NHAT LY.

AUTOMOTIVE TECHNOLOGY

A Systems Approach
2ND EDITION

Jack Erjavec ■ **Robert Scharff**

Delmar Publishers

I(T)P™ An International Thomson Publishing Company

Albany • Bonn • Boston • Cincinnati • Detroit • London • Madrid • Melbourne
Mexico City • New York • Pacific Grove • Paris • San Francisco • Singapore • Tokyo
Toronto • Washington

NOTICE TO THE READER

COVER PHOTO: Courtesy of Pontiac

PHOTO SEQUENCES: Photography by Rod Dixon Associates, Michael A. Gallitelli (Metroland Photo), and Jeff Hinkley

DELMAR STAFF

Acquisitions Editor: Vernon Anthony
Developmental Editor: Catherine Eads
Project Editor: Thomas Smith
Production Coordinator: Karen Smith
Art/Design Coordinators: Denise Denisoff and Michael Prinzo

COPYRIGHT © 1996
By Delmar Publishers
a division of International Thomson Publishing Inc.

The ITP logo is a trademark under license

Printed in the United States of America

For more information, contact:

Delmar Publishers
3 Columbia Circle, Box 15015
Albany, New York 12212-5015

International Thomson Publishing Europe
Berkshire House 168-173
High Holborn
London, WC1V7AA
England

Thomas Nelson Australia
102 Dodds Street
South Melbourne, 3205
Victoria, Australia

Nelson Canada
1120 Birchmount Road
Scarborough, Ontario
Canada M1K 5G4

International Thomson Editores
Campos Eliseos 385, Piso 7
Col Polanco
11560 Mexico D F Mexico

International Thomson Publishing Gmbh
Königswinterer Strasse 418
53227 Bonn
Germany

International Thomson Publishing Asia
221 Henderson Road #05-10
Henderson Building
Singapore 0315

International Thomson Publishing - Japan
Hirakawacho Kyowa Building, 3F
2-2-1 Hirakawacho
Chiyoda-ku, 102 Tokyo
Japan

5 6 7 8 9 10 XXX 02 01 00 99 98

Library of Congress Cataloging-in-Publication Data

Erjavec, Jack.
    Automotive technology: a systems approach / Jack Erjavec, Robert Scharff. — 2nd ed.
      p.   cm.
    Includes index.
    ISBN 0-8273-6724-4 (case)
    1. Automobiles—Maintenance and repair. I. Scharff, Robert. II. Title.
TL152.E67 1996
629.28'72—dc20
                                  95-42891
                                    CIP

CONTENTS

SECTION ONE   AUTOMOTIVE TECHNOLOGY

SECTION 3   ELECTRICITY

SECTION 4   ENGINE PERFORMANCE

SECTION 5 MANUAL TRANSMISSIONS AND TRANSAXLES

CHAPTER 31

SECTION 6 AUTOMATIC TRANSMISSIONS AND TRANSAXLES

CHAPTER 32

CHAPTER 33

SECTION 7   Suspensions

SECTION 8   BRAKES

SECTION 9 PASSENGER COMFORT

PHOTO SEQUENCES

Changing the Oil and Oil Filter / 48

Using a Micrometer / 56

Conducting a Cylinder Compression Test / 94

Checking Main Bearing Clearance with Plastigage / 167

Measuring and Fitting Valve Springs / 203

Replacing a Timing Belt on an OHC Engine / 229

Performing a Voltage Drop Test / 349

Soldering Two Copper Wires Together / 354

Using a Volt and Amp Tester to Test the Battery and the Starting System / 422

Using a Volt and Amp Tester to Test the Charging System / 445

Installing a Distributor and Setting the Timing of an Engine / 562

Removing and Replacing Various DIS Components / 565

Checking the Fuel Pressure on a PFI System / 589

Typical Procedure for Testing Injector Balance / 644

Removing and Replacing a Fuel Injector on a PFI System / 648

Installing and Aligning a Clutch Disc / 732

Removing and Replacing a CV Joint Boot / 778

Performing an Automatic Transmission Fluid and Filter Change / 882

Typical Procedure for Disassembling a Warner 13-56 Transfer Case / 903

Typical Procedure for Reassembling a Warner 13-56 Transfer Case / 905

Dismounting and Mounting a Tire on a Wheel Assembly / 923

Typical Procedure for Measuring Front and Rear Curb Riding Height / 953

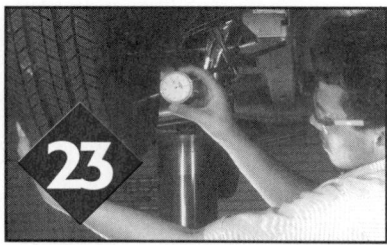

Typical Procedure for Measuring the Lower Ball Joint Radial Movement on a MacPherson Strut Front Suspension / 956

Removing and Replacing a MacPherson Strut / 959

Typical Procedure for Measuring Front Wheel Camber and Caster / 1013

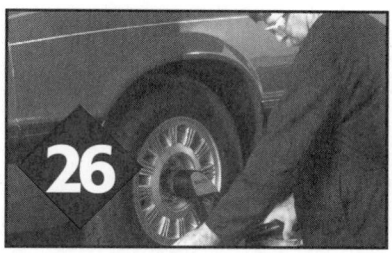

Typical Procedure for Measuring Front Wheel Toe / 1014

Typical Procedure for Performing Four-Wheel Alignment with a Computer Wheel Aligner / 1018

Adjusting Rear Drum Parking Brake / 1074

Removing and Replacing Brake Pads / 1088

Evacuating and Recharging an A/C System with a Recycling and Charging Station / 1136

PREFACE

This new edition of *Automotive Technology: A Systems Approach* reflects changes in the automotive industry since the publication of the first edition. Changes in vehicle design and automobile service have been mandated by legislation. New technologies provide safer, more efficient, and more reliable automobiles.

New chapters in the Electricity section reflect the use of electronic controls throughout most of the systems of an automobile. Basics of electricity and electronics are covered more simply and more completely. The Engine Performance section covers OBD-II systems, introduces OBD-II terminology, and discusses I/M testing and alternative fuels.

The Transmission sections cover basic manual and automatic transmissions and transaxles, as well as electronically-controlled transmissions. Additional information on electronic controls and four-wheel steering has been added to the Steering and Suspension section.

We have added a new chapter on antilock brake systems to the Brakes section. Our section on Comfort and Safety includes updated information on air-conditioning service procedures to comply with new federal mandates, as well as information on air bags.

The second edition of *Automotive Technology: A Systems Approach* is a comprehensive guide to the service and repair of contemporary automobiles. It is divided into nine sections that relate to specific automotive systems. The chapters in each section describe the various subsystems and individual components. Diagnostic and service procedures, unique to different automobile manufacturers, are included in these chapters. The relationships between integrated automotive systems are explained, as well.

Effective diagnostic skills begin with learning to isolate the problem. By identifying the system that contains the problem, the exact cause is easier to pinpoint. Troubleshooting techniques are discussed throughout this text because troubleshooting is an essential skill that must be mastered. Each chapter describes techniques to isolate the individual components of the problem system.

This systems approach prepares the student for the ASE certification exams, which are categorized by the automobile's major systems. The book's sections are outlined to match the ASE test specifications and competency task lists. The review questions at the end of each chapter give students practice in answering ASE-style questions.

FEATURES OF THE TEXT

We have added a series of features to ease the teaching and learning processes because learning to maintain and repair today's automobiles can be intimidating.

PHOTO SEQUENCES

Step-by-step photo sequences illustrate practical shop techniques. The photo sequences focus on standard service and maintenance procedures, and give students a clean, detailed image to look at when they perform these procedures.

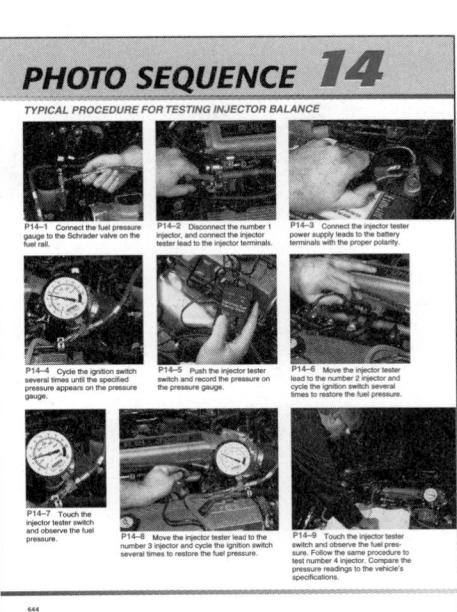

PHOTO SEQUENCE 14

TYPICAL PROCEDURE FOR TESTING INJECTOR BALANCE

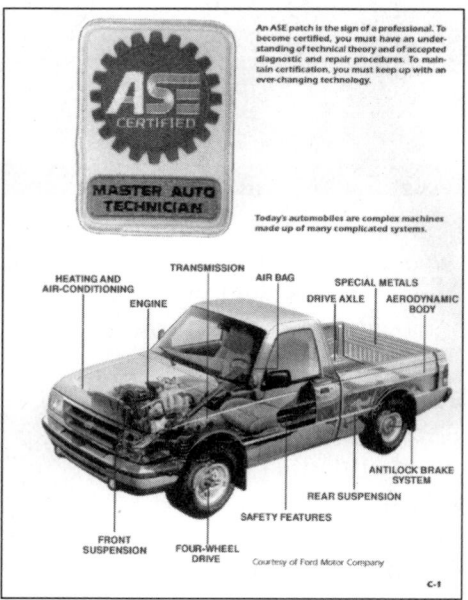

COLOR INSERT

The sixteen page, color insert contains full color cutaways and functional details from the eight ASE systems. Many of these up-to-date illustrations are gathered from industry and show the details of system operation.

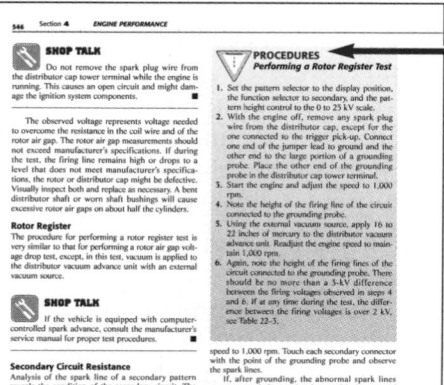

PROCEDURES

This feature gives detailed, step-by-step instructions for important service and maintenance procedures. These hands-on procedures appear frequently because they help to develop good shop skills and help to meet ASE competencies.

CASE STUDIES

Case Studies highlight our emphasis on logical troubleshooting. A service problem is outlined at the end of each chapter, then a technician's solution is described. This gives the student a practical example of logical troubleshooting. The Tech Manual provides many open-ended case studies for more practice.

KEY TERMS

Each chapter also ends with a list of terms that were highlighted when they were introduced in the text. These terms are defined in the glossary.

TECH MANUAL REFERENCES

Each chapter ends with a reference to the Tech Manual that accompanies this text. Each reference lists the procedure that is detailed in the Tech Manual.

SHOP TALK

These features are sprinkled throughout each chapter to give common-sense advice on service and maintenance procedures.

CUSTOMER CARE

A professional image is important in automotive technology today. The customer care tips encourage professional integrity, customer education, and customer satisfaction.

USING SERVICE MANUALS

Learning to use service manuals can be confusing and time-consuming. Therefore, we have included this feature to familiarize the reader with the information available in this important resource. Tips and instructions on how to locate information are found throughout the text. Students will practice recording and analyzing service manual data in the Tech Manual.

CAUTIONS AND WARNINGS

Instructors often tell us that shop safety is their most important concern. Cautions and warnings appear frequently in each chapter to alert students to important safety concerns.

SUPPLEMENTS

The *Automotive Technology* package offers a full complement of supplements to keep instructors up-to-date in the classroom.

Tech Manual

The student tech manual gives hands-on, practical shop experience. The tech manual contains hundreds of shop activities and competency-based interactive job sheets, with practice in troubleshooting, and using diagnostic charts and service manuals. Service manual report sheets, open-ended case studies, review questions, and ASE prep tests reinforce hands-on learning.

Instructor's Guide

This comprehensive guide provides teaching hints, answers to review questions and Tech Manual questions, transparency masters, and guidelines for using the Tech Manual. A unique Crossover Guide is included to help you switch from your current text to *Automotive Technology*.

Test Bank

More than 2,000 questions, including sample ASE tests, are available on hard copy or disk. The computerized version is designed for easy tailoring and contains graphics.

ACKNOWLEDGMENTS

We gratefully acknowledge the contributions of the following text reviewers:

Walter M. Bertotti
Porter and Chester Institute
Watertown, CT

Richard J. Caissie
TAD Technical Institute
Chelsea, MA

Wallace P. Fish
Central Maine Technical College
Auburn, ME

C. Neel Flannagan
Aiken Technical College
Aiken, SC

Robert G. Koch
Community College of Allegheny County
Pittsburgh, PA

Michael E. Kozenko
Vale Technical Institute
Blairsville, PA

Timothy McCluskey
Dakota County Technical College
Rosemount, MN

James J. Pinto
Porter and Chester Institute
Wethersfield, CT

Fred Raadsheer
British Columbia Institute of Technology
Burnaby, British Columbia
CANADA

Harry T. Runyon
Gaston College
Dallas, NC

Bob Swanner
Tennessee Technical Center at Nashville
Nashville, TN

We also acknowledge the following individuals from Columbus State Community College's Automotive Maintenance Technology Department, who provided valuable assistance in preparing the step-by-step photos in this text:

Bill Ackley
Chuck Frieze
Rusty Gillman
Steve Levin

Tadashi Nakamura
Dave Slater
Rez Talbert
Bill Warner

The following individuals were also instrumental in producing the step-by-step photos.

Photographers: Rod Dixon
                Michael Gallitelli
                Jeff Hinkley

Models: Connie Cittadino
         John Flores
         Rosemary Flores
         John Ising
         Robert Jones
         Maureen McDermott
         Cliff Widener

DEDICATION

We dedicate this book to Mary Puschack Scharff, whose commitment and hard work on the first edition was greatly appreciated.

ROBERT SCHARFF
February 16, 1921–October 26, 1995

Author of hundreds of books used by thousands of students, Bob Scharff was a great entrepreneur and a true character those who knew him will never forget. This book is dedicated to his memory.

SECTION 1

AUTOMOTIVE TECHNOLOGY

Servicing today's cars and trucks is much different than it was just a few years ago. Demands on the automotive industry to build more reliable, cleaner, safer, and more fuel efficient vehicles has greatly changed the way products are built, operated, and serviced.

Today's automotive technicians must keep up with these changes. Electronic controls are now part of nearly every system, from the engine and the ignition system to brakes and transmissions. Automobile mechanics who have not kept up with these changes have left or been forced out of the industry. This has resulted in a shortage of qualified technicians. This shortage comes at a time when more cars are on the road and, therefore, more cars need to be serviced. As a result, excellent career opportunities for skilled and certified service technicians have never been greater.

The material covered in Section 1 explains these career opportunities. It also presents a quick look at the major systems of an automobile. In the later chapters, important safety practices are covered, as are the correct uses of common shop tools, equipment, and diagnostic testers.

WE ENCOURAGE
PROFESSIONALISM

THROUGH TECHNICIAN

THE AUTOMOTIVE INDUSTRY

1

OBJECTIVES

◆ Describe the reasons why today's automotive industry is considered a global industry. ◆ Explain how computer technology has changed the way vehicles are built and serviced. ◆ Explain why the need for qualified automotive technicians is increasing. ◆ Describe the major types of business that employ automotive technicians. ◆ List some of the many job opportunities available to people with a background in automotive technology. ◆ Describe what it takes to be a good technician. ◆ Explain the role ASE now plays within the automotive service industry. ◆ Describe the requirements for ASE certification as an automotive technician and a master auto technician.

Personal transportation has become a way of life for Americans. People spend hours each week traveling to and from work. The drive-through lanes at banks and fast-food restaurants are often busier than the service counters inside. We drive to shopping malls to shop, see a motion picture, or get something to eat. We spend much of our free time traveling. We think little of driving hundreds of miles to beaches, ski resorts, amusement parks, or historical sites.

There are more than 85 passenger cars for every 100 drivers in the United States. In fact, there is one passenger car for every 1.8 people. Table 1–1 shows how the United States compares to other countries, in regard to car ownership.

The automotive industry's part in the total economy of the United States is second only to the food industry. Manufacturing, selling, and servicing these vehicles is an incredibly large, diverse, and expanding industry.

INTRODUCTION

Not too long ago, America's "big three" auto makers—General Motors, Ford Motor Company, and Chrysler Corporation—dominated the auto industry. This is no longer true. The industry is now a global industry. Auto makers from Japan, Korea, Germany, Sweden, and other European and Asian countries compete with U.S. companies for domestic and foreign sales (Table 1–2).

Several foreign manufacturers, such as Honda, operate assembly plants in the United States and

Canada. In fact, Honda is often referred to as a member of the "big four." A number of car models are built jointly by the United States and foreign manufacturers. These vehicles are built in North America or overseas and imported into North America.

This cooperation between manufacturers and the public acceptance of imported vehicles has resulted in an extremely wide selection of vehicles from which customers may choose. This has also created new challenges for automotive technicians. These

TABLE 1–1 PASSENGER CAR COUNT OF SELECT COUNTRIES		
Country	Passenger Cars (Millions)	People Per Passenger Car
United States	140.1	1.8
Canada	25.3	2.3
Germany	31.3	2.4
Italy	22.3	2.5
France	21.2	2.6
United Kingdom	17.4	3.2
Spain	9.7	4.1
Japan	28.6	4.3
Brazil	10.0	15.4
Mexico	5.0	17.6
China	0.79	1,345.0

TABLE 1–2 TODAY'S FOREIGN CARS AND THEIR ORIGINS	
Vehicle	**Exporting Country**
Acura	Japan
Audi/Porsche	Germany
BMW	Germany
Honda	Japan
Hyundai	Korea
Infiniti	Japan
Isuzu	Japan
Jaguar	Great Britain
Lexus	Japan
Mazda	Japan
Mercedes-Benz	Germany
Mitsubishi	Japan
Nissan	Japan
Saab	Sweden
Sterling	Great Britain
Subaru	Japan
Toyota	Japan
Volkswagen	Germany
Volvo	Sweden

challenges are based on one simple fact: with the different models come different systems.

The Technology Boom

The same advances in electronics that are responsible for the development of affordable personal computers (PCs), calculators, videocassette recorders (VCRs), compact disc players, and other equipment has also changed the way automotive systems operate and are serviced.

Because electronics play an important part in the operation of all automotive systems, an understanding of electronics is a must for all automotive technicians. The needed level of understanding is not that of an engineer, rather technicians need a practical understanding of electronics. In addition to mastering the mechanical skills needed to remove, repair, and replace faulty or damaged components, today's technician also must be able to diagnose electronic systems.

Computers and electronic devices are used to control the engine and its support systems. Because of these controls, cars of today use less fuel, perform better, and run cleaner than those in the past.

Electronic controls also are used to activate shifting in automatic transmissions, eliminate brake lockup in antilock braking systems (ABS), and improve handling by controlling steering and suspension systems. The amount of electronics used on cars and

trucks is increasing with each model year. Consider these projections for the 1990s and beyond.

◆ In 1991, about 20 percent of all functions on new cars were controlled by electronics. By 1998, this figure will jump to over 80%.
◆ By the year 2000, antilock braking systems, now an option on many vehicles, will become standard equipment on nearly all cars.
◆ Some vehicles do use and others will use three or more different computers to control different systems on the car. Separate computers will be used to control the engine, the transmission/transaxle, instrumentation and climate control, the suspension system, steering system, and antilock brakes.
◆ Vehicle diagnostic systems will anticipate breakdowns, contact emergency road service, and guide technicians through the repair process.
◆ By the year 2000, some model vehicles will have multiple video cameras to view the area all around the car, eliminating blind spots, and an infrared system to provide good vision at night and in bad weather.
◆ Electronic mufflers will analyze engine noise in the exhaust pipe and generate antinoise, a sound wave exactly 180 degrees out of phase with the offending noise. The original noise and mirror-image antinoise cancel out each other when they meet. The result is a soundless exhaust system.
◆ Intelligent cruise control devices will combine speed control with braking. The vehicle's brakes will apply automatically to keep safe distances between moving cars.
◆ Global navigation and satellite tracking systems will allow the driver to know the best route to take. These systems will keep track of traffic and road conditions.

Not only will electronics shape the cars of the future, but so will laws. The government passes laws to try to make cars cleaner and safer. These laws will also affect the lives of automotive technicians.

One recently passed law, called OBD-II, will make life easier for technicians. It gives all technicians a chance to repair the computer controls of all makes and models of cars. It does this by ordering the manufacturers to use a common system and common terms to describe it. This is a big change. For many years, each manufacturer took its own approach to computer controls. The result was nearly as many different systems as there were car models.

Many states have passed laws that require car owners to have their vehicles' exhaust tested on an annual basis. Most states are requiring the vehicles to pass an I/M-240 test. This test examines the exhaust while a car is being driven under a number of different conditions. This test, and the laws that tell the owners their vehicles must pass the test, will also affect the life of a technician.

The Need for Quality Service

As vehicles continue to become more complex, the need for good technicians continues to grow. Good technicians have been trained on the systems they service and the equipment they use for diagnostics (Figure 1–1).

Good **diagnostic skills** are especially important for today's technicians. Those who can identify and solve problems the first time the vehicle is brought into the shop are those who are wanted by the industry. For them, there are many excellent opportunities. The high cost of electronic components and many mechanical parts has made the "hit-and-miss" method of repair too expensive. Too often, mechanics who do not understand how to properly troubleshoot an electronic system automatically replace its most expensive component—the computer. This often results in a very expensive wrong guess. Computers are very reliable. Normally, the cause of a problem in a computer system is an inexpensive switch or sensor, a poor electrical connection, or a bad mechanical part within the system.

Proper diagnostic techniques are important also for finding the cause of a vehicle that failed an exhaust gas test, especially an I/M-240 test. Technicians must be able to find the reason why the vehicle failed and correct the problem.

The Need for On-Going Service

The use of electronic controls has not eliminated the need for routine service and scheduled maintenance (Figure 1–2). In fact, it has made it more important

FIGURE 1–1 Sophisticated diagnostic equipment is required to service today's automotive systems. *Courtesy of Environmental Systems Products*

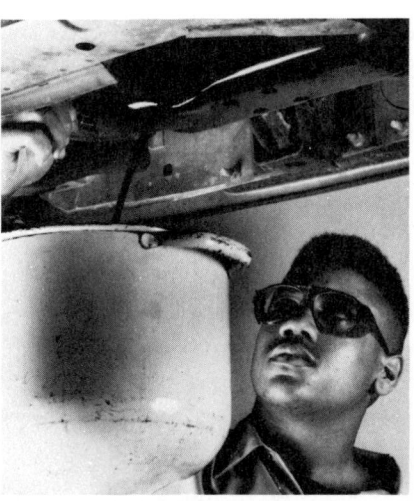

FIGURE 1–2 Regular preventive maintenance is important in keeping electronic control systems operating smoothly. A common part of PM is changing the engine's oil and filter.

than ever. Although the computer systems can make adjustments to cover up some problems, a computer cannot replace parts that wear. A computer cannot tighten loose belts, change weak or dirty coolant, or change dirty engine oil. Simple problems such as these can set off a chain of unwanted events in an engine control system. Electronic controls are designed to help a well-maintained vehicle operate effectively. They are not designed to repair systems.

The computer, through its control devices, may attempt to compensate for a problem by making adjustments to the engine's systems. As a result, the engine will run reasonably well, but its overall performance and efficiency will be lowered.

Various maintenance procedures usually are performed according to a schedule recommended by the vehicle's manufacturer. These maintenance procedures are referred to as **preventive maintenance** (PM) because they are designed to prevent problems. Scheduled preventive maintenance normally includes oil and filter changes, coolant and lubrication services, replacement of belts and hoses, and replacement of spark plugs, filters, and worn electrical parts.

If a car owner fails to follow the recommended maintenance schedule, the car's warranty might not cover problems that result. For example, if the car's engine fails during the period of time covered by the warranty, the warranty may not cover the engine if the owner does not have proof that the engine's oil was changed according to the recommended schedule.

In order to meet federal regulations controlling the amount of pollution that is given off by a car and the amount of fuel used, automobile manufacturers have installed many components that do nothing more than help the vehicle meet these regulations. The parts of these emission control systems have a

5-year, 50,000-mile warranty. This warranty is mandated by law. The time and mileage of this warranty will soon increase, a step at a time, until it reaches 10 years and 100,000 miles. Periodic maintenance or replacement of these parts is required to keep these systems working properly. In some cases, service guidelines for these systems are mandated by law.

Warranties   A **warranty** is an agreement by the auto manufacturer to have its authorized dealers repair, replace, or adjust certain parts if they become defective. This agreement normally lasts until the vehicle has been driven a certain amount of miles, typically 50,000, and/or until the vehicle has been owned for a certain length of time, typically 5 years. In order for the warranty to cover the cost of the repair, the problem must occur during the time or miles covered by the warranty. There are basically two types of warranties: those offered by the manufacturer and those ordered by federal and state laws.

The details of most manufacturer warranties normally vary with the manufacturer, vehicle model, and year. Most manufacturers provide several levels of warranty coverage. There is often a basic warranty that covers the complete vehicle for the first year or first 12,000 miles, whichever comes first. Additional warranties may cover the engine, transmission, drive axles, powertrain, battery, safety restraint systems, the body, or other parts of the vehicle. These warranties extend the warranty time for these items. Sometimes on these warranties, a certain amount of money, called the **deductible**, must be paid by the owner. The manufacturer pays for all repair costs over the deductible amount. Some warranties are prorated. This means that the amount of the repair bill covered by the warranty decreases over time.

The two government-mandated warranties are the Federal Emissions Defect Warranty and the Federal Emissions Performance Warranty. The Federal Emissions Defect Warranty ensures that the vehicle meets all required emissions regulations and that the vehicle's emission control system works as designed. The Federal Emissions Performance Warranty covers a vehicle if it is registered in a state or city that has an inspection and maintenance program that meets the requirements of the Environmental Protection Agency (EPA). If the owner properly maintains the vehicle and it fails an EPA-approved emissions test, the manufacturer's dealer will repair those emission-related parts covered by the warranty, free of charge. Some states, such as California, require the manufacturers to offer additional warranties.

All warranty information can be found in the vehicle's owner's manual. Whenever there are questions about the warranties, carefully read that section in the owner's manual.

Increased Vehicle Age   Like the price of everything else, the price of a new car has risen sharply. To purchase a new car, many people have taken out loans and have committed to make car payments for up to 7 years. These long-term loans are the only way many can afford a new car. These loans are also the reason why people are keeping their cars longer than they did in the past when it was common for many to buy a new car every 3 years. With a small downpayment, the car could be financed for 3 years.

Purchasing a car today is a major, long-term investment. The average age of on-the-road automobiles ranges from 4 to 7 years. There are no signs that the trend of keeping cars longer will stop.

Older vehicles provide most of the major repair and overhaul work performed in dealerships and independent garages. However, this does not mean that these cars are not complex. Most of the cars on the road have electronic controls, and servicing them requires training and specialized equipment.

Emissions and Fuel Economy Requirements   Concerns about our environment and safety are two more reasons the need for vehicle service is increasing. Most states now have laws that require periodic inspections of passenger vehicles. In many cases, vehicles must pass exhaust emission and safety inspections before the vehicle's registration can be renewed. A vehicle that fails these inspections must be brought up to the required standards at the owner's expense, before a new license can be issued.

Career Opportunities

Automotive service technicians can enjoy careers in many different types of automotive business. Because of the skills required to be a qualified technician, there are also career opportunities for those who don't want to repair cars the rest of their lives.

Dealerships   New car dealerships (Figure 1–3) serve as the link between the vehicle manufacturer and the customer. They are privately owned businesses. Most dealerships are franchised operations. This means the owners have signed a contract with a particular auto manufacturer and have agreed to sell and service their vehicles. Many dealerships have more than one franchise and sell more than one type of vehicle.

The sales and service policies of the dealership are usually set by the manufacturer. Most warranty repair work is done at the dealership. The manufacturer then pays the dealership for making the repair.

FIGURE 1–3   Dealerships sell and service vehicles made by a specific auto manufacturer.

FIGURE 1–4   Full-service gasoline stations are one type of independent service shop.

The manufacturer also provides the service department at the dealership with the special tools, equipment, and information needed to repair their vehicles. The manufacturers also help the dealerships get service business. Often, their commercials stress the importance of using their replacement parts and promote their technicians as the most qualified to work on their products.

Working for a new car dealership can have many advantages. Technical support, equipment, and the opportunity for on-going training are usually excellent. However, being tied into one or two particular model lines may limit the scope of your servicing expertise.

Independent Service Shops   Independent shops (Figure 1–4) normally service all types of vehicles. Some shops may specialize in particular types of cars or specific systems of the car. Independent shops outnumber dealerships by six to one. As the name states, an independent service shop is not associated with any particular automobile manufacturer.   Many independent shops are started by technicians eager to be their own boss and run their own business.

An independent shop may range in size from a two-bay garage with two to four technicians, to a multiple-bay service center with twenty to thirty technicians. The amount of equipment in an independent shop varies; however, most are well-equipped to do the work they do best. Working in an independent shop may present diagnostic and servicing challenges, which can develop you into a well-rounded technician.

Specialty service shops specialize in areas such as engine rebuilding, transmission/transaxle overhauling, and brake, exhaust, cooling, emissions, and electrical work.

The number of specialty shops that service and repair only one or two systems of the automobile has steadily increased over the past ten to twenty years.

Technicians employed by these shops have the opportunity to become very good in one particular area of service and repair.

Franchise Repair Shops   A great number of jobs are available at service shops that are run by large companies. Firestone, Goodyear, Precision Tune, Midas, and Procare are examples of this type of shop. These shops do not normally service and repair all of the systems of the automobile. However, their customers come in with a variety of service needs. Technicians employed by these shops have the opportunity to become very good in many areas of service and repair.

Store-Associated Shops   Other major employers of auto technicians are the service departments of department stores. Many large stores that sell automotive parts often offer certain types of automotive services, such as brake, exhaust system, and wheel and tire work (Figure 1–5).

Fleet Service and Maintenance   Any company that relies on several vehicles to do their business faces an

FIGURE 1–5   Many major retail store chains sell auto parts and have well-organized service facilities. These facilities typically offer limited service and installation work.

on-going vehicle service and preventive maintenance problem. Small fleets often send their vehicles to an independent shop for maintenance and repair. Large fleets, however, usually have their own preventive maintenance and repair facilities and technicians.

Utility companies (electric, telephone, cable TV, etc.), car rental companies, overnight delivery services, and taxicab companies are good examples of businesses that usually have their own service departments. Many career opportunities are available in this segment of the auto service industry.

JOB CLASSIFICATIONS

The automobile industry offers numerous types of employment for people with a good understanding of automotive systems.

Service Technician

A **service technician** (Figure 1–6) assesses vehicle problems, performs all necessary diagnostic tests, and competently repairs or replaces faulty components. The skills to do this job are based on a sound understanding of auto technology, on-the-job experience, and continuous training in new technology as it is introduced by auto manufacturers.

Someone skilled in automotive service is now referred to as a technician, not a mechanic. There is a good reason for this. *Mechanic* stresses the ability to repair and service mechanical systems. While this skill is still very much needed, it is only part of the technician's overall job. Today's vehicles require mechanical knowledge plus an understanding of other technologies, such as electronics, hydraulics, and pneumatics.

A technician may work on all systems of the car or may become specialized. Specialty technicians concentrate on serving one or more systems of the automobile, such as electrical, brakes, or transmission (Figure 1–7). These specialties require advanced and continuous training in that particular field.

FIGURE 1–6 Service technicians perform all types of general repair work.

FIGURE 1–7 Specialty technicians repair only one or more systems on a vehicle, such as brakes.

Service Advisor

The person who greets customers at a service center is the service advisor, sometimes called a service writer. The service writer must have a good knowledge of automobiles and the parts of a car. A friendly attitude and the ability to deal with people effectively are also important. Customers discuss their automotive problems and needs with the service writer. The service writer then consults with a technician. Based on these discussions and the technician's diagnosis, the service writer prepares a detailed cost estimate for the customer.

Service Manager

The service manager is responsible for the operation of the entire service department at a large dealership or independent shop. Normally, customer concerns and complaints are handled by the service manager. Therefore, a good service manager has good people skills in addition to organizational skills and a solid automotive background.

In a dealership, the service manager makes sure the manufacturers' policies on warranties, service procedures, and customer relations are carried out. The service manager also arranges for technician training and keeps all other shop personnel informed and working together.

Parts Manager

The parts manager is in charge of ordering all replacement parts for the repairs the shop performs. The ordering and timely delivery of parts is extremely important for smooth operation of the shop. Delays in obtaining parts or omitting a small but crucial part from the initial parts order can cause frustrating holdups for both the service technicians and customers.

Most dealerships and large independent shops

keep an inventory of commonly used parts, such as filters, belts, hoses, and gaskets. The parts manager is responsible for maintaining this inventory.

An understanding of automotive systems and their parts, thoroughness, attention to detail, and the ability to work with people face-to-face and over the phone are a must for a parts manager.

RELATED CAREER OPPORTUNITIES

In addition to careers in automotive service, there are many other job opportunities directly related to the automotive industry.

Parts Distribution

The automotive aftermarket refers to the network of businesses that supplies replacement parts (Figure 1–8) to independent service shops, car and truck dealerships, fleet operations, and the general public.

Vehicle manufacturers and independent parts manufacturers sell and supply parts to approximately 1,000 warehouse distributors throughout the United States. These warehouse distributors (**WD**s) carry substantial inventories of many part lines.

Warehouse distributors serve as large distribution centers. WDs sell and supply parts to part wholesalers who are commonly known as jobbers.

Jobbers sell parts and supplies to shops. They also sell to "do-it-yourselfers." Many jobbers operate machine shops that offer another source of employment for skilled technicians.

Jobbers or parts stores can be independently owned and operated. They can also be part of a larger national chain (Figure 1–9). Auto manufacturers have also set up their own parts distribution systems to their dealerships and authorized service outlets. Parts manufactured by the original vehicle manufacturer are called original equipment manufacturer or **OEM** parts.

Opportunities for employment exist at all levels in the parts distribution network, from warehouse distributors to the counterpeople at local jobber outlets.

Marketing and Sales

Companies that manufacture equipment and parts for the service industry are constantly searching for knowledgeable people to represent and sell their products. For example, a sales representative working for an aftermarket parts manufacturer should have a good knowledge of the company's products. The sales representative also works with WDs, jobbers, and service shops to make sure the parts are being sold and installed correctly. They also help coordinate training and supply information so that everyone using their products is properly trained and informed.

Other Opportunities

Other career possibilities for those trained in automotive service include insurance company claims adjusters, auto body shop technicians, and trainers for the various manufacturers or instructors for an automotive program. The latter two careers require solid experience and a thorough understanding of the automobile.

WORKING AS AN AUTOMOTIVE TECHNICIAN

To be a successful automotive technician you need to have good training, a desire to succeed, and a commitment to be a good technician and a good employee. A good employee works well with other employees and strives to make the entire organization successful.

Employer-Employee Relationships

Being a good employee requires more than learning job skills. When you begin a job, you enter into a business agreement with your employer. When you become an employee, you sell your time, skills, and efforts. In return, your employer pays you for these resources.

Employer Obligations As part of the employment agreement, your employer also has certain responsibilities.

INSTRUCTION AND SUPERVISION You should be told what is expected of you. A supervisor should observe your work and tell you if it is satisfactory.

CLEAN, SAFE PLACE TO WORK An employer should provide a clean and safe work area as well as a place for personal cleanup.

WAGES You should know how much you are to be paid before accepting a job. Your employer should pay you on designated pay days.

FRINGE BENEFITS When you are hired, you should be told what benefits, in addition to wages, you can expect. Fringe benefits usually include paid vacations and employer contributions to health insurance and retirement plans.

OPPORTUNITY AND FAIR TREATMENT Opportunity means you are given a chance to succeed and possibly advance within the company. Fair treatment means all employees are treated equally, without prejudice or favoritism.

Employee Obligations On the other side of this business transaction, employees have responsibilities to their employers. Your obligations as a worker include the following.

ROCKER ARM ASSEMBLY

VALVE ADJUSTING SCREW

DOWEL PIN

SEAL

CAMSHAFT PULLEY

KEY

SPECIAL WASHER

CAMSHAFT

VALVE KEEPERS

SPRING RETAINER

VALVE SPRING SEAT

EX. VALVE SPRING

EX. VALVE SEAL

EX. VALVE GUIDE

VALVE KEEPERS

SPRING RETAINER

IN. VALVE SPRING

VALVE SEAL

VALVE SPRING SEAT

IN. VALVE GUIDE

TIMING BELT BACK COVER

CYLINDER HEAD

IN. VALVE

EX. VALVE

FIGURE 1–8 Correctly identifying and ordering replacement parts is a crucial step in the repair process. *Courtesy of American Honda Motor Company, Inc.*

FIGURE 1–9 Many auto parts stores are part of a national corporation with stores located across the country.

REGULAR ATTENDANCE A good employee is reliable. Businesses cannot operate successfully unless their workers are on the job. This is important to employers. One of the first things a potential employer will ask a student's instructor about is the student's class attendance.

FOLLOWING DIRECTIONS As an employee, you are part of a team. Doing things your way may not serve the best interests of the company.

RESPONSIBILITY Be willing to answer for your behavior and work habits.

PRODUCTIVITY Remember, you are paid for your time as well as your skills and effort. You have a duty to be as effective as possible when you are at work.

LOYALTY Loyalty is expected by any employee. Being loyal means that you act in the best interests of your employer, both on and off the job.

Getting Along at Work You also have certain responsibilities toward your fellow workers. You will be a member of a team. Teamwork means cooperating with and caring about other workers.

Customer Relations Good customer relations begin at the technician level (Figure 1–10). Learn to listen and communicate clearly. Be polite and organized, particularly when dealing with customers on the telephone.

Respect the vehicles on which you work. They are important to the lives of your customers. Always return the vehicle to the owner in a clean, undamaged condition. Remember, a car is the second largest expense a customer has. Treat it that way. It doesn't matter if you like the car. It belongs to the customer; treat it respectfully.

Explain the repair process to the customer in understandable terms. Make repair estimates as precisely as possible. No one likes surprises, particularly when substantial amounts of money are involved.

To help you develop your customer relation skills, special customer care tips appear throughout this text. They contain sound advice you can share with customers on personal car care. They also give you advice on how to conduct business in a courteous and professional manner.

TRAINING FOR A CAREER IN AUTOMOTIVE SERVICE

Those interested in a career in auto service can receive training in formal school settings—secondary, post-secondary, and vocational schools, and technical or community colleges, both private and public. To help these schools keep pace with the rapidly changing technology and equipment needed for training and maintaining a curriculum that meets the service industry's needs, many auto manufacturers now work with these schools through their own cooperative training programs. These apprenticeship-type programs blend work experience at a dealership with formal training at local schools. Programs vary, but generally the manufacturer provides specific product-training curriculum, test equipment, vehicles, and components to participating schools and on-the-job training at local dealerships. Examples of this type of program are the Chrysler CAPS, Ford ASSET, GM ASEP, and Toyota T-Ten programs.

Training in automotive technology and service does not end with graduation from school. A professional auto technician must constantly learn and keep up to date. Car manufacturers, equipment manufacturers, aftermarket parts manufacturers, and publishers are always producing new training materials to keep technicians informed on how to service the late-model cars and trucks.

In addition, technical clinics are often sponsored by car manufacturers, aftermarket parts manufacturers, and parts dealers. Reading trade magazines and publications is also an excellent way to stay up to date. A good technician takes advantage of every opportunity to learn.

ASE CERTIFICATION

The National Institute for Automotive Service Excellence (**ASE**) has established a certification program for automotive, heavy-duty truck, auto body repair, and engine machine shop technicians. In addition to these programs, ASE also offers individual testing in the areas of parts, alternate fuels, and advanced engine performance. This certification sys-

FIGURE 1–10 Keeping the customer informed and satisfied is the responsibility of everyone involved in the service industry.

An ASE patch is the sign of a professional. To become certified, you must have an understanding of technical theory and of accepted diagnostic and repair procedures. To maintain certification, you must keep up with an ever-changing technology.

Today's automobiles are complex machines made up of many complicated systems.

TRANSMISSION

AIR BAG

SPECIAL METALS

HEATING AND AIR-CONDITIONING

DRIVE AXLE

AERODYNAMIC BODY

ENGINE

ANTILOCK BRAKE SYSTEM

REAR SUSPENSION

FRONT SUSPENSION

FOUR-WHEEL DRIVE

SAFETY FEATURES

Courtesy of Ford Motor Company

ENGINES

Modern automobile engines are basically the same as older ones. However, technological advances have resulted in many new engine designs, as well as the use of new materials in the manufacturing process.

Courtesy of Cadillac Motor Division—GMC

FRONT-WHEEL TRANSVERSE

ALL-WHEEL TRANSVERSE

FRONT-WHEEL LONGITUDINAL

REAR-WHEEL LONGITUDINAL

Aerodynamics, fuel economy, and passenger safety and comfort have influenced the overall design of the automobile and the layout of the engine and its driveline.

ELECTRICAL SYSTEMS

Advances made in electronics have made the biggest impact on the industry. Microprocessors are used to control and monitor engine and driveline systems. Due to this electronic revolution, manufacturers have been able to produce cars that are more comfortable, safer, and more efficient.

TO A/C RELAY

TO REAR WIRING HARNESS

TO HEADLIGHT

TO AIR FLOW METER

TO HEADLIGHT DOOR

TO COOLING FAN

TO TRANSMISSION

TO STARTER MOTOR

TO WATER TEMPERATURE SWITCH

TO ALTERNATOR

TO IGNITION COIL

TO HORNS

TO SIDE MARKER LIGHT

TO AIR SUSPENSION SYSTEM

Diagnostic and repair procedures are rapidly changing. Electronics has introduced new terms and components, as well as new test equipment and procedures.

TO REAR
DEFOGGER

CHECK CONNECTOR

TO PASSIVE
RESTRAINT

READ
MEMORY
CONNECTOR

TO
REAR LAMPS

TO BACK-UP
LAMP

HIGH
MOUNT
BRAKE
LAMP

TO
LICENSE
PLATE
LAMP

TO
BLOWER
SWITCH

TO
FUEL PUMP

TO MPFI
CONTROL
UNIT

TO TURN
SIGNAL
LAMP

TO
LAP BELT

TO
AIR
SUSPENSION

TO TRANSMISSION
CONTROL

HEIGHT CONTROL
UNIT

DIGITAL INSTRUMENT PANEL

Courtesy of Cadillac Motor Car Division—GMC

ANALOG INSTRUMENT PANEL

Courtesy of Nissan Motors

ENGINE PERFORMANCE

No other major component of a car shows move evidence of the electronic revolution than the engine. A computer is used to integrate the various systems of the engine to ensure maximum efficiency.

Courtesy of the Cleveland Institute of Electronics

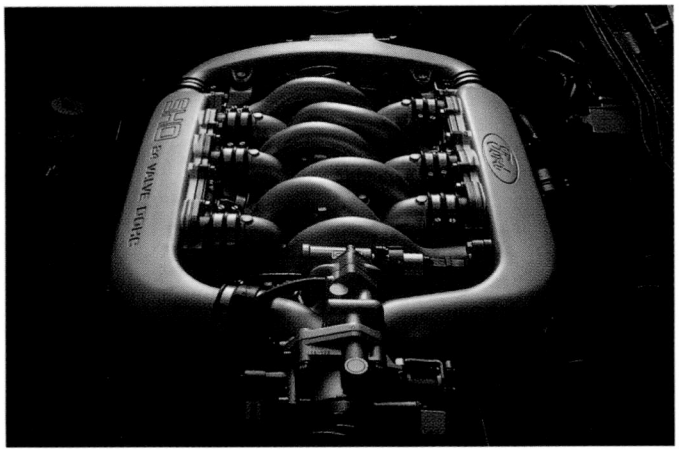

Emission controls, the induction system, and the ignition circuit work together to improve driveability. Purely electronic systems have replaced many mechanical components, such as the distributor.

Courtesy of Ford Motor Company

Courtesy of Ford Motor Company

Today's engines are much smaller than the engines of yesterday. Technology allows them to perform as well or better than the older-style engines. Many engines rely on superchargers or turbochargers for this performance.

Courtesy of Ford Motor Company

INJECTORS

FUEL RAIL

AIR INTAKE

INTAKE MANIFOLD

CARBON CANISTER

FUEL FILTER

INDUCTION SYSTEMS

Engine efficiency is affected by the induction system's ability to provide the correct air/fuel mixture under all conditions. Electronically-controlled fuel injection systems, multiple valves, and tuned manifolds provide this desired efficiency.

FILLER NECK

FUEL PUMP

INERTIA SWITCH

ROLLOVER VALVE

Courtesy of Toyota Motor Sales USA, Inc.   Courtesy of Cadillac Motor Division–GMC

TRANSMISSIONS

Power from the engine is sent to the wheels by an efficient transmission. Both automatic and manually-shifted transmissions and transaxles have been modified to include additional speed gears and electronic controls to limit power loss.

Courtesy of Cadillac Motor Division–GMC

Courtesy of Chrysler Corporation

Courtesy of Chrysler
Corporation

STEERING AND SUSPENSION SYSTEMS

Modifications to the car's steering and suspension systems permit aerodynamic styling and improve fuel economy by reducing the vehicle's weight.

Electronic steering and suspension systems provide safety and comfort to passengers without sacrificing engine power.

Courtesy of Chrysler Corporation

Courtesy of Ford Motor Company

BRAKE SYSTEMS

Passenger safety has been a major focus of engineers. Today's cars are equipped with disc brakes on two or four wheels. The clamping power of this type of brake allows for quick and sure braking power, even after repeated use.

MASTER CYLINDER

SPEED SENSOR

DISC BRAKE

Courtesy of Cadillac Motor Division—GMC

Ventilated rotors stay cool, reducing brake fade. The caliper fits over the rotor, housing the brake pistons and pads.

Courtesy of Buick Motor Division—GMC

C-14

Many late-model vehicles are fitted with electronically-controlled antilock brake systems that increase the vehicle's stability during hard braking.

Courtesy of Chrysler Corporation

THERMOSTAT   HEATER CORE

RADIATOR   WATER PUMP

HEATING SYSTEMS

New engine designs run at very high temperatures. Today's heater systems have been modified for this high heat and provide for quick passenger comfort in cold weather.

Courtesy of Chrysler Corporation

AIR-CONDITIONING SYSTEMS

Electronic controls are used in the air-conditioning systems of most newer cars. These controls provide passenger comfort, while minimizing engine power used to run the system.

Courtesy of Nissan Motors

COMPRESSOR   CONDENSER

EVAPORATOR

DRIER

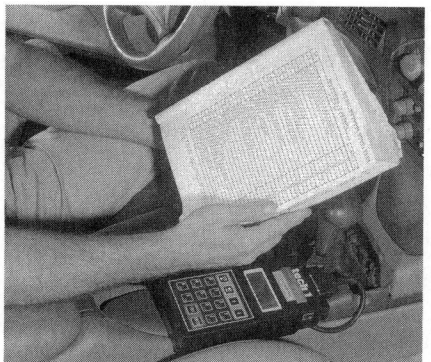

FIGURE 1–11 Master automotive technicians have proven their ability to work on the most complex repair jobs, such as diagnosing driveability problems.

FIGURE 1–12 ASE certification shoulder patches worn by (left) automotive technicians and (right) master automotive technicians.

tem combines voluntary testing with on-the-job experience to confirm that technicians have the skills needed to work on today's more complex vehicles. ASE recognizes two distinct levels of service capability—the automotive technician and the master automotive technician. The master automotive technician is certified by ASE in all major automotive systems (Figure 1–11). The automotive technician may have certification in only several areas.

To become ASE certified, a technician must pass one or more tests that stress diagnostic and repair problems. Eight different tests are offered in automotive repair. They are as follows.

1. Engine repair
2. Automatic transmission/transaxle
3. Manual transmissions and drive axles
4. Suspension and steering
5. Brakes
6. Electrical systems
7. Heating and air conditioning
8. Engine performance (driveability)

ASE also offers certification programs for parts counterpersons, engine machinists, body and paint technicians, and heavy-duty truck technicians. ASE also offers advanced level testing for auto technicians in the areas of alternate fuels and engine performance.

After passing at least one exam and providing proof of 2 years of hands-on work experience, the technician becomes ASE certified. Retesting is necessary every 5 years to remain certified. A technician who passes one examination receives an automotive technician shoulder patch. The master automotive technician patch is awarded to technicians who pass all eight of the basic automotive certification exams (Figure 1–12).

As mentioned, ASE certification requires that you have 2 years of full-time, hands-on working experience as an automotive technician. You may receive credit for one of the 2 years by substituting relevant formal training in one, or a combination, of the following.

◆ High school training. Three full years of training, either in automotive repair or in body repair and refinishing, may be substituted for 1 year of work experience.
◆ Post-high school training. Two full years of post-high school training in a public or private trade school, technical institute, community or 4-year college, or in an apprenticeship program may be counted as 1 year of work experience.
◆ Short courses. For shorter periods of post-high school training, you may substitute 2 months of training for 1 month of work experience.

You may receive full credit for the experience requirement by satisfactorily completing a 3- or 4-year apprenticeship program.

Each certification test consists of 40 to 80 multiple-choice questions. The questions are written by a panel of technical service experts, including domestic and import vehicle manufacturers, repair and test equipment and parts manufacturers, working automotive technicians, and automotive instructors. All questions are pretested and quality-checked on a national sample of technicians before they are included in the actual test. Many test questions force the student to choose between two distinct repair methods. Questions similar to this Technician A/Technician B format are included in the review questions at the end of each chapter in this text.

The knowledge and skills needed to pass the tests follows.

BASIC TECHNICAL KNOWLEDGE What is it? How does it work? This requires knowing what is in a system and how the system works. It also calls for knowing the procedures and precautions to be followed in making repairs and adjustments.

REPAIR KNOWLEDGE AND SKILL What is a likely source of a problem? How do you fix it? This requires you to understand and to apply generally accepted procedures and precautions in disassembly, assembly, and reconditioning operations; and in making major inspections and adjustments. It also calls for an ability to use service manuals and the precision tools of the trade.

TESTING AND DIAGNOSTIC KNOWLEDGE AND SKILL How do you find what is wrong? How do you determine the effectiveness of work done? This requires that you be able to recognize the existence of a problem and use generally available measuring and testing equipment to diagnose the difficulty. You also must be able to trace the effects of a particular condition and efficiently find the cause of a particular set of symptoms.

For further information on the ASE certification program, write: National Institute for Auto Service Excellence (ASE), 13505 Dulles Technology Drive, Herndon, VA 22071.

KEY TERMS

ASE	OEM
Deductible	Preventive maintenance
Diagnostic skills	Service technician
Independent shops	Warranty
Jobbers	WD

SUMMARY

◆ The modern auto industry is a global industry involving vehicle and parts manufacturers from many countries.

◆ Electronic computer controls are found on many auto systems, such as engines, ignition systems, transmissions, steering systems, and suspensions. The use of electronics in automobiles is increasing rapidly.

◆ The increasing complexity of vehicles, the increasing age of vehicles on the road, and the need to comply to federal laws concerning emission control and mileage are three reasons the need for quality service technicians is increasing.

◆ Preventive maintenance is extremely important in keeping today's electronically controlled systems in good working order.

◆ New car dealerships, independent service shops, specialty service shops, fleet operators, and many other businesses are in great need of qualified service technicians.

◆ A solid background in auto technology may be the basis for many other types of careers within the industry. Some examples are parts management, collision damage appraisal, sales, and marketing positions.

◆ Besides learning technical and mechanical skills, service technicians must learn to work as part of a team. As an employee, you will have certain responsibilities to both your employer and customers.

◆ Customer relations is an extremely important part of doing business. Professional, courteous treatment of customers and their vehicles is a must.

◆ Training in auto technology is available from many types of secondary and vocational and technical schools. Auto manufacturers also have cooperative programs with schools to ensure graduates understand modern systems and the equipment to service them.

◆ The National Institute for Automotive Service Excellence (ASE) actively promotes professionalism within the industry. Its certification program for automotive technicians and master auto technicians helps guarantee a high level of quality service.

◆ The ASE certification process involves both written tests and credit for on-the-job experience. Testing is available in many areas of auto technology.

 REVIEW QUESTIONS

1. Give three examples of how the automotive industry has evolved into a global industry.
2. Explain the basic requirements for becoming a successful automotive technician.
3. List at least five different types of businesses that hire service technicians. Describe the types of work these businesses handle and the advantages and disadvantages of working for them.
4. List some of the responsibilities of both employee and employer in maintaining a good working relationship.
5. Explain the role of ASE in the auto service industry and the ASE certification process of service technicians.
6. Repair work performed on vehicles still under manufacturer's warranty is usually performed by ____.
   a. independent service shops **c.** specialty shops
   b. dealerships   **d.** either a or b
7. Which of the following businesses perform work on only one or two automotive systems?
   a. dealerships
   b. independent service shops
   c. specialty shops
   d. fleet service departments

8. Normally whose job is it to prepare a repair cost estimate for a customer?
   a. service manager
   b. parts manager
   c. master automotive technician
   d. service advisor

9. Technician A says the Federal Emissions Performance Warranty is applicable only in certain states. Technician B says the Federal Emissions Defect Warranty is applicable for the entire United States. Who is correct?
   a. Technician A
   b. Technician B
   c. Both A and B
   d. Neither A nor B

10. In which of the following areas could an automotive technician become a specialist?
    a. brakes
    b. electrical system
    c. transmission
    d. all of the above

11. A technician must have a minimum of ____ year(s) of hands-on work experience to get ASE certification.
    a. 1
    b. 2
    c. 3
    d. 4

12. A technician who passes all eight basic ASE automotive certification tests is certified as a(n) ____.
    a. automotive technician
    b. master automotive technician
    c. service manager
    d. parts manager

13. Technician A says battery warranties are often prorated. Technician B says prorated warranties have a deductible. Who is correct?
    a. Technician A
    b. Technician B
    c. Both A and B
    d. Neither A nor B

14. Wholesale auto parts stores that sell aftermarket parts and supplies to service shops and the general public are called ____.
    a. warehouse distributors
    b. mass merchandisers
    c. jobbers
    d. freelancers

15. On-going technical training and support is available from ____.
    a. aftermarket parts manufacturers
    b. auto manufacturers
    c. jobbers
    d. all of the above

PRACTICING SAFETY IN THE SHOP

2

OBJECTIVES

◆ *Understand the importance of safety and accident prevention in an automotive shop.* ◆ *Explain the basic principles of personal safety, including protective eye wear, clothing, gloves, shoes, and hearing protection.* ◆ *Explain the procedures and precautions for safely using tools and equipment.* ◆ *Explain what should be done to maintain a safe work area, including handling vehicles in the shop and venting carbon monoxide gases.* ◆ *Describe the purpose of the laws concerning hazardous wastes and materials, including the right-to-know laws.*

Safety and accident prevention must be a priority in all automotive shops. There is great potential for serious accidents, simply because of the nature of the business and the equipment used. In fact, the automotive repair industry is rated as one of the most dangerous occupations in the country.

Vehicles, equipment, and many parts are very heavy; and parts often fit tightly together. Many components become hot during operation and high fluid pressures can build up inside the cooling system, fuel system, or battery. Batteries contain highly corrosive and potentially explosive acids. Fuels and cleaning solvents are flammable. Exhaust fumes are poisonous. During some repairs, technicians can be exposed to harmful dust particles and vapors.

Good safety practices eliminate these potential dangers. A careless attitude and poor work habits invite disaster. Shop accidents can cause serious injury, temporary or permanent disability, and death.

Safety is a very serious matter. Both the employer and employees must work together to protect the health and welfare of all who work in the shop.

This chapter contains many safety guidelines concerning personal, work area, tool and equipment, and hazardous material safety. In addition to these rules, special warnings have been used throughout this book to alert you to situations in which carelessness could result in personal injury. Finally, when working on cars, always follow safety guidelines given in service manuals and other technical literature. They are there for your protection.

PERSONAL SAFETY

Personal safety simply involves those precautions you take to protect yourself from injury. This includes wearing protective gear, dressing for safety, and correctly handling tools and equipment.

EYE PROTECTION Your eyes can become infected or permanently damaged by many things in a shop.

Some repair procedures, such as grinding, result in tiny particles of metal and dust that are thrown off at very high speeds. These metal and dirt particles can easily get into your eyes, causing scratches or cuts on your eyeball. Pressurized gases and liquids escaping a ruptured hose or fuel line fitting can spray a great distance. If these chemicals get into your eyes, they can cause blindness. Dirt and sharp bits of corroded metal can easily fall down into your eyes while you are working under a vehicle.

Eye protection should be worn whenever you are exposed to these risks. To be safe, you should wear **safety glasses** whenever you are working in the shop. There are many types of eye protection available (Figure 2–1). To provide adequate eye protection, safety glasses have lenses made of safety glass. They also offer some sort of side protection. Regular prescription glasses do not offer sufficient protection and, therefore, should not be worn as a substitute for safety glasses.

Wearing safety glasses at all times is a good habit to get into. To help develop this habit, wear safety glasses that fit well and feel comfortable.

FIGURE 2–2 Typical (A) earmuffs and (B) earplugs. *Courtesy of Willson Safety Products, Inc.*

FIGURE 2–1 (A) Safety glasses; (B) splash goggles; (C) face shield. *Courtesy of Goodson Shop Supplies*

If chemicals such as battery acid, fuel, or solvents get into your eyes, flush them continuously with clean water. Have someone call a doctor and get medical help immediately.

CLOTHING Your clothing should be well-fitted and comfortable but made with strong material. Loose, baggy clothing can easily get caught by moving parts and machinery. Neckties should not be worn. Some technicians prefer to wear coveralls or shop coats to protect their personal clothing. Cutoffs and short pants are inappropriate for shop work.

SHOES Automotive work involves the handling of many heavy objects, which can be accidentally dropped on your feet or toes. Always wear leather or similar material shoes or boots with nonslip soles. Steel-tipped safety shoes can give added protection to your feet. Jogging or basketball shoes, street shoes, and sandals are inappropriate in the shop.

GLOVES Good hand protection is often overlooked. A scrape, cut, or burn can limit your effectiveness at work for many days. A well-fitted pair of heavy work gloves should be worn during operations such as grinding and welding or when handling high-temperature components. Always wear approved rubber gloves when handling strong and dangerous caustic chemicals. They can easily burn your skin. Be very careful when handling these types of chemicals.

EAR PROTECTION Exposure to very loud noise levels for extended periods of time can lead to a loss of hearing. Air wrenches, engines running under a load, and vehicles running in enclosed areas can all generate annoying and harmful levels of noise. Simple earplugs or earphone-type protectors (Figure 2–2) should be worn in environments that are constantly noisy.

HAIR AND JEWELRY Long hair and loose, hanging jewelry can create the same type of hazard as loose-fitting clothing. They can become caught in moving engine parts and machinery. If you have long hair, tie it back or cover it with a cap.

Never wear rings, watches, bracelets, and neck chains. These can easily get caught in moving parts and cause serious injury.

LIFTING AND CARRYING Knowing the proper way to lift heavy objects is important. You should also use back-protection devices when you are lifting a heavy object. Always lift and work within your ability and ask others to help when you are not sure whether or not you can handle the size or weight of an object. Even small, compact parts can be surprisingly heavy or unbalanced. Think about how you are going to lift something before beginning. When lifting any object, follow these steps.

1. Place your feet close to the object. Position your feet so you will be able to maintain a good balance.
2. Keep your back and elbows as straight as possible. Bend your knees until your hands reach the best place to get a strong grip on the object (Figure 2–3).
3. If the part is in a cardboard box, make sure the box is in good condition. Old, damp, or poorly sealed boxes will tear and the part will fall out.
4. Firmly grasp the object or container. Never try to change your grip as you move the load.
5. Keep the object close to your body, and lift it up by straightening your legs. Use your leg muscles, not your back muscles.
6. If you must change your direction of travel, never twist your body. Turn your whole body, including your feet.
7. When placing the object on a shelf or counter, do not bend forward. Place the edge of the load on

POSITION BODY OVER LOAD.

KEEP BACK AS ERECT AS POSSIBLE.

USE LEG MUSCLES.

STRAIGHT BACK

WEIGHT CLOSE TO BODY

LEGS BENT

FIGURE 2–3 Use your leg muscles—never your back—when lifting any heavy load.

the shelf and slide it forward. Be careful not to pinch your fingers.

8. When setting down a load, bend your knees and keep your back straight. Never bend forward. This strains the back muscles.

9. When lowering something heavy to the floor, set the object on blocks of wood to protect your fingers.

OTHER PERSONAL SAFETY WARNINGS Never smoke while working on a vehicle or while working with any machine in the shop.

Playing around or "horseplay" is not fun when it sends someone to the hospital. Such things as air nozzle fights, creeper races, and practical jokes have no place in the shop.

To prevent serious burns, keep your skin away from hot metal parts such as the radiator, exhaust manifold, tailpipe, catalytic converter, and muffler.

When working with a hydraulic press, make sure the pressure is applied in a safe manner. It is generally wise to stand to the side when operating the press. Always wear safety glasses.

Properly store all parts and tools by putting them away in a place where people will not trip over them. This practice not only cuts down on injuries, it also reduces time wasted looking for a misplaced part or tool.

TOOL AND EQUIPMENT SAFETY

An automotive technician must follow these shop safety guidelines.

HAND TOOL SAFETY Careless use of simple hand tools such as wrenches, screwdrivers, and hammers causes many shop accidents that could be prevented.

Keep all hand tools grease-free and in good condition. Tools that slip can cause cuts and bruises. If a tool slips and falls into a moving part, it can fly out and cause serious injury.

Use the proper tool for the job. Make sure the tool is of professional quality. Using poorly made tools or the wrong tools can damage parts or the tool itself, or could cause injury. Do not use broken or damaged tools.

Be careful when using sharp or pointed tools. Do not place sharp tools or other sharp objects into your pockets. They can stab or cut your skin, ruin automotive upholstery, or scratch a painted surface. If a tool is supposed to be sharp, make sure it is sharp. Dull tools can be more dangerous than sharp tools.

POWER TOOL SAFETY Power tools are operated by an outside source of power, such as electricity, compressed air, or hydraulic pressure. Safety around power tools is very important. Serious injury can result from carelessness. Always wear safety glasses when using power tools.

If the tool is electrically powered, make sure it is properly grounded. Check the wiring for cracks in the insulation, as well as for bare wires, before using it. Also, when using electrical power tools, never stand on a wet or damp floor. Disconnect the power source before performing any service on the machine or tool. Before plugging in any electric tool, make sure the switch is off to prevent serious injury. When you are done using the tool, turn it off and unplug it. Never leave a running power tool unattended. When you leave, turn it off.

When using power equipment on a small part, never hold the part in your hand. Always mount the part in a bench vise or use vise grip pliers. Never try to use a machine or tool beyond its stated capacity or for operations requiring more than the rated power of the tool.

When working with larger power tools, such as bench or floor equipment, check the machines for signs of damage before using them. Place all safety guards in position (Figure 2–4). A safety guard is a protective cover over a moving part. It is designed to prevent injury. Wear safety glasses or a face shield. Make sure there are no people or parts around the machine before starting it. Keep your hands and clothing away from the moving parts. Maintain a balanced stance while using the machine.

COMPRESSED AIR EQUIPMENT SAFETY Tools that use compressed air are called **pneumatic tools**. Compressed air is used to inflate tires, apply paint, and drive tools. Compressed air can be dangerous when it is not used properly.

FIGURE 2–4 Safety guards in position on a bench grinder. *Courtesy of Snap-on Tools Corporation*

	OUTBOARD TWIN POST HOIST		DRIVE ON HOIST
	FLOOR JACK		FRAME CONTACT HOIST

FIGURE 2–5 Hoisting and lifting points for a typical unibody vehicle. *Courtesy of Chrysler Corporation*

When using compressed air, safety glasses or a face shield should be worn. Particles of dirt and pieces of metal, blown by the high-pressure air, can penetrate your skin or get into your eyes.

Before using a compressed air tool, check all hose connections. Always hold an air nozzle or air control device securely when starting or shutting off the compressed air. A loose nozzle can whip suddenly and cause serious injury. Never point an air nozzle at anyone. Never use compressed air to blow dirt from your clothes or hair. Never use compressed air to clean the floor or workbench.

Never spin bearings with compressed air. If the bearing is damaged, one of the steel balls or rollers might fly out and cause serious injury.

Finally, pneumatic tools must always be operated at the pressure recommended by the manufacturer.

LIFT SAFETY Always be careful when raising a vehicle on a lift or a hoist. Adapters and hoist plates must be positioned correctly on twin post and rail-type lifts to prevent damage to the underbody of the vehicle. There are specific lift points. These points allow the weight of the vehicle to be evenly supported by the adapters or hoist plates. The correct lift points can be found in the vehicle's service manual. Figure 2–5 shows typical locations for unibody and frame cars. These diagrams are for illustration only. Always follow the manufacturer's instructions. Before operating any lift or hoist, carefully read the operating manual and follow the operating instructions.

⚠️ *WARNING!*

Never use a lift or jack to move something heavier than it is designed for. Always check the rating before using a lift or jack. If a jack is rated for 2 tons, do not attempt to use it for a job requiring 5 tons. It is dangerous for you and the vehicle. ∎

Before driving a vehicle over a lift, position the arms and supports to provide an unobstructed clearance. Do not hit or run over lift arms, adapters, or axle supports. This could damage the lift, vehicle, or tires.

Position the lift supports to contact the vehicle at its lifting points. Raise the lift until the supports contact the vehicle. Then, check the supports to make sure they are in full contact with the vehicle. Raise the lift to the desired working height.

Make sure the vehicle's doors, hood, and trunk are closed before raising the vehicle. Never raise a car with someone inside.

⚠️ *WARNING!*

Before working under a car, make sure the lift's locking device is engaged. ∎

After lifting a vehicle to the desired height, always lower it onto its mechanical safeties. On some vehicles, the removal (or installation) of components can cause a critical shift of the vehicle's weight, which may cause the vehicle to be unstable on the lift. Refer to the vehicle's service manual for the recommended procedures to prevent this from happening.

Make sure tool trays, stands, and other equipment are removed from under the vehicle. Release the lift's locking devices according to the instructions before attempting to lower the lift.

FIGURE 2–6   Typical hydraulic jacks. *Courtesy of Blackhawk Automotive, Inc.*

FIGURE 2–7   Jack stands are used in combination with jacks and hoists. *Courtesy of Lincoln, St. Louis*

FIGURE 2–8   Using a chain hoist to lift an engine. *Courtesy of American Honda Motor Company, Inc.*

JACK AND JACK STAND SAFETY An automobile can be raised off the ground by a hydraulic jack (Figure 2–6). **Jack stands**, also called **safety stands** (Figure 2–7), are supports of different heights that sit on the floor. They are placed under a sturdy chassis member, such as the frame or axle housing, to support the vehicle. Like jacks, jack stands also have a capacity rating. Always use the correct rating of jack stand.

The jack should be removed after the jack stands are set in place. This eliminates a hazard, such as a jack handle sticking out into a walkway. A jack handle that is bumped or kicked can cause a tripping accident or cause the vehicle to fall. Never use a jack by itself to support an automobile. Always use a jack stand with the jack as a safety precaution. Make sure the jack stands are properly placed under the vehicle.

CHAIN HOIST AND CRANE SAFETY Heavy parts of the automobile, such as engines, are removed by using chain hoists (Figure 2–8) or cranes. Another term for a chain hoist is chain fall. Cranes often are called cherry pickers.

To prevent serious injury, chain hoists and cranes must be properly attached to the parts being lifted. Always use bolts with enough strength to support the object being lifted. After you have attached the lifting chain or cable to the part that is being removed, have your instructor check it. Place the chain hoist or crane directly over the assembly. Then, attach the chain or cable to the hoist.

CLEANING EQUIPMENT SAFETY Parts cleaning is a necessary step in most repair procedures. Cleaning automotive parts can be divided into four basic categories.

Chemical cleaning relies primarily on some type of chemical action to remove dirt, grease, scale, paint, or rust (Figure 2–9). A combination of heat, agitation, mechanical scrubbing, or washing may be used to help remove dirt. Chemical cleaning equipment includes small parts washers, hot/cold tanks, pressure washers, spray washers, and salt baths.

Thermal cleaning relies on heat, which bakes off or oxidizes the dirt (Figure 2–10). Thermal cleaning leaves an ash residue on the surface that must be removed by an additional cleaning process, such as airless shot blasting or spray washing.

Abrasive cleaning relies on physical abrasion to clean the surface. This includes everything from a

FIGURE 2–9 Automotive parts washer. *Courtesy of Broadhead-Garrett*

FIGURE 2–11 Heads undergoing abrasive cleaning in a steel shot blaster. *Courtesy of Kansas Instruments, Inc.*

FIGURE 2–12 Open steam cleaning was once a popular means of cleaning engines.

wire brush to glass bead blasting, airless steel shot blasting, abrasive tumbling, and vibratory cleaning (Figure 2–11). Chemical in-tank solution sonic cleaning might also be included here because it relies on the scrubbing action of ultrasonic sound waves to loosen surface contaminants.

Steam cleaning uses hot water vapor mixed with chemical cleaning agents to clean dirt from an object (Figure 2–12). After steam cleaning, the object should be thoroughly hosed down with clean water, then air dried.

There are several reasons why steam cleaning has rapidly declined in recent years. Concerns about our environment have led to mandates that a closed loop system must be used for steam cleaning. This means that the runoff from the cleaning process must be collected by and contained within the steam cleaning system. The runoff can not flow into a public sewage system.

Steam cleaning is normally done in an uncongested portion of the shop or in a separate building. Care

must be taken to protect all painted surfaces and exposed skin from contact with the steam's heat and chemicals. Injury or damage would result. In addition, care must also be taken when working on the slippery floor that this process creates.

Before using a steam cleaning machine, check the electrical cords. Pay special attention to the ground-

FIGURE 2–10 Complete thermal cleaning system. *Courtesy of Bayco, Inc.*

ing connector at the plug. If the machine is not properly grounded, there is a great possibility of getting an electrical shock.

Finally, steam cleaning takes a lot of time and work. Most shops cannot justify the labor cost for using an open steam cleaning system.

VEHICLE OPERATION When the customer brings a vehicle in for service, certain shop safety guidelines should be followed. For example, when moving a car into the shop, check the brakes before beginning. Then, buckle the safety belt. Drive carefully in and around the shop. Make sure no one is near, the way is clear, and there are no tools or parts under the car before you start the engine.

When road testing the car, obey all traffic laws. Drive only as far as is necessary to check the automobile. Never make excessively quick starts, turn corners too quickly, or drive faster than conditions allow.

If the engine must be running while working on the car, block the wheels to prevent the car from moving. Place the transmission into park for automatic transmissions or in neutral for manual transmissions. Set the emergency brake. Never stand directly in front of or behind a running vehicle.

Run the engine only in a well-ventilated area to avoid the danger of poisonous carbon monoxide (**CO**) in the engine exhaust. If the shop is equipped with an exhaust ventilation system (Figure 2–13), use it. If not, use a hose to direct the exhaust out of the building.

WORK AREA SAFETY

Your work area should be kept clean and safe. The floor and bench tops should be kept clean, dry, and orderly. Any oil, coolant, or grease on the floor can make it slippery. Slips can result in serious injuries. To clean up oil, use a commercial oil absorbent. Keep all water off the floor. Water is slippery on smooth floors, and electricity flows well through water. Aisles and walkways should be kept clean and wide enough to easily move through. Make sure the work areas around machines are large enough to safely operate the machine.

Proper ventilation of space heaters, used in some shops, is necessary to reduce the CO levels in the shop. Also, proper ventilation is very important in areas where volatile solvents and chemicals are used. A volatile liquid is one that vaporizes very quickly.

Keep an up-to-date list of emergency telephone numbers clearly posted next to the telephone. These numbers should include a doctor, hospital, and fire and police departments. Also, the work area should have a first-aid kit for treating minor injuries and eye-flushing kits readily available.

FIGURE 2–13 Removing carbon monoxide.

Gasoline is a highly flammable volatile liquid. Always keep gasoline or diesel fuel in an approved safety can, and never use it to clean your hands or tools. Oily rags should also be stored in an approved metal container. When these oily, greasy, or paint-soaked rags are left lying about or are not stored properly, they can cause spontaneous combustion. Spontaneous combustion results in a fire that starts by itself, without a match.

Make sure all drain covers are snugly in place. Open drains or covers that are not flush to the floor can cause toe, ankle, and leg injuries.

Handle all solvents (or any liquids) with care to avoid spillage. Keep all solvent containers closed, except when pouring. Be extra careful when transferring flammable materials from bulk storage (Figure 2–14). Static electricity can build up enough to create a spark that could cause an explosion. Discard or clean all empty solvent containers. Solvent fumes in the bottom of these containers are very flammable. Never light matches or smoke near flammable solvents and chemicals, including battery acids. Solvent and other combustible materials must be stored in approved and designated storage cabinets or rooms (Figure 2–15). Storage rooms should have adequate ventilation.

FIGURE 2–14 Flammable liquids should be stored in safety-approved containers. *Courtesy of Gutman Advertising Agency*

FIGURE 2–15
Store combustible
materials in
approved safety
cabinets. *Courtesy
of Sherwin-Williams
Company*

Know where the fire extinguishers are and what types of fires they put out (Table 2–1). A multipurpose dry chemical fire extinguisher will put out ordinary combustibles, flammable liquids, and electrical fires. Never put water on a gasoline fire. The water will just spread the fire. Use a fire extinguisher to smother the flames. Remember, during a fire, never open doors or windows unless it is absolutely necessary; the extra draft will only make the fire worse. A good rule is to call the fire department first and then attempt to extinguish the fire.

To extinguish a fire, stand 6 to 10 feet from the fire. Hold the extinguisher firmly in an upright posi-

	Class of Fire	Typical Fuel Involved	Type of Extinguisher
TABLE 2–1 GUIDE TO EXTINGUISHER SELECTION			
Class **A** Fires (green)	**For Ordinary Combustibles** Put out a class A fire by lowering its temperature or by coating the burning combustibles.	Wood Paper Cloth Rubber Plastics Rubbish Upholstery	Water*[1] Foam* Multipurpose dry chemical[4]
Class **B** Fires (red)	**For Flammable Liquids** Put out a class B fire by smothering it. Use an extinguisher that gives a blanketing, flame-interrupting effect; cover whole flaming liquid surface.	Gasoline Oil Grease Paint Lighter fluid	Foam* Carbon dioxide[5] Halogenated agent[6] Standard dry chemical[2] Purple K dry chemical[3] Multipurpose dry chemical[4]
Class **C** Fires (blue)	**For Electrical Equipment** Put out a class C fire by shutting off power as quickly as possible and by always using a nonconducting extinguishing agent to prevent electric shock.	Motors Appliances Wiring Fuse boxes Switchboards	Carbon dioxide[5] Halogenated agent[6] Standard dry chemical[2] Purple K dry chemical[3] Multipurpose dry chemical[4]
Class **D** Fires (yellow)	**For Combustible Metals** Put out a class D fire of metal chips, turnings, or shavings by smothering or coating with a specially designed extinguishing agent.	Aluminum Magnesium Potassium Sodium Titanium Zirconium	Dry powder extinguishers and agents only

*Cartridge-operated water, foam, and soda-acid types of extinguishers are no longer manufactured. These extinguishers should be removed from service when they become due for their next hydrostatic pressure test.
Notes:
(1) Freezes in low temperatures unless treated with antifreeze solution, usually weighs over 20 pounds, and is heavier than any other extinguisher mentioned.
(2) Also called ordinary or regular dry chemical. (sodium bicarbonate)
(3) Has the greatest initial fire-stopping power of the extinguishers mentioned for class B fires. Be sure to clean residue immediately after using the extinguisher so sprayed surfaces will not be damaged. (potassium bicarbonate)
(4) The only extinguishers that fight A, B, and C classes of fires. However, they should not be used on fires in liquefied fat or oil of appreciable depth. Be sure to clean residue immediately after using the extinguisher so sprayed surfaces will not be damaged. (ammonium phosphates)
(5) Use with caution in unventilated, confined spaces.
(6) May cause injury to the operator if the extinguishing agent (a gas) or the gases produced when the agent is applied to a fire is inhaled.

tion. Aim the nozzle at the base and use a side-to-side motion, sweeping the entire width of the fire. Stay low to avoid inhaling the smoke. If it gets too hot or too smoky, get out. Remember, never go back into a burning building for anything.

MANUFACTURER'S WARNINGS AND GOVERNMENT REGULATIONS

The solvents and other chemical products used in an auto shop carry warnings and caution information that must be read and understood by all that use them. Likewise, all federal (including Occupational Safety and Health Administration [**OSHA**], Mine Safety and Health Administration [**MSHA**], and National Institute for Occupational Safety and Health [**NIOSH**]), state, and local safety regulations must be fully understood, and strictly followed.

Many repair and service procedures generate what are known as **hazardous wastes**. Dirty solvents and cleaners are good examples of hazardous wastes. Not only are the waste materials of concern but so also are the different chemicals used by the shop. Every employee in the shop is protected by **right-to-know laws** concerning all chemicals. These laws started with OSHA's Hazard Communication Standard, which was published in 1983. This document was originally intended for chemical companies and manufacturers that require employees to handle potentially hazardous materials in the workshop. Since then, the majority of states have enacted their own right-to-know laws. The federal courts have decided that these regulations should apply to all companies, including auto repair shops.

The general intent of right-to-know laws is for employers to provide their employees with a safe working place as it relates to hazardous materials. Specifically, there are three areas of employer responsibility.

Primarily, all employees must be trained about their rights under the legislation, the nature of the hazardous chemicals in their workplace, and the contents of the labels on the chemicals. All of the information about each chemical must be posted on material safety data sheets (**MSDS**) and must be accessible. The manufacturer of the chemical must give these sheets to its customers, if they are requested to do so (Figure 2–16). They detail the chemical composition and precautionary information for all products that can present a health or safety hazard. Employees must become familiar with the general uses, protective equipment, accident or spill procedures, and any other information regarding the safe handling of the hazardous material. This training

must be given to employees annually and provided to new employees as part of their job orientation. The Canadian equivalents to MSDS are called workplace hazardous materials information systems (**WHMIS**).

Secondly, all hazardous material must be properly labeled, indicating what health, fire, or reactivity hazard it poses and what protective equipment is necessary when handling each chemical. The manufacturer of the hazardous waste materials must provide all warnings and precautionary information, which must be read and understood by the user before application. Attention to all label precautions is essential for the proper use of the chemical and for prevention of hazardous conditions. A list of all hazardous materials used in the shop must be posted for the employees to see.

Finally, shops must maintain documentation on the hazardous chemicals in the workplace, proof of training programs, records of accidents or spill incidents, satisfaction of employee requests for specific chemical information via the MSDS, and a general right-to-know compliance procedure manual utilized within the shop.

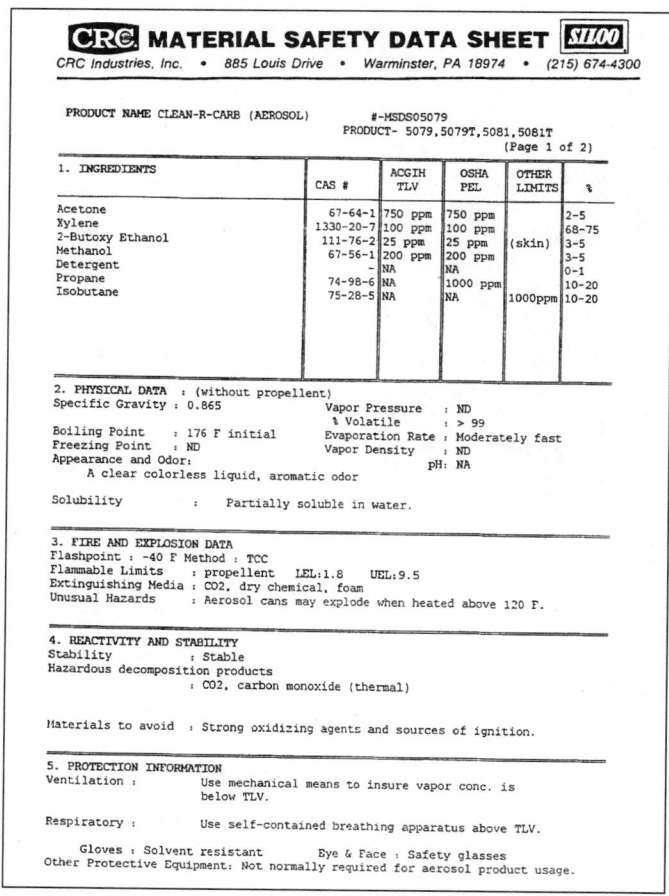

FIGURE 2–16 Material safety data sheets are an important part of employee training and should be readily accessible. *Courtesy of CRC Industries, Inc.*

FIGURE 2–17 Wear proper safety equipment when handling hazardous waste. *Courtesy of DuPont Company*

⚠ WARNING!

When handling any hazardous waste material, be sure to wear the proper safety equipment (Figure 2–17) covered under the right-to-know law. Follow all required procedures correctly. This includes the use of approved respirator equipment. ■

Something is classified as a hazardous waste by the Environmental Protection Agency if it is on the EPA list of known harmful materials or has one or more of the following characteristics.

◆ **Ignitability.** If it is a liquid with a flash point below 140°F or a solid that can spontaneously ignite.

◆ **Corrosivity.** If it dissolves metals and other materials or burns the skin.

◆ **Reactivity.** Any material that reacts violently with water or other materials or releases cyanide gas, hydrogen sulfide gas, or similar gases when exposed to low pH acid solutions. This also includes material that generates toxic mists, fumes, vapors, and flammable gases.

◆ **EP toxicity.** Materials that leach one or more of eight heavy metals in concentrations greater than 100 times primary drinking water standard concentrations.

Complete EPA lists of hazardous wastes can be found in the Code of Federal Regulations. It should be noted that no material is considered hazardous waste until the shop is finished using it and ready to dispose of it.

⚠ WARNING!

The shop is ultimately responsible for the safe disposal of hazardous wastes, even after the waste leaves the shop. Only licensed waste removal companies should be used to dispose of the waste. Make sure you know what the company is planning to do with the waste. Make sure you have a written contract stating what is supposed to happen with the waste. Leave nothing to chance. In the event of an emergency hazardous waste spill, contact the National Response Center (1-800-424-8802) immediately. Failure to do so can result in a $10,000 fine, a year in jail, or both. ■

Many shops use full-service haulers to remove hazardous waste from the property (Figure 2–18). Besides hauling the hazardous waste away, the hauler will also take care of all the paperwork, deal with the various government agencies, and advise the shop on how to recover the disposal costs.

Asbestos had been used as a lining for many auto parts. However, it is used very seldom now. This is because asbestos has been identified as a health hazard. When working with asbestos materials, such as brake pads, clutch discs, and some engine gaskets, there are certain guidelines you should follow. All asbestos waste must be disposed of in accordance with OSHA and EPA asbestos regulations. An industrial vacuum equipped with multiple-stage, high-efficiency filters and housing must be used when doing brake work. These machines are used to remove any accumulation of asbestos dust on the brake parts. The dust is collected in a vacuum bag. These bags must be disposed of properly. When you remove one of these vacuum bags, an approved respirator should

FIGURE 2–18 Many automotive shops hire full-service and certified companies to remove hazardous waste from their area. *Courtesy of DuPont Company*

be worn. Never use compressed air or dry sweeping for cleaning up asbestos dust. Water or another dust suppressant should be applied to the floor if brooms are going to be used to clean it.

To minimize the risks of working around asbestos, follow these simple personal hygiene guidelines.

- Do not smoke while or after working with the materials.
- Thoroughly wash yourself before eating.
- Shower after work.
- Change into work clothes when you arrive at work, and change from your work clothes after work. Work clothing should not be taken home.

OSHA and the EPA have other strict rules and regulations that help to promote safety in the auto shop. These are described throughout this text whenever they are applicable.

KEY TERMS

Abrasive cleaning	OSHA
Chemical cleaning	Pneumatic tools
CO	Power tools
Corrosivity	Reactivity
EP toxicity	Right-to-know laws
Hazardous waste	Safety glasses
Ignitability	Safety stands
Jack stands	Thermal cleaning
MSDS	WHMIS

SUMMARY

- Dressing safely for work is very important. This includes snug-fitting clothing, eye and ear protection, protective gloves, strong shoes, and caps to cover long hair.
- When choosing eye protection, make sure it has safety glass and offers side protection.
- When shop noise exceeds safe levels, protect your ears by wearing earplugs or earmuffs.
- Safety while using any tool is a must, particularly power tools. Before plugging in a power tool, make sure the power switch is off. Disconnect the power before servicing the tool.
- Always observe all relevant safety rules when operating a vehicle lift or hoist. Jacks, jack stands, chain hoists, and cranes can also cause injury if not operated safely.
- Steam cleaning must be done in an uncongested area. Due to environmental considerations and because it is so labor intensive, its use has declined.
- Use care whenever it is necessary to remove a vehicle in the shop. Carelessness and playing around can lead to a damaged vehicle and serious injury.

- Carbon monoxide gas is a poisonous gas present in engine exhaust fumes. It must be properly vented from the shop using tailpipe hoses or other reliable methods.
- Adequate ventilation is also necessary when working with any volatile solvent or material.
- Gasoline and diesel fuel are highly flammable and should be kept in approved safety cans. Never light matches near any combustible materials.
- It is important to know when to use each of the various types of fire extinguishers. When fighting a fire, aim the nozzle at the base and use a side-to-side sweeping motion.
- Right-to-know laws began in 1983 and are designed to protect employees who must handle hazardous materials and wastes on the job. The EPA lists many materials as hazardous, provided they have one or more of the following characteristics: ignitability, corrosivity, reactivity, and EP toxicity.
- Material safety data sheets contain important chemical information and must be furnished to all employees annually. New employees should be given the sheets as part of their job orientation.
- All asbestos waste should be disposed of according to OSHA and EPA regulations.

 REVIEW QUESTIONS

1. At what point is a material considered hazardous?
2. Where in the shop should a list of emergency telephone numbers be posted?
3. When should eye protection be worn?
4. How should a class B fire be extinguished?
5. Where can complete EPA lists of hazardous wastes be found?
6. Safety glasses should have ____.
   a. side protection
   b. shatterproof lenses
   c. comfortable fit
   d. all of the above
7. Gasoline is ____.
   a. highly volatile
   b. highly flammable
   c. dangerous especially in vapor form
   d. all of the above
8. Technician A says it is recommended that you wear shoes with nonslip soles in the shop. Technician B says steel-toed shoes offer the best foot protection. Who is correct?
   a. Technician A   c. Both A and B
   b. Technician B   d. Neither A nor B

9. Technician A does steam cleaning in a building separate from the shop. Technician B does it in an uncongested part of the shop. Who is correct?
    a. Technician A
    b. Technician B
    c. Both A and B
    d. Neither A nor B

10. Which type of parts cleaning method leaves an ash residue that must be removed by further cleaning?
    a. chemical
    b. abrasive
    c. thermal
    d. steam

11. Federal right-to-know laws concern ____.
    a. auto emission standards
    b. hazards associated with chemicals used in the workplace
    c. employee benefits
    d. hiring practices

12. Which of the following is/are important when working in the automotive shop?
    a. Use the proper tool for the job.
    b. Avoid loose-fitting clothes.
    c. Wear steel-tipped shoes.
    d. All of the above.

13. Which exhaust gas from automobiles is considered dangerous?
    a. carbon dioxide
    b. carbon monoxide
    c. nitrogen
    d. both a and b

14. Which of the following is *not* recommended to extinguish flammable liquid fires?
    a. foam
    b. carbon dioxide
    c. water
    d. dry chemical

15. Technician A says some machines can be routinely used beyond their stated capacity.

Technician B says a power tool can be left running unattended if the technician puts up a power on sign. Who is correct?
    a. Technician A
    b. Technician B
    c. Both A and B
    d. Neither A nor B

16. If a substance dissolves metals and other materials, or burns the skin, it is said to possess ____.
    a. toxicity
    b. reactivity
    c. ignitability
    d. corrosivity

17. Technician A ties his long hair behind his head while working in the shop. Technician B covers her long hair with a brimless cap. Who is correct?
    a. Technician A
    b. Technician B
    c. Both A and B
    d. Neither A nor B

18. Technician A uses compressed air to blow dirt from his clothes and hair. Technician B says this should only be done outside. Who is correct?
    a. Technician A
    b. Technician B
    c. Both A and B
    d. Neither A nor B

19. Protective gloves should be worn when ____.
    a. welding
    b. grinding metal
    c. working with caustic cleaning solutions
    d. all of the above

20. Jack stands are used ____.
    a. with a jack or hoist
    b. in place of a jack or hoist
    c. under sturdy chassis members
    d. both a and c

AUTOMOTIVE SYSTEMS

3

OBJECTIVES

◆ *Explain the major events that have influenced the development of the automobile during the last 30 years.* ◆ *Explain the difference between unitized and body-over-frame vehicles.* ◆ *Describe the manufacturing process used in a modern automated automobile assembly plant.* ◆ *List the basic systems that make up an automobile and name their major components and functions.* ◆ *Explain the importance of preventive maintenance, and list at least six examples of typical preventive maintenance.*

The automobile has changed quite a bit since the first horseless carriage went down an American street. In 1896, both Henry Ford and Ransom Eli Olds test drove their first gasoline-powered vehicles. At that time, the automobile looked like the horse-drawn carriages it was designed to replace (Figure 3–1). In fact, for many years most cars looked like carriages. In 1919, ninety percent of the cars had carriagelike open bodies. Although body styles changed, cars continued to have carriagelike features. It was not until 1939 that running boards began disappearing. In fact, some very popular cars in the 1960s and 1970s (such as the Volkswagen Beetle) still had them.

These early cars had rear-mounted engines and very tall tires. They were designed to move people down dirt roads. As the roads improved and became paved, the automobile changed. As more people owned cars, automobiles changed. As manufacturers tried to sell more cars, automobiles changed. As concerns for safety and environment grew, automobiles changed. As automobiles changed, they became more practical, more affordable, safer, more comfortable, and faster. The automobile had slowly evolved into a sturdy, dependable, and comfortable machine (Figure 3–2). Although many improvements have been made to the original design, the basic structure of the automobile has changed very little.

Most cars still use gasoline engines to drive two or more wheels. A steering system is used to control the direction of the car. A brake system is used to slow down and stop the car. A suspension system is

FIGURE 3–1   The modern automobile has changed greatly from the days of the first horseless carriages. *Camaro is courtesy of the Chevrolet Division, General Motors Corporation*

FIGURE 3–2 The 1925 Pierce Arrow, like most older cars, had the same basic systems found on today's cars.

FIGURE 3–4 A mid-1960s 7-liter (427 cid) V-8 engine. *Courtesy of* Super Ford Magazine

used to absorb road shocks and help the driver maintain control on bumpy roads. The parts of these major systems are mounted on steel frames and the frame is covered with body panels. These panels give the car its shape and protect those inside from the weather and dirt. The body panels also offer some protection for the passengers in an accident.

Although the basics of an automobile have changed little in the past 100 years, the parts and the control systems have greatly changed. The entire automobile is technologically light-years ahead of Ford's and Olds's early models (Figure 3–3). The use of new technology has changed the slow, unreliable, user-hostile vehicles of the early 1900s into vehicles that travel at speeds in excess of 200 mph, operate trouble-free for thousands of miles, and provide comforts that even the rich had not dreamed of in 1896.

The most dramatic changes have occurred during the past 30 years. By the mid-1960s, American cars became heavy, big, and had large engines. As a result, those cars were fast and comfortable but used a lot of fuel and cornered and stopped poorly; their exhaust seriously polluted the air. The car manufacturers produced and sold what Americans wanted. Both

Chevrolet and Ford had full-sized cars with 7-liter (427 cubic inches) engines that produced more than 425 horsepower (Figure 3–4). These cars were fast and were constantly battling each other at race tracks. They were built for street use and it seemed everyone wanted one, in spite of the fact they were lucky to go 6 miles on a gallon of gasoline.

The drive to go faster resulted in putting these large engines in smaller cars. The power race between the manufacturers was getting ridiculously wonderful but suddenly it was brought to a halt. In 1965, legislation was passed limiting the levels of fuel and exhaust emissions. Automotive manufacturers were forced to build cleaner-burning engines. In the following years, stricter emissions laws were passed; manufacturers developed systems to control emissions.

The different emission control systems that were developed and added to cars over the next 10 years drastically affected the power output and performance of the big engines of the 1960s. Manufacturers were forced to make many changes to the design of their engines. As a result, horsepower output was reduced.

World events in the 1970s continued to shape the development of today's automobile. An oil embargo by Arab nations in 1973 caused the price of gasoline to quickly increase to four times its normal price. This event caused most Americans to realize that the supply of gasoline and other nonrenewable resources was limited. Car buyers wanted cars that were not only kind to the atmosphere but that also used little fuel.

In 1975, Congress passed the Corporate Average Fuel Economy (**CAFE**) standards, which requires auto makers not only to manufacture clean-burning

FIGURE 3–3 Today's automobile is the result of almost 100 years of innovation. *Courtesy of Pontiac Motor Division, General Motors Corporation*

engines but also to equip their vehicles with engines that burn gasoline efficiently. Under the CAFE standards, different models from each manufacturer were tested for the number of miles they could be driven on a gallon of gas. The fuel efficiencies of these vehicles were averaged together to arrive at a corporate average. The CAFE standards have increased many times since it was established. A manufacturer that does not meet CAFE standards for a given model year faces heavy fines.

MODERN POWER PLANTS

While trying to produce more efficient vehicles, American manufacturers put four-cylinder and other small engines into their cars, instead of large eight-cylinder engines. Some basic engine systems like carburetors and ignition breaker points were replaced by fuel injection systems and electronic ignition systems.

By the mid-1980s the American automobile had gained a measure of self-control over emissions and fuel efficiency through the use of computers and other electronics. Fuel and air were carefully monitored and consumed in proportions that maximized the performance of the smaller engines while minimizing the production of harmful pollutants.

After a prolonged period of economic growth in the 1980s, the demand for good performance is once again a shaping force in automotive developments. However, this time the industry is responding with responsibility. Electronic sensors are used to monitor engine functions. Computerized engine control systems control air and fuel delivery, ignition timing, emission systems operation, and a host of other related operations. The result is a clean-burning, fuel-efficient, and powerful engine. Examples of late-model, high-tech, high-performance engines are the Northstar engine from General Motors and the DOHC 4.6-liter engine from Ford Motor Co. These engines (Figure 3–5) have approximately 260 cubic inches and put out about 280 horsepower. They provide enough power to have these cars accelerate at nearly the same rate as the larger engined cars of the 1960s. They do this while achieving at least four times the gas mileage. They also do this in cars that corner and stop very well.

DESIGN EVOLUTION

Through the 1960s and early 1970s, virtually all American automobiles were manufactured with body-over-frame construction, rear-wheel drive, and symmetrical designs.

In the mid-1970s, foreign car manufacturers were already offering small, fuel-efficient vehicles to

FIGURE 3–5 A late-model, high-tech, high-performance V-8 engine. *Courtesy of General Motors Corporation*

the American market. When gasoline prices skyrocketed, cars and light trucks from Japan and Europe began "selling like hot cakes."

To meet this foreign challenge, domestic auto makers began to use many of the design features introduced to America by foreign manufacturers.

In 1977, most American cars used a perimeter-type frame and weighed around 4,500 pounds. In 1978, unitized construction was used on American-made cars. Body weight began to decrease and the first American-made transverse engine, front-wheel-drive cars were introduced.

By 1981, unibodies were used in almost half the American-made cars. Today, all but a handful of domestic cars are unibodies. The average weight of today's car is approximately 3,000 pounds.

UNITIZED CONSTRUCTION

A **unibody** has no separate frame (Figure 3–6). It is a stressed hull structure in which each of the body

FIGURE 3–6 Structure of a typical unibody vehicle. *Courtesy of Toyota Motor Corporation*

FIGURE 3–7 Location of rubber biscuits or mounts.
Courtesy of Toyota Motor Corporation

TWO-DOOR SEDAN

FOUR-DOOR SEDAN

FIGURE 3–8 Typical sedan body shapes.

parts supplies structural support and strength to the entire vehicle.

The major advantage of unibody vehicles is that they tend to be more tightly constructed because the major parts are all welded together. This design characteristic helps protect the occupants during a collision. However, it causes damage patterns that differ from those of body-over-frame vehicles. Rather than localized damage, the stiffer sections used in unibody design tend to transmit and distribute impact energy throughout more of the vehicle.

BODY-OVER-FRAME CONSTRUCTION

In body-over-frame construction, the frame is the vehicle's foundation. The body and all major parts of the vehicle are attached to the frame. The frame must also be strong enough to keep the other car parts in alignment should a collision occur.

The frame is an independent, separate component, which is not welded to any of the major units of the body. The body is generally bolted to the frame. Large, specially designed rubber or mounts are placed between the frame and body structure to reduce noise and vibration from entering the passenger compartment (Figure 3–7). Quite often two layers of rubber are used in the mounting pads to provide a smoother ride. In higher priced vehicles, shock absorbers are mounted between the body and the rear frame, which serve to minimize vibrations when cars are traveling at high speeds.

Modern body-over-frame designs are still used on many of today's pick-up trucks, full-size vans, and some full-size passenger cars.

BODY SHAPES

Various methods of classifying vehicles exist. Vehicles may be classified by engine type, body/frame construction, fuel consumption structure, type of drive, or the classifications most common to consumers, which are body shape, seat arrangement, and number of doors.

Seven basic body shapes are used today.

1. **Sedan.** A vehicle with front and back seats that accommodates four to six persons is classified as either a two- or four-door sedan (Figure 3–8). If the vehicle does not have door or B pillars, it is called a hardtop. It can also be classified as either a two- or four-door hardtop.
2. **Convertible top.** After an absence from the domestic market for several years, the convertible top made a comeback in 1985. Convertibles have vinyl roofs that can be raised or lowered (Figure 3–9). Like a hardtop, a convertible top has no door pillars. It can be available in two- and four-door models. Some convertibles have both front and rear seats. Those without rear seats are commonly referred to as sports cars.
3. **Liftback** or **hatchback.** The distinguishing feature of this vehicle is its rear luggage compartment, which is an extension of the passenger compartment. Access to the luggage compartment is gained through an upward opening hatch-type door (Figure 3–10). The vehicle comes in three- and five-door models.

TWO-DOOR CONVERTIBLE

SPORTS CAR TYPE-CONVERTIBLE

FIGURE 3–9 Typical convertible body shapes.

THREE-DOOR LIFTBACK

FIVE-DOOR LIFTBACK

FIGURE 3–10 Typical liftback or hatchback body shapes.

TWO-DOOR STATION WAGON

FOUR-DOOR STATION WAGON

FIGURE 3–11 Typical station wagon body shapes.

PICK-UP TRUCK

CREW-CAB PICK-UP TRUCK

FIGURE 3–12 Typical pick-up body shapes.

MINIVAN

FULL-SIZED CARGO VAN

FIGURE 3–13 Typical van body shapes.

4. **Station wagon.** A station wagon (Figure 3–11) is characterized by its roof, which extends straight back, allowing a spacious interior luggage compartment in the rear. The rear door, which can be opened in various ways depending on the model, provides access to the luggage compartment. Station wagons come in two- and four-door models and have space for up to nine passengers.

5. **Pick-ups.** Pick-up truck body designs (Figure 3–12) have an open cargo area behind the driver's compartment. They are available with standard cab designs, with extended cab areas (some have added seats in back of the front seat), and some with open or closed cargo spaces. They are available in two-wheel drive, four-wheel drive (4 × 4), or all-wheel drive.

6. **Vans.** The van body design (Figure 3–13) has a tall roof and a totally enclosed large cargo or passenger area. Vans can seat from two to twelve passengers, depending on size and design.

7. **Sport utility** or **multipurpose vehicles.** This classification of vehicles covers a range of body designs (Figure 3–14). Vehicles are available in two-wheel drive, four-wheel drive (4 × 4), or all-wheel drive. Sports vehicles are best described as multipurpose vehicles and can carry a wide range of passengers, depending on their size and design.

FIGURE 3–14 Typical sports utility vehicle body shapes.
Courtesy of McGard, Inc.

THE ELECTRONIC REVOLUTION

Perhaps the thing that has brought about the most change to the automotive industry is the computer. Not only are engine support systems controlled by computers, nearly every other major system on a car has some sort of electronic control. Initially, electronic controls were added to help maintain the emissions levels that the vehicle had when it was new. As these controls became more sophisticated, they improved engine performance. These electronic controls have done so much for engine efficiency that some of the early emission control systems have been eliminated.

The use of electronics has and will continue to change the automobile, as will advances made in other technologies. New composite materials are being used for engine parts. Soon a majority of the engine will be made with plastic-based materials. Steel body panels are being replaced with aluminum and plastic parts that are glued to a frame. The increased use of plastics and composites are the result of the manufacturer's efforts to reduce the weight of the vehicles. Reduced weight normally results in better performance and fuel economy. This is especially true when the weight of moving engine parts is reduced. A loss of weight here reduces the frictional drag of the engine, resulting in great increases in power output.

Systems have been developed and are being installed to allow engines to run on cleaner burning fuels. Advances in this area are sure to be more popular in the near future. Research is being done that may result in different types of engines powering cars of the future. Some of these engine designs are currently in a few car models and may spread throughout the industry. Some of the engine designs being developed are clean-burning, such as two-stroke cycle engines, Miller-stroke engines, Stirling engines, hydrogen-powered engines, and solar-powered and/or battery-powered electronic motors. The state of California (and soon other states) has passed legislation that requires manufacturers to have at least one model of their vehicles produce zero emissions. This law has lead to research and development of electric vehicles.

BUILDING MODERN VEHICLES

Technology has also changed the way vehicles are manufactured. The basics of assembly line production introduced by Henry Ford in 1914 still hold true. However, much of the labor is now performed by computer-controlled robotics systems. Workers now spend the majority of their time monitoring these systems and performing constant quality control checks and tests.

FIGURE 3–15 Modern vehicle assembly lines use computer-controlled robotics systems. *Courtesy of Chrysler Corporation*

In a state-of-the-art automobile assembly plant, all handling of parts and materials is fully automated and computer controlled (Figure 3–15). This provides for just-in-time delivery of parts and materials.

Automated guided vehicles (**AGV**s) move the vehicle bodies through the assembly process. Robotic welders also communicate electronically, signalling to each other as to when to move and work. A typical car body shell may contain 840 different welds made by 225 robots.

The entire assembly process is run by a system known as programmable logic control (**PLC**). This system gives orders, monitors conditions and adjusts the plant's rhythm, recognizes problems, recalls past problems and recommends corrections, and controls maintenance.

It normally takes about a day and a half to complete a vehicle. The assembly process begins with the delivery of the engine, transaxle, suspension components, electrical system, and some inner body parts. As these are being fed into the system, the stamping department is making outer body panels—roofs, hoods, deck lids, fenders, quarter panels—from rolls of galvanized steel.

The unwelded body panels are assembled together on an AGV that moves it through the welding process. The entire welding process takes 11.5 minutes. The body then is taken off the AGV and put on a conveyor system that moves it through the paint shop. The entire body is washed then dropped into an electrically charged dip tank. This process uses an electrical charge to coat the body with corrosion-resistant primer.

The body then moves on to be inspected for flaws, and any minor surface imperfections are hand sanded. Next, the body is given an alcohol bath. Then it is moved into an electrically charged paint booth. It takes 1.5 minutes to apply the color coat. The color coat is baked dry, then the clear coat is applied and baked. The total time in the paint shop is 10 hours.

After the paint shop, the interior and instrument panels are installed. At the same time, on the engine line, the transaxle, wiring, hoses, and exhaust system are being attached to the engine. Then the engine and drivetrain are dropped into place.

The body goes to the glass installation section for the windshield, backlight, and rear quarter windows. The vehicle then moves down the line for tires, wheels, moldings, and bumpers. It then moves into a station where headlights are aimed and wheels aligned.

Finally, at the last station, several wires from a computer are hooked to appropriate points on the car. This allows for a careful check of the electrical systems (including the gauges and lights), engine performance, transaxle performance, and steering. If all quality checks are met, the vehicle is moved out to the holding lot for shipment to a dealership.

THE BASIC ENGINE

The engine provides the power to drive the wheels of the vehicle. All automobile engines, both gasoline and diesel, are classified as internal combustion engines because the combustion or burning that creates energy takes place inside the engine. The combustion process is the burning of an air and fuel mixture. As a result of combustion, large amounts of pressure are generated in the engine. This pressure or energy is used to power the car. The engine must be built strong enough to hold the pressure and temperatures formed by combustion.

The following sections cover the basic parts (Figure 3–16) and the major systems of a gasoline engine.

Cylinder Block

The biggest part of the engine is the **cylinder block**, which is also called an **engine block** (Figure 3–17).

FIGURE 3–16 Basic parts of a reciprocating piston gasoline engine.

The cylinder block is a large casting of metal that is drilled with holes to allow for the passage of lubricants and coolant through the block and provide spaces for movement of mechanical parts. The block contains the cylinders, which are round passageways fitted with pistons. The block houses or holds the major mechanical parts of the engine.

Cylinder Head

The **cylinder head** fits on top of the cylinder block to close off and seal the top of the cylinder. The **combustion chamber** is an area into which the air/fuel mixture is compressed and burned. The cylinder

FIGURE 3–17 The cylinder block is the foundation of the engine.

FIGURE 3–18 The valve train opens and closes the intake and exhaust ports.

FIGURE 3–19 The crankshaft changes reciprocating motion to rotary motion.

head contains all or most of the combustion chamber. The cylinder head also contains **ports**, which are passageways through which the air/fuel mixture enters and burned gases exit the cylinder.

Valve Train

A **valve train** is a series of parts used to open and close the intake and exhaust ports. A valve is a movable part that opens and closes a passageway. A camshaft controls the movement of the valves (Figure 3–18), causing them to open and close at the proper time. Springs are used to help close the valves.

Piston

The burning of air and fuel takes place between the cylinder head and the top of the piston. The **piston** is a can-shaped part closely fitted inside the cylinder. In an engine with a four-stroke cycle, the piston has four strokes or movements: intake, compression, power, and exhaust. On the intake stroke, the piston moves downward, and a charge of air/fuel mixture is introduced into the cylinder. As the piston travels upward, the air/fuel mixture is compressed in preparation for burning. When the piston returns to the top of the cylinder, combustion occurs and forces the piston downward on its power stroke. When it reciprocates, or moves upward again, the piston is on the exhaust stroke. During the exhaust stroke, the piston pushes the burned gases out of the cylinder.

Connecting Rods and Crankshaft

The reciprocating motion of the pistons must be converted to rotary motion before it can drive the wheels of a vehicle. As shown in Figure 3–19, this conversion is achieved by linking the piston to a **crankshaft** with a **connecting rod**. The upper end of the connecting rod moves with the piston as it moves up and down in the cylinder. The lower end of the connecting rod is attached to the crankshaft and moves in a circle. The end of the crankshaft is connected to the transmission to continue the power flow through the drivetrain and to the wheels.

Manifolds

A **manifold** is metal ductwork assembly used to direct the flow of gases to or from the combustion chambers. Two separate manifolds are attached to the cylinder head (Figure 3–20). The **intake manifold** delivers a mixture of outside air and fuel vapor to the intake ports. The **exhaust manifold** mounts over the exhaust ports and carries exhaust gases away from the cylinders. The design of the manifolds has a critical effect on volumetric efficiency, or how easily an engine breathes. The more air an engine can bring into its cylinders, the more power the engine will be able to produce.

FIGURE 3–20 Manifolds direct gases in and out of the combustion chambers.

FIGURE 3–21   The lubrication system distributes oil throughout the engine. *Courtesy of General Motors Corporation*

ENGINE SYSTEMS

The following sections present a brief explanation of the systems that help an engine run and keep running.

Lubrication System

The moving parts of an engine need constant lubrication. Lubrication limits the amount of wear and reduces the amount of friction in the engine. **Friction** is a heat generated when two objects rub against each other.

Motor or engine oil is the fluid used to lubricate the engine. Several quarts of oil are stored in an **oil pan** bolted to the bottom of the engine block. The oil pan is sometimes called the **oil sump**. When the engine is running, an oil pump draws oil from the pan and forces it through oil galleries. These galleries are small passageways that direct the oil to the moving parts of the engine.

Oil from the pan passes through an oil filter before moving through the engine (Figure 3–21). The filter removes dirt and metal particles from the oil. Premature wear and damage to parts can result from dirt in the oil. Regular replacement of the oil filter and oil is an important step in a preventive maintenance program.

Cooling System

The burning of the air/fuel mixture in the combustion chambers of the engine produces large amounts of heat. This heat must not be allowed to build up and must be reduced. This heat can easily damage and warp the metal parts of an engine. To prevent this, engines have a cooling system (Figure 3–22).

The most common way to cool an engine is to circulate a liquid coolant through passages in the engine block and cylinder head. An engine can also be cooled by passing air over and around the engine. Liquid cooling is preferable to air cooling because it is less noisy and better able to maintain a constant temperature at the cylinders. If the engine is maintained at a constant temperature, it will run more efficiently. A liquid cooling system also has a supply of hot coolant available to operate a heater for the passenger compartment. The cooling system is designed to cool the engine, not the passengers inside

FIGURE 3–22   Typical automotive cooling system. *Courtesy of Buick Motor Division, General Motors Corporation*

FIGURE 3–23 Parts of a fuel system. *Courtesy of Chevrolet Motor Division, General Motors Corporation*

the car. Cooling the passengers is the responsibility of the air-conditioning system.

A cooling system is made up of the following components.

- **Water pump.** Circulates the cooling liquid through the system. The pump is typically driven by the engine. The liquid is a mixture of water and antifreeze and is commonly referred to as coolant.
- **Water jackets.** Passages in the cylinder block and cylinder head that carry the coolant around the cylinder's combustion chambers.
- **Radiator.** Transfers the coolant's heat to the outside air as the coolant flows through its tubes.
- **Fan.** A device that pulls cool outside air through the fins of the radiator to help cool the coolant.
- **Pressure cap.** Maintains a pressure in the system to raise the boiling point of the coolant. Also provides relief from excess pressure or vacuum.
- Hoses. Connect the components of the system to one another.
- **Thermostat.** Blocks off circulation in the system until a preset temperature is reached to speed engine warmup. Also, keeps engine temperature to a predetermined level.
- Temperature indicator. Warns the driver in case of overheating.

Fuel and Air System

The fuel and air system is designed to supply the correct amount of fuel mixed with the correct amount of

air to the cylinders of the engine. Liquid gasoline does not burn; therefore, the fuel delivered to the cylinders must be in vapor form in order for it to ignite. This system stores the fuel for later use, collects and cleans the outside air, delivers fuel to a device that will control the amount of fuel going to the engine, break down the fuel into very fine droplets and mix the fuel with air to form a vapor, and change the fuel and air ratios to meet the needs of the engine during different operating conditions.

The fuel system is made up of several different parts. A fuel tank stores the liquid gasoline. Fuel lines carry the liquid from the tank to the other parts of the system. A pump moves the gasoline from the tank through the lines. A filter removes dirt or other particles from the fuel. A fuel pressure regulator keeps the pressure below a specified level. An air filter cleans the outside air before it is delivered to the cylinders. An intake manifold directs the air/fuel mixture to each of the cylinders. Fuel injectors or a carburetor mix the liquid gasoline with air for delivery to the cylinders. The components of a typical fuel system are shown in Figure 3–23.

Emission Control System

Car manufacturers are required by law to produce cars that emit less than a certain amount of pollutants. Some of the major vehicle emissions that are harmful to individual health and to the environment are hydrocarbons (**HC**), carbon monoxide (**CO**), and oxides of nitrogen (**NO$_X$**). The Environmental

FIGURE 3–24 Parts of an exhaust system.

Protection Agency establishes emissions standards that limit the amount of these pollutants a vehicle can emit.

Since the standards have been in place, engines have been equipped with a variety of emission control devices and systems. A list of the most common follows.

◆ Positive crankcase ventilation (**PCV**) system. This system reduces HC emissions by drawing fuel and oil vapors from the oil pan or crankcase and sends them into the intake manifold where they are delivered to and burned in the cylinders. This system prevents the vapors from escaping the engine and entering into the atmosphere. It also prevents a buildup of pressure in the oil pan.
◆ Evaporative emission control system. This system reduces HC emissions by drawing fuel vapors from the fuel tank and the carburetor bowl and introduces them into the intake air to be burned. This system stops these vapors from leaking into the atmosphere.
◆ Exhaust gas recirculation (**EGR**) system. Introduces exhaust gases into the intake air to reduce the temperatures reached during combustion. This reduces the chances of forming NO_X during combustion.
◆ Catalytic converter. Located in the exhaust system, it allows for the burning or converting of the hydrocarbons and CO present in the exhaust stream. Also, breaks down NO_X into harmless nitrogen and oxygen.
◆ Air injection system. This system reduces CO and

HC emissions by introducing fresh air into the exhaust stream to cause minor combustion of the HC in the engine's exhaust stream.
◆ Early fuel evaporation (**EFE**) system. This system reduces CO emissions by warming the incoming air to reduce the condensation of fuel on the walls of the intake manifold and speed the warmup of the vehicle.

Exhaust System

As each piston reaches its top dead center position on its exhaust stroke, the burned air/fuel mixture, or exhaust, is forced out of the combustion chamber and into the exhaust manifold. From the manifold, the gases travel through the other parts of the exhaust system until they are expelled out of the car (Figure 3–24). The exhaust system is designed to direct toxic exhaust fumes away from the passenger compartment, to quiet the sound of the exhaust pulses, and to burn or catalyze emissions in the exhaust. A typical exhaust system contains the following components.

◆ Exhaust manifold and gasket
◆ Exhaust pipe, seal, and connector pipe
◆ Intermediate pipes
◆ Catalytic converter
◆ Muffler
◆ Resonator
◆ Tailpipe
◆ Heat shields
◆ Clamps, gaskets, and hangers

On some engines, the exhaust system performs several other functions. Some vehicles have a stove on the exhaust manifold that is used to heat the incoming air. A hot-air pipe or hose leads up from the manifold to the air cleaner snorkel and carries heated air to mix with the normal intake air. This setup improves cold engine performance and helps vaporize the fuel.

Some engines use manifold heat to warm a section of the intake manifold. An exhaust crossover passage directs exhaust under the intake manifold, warming the air/fuel charge. This improves cold engine operation.

Electrical and Electronic Systems

Automobiles have many circuits that carry electrical current from the battery to individual components. The total electrical system includes such major subsystems as the ignition system, starting system, charging system, and the lighting and other electrical systems.

Ignition System After the air/fuel mixture has been delivered to the cylinder and compressed by the piston, it must be ignited. A gasoline engine uses an electrical spark to ignite the mixture. Generating this spark is the role of the ignition system (Figure 3–25).

The electricity that creates this spark is generated by the **ignition coil**. The coil transforms the low voltage of the battery into a burst of 30,000 to 100,000 volts. The release of this high voltage must occur at the correct time. The compressed air/fuel mixture must be ignited at the proper time in order for com-

plete combustion to occur. Ignition occurs when the piston has nearly completed its compression stroke.

On many engines, the motion of the piston and the rotation of the crankshaft is monitored by a **crankshaft position sensor**. The sensor electronically tracks the position of the crankshaft and relays that information to an ignition control module. Based on input from the crankshaft position sensor, and, in some systems, the electronic engine control computer, the ignition control module then turns the battery current to the coil on and off at just the precise time so that the voltage surge arrives at the cylinder at the right time.

The voltage surge from the coil must be distributed to the correct cylinder since only one cylinder is fired at a time. In some systems, this is the job of the **distributor**. The distributor is driven by a gear on the camshaft at one-half of the crankshaft speed. It transfers the high-voltage surges from the coil to high-tension spark plug wires in the correct firing order.

The spark plug wires deliver the high voltage to the spark plugs, which are screwed into the cylinder head. The voltage jumps across a space between two electrodes on the end of each **spark plug** and a spark is created. This spark causes the air/fuel mixture in the combustion chamber to ignite.

Many ignition systems do not have a distributor. Instead, these systems have several coils—one for each pair of spark plugs (Figure 3–26). When a coil is activated by the electronic control module, high voltage is sent through the spark plug circuit. Each

FIGURE 3–25 The ignition system generates the necessary electrical spark. *Courtesy of Ford Motor Company*

FIGURE 3–26   Typical distributorless ignition system.

spark plug circuit includes two spark plugs, which fire at the same time. One spark plug fires during the compression stroke of a cylinder and the other fires during the exhaust stroke of another cylinder and is wasted. In this way, the electronic control module controls both the timing and the distribution of the coil's spark-producing voltage.

Starting and Charging Systems   The starting system is responsible for getting the engine started (Figure 3–27). When the ignition key is turned to the start position, a small amount of current flows from the battery to a **solenoid** or relay switch. This causes the solenoid or relay to activate and close another electrical circuit that allows full battery voltage to reach the starter motor. The starter motor then turns the flywheel mounted on the rear of the crankshaft. As the crankshaft turns, so do the other parts of the engine. As the pistons move through their strokes, the ignition system provides a spark that ignites the air/fuel mixture. If good combustion takes place, the engine will now rotate on its own without the need of the starter motor. The ignition key is now allowed to return to the on position. From this point on, the engine will continue to run until the ignition key is turned off. This action turns off the ignition system.

FIGURE 3–27   Schematic of a typical starting system.

FIGURE 3–28 Typical charging system circuit.

The electrical power for the engine and the rest of the car comes from the car's battery. The battery is especially important for the operation of the starting system. While the engine is starting, a lot of electricity is required to rotate the engine. This tends to lower the amount of power in the battery. Therefore, a system must be present to recharge the battery so that engine starts can be made in the future.

The charging system is designed to recharge and maintain the battery's state of charge. It also provides electrical power for the ignition system, air conditioner, heater, lights, radio, and all electrical accessories when the engine is running.

In addition to the battery, the charging system includes the alternator or generator, voltage regulator, indicator light, and the necessary wiring (Figure 3–28).

Turned by the engine's crankshaft through a drive belt, the charging unit—either a generator (very early model vehicles) or, most likely, an **alternator**—converts mechanical energy into electrical energy. When the output or electrical current from the charging system flows back to the battery, the battery is being charged. When the current flows out of the battery, the battery is said to be discharging.

Electronic Engine Controls An electronic engine control system is an assembly of electronic and electromechanical components. Electronic components are often called solid-state components. The system is designed to continuously monitor the operation of the engine and to make adjustments that will cause the engine to run more efficiently.

Electronic control systems have three main types of components: input sensors, a microprocessor or computer, and output devices (Figure 3–29). The computer analyzes data from the input sensors. Then, based on the inputs and the instructions held in its memory, the computer directs the output devices to make the necessary changes in the operation of some engine systems. The use of electronic engine controls has given the automobile manufacturer the capability to meet federal government regulations by accurately controlling many different engine systems. In addition, electronic control systems have fewer moving parts than old style mechanical and vacuum controls. Therefore, the engine and other support systems can maintain their calibration almost indefinitely.

As an added advantage, an electronic control system is very flexible. Because it uses microcomputers, it can be modified through programming changes to meet a variety of different vehicle engine combinations or calibrations. Critical quantities that determine an engine's performance can be changed easily by changing data that is stored in the system's computer memory.

DRIVETRAIN

The **drivetrain** is made up of all components that transfer power from the engine to the driving wheels of the vehicle. The exact components used in a vehicle's drivetrain depend on whether the vehicle is equipped with rear-wheel drive, front-wheel drive, or four-wheel drive (Figure 3–30).

Power flow through the drivetrain of a rear-wheel-drive vehicle passes through the **clutch** or **torque converter**, manual or automatic transmission, and the driveline (drive shaft assembly). Then it goes through the rear differential, the rear-driving axles, and onto the rear wheels.

Power flow through the drivetrain of a front-wheel-drive vehicle passes through the clutch or torque converter, manual or automatic transmission, then it goes through a front differential, the driving axles, and onto the front wheels.

Four-wheel-drive or all-wheel-drive vehicles combine features of both rear- and front-wheel-drive systems so that power can be delivered to all wheels either on a permanent or on-demand basis.

Clutch

The clutch is used on vehicles with manual transmissions/transaxles. It is used to mechanically connect the engine's flywheel to the transmission/transaxle input shaft (Figure 3–31). It does this through the use of a special friction plate that is splined to the input shaft. When the clutch is engaged, the friction plate contacts the flywheel, transferring power through the plate to the input shaft.

COMPUTER HARNESS

- C1 Engine Control Module (ECM) (Beneath Passenger Side Underhood Electrical Center)
- C2 Data Link Connector (DLC)
- C3 Malfunction Indicator Lamp (MIL) "Service Engine Soon"
- C4 Fuel/ECM Power Fuse**
- C5 ECM Harness Grounds
- C6 Fuse Panel
- C8 Fuel Pump Test Connector
- C10 Remote Battery Feed Stud

NOT ECM CONNECTED

- N1 Crankcase Vent Valve (PCV)
- N2 Evaporative Emission Canister Control Valve

NOTICE: Evaporative Emission Canister (not shown) located at rear of vehicle next to fuel filler neck.

CONTROLLED DEVICES

- 1 Fuel Injector
- 2 Idle Air Control (IAC) Valve
- 3 Fuel Pump Relay**
- 5 Torque Converter Clutch (TCC) Solenoid
- 8 Cooling Fan #1 Control (FC) Relay**
- 12 Cooling Fan #2 Control (FC) Relay
- 13 A/C Compressor Clutch Control Relay**
- 14 Ignition Coil Assembly
- 15 Primary Cooling Fan #1
- 16 Secondary Cooling Fan #2 (A/C equipped vehicles only)
- 17 EGR Control Valve Relay Solenoid (Beneath MAP Sensor)

Exhaust Gas Recirculation (EGR) Valve

** Passenger Side Underhood Electrical Center

INFORMATION SENSORS

- A Manifold Absolute Pressure (MAP) Sensor
- B Oxygen Sensor (O2S)
- C Throttle Position (TP) Sensor
- D Engine Coolant Temperature (ECT) Sensor
- F₁ Vehicle Speed Sensor (VSS)
- M Park/Neutral Position (PNP) Switch
- T Intake Air Temperature (IAT) Sensor (On Rear Air Duct Assembly)
- U A/C Refrigerant Pressure Sensor

FIGURE 3–29 Electronic control systems rely on input sensors, central processing computers, and output devices. _Courtesy of Chevrolet Motor Division, General Motors Corporation_

FIGURE 3–30 Typical drivetrains: (A) rear-wheel drive, (B) front-wheel drive, and (C) four-wheel drive.

FIGURE 3–31   Parts of a clutch assembly. *Courtesy of Ford Motor Company*

When stopping, starting, and shifting from one gear to the next, the clutch is disengaged by pushing down on the clutch pedal. This moves the clutch plate away from the flywheel. Power flow to the transmission stops. The driver can then shift gears without damaging the transmission or transaxle. Allowing the clutch pedal to come up, re-engages the clutch. This allows power to flow from the engine through the transmission.

Manual Transmission

Whenever two or three gears have their teeth meshed together, a gearset is formed. The movement of one gear in the set will cause the others to move. If any of the gears in the set are a different size than the others, the gears will move at different speeds. The size ratio of a gearset is called the **gear ratio** of that gearset.

A manual or standard transmission houses a number of individual gearsets, which produce different gear ratios (Figure 3–32). The driver selects the desired operating gear or gear ratio. The driver has a selection of speed- and power- (torque-) producing gear ranges. A typical manual transmission has four or five forward gear ranges, neutral, and reverse.

The driver selects the desired range by disengaging the clutch and moving a shift lever to the required

FIGURE 3–32   Typical manual transmission.

1 Converter housing	7 Intermediate shaft	13 One-way clutch	19 Oil distributor
2 Torque converter	8 2nd band brake	14 Low & reverse clutch	20 Control valve assembly
3 Oil pump assembly	9 Front clutch	15 Transmission case	21 Oil pan
4 O.D. planetary gear	10 Rear clutch	16 Governor valve assembly	22 O.D. band brake
5 Direct clutch	11 Front planetary gear	17 Rear extension	23 O.D. case
6 Drum support	12 Rear planetary gear	18 Output shaft	24 Input shaft
			25 O.D. one-way clutch

FIGURE 3–33   Typical torque converter and automatic transmission. *Courtesy of General Motors Corporation*

position. This action engages the desired gearset, and the desired output shaft rotation speed is produced.

Automatic Transmission

An automatic transmission eliminates the use of a mechanical clutch and shift lever. In place of a clutch, it uses a fluid coupling called a torque converter to transfer power from the engine's flywheel to the transmission input shaft. The torque converter allows for smooth transfer of power at all engine speeds (Figure 3–33).

Shifting in an automatic transmission is controlled by a hydraulic system. Most late-model automatic transmissions use electronics to control shifting by controlling the hydraulic system. In a hydraulic system, an intricate network of valves and other components use hydraulic pressure to control the operation of planetary gearsets. These gearsets generate the three or four forward speeds, neutral, park, and reverse gears normally found on automatic transmissions. Newer electronic shifting systems use electric solenoids to control shifting mechanisms. Electronic shifting is precise and can be varied to suit certain operating conditions.

Driveline

Drivelines are used on rear-wheel-drive vehicles and four-wheel-drive vehicles. They connect the output shaft of the transmission with the gearing in the rear axle housing (Figure 3–34), on rear-wheel-drive vehi-

cles. They are also used to connect the output shaft to the front and rear drive axles on a four-wheel-drive vehicle.

A driveline consists of a hollow drive or propeller shaft that is connected to the transmission and drive axle differential by universal joints (U-joints). These U-joints allow the drive shaft to move up and down with the rear suspension, preventing damage to the shaft.

Differential

On rear-wheel-drive vehicles, the drive shaft turns perpendicular to the forward motion of the vehicle. The differential gearing in the rear axle housing is designed to turn the direction of the power so that it can be used to drive the wheels of the vehicle. The power flows into the **differential**, where it changes direction, then to the rear axles and wheels (Figure 3–35).

The differential also performs two other important jobs. It multiplies the torque of the power it receives from the drive shaft by providing a final gear reduction. Also, it divides this power between the left and right driving axles and wheels in such a way that a differential wheel speed is possible. This means one wheel can turn faster than the other when going around turns.

Driving Axles

Driving axles are solid steel shafts that transfer differential torque to the driving wheels. A separate axle shaft is used for each driving wheel. The driving axles and part of the differential are enclosed in an

FIGURE 3–34   Output power from the transmission is connected to the differential in the drive axle housing by a drive shaft.

FIGURE 3–35   Rear differential components.

axle housing that protects and supports these parts. Figure 3–36 shows a housing and axle setup for a rear-wheel-drive automobile.

Each driving axle is connected to the side gears in the differential. The inner, or differential ends of the axles are splined to fit into the side gears. As the side gears are turned, the axles to which they are splined turn at the same speed.

At their outer or wheel ends, the axles are attached to the driving wheels. For attachment to a wheel, the outer end of each axle has a flange mounted to it. A **flange** is a rim for attaching one part to

another part. To hold the wheel in place against the flange, studs are used. **Studs** are threaded shafts, resembling bolts without heads. One end of the stud is screwed or pressed into the flange. The wheel fits over the studs and a nut, called the **lug nut**, is tightened over the open end of the stud. This holds the wheel in place.

The inner end of each axle is supported by the differential carrier. The outer end of the axle shaft is supported by a bearing inside the axle housing. A bearing supports and holds a rotating part in place. This bearing, called the axle bearing, allows the axle to rotate smoothly inside the axle housing.

Transaxle

The transaxle is used on front-wheel-drive vehicles. A transaxle assembly consists of a transmission and differential housed in a single unit (Figure 3–37). The gearsets in the transaxle provide the required gear ratios and direct the power flow into the differential. The differential gearing provides the final gear reduction and splits the power flow between the left and right front drive axles.

The drive axles on front-wheel-drive cars extend from the sides of the transaxle. These axles can be hollow or solid. The outer end of the axles are fitted

FIGURE 3–36   Housing and axle setup for a rear-wheel-drive automobile.

ENGINE

TRANSMISSION COMPONENTS

FRONT

DIFFERENTIAL COMPONENTS

DRIVE AXLE

DRIVE AXLE

FIGURE 3–37 Vehicles with a transaxle have the entire driveline in the front of the vehicle. *Courtesy of Chrysler Corporation*

to the hubs of the drive wheels. **Constant velocity joints** mounted on each end of the drive axles allow for steering and suspension (up-and-down) motion without affecting the power flow to the wheels.

Four-Wheel-Drive System

Four-wheel- or all-wheel-drive vehicles combine features of rear-wheel-drive transmissions and front-wheel-drive transaxles. Additional **transfer case** gearing splits the power flow between a differential driving the front wheels and a rear differential that drives the rear wheels. This transfer case can be a housing bolted directly to the transmission/transaxle, or it can be a separate housing mounted somewhere in the driveline.

RUNNING GEAR

The **running gear** consists of components that are used to control the vehicle. The running gear includes the suspension system, the steering system, the braking system, and the wheels and tires.

Suspension System

The suspension system on the automobile includes such components as the springs, shock absorbers,

MacPherson struts, torsion bars, axles, and connecting linkages. These components are designed to support the body and frame, the engine, and the drivelines. Without these systems, the comfort and ease of driving the vehicle would be reduced. Figure 3–38 illustrates some of the components that are used in a suspension system.

Springs and **torsion bars** are used to support the axles of the vehicle. The two types of springs commonly used are the coil spring and the leaf spring (Figure 3–39, page 46).

Torsion bars are made of long spring steel rods. One end of the rod is connected to the frame, while the other end is connected to the movable parts of the axles. As the axles move up and down, the rod twists and acts as a spring.

Shock absorbers slow the upward and downward movement of the springs. This is necessary to limit the car's reaction to a bump in the road.

Steering System

A steering system allows the driver to control the direction of the vehicle. A steering system includes the steering wheel, steering gear, steering shaft, and steering linkage.

FIGURE 3–38 Typical (A) front and (B) rear suspension systems. *Courtesy of Ford Motor Company*

There are two basic types of steering systems used in today's vehicles: **rack-and-pinion** and **recirculating ball** systems (Figure 3–40). The rack-and-pinion system is commonly used in passenger cars. The recirculating ball system is normally used only on heavy vehicles, such as large pick-up trucks, station wagons, and full-size luxury cars.

Steering gears provide a gear reduction to make changing the direction of the wheels easier. On all but a few subcompact and compact car models, the steering gear is also power assisted to ease the effort of turning the wheels. In a power-assisted system, a pump provides hydraulic fluid under pressure to the steering gear. A spool valve directs fluid to one side or the other of the steering gear to assist the operator in turning the wheels.

Some new vehicles have four-wheel steering. Some of these systems use a mechanical gearbox

directly linked to the front steering gear to turn the rear wheels. Other systems use a second power steering gearbox that is computer controlled. In a low-speed turning mode, the rear wheels turn in the opposite direction of the front wheels to reduce the turning radius. When turning the wheels at high speeds, the rear wheels turn in the same direction as the front wheels so that the back wheels follow the front wheels in quick lane changes and other high-speed maneuvers.

Brakes

Automobiles are stopped by activating the brake system (Figure 3–41). Brakes, which are located at each wheel, utilize friction to slow and stop the automobile.

The brakes are activated when the vehicle operator depresses a brake pedal. The brake pedal is connected to a plunger in a **master cylinder**, which is

RACK-AND-PINION STEERING LINKAGE

PARALLELOGRAM STEERING LINKAGE

FIGURE 3—40   Common steering systems.

FIGURE 3—39   Leaf springs help support the rear axles on some systems. *Courtesy of Ford Motor Company*

filled with hydraulic fluid. When the brake pedal is depressed, a force is put onto the hydraulic fluid in the master cylinder. The force is increased by the master cylinder and transferred through brake hoses and lines to the four brake assemblies.

Two types of brakes are used on automobiles—**disc brakes** and **drum brakes**. Many automobiles use a combination of the two types: disc brakes at the front wheels and drum brakes at the rear wheels.

Most vehicles have power-assisted brakes. A **brake booster** typically uses manifold vacuum to increase the pressure applied to the plunger in the master cylinder. This lessens the amount of pressure that must be applied to the brake pedal by the operator and increases the responsiveness of the brake system.

FIGURE 3—41   Many automobiles feature a combination of drum and disc brakes.

Wheels and Tires

The only contact a vehicle has with the road is through its tires and wheels. Tires are filled with air and made of rubber and other materials to give them strength. The air in the tires cushions the ride of the vehicle.

Wheels are made of metal and are bolted to the axles or spindles. Wheels hold the tires in place. Wheels and tires come in many different sizes. Their sizes must be matched to one another and to the automobile.

PREVENTIVE MAINTENANCE

Preventive maintenance (PM) involves performing certain services to a vehicle on a regularly scheduled basis, before there is any sign of trouble. Regular inspection and routine maintenance can prevent major breakdowns and expensive repairs. It also keeps cars and trucks running efficiently and safely.

A recent survey of 2,375 vehicles conducted during National Car Care Month found that more than 90% of the cars looked at needed some form of service. The cars were inspected for exhaust emissions, fluid levels, tire pressure, and other safety features. The results indicated that 34% of the cars had restricted air filters, 27% had worn belts, 25% had clogged PCV filters, 14% had worn hoses, and 20% had bad batteries, battery cables, or terminals.

During the fluid and cooling system inspection, 39% failed due to bad or contaminated transmission or power steering fluid, 36% had worn out or dirty engine oil, 28% had inadequate cooling system protection, and 8% had a faulty radiator cap.

In the safety category, 50% failed due to worn or improperly inflated tires, 32% had inoperative headlights or brake lights, and 14% had worn wipers.

Professional technicians constantly remind their customers about the need for preventive maintenance. The schedule for a particular vehicle's PM program is outlined in the owner's or maintenance manual. These books list the recommended service intervals and the specifications for the various fluids to be used.

A typical preventive maintenance schedule is shown in Figure 3–42. Driving habits and conditions should be used to determine the frequency of PM service intervals. For example, vehicles that frequently are driven for short distances in city traffic may require more frequent oil changes due to the more rapid accumulation of condensation and unburned fuel in the oil. Oil change intervals as short as 3 months or 3,000 miles are sometimes recommended. The steps involved in changing engine oil and filter are illustrated in Photo Sequence 1.

SCHEDULED MAINTENANCE SERVICES

SCHEDULE I

Follow Schedule I if the car is MAINLY driven under one or more of the following conditions:

- When most trips are less than 6 kilometers (4 miles).
- When most trips are less than 16 kilometers (10 miles) and outside temperature remains below freezing.
- When most trips include extended idling and/or frequent low-speed operation as in stop-and-go traffic.†
- Towing a trailer.**
- Operating in dusty areas.

ITEM NO.	TO BE SERVICED	WHEN TO PERFORM Kilometers (Miles) or Months, Whichever Occurs First		The services shown in this schedule up to 80 000 km (48,000 miles) are to be performed after 80 000 km (48,000 miles) at the same intervals.															
			KILOMETERS (000)	5	10	15	20	25	30	35	40	45	50	55	60	65	70	75	80
			MILES (000)	3	6	9	12	15	18	21	24	27	30	33	36	39	42	45	48
1.	Engine Oil & Oil Filter Change*	Every 5 000 km (3,000 Miles) or 3 mos. or when "CHANGE OIL" light comes on.		•	•	•	•	•	•	•	•	•	•	•	•	•	•	•	•
2.	Chassis Lubrication	Every other oil change.			•		•		•		•		•		•		•		•
3.	Tire and Wheel Assembly Inspection & Rotation	At 10 000 km (6,000 mi.) and then every 25 000 km (15,000 mi.)			•					•					•				
4.	Serpentine Drive Belt Inspection*	Every 50 000 km (30,000 mi.) or 24 mos.											•						
5.	Cooling System Service*												•						
6.	Front Wheel Bearing Assembly Repack	See explanation for service interval.																	
7.	Transmission Service																		
8.	Spark Plug Assembly Replacement*	Every 160 000 km (100,000 mi.)																	
9.	Spark Plug Wire Assembly Inspection* ‡	Every 50 000 km (30,000 mi.)											•						
10.	Positive Crankcase Ventilation (PCV) Valve Inspection* ‡												•						
11.	Air Cleaner Filter Replacement*												•						
12.	Fuel Tank, Cap & Lines Inspection* ‡												•						
13.	Rear Axle Lubricant Change	See explanation for service interval																	

† Note: Schedule I should also be followed if the vehicle is used for delivery service, police, taxi or other commercial applications.

‡ The U.S. Environmental Protection Agency or the California Air Resources Board has determined that the failure to perform this maintenance item will not nullify the emission warranty or limit recall liability prior to the completion of vehicle useful life. General Motors, however, urges that all recommended maintenance services be performed at the indicated intervals and the maintenance be recorded in section E of the owner's maintenance schedule.

* An Emission Control Service

** Do not exceed trailering limits. See your Owner's Manual for details.

Figure 3–42 Typical preventive maintance schedule. *Courtesy of General Motors Corporation*

CHANGING THE OIL AND OIL FILTER

P1–1 Always make sure the car is positioned safely on a lift before working under it.

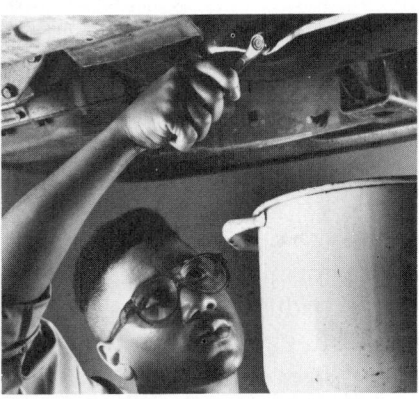

P1–4 Loosen the drain plug with the appropriate wrench. After the drain plug is loosened, quickly remove it so that the oil can freely drain from the pan.

P1–7 Place the old filter in the drain pan so it can drain. Then, discard the filter according to local regulations.

P1–2 The tools and other items needed to change the engine's oil and oil filter are rags, a funnel, an oil filter wrench, safety glasses, and a wrench for the drain plug.

P1–5 Make sure the drain pan is positioned so it can catch all of the oil.

P1–8 After wiping the oil filter sealing area on the engine, apply a coat of clean engine oil on the new filter's seal.

P1–3 Place the oil drain pan under the drain plug before beginning to drain the oil.

P1–6 While the oil is draining, use an oil filter wrench to loosen and remove the oil filter.

P1–9 Hand-tighten the filter to the block. Oil filters should be tightened according to the directions given on the filter.

P1–10 Prior to reinstalling the drain plug, wipe off its threads and sealing surface with a clean rag.

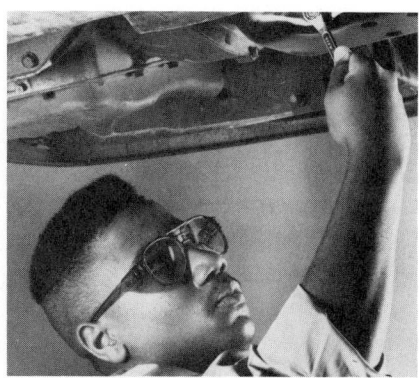

P1–11 The drain plug should be tightened according to the manufacturer's recommendations. Overtightening can cause thread damage, while undertightening may result in oil leakage.

P1–12 With the oil filter and drain plug installed, lower the car to the ground and remove the oil filler cap.

P1–13 Carefully pour the oil into the engine. The use of a funnel usually keeps oil from spilling on the engine.

P1–14 After the recommended amount of oil has been put in the engine, check the oil level.

P1–15 Start the engine and allow it to reach operating temperature. While the engine is running, check the engine for oil leaks. Extra attention should be given to the seal of the oil filter. If there is evidence of a leak, turn off the engine and correct the problem.

P1–16 After the engine has been turned off, recheck the oil level and correct it if necessary.

Most manufacturers also specify more frequent service intervals for vehicles that are used to tow a trailer, or those that operate in extremely dusty or unusual conditions.

The following PM checks should also be performed at the suggested time intervals to help ensure safe, dependable vehicle operation.

TIME: Whenever refueling

◆ Check the engine oil level.
◆ Check the windshield washer fluid level.
◆ Look for low or underinflated tires.

TIME: At least monthly

◆ Check the tire pressure. (Check tires when cold, not after a long drive.)
◆ Check the coolant in the coolant recovery reservoir.
◆ Check the operation of all exterior lights, including the brake lights, turn signals, and hazard warning flashers.

TIME: At least twice a year

◆ Check windshield washer spray and wiper operation. Check and replace worn wiper blades.
◆ Check for worn tires and loose wheel lug nuts.
◆ Check pressure in spare tire.
◆ Check headlight alignment.
◆ Check muffler, exhaust pipes, and clamps.
◆ Check the brake fluid level.
◆ Inspect the lap/shoulder belts for wear.
◆ Check radiator, heater, and air-conditioning hoses for leaks or damage.

TIME: At least once a year

◆ Lubricate all hinges and all outside key locks.
◆ Lubricate the rubber weatherstrips for the doors.
◆ Clean the body's water drain holes.
◆ Check the power steering fluid level.
◆ Check the connections at the battery.
◆ Lubricate the transmission controls and linkage.

TIME: While operating the vehicle

◆ Pay attention to and note any changes in the sound of the exhaust or any smell of exhaust fumes in the vehicle.
◆ Check for vibrations in the steering wheel. Notice any increased steering effort or looseness in the steering wheel.
◆ Notice if the vehicle constantly turns slightly or pulls to one side of the road.
◆ When stopping, listen and check for strange sounds, pulling to one side, increased brake pedal travel, or hard-to-push brake pedal.

◆ If any slipping or changes in the operation of the transmission occur, check the transmission fluid level.
◆ Check for fluid leaks under the vehicle. (Water dripping from the air-conditioning system after use is normal.)
◆ Check the automatic transmission's park function.
◆ Check the parking brake.

KEY TERMS

AGV	Master cylinder
Alternator	Multipurpose vehicle
Brake booster	NO_X
CAFE	Oil pan
Clutch	Oil sump
CO	PCV
Combustion chamber	Pick-up
Connecting rod	Piston
Constant velocity joint	PLC
Convertible top	Port
Crankshaft	Pressure cap
Crankshaft position sensor	Rack and pinion
	Radiator
Cylinder block	Recirculating ball
Cylinder head	Running gear
Differential	Sedan
Disc brakes	Shock absorber
Distributor	Solenoid
Drivetrain	Spark plug
Drum brakes	Sport utility vehicle
EFE	Spring
EGR	Station wagon
Engine block	Steering gear
Exhaust manifold	Stud
Fan	Thermostat
Flange	Torque converter
Friction	Torsion bar
Gear ratio	Transaxle
Hatchback	Transfer case
HC	Unibody
Ignition coil	Valve train
Intake manifold	Van
Liftback	Water jacket
Lug nut	Water pump
Manifold	

SUMMARY

◆ Dramatic changes to the automobile have occurred over the last 30 years, including the addition of emission control systems, more fuel efficient and cleaner-burning engines, and lighter body weight.

- In addition to being lighter than body-over-frame vehicles, unibodies offer better occupant protection by distributing impact forces throughout the vehicle.
- There are seven basic vehicle body shapes: sedan, convertible, liftback or hatchback, station wagon, pick-up, van, and sport utility vehicle.
- Today's computerized engine control systems regulate such things as air and fuel delivery, ignition timing, and emissions. The result is an increase in overall efficiency.
- In modern automated and computer-controlled vehicle assembly plants, automatic guided vehicles move the vehicle bodies through the assembly process. Conditions in the plant are constantly monitored and adjusted by programmable logic control, which also controls maintenance operations.
- All automobile engines are classified as internal combustion, because the burning of the fuel and air occurs inside the engine. Diesel engines share the same major parts as gasoline engines, but they do not use a spark to ignite the air/fuel mixture.
- The cooling system maintains proper engine temperatures. Liquid cooling is more efficient than air cooling and more commonly used.
- The lubrication system distributes motor oil throughout the engine. This system also contains the oil filter necessary to remove dirt and other foreign matter from the oil.
- The fuel system is responsible not only for fuel storage and delivery, but also for atomizing and mixing it with the air in the correct proportion.
- The exhaust system has three primary purposes: to channel toxic exhaust away from the passenger compartment, to quiet the exhaust pulses, and to burn the emissions in the exhaust.
- The total electrical system of an automobile includes the ignition, starting, charging, and lighting systems. Electronic engine controls regulate these systems very accurately through the use of microcomputers.
- Modern automatic transmissions use a computer to match the demand for acceleration with engine speed, wheel speed, and load conditions. It then chooses the proper gear ratio and, if necessary, initiates a gear change.
- The running gear is critical to controlling the vehicle. It consists of the suspension system, braking system, steering system, and wheels and tires.
- Preventive maintenance involves regularly scheduled service on a vehicle to keep it operating efficiently and safety. Professional technicians should stress the importance of PM to their customers.

 REVIEW QUESTIONS

1. Under the CAFE standards, for what are vehicles tested?
2. Describe how a unitized vehicle is constructed.
3. Define internal combustion.
4. In addition to the battery, what does the charging system include?
5. What preventive maintenance checks should be made whenever the vehicle is refueled?
6. Which of the following is *not* a typical emission control system?
   a. EGR
   b. PCV
   c. EPA
   d. EFE
7. Automatic transmissions use a ____ instead of a clutch to transfer power from the flywheel to the transmission's input shaft.
   a. differential
   b. U-joint
   c. torque converter
   d. constant velocity joint
8. Technician A stresses the need to follow the manufacturer's recommendations for preventive maintenance to his customers. Technician B says the proper PM service intervals depends on the customer's driving habits and typical driving conditions. Who is correct?
   a. Technician A   c. Both A and B
   b. Technician B   d. Neither A nor B
9. How many basic vehicle body shapes are used today?
   a. four   c. six
   b. five   d. seven
10. Technician A says today's cars are more efficient than the cars of the 1960s. Technician B says high-performance cars in the 1990s are nearly as fast as those in the 1960s. Who is correct?
    a. Technician A   c. Both A and B
    b. Technician B   d. Neither A nor B
11. Which type of engine is classified as internal combustion?
    a. gasoline   c. both a and b
    b. diesel   d. neither a nor b
12. What is the function of the valve train?
    a. close off and seal the top of the cylinder
    b. house the major parts of the engine
    c. convert reciprocating motion to rotary motion
    d. open and close the intake and exhaust ports

13. Technician A says liquid cooling an engine maintains a constant operating temperature. Technician B says that air cooling lets the engine operate more efficiently. Who is correct?
    a. Technician A   c. Both A and B
    b. Technician B   d. Neither A nor B

14. An engine is experiencing trouble generating the electrical spark needed to ignite the air/fuel mixture. Technician A says the problem is probably in the starting system, while Technician B says the ignition system is most likely at fault. Who is correct?
    a. Technician A   c. Both A and B
    b. Technician B   d. Neither A nor B

15. Which emission control system introduces exhaust gases into the intake air to reduce the formation of NO_X in the combustion chamber?
    a. evaporative emission controls
    b. exhaust gas recirculation
    c. air injection
    d. early fuel evaporation

16. Technician A says most vehicles use a solenoid as the charging unit. Technician B says new vehicles use an alternator as the charging unit. Who is correct?
    a. Technician A   c. Both A and B
    b. Technician B   d. Neither A nor B

17. Technician A says a transaxle is used in combination with a drive shaft in front-wheel-drive vehicles. Technician B says the transaxle eliminates the need for a final drive gearset. Who is correct?
    a. Technician A   c. Both A and B
    b. Technician B   d. Neither A nor B

18. Which of the following is *not* part of the running gear?
    a. differential
    b. steering
    c. suspension
    d. brakes

19. Which of the following PM checks should be made most often?
    a. coolant in the coolant recovery reservoir
    b. operation of all exterior lights
    c. engine oil level
    d. spare tire pressure

20. Technician A says water dripping from the air-conditioning system often after use indicates a problem in the system. Technician B says the dripping could be coolant from the cooling system. Who is correct?
    a. Technician A
    b. Technician B
    c. Both A and B
    d. Neither A nor B

SHOP TOOLS

4

OBJECTIVES

◆ *List the basic units of measure for length, volume, and mass in the two measuring systems.* ◆ *List the various mechanical measuring tools used in the automotive shop.* ◆ *Describe the proper procedure for measuring with a micrometer.* ◆ *List some of the common hand tools used in auto repair.* ◆ *Describe the use of common pneumatic, electrical, and hydraulic power tools found in an automotive service department.*

Repairing the modern automobile requires the use of various tools. Many of these tools are common hand and power tools used every day by a technician. Other tools are very specialized and are only for specific repairs on specific systems and/or vehicles. This chapter will present some of the more commonly used hand and power tools with which every technician must be familiar. Since units of measurement play such an important part in tool selection and in diagnosing automotive problems, this chapter begins with a presentation of measuring systems. A description of the measuring systems and some important measuring tools follows.

MEASURING SYSTEMS

Two systems of weights and measures now exist side by side in the United States—the United States customary systems (**UCS**) and the international system (**SI**). The UCS is commonly known as the English system, while the international system is normally called the metric system.

The basic unit of linear measurement in the UCS is the inch. The basic unit of linear measurement in the metric system is the meter. The meter is easily broken down into smaller units, such as the centimeter (1/100 meter) and millimeter (1/1,000 meter).

All units of measurement in the metric system are related to each other by a factor of 10. Every metric unit can be multiplied or divided by the factor of 10 to get larger units (multiples) or smaller units (submultiples). This makes the metric system much easier to use, with less chance of math errors than in the English system (Figure 4–1).

The United States passed the Metric Conversion Act in 1975 in an attempt to get American industry and the general public to use the metric system, as the rest of the world does. While the general public has been slow to drop the customary measuring system of inches, gallons, and pounds, many industries, led by the automotive industry, are now predominantly metric.

Nearly all vehicles are now built to metric standards. Technicians must be able to measure and work

FIGURE 4–1   A meter stick is made of 1,000 increments known as millimeters.

with both systems of measurement. The following are some common equivalents between the two systems.

1 meter (m) = 39.37 inches (in.)
1 centimeter (cm) = 0.3937 inch
1 millimeter (mm) = 0.03937 inch
1 inch = 2.54 centimeters
1 inch = 25.4 millimeters

ENGINE MEASURING TOOLS

Engine work requires very exact measurements, often in ten thousandths (0.0001) of an inch or thousandths (0.001) of a millimeter. Accurate measurements with this kind of precision can only be made through the use of precise measuring devices.

Measuring tools are precise and delicate instruments. In fact, the more precise they are, the more delicate they are. They should be handled with great care. Never pry, strike, drop, or force these instruments. They may be permanently damaged.

Precision measuring instruments, especially micrometers, are extremely sensitive to rough handling. Clean them before and after every use. All measuring should be performed on parts that are at room temperature. This eliminates the chance of measuring something that has contracted because it was cold or has expanded because it was hot.

SHOP TALK

Check measuring instruments regularly against known good equipment to ensure that they are operating properly and capable of accurate measurement. Always refer to the appropriate service manual or other reference material for the correct specifications before performing any service or diagnostic procedures. The close tolerances required for the proper operation of some automotive parts make using the correct specifications and taking accurate measurements very important. Even the slightest error in measurement can be critical to the durability and operation of an engine and other systems. ■

Machinist's Rule

The **machinist's rule** looks very much like an ordinary ruler. Each edge of this basic engine measuring tool is divided into increments based on a different scale. As shown in Figure 4–2, a typical machinist's rule based on the English system of measurement may have scales based on 1/8-, 1/16-, 1/32-, and 1/64-inch intervals.

FIGURE 4–2 Typical machinist's rule graduations.

Some English system machinist rules may be based on decimal intervals. These are typically divided into 1/10-, 1/50-, and 1/1,000-inch (0.1, 0.03, and 0.01) increments. Decimal machinist rules are very helpful when measuring dimensions that are specified in decimal fractions; they make such measurements much easier.

Of course, metric machinist rules are also available. Metric rules are usually divided into 0.5-mm and 1-mm increments. As stated earlier, the metric system is based on a decimal system of measurement.

Dial Caliper

The **dial caliper** (Figure 4–3) is a versatile measuring instrument capable of taking inside, outside, depth, and step measurements. UCS calipers commonly measure dimensions from 0 to 6 inches. Metric dial calipers typically measure from 0 to 150 mm in increments of 0.02 mm. The dial caliper features a depth scale, bar scale, dial indicator, inside measurement jaws, and outside measurement jaws.

The bar scale of an English system dial caliper is divided into one-tenth (0.1) inch graduations. The dial indicator is divided into one-thousandth (0.001) inch graduations. Therefore, one revolution of the dial indicator needle equals one-tenth inch on the bar scale. (One hundred-thousandths inch equals one-tenth inch.)

A metric dial caliper is similar in appearance to the UCS model. However, the bar scale is divided

FIGURE 4–3 Typical dial caliper. *Courtesy of Central Tools, Inc.*

FIGURE 4–4 Major components of (A) an outside and (B) an inside micrometer.

into 2-mm increments. Additionally, on a metric dial caliper, one revolution of the dial indicator needle equals 2 mm.

Both English and metric dial calipers use a thumb-operated roll knob for fine adjustment. When you use a dial caliper, always move the measuring jaws backward and forward to center the jaws on the object being measured. Make sure the caliper jaws lay flat on or around the object. If the jaws are tilted in any way, you will not obtain an accurate measurement.

Although dial calipers are precision measuring instruments, they are only accurate to plus or minus two-thousandths (± 0.002) of an inch. Micrometers are preferred when extremely precise measurements are desired.

Micrometers

The **micrometer** is used to measure linear outside and inside dimensions. Both outside and inside micrometers are calibrated and read in the same manner. Measurements on both are taken with the measuring points in contact with the surfaces being measured.

The major components and markings of a micrometer include the frame, anvil, spindle, locknut, sleeve, sleeve numbers, sleeve long line, thimble marks, thimble, and ratchet (Figure 4–4). Micrometers are calibrated in either inch or metric graduations and are available in a range of sizes. The proper procedure for measuring with an inch-graduated outside micrometer is outlined in Photo Sequence 2. Some micrometers use a digital display to show the measurement. Obviously, the procedure shown in the photo sequence does not apply to them.

Reading a Metric Outside Micrometer The metric micrometer is read in the same manner as the inch-graduated micrometer, except the graduations are

expressed in the metric system of measurement. Readings are obtained as follows.

- Each number on the sleeve of the micrometer represents 5 millimeters (mm) or 0.005 meter (m) (Figure 4–5A).
- Each of the ten equal spaces between each number, with index lines alternating above and below the horizontal line, represents 0.5 mm or five

FIGURE 4–5 Reading a metric micrometer: (A) 5 mm plus (B) 0.5 mm plus (C) 0.01 mm, equals 5.51 mm.

USING A MICROMETER

P2–1 Micrometers can be used to measure the diameter of many objects. By measuring the stem of a valve in two places, the wear of the stem can be determined.

P2–3 The graduations on the sleeve each represent 0.025 inch. To read a measurement on a micrometer, begin by counting the visible lines on the sleeve by 0.025.

P2–4 The graduations on the thimble assembly define the area between the lines on the sleeve. The number indicated on the thimble is added to the measurement shown on the sleeve.

P2–2 Because the diameter of the stem is less than one inch, a 0-to-1-inch micrometer is used.

P2–5 Micrometer reading of 0.500 inch.

P2–6 Micrometer reading of 0.375 inch.

P2–7 Normally little stem wear is evident directly below the keeper grooves. To measure the diameter of the stem at that point, close the micrometer around the stem.

P2–8 To get an accurate reading, slowly close the micrometer until a slight drag is felt while passing the valve in and out of the micrometer.

P2–9 To prevent the reading from changing while you move the micrometer away from the stem, use your thumb to activate the lock lever.

P2–10 This reading (0.311 inch) represents the diameter of the valve stem at the top of the wear area.

P2–11 Some micrometers are able to measure in 0.0001 inch. Use this type of micrometer if the specifications call for this type of accuracy. Note that the exact diameter of the valve stem is 0.3112 inch.

P2–12 Most valve stem wear occurs above the valve head. The diameter here should also be measured. The difference between the diameter of the valve stem just below the keepers and just above the valve head represents the amount of valve stem wear.

FIGURE 4–6 The total reading on this micrometer is 7.28 mm.

FIGURE 4–7 Using a digital micrometer.

tenths of a mm. One revolution of the thimble changes the reading one space on the sleeve scale or 0.5 mm (Figure 4–5B).

◆ The beveled edge of the thimble is divided into 50 equal divisions with every fifth line numbered: 0, 5, 10, . . . 45. Since one complete revolution of the thimble advances the spindle 0.5 mm, each graduation on the thimble is equal to 1/50 of 0.5 mm or one hundredth of a millimeter (Figure 4–5C).

As with the inch-graduated micrometer, the three separate readings are added together to obtain the total reading (Figure 4–6).

PROCEDURES
Using a Metric Outside Micrometer

1. Read the largest number on the sleeve that has been uncovered by the thimble. In the illustration it is 5, which means the first number in the series is 5 mm.

2. Count the number of lines past the number 5 that the thimble has uncovered. In the example, this is 4. Since each space is equal to 0.5 mm, 4 spaces equal 4 × 0.5, or 2 mm. This, added to the figure obtained in step 1, gives 7 mm.

3. Read the graduation line on the thimble that coincides with the horizontal line of the sleeve scale, and add this to the total obtained in step 2. In the example, the thimble scale reads 28 or 0.28 mm. This, added to the 7 mm for step 2, gives a total reading of 7.28 mm.

Using an Outside Micrometer To measure small objects using an outside micrometer, open the jaws of the tool and slip the object between the spindle and anvil. While holding the object against the anvil, turn

the thimble using your thumb and forefinger until the spindle contacts the object. Never clamp the micrometer tightly. Use only enough pressure on the thimble to allow the work to just fit between the anvil and spindle. To get an accurate reading, the object must slip through the micrometer with only a very light resistance. When a satisfactory adjustment has been made, lock the micrometer. Read the measurement scale. Be careful not to change the setting if the tool is not equipped with a lock.

Some technicians use a digital micrometer, which is easier to read. These tools do not have the various scales, rather the measurement is displayed and read directly off the micrometer. Figure 4–7 shows a digital outside micrometer in use.

In order to get accurate readings, you should slip the micrometer back and forth over the object until you feel a very light resistance, while at the same time rocking the tool from side to side to make certain the spindle cannot be closed any further (Figure 4–8). These steps should be taken with any precision measuring device to ensure correct measurements.

SLIP BACK AND FORTH OVER OBJECT. **ROCK FROM SIDE TO SIDE.**

FIGURE 4–8 Slip the micrometer when measuring larger objects.

INSIDE MICROMETER

FIGURE 4–9   Obtaining a precise measurement with an inside micrometer.

FIGURE 4–10   Typical depth micrometer. *Courtesy of Central Tools, Inc.*

To measure larger objects such as a piston, select a micrometer of the proper size. Micrometers are available in a number of different sizes. The size is dictated by the smallest measurement it can make to the largest. Examples of these sizes are the 0-to-1-inch, 1-to-2-inch, 2-to-3-inch, and 3-to-4-inch micrometers.

Measurements with any micrometer will be reliable if the micrometer is calibrated correctly. To calibrate a micrometer, close the micrometer over a micrometer standard. If the reading differs from that of the standard, the micrometer should be adjusted according to the instructions provided by the tool manufacturer.

Reading an Inside Micrometer   Inside micrometers (Figure 4–9) are used to measure the inside diameter of a bore or hole. To use an inside micrometer, place it inside the bore and extend the measuring surfaces until each end touches the bore's surface. If the bore is large, it might be necessary to use an extension rod to increase the micrometer's range. These extension rods come in various lengths. The inside micrometer is read in the same manner as an outside micrometer.

To obtain a precise measurement, keep the anvil firmly against one side of the bore and rock the micrometer back and forth and side to side. This makes sure the micrometer is in the center of the bore. As with the outside micrometer, this procedure will require a little practice until you get the feel of the correct resistance on both ends of the tool.

Reading a Depth Micrometer   The depth micrometer (Figure 4–10) is used to measure the distance between two parallel surfaces. Depth micrometers are available in inch- and metric-graduated models. The sleeves, thimbles, and ratchet screws operate in the same way as other micrometers. Likewise, depth micrometers are read in the same way as other micrometers.

If a depth micrometer is used with a gauge bar, it is important to keep both the bar and the micrometer from rocking. Any movement of either part will result in an inaccurate measurement.

SHOP TALK

Follow these tips for taking care of a micrometer.

◆ Always clean the micrometer before using it.
◆ Do not touch measuring surfaces.
◆ Store the tool properly. The spindle face should not touch the anvil face, or a change in temperature might spring the micrometer.
◆ Clean the micrometer after use. Wipe it clean of any oil, dirt, or dust using a lint-free cloth.
◆ Do not drop the tool. It is a sensitive instrument and must be handled with care.
◆ Check the calibration weekly.   ■

Telescoping Gauge

Telescoping gauges (Figure 4–11) are used for measuring bore diameters and other clearances. They may also be called **snap gauges**. They are normally offered in sizes ranging from fractions of an inch through 6 inches. Each gauge consists of two telescoping plungers, a handle, and a lock screw. Telescoping gauges are normally used with an outside micrometer.

To use the telescoping gauge, insert it into the bore and loosen the lock screw. This will allow the plungers to snap against the bore. Once the plungers have expanded, tighten the lock screw. Then, remove

FIGURE 4–11 Typical telescoping gauge.

FIGURE 4–12 Measuring a telescoping gauge with a micrometer.

FIGURE 4–13 Measuring a small hole gauge with a micrometer.

FIGURE 4–14 Typical feeler gauge pack.

the gauge and measure the expanse with a micrometer (Figure 4–12).

Small Hole Gauge

The small hole or **ball gauge** works just like a telescoping gauge. However, it is designed to be used on small bores. After it is placed into the bore and expanded, it is removed and measured with a micrometer (Figure 4–13). Like the telescoping gauge, the small hole gauge consists of a lock, handle, and an expanding end. The end expands or retracts by turning the gauge handle. The small hole gauge is commonly used to measure the inside diameter of valve guides.

Feeler Gauge

The **feeler gauge** is a thin strip of metal of known and closely controlled thickness. Several of these metal strips are often assembled together as a feeler

gauge set that looks like a pocket knife (Figure 4–14). The desired thickness gauge can be pivoted away from others for convenient use. A steel feeler gauge pack usually contains strips or leaves of 0.002- to 0.010-inch thickness (in steps of 0.001 inch) and leaves of 0.012- to 0.024-inch thickness (in steps of 0.002 inch).

A feeler gauge can be used by itself to measure piston ring side clearance, piston ring end gap, connecting rod side clearance, crankshaft end play, and other distances. It can also be used with a precision straightedge to measure main bearing bore alignment and cylinder head/block warpage (Figure 4–15).

Radius Gauge

A **radius gauge** (Figure 4–16) is used to check the crankshaft fillet radii at the edge or side of the rod and main bearing journals. All of them should be the same size and should be at the specified radius.

Screw Pitch Gauge

The use of a **screw pitch gauge** (Figure 4–17) provides a quick and accurate method of checking the threads per inch (pitch) of a fastener. The leaves of

FIGURE 4–15 Using a feeler gauge and precision straight-edge to check for warpage. *Courtesy of Fel-Pro, Inc.*

FIGURE 4–16 A set of radius gauges. *Courtesy of Goodson Shop Supplies.*

FIGURE 4–17 Typical screw pitch gauge. *Courtesy of Central Tools, Inc.*

FIGURE 4–18 Typical dial indicator. *Courtesy of The Dyer Company*

and crankshaft end play. Dial indicators are available with various face markings and measurement ranges to accommodate many measuring tasks.

To use a dial indicator, position the indicator rod against the object to be measured. Then, push the indicator toward the work until the indicator needle travels far enough around the gauge face to permit movement to be read in either direction (Figure 4–19). Zero the indicator needle on the gauge. Always be sure the range of the dial indicator is sufficient to allow the amount of movement required by the measuring procedure. For example, never use a 1-inch indicator on a component that will move 2 inches.

this measuring tool are marked with the various pitches. To check the pitch of threads, simply match the teeth of the gauge with the threads of the fastener. Then, read the pitch from the leaf.

Screw pitch gauges are available for the various types of fastener threads used in the automotive industry: American National coarse and fine threads, metric threads, International Standard threads, and Whitworth threads.

Dial Indicator

The **dial indicator** (Figure 4–18) is calibrated in 0.001-inch (one-thousandth inch) increments. Metric dial indicators are also available. Both types are used to measure movement. Common uses of the dial indicator include measuring valve lift, journal concentricity, flywheel or brake rotor runout, gear backlash,

FIGURE 4–19 Using a dial indicator to measure crankshaft end play.

FIGURE 4–20 Typical valve seat runout gauge. *Courtesy of Central Tools, Inc.*

FIGURE 4–21 Typical cylinder bore dial gauges. *Courtesy of Goodson Shop Supplies*

Valve Seat Runout Gauge

The valve seat **runout gauge**, also called a **concentricity gauge**, is similar to the dial indicator. It features a gauge face divided into 0.001-inch (one-thousandth inch) increments, an arbor that centers the instrument in the valve guide bore, and an indicator bar that can be adjusted so it bears on the valve seat (Figure 4–20). The tool is then slowly rotated around the diameter of the valve seat to check its concentricity (runout).

Cylinder Bore Dial Gauge

The cylinder bore dial gauge is used to determine cylinder bore size, out-of-roundness, and taper. These three measurements, in addition to main bearing saddle alignment, provide basic information about the condition of the engine block.

Cylinder bore dial gauges are read in the same way as a dial indicator. As with the inside micrometer and telescoping gauge, the cylinder bore micrometer must be rocked to obtain the correct measurement.

The parts of the cylinder bore dial gauge include the handle, guide blocks, lock, indicator contact, and dial indicator (Figure 4–21). Various indicator contacts can be installed to measure different bore sizes with one gauge.

Cylinder bores do not always wear in a perfectly round pattern. One side of the cylinder wall usually wears more than the other. For this reason, cylinder roundness is checked during engine overhaul procedures (Figure 4–22). To measure out-of-roundness, take three measurements at the same depth in the cylinder. These measurements should be taken in these directions: front/rear, right/left, and diagonally (Figure 4–23). Then, the smallest reading obtained from the cylinder is subtracted from the largest reading. The answer is the amount the cylinder is out-of-round.

FIGURE 4–22 Determining cylinder roundness using a cylinder bore dial gauge. *Courtesy of Central Tools, Inc.*

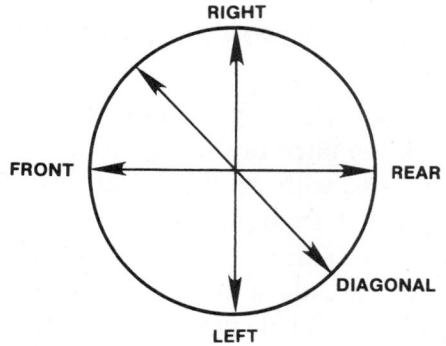

THE DIFFERENCE BETWEEN THE LARGEST AND SMALLEST DIAMETERS EQUALS OUT-OF-ROUND.

FIGURE 4–23 Recommended directions for measuring cylinder out-of-roundness.

By measuring the top of the cylinder bore and comparing it to the measurement at the bottom, you can determine the amount of taper the bore has. The top of the cylinder should be measured right below

FIGURE 4–24 Another common type of cylinder bore dial gauge. *Courtesy of L. S. Starrett Company*

FIGURE 4–26 Checking crankcase saddle bore alignment with an aligning bar. *Courtesy of Sunnen Products Company*

the point where the piston rings ride. Manufacturers recommend a maximum amount of allowable taper.

Another cylinder bore gauge that is used to check cylinder taper and out-of-roundness is shown in Figure 4–24. The diameter of a cylinder can also be measured with an inside micrometer.

Out-of-Roundness Gauge

The bearings used with many critical engine parts are designed to have complete contact with the back of the bearing back and the saddle bore. Therefore, if these insert bearings are fitted properly, they will conform exactly to the contour of the saddle bore. This is why the saddle bores in an engine block and the bores in a connecting rod must be perfectly round. Special gauges are available for checking these bores.

The gauge shown in Figure 4–25 consists of a base with a dial indicator mounted to it and an adjustable slide on the bottom. The bottom is adjusted to fit the bore it is measuring. To check a bore for out-of-roundness, move the locking adjustable slide to fit the diameter of the bore, then set the dial indicator to zero. As the gauge is rotated, the dial will show a plus or minus reading in thousandths of an inch for any variation in the diameter.

Out-of-roundness can also be checked with an inside micrometer. However, the out-of-roundness gauge is a much quicker and easier method.

Aligning Bar

An aligning bar is an excellent tool for checking the alignment of the block's saddle bores (Figure 4–26).

With the bearings removed, insert the aligning bar into the full length of the crankcase and tighten the bearing caps. If the bar can be turned by hand using a short bar (12 inches) for leverage, the saddle bores are in alignment. If the aligning bar will not turn, the saddle bores are out of alignment.

V-Blocks

The use of **V-blocks** and a dial indicator is the recommended method for checking crankshaft alignment (Figure 4–27). With the front and rear main journals in the V-blocks, the dial indicator is used to track the movement of the main journals. If the journal is perfectly round and the shaft is straight, there will be no movement on the dial indicator.

On short crankshafts with three or four main journals, the shaft can be supported and rotated on the front and rear journals. The dial indicator can be set so it measures concentricity at the vertical centerline of the other main journals. On longer shafts having five or seven main journals, it is recommended that the shaft be supported at the intermediate main bearing journal to prevent possible sag.

Each of the end journals is checked by moving one of the V-blocks to the center main journal and taking the dial indicator reading on the unsupported

FIGURE 4–25 Typical out-of-roundness gauge. *Courtesy of L. S. Starrett Company*

FIGURE 4–27 Using V-blocks and a dial indicator to check crankshaft alignment. *Courtesy of Perfect Circle/Dana*

journal. A strip of paper should be placed in each V-block to prevent damage to the journals. It is also important to check the nose of the crankshaft for excessive runout.

Torque-Indicating Wrench

The fact that practically every vehicle and engine manufacturer publishes a list of torque recommendations is ample proof of the importance of using proper amounts of torque when tightening nuts or bolts.

SHOP TALK

Following torque specifications is critical. However, there is a possibility that the torque spec is wrong as printed. In other words, someone made a mistake. If the torque spec seems way too tight or loose for the size of bolt, find the torque spec in a different source. If they are the same, use it. If they are different, use the one that seems right. ■

Several types of **torque-indicating wrenches** are available. One of the most popular is the dial type (Figure 4–28). Any design of torque wrench allows a technician to duplicate the tightening pressure used when the engine was originally assembled. This, therefore, duplicates the tightness and stress that the manufacturer has found to be the most desirable and reliable (Figure 4–29).

FIGURE 4–28 Dial-type torque-indicating wrenches. *Courtesy of Central Tools, Inc.*

FIGURE 4–29 Using a torque-indicating wrench. *Courtesy of Perfect Circle/Dana*

Bearing caps that are too tight distort the bearings, causing excessive wear and incorrect oil clearance, which often results in rapid wear of other engine parts due to decreased oil flow.

Insufficient torque can result in out-of-round bores and subsequent failure of the parts. In extreme cases of inadequate bolt torque, bolt and rod or cap breakage can result, causing major engine failure.

SHOP TALK

The torque wrench, as already noted, has long been the standard tool for tightening bolts and nuts that clamp parts together. Torque is the twisting force used to turn a fastener (bolt or nut) against friction (between threads and between fastener head and component surface). It is a fact that up to 90% of the torque is used up by friction. The remaining 10% is used to clamp parts together. Therefore, clamping forces can vary significantly over a single cylinder head or other engine component.

Because new high-tech engines are designed with extremely close tolerances, it is not surprising that torque alone is no longer adequate for proper service procedures. The torque/angle measurements of fasteners is a method of clamping parts together that makes sure similar fasteners will exert the same clamping force. Without proper clamping forces, distortion of cylinder bores and bearing bores can occur as well as leaking head gaskets. This method of tightening begins with tightening the fastener to a low torque setting. This puts the parts in close contact with each other, and the actual torque values are less affected by fastener friction at these low values. The fasteners are then turned to a specified angle. The clamping force of each fastener will now be consistent.

The unit shown in Figure 4–30 is a precision, microprocessor-controlled torque/angle meter that makes sure fasteners are easily and consistently tightened to true clamp load specifications. ■

FIGURE 4–30   Typical precision torque/angle meter. *Courtesy of Kent-Moore Tools*

HAND TOOLS

Most service procedures require the use of hand tools. Therefore, technicians have a wide assortment of these tools. Each of these tools has a specific job and should be used in a specific way. Most service departments and garages require their technicians to buy their own hand tools. A set of master technician's hand tools and a tool chest are shown in Figure 4–31.

FIGURE 4–31   Professional set of automotive hand tools. *Courtesy of Snap-on Tools Corporation*

FIGURE 4–32   Wrench assortment. *Courtesy of Snap-on Tools Corporation*

Wrenches

All technicians should have a complete collection of **wrenches**. This includes both metric and SAE wrenches in a variety of sizes and styles (Figure 4–32).

The word *wrench* means twist. A wrench is a tool for twisting and/or holding bolt heads of nuts. The width of the jaw opening determines its size. For example, a 1/2-inch wrench has a jaw opening (from face to face) of 1/2 inch. The size is actually slightly larger than its nominal size so the wrench fits around a nut or bolt head of equal size.

⬛ SHOP TALK

Metric and SAE wrenches are not interchangeable. For example, a 9/16-inch wrench is 0.02 inch larger than a 14-millimeter nut. If the 9/16-inch wrench is used to turn or hold a 14-millimeter nut, the wrench will probably slip. This may cause rounding of the points of the nut and possibly skinned knuckles as well. ⬛

OPEN-END WRENCH   The jaws of the open-end wrench (Figure 4–33) allow the wrench to slide

FIGURE 4–33   The open-end wrench grips only two faces of a fastener.

FIGURE 4–34 Box-end wrenches are closed to provide better holding power. *Courtesy of Snap-on Tools Corporation*

around bolts or nuts where there might be insufficient clearance above or on one side of the nut to accept a box wrench.

BOX-END WRENCH The end of the box-end wrench is boxed or closed rather than open (Figure 4–34). The jaws of the wrench fit completely around a bolt or nut, gripping each point on the fastener. The box-end wrench is not likely to slip off a nut or bolt. It is safer than an open-end wrench.

COMBINATION WRENCH The combination wrench has an open-end jaw on one end and a box-end on the other. Both ends are the same size. Every auto technician should have two sets of wrenches: one for holding and one for turning. The combination wrench is probably the best choice for the second set. It can be used with either open-end or box-end wrench sets and can be used as an open-end or box-end wrench.

ADJUSTABLE WRENCH An adjustable wrench has one fixed jaw and one movable jaw. The wrench opening can be adjusted by rotating a helical adjusting screw that is mated to teeth in the lower jaw. Because this type of wrench does not firmly grip a bolt's head, it is likely to slip. Adjustable wrenches should be used carefully only when it is absolutely necessary. Be sure to put all of the turning pressure on the fixed jaw (Figure 4–35).

ALLEN WRENCH Set screws are used to fasten door handles, instrument panel knobs, engine parts, and even brake calipers. A set of hex head wrenches, or Allen wrenches (Figure 4–36), should be in every technician's tool box.

SOCKET WRENCH In many situations, a socket wrench is much safer, faster, and easier to use than

APPLY FORCE IN DIRECTION INDICATED.

FIGURE 4–35 Pull the adjustable wrench so that the force bears against the fixed jaw.

FOLDING WRENCH SETS

L-SHAPED HEX KEYS

T-SHAPED HEX KEYS

FIGURE 4–36 Typical Allen wrench set. *Courtesy of Snap-on Tools Corporation*

an open-end or box-end wrench. Sometimes it is the only wrench that will work.

The basic socket wrench set consists of a ratchet handle and several barrel-shaped sockets. The socket fits over and around a bolt or nut (Figure 4–37). Inside, it is shaped like a box-end wrench. Sockets are

TOP VIEW

1/2-INCH SQUARE DRIVE HOLE

9/16-INCH SOCKET

9/16 INCH ACROSS FLATS

9/16-INCH HEX HEAD BOLT

9/16 INCH ACROSS FLATS

FIGURE 4–37 The size of a socket is the same as the bolt or nut size it fits.

FIGURE 4–38 The socket drive size is equal to the diameter of the handle lug.

available in 6, 8, or 12 points. The top side of a socket has a square hole that accepts a square lug on the socket handle (Figure 4–38). This square hole is the drive hole. The size of the hole and handle lug (1/4 inch, 3/8 inch, 1/2 inch, and so on) indicates the drive size of the socket wrench. One handle fits all the sockets in a set. On better quality handles, a spring-loaded ball in the square drive lug fits into a depression in the socket. This ball holds the socket to the handle.

Sockets are available in various sizes, lengths, and bore depths. Both standard UCS and metric socket wrench sets are necessary for automotive service. Normally, the larger the socket size, the longer the socket or the deeper the well. Deep-well sockets (Figure 4–39) are made extra long to fit over bolt ends

or studs. A spark plug socket is an example of a deep-well socket. Heavier walled sockets made of hardened steel are designed for use with an impact wrench and are called impact sockets. Most sockets are chrome-plated, except for impact sockets, which are not.

⚠️ WARNING!

Deep-well sockets are also good for reaching nuts or bolts in limited access areas. Deep-well sockets should not be used when a regular size socket will do the job. The longer socket develops more twist torque and tends to slip off the fastener. ∎

Figure 4–40 shows a number of socket wrench set accessories. Accessories multiply the usefulness of

FIGURE 4–39 Deep-well sockets fit over bolt ends and studs.

FIGURE 4–40 Typical ⅜-inch and ½-inch socket wrench sets. *Courtesy of Snap-on Tools Corporation*

FIGURE 4–41 Typical screwdriver attachment set including (A) hex driver, (B) Phillips driver, (C) flat tip driver, (D) clutch head driver, (E) Torx® driver, (F) three-wing socket, (G) double square socket, and (H) Torx® socket. *Courtesy of Snap-on Tools Corporation*

a socket wrench. A good socket wrench set has a variety of accessories.

Screwdriver attachments are also available for use with a socket wrench. Figure 4–41 shows a typical set of screwdriver attachments and three specialty sockets. These socket wrench attachments are very handy when a fastener cannot be loosened with a regular screwdriver. The leverage given by the ratchet handle is often just what it takes to break a stubborn screw loose.

Screwdrivers

A variety of threaded fasteners used in the automotive industry are driven by a screwdriver. Each fastener requires a specific kind of screwdriver, and the well-equipped technician will have several sizes of each (Figure 4–42).

All screwdrivers, regardless of the type of fastener they were designed for, have several things in common. The size of the screwdriver is determined by the length of the shank or blade and the working end of the tool. The smallest size is a No. 1, the next largest and most common is the No. 2. The size of the handle is important, too. The larger the diameter of the handle, the better grip it has and the more torque it can generate when turned. Screwdriver handles should also be insulated from the blade and made with a material that does not conduct electricity.

FIGURE 4–42 The prepared technician keeps several sizes of screwdrivers on hand. ©1995 Stanley Tools, Division of the Stanley Works, New Britain, Connecticut 06053 USA

A screwdriver should not be used as a chisel, punch, or pry bar. Screwdrivers were not made to withstand blows or bending pressures. When misused in such a fashion, the tips will wear, become rounded, and tend to slip out of the fastener. At that point, a screwdriver becomes unusable. Remember a defective tool is a dangerous tool. ■

STANDARD TIP SCREWDRIVER A slotted screw accepts a screwdriver with a standard or blade-type tip. The standard tip screwdriver is probably the most common type (Figure 4–43). It is useful for turning carriage bolts, machine screws, and sheet metal screws.

PHILLIPS SCREWDRIVER The tip of a **Phillips screwdriver** has four prongs that fit the four slots in a Phillips head screw (Figure 4–44). This type of fastener is used very often in the automotive field. Not only does it look nicer than the slot head screw, but it also is easier to install, tighten, and loosen. The four

FIGURE 4–43 The standard tip screwdriver fits slotted head screws.

FIGURE 4–44 The tip of a Phillips screwdriver has four prongs that help prevent slippage of the fastener.

surfaces enclose the screwdriver tip so it is less likely the screwdriver will slip out of the fastener.

SPECIALTY SCREWDRIVERS A number of specialty fasteners have been replacing the slot and Phillips head screws. This new breed of fasteners is designed to improve transfer of torque from the screwdriver to the fastener, to slip less, and to offer some tamper resistance.

The **Posidriv® screwdriver** is like a Phillips but its tip is flatter and blunter (Figure 4–45). The squared tip grips the screw's head and slips less than a Phillips screwdriver. The **Torx®** screwdriver is used to secure headlight assemblies, mirrors, and luggage racks. Not only does the six-prong tip provide greater turning power and less slippage (Figure 4–46), but the Torx® fastener also provides a measure of tamper resistance.

Pliers

Pliers are gripping tools used for working with wires, clips, and pins. An auto technician should own several types: standard pliers for common parts and wires, needle nose for small parts, and large, adjustable pliers for large items and heavy-duty work.

FIGURE 4–45 The Posidriv® screwdriver is similar to a Phillips. ©1995 Stanley Tools, Division of the Stanley Works, New Britain, Connecticut 06053 USA

FIGURE 4–46 Torx® screwdrivers feature a six-prong tip. ©1995 Stanley Tools, Division of the Stanley Works, New Britain, Connecticut 06053 USA

FIGURE 4–47 Combination, or slip-joint, pliers. *Courtesy of Snap-on Tools Corporation*

FIGURE 4–48 Adjustable pliers. *Courtesy of Snap-on Tools Corporation*

COMBINATION PLIERS Combination pliers (Figure 4–47) are the most common type of pliers and are frequently used in many kinds of automotive repair. The jaws have both flat and curved surfaces for holding flat or round objects. Also called slip-joint pliers, the combination pliers have many jaw-opening sizes. One jaw can be moved up or down on a pin attached to the other jaw to change the size of the opening.

ADJUSTABLE PLIERS Adjustable pliers, commonly called channel locks (Figure 4–48), have a multiposition slip joint that allows for many jaw-opening sizes.

NEEDLE NOSE PLIERS Needle nose pliers have long, tapered jaws (Figure 4–49). They are indispensable for grasping small parts or for reaching into tight spots. Many needle nose pliers also have wire cutting edges and a wire stripper.

LOCKING PLIERS Locking pliers, or vise grips, are similar to the standard pliers, except they can be tightly locked around an object (Figure 4–50). They are extremely useful for holding parts together. They are also useful for getting a firm grip on a badly rounded fastener, which is impossible to turn with a wrench or socket. Locking pliers come in several sizes and jaw configurations for use in many auto repair jobs.

DIAGONAL CUTTING PLIERS Diagonal cutting pliers, or cutters, are used to cut electrical connections,

FIGURE 4–49 Needle nose pliers. *Courtesy of Snap-on Tools Corporation*

FIGURE 4–50 Locking pliers, or vise grips, can be locked closed.

FIGURE 4–51 Diagonal cutting pliers.

cotter pins, and other wires on an automobile. Jaws on these pliers have extra-hard cutting edges that are squeezed around the item to be cut (Figure 4–51).

SNAP RING PLIERS Snap ring, or lock ring pliers generally consist of a linkage that permits the movable jaw to stay parallel throughout the range of opening (Figure 4–52). The jaw surface is usually serrated (notched or toothed) to prevent slipping.

RETAINING RING PLIERS Retaining ring pliers, sometimes called snap ring pliers, are identified by their pointed tips that fit into holes in retaining rings (Figure 4–53). Retaining ring pliers come in fixed sizes but are also available in sets with interchangeable jaws.

FIGURE 4–52 Snap ring pliers.

FIGURE 4–53 Retaining ring pliers.

Hammers

Hammers are identified by the material and weight of the head. There are two groups of hammer heads: steel and soft face (Figures 4–54 and 4–55). The heads

PARTS OF A BALLPEEN HAMMER HEAD

CROSS PEEN HAMMER

SLEDGEHAMMER

FIGURE 4–54 Steel-face hammers.

PLASTIC-TIP HAMMER

BRASS-HEADED HAMMER

SOFT-FACE COMPOSITION HAMMER
WITH REPLACEMENT TIPS

RUBBER MALLET

FIGURE 4–55 Soft-face hammers.

ADJUSTING SCREW

ADJUSTABLE ROUND   ADJUSTABLE ROUND

SOLID HEXAGON   SOLID SQUARE

FIGURE 4–57 Common die shapes.

of steel-faced hammers are made from high-grade alloy steel. The steel is deep forged and heat treated to a suitable degree of hardness. Soft-face hammers have a surface that yields when it strikes an object. Soft-face hammers should be used on machined surfaces and when marring a finish is undesirable. For example, a brass hammer should be used to strike gears or shafts because they will not damage them.

Taps and Dies

The hand **tap** is a small tool used for hand cutting internal threads (Figure 4–56). An internal thread is cut on the inside of a part, such as a thread on the inside of a nut. Taps are also available that only clean and restore threads that were previously cut. Taps are selected by size and thread pitch.

Hand-threading **dies** (Figure 4–57) are the opposite of taps because they cut external (outside) threads on bolts, rods, and pipes rather than internal

threads. Dies are made in various sizes and shapes, depending on the particular work for which they are intended. Dies may be solid (fixed size), split on one side to permit adjustment, or have two halves held together in a collet that provides for individual adjustments. Dies fit into holders called die stocks.

Chisels and Punches

Chisels (Figure 4–58) are used to cut metal by driving them with a hammer. Automotive technicians use a variety of chisels for cutting sheet metal, shearing off rivet and bolt heads, splitting rusted nuts, and chipping metal.

CUTTING THREADS

CHAMFER   SQUARE DRIVE END

FLUTE   SHANK

FIGURE 4–56 Parts of a hand tap.

RIVET BUSTER CHISEL

DIAMOND POINT CHISEL

ROUND NOSE CAPE CHISEL

CAPE CHISEL

FLAT CHISEL

LONG FLAT CHISEL

FIGURE 4–58 Chisels and their correct cutting edges.

Punches (Figure 4–59) are used for driving out pins, rivets, or shafts; aligning holes in parts during assembly; and marking the starting point for drilling a hole. Punches are designated by their point diameter and punch shape.

Rust, corrosion, and prolonged heat can cause automotive fasteners, such as cap screws and studs, to become stuck. A box wrench or socket is used to loosen cap screws. A special gripping tool is designed to remove studs. However, if the fastener breaks off, special extracting tools and procedures must be employed.

Removers

Several stud removers are shown in Figure 4–60. These tools are also used to install studs. Stud removers have hardened, knurled, or grooved eccentric rollers or jaws that grip the stud tightly when operated. Stud removers/installers are turned by a socket wrench drive handle, a socket, or wrench.

CENTER PUNCH (SHOWING INCLUDED ANGLE)

STARTING PUNCH

PIN PUNCH

ALIGNING PUNCH

STRAIGHT SHANK BRASS PUNCH

FIGURE 4–59 Punches are designated by point diameter and punch shape.

FIGURE 4–60 Various stud removers.

FIGURE 4–61 Screw extractor set.

Screw Extractors

Extractors are used on screws and bolts that are broken off below the surface. Twist drills, fluted extractors, and hex nuts are included in a screw extractor set (Figure 4–61). This type of extractor lessens the tendency to expand the screw or stud that has been drilled out by providing gripping power along the full length of the stud.

Tubing Tools

Tubing made from steel, copper, aluminum, and plastic is used frequently on the automobile. During service work, tubing often needs to be repaired or replaced. Tubing tools are made for such tasks as cutting, deburring, flaring, swaging, bending, and removing fittings. Figure 4–62 illustrates some of these tools.

Gear and Bearing Pullers

Many precision gears and bearings have a slight interference fit (**press-fit**) when installed on a shaft or a housing. The press-fit allows no motion between parts and, therefore, prevents wear. The removal of gears and bearings must be done carefully. Prying or hammering can break or bind the parts. A puller with the proper jaws and adapters should be used when applying force to remove gears and bearings. Using proper tools, the force can be applied with a slight and steady motion. Various gear and bearing puller styles and sizes are shown in Figure 4–63.

POWER TOOLS

Power tools make a technician's job easier. They operate faster and with more torque than hand tools. However, power tools require greater safety measures. Power tools do not stop unless they are turned

A

GROOVED SUPPORTING ROLLERS

CUTTING WHEEL

ADJUSTING KNOB

RETRACTABLE REAMER AND FILE

B

KNURLED ADJUSTING NUT

CUTTING CONE

IMPERIAL

C

CLAMPING LEVER

SLIDING DIE BLOCKS

IMPERIAL EASTMAN

FIGURE 4–62 Common tubing tools: (A) tubing cutter, (B) deburring tool, and (C) single-lap flaring tool.

FIGURE 4–63 Various gear and bearing pullers.

off. Power is furnished by either air (pneumatic), electricity, or hydraulic fluid. Power tools should only be used for loosening nuts and/or bolts.

SHOP TALK

Safety is critical when using power tools. Carelessness or mishandling of power tools can cause serious injury. Do not use a power tool without obtaining permission from your instructor. Be sure you know how to operate the tool properly before using it. Prior to using a power tool, read the instructions carefully. ∎

IMPACT WRENCH An **impact wrench** (Figure 4–64) is a portable hand-held reversible wrench. A heavy-duty model can deliver up to 450 foot-pounds of torque. When triggered, the output shaft, onto which the impact socket is fastened, spins freely at 2,000 to 14,000 rpm, depending on the wrench's make and model. When the impact wrench meets resistance, a small spring-loaded hammer, which is situated near the end of the tool, strikes an anvil attached to the drive shaft onto which the socket is mounted. Each impact moves the socket around a little until torque equilibrium is reached, the fastener breaks, or the trigger is released. Torque equilibrium occurs when the torque of the bolt equals the output torque of the wrench.

SHOP TALK

When using an air impact wrench, it is important that only impact sockets and adapters are used. Other types of sockets and adapters, if used, might shatter and fly off, endangering the safety of the operator and others in the immediate area. ∎

FIGURE 4–64   Typical impact wrenches. *Courtesy of Matco Tools Company*

FIGURE 4–66   Using a pneumatic drill.

FIGURE 4–67   The air chisel is a very versatile tool.

AIR RATCHET An air ratchet, like the hand ratchet, has a special ability to work in hard-to-reach places. Its angle drive reaches in and loosens or tightens where other hand or power wrenches just cannot work (Figure 4–65). The air ratchet looks like an ordinary ratchet but has a fat handgrip that contains the air vane motor and drive mechanism.

AIR DRILL Air drills are usually available in 1/4-, 3/8-, and 1/2-inch sizes, operate in much the same manner as an electric drill, but are smaller and lighter. This compactness makes them a great deal easier to use for drilling operations in auto work (Figure 4–66).

AIR CHISEL OR HAMMER Of all auto air tools, the air chisel or hammer (Figure 4–67) is one of the most useful. It is also one of the most dangerous. Always wear eye protection when using an air chisel,

hammer, or drill. Used with the accessories illustrated in Figure 4–68, this tool can be used as the following tools.

- Universal joint and tie-rod tool
- Ball joint separator
- Shock absorber chisel
- Tailpipe cutter
- Tapered punch
- Rubber bushing splitter
- Bushing removal
- Bushing installer

BLOWGUN **Blowguns** are used for blowing off parts during cleaning. Never point a blowgun at yourself or someone else. A blowgun (Figure 4–69) snaps into one end of an air hose and directs airflow when a button is pressed. Before using a blowgun, be sure it has not been modified to eliminate air-bleed holes on the side.

BENCH GRINDER This electric power tool is generally bolted to a workbench. The grinder should have safety shields and guards. Always wear face protection when using a grinder. A bench grinder is classified by wheel size. Six- to ten-inch wheels are the most common in auto repair shops. Three types of wheels are available with this bench tool.

- Grinding wheel. For a wide variety of grinding jobs from sharpening cutting tools to deburring.

FIGURE 4–65   Using an air ratchet wrench.

FIGURE 4–68 Air chisel accessories: (A) universal joint and tie-rod tool; (B) smoothing hammer; (C) ball joint separator; (D) panel crimper; (E) shock absorber chisel; (F) tailpipe cutter; (G) scraper; (H) tapered punch; (I) edging tool; (J) rubber bushing splitter; (K) bushing remover; and (L) bushing installer.

FIGURE 4–69 Typical blowgun. *Courtesy of DeVilbiss Company*

◆ Wire wheel brush. Used for general cleaning and buffing, removing rust and scale, paint removal, deburring, and so forth.

◆ Buffing wheel. For general purpose buffing, polishing, light cutting, and finish coloring operations.

TROUBLE LIGHT Adequate light is necessary when working under and around automobiles. A **trouble light** can be hand-held or hung in a convenient location. It should be insulated to protect you from electrical shocks. Trouble lights use either a bulb or fluorescent tube. The bulb or tube is sur-rounded by a cage or enclosed in clear plastic to prevent accidental breaking and burning. The heat generated by the bulb can easily burn your skin. The light has a long cord so that the light can be moved throughout the shop.

FLOOR JACK A floor jack is a portable tool on wheels that is used to raise an automobile. A control lever at the end of the long handle directs hydraulic fluid to a cylinder, which in turn raises or lowers a pad at the end of the jack. The pad is a portion of the jack that contacts the automobile. Always use jack stands to support the automobile after it has been raised by a jack.

HOIST The lift, or hoist, raises the entire automobile. This allows the technician to have extra working space underneath. A hoist is lowered onto the floor when it is not being used and is raised when an automobile is to be lifted. Most modern hoists are double-post designs, although some single-post models remain in use. Hydraulic pressure and compressed air are used to move hoists up and down. A control lever is placed at a convenient location near the hoist.

PRESSES Many automotive jobs require the use of powerful force to assemble or disassemble parts that are press-fit together. Removing and installing piston pins, servicing rear axle bearings, pressing brake drum and rotor studs, and transmission assembly work are just a few of the examples. Presses can be hydraulic, electric, air, or hand driven. Capacities range up to 150 tons of pressing force, depending on the size and design of the press. Smaller arbor and C-frame presses can be bench or pedestal mounted (Figure 4–70), while high capacity units are free-standing or floor mounted (Figure 4–71).

FIGURE 4–70 Small bench-mounted, manually operated arbor press. *Courtesy of Auto Electric Supplier and Equipment Company*

FIGURE 4–71 Typical heavy-duty electro-hydraulic shop press. *Courtesy of LS Industries*

FIGURE 4–72 Service manuals are separated into major sections. *Courtesy of Ford Motor Company*

SERVICE MANUALS

The most important tool of the trade is the service manual. There are many different sources of information that should be available to automotive technicians.

AUTO MANUFACTURER'S SERVICE MANUALS The primary source of repair and specification information for any car, van, or truck is the manufacturer. Service manuals are published by the manufacturer each year, for every vehicle built. These manuals are written for professional technicians.

Because of the enormous amount of information, some manufacturers publish more than one manual per year per car model. They may be separated into sections such as chassis, suspension, steering, emission control, fuel systems, brakes, basic maintenance and tuneup, engine, transmission, body, and so on (Figure 4–72).

When complete information with step-by-step testing, repair, and assembly procedures is desired, nothing can match auto manufacturers' repair manuals. They cover all repairs, adjustments, specifications, detailed diagnostic procedures, and special tools required. They can be purchased directly from the automobile manufacturer.

To help you learn how to effectively use service manuals, you will find service manual references and tips throughout this text.

Since many technical changes occur on specific vehicles each year, manufacturers' service manuals need to be constantly updated. Updates are published as service bulletins (often referred to as Technical Service Bulletins or TSBs) that show the changes in specifications and repair procedures during the model year (Figure 4–73). These changes do not appear in the service manual until the next year. The car manufacturer provides these bulletins to dealers and repair facilities on a regular basis.

Automotive manufacturers also publish a series of technician reference books. The publications provide general instructions on the service and repair of their vehicles with their recommended techniques.

NOVEMBER 14, 1994   BULLETIN NO. 94-23

TECHNICAL SERVICE BULLETIN

FEATURED IN THIS BULLETIN:

- Special Handling Procedures For Laser
  Red Mustangs Exhibiting Reduced Chip
  Resistance On Vehicles Built 12/1/93
  Through 2/8/94 Only. . . . . 1994 MUSTANG

PARTNERS IN CUSTOMER SATISFACTION

FIGURE 4–73 Service bulletins are used to provide the latest repair procedures and other changes. *Courtesy of Ford Motor Company*

AFTERMARKET SUPPLIERS' GUIDES AND CATALOGS Many of the larger parts manufacturers have excellent guides on the various parts they manufacture or supply. They also provide updated service bulletins on their products.

GENERAL AND SPECIALTY REPAIR MANUALS These are published by independent companies rather than the manufacturers. However, they pay for and get most of their information from the car makers. They may contain component information, diagnostic steps, repair procedures, and specifications for several car makes in one book. Information is usually condensed and is more general in nature than the manufacturer's manuals. The condensed format allows for more coverage in less space and, therefore, is not always specific. They may also contain several years of models as well as several car makes in one book.

FLAT-RATE MANUALS Flat-rate manuals contain figures relating to the length of time a specific repair is supposed to require. Normally, they also contain a

parts list with approximate or exact prices of parts. They are excellent for making cost estimates and are published by the manufacturers and independents.

The same information that is available in service manuals and bulletins is also available on compact disk-read only memory systems (**CD-ROM**). A single compact disk can hold a quarter million pages of text. One great advantage of this system is that finding information is easier and quicker. The disks are normally updated monthly and not only contain the most recent service bulletins but also engineering and field service fixes. Other sources for up-to-date technical information are trade magazines and trade associations.

CASE STUDY

*T*he word diagnosis is commonly used in automotive textbooks and service manuals. However, it is a term that is seldom explained. It is more than following a series of interrelated steps in order to find the solution to a specific condition. Diagnosis is a way of looking at systems that are not functioning the way they should and finding out why. It is knowing how the system should work and deciding whether it is working correctly. Through an understanding of the purpose and operation of the car's system, a technician can accurately diagnose problems.

Most good diagnosticians use the same basic diagnostic procedure. Because of its logical approach, this procedure can quickly lead a technician to the cause of a problem. Accurate diagnostics include the following steps.

1. **Gather information about the condition or problem.**
2. **Verify that the condition exists.**
3. **Thoroughly define what the problem is and when it occurs.**
4. **Determine the possible causes of the problem.**
5. **Isolate the problem by general testing.**
6. **Test to pinpoint the cause of the problem.**
7. **Repair the problem and verify the repair.**

Most service manuals contain diagnostic charts that help technicians pinpoint the cause of the problem (Figure 4–74). The steps of diagnostic charts or trees are designed to be followed in order. These charts contain the most probable causes of a particular problem and simple tests that lead to the exact cause.

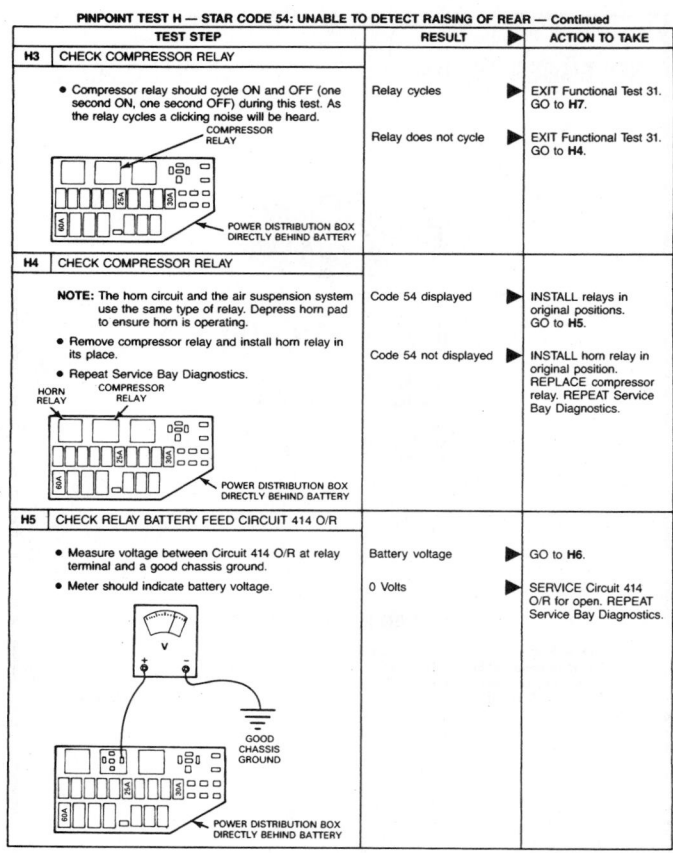

FIGURE 4–74 Typical diagnostic chart or tree. *Courtesy of Ford Motor Company*

KEY TERMS

Ball gauge
Blowgun
CD-ROM
Chisel
Concentricity gauge
Dial caliper
Dial indicator
Die
Extractor
Feeler gauge
Flat-rate
Impact wrench
Machinist's rule
Micrometer
Phillips screwdriver
Pliers
Posidriv screwdriver

Press-fit
Punch
Radius gauge
Runout gauge
Screw pitch gauge
SI
Snap gauge
Tap
Telescoping gauge
Torque-indicating wrench
Torx screwdriver
Trouble light
UCS
V-block
Wrench

SUMMARY

◆ Repairing the modern automobile requires the use of many different hand and power tools. Units of measurement play a major role in tool selection. Therefore, it is important to be knowledgeable in not only the UCS system but also the metric system of measurement.

◆ Engine measuring tools must be able to measure objects to a high degree of precision. They should be handled with care at all times and cleaned before and after every use.

◆ A micrometer can be used to measure the outside diameter of shafts and the inside diameter of holes. It is calibrated in either inch or metric graduations.

◆ Telescoping gauges are designed to measure bore diameters and other clearances. They usually are used with an outside micrometer. Small hole gauges are used in the same manner as the telescoping gauge, usually to determine valve guide diameter.

◆ The screw pitch gauge provides a fast and accurate method of measuring the threads per inch (pitch) of fasteners. This is done by matching the teeth of the gauge with the fastener threads and reading the pitch directly from the leaf of the gauge.

◆ While out-of-roundness can be checked with an inside micrometer, an out-of-roundness gauge does the job better. Any reading on the gauge indicates the amount of variation or out-of-roundness.

◆ It is crucial to use the proper amount of torque when tightening nuts or cap screws on any part of a vehicle, particularly the engine. A torque-indicating wrench makes it possible to duplicate the conditions of tightness and stress recommended by the manufacturer.

◆ Metric and SAE size wrenches are not interchangeable. An auto technician should have a variety of both types.

◆ The handle of a screwdriver is important. The larger the diameter, the better grip and torque it will provide. A screwdriver, no matter what type, should never be used as a chisel, punch, or pry bar.

◆ The hand tap is used for hand cutting internal threads and for cleaning and restoring previously cut threads. Hand-threading dies cut external threads and fit into holders called die stocks.

◆ Carelessness or mishandling of power tools can cause serious injury. Safety measures are needed when working with such tools as impact and air ratchet wrenches, blowguns, bench grinders, lifts, hoists, and hydraulic presses.

◆ The primary source of repair and specification information for any vehicle is the manufacturer's service manual. Updates are published as service bulletins. These include changes made during the model year, which will not appear in the manual until the following year.

◆ Flat-rate manuals are ideal for making cost estimates. Published by manufacturers and independent companies, they contain figures showing how long specific repairs should take to complete, as well as a list of the necessary parts and their prices.

◆ Diagnosis means finding the cause or causes of a problem. It requires a thorough understanding of the purpose and operation of the various automotive systems. Diagnostic charts found in service manuals can aid in diagnostics.

TECH MANUAL

The following procedures are included in Chapter 4 of the *Tech Manual* that accompanies this book:

1. How to cut with a chisel.

2. Using a punch to remove a rivet.

3. How to repair and/or replace damaged threads.

4. Proper use of a stationary grinder.

5. Proper use of a hydraulic floor jack.

6. Proper use of a vehicle hoist.

7. Proper use of a service manual.

 REVIEW QUESTIONS

1. How often should the calibration of a micrometer be checked?

2. List some common uses of the dial indicator.

3. What determines the size of a wrench?

4. Name the three types of wheels available for use with a bench grinder.

5. How do manufacturers inform technicians about changes in vehicle specifications and repair procedures during the model year?

6. Which of the following wrenches is the best choice for turning a bolt?

a. open-end
b. box-end
c. combination
d. none of the above

7. Technician A says a screwdriver can be used as a chisel. Technician B says a screwdriver makes a handy small pry bar. Who is correct?

a. Technician A   c. Both A and B
b. Technician B   d. Neither A nor B

8. Technician A says a tap cuts external threads. Technician B says a die cuts internal threads. Who is correct?

a. Technician A   c. Both A and B
b. Technician B   d. Neither A nor B

9. Which of the following screwdrivers is like a Phillips but has a flatter and blunter tip?
   a. standard
   b. Torx
   c. Posidriv
   d. clutch head

10. Which of the following types of pliers is best for grasping small parts?
    a. adjustable
    b. needle nose
    c. retaining ring
    d. snap ring

11. Technician A uses a punch to align holes in parts during assembly. Technician B uses a punch to drive out rivets. Who is correct?
    a. Technician A
    b. Technician B
    c. Both A and B
    d. Neither A nor B

12. An extractor is used for removing broken ____.
    a. seals
    b. bushings
    c. pistons
    d. bolts

13. Which of the following operations can an air chisel or hammer perform?
    a. bushing installation
    b. bushing removal
    c. shock absorber chisel
    d. all of the above

14. Technician A uses a blowgun to blow off parts during cleaning. Technician B uses a blowgun to clean off his uniform after working. Who is correct?
    a. Technician A
    b. Technician B
    c. Both A and B
    d. Neither A nor B

15. Always use jack stands to support a vehicle after it has been raised by a ____.
    a. floor jack
    b. hoist
    c. hydraulic press
    d. all of the above

16. Technician A uses a dial caliper to take inside and outside measurements. Technician B uses a dial caliper to take depth measurements. Who is correct?
    a. Technician A
    b. Technician B
    c. Both A and B
    d. Neither A nor B

17. For a measurement that must be made within one ten-thousandth of an inch, Technician A uses a machinist's rule. For the same measurement, Technician B uses a standard micrometer. Who is correct?
    a. Technician A
    b. Technician B
    c. Both A and B
    d. Neither A nor B

18. Which of the following feeler gauge measurements requires the use of a precision straightedge as well?
    a. piston ring end gap
    b. connecting rod side clearance
    c. crankshaft end play
    d. cylinder head warpage

19. Technician A uses a 9/16-inch wrench to turn a 14-millimeter nut. Technician B uses a 9/16-inch wrench to hold a 14-millimeter nut. Who is correct?
    a. Technician A
    b. Technician B
    c. Both A and B
    d. Neither A nor B

20. When using an air impact wrench, Technician A uses only impact sockets and adapters. Technician B uses only chrome-plated sockets. Who is correct?
    a. Technician A
    b. Technician B
    c. Both A and B
    d. Neither A nor B

DIAGNOSTIC EQUIPMENT

5

OBJECTIVES

◆ *Explain the basic principles of electricity.* ◆ *Name the diagnostic tools and equipment commonly used in vehicle repair work.* ◆ *Describe the basic applications and operation of these tools.* ◆ *Explain why it is important for technicians to be skilled in the use of electrical, electronic, and computerized test equipment.*

As the trend toward the integration of ignition, fuel, and emission systems progresses, diagnostic test equipment must also keep up with these changes. New tools and techniques are constantly being developed to diagnose electronic engine control systems.

Today's technician must not only keep up with changes in automotive technology but must also keep up with the new testing procedures and specialized diagnostic equipment. To be successful, a shop must continuously invest in this equipment and the training necessary to troubleshoot today's electronic engine systems.

Fortunately, many of the testers for noncomputerized cars will still work on some systems of late-model cars. Also, some of the latest testers, can be used on early models even though they feature test procedures for computerized systems. This interchangeability limits the expense for diagnostic equipment.

Not all engine performance problems are related to electronic control systems. Therefore, technicians still need to understand basic engine tests. Pressure tests and basic electrical checks are still an important part of modern engine diagnosis.

ELECTRICAL FUNDAMENTALS

There is often confusion concerning the terms electrical and electronic. In this book, electrical and electrical systems will refer to wiring and electrical parts, such as alternators, lights, and voltage regulators. **Electronics** will mean computers and other black box-type items used to control engine and vehicle systems.

A basic understanding of electrical principles is important to properly diagnose any system that is monitored, controlled, or operated by electricity.

Although the subject will be covered in greater detail in later chapters, a quick overview of electricity and its principles is presented here.

Flow of Electricity

All things are made up of atoms. An **atom** is the smallest particle of something. Atoms are very small and cannot be seen with your eye. This may be the reason many technicians struggle to understand electricity. The basics of electricity focus in on atoms. Understanding the structure of the atom is the first step in understanding how electricity works. The following principles describe atoms, which are the building blocks of all materials.

◆ In the center of every atom is a **nucleus**.
◆ The nucleus contains positively charged particles called **protons** and particles called **neutrons** that have no charge.
◆ Negatively charged particles called **electrons** orbit around every nucleus.
◆ Every type of atom has a different number of protons and electrons, but each atom has an equal number of protons and electrons. Therefore, the total electrical charge of an atom is zero, or neutral.

In all atoms, the electrons are arranged in different orbits, called shells. Each shell contains a specific number of electrons. Figure 5–1A shows a copper atom. This atom has 29 electrons and 29 protons. The 29 electrons are arranged in shells. Notice that the outer shell has only 1 electron. This outer shell needs 32 electrons to be completely full. This means that the 1 electron in the outer shell is loosely tied to the atom and can be easily removed.

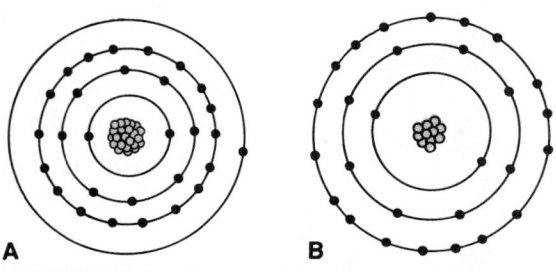

FIGURE 5–1 Electron arrangement of (A) a copper atom and (B) a nickel atom.

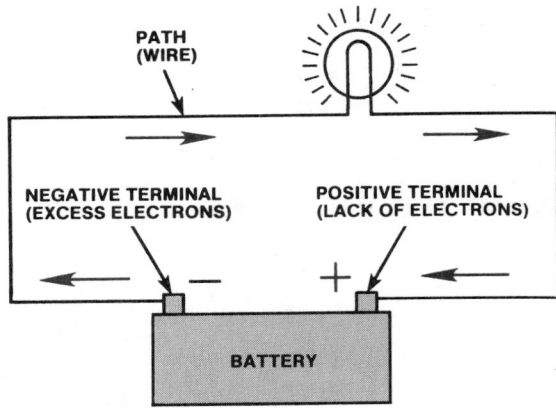

FIGURE 5–2 Electricity results from the flow of electrons from the negative side of the battery to the positive side.

Figure 5–1B shows a simplified drawing of a nickel atom. This atom contains 28 protons in the nucleus and 28 electrons arranged in shells. The third shell of any atom can contain only 18 electrons. In the nickel atom, the outer shell is completely filled. Therefore, its electrons are closely tied to the atom and cannot be removed easily.

The looseness or tightness of the electrons in orbit around the neutron of an atom explains the behavior of electricity. Electricity is caused by the flow of electrons from one atom to another. The release of energy as one electron leaves the orbit of one atom and jumps into the orbit of another is electricity. The key behind creating electricity is to give a reason for the electrons to move.

There is a natural attraction of electrons to protons. Electrons have a negative charge and are attracted to something with a positive charge. When an electron leaves the orbit of an atom, the atom then has a positive charge. An electron moves from one atom to another because the atom next to it appears to be more positive than the one it is orbiting around. An electrical power source provides for a more positive charge and to allow for a continuous flow of electricity, it supplies free electrons. To have a continuous flow of electricity, three things must be present: an excess of electrons in one place, a lack of electrons in another place, and a path between the two places.

Two power or energy sources are used in an automobile's electrical system. These are based on a chemical reaction and on **magnetism**. A car's battery is a source of **chemical energy**. A chemical reaction in the battery provides for an excess of electrons and a lack of electrons in another place. Batteries have two terminals, a positive and a negative. Basically, the negative terminal is the outlet for the electrons and the positive terminal is the inlet for the electrons to get to the protons. The chemical reaction in a battery causes a lack of electrons at the positive (+) terminal and an excess at the negative (–) terminal. This creates an electrical imbalance, causing the electrons to flow through the path provided by a wire. A simple example of this process is shown in the battery and light arrangement in Figure 5–2.

The chemical process in the battery continues to provide electrons until the chemicals become weak. At that time, either the battery has run out of electrons or all of the protons are matched with an electron. When this happens, there is no longer a reason for the electrons to want to move to the positive side of the battery. It no longer looks more positive. Fortunately, the vehicle's charging system restores the battery's supply of electrons. This allows the chemical reaction in the battery to continue indefinitely.

Electricity and magnetism are interrelated. One can be used to produce the other. Moving a wire (a conductor) through an already existing magnetic field (such as a permanent magnet) can produce electricity. This process of producing electricity through magnetism is called **induction**. In a generator, a coil of wire is moved through a magnetic field. In an alternator, a magnetic field is moved through a coil of wire. In both cases, electricity is produced. The amount of electricity produced depends on a number of factors, including the strength of the magnetic field, the number of wires that pass through the field, and the speed at which the wire moves through the magnetic field.

MEASURING ELECTRICITY

Electrical **current** is a term used to describe the movement or flow of electricity. The greater the number of electrons flowing past a given point in a given amount of time, the more current the circuit has. This current, like the flow of water or any other substance, can be measured. **Voltage** is electrical pressure. Voltage is the force developed by the attraction of the electrons to the protons. The more positive one side of the circuit is, the more voltage is present in the circuit. Voltage does not flow, rather it is the pressure that causes current flow.

When any substance flows, it meets **resistance**. The resistance to electrical flow can be measured. **Power** is the rate at which work can be done. Forcing a current through a resistance is work. The power used in a circuit can also be determined. The following section explains the measurement of flow (current), resistance (**ohms**), pressure (voltage), and power (**wattage**).

Electrical Flow (Current)

The unit for measuring electrical current is the **ampere**. The instrument used to measure electrical current flow in a circuit is called an **ammeter**. There are two types of electrical flow, or current: direct current (**DC**) and alternating current (**AC**). In direct current, the electrons flow in one direction only. The example of the battery and light shown earlier is based upon direct current. In alternating current, the electrons change direction at a fixed rate. An automobile uses DC current while the current in homes and buildings is AC.

Resistance

In every atom, the electrons resist being moved out of their shell. The amount of resistance depends on the type of atom. As explained earlier, in some atoms (such as those in copper) there is very little resistance to electron flow because the outer electron is loosely held. In other substances (such as nickel) there is more resistance to flow, because the outer electrons are tightly held.

The resistance to current flow produces heat. This heat can be measured to determine the amount of resistance. A unit of measured resistance is called an ohm. Resistance can be measured by an instrument called an **ohmmeter**. Differing amounts of resistance are measured by changing scales (such as × 1, × 10, × 100) on the ohmmeter.

Pressure

In electrical flow, some force is needed to move the electrons between atoms. This force is the pressure that exists between a positive and negative point within an electrical circuit. This force, also called electromotive force (**EMF**), is measured in units called volts. One volt is the amount of pressure (force) required to move 1 ampere of current through a resistance of 1 ohm. Voltage is measured by an instrument called a voltmeter.

Power

Electrical power, or the rate of work, is found by multiplying the amount of electrical pressure by the amount of current flow (power = voltage × amperage). Power is measured in watts. Although power measurements are rarely, if ever, needed in automotive service, knowing the power requirements of light bulbs, electric motors, and other components is sometimes useful when troubleshooting electrical systems.

Circuits

When electrons are able to flow along a path (wire) between two points, an electrical circuit is formed. An electrical circuit is considered complete when there is a path that connects the positive and negative terminals of the electrical power source. Somewhere in the circuit there must be a load or resistance to control the amount of current in the circuit. Most automotive electrical circuits use the chassis as the path to the negative side of the battery. Electrical components have a lead that connects them to the chassis. These are called the **chassis ground** connections. In a complete circuit, the flow of electricity can be controlled and applied to do useful work, such as light a headlamp or turn over a starter motor. Components that use electrical power put a load on the circuit and consume electrical energy.

The amount of current that flows in a circuit is determined by the resistance in that circuit. As resistance goes up, the current goes down. The energy used by a load is measured in volts. Amperage stays constant in a circuit, but the voltage is dropped as it powers a load. Measuring voltage drop determines the amount of energy consumed by the load.

Electrical test equipment is often used to troubleshoot problems in an electrical circuit. Electrical problems are normally one of the following.

OPEN CIRCUIT An **open** circuit is one that has a break in the wire, often called a break in the circuit's continuity. Without a completed path, current cannot flow. An open circuit can be caused by a disconnected wire, a broken wire, or a switch in the off position. When a circuit is off, it is open. When the circuit is on, it is closed.

SHORTED CIRCUIT A shorted circuit is an unwanted current path. **Short** circuits cause an increase in current flow. This increased current flow can burn wires or components. Sometimes two circuits become shorted together. When this happens, one circuit powers another. This may result in strange happenings, such as the horn sounding every time the brake pedal is depressed. In this case, the brake light circuit is shorted to the horn circuit. Improper wiring and damaged insulation are the two major causes of short circuits.

A short can also be an unwanted short to ground. This problem provides a low resistance path to ground. This problem causes extremely high current flow, which will damage wires and electrical components. Some call this problem a grounded circuit.

HIGH-RESISTANCE CIRCUIT This problem occurs when there is unwanted high resistance in the circuit. The higher-than-normal resistance causes the current flow to be lower than normal and the components in the circuit will be unable to operate properly. A common cause of this type of problem is corrosion at a connector. The corrosion becomes an additional load in the circuit. This load uses some of the circuit's voltage, which prevents full voltage to the normal loads in the circuit.

With a basic understanding of electricity and simple circuits, it is easier to understand the operation and purpose of the various types of electrical test equipment described in the following sections.

Circuit Tester

Circuit testers (Figure 5–3) are used to identify short and open circuits in any electrical circuit. Low-voltage testers are used to troubleshoot 6- to 12-volt circuits. High-voltage circuit testers diagnose primary and secondary ignition circuits.

A circuit tester, commonly called a **testlight**, looks like a stubby ice pick. Its handle is transparent and contains a light bulb. A probe extends from one end of the handle and a ground clip and wire from the other end. When the ground clip is attached to a good ground and the probe touched to a live connector, the bulb in the handle will light up. If the bulb does not light, voltage is not available at the connector.

A self-powered testlight is called a **continuity tester** (Figure 5–4). It is used on open circuits. It looks like a regular testlight, except that it has a small internal battery. When the ground clip is attached to the negative side of a component and the probe touched to the positive side, the lamp will light if there is conti-

FIGURE 5–5 A voltmeter can be used to measure the voltage available at any point in an electrical system. *Courtesy of MAC Tools, Inc.*

nuity in the circuit. If an open circuit exists, the light will not be illuminated. Typically, the negative side of a component is called the ground side, while the positive side is called the power or feed side.

Electrical Test Meters

Several meters are used to test and diagnose electrical systems. These are the voltmeter, ohmmeter, and ammeter.

VOLTMETER The **voltmeter** (Figure 5–5) measures the voltage available at any point in an electrical system. For example, it can be used to measure the voltage available at the battery. It can also be used to test the voltage available at the terminals of any component or connector. A voltmeter can also be used to test voltage drop across an electrical circuit, component, switch, or connector.

A voltmeter has two leads: a red positive lead and a black negative lead. The red lead should be connected to the positive side of the circuit or component. The black should be connected to ground or to the negative side of the component. Voltmeters should always be connected across the circuit being tested.

OHMMETER As mentioned earlier, an ohmmeter (Figure 5–6) measures resistance to current flow in a circuit. In contrast to the voltmeter, which uses the voltage available in the circuit, the ohmmeter is battery powered. The circuit being tested must be open. If the power is on in the circuit, the ohmmeter will be damaged.

The two leads of the ohmmeter are placed across or in parallel with the circuit or component being tested. The red lead is placed on the positive side of the circuit and the black lead is placed on the negative side of the circuit. The meter sends current through the component and determines the amount of resis-

FIGURE 5–3 Typical circuit tester, commonly called a testlight. *Courtesy of MAC Tools, Inc.*

FIGURE 5–4 Typical self-powered circuit tester, commonly called a continuity tester. *Courtesy of MAC Tools, Inc.*

FIGURE 5–6 Typical ohmmeter.

tance based on the voltage dropped across the load. The scale of an ohmmeter reads from zero to infinity (∞). A zero reading means there is no resistance in the circuit and may indicate a short in a component that should show a specific resistance. An infinity reading indicates a number higher than the meter can measure. This usually is an indication of an open circuit.

AMMETER As previously discussed, an ammeter (Figure 5–7) measures current flow in a circuit. Current is measured in amperes. Unlike the voltmeter and ohmmeter, the ammeter must be placed into the circuit or in series with the circuit being tested. Normally, this requires disconnecting a wire or connector from a component and connecting the ammeter between the wire or connector and the component. The red lead of the ammeter should always be connected to the side of the connector closest to the positive side of the battery and the black lead should be connected to the other side.

FIGURE 5–7 Typical ammeter. *Courtesy of MAC Tools, Inc.*

FIGURE 5–9
Typical battery tester.
Courtesy of Kent-Moore Tools

FIGURE 5–8 The volt/ampere tester is used for testing batteries and the starting and charging systems. *Courtesy of Sun Electric Corporation*

It is much easier to test current using an ammeter with an inductive pickup. The pickup clamps around the wire or cable being tested. The ammeter determines amperage based on the magnetic field created by the current flowing through the wire. This type of pickup eliminates the need to separate the circuit to insert the meter.

VOLT/AMPERE TESTER A volt/ampere tester (**VAT**), shown in Figure 5–8, is used to test batteries, starting systems, and charging systems. The tester contains a voltmeter, ammeter, and carbon pile. The carbon pile is a variable resistor. A knob on the tester allows the technician to vary the resistance of the pile. When the tester is attached to the battery, the carbon pile will draw current out of the battery. The ammeter will read the amount of current draw. When testing a battery, the resistance of the carbon pile must be adjusted to match the ratings of the battery.

Figure 5–9 shows a small battery tester. This battery tester does not have a carbon pile. However, it can be used to test circuit voltage and to perform battery load tests on 6- and 12-volt batteries. It can also be used to check the condition of battery cables and connectors, and to check running voltage.

MULTIMETER It is not necessary for a technician to own separate voltmeters, ohmmeters, and ammeters. These meters are combined in a single tool called a **multimeter**. A multimeter is one of the most versatile tools used in diagnosing engine performance

FIGURE 5–10   The digital volt/ohmmeter can be used to test voltage and resistance.

FIGURE 5–11   Typical multifunctional, low-impedance multimeter. *Courtesy of OTC Tool and Equipment Division of SPX Corporation*

TABLE 5–1 ELECTRICAL TESTING WITH A MULTIMETER				
System/ Component	**Measurement Type**			
	Voltage Presence & Level	**Voltage Drop**	**Current**	**Resistance**
Charging System				
Alternators	•		•	
Regulators	•			
Diodes		•		•
Connectors	•	•		•
Starting System				
Batteries	•	•	•	
Starters		•	•	
Solenoids	•	•		•
Connectors	•	•		•
Cables	•	•		•
Ignition System				
Coils	•			•
Connectors	•	•		•
Distributor caps				•
Plug wires				•
Rotors				•
Magnetic pickup	•			•

and electrical systems. The most commonly used multimeter is the digital volt/ohmmeter (**DVOM**), which is often referred to as a digital multimeter (**DMM**). As its name implies, the DVOM tests both voltage and resistance (Figure 5–10). These meters do not use a sweeping needle and scales to display the measurement. Rather, they display the measurement digitally on the meter.

Top-of-the-line multimeters are multifunctional. Most test—DC and AC—volts, ohms, and amperes. Usually there are several test ranges provided for each of these functions. In addition to these basic electrical tests, multimeters also test engine revolutions per minute (rpm), ignition dwell, diode condition, distributor conditions, frequency, and even temperature (Figure 5–11). Table 5–1 shows some of the many tests that can be performed with a multimeter.

Multimeters are available with either analog or digital displays. Analog meters (Figure 5–12) enjoyed wide popularity prior to electronic control systems. They are still favored by technicians who have used them for years and prefer the visual reference provided by a moving needle.

However, there are several drawbacks to using most analog-type meters for testing electronic control systems. Many electronic components require very precise test results. Digital meters can measure volts, ohms, or amperes in tenths and hundredths. Some have multiple test ranges that must be manually selected. Others are auto ranging. The multimeter shown in Figure 5–13 has many different test ranges.

Another problem with analog meters is their low internal resistance (input impedance). The low input

FIGURE 5–12 Analog multimeters provide a visual reference point in the form of the moving needle. *Courtesy of Bill Johnson*

FIGURE 5–13 This multimeter has eighteen test ranges. *Courtesy of TIF Instruments, Inc.*

impedance allows too much current to flow through circuits and should not be used on delicate electronic devices.

Digital meters, on the other hand, have a high input impedance, usually at least 10 megohms (10 million ohms). Metered voltage for resistance tests is well below 5 volts, reducing the risk of damage to sensitive components and delicate computer circuits.

IGNITION SYSTEM TEST EQUIPMENT

Some of the tools used to troubleshoot ignition systems have been in use for years. Others are relatively

FIGURE 5–14 Typical tach-dwellmeter. *Courtesy of Snap-on Tools Corporation*

new, having been developed in response to electronic ignition and computer-controlled ignition systems.

Tach-Dwellmeter

A tool commonly used for tuneup and engine diagnosis is the tach-dwellmeter (Figure 5–14). This meter is a combination tachometer and dwellmeter. A **tachometer** measures engine speed. Engine speed is measured in **rpm**s (revolutions per minute). A **dwellmeter** measures the time a circuit is on. On ignition systems, the dwell time is the degree of crankshaft rotation during which the primary circuit is on. On older GM vehicles with the C-4 or computer-controlled catalytic converter systems, a dwellmeter can be used to test the carburetor's mixture control solenoid. A tach-dwellmeter has little value on late-model, fuel injection cars. Therefore, it is a tester that is doomed to extinction.

A typical tach-dwellmeter has three leads. Two heavy-duty leads connect the meter to the battery terminals. The third lead usually connects the meter to the distributor or tach terminal on the coil. As the current flow in the primary ignition system is turned on and off, the tach-dwellmeter is able to determine the speed of the engine and the dwell angle.

Tachometer

Tachometers are used to measure engine speed. Like other meters, they are available in analog and digital types. Digital meters are the most common. Tachometers are connected to the ignition system to monitor ignition pulses. These pulses are then converted to engine speed by the meter.

Several types of inductive pickup tachometers that simplify rpm testing are now available. The inductive tachometer shown in Figure 5–15 simply clamps over the number 1 spark plug wire. The digital display gives the engine rpm, based on the magnetic pulses created by the secondary voltage in the wire.

Another type of digital tachometer is the photoelectric tachometer (Figure 5–16). The photoelectric

FIGURE 5–15 An inductive pick-up tachometer clamps over the spark plug wires for testing engine rpm. *Courtesy of TIF Instruments, Inc.*

mechanical components rotate, voltage pulses are magnetically induced in the sensor. An electronic control module monitors the voltage pulses to determine crankshaft position and engine speed.

Figure 5–17 illustrates a magnetic probe receptacle provided on the sensing device. This permits a probe to be placed in the receptacle and the electrical pulses to be remotely monitored. Figure 5–18 shows a digital tachometer with a magnetic coil pickup, or inductive probe. The tachometer counts the number of pulses and, based on the number of pulses generated per minute by the vehicle's crankshaft position sensor, determines the rpm.

Timing Light

A **timing light** (Figure 5–19) is an essential tool for tuneups on early model vehicles. A timing light is

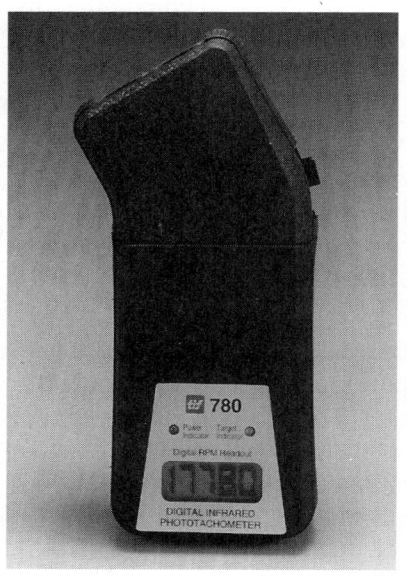

FIGURE 5–16 The photoelectric tachometer converts light pulses into rpm readings. *Courtesy of TIF Instruments, Inc.*

MAGNETIC TIMING PROBE RECEPTACLE

FIGURE 5–17 Location of the magnetic timing probe receptacle.

FIGURE 5–18 Digital tachometer with inductive probe. *Courtesy of Alltest, Inc.*

tachometer converts light pulses into rpm readings. This type of meter has an internal light source, powered either by an internal battery or by the car's battery. Reflective tape is applied to any rotating part of the engine, such as the crankshaft pulley. When the meter light is pointed at the revolving tape, a photoelectric eye in the meter reacts to the reflected light. The flashes of light are converted into electrical signals, which the meter uses to determine the engine rpm.

When electronic distributor ignitions replaced breaker-point ignitions, magnetic pulse sensors were used to determine crankshaft position and rotational speed. The sensors were usually mounted over the harmonic balancer, the flywheel, beside a crankshaft-mounted reluctor, or inside the distributor. As the

FIGURE 5–19 Timing light with inductive pickup. *Courtesy of Actron Manufacturing Company*

FIGURE 5–20 Typical timing marks.

used to show when the spark plugs are firing in relation to the piston position. A timing light normally consists of a strobe light and three leads. Two of the leads connect to the car battery to power the strobe. The third lead (pickup lead) is clamped around the number 1 spark plug wire. When the engine is running, the timing light will flash every time the number 1 plug fires.

To check the ignition timing, the flashing timing light is aimed at the ignition timing marks. The timing marks (Figure 5–20) are located either in front of the engine on the harmonic balancer or crankshaft pulley or at the rear of the engine on the flywheel.

The timing marks consist of a pointer, line, or notch and a scale. The scale represents degrees of crankshaft rotation. The scale usually has a zero reference mark that refers to the crankshaft position when the number 1 piston is at top dead center (**TDC**) on the compression stroke. On either side of the zero reference mark are marks spaced every 2 or 3 degrees. These marks indicate degrees of crankshaft rotation before top dead center (**BTDC**) and after top dead center (**ATDC**).

When the number 1 piston is at TDC on the compression stroke, the line or notch will line up with the zero reference mark on the timing plate. Usually an engine is timed so the number 1 spark plug fires several degrees BTDC.

When the timing light is connected to the battery and the number 1 spark plug wire, it will flash every time the number 1 spark plug fires. When pointed at the timing marks, the strobe effect of the light will freeze the spinning timing marks as it passes the timing scale. The ignition timing is checked by observing the degree of crankshaft rotation BTDC or ATDC when the spark plug fires.

Base timing is checked at base, or curb, idle. Advanced timing is checked at a higher rpm specified by the vehicle's manufacturer. As engine speed increases, the timing is advanced (either mechanically, by vacuum, or electronically). The actual amount of timing advance can be measured with an advance timing light (Figure 5–21).

The advance timing light has either a scale or meter that indicates the degrees of timing advance. The advance knob on the light can be turned to delay

TIMING ADVANCE KNOB

FIGURE 5–21 Advance timing light. *Courtesy of Actron Manufacturing Company*

the flash of the light. By pointing the flashing light at the timing marks and turning the dial until the timing marks appear to line up again at the base timing position, the dial will indicate the amount of timing advance.

A more versatile advanced timing light is the digital timing light. The timing light shown in Figure 5–22 electronically measures timing advance as the engine rpm is increased and displays timing advance on an LED display. This light flashes only when a trigger is squeezed. When the trigger is released, the LED displays engine rpm. This combined feature eliminates the need for a separate tachometer when setting timing.

Magnetic Timing Probe

A timing light is not necessary for tuning many cars. A magnetic probe receptacle on the crankshaft posi-

tion sensor allows the ignition timing to be electronically monitored with a magnetic timing probe (Figure 5–23). Changes in the magnetic field create electrical pulses in the tip of the timing probe. These pulses are monitored by the timing meter to determine crankshaft position and ignition timing. The timing indicated by this type of equipment is extremely accurate.

The only trick to using a magnetic timing probe is correcting the offset of the probe receptacle. The receptacle is usually situated on either side of the vehicle's coil pickup. The degree of offset must be factored into the timing probe's reading or the timing readout will be inaccurate by that many degrees. The timing meter must be programmed for the degree of offset specified by the car manufacturer.

The magnetic timing unit shown in Figure 5–23 measures not only timing but engine rpm as well.

Electronic Ignition Module Tester

A defective electronic ignition module can cause a variety of problems. Some may be as obvious as a no-spark, no-start condition. Others may be only intermittent problems, such as a misfire at cruising speeds or under certain load or temperature conditions. Tracing the source of intermittent problems to the ignition module can be difficult without an ignition module tester (Figure 5–24).

An electronic module ignition tester evaluates and determines if the module is operating within a given set of design parameters. It does so by simulating normal operating conditions while looking for

FIGURE 5–22 Digital timing light with LED display. *Courtesy of Alltest, Inc.*

MAGNETIC TIMING PROBE

FIGURE 5–23 Ignition timing tester with a magnetic probe attachment. *Courtesy of Alltest, Inc.*

FIGURE 5–24 Typical electronic ignition module tester. *Courtesy of Alltest, Inc.*

faults in key components. A typical ignition module tester will perform the following tests.

◆ Shorted module test
◆ Cranking current test
◆ Key on/engine off current test
◆ Idle current test
◆ Cruise current test
◆ Cranking primary voltage test
◆ Idle primary voltage test
◆ Cruise primary voltage test

Some ignition module testers are also able to perform an ignition coil-spark test (actually firing the coil) and a distributor pickup test.

Test selection is made by pushing the appropriate button. The module tester usually responds to these tests with a pass or fail indication.

Oscilloscope

The **oscilloscope** (Figure 5–25) was developed for automotive diagnostics in the 1950s. It is still one of the most important diagnostic tools. In fact, it performs some very valuable tests on today's electronic systems. Some of the tests that can be performed with an oscilloscope are shown in Table 5–2. An oscilloscope converts electrical signals into a visual image representing voltage changes over a specific period of time. This information is displayed on a CRT in the form of a continuous voltage line called a **waveform** pattern or **trace** (Figure 5–26).

Dual-trace oscilloscopes (Figure 5–27) can display two different waveform patterns at the same time. Dual-trace oscilloscopes can show how fuel-injector pulse width affects the oxygen sensor voltage signal, and other highly useful cause-and-effect electrical tests.

TABLE 5–2 IGNITION SYSTEM SCOPE TESTS	
Breaker Point Systems	**Electronic Systems**
Cranking coil output	Cranking spark duration
Coil polarity	Coil polarity
Spark plug firing voltage	Spark plug firing voltage
Rotor air gap voltage drop	Rotor air gap voltage drop
Rotor register	Rotor register
Secondary circuit resistance	Secondary circuit resistance
Maximum coil output	Running spark duration
Secondary insulation	Secondary insulation
Spark plugs under load	Spark plugs under load
Coil and condenser	Coil condition
Cylinder timing accuracy	Cylinder timing accuracy
Dwell variation	Dwell and dwell variation
Battery voltage	Battery voltage
Charging voltage	Charging voltage
Alternator condition	Alternator condition

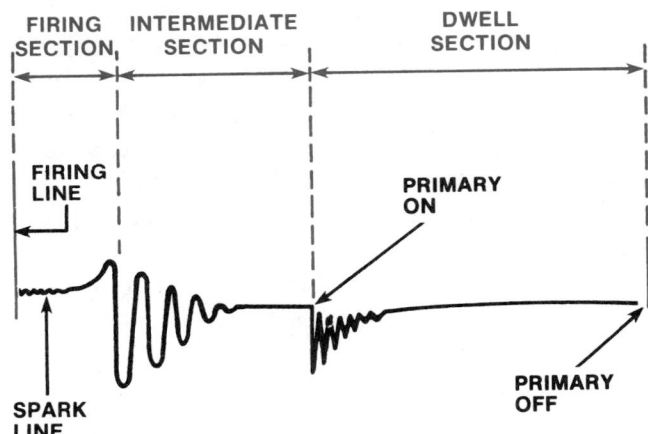

FIGURE 5–26 Typical oscilloscope waveform pattern.

FIGURE 5–25 The oscilloscope is sometimes referred to as a tuneup scope. *Courtesy of Snap-on Tools Corporation*

FIGURE 5–27 A dual-trace scope allows you to watch the electrical activity of two circuits at one time.

COMPRESSION AND VACUUM TESTERS

Internal combustion engines depend on compression of the air/fuel mixture to maximize the power produced by the engine. The upward movement of the piston on the compression stroke compresses the air/fuel mixture within the combustion chamber. The air/fuel mixture gets hotter as it is compressed. The hot mixture is easier to ignite, and when ignited it will generate much more power than the same mixture at a lower temperature.

If the combustion chamber leaks, some of the air/fuel mixture will escape when it is compressed, resulting in a loss of power and a waste of fuel. The leaks can be caused by burned valves, a blown head gasket, worn rings, slipped timing belt or chain, worn valve seats, a cracked head, and more.

An engine with poor compression (lower compression pressure due to leaks in the cylinder) will not run correctly and cannot be tuned to factory specifications. To see if a driveability problem is caused by poor compression, a compression test is performed.

A **compression gauge** is used to check cylinder compression. The dial face on the typical compression gauge indicates pressure in both pounds per square inch (**psi**) and metric kilopascals (**kPa**). The range is usually 0 to 300 psi and 0 to 2,100 kPa.

There are two basic types of compression gauges: the push-in gauge (Figure 5–28) and a screw-in gauge.

The push-in type has a short stem that is either straight or bent at a 45-degree angle. The stem ends in a tapered rubber tip that fits any size spark plug hole. The rubber tip is placed in the spark plug hole, after the spark plugs have been removed, and held there while the engine is cranked through several compression cycles. Although simple to use, the push-in gauge may give inaccurate readings if it is not held tightly in the hole.

The screw-in gauge has a long, flexible hose that ends in a threaded adapter. This type compression tester is often used because its flexible hose can reach into areas that are difficult to reach with a push-in type tester. The threaded adapters are changeable and come in several thread sizes to fit 10-mm, 12-mm, 14-mm, and 18-mm diameter holes. The adapters screw into the spark plug holes in place of the spark plugs.

Most compression gauges have a vent valve that holds the highest pressure reading on its meter. Opening the valve releases the pressure when the test is complete. The steps for conducting a cylinder compression test are shown in Photo Sequence 3.

Cylinder Leakage Tester

If a compression test shows that any of the cylinders are leaking, a **cylinder leakage** test can be performed to measure the percentage of compression lost and help locate the source of leakage.

A cylinder leakage tester (Figure 5–29) applies compressed air to a cylinder through the spark plug hole. Before the air is applied to the cylinder, the piston of that cylinder must be at TDC on its compression stroke. A threaded adapter on the end of the air pressure hose screws into the spark plug hole. The source of the compressed air is normally the shop's compressed air system. A pressure regulator in the tester controls the pressure applied to the cylinder. An analog gauge registers the percentage of air pressure lost from the cylinder when the compressed air is applied. The scale on the dial face reads 0 to 100 percent.

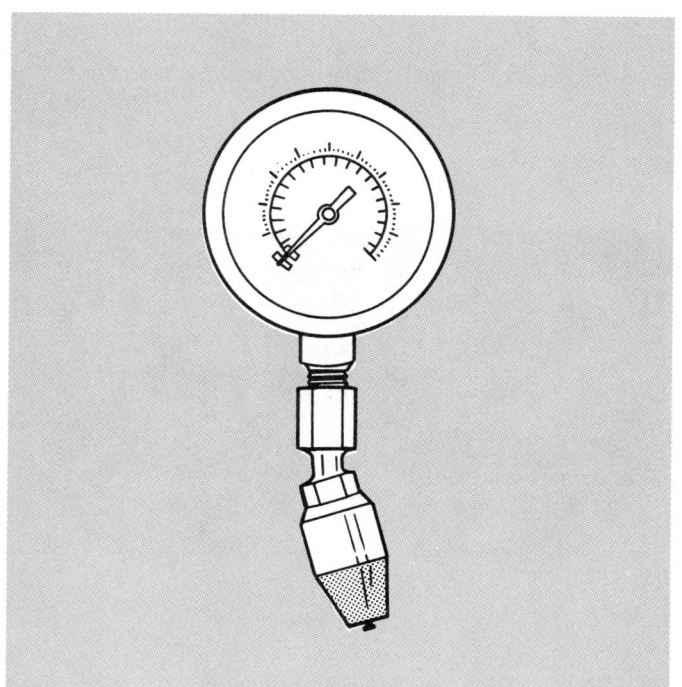

FIGURE 5–28   Push-in compression gauge.

FIGURE 5–29   Typical cylinder leakage tester. *Courtesy of Snap-on Tools Corporation*

A zero reading means there is no leakage from the cylinder. Readings of 100 percent would indicate that the cylinder will not hold any pressure. The location of the compression leak can be found by listening and feeling around various parts of the engine. If air is felt or heard leaving the throttle plate assembly, a leaking intake valve is indicated. If a bad exhaust valve is responsible for the leakage, air can be felt leaving the exhaust system during the test. Air leaving the radiator would indicate a faulty head gasket or a cracked block or head. If the piston rings are bad, air will be heard leaving the valve cover's breather cap or the oil dipstick tube.

Most vehicles, even new cars, experience some leakage around the rings. Up to 20 percent is considered acceptable during the leakage test. When the engine is actually running, the rings will seal much better and the actual percent of leakage will be lower. However, there should be no leakage around the valves or the head gasket.

Vacuum Gauge

Measuring intake manifold vacuum is another way to diagnose the condition of an engine. Manifold vacuum is tested with a vacuum gauge (Figure 5–30). Vacuum is formed on a piston's intake stroke. As the piston moves down, it lowers the pressure of the air in the cylinder—if the cylinder is sealed. This lower cylinder pressure is called engine vacuum. Vacuum is best defined as any pressure lower than atmospheric pressure. Atmospheric pressure is the pressure of the air around us. If there is leak, atmospheric pressure will force air into the cylinder and the resultant pressure will not be as low. The reason atmospheric pressure will enter is simply that whenever there is a low and high pressure, the high pressure will always move toward the low pressure.

FIGURE 5–30 Vacuum gauge kit. *Courtesy of MAC Tools, Inc.*

The vacuum gauge measures the difference in pressure between intake manifold vacuum and atmospheric pressure. If the manifold pressure is lower than atmospheric pressure, a vacuum exists. Vacuum is measured in inches of mercury (in./Hg) and in kilopascals (kPa) or millimeters of mercury (mm/Hg).

To measure vacuum, a flexible hose on the vacuum gauge is connected to a source of manifold vacuum, either on the manifold or a point below the throttle plates. Sometimes this requires removing a plug from the manifold and installing a special fitting.

The test is made with the engine cranking or running. A good vacuum reading is typically at least 16 in./Hg. However, a reading of 15 to 20 in./Hg (50 to 65 kPa) is normally acceptable. Since the intake stroke of each cylinder occurs at a different time, the production of vacuum occurs in pulses. If the amount of vacuum produced by each cylinder is the same, the vacuum gauge will show a steady reading. If one or more cylinders are producing different amounts of vacuum, the gauge will show a fluctuating reading.

Low or fluctuating readings can indicate many different problems. For example, a low, steady reading might be caused by retarded ignition timing or incorrect valve timing. A sharp vacuum drop at regular intervals might be caused by a burned intake valve.

Other conditions that can be revealed by vacuum readings follow.

◆ Stuck or burned valves
◆ Improper valve or ignition timing
◆ Weak valve springs
◆ Leaking intake manifold or EGR valve
◆ Uneven compression
◆ Worn rings or cylinder walls
◆ Leaking head gaskets
◆ Incorrect carburetor adjustments
◆ Restricted exhaust system
◆ Ignition defects

Vacuum Pump

There are many vacuum-operated devices and vacuum switches of cars. These devices use engine vacuum to cause a mechanical action or to switch something on or off. The tool used to test vacuum-actuated components is the vacuum pump (Figure 5–31). There are two types of vacuum pumps: an electrically operated pump and a hand-held pump. The hand-held pump is most often used for diagnostics. A hand-held vacuum pump consists of a hand pump, a vacuum gauge, and a length of rubber hose used to attach the pump to the component being tested. Tests with the vacuum pump can usually be performed without removing the component from the car.

CONDUCTING A CYLINDER COMPRESSION TEST

P3–1 Before conducting a compression test, disable the ignition and the fuel injection system (if the engine is so equipped).

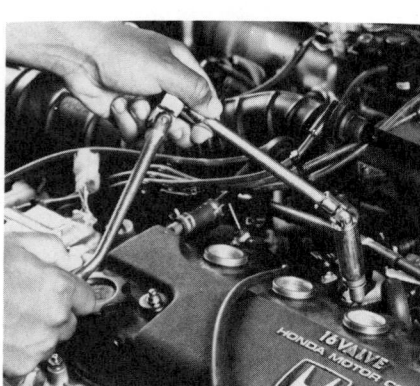

P3–3 Remove all of the engine's spark plugs.

P3–4 Connect a remote starter button to the starter system.

P3–5 Many types of compression gauges are available. The screw-in type tends to be the most accurate and easiest to use.

P3–6 Carefully install the gauge into the spark plug hole of the first cylinder.

P3–7 Connect a battery charger to the car. This will allow the engine to crank at consistent and normal speeds that are needed for accurate test results.

P3–8 Depress the remote starter button and observe the gauge's reading after the first engine revolution.

P3–9 Allow the engine to turn through four revolutions, and observe the reading after the fourth. The reading should increase with each revolution.

P3–2 Prop the throttle plate into a wide open position. This will allow an unrestricted amount of air to enter the cylinders during the test.

P3–10 Readings observed should be recorded. After all cylinders have been tested, a comparison of cylinders can be made.

P3–11 Before removing the gauge from the cylinder, release the pressure from it using the release valve on the gauge.

P3–12 Each cylinder should be tested in the same way.

P3–13 After completing the test on all cylinders, compare them. If a cylinder is much lower than the others, continue testing that cylinder.

P3–14 Squirt a small amount of oil into the weak cylinder.

P3–15 Reinstall the compression gauge into that cylinder and conduct the test.

P3–16 If the reading increases with the presence of oil in the cylinder, the most likely cause of the original low readings was poor piston ring sealing. Using oil during a compression test is normally referred to as a wet test.

FIGURE 5–31 Typical vacuum pump with accessories. *Courtesy of Actron Manufacturing Company*

When the handles of the pump are squeezed together, a piston inside the pump body draws air out of the component being tested. The partial vacuum created by the pump is registered on the pump's vacuum gauge. While forming a vacuum in a component, watch the action of the component. The vacuum level needed to actuate a given component should be compared to the specifications given in the factory service manual.

The vacuum pump is also commonly used to locate vacuum leaks. This is done by connecting the vacuum pump to a suspect vacuum hose or component and applying vacuum. If the needle on the vacuum gauge begins to drop after the vacuum is applied, a leak exists somewhere in the system.

The following list shows some of the systems and components that can be tested with a vacuum pump.

1. Fuel injection service—fuel pressure regulators
2. Carburetor service
   a. Choke pull-off diaphragm
   b. Vacuum break diaphragm
3. Ignition system service
   a. Vacuum advance unit
   b. Vacuum retard unit
4. Computerized engine control system—vacuum transducer MAP sensor
5. Emission control system
   a. Thermal vacuum switch
   b. Vacuum delay valve
   c. Heated air intake system
   d. EGR (exhaust gas recirculation) valve
   e. Vacuum control valves
6. Automatic transmission modulator valve

Vacuum Leak Detector

A vacuum or compression leak might be revealed by a compression check, a cylinder leak down test, or a manifold vacuum test. However, finding the location of the leak can often be very difficult.

A simple, but time-consuming way to find leaks in a vacuum system is to check each component and vacuum hose with a vacuum pump. Simply apply vacuum to the suspected area and watch the gauge for any loss of vacuum. A good vacuum component will hold the vacuum that is applied to it.

Another method of leak detection is done by using an ultrasonic leak detector (Figure 5–32). Air rushing through a vacuum leak creates a high-frequency sound, higher than the range of human hearing. An ultrasonic leak detector is designed to hear the frequencies of the leak. When the tool is passed over a leak, the detector responds to the high-frequency sound by emitting a warning beep. Some detectors also have a series of LEDs that light up as the frequencies are received. The closer the detector is moved to the leak, the more LEDs light up or the faster the beeping occurs. This allows the technician to zero in on the leak. An ultrasonic leak detector can sense leaks as small as 1/500 inch and accurately locate the leak to within 1/16 inch.

An ultrasonic leak detector can also be used to detect the source of compression leaks, bearing wear, and electrical arcing. It can also be used to diagnose fuel injector operation.

FIGURE 5–32 An ultrasonic leak detector picks up the sound frequencies of the leak. *Courtesy of TIF Instruments, Inc.*

FIGURE 5–33 Fuel pressure gauge and various adapters. *Courtesy of OTC Tool and Equipment Division of SPX Corporation*

FIGURE 5–34 Checking fuel pump discharge volume.

FUEL SYSTEM TEST EQUIPMENT

The proper amount of fuel is essential to the proper operation of an engine. Therefore, misadjusted or faulty fuel system components will adversely affect engine performance. The following tools are used to test the parts of the fuel system.

Pressure Gauge

A **pressure gauge** (Figure 5–33) is used to measure the pressure in the fuel system. This tester is very important for diagnosing fuel injection systems. These systems rely on very high fuel pressures, from 35 to 70 psi. A drop in fuel pressure will reduce the amount of fuel delivered to the injectors and result in a lean air/fuel mixture.

A fuel pressure gauge is used to check the discharge pressure of fuel pumps, the regulated pressure of fuel injection systems, and injector pressure drop. This test can identify faulty pumps, regulators, or injectors and can identify restrictions present in the fuel delivery system. Restrictions are typically caused by dirty fuel filter, collapsed hoses, or damaged fuel lines.

🔧 SHOP TALK

The fuel system on fuel-injected vehicles is highly pressurized. The pressure must be relieved before servicing any component in the fuel system and before any hoses or lines are disconnected. ■

Some fuel pressure gauges also have a valve and outlet hose for testing fuel pump discharge volume (Figure 5–34). The manufacturer's specification for discharge volume will be given as a number of pints or liters of fuel that should be delivered in a certain number of seconds.

Fuel Injector Cleaner

Fuel injectors spray a certain amount of fuel into the intake system. If the fuel pressure is low, not enough fuel will be sprayed. This is also true if the fuel injector is dirty. Normally clogged injectors are the result of inconsistencies in gasoline detergent levels and the high sulfur content of gasoline. When these sensitive fuel injectors become partially clogged, fuel flow is restricted. Spray patterns are altered, causing poor performance and reduced fuel economy.

The solution to a sulfated and/or plugged fuel injector is to clean it, not replace it. There are two kinds of fuel injector cleaners. One is a pressure tank (Figure 5–35). A mixture of solvent and unleaded gasoline is placed in the tank, following the manufacturer's instructions for mixing, quantity, and safe han-

FIGURE 5–35 Pressurized tank used to clean fuel injectors. *Courtesy of OTC Tool and Equipment Division of SPX Corporation*

FIGURE 5–36 Throwaway canister of fuel injector cleaner. *Courtesy of Penray Company*

dling. The vehicle's fuel pump must be disabled and, on some vehicles, the fuel line must be blocked between the pressure regulator and the return line. Then, the hose on the pressure tank is connected to the service port in the fuel system. The in-line valve is then partially opened and the engine is started. It should run at approximately 2,000 rpm for about 10 minutes to clean the injectors thoroughly.

An alternative to the pressure tank is a pressurized canister (Figure 5–36) in which the solvent solution is premixed. Use of the canister-type cleaner is similar to this procedure but does not require mixing or pumping.

The canister is connected to the injection system's servicing fitting, and the valve on the canister is opened. The engine is started and allowed to run until it dies. Then, the canister is discarded.

Fuel Injector Pulse Tester

To check the operation and the balance of the injectors, a fuel injector pulse tester (Figure 5–37) is used. This electronic tool turns on individual fuel injectors in 1/2-second increments according to three different time ranges: 1 pulse of 500 milliseconds, 50 pulses of 10 milliseconds, and 100 pulses of 5 milliseconds. While the injector is being pulsed, the technician monitors the pressure drop. Ideally, each injector should create the same pressure drop when activated for the same amount of time. Little or no pressure drop indicates a plugged or defective injector.

A fuel injector load tester can also be used to check the operation of the injectors. This tester duplicates the normal operational amperage of an injector circuit. Doing this, the tester is capable of identifying injectors that break down under a load.

Injector Circuit Testlight

A special testlight called a **noid light** can be used to determine if a fuel injector is receiving its proper voltage pulse from the computer. The wiring harness connector is disconnected from the injector and the

FIGURE 5–37 A fuel injector pulse tester monitors fuel pressure while the injector is pulsed by the tester's control box. *Courtesy of OTC Tool and Equipment Division of SPX Corporation*

HARNESS CONNECTOR

NOID LIGHT

TO FUEL INJECTOR

FIGURE 5–38 A noid light is used to check for voltage pulses at the fuel rail harness.

noid light is plugged into the connector (Figure 5–38). After disabling the ignition to prevent starting, the engine is turned over by the starter motor. The noid light will flash rapidly if the voltage signal is present. No flash usually indicates an open in the power feed or ground circuit to the injector.

EXHAUST ANALYZER

Federal laws require new cars and light trucks to meet specific emissions levels. State governments have also passed laws requiring that car owners maintain their vehicles so that the emissions remain below an acceptable level. Most states require an annual emissions inspection to meet that goal. Many shops have an exhaust analyzer for inspection purposes.

Exhaust analyzers are also very valuable diagnostic tools. By looking at the quality of an engine's exhaust, a technician is able to see the effects of the combustion process. Any defect can cause a change in exhaust quality. The amount and type of change serves as the basis of diagnostic work.

Early emission analyzers measured the amount of hydrocarbons (HC) and carbon monoxides (CO) in the exhaust. Hydrocarbons in the exhaust is raw, unburned fuel. HC emissions indicate that complete combustion is not occurring in the engine. Emissions analyzers measure HC in parts per million (ppm) or grams per mile (g/mi). Carbon monoxide is an odorless, toxic gas that is the product of combustion and is typically caused by a lack of air or excessive fuel. CO is measured as a percent of the total exhaust.

The levels of HC and CO in the exhaust are a direct indication of engine performance. A high level of hydrocarbons could indicate a fouled spark plug, a defective spark plug wire, or a burned valve. All of these problems would decrease the effectiveness of combustion and allow fuel to leave the cylinder unburned. A high CO level indicates an excessively rich air/fuel mixture caused by a restriction in the air intake system or too much fuel being delivered to the cylinders.

Many of the emission control devices that have been added to vehicles over the past 30 years have decreased the amount of HC and CO in the exhaust. This is especially true of catalytic converters. These devices alter the contents of the exhaust. Therefore, checking the HC and CO contents in the exhaust may not be a true indication of the operation of an engine.

The manufacturers of exhaust analyzers have altered their machines so they can look at the efficiency of an engine, in spite of the effectiveness of the emission controls. These machines are four-gas exhaust analyzers. In addition to measuring HC and CO levels, a four-gas exhaust analyzer also monitors carbon dioxide (CO_2) and oxygen (O_2) levels in the exhaust. The latter two gases are changed only slightly by the emission controls and, therefore, can be used to check engine efficiency. Four-gas analyzers can be used to diagnose the following conditions.

- Rich or lean mixtures (Table 5–3)
- Air pump malfunctions
- Catalytic converter malfunction
- Blown head gaskets
- Faulty carburetors or injectors
- Intake manifold leaks
- Leaking EGR valves
- Excessive misfire
- Excessive spark advance
- Leaks or restrictions in the exhaust system

TABLE 5–3 ANALYSIS OF FOUR-GAS EMISSIONS ANALYZER RESULTS

Gas Condition		With Catalytic Converter	Without Catalytic Converter
HC*	Over 110 ppm	Misfire	—
	Over 250 ppm	—	Misfire
CO	Over 3%	—	Rich
	Over 1%	Rich	—
O_2	Over 2%	Lean mixture or misfire	
	Under 1%	Rich mixture	
CO_2	Less than 10%	Rich mixture or misfire	

*HC readings can vary significantly depending on the age and condition of the engine, and the temperature of the engine.

COMPUTER SCAN TOOLS

The introduction of computer-controlled ignition and fuel systems brought with it the need for tools capable of troubleshooting electronic engine control systems. There are a variety of computer scan tools available today that do just that. A **scan tool** (Figure 5–39) is a microprocessor designed to communicate with the vehicle's computer. Connected to the computer through diagnostic connectors, a scan tool can access trouble codes, run tests to check system operations, and monitor the activity of the system. Trouble codes and test results are displayed on an LED screen, or printed out on the scanner printer.

A scan tool receives its testing information from one of several sources. Some scan tools have a programmable read-only memory (**PROM**) chip that contains all the information needed to diagnose specific model lines (usually GM, Ford, or Chrysler). This chip is normally contained in a cartridge that is

FIGURE 5–39   This scan tool has a coded identification card for each car model and a built-in printer. *Courtesy of OTC Tool and Equipment Division of SPX Corporation*

FIGURE 5–40   Using a scan tool during a road test. *Courtesy of OTC Tool and Equipment Division of SPX Corporation*

FIGURE 5–41   The wiring harness breakout box allows for detailed testing of individual circuits and components.

plugged into the tool. The type of vehicle being tested determines the appropriate cartridge that should be inserted. These cartridges contain the test information for that particular car. A cartridge is typically needed for each make and model vehicle. As new systems are introduced on new car models, a new cartridge is made available.

Some scan tools can be used during a road test (Figure 5–40). This allows the technician to record data from the on-board vehicle computer at the exact time an intermittent fault is occurring. After the test drive, the data is retrieved from the memory of the scan tool for analysis.

LED displays are generally only large enough to display four short lines of information. This feature limits the technician's ability to compare test data. However, most scan tools overcome this inadequacy by storing the test data in a random access memory (**RAM**). The scan tool then can be interfaced with a printer, personal computer, or larger engine analyzer that can retrieve the information stored in the memory. Some scan tools have a built-in printer so the test results can be printed as soon as they are entered into the scan tool's memory.

Trouble codes are only set by the vehicle's computer when a voltage signal is entirely out of its normal range. The codes help technicians identify the cause of the problem when this is the case. If a signal is within its normal range but is still not correct, the vehicle's computer will not display a trouble code. However, a driveability problem will still exist. As an aid to identify this type of problem, most manufacturers recommend that the signals to and from the computer be carefully looked at. This is done through the use of a **breakout box** (Figure 5–41). A breakout box allows the technician to check voltage and resistance readings between specific points within the computer's wiring harness.

ENGINE ANALYZER

When performing a complete engine performance analysis, an engine analyzer is used. An engine analyzer houses all of the necessary test equipment. Although the term engine analyzer is often loosely applied to any multipurpose test meter, a complete engine analyzer will incorporate most, if not all, of the test instruments mentioned in this chapter. Most engine analyzers are based on a computer that guides a technician through the tests. Most will also do the work of the following tools.

- Compression gauge
- Pressure gauge
- Vacuum gauge
- Vacuum pump
- Tachometer
- Timing light/probe
- Emissions analyzer
- Voltmeter
- Ohmmeter
- Ammeter
- Oscilloscope
- Computer scan tool

With an engine analyzer, you can perform tests on the battery, starting system, charging system, primary and secondary ignition circuits, electronic control systems, the fuel system, the emissions system, and the engine assembly. The analyzer is connected to these systems by a variety of leads, inductive clamps, probes, and connectors. The data received from these connections is processed by several computers within the analyzer.

The microprocessors in some computerized engine analyzers are programmed with specifications for specific model vehicles. Diagnostic trouble codes have also been loaded into the analyzer's memory. Based on the input from the leads and connectors, the microprocessors can identify worn, misadjusted, or faulty components in all major engine systems. The analyzer will also list the probable causes of specific performance problems and will prompt, or guide, the technician step by step through a troubleshooting procedure designed to verify and correct the problem.

FIGURE 5–42 Engine analyzer with PC technology. *Courtesy of Automotive Diagnostics, a division of SPX Corporation*

Commands and specifications can be entered into the analyzer on a computerlike keyboard. Specifications, commands, and test results are displayed on the CRT screen. Some analyzers will graphically display test results on their CRT screen (Figure 5–42). The analyzer's printer can also print out copies of the information that appears on the screen.

Most engine analyzers have both manual and automatic test modes. In the manual modes, any single test, such as cylinder compression or alternator output, can be performed. The manual test mode is useful when there is little need to do a complete test. The automatic test mode is useful when performing a general tuneup. When the automatic test mode is selected, specific tests are automatically performed in a specific sequence. The following is a typical test sequence performed by a analyzer when it is placed in the automatic test mode.

- Cranking voltage
- Relative compression
- Charging voltage
- Running voltage
- Primary circuit voltage
- Secondary circuit kilovoltage
- Dwell per cylinder
- Cylinder power balance
- Engine vacuum

These tests provide for a general analysis of the engine, starting system, charging system, and ignition system. Some engine analyzers have automatic test modes for specific systems (cranking, charging, timing, fuel system, primary ignition circuit/dwell, secondary ignition circuit/power analysis and cylinder balance, and exhaust analysis).

KEY TERMS

AC	Noid light
Ammeter	Nucleus
Ampere	O_2
ATDC	Ohmmeter
Atoms	Ohms
Breakout box	Open
BTDC	Oscilloscope
Chassis ground	Power
Chemical energy	Pressure gauge
CO_2	PROM
Compression gauge	Protons
Continuity tester	psi
Current	RAM
Cylinder leakage	Resistance
DC	rpm
DMM	Scan tool
Dual-trace oscilloscopes	Short
DVOM	Tachometer
Dwellmeter	TDC
Electronics	Testlight
Electrons	Timing light
EMF	Trace
Fuel injector	VAT
Induction	Voltage
kPa	Voltmeter
Magnetism	Wattage
Multimeter	Waveform
Neutrons	

SUMMARY

- A basic understanding of electrical principles is important for effective electrical diagnosis and for the proper operation and interpretation of diagnostic tools. The flow of electricity is called current and is measured in amperes. There are two types of electrical flow: direct current (DC) and alternating current (AC).
- Resistance to current flow produces heat. The amount of resistance is measured in ohms.
- In a complete electrical circuit, the flow of electricity is controlled and applied to perform tasks such as lighting headlights and turning over the starter motor. Circuit testers are used to identify short and open circuits.
- Voltage is electrical pressure and it is measured in volts.
- There are three basic types of problems that can occur in an electrical circuit: an open, high resistance, and a short.
- Three important electrical test meters are the voltmeter, which measures the voltage available at

any point in an electrical system; the ohmmeter, which measures resistance to current flow in a circuit; and the ammeter, which measures current flow in a circuit.

◆ A volt/ampere tester can be used to test batteries, starting systems, and charging systems. This tester contains a carbon pile, which is a variable resistor used to draw current out of the battery. The resistance of the carbon pile must be adjusted to match the ratings of the battery.

◆ The timing light is an essential tool for tuning up most vehicles. It reveals when the spark plugs are firing in relation to the piston position. Base timing is checked at base, or curb, idle. Advanced timing is checked at a higher rpm specified by the vehicle manufacturer.

◆ An electronic ignition module tester is capable of performing a series of tests to trace the source of ignition problems. Intermittent problems, such as misfire at cruising speeds under certain load or temperature conditions, can be difficult without the use of this tester.

◆ Compression is an indicator of engine condition. Two types of compression gauges (push-in and screw-in) are available to test each cylinder for compression.

◆ Vacuum is another indicator of engine condition. The vacuum gauge measures the difference in pressure between the intake manifold and the outside atmosphere. If manifold pressure is lower, a vacuum exists.

◆ Fuel system pressure is particularly important in fuel-injected systems. A pressure gauge can be used to check fuel pump discharge pressure, the regulated pressure of injection systems, and injector pressure drop.

◆ Even partially clogged fuel injectors can cause poor engine performance and reduced fuel economy. There are two types of injector cleaners available: a pressure tank and a canister-type cleaner.

◆ On most new cars, the amounts of hydrocarbons (HC) and carbon monoxide (CO) in the exhaust are no longer a good indicator of engine operation. A four-gas exhaust analyzer is now used because it monitors carbon dioxide (CO_2) and oxygen (O_2) levels, in addition to HC and CO.

◆ Computer scan tools are connected to the vehicle's on-board computer. A scan tool will access trouble codes, run tests that activate various engine controls, and display the communications that take place within the system.

◆ A typical engine analyzer does the work of the following tools: compression, pressure, and vacuum gauge; vacuum pump; tachometer; timing light/probe; voltmeter, ohmmeter, and ammeter; oscilloscope; computer scan tool; and exhaust analyzer. The engine analyzer points out the probable cause of a specific problem and guides the technician through a step-by-step troubleshooting procedure.

 REVIEW QUESTIONS

1. Name the two energy sources used in automobile electrical systems.

2. What are circuit testers used to identify?

3. Name the two basic types of compression gauges.

4. What tool is used to test manifold vacuum?

5. Define induction.

6. The center of an atom is known as the ____.
   - **a.** shell
   - **b.** proton
   - **c.** nucleus
   - **d.** neutron

7. Resistance is measured in ____.
   - **a.** current
   - **b.** volts
   - **c.** ohms
   - **d.** watts

8. What type of circuit allows electricity to flow through its normal load?
   - **a.** grounded
   - **b.** open
   - **c.** shorted
   - **d.** closed

9. When using a voltmeter, Technician A connects it across the circuit being tested. Technician B connects the red lead of the voltmeter to the most positive side of the circuit. Who is correct?
   - **a.** Technician A
   - **b.** Technician B
   - **c.** Both A and B
   - **d.** Neither A nor B

10. Technician A uses a digital volt/ohmmeter to test voltage. Technician B uses the same tool to test resistance. Who is correct?
    - **a.** Technician A
    - **b.** Technician B
    - **c.** Both A and B
    - **d.** Neither A nor B

11. Recent advances in automotive electronics have lessened the usefulness of the ____.
    - **a.** multimeter
    - **b.** volt/ampere tester
    - **c.** tach-dwellmeter
    - **d.** magnetic timing probe

12. Which of the following is *not* a typical electrical problem?
    - **a.** high resistance in the circuit
    - **b.** an open circuit
    - **c.** a short circuit
    - **d.** a closed circuit

13. Technician A says a push-in compression gauge must be held tightly in the spark plug hole in order to get an accurate reading. Technician B says the gauge will read a vacuum when the cylinder is on the compression stroke. Who is correct?

    a. Technician A   **c.** Both A and B
    b. Technician B   **d.** Neither A nor B

14. When conducting a cylinder leakage test, Technician A says 20 percent leakage around the rings means the cylinder in question is defective. Technician B says 20 percent leakage past the intake valve is considered acceptable. Who is correct?

    a. Technician A   **c.** Both A and B
    b. Technician B   **d.** Neither A nor B

15. Which of the following conditions can be revealed by vacuum readings?

    a. leaking intake manifold
    b. uneven compression
    c. restricted exhaust system
    d. all of the above

16. Technician A uses an ultrasonic leak detector to check bearing wear. Technician B uses it to detect electrical arcing. Who is correct?

    a. Technician A   **c.** Both A and B
    b. Technician B   **d.** Neither A nor B

17. Technician A says a sulfated and plugged fuel injector is caused by electrical problems. Technician B says a sulfated and plugged fuel injector can be cleaned. Who is correct?

    a. Technician A   **c.** Both A and B
    b. Technician B   **d.** Neither A nor B

18. The tests conducted by a computer scan tool also can be done by some ____.

    a. fuel injector pulse testers
    b. exhaust analyzers
    c. engine analyzers
    d. digital volt/ohmmeters

19. When using a fuel injector pulse tester, Technician A says little or no pressure drop indicates a plugged or defective injector. Technician B says no pressure drop indicates an overly rich condition. Who is correct?

    a. Technician A   **c.** Both A and B
    b. Technician B   **d.** Neither A nor B

20. It is much easier to test current using an ammeter equipped with a(n) ____.

    a. continuity tester   **c.** inductive pickup
    b. carbon pile   **d.** tachometer

SECTION 2

ENGINES

The engine of a car or truck is a complex piece of precision-built machinery. You should have a clear understanding of how the internal combustion process of an engine generates usable power before you attempt any engine work.

Engine repair and rebuilding procedures are among the most demanding jobs performed by technicians. Components must be handled with great care and assembled to exacting tolerances. Absolute cleanliness must be maintained. Bolt torque and sealing requirements must be met.

The information found in Section 2 of this textbook explains all of the engine's systems and components, including disassembly, inspection, repair, and reassembly procedures. It corresponds to the materials covered on the ASE certification test for engine repair.

AUTOMOTIVE ENGINES

6

OBJECTIVES

◆ *Describe the various ways in which engines can be classified.* ◆ *Explain what takes place during each stroke of the four-stroke cycle.* ◆ *Describe the differences between two-stroke and four-stroke engines.* ◆ *Outline the advantages and disadvantages of the in-line and V-type engine designs.* ◆ *Define important engine measurements and performance characteristics, including bore and stroke, displacement, compression ratio, engine efficiency, torque, and horsepower.* ◆ *Explain how to evaluate the condition of an engine.* ◆ *List and describe nine abnormal engine noises.* ◆ *Outline the basics of diesel, rotary, and stratified engine operation.*

Modern engines are highly engineered power plants. These engines are designed to meet the performance and fuel efficiency demands of the public. The days of the heavy, cast-iron V-8 engine with its poor gas mileage are quickly drawing to a close. Today, these engines have been replaced by compact, lightweight, and fuel-efficient engines (Figure 6–1). Modern engines are made of lightweight engine castings and stampings; non-iron materials (for example, aluminum, magnesium, fiber-reinforced plastics); and fewer and smaller fasteners to hold things together. These fasteners are made possible through computerized joint designs that optimize loading patterns. Each of these newer engine designs has its own distinct personality, based on construction materials, casting configurations, and design.

These modern engine building techniques have changed how engine repair technicians make their money. Before these changes can be explained, it is

FIGURE 6–2   Modern V-6 engine. *Courtesy of Chrysler Corporation*

important to explain the "basics" of engine design and operation (Figure 6–2).

ENGINE CLASSIFICATIONS

Today's automotive engines can be classified in several ways depending on the following design features.

◆ Operational cycles. Most technicians will generally come in contact with only four-stroke cycle engines (Figure 6–3). However, a few older cars

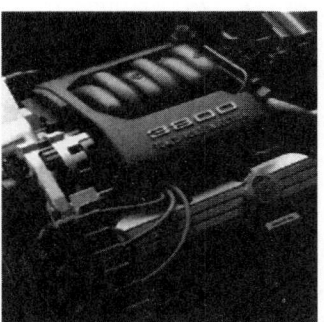

FIGURE 6–1   Typical late-model engine. *Courtesy of General Motors Corporation*

FIGURE 6–3   Major components of a four-stroke engine. *Courtesy of American Honda Motor Company, Inc.*

have used and some cars in the future will use a two-stroke engine.

- Number of cylinders. Current engine designs include 3-, 4-, 5-, 6-, 8-, and 12-cylinder engines.
- Cylinder arrangement. An engine can be flat (opposed), in-line, or V-type. Other more complicated designs have also been used.
- Valve train type. Engine valve trains can be either the overhead camshaft (**OHC**) type or the camshaft in-block overhead valve (**OHV**) type. Some engines separate camshafts for the intake and exhaust valves. These are based on the OHC design and are called dual overhead camshaft (**DOHC**) engines. V-type DOHC engines have four camshafts—two on each side.
- Ignition type. There are two types of ignition systems: spark and compression. Gasoline engines use a spark ignition system. In a spark ignition system, the air/fuel mixture is ignited by an electrical spark. Diesel engines, or compression ignition engines, have no spark plugs. An automotive diesel engine relies on the heat generated as air is compressed to ignite the air/fuel mixture for the power stroke.
- Cooling systems. There are both air-cooled and liquid-cooled engines in use. Nearly all of today's engines have liquid-cooling systems.
- Fuel type. Several types of fuel currently used in automobile engines include gasoline, natural gas, diesel, and propane. The most commonly used is gasoline.

FOUR-STROKE GASOLINE ENGINE

In a passenger car or truck, the engine provides the rotating power to drive the wheels through the transmission and driving axles. All automobile engines, both gasoline and diesel, are classified as internal combustion because the combustion or burning takes place inside the engine. These systems require an air/fuel mixture that arrives in the combustion chamber at the correct time and an engine constructed to withstand the temperatures and pressures created by the burning of thousands of fuel droplets.

The **combustion chamber** is the space between the top of the piston and cylinder head. It is an enclosed area in which the gasoline and air mixture is burned. The piston is a hollow metal tube with one end closed that moves up and down in the cylinder. This reciprocating motion is caused by an increase of pressure, due to combustion, in the cylinder.

The reciprocating motion must be converted to a rotary motion before it can drive the wheels of a vehicle. This change of motion is accomplished by connecting the piston to a crankshaft with a connecting rod (Figure 6–4). The upper end of the connecting rod moves with the piston as it moves up and down in the cylinder. The lower end of the connecting rod is attached to the crankshaft and moves in a circle. The end of the crankshaft is connected to the flywheel, which transfers the engine's power through the drivetrain to the wheels.

In order to have complete combustion in an engine, the right amount of fuel must be mixed with the right amount of air. This mixture must be compressed in a sealed container then shocked by the right amount of heat at the right time. When these condi-

FIGURE 6–4   The reciprocating motion of the pistons is converted to rotary motion by the crankshaft.

tions exist, all the fuel that enters a cylinder is burned and converted to power. This power is used to move the vehicle. The ignition system is responsible for providing the heat, and the air and fuel system is responsible for providing the air/fuel mixture. The construction of the engine and its different parts are responsible for providing a container for the combustion process. This container is the cylinder of an engine. Automotive engines have more than one cylinder. Each cylinder should receive the same amount of air, fuel, and heat, if the engine is to run efficiently.

Although the combustion must occur in a sealed cylinder, the cylinder must also have some means of allowing heat, fuel, and air into it. There must also be a means to allow the burnt air/fuel mixture out so a fresh mixture can enter and the engine can continue to run. To accommodate these requirements, engines are fitted with valves.

There are at least two valves at the top of each cylinder. The air/fuel mixture enters the combustion chamber through an intake valve and leaves (after having been burned) through an exhaust valve. The valves are accurately machined plugs that fit into machined openings. A valve is said to be seated or closed when it rests in its opening. When the valve is pushed off its seat, it opens.

A rotating camshaft, driven by the crankshaft, opens and closes the intake and exhaust valves. **Cams** are raised sections of a shaft that have high spots called **lobes**. As the camshaft rotates, the lobes rotate and push the valve open by pushing it away from its seat. Once the cam lobe rotates out of the way, the valve, forced by a spring, closes. The camshaft can be located either in the cylinder block or in the cylinder head.

When the action of the valves and the spark plug is properly timed to the movement of the piston, the combustion cycle takes place in four strokes of the piston: the intake stroke, the compression stroke, the power stroke, and the exhaust stroke. A **stroke** is the full travel of the piston either up or down in the cylinder bore.

The up-and-down movement of the piston on all four strokes is converted to a rotary motion by the crankshaft. It takes two full revolutions of the crankshaft to complete the four-stroke cycle.

The piston moves by the pressure produced during combustion only about half a stroke or one-quarter of crankshaft revolution. This explains why a flywheel is needed. The flywheel stores some of the power produced by the engine. This power is used to keep the pistons in motion during the rest of the four-stroke cycle. This power is also used to compress the air/fuel mixture just before combustion.

INTAKE STROKE The first stroke of the cycle is the intake stroke. As the piston moves away from top dead center (TDC), the intake valve opens (Figure 6–5A). The downward movement of the piston increases the volume of the cylinder above it. This reduces the pressure in the cylinder. This reduced pressure, commonly referred to as engine vacuum, causes the atmospheric pressure to push a mixture of air and fuel through the open intake valve. (Some engines are equipped with a super- or turbocharger that pushes more air past the valve.) As the piston reaches the bottom of its stroke, the reduction in pressure stops. This causes the intake of air/fuel mixture to slow down. It does not stop because of the weight and movement of the air/fuel mixture. It continues to enter the cylinder until the intake valve closes. The intake valve closes after the piston has reached bottom dead center (BDC). This delayed closing of the valve increases the volumetric efficiency of the cylinder by packing as much air and fuel into it as possible.

COMPRESSION STROKE The compression stroke begins as the piston starts to move from BDC. The intake valve closes, trapping the air/fuel mixture in the cylinder (Figure 6–5B). The upward movement of the piston compresses the air/fuel mixture, thus heating it up. At TDC, the piston and cylinder walls form a combustion chamber in which the fuel will be burned. The volume of the cylinder with the piston at BDC compared to the volume of the cylinder with the piston at TDC determines the compression ratio of the engine.

POWER STROKE The power stroke begins as the compressed fuel mixture is ignited (Figure 6–5C). An electrical spark across the electrodes of a spark plug ignites the air/fuel mixture. The burning fuel rapidly expands, creating a very high pressure against the top of the piston. This drives the piston down toward BDC. The downward movement of the piston is transmitted through the connecting rod to the crankshaft.

EXHAUST STROKE The exhaust valve opens just before the piston reaches BDC on the power stroke (Figure 6–5D). Pressure within the cylinder causes the exhaust gas to rush past the open valve and into the exhaust system. Movement of the piston from BDC pushes most of the remaining exhaust gas from the cylinder. As the piston nears TDC, the exhaust valve begins to close as the intake valve starts to open. The exhaust stroke completes the four-stroke cycle. The opening of the intake valve begins the cycle again. This cycle occurs in each cylinder and is repeated over and over, as long as the engine is running.

FIGURE 6–5 (A) Intake stroke, (B) compression stroke, (C) power stroke, and (D) exhaust stroke.

TWO-STROKE GASOLINE ENGINE

In the past, several imported vehicles have used two-stroke engines. As the name implies, this engine requires only two strokes of the piston to complete all four operations: intake, compression, power, and exhaust. As shown in Figure 6–6, this is accomplished as follows.

1. Movement of the piston from BDC to TDC completes both intake and compression (Figure 6–6A).
2. When the piston nears TDC, the compressed air/fuel mixture is ignited, causing an expansion of the gases. Note that the reed valve is closed and the piston is blocking the intake port (Figure 6–6B).
3. Expanding gases in the cylinder force the piston down, rotating the crankshaft (Figure 6–6C).
4. With the piston at BDC, the intake and exhaust ports are both open, allowing exhaust gases to leave the cylinder and air/fuel mixture to enter (Figure 6–6D).

Although the two-stroke-cycle engine is simple in design and lightweight because it lacks a valve train, it has not been widely used in automobiles. They tend to be less fuel efficient and have dirtier exhaust than four-stroke engines. Oil is often in the exhaust

FIGURE 6–6 Steps of a two-stroke engine cycle.

stream because these engines require constant oil delivery to the cylinders to keep the piston lubricated. Some of these engines require a certain amount of oil to be mixed with the fuel.

In recent years, however, thanks to a revolutionary pneumatic fuel injection system, there has been increased interest in the two-stroke engine. The injection system, which works something like a spray paint gun, uses compressed air to flow highly atomized fuel directly into the top of the combustion chamber. The system becomes the long sought-after answer to the fuel economy and emissions problems of the conventional two-stroke engine. This fuel injection system is the basis for orbital two-stroke direct injection piston engine, which may be used in cars in the future.

A small two-stroke engine can deliver as much horsepower, with less fuel, as a larger displacement four-stroke engine because in a two-stroke engine, combustion occurs every crankshaft revolution rather than every other revolution (Figure 6–7). This fact explains why the orbital engine has gained promise for the future. The improvement in fuel economy the orbital engine has achieved is due in part to a number of mechanical design features in addition to its pneumatic direct injection fuel system.

One of these features is the use of a three-cylinder engine block (Figure 6–8). Although the same

direct injection technology can be used with a four-cylinder or a V-6, a three-cylinder block saves the weight, bulk, and manufacturing expenses. The reduction in internal engine friction achieved by eliminating additional pistons and the absence of a valve train is in itself worth a significant improvement in fuel economy.

Additional performance improvements are obtained in the orbital two-stroke design by using a high-turbulence combustion chamber. The engine also has an exhaust port scavenge flow control valve, which is controlled by the engine computer to increase low-speed torque and assist in emissions control. The valve can be partially closed to restrict the

FIGURE 6–7 Cutaway of a two-stroke engine.

FIGURE 6–8   Main castings of the 3-cylinder orbital engine.

8 CYLINDER   **6 CYLINDER**

FIGURE 6–10   V-type engine designs.

flow of exhaust out of the cylinder. This accomplishes the same results as an EGR, a reduction in NO_X.

CHARACTERISTICS OF FOUR-STROKE ENGINE DESIGN

Depending on the vehicle, either an in-line, V-type, slant, or opposed cylinder design can be used. The most popular designs are in-line and V-type engines.

IN-LINE ENGINE In the in-line engine design (Figure 6–9), the cylinders are all placed in a single row. There is one crankshaft and one cylinder head for all of the cylinders. The block is cast so all cylinders are located in an upright position.

In-line engine designs have certain advantages and disadvantages. They are easy to manufacture and service. However, because the cylinders are positioned vertically, the front of the vehicle must be higher. This affects the aerodynamic design of the car. Aerodynamic design refers to the ease at which the car can move through the air. When equipped with an in-line engine, the front of a vehicle cannot be made as low as it can with other engine designs.

V-TYPE ENGINE The V-type engine design has two rows of cylinders (Figure 6–10) located 60 to 90

degrees away from each other. A V-type engine uses one crankshaft, which is connected to the pistons on both sides of the V. This type of engine has two cylinder heads, one over each row of cylinders.

One advantage of using a V-configuration is that the engine is not as high or long as an in-line configuration. The front of a vehicle can now be made lower. This design improves the outside aerodynamics of the vehicle. If eight cylinders are needed for power, a V configuration makes the engine much shorter, lighter, and more compact. Many years ago, some vehicles had an in-line eight-cylinder engine. The engine was very long and its long crankshaft also caused increased torsional vibrations in the engine.

SLANT CYLINDER ENGINE Another way of arranging the cylinders is in a slant configuration (Figure 6–11A). This is much like an in-line engine, except the entire block has been placed at a slant. The slant engine was designed to reduce the distance from the top to the bottom of the engine. Vehicles using the slant engine can be designed more aerodynamically.

OPPOSED CYLINDER ENGINE In this design, two rows of cylinders are located opposite the crankshaft (Figure 6–11B). Opposed cylinder engines are used in applications in which there is very little vertical room for the engine. For this reason, opposed cylinder designs are commonly used on vehicles that have the engine in the rear. The angle between the two cylinders is typically 180 degrees. One crankshaft is used with two cylinder heads.

4 CYLINDER

6 CYLINDER

FIGURE 6–9   In-line engine designs.

A   **B**

FIGURE 6–11   (A) Slant cylinder and (B) opposed cylinder engine designs.

FIGURE 6–12 Basic valve and camshaft placement configurations: (A) overhead valve and (B) overhead cam.

Valve and Camshaft Placement Configurations

Two basic valve and camshaft placement configurations of the four-stroke gasoline engines are used in automobiles (Figure 6–12).

OVERHEAD VALVE (OHV) As the name implies, the intake and exhaust valves on an overhead valve engine are mounted in the cylinder head and are operated by a camshaft located in the cylinder block. This arrangement requires the use of valve lifters, pushrods, and rocker arms to transfer camshaft rotation to valve movement. The intake and exhaust manifolds are attached to the cylinder head.

OVERHEAD CAM (OHC) An overhead cam engine also has the intake and exhaust valves located in the cylinder head. But as the name implies, the cam is located in the cylinder head. In an overhead

FIGURE 6–13 Other valve arrangements.

cam engine, the valves are operated directly by the camshaft or through cam followers or tappets.

Valve Arrangement

As shown in Figure 6–13, there are several valve arrangements. Most of these designs are not used in current automotive engines.

L-HEAD ENGINE DESIGN Engines that use the L-head engine design also are called flathead or side valve engines. This was a popular valve arrangement. This engine type is characterized by having no moving parts contained in the cylinder head. The head serves only as the combustion chamber. The valves are located in the cylinder block beside each cylinder. The intake and exhaust manifolds mount to the cylinder block. The valves were opened and closed directly by the camshaft. A major drawback of this design was the air/fuel mixture had to change direction to reach the combustion chamber. This limited the overall performance of the engine.

I-HEAD ENGINE DESIGN I-head means the valves are directly above the piston (overhead valves). The valves are located in the cylinder head. The design allows air and fuel to move easily into and out of the cylinder with little restriction. Variations of this design are used in today's engines.

T-HEAD ENGINE DESIGN In the T-head design, the valves are located within the block. The difference between this design and the L-head design is that two camshafts are needed. Because of this extra expense, T-head designs have not been used in the automotive industry for many years.

F-HEAD ENGINE DESIGN The F-head engine design is a combination of the I-head and the L-head designs. There are valves located in the head as well as in the block. It has some of the advantages of the L-head and I-head designs. However, the increased cost of parts is a disadvantage.

Valve and Camshaft Operation

In OHV engines with the camshaft in the block (Figure 6–14), the valves are operated by valve lifters and pushrods that are actuated by the camshaft. On overhead cam engines, the cam lobes operate the valves directly and there is no need for pushrods or lifters.

Cam lobes are oval shaped. The placement of the lobe on the shaft determines when the valve will open. Design of the lobe determines how far the valve will open and how long it will remain open in relation to piston movement.

The camshaft is driven by the crankshaft through gears, or sprockets, and a cogged belt, or timing chain. The camshaft turns at half the crankshaft speed and rotates one complete turn during each complete four-stroke cycle.

Engine Location

The engine is typically placed in one of three locations. In the vast majority of vehicles, it is located at the front of the vehicle, in front of the passenger compartment. Front-mounted engines can be positioned either longitudinally or transversely with respect to the vehicle.

The second engine location is a mid-mount position between the passenger compartment and rear suspension. Mid-mount engines are normally transversely mounted. The third, and least common, engine location is the rear of the vehicle. The engines are typically opposed-type engines.

Each of these engine locations offers advantages and disadvantages. Typical engine locations and drivetrain configurations are illustrated in the color insert of the text.

FIGURE 6–14 Valve operation in an overhead engine.

FRONT ENGINE LONGITUDINAL In this type of vehicle, the engine, transmission, front suspension, and steering equipment are installed in the front of the body, and the differential and rear suspension are installed in the rear of the body. Most front engine longitudinal vehicles are rear-wheel drive. Some front-wheel-drive cars with a transaxle have this configuration, and most four-wheel-drive vehicles are equipped with a transfer case and have the engine mounted longitudinally in the front of the vehicle.

Total vehicle weight can be evenly distributed between the front and rear wheels with this configuration. This lightens the steering force and equalizes the braking load. With this design, it is possible to independently remove and install the engine, propeller shaft, differential, and suspension. Longitudinally mounted engines require large engine compartments. The need for a rear-drive propeller shaft and differential also cuts down passenger compartment space.

FRONT ENGINE TRANSVERSE Front engines that are mounted transversely sit sideways in the engine compartment. They are used with transaxles that combine transmission and differential gearing into a single compact housing, fastened directly to the engine. Transversely mounted engines reduce the size of the engine compartment and overall vehicle weight.

Transversely mounted front engines allow for down-sized, lighter vehicles with increased interior space. However, most of the vehicle weight is toward the front of the vehicle. This provides for increased traction by the drive wheels. The weight also places a greater load on the front suspension and brakes.

MID-ENGINE TRANSVERSE In this design, the engine and drivetrain are positioned between the passenger compartment and rear axle. Mid-engine location is used in smaller, rear-wheel-drive, high-performance sports cars for several reasons. The central location of heavy components results in a center of gravity very near the center of the vehicle. This vastly improves steering and handling. Since the engine is not under the hood, the hood can be sloped downward, improving aerodynamics and increasing the driver's field of vision. However, engine access and cooling efficiency are reduced. A barrier is also needed to reduce the transfer of noise, heat, and vibration to the passenger compartment.

GASOLINE ENGINE SYSTEMS

The operation of an engine relies on several other systems. The efficiency of these systems affects the overall operation of the engine.

AIR/FUEL SYSTEM This system makes sure the engine gets the right amount of both air and fuel needed for efficient operation. For many years air and fuel were mixed in a carburetor, which supplied the resulting mixture to the cylinder. Today, most late-model automobiles have a fuel injection system, which replaces the carburetor but performs the same basic function.

IGNITION SYSTEM This system delivers a spark to ignite the compressed air/fuel mixture in the cylinder at the end of the compression stroke. The **firing order** of the cylinders is determined by the engine's manufacturer and can be found in the vehicle's service manual. Typical firing orders are illustrated in Figure 6–15.

LUBRICATION SYSTEM This system supplies oil to the various moving parts in the engine. The oil lubricates all parts that slide in or on other parts, such as the piston, bearings, crankshaft, and valve stems. The oil enables the parts to move easily so little power is lost and wear is kept to a minimum. The lubrication system also helps transfer heat from one part to another for cooling.

COOLING SYSTEM This system is also extremely important. Coolant circulates in jackets around the cylinder and in the cylinder head. This removes part of the heat produced by combustion and prevents the engine from being damaged by overheating.

EXHAUST SYSTEM This system removes the burned gases from the combustion chamber and limits the noise produced by the engine.

FIGURE 6–15 Common cylinder firing orders.

EMISSION CONTROL SYSTEM Several control devices, which are designed to reduce the amount of pollutants released by the engine, have been added to the engine. Engine design changes, such as reshaped combustion chambers and altered valve timing, have also been part of the manufacturers' attempt to reduce emission levels.

ENGINE MEASUREMENT AND PERFORMANCE

Some of the engine measurements and performance characteristics a technician should be familiar with follow.

BORE AND STROKE The **bore** of a cylinder is simply its diameter measured in inches (in.) or millimeters (mm). The stroke is the length of the piston travel between TDC and BDC. Between them, bore and stroke determine the displacement of the cylinders (Figure 6–16). When the bore of the engine is larger than its stroke, it is said to be oversquare. When the stroke is larger than the bore, the engine is said to be undersquare. Generally, an oversquare engine will provide for high engine speeds, such as for automobile use. An undersquare or long-stroke engine will deliver good low-speed power, such as an engine for a truck or tractor.

The **crank throw** is the distance from the crankshaft's main bearing centerline to the crankshaft throw centerline. The stroke of any engine is twice the crank throw (Figure 6–17).

DISPLACEMENT Displacement is the volume of a cylinder between the TDC and BDC positions of the piston. It is usually measured in cubic inches, cubic centimeters, or liters (Figure 6–18). The total displacement of an engine (including all cylinders) is a

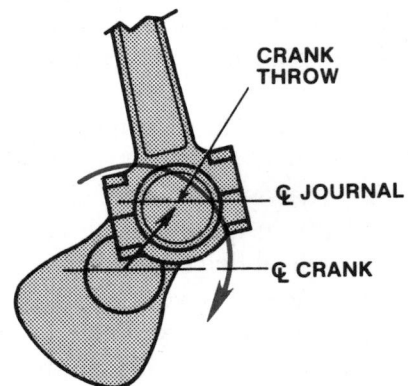

FIGURE 6–17   The stroke of an engine is equal to twice the crank throw.

FIGURE 6–18   Displacement is the volume the cylinder holds between TDC and BDC.

rough indicator of its power output. Displacement can be increased by opening the bore to a larger diameter or by increasing the length of the stroke. Total displacement is the sum of displacements for all cylinders in an engine. Cubic inch displacement (CID) may be calculated as follows.

$$CID = \pi \times R^2 \times L \times N$$

in which $\pi = 3.1416$

R = bore radius or bore diameter/2

L = length of stroke

N = number of cylinders

Example: Calculate the cubic inch displacement (CID) of a six-cylinder engine with a 3.7-in. bore and 3.4-in. stroke.

$$CID = 3.1416 \times 1.85^2 \times 3.4 \times 6$$
$$CID = 219.66$$

Most of today's engines are described by their metric displacement. Cubic centimeters and liters are determined by using metric measurements in the displacement formula.

PISTON AT BDC
(BOTTOM DEAD CENTER)

PISTON AT TDC
(TOP DEAD CENTER)

$$\frac{BORE}{STROKE} = BORE\ STROKE\ RATIO$$

FIGURE 6–16   The bore and stroke of a cylinder.

Example: Calculate the metric displacement of a four-cylinder engine with a 78.9-mm stroke and a 100-mm bore.

$$Displacement = 3.1415 \times 100^2 \times 78.9 \times 4$$
$$Displacement = 2479 \text{ cubic centimeters (cc)}$$
$$= 2.5 \text{ liters (L)}$$

Larger, heavier vehicles are provided with large displacement engines. Large displacement engines produce more torque than smaller displacement engines. They also consume more fuel. Smaller, lighter vehicles can be adequately powered by lower displacement engines that use less fuel.

COMPRESSION RATIO The **compression ratio** of an engine expresses how much the air/fuel mixture will be compressed during the compression stroke. The compression ratio is defined as the ratio of the volume in the cylinder above the piston when the piston is at BDC to the volume in the cylinder above the piston when the piston is at TDC (Figure 6–19). The formula for calculating the compression ratio is as follows.

$$\frac{\text{volume above the piston at BDC}}{\text{volume above the piston at TDC}}$$

or

$$\frac{\text{total cylinder volume}}{\text{total combustion chamber volume}}$$

In many engines, the top of the piston is even or level with the top of the cylinder block at TDC. The combustion chamber is in the cavity in the cylinder head above the piston. This is modified slightly by the shape of the top of the piston. The volume of the combustion chamber must be added to each volume in the formula in order to get an accurate calculation of compression ratio.

Example: Calculate the compression ratio if the total piston displacement is 45 cubic inches and the combustion chamber volume is 5.5 cubic inches.

VOLUME BEFORE COMPRESSION: 480 cc **VOLUME AFTER COMPRESSION: 60 cc**

BDC TDC

COMPRESSION RATIO: 8 TO 1

FIGURE 6–19 Compression ratio measures the amount the air and fuel have been compressed.

$$\frac{45 + 5.5}{5.5} = \text{compression ratio}$$
$$9.1:1 = \text{compression ratio}$$

(Be sure to add the combustion chamber volume to the piston displacement to get the total cylinder volume.)

The higher the compression ratio, the more power an engine theoretically can produce. Also, as the compression ratio increases, the heat produced by the compression stroke also increases. Gasoline with a low octane rating burns fast and may explode rather than burn when introduced to a high compression ratio. This can cause preignition. The higher a gasoline's octane rating, the less likely it is to explode.

As the compression ratio increases, the octane rating of the gasoline also should be increased to prevent abnormal combustion.

ENGINE EFFICIENCY Engine **efficiency** is a measure of the relationship between the amount of energy put into the engine and the amount of available energy from the engine. Engine efficiency is expressed in a percentage. The formula for determining efficiency is:

$$\text{efficiency} = \frac{\text{output energy}}{\text{input energy}} \times 100$$

There are other aspects of the engine that are expressed in efficiencies. These include mechanical efficiency, volumetric efficiency, and thermal efficiency. They are expressed as a ratio of input (actual) to output (maximum or theoretical). Efficiencies are expressed as percentages. They are always less than 100 percent. The difference between the efficiency and 100 percent is the percentage lost during the process. For example, if there were 100 units of energy put into the engine and 28 units came back, the efficiency would be equal to 28 percent. This would mean that 72 percent of the energy received was wasted or lost.

TORQUE AND HORSEPOWER **Torque** is a turning or twisting force. The engine's crankshaft rotates with a torque that is transmitted through the drivetrain to turn the drive wheels of the vehicle. **Horsepower** is the rate at which torque is produced.

Engines produce power by turning a crankshaft in a circular motion. To convert terms of force applied in a straight line to a force applied in a circular motion, the formula is:

$$\text{torque} = \text{force} \times \text{radius}$$

Example: A 10-pound force applied to a wrench 1 foot long will produce 10 pound-feet (lb-ft) of torque.

FIGURE 6–20 Force applied to a wrench produces torque.

Imagine that the 1-foot-long wrench is connected to a shaft. If 1 pound of force is applied to the end of the wrench, 1 pound-foot of torque is produced. Ten pounds of force applied to a wrench 2 feet long will produce 20 pound-feet of torque (Figure 6–20).

The technically correct torque measurement is stated in pound-feet (lb-ft). However, it is rather common to state torque in terms of foot-pounds (ft-lb). In the metric or SI system, torque is stated in Newton-meters (N-m) or kilogram-meters (kg-m).

If the torque output of an engine at a given speed (rpm) is known, horsepower (HP) can be calculated by the following formula.

$$HP = (torque \times rpm) \div 5{,}252$$

An engine produces different amounts of torque based on the rotational speed of the crankshaft and other factors. A mathematical representation, or graph, of the relationship between the horsepower and torque of an engine is shown in Figure 6–21.

FIGURE 6–21 The relationship between horsepower and torque.

GENERAL SPECIFICATIONS	
DISPLACEMENT	1.9L
NUMBER OF CYLINDERS	1–4
BORE AND STROKE	
1.9L	82 x 88 (3.23 x 3.46)
FIRING ORDER	1-3-4-2
OIL PRESSURE (HOT 2000 RPM)	240-450 kPa (35-65 PSI)
DRIVE BELT TENSION	178-311 (40-70 Lb-Ft)

CYLINDER HEAD AND VALVE TRAIN ① ②	
COMBUSTION CHAMBER VOLUME (cc)	EFI-HO 55 ± 1.6
VALVE GUIDE BORE DIAMETER	EFI 39.9 ± 0.8
Intake	13.481-13.519mm (0.531-0.5324 in.)
Exhaust	13.481-13.519mm (0.531-0.532 in.)
VALVE GUIDE I.D.	
Intake and Exhaust	8.063-8.094 N-m (.3174-.3187 in.)
VALVE SEATS	
Width — Intake & Exhaust	1.75-2.32mm (0.069-0.091 in.)
Angle	45°
Runout (T.I.R.)	0.076mm (0.003 in.) MAX.
Bore Diameter (Insert Counterbore Diameter)	
Intake	(EFI-HO) 43.763mm (1.723 in.) MIN.
	43.788mm (1.724 in.) MAX.
	(EFI) 39.940 mm (1.572 in.) MIN
	39.965 mm (1.573 in.) MAX.
Exhaust	(EFI-HO) 38.263mm (1.506 in.) MIN.
	38.288mm (1.507 in.) MAX.
	(EFI) 34.940 mm (1.375 in.) MIN.
	39.965 mm (1.573 in.) MAX.
GASKETS SURFACE FLATNESS	0.04mm (0.0016 in.)/26mm (1 in.)
	0.08mm (0.003 in.)/156mm (6 in.)
	0.15mm (0.006 in.) Total
HEAD FACE SURFACE FINISH	0.7/2.5 0.8 (28/100 .030)
VALVE STEM TO GUIDE CLEARANCE	
Intake	0.020-0.069mm (0.0008-0.0027 in.)
Exhaust	0.046-0.095mm (0.0018-0.0037 in.)
VALVE HEAD DIAMETER	
Intake	42.1-41.9mm (1.66-1.65 in.)
Exhaust	37.1-36.9mm (1.50-1.42 in.)
VALVE FACE RUNOUT	
LIMIT	Intake & Exhaust .05mm (0.002 in.)
VALVE FACE ANGLE	45.6°
VALVE STEM DIAMETER (Std.)	
Intake	8.043-8.025mm (0.3167-0.3159 in.)

FIGURE 6–22 Service manuals contain engine specifications. *Courtesy of Ford Motor Company*

This graph shows that torque begins to decrease when the engine's speed reaches about 1,700 rpm. Brake horsepower increases steadily until about 3,500 rpm. Then it drops. The third line on the graph indicates the horsepower needed to overcome the friction or resistance created by the internal parts of the engine rubbing against each other.

Complete engine specifications can usually be found in service manuals as shown in Figure 6–22.

ENGINE IDENTIFICATION

To find the correct specifications for an engine, a technician must know how to use the vehicle identification number (**VIN**). The VIN is a code of seventeen numbers and letters stamped on a metal tab that is riveted to the instrument panel close to the windshield (Figure 6–23). From this number much information about the vehicle can be found.

FIGURE 6–23 The VIN is visible through the driver's side of the windshield.

SAMPLE VIN NUMBER

1 F T B F 2 5 G 5 H L A 0 0 0 0 1

① POSITION 1, 2, AND 3—MANUFACTURER, MAKE, AND TYPE (WORLD MANUFACTURER IDENTIFIER)
② POSITION 4—BRAKE SYSTEM
③ POSITION 5, 6, AND 7—MODEL OR LINE, SERIES, CHASSIS, CAB OR BODY TYPE
④ POSITION 8—ENGINE TYPE
⑤ POSITION 9—CHECK DIGIT
⑥ POSITION 10—MODEL YEAR
⑦ POSITION 11—ASSEMBLY PLANT
⑧ POSITION 12—CONSTANT A UNTIL SEQUENCE NUMBER 99,999 IS REACHED, THEN CHANGES TO A CONSTANT B AND SO ON.
⑨ POSITION 13 THROUGH 17—SEQUENCE NUMBER— BEGINS AT 00001

FIGURE 6–24 The VIN provides a great deal of information.

USING SERVICE MANUALS

Normally, information used to identify the size of an engine is given in service manuals at the beginning of the section covering that particular manufacturer. ∎

The adoption of the seventeen-number-and-letter code became mandatory beginning with 1981 vehicles. The standard VIN of the United States National Highway Transportation and Safety Administration Department of Transportation is being used by all manufacturers of vehicles, both domestic and foreign.

By referring to the VIN, much information about the vehicle can be determined (Figure 6–24). An engine serial number is also stamped on many blocks (Figure 6–25). Its location is different for the different manufacturers. The service manual will tell you where to look for it. The engine code is generally found beside the serial number. A typical engine code might be DZ or MO. These letters indicate the horsepower rating of the engine, whether it was built for an automatic or manual transmission, and other important details. The engine code will help you determine the correct specifications for that particular engine.

Casting numbers are often mistaken for serial numbers and engine codes. Manufacturers use a casting number to identify major engine parts on the assembly line. They seldom can be used to identify the type of engine.

ENGINE DIAGNOSTICS

In the previous chapter, different types of test equipment were discussed. Many of these tested the mechanical condition of an engine, such as the wet and dry compression, cylinder leakage, and engine vacuum. In addition to these, two other common tests can be performed to evaluate the condition of an engine and to identify any problem areas. The cylinder power balance test checks the efficiency of individual cylinders. The results of this test are often used in conjunction with the results of compression and cylinder leakage tests.

Unlike other engine tests, an oil pressure test does not test a cylinder's ability to seal. It is used to determine wear on the engine's parts. Excessive clearances, often the result of wear, between a shaft and its bearings will have an affect on oil pressure. The oil pressure test is performed with an oil pressure gauge and measures the pressure of the oil while it is circulating through the engine. The pressure of the oil depends upon the efficiency of the oil pump and the clearances through which it travels.

USING SERVICE MANUALS

Whenever you test oil pressure, be sure to refer to the service manual to find out the required conditions for the test and the desired pressure readings. ∎

FRONT

FRONT

FRONT

REAR OF ENGINE

FIGURE 6–25 Common engine serial number locations.

OIL PRESSURE TESTING

Loss of performance, excessive engine noise, and poor starting can be caused by abnormal oil pressures. An insufficient amount of pressure may also cause premature wear on rotating parts. An oil pressure tester is a gauge with a high-pressure hose attached to it. The scale of the gauge typically reads from 0 to 100 psi. The hose is connected to the engine block in a place where oil pressure can be measured (usually where the oil pressure indicator light sensor is screwed into the block).

To conduct the test, simply follow the guidelines given in the service manual and observe the gauge. The pressure is read when the engine is at normal operating temperatures and at a fast idle speed. Low oil pressures can be caused by a worn oil pump, excessive wear on the crankshaft or camshaft and their bearings, a plugged oil pickup screen, or a weak or broken oil pressure relief valve. High oil pressure is normally caused by restrictions in the oil passages or a faulty pressure regulator.

CYLINDER POWER BALANCE TESTING

The **cylinder power balance** test is used to see if all the engine's cylinders are producing the same amount of power. Ideally, all cylinders produce the same amount. This minimizes the amount of power that is lost by keeping the engine running and allows the engine to run smoothly. To check the balance of the cylinders, the cylinders are shorted out one at a time and the change in engine speed is recorded. Ideally, the changes in engine rpm should be about equal as each cylinder is shorted out. Unequal cylinder power can mean a problem in the cylinders themselves, as well as the rings, valves, intake manifold, head gasket, fuel system, or ignition system.

The power balance test is performed quickly and easily using an engine analyzer, because the spark plugs can be controlled with push buttons. Changes are measured in rpm drop. Keep in mind that the push-button numbers refer to the cylinder firing order, not the cylinder number designation. For example, when testing an engine with a firing order of 1-3-4-2, pushing the first button shorts out the number of 1 cylinder, pushing the second button shorts out the number 3 cylinder, and so on.

SHOP TALK

A cylinder power balance test can be conducted with just a tachometer. To do this, simply remove a spark plug wire and ground it. Do this to each spark plug, one at a time, and observe the change in engine rpm. If the engine is equipped with electronic ignition, do not ground the spark plug wire directly to ground. Insert a test spark into the end of the wire and ground the test plug before running the engine. ∎

Test Precautions

On some computer-controlled or fuel-injected engines, certain components must be disconnected before attempting the power balance test. Because of the wide variations from manufacturer to manufacturer, consult the vehicle's service manual for specific instructions.

If the engine being tested has an exhaust gas recirculation (EGR) system, added precautions must be taken. If the system is valve controlled, disconnect the vacuum or electrical connection to the EGR valve. This will prevent the valve from cycling due to vacuum changes when the cylinders are shorted out. For engines with a floor jet EGR system, the power balance test cannot be performed accurately because of the possibility of the unburned fuel mixture being sent back into the cylinders. The compression test is the recommended alternative in such cases.

Care must be taken when performing the power balance test on vehicles with catalytic converters. To prevent unburned fuel from building up in the converter, short each spark plug for less than 15 seconds, then allow the engine to run for another 30 seconds before shorting another one.

Performing the Test

The standard power balance test is fairly simple. If the engine has an air/fuel mixture feedback control or O_2 sensor (Figure 6–26A), disconnect the plug, either the air pump hose going to the catalytic converter or the downstream hose between the air switching valve and the check valve. On some Ford models, the air switching valve can routinely have up to 10 percent leakage, in which case both hoses must be disconnected and plugged. If the engine does not have an air/fuel mixture feedback control or O_2 sensor (Figure 6–26B), disconnect and block the air pump on the valve side.

Override the controls of the electric cooling fan by jumper wiring the controls so the fan runs constantly. If the fan cannot be bypassed, disconnect it. Be careful that the engine does not overheat during the test.

Connect the engine analyzer's leads, referring to the equipment's instruction manual for specific instructions.

FIGURE 6–26 The procedure for conducting a cylinder power balance test differs, depending on whether the engine (A) has an air/fuel mixture feedback control or (B) does not have an air/fuel mixture feedback control.

Turn on the engine and let it reach its normal operating temperature before beginning the test. Engine speed should be stabilized at approximately 1,000 rpm. When a cylinder is shorted, note any drop in rpm or manifold vacuum.

As each cylinder is shorted out, a noticeable drop in engine speed should occur. Little or no decrease in rpm indicates a weak cylinder. If all the readings are fairly close to each other, the engine is in sound mechanical condition. If a reading in one or more cylinders differs greatly from the rest, there is a problem. Further testing should be done to determine the exact cause of the problem.

EVALUATING THE ENGINE'S CONDITION

Once the compression, cylinder leakage, vacuum, and power balance tests are performed, a technician is ready to evaluate the engine's condition. For example, an engine with good relative compression but high cylinder leakage past the rings is typical of a high-mileage worn engine. This engine would have these symptoms: excessive blowby, lack of power, poor performance, and reduced fuel economy.

If these same compression and leakage test results are found on an engine with comparatively low mileage, the problem is probably stuck piston rings that are not expanding properly. If this is the case, try treating the engine with a combustion chamber cleaner, oil treatment, or engine flush. If this fails to correct the problem, an engine overhaul is required.

A cylinder that has poor compression but minimal leakage indicates a valve train problem. Under these circumstances, a valve might not be opening at the right time, might not be opening enough, or might not be opening at all. This condition can be confirmed on engines with a pushrod-type valve train by pulling the rocker covers and watching the valves operate while the engine is cycled. If one or more valves fail to move, either the lifters are collapsed or the cam lobes are worn. If all of the cylinders have low compression with minimal leakage, the most likely cause is incorrect valve timing.

If compression and leakage are both good, but the power balance test reveals weak cylinders, the cause of the problem is outside the combustion chamber. Assuming there are no ignition or fuel problems, check for broken, bent, or worn valve train components, collapsed lifters, leaking intake manifold, or excessively leaking valve guides. If the latter is suspected, squirt some oil on the guides. If they are leaking, blue smoke will be seen in the exhaust.

NOISE DIAGNOSIS

More often than not, malfunction in the engine will reveal itself first as an unusual noise. This can happen before the problem affects the driveability of the vehicle. Problems such as loose pistons, badly worn rings or ring lands, loose piston pins, worn main bearings and connecting rod bearings, loose vibration damper or flywheel, and worn or loose valve train components all produce telltale sounds. Unless the technician has experience in listening to and interpreting engine noises, it can be very hard to distinguish one from the other.

CUSTOMER CARE

When attempting to diagnose the cause of abnormal engine noise, it may be necessary to temper the enthusiasm of a customer who thinks they have pinpointed the exact cause of the noise using nothing more than their own two ears. While the owner's description may be helpful (and should always be asked for), it must be stressed that one person's "rattle" can be another person's "thump." You are the professional. The final diagnosis is up to you. If customers have been proven correct in their diagnosis, make it a point to tell them so. Everyone feels better about dealing with an automotive technician who listens to them. ∎

When correctly interpreted, engine noise can be a very valuable diagnostic aid. For one thing, a costly and time-consuming engine teardown might be avoided. Always make a noise analysis before doing any repair work. This way, there is a much greater likelihood that only the necessary repair procedures will be done. Careful noise diagnosis also reduces the chances of ruining the engine by continuing to use the vehicle despite the problem.

⚠ WARNING!

Be very careful when listening for noises around moving belts and pulleys at the front of the engine. Keep the end of the hose or stethoscope probe away from the moving parts. Physical injury can result if the hose or stethoscope is pulled inward or flung outward by moving parts. ∎

Using a Stethoscope

Some engine sounds can be easily heard without using a listening device, but others are impossible to hear unless amplified. A stethoscope or rubber hose (as mentioned earlier) is very helpful in locating engine noise by amplifying the sound waves. It can also distinguish between normal and abnormal noise. The procedure for using a stethoscope is simple. Use the metal prod to trace the sound until it reaches its maximum intensity. Once the precise location has been discovered, the sound can be better evaluated. A sounding stick, which is nothing more than a long, hollow tube, works on the same principle, though a stethoscope gives much clearer results.

The best results, however, are obtained with an electronic listening device. With this tool you can tune into the noise. Doing this allows you to eliminate all other noises that might distract or mislead you.

Common Noises

Following are examples of abnormal engine noises, including a description of the sound, its likely cause,

and ways of eliminating it. An important point to keep in mind is that insufficient lubrication is the most common cause of engine noise. For this reason, always check the oil level first before moving on to other areas of the vehicle. Some noises are more pronounced on a cold engine because clearances are greater when parts are not expanded by heat. Remember that aluminum and iron expand at different rates as temperatures rise. For example, a knock that disappears as the engine warms up is probably piston slap or knock. An aluminum piston expands more than the iron block, allowing the piston to fit more closely as engine temperature rises.

RING NOISE This sound can be heard during acceleration as a high-pitched rattling or clicking in the upper part of the cylinder. It can be caused by worn rings or cylinders, broken piston ring lands, or insufficient ring tension against the cylinder walls. Ring noise is corrected by replacing the rings, pistons, or sleeves or reboring the cylinders.

PISTON SLAP This is commonly heard when the engine is cold. It often gets louder when the vehicle accelerates. When a piston slaps against the cylinder wall, the result is a hollow, bell-like sound. Piston slap is caused by worn pistons or cylinders, collapsed piston skirts, misaligned connecting rods, excessive piston-to-cylinder wall clearance, or lack of lubrication, resulting in worn bearings. Correction requires either replacing the pistons, reboring the cylinder, replacing or realigning the rods, or replacing the bearings. Shorting out the spark plug of the affected cylinder might quiet the noise.

PISTON PIN KNOCK Piston pin knock is a sharp, metallic rap that can sound more like a rattle if all the pins are loose. It originates in the upper portion of the engine and is most noticeable when the engine is idling and the engine is hot. Piston pin knock sounds like a double knock at idle speeds. It is caused by a worn piston pin, piston pin boss, piston pin bushing, or lack of lubrication, resulting in worn bearings. To correct it, either install oversized pins, replace the boss or bushings, or replace the piston.

RIDGE NOISE This noise is less common but very distinct. As a piston ring strikes the ridge at the top of the cylinder, the result is a high-pitched rapping or clicking noise that becomes louder during deceleration (Figure 6–27).

There can be more than one reason for the ridge interfering with the ring's travel. For one thing, if new rings are installed without removing the old ridge, the new rings will contact the ridge and make a noise. Also, if the piston pin is very loose or the

FIGURE 6–27 When the piston strikes the ridge at the top of the cylinder, a high-pitched rapping or clicking sound is made.

connecting rod has a loose or burned-out bearing, the piston will go high enough in the cylinder for the top ring to contact the ridge. Thus, in order to eliminate ridge noise, remove the old ring ridge and replace the piston pin or piston.

ROD-BEARING NOISE The result of worn or loose connecting rod bearings, this noise is heard at idle as well as at speeds over 35 mph. Depending on how badly the bearings are worn, the noise can range from a light tap to a heavy knock or pound. Shorting out the spark plug of the affected cylinder can lessen the noise, unless the bearing is extremely worn. In this case, shorting out the plug will have no effect. Rod-bearing noise is caused by a worn bearing or crankpin, a misaligned rod, or lack of lubrication, resulting in worn bearings. To correct it, service or replace the crankshaft, realign or replace the connecting rods, and replace the bearings.

MAIN OR THRUST BEARING NOISE A loose crankshaft main bearing produces a dull, steady knock, while a loose crankshaft thrust bearing produces a heavy thump at irregular intervals. The thrust bearing noise might only be audible on very hard acceleration. Both of these bearing noises are usually caused by worn bearings or crankshaft journals. To correct the problem, replace the bearings or crankshaft.

TAPPET NOISE Tappet noise is characterized by a light, regular clicking sound that is more noticeable when the engine is idling. It is the result of excessive clearance in the valve train. The clearance problem area is located by inserting a feeler gauge between each lifter and valve, or between each rocker arm and valve tip, until the noise subsides. Tappet noise can be caused by improper valve adjustment, worn or damaged parts, dirty hydraulic lifters, or lack of lubrication. To correct the noise, adjust the valves,

replace any worn or damaged parts, or clean or replace the lifters.

ABNORMAL COMBUSTION NOISES Preignition and detonation noises are caused by abnormal engine combustion. For instance, **detonation** knock or **ping** is a noise most noticeable during acceleration with the engine under load and running at normal temperature. Excessive detonation can be very harmful to the engine. It is often caused by advanced ignition timing or substantial carbon buildup in the combustion chambers that increases combustion pressure. Carbon deposits that get so hot they glow will also preignite the air/fuel mixture, causing detonation. Another possible cause is fuel with octane that is too low. Detonation knock can usually be cured by removing carbon deposits from the combustion chambers with a rotary wire brush as well as recommending the use of a higher octane gasoline. A malfunctioning EGR valve can also cause detonation and even rod knock.

Sometimes abnormal combustion combines with other engine parts to cause noise. For example, rumble is a term that is used to describe the knock or noise resulting from another form of abnormal ignition. Rumble is a vibration of the crankshaft and connecting rods that is caused by multi-surface ignition. Rumble is a form or preignition in which several flame fronts occur simultaneously from overheated deposit particles. Multi-surface ignition causes a tremendous sudden pressure rise near top dead center. It has been reported that the rate of pressure rise during rumble is five times the rate of normal combustion.

A loose vibration damper causes a heavy rumble or thump in the front of the engine that is more apparent when the vehicle is accelerating from idle under load or is idling unevenly. A loose flywheel causes a heavy thump or light knock at the back of the engine, depending on the amount of play and the type of engine. Both of these problems are corrected either by tightening or replacing the damper or flywheel.

OTHER ENGINE DESIGNS

The gasoline-powered, internal combustion piston engine has been the primary automotive power plant for many years and probably will remain so for years to come. Present-day social requirements and new technological developments, however, have necessitated searches for ways to modify or replace this time-proven workhorse. This portion of the chapter takes a brief look at the most likely contenders, and how they work. The orbital two-stroke cycle engine was discussed earlier and is not explained in the following. This certainly does not mean that this engine design is not a viable one.

FIGURE 6–28 Typical four-stroke diesel engine. *Courtesy of Ford Motor Company*

Diesel Engine

Diesel engines represent tested, proven technology with a long history of success. Invented by Dr. Rudolph Diesel, a German engineer, and first marketed in 1897, the diesel engine is now the dominate power plant in heavy-duty trucks, construction equipment, farm equipment, buses, and marine applications.

During the late 1970s and early 1980s, many predicted small diesel engines would replace gasoline engines in passenger vehicles. However, stabilized gas prices and other factors dampened the enthusiasm for diesels in these markets. The use of diesel engines in cars and light trucks is now limited to a few manufacturers.

Diesel engines (Figure 6–28) and gasoline-powered engines share several similarities. They have a number of components in common, such as the crankshaft, pistons, valves, camshaft, and water and oil pumps. They both are available in four-stroke

combustion cycle models. However, the diesel engine and four-stroke compression-ignition engine are easily recognized by the absence of a ignition system. Instead of relying on a spark for ignition, a diesel engine uses the heat produced by compressing air in the combustion chamber to ignite the fuel. The systems used in diesel-powered vehicles are essentially the same as those used in gasoline vehicles.

Figure 6–29 shows the four-strokes of a diesel engine. Fuel injection is used on all diesel engines. Injectors spray pressurized fuel into the cylinders just as the piston is completing its compression stroke. The heat of the compressed air ignites the fuel and begins the power stroke.

Glow plugs are used only to warm the combustion chamber when the engine is cold. Cold starting is impossible without these plugs because even the high-compression ratios cannot heat cold air enough to cause combustion.

Diesel combustion chambers are different from gasoline combustion chambers because diesel fuel burns differently. Three types of combustion chambers are used in diesel engines: open combustion chamber, precombustion chamber, and turbulence combustion chamber. The open combustion chamber has the combustion chamber located directly inside the piston. Diesel fuel is injected directly into the center of the chamber. The shape of the chamber and the quench area produces turbulence. The precombustion chamber is a smaller, second chamber connection to the main combustion chamber. On the power stroke, fuel is injected into the small chamber. Combustion is started there and then spreads to the main chamber. This design allows lower fuel injection pressures and simpler injection systems on diesel engines.

The turbulence combustion chamber is designated to create an increase in air velocity or turbulence in the combustion chamber. The fuel is injected into the turbulent air and burns more completely. The prechambers on a diesel engine head must be proper-

INTAKE **COMPRESSION** **POWER** **EXHAUST**

FIGURE 6–29 Four-stroke diesel engine cycle.

FIGURE 6–30 Correctly installed diesel prechambers.

TABLE 6–1 COMPARISON BETWEEN GASOLINE AND DIESEL ENGINES

	Gasoline	**Diesel**
Intake	Air/fuel	Air
Compression	8–10 to 1 130 psi 545°F	13–25 to 1 400–600 psi 1,000°F
Air/fuel mixing point	In intake manifold near the intake valve.	In cylinder near TDC by injection
Combustion	Spark ignition	Compression ignition
Power	464 psi	1,200 psi
Exhaust	1,300°–1,800°F CO = 1%	700°–900°F CO = 0.5%
Efficiency	22–28%	32–38%

ly indexed with the head and correctly installed (Figure 6–30). They must be perfectly flush (not above or below) with the cylinder head. Failure to follow this will cause the head gasket to fail.

Table 6–1 compares the gasoline and diesel four-stroke-cycle engines. Diesel engines are also available in two-stroke-cycle models (Figure 6–31).

Rotary Engine

The **rotary** engine, or **Wankel** engine, is somewhat similar to the standard piston engine in that it is a four-cycle, spark ignition, internal combustion engine. Its mechanical design, however, is quite different. For one thing, the rotary engine uses a rotating motion rather than a reciprocating motion. In addition, it uses ports rather than valves for controlling the intake of the air/fuel mixture and the exhaust of the combusted charge.

As shown in Figure 6–32 the heart of a rotary engine is a roughly triangular rotor that "walks" around a smaller, rigidly mounted gear. The rotor is connected to the crankshaft through additional gears in such a manner that for every rotation of the rotor the crankshaft revolves three times. The tips of the triangular rotor move within the housing and are in constant contact with the housing walls. As the rotor moves, the volume between each side of the rotor and the housing walls continually changes.

Referring to Figure 6–33, when side A of the rotor is in position 1, the intake port is uncovered and the air/fuel mixture is entering the upper chamber. As the rotor moves to position B, the intake port

FIGURE 6–31 Two-stroke diesel engine cycle.

FIGURE 6–32   Typical rotary engine. *Courtesy of Mazda*

FIGURE 6–33   Rotary engine cycle.

closes and the upper chamber reaches its maximum volume. When full compression has reached position C, the two spark plugs fire, one after the other, to start the power stroke. At position D, rotor side A uncovers the exhaust port and exhaust begins. This cycle continues until position 1 is reached where the chamber volume is at minimum and the intake cycle starts once again.

The fact that the rotating combustion chamber engine is small and light for the amount of power it produces makes it attractive for use in automobiles. Using this small, lightweight engine can provide the same performance as a larger engine. But, the rotary engine, at present, cannot compete with the piston gasoline on durability, exhaust emission control, and economy.

FIGURE 6–34   Typical stratified charge engine.

Stratified Charge Engine

The stratified charge engine (Figure 6–34) combines the features of both the gasoline and diesel engines. It differs from the conventional gasoline engine in that the air/fuel mixture is deliberately stratified to produce a small rich mixture at the spark plug while providing a leaner, more efficient and cleaner burning main mixture. In addition, the air/fuel mixture is swirled for more complete combustion.

Referring to position A in Figure 6–35, a large amount of very lean mixture is drawn through the main intake valve on the intake stroke to the main combustion chamber. At the same time, a small amount of rich mixture is drawn through the auxiliary intake valve into the precombustion chamber. At the end of the compression stroke in position B, the

FIGURE 6–35   Four-stroke cycle of a stratified charge engine.

spark plug fires the rich mixture in the precombustion chamber. As the rich mixture ignites, it in turn ignites the lean mixture in the main chamber. The lean mixture minimizes the formation of carbon monoxide during the power stroke (position C). In addition, the peak temperature stays low enough to minimize the formation of oxides of nitrogen, and the mean temperature is maintained high enough and long enough to reduce hydrocarbon emissions. During the exhaust stroke (position D) the hot gases exit through the exhaust valve.

A great deal of automobile engineering research, especially by Japanese and European manufacturers, is being done on these engines. In fact, the Honda CVCC engine uses a stratified charge design. This engine uses a third valve to release the initial charge. The stratified charge combustion chamber has three important advantages. It produces good part-load fuel economy. It can run efficiently on low-octane fuel and has low exhaust emissions.

Electric Motors

In the early days of the automobile, electric cars outnumbered gasoline cars. An electric motor is quiet, has little or no emissions, and has few moving parts. It starts well in the cold, is simple to maintain, and does not burn petroleum products to operate. Its disadvantages are limited speed, power, and range as well as the need for heavy, costly batteries. Experimental vehicles employing solar-charged batteries are being considered as sources of automotive power.

CASE STUDY

A customer complains that the engine has a rough idle and does not have as much power as it used to. Also, the customer says that the engine is difficult to start when it is cold and runs better while cruising at highway speeds. Upon examining the car, it is found that it has a four-cylinder engine with nearly 65,000 miles on it. Driving the car verifies the customer's complaint.

Diagnosis begins with a visual inspection that reveals only that the car has been well-maintained. Because there is an endless list of possible causes for these problems, the first test is for engine vacuum. With the vacuum gauge connected to the manifold and the engine at idle speed, the gauge's needle constantly drops from a normal reading to 10 in. Hg. The rhythm of the drop matches the rhythm of the idle. The

behavior of the gauge indicates a probable problem in one cylinder.

To verify this, a cylinder power balance test is conducted. The results show an engine speed drop of 100 to 125 rpm when cylinders 1, 2, and 4 are shorted, and a drop of only 10 rpm when cylinder 3 is shorted. Based on this test, cylinder 3 is identified as having the problem.

To identify the exact fault, further testing is required. The spark plugs are removed and inspected. All look normal, including cylinder 3. Next, a compression test is taken. All cylinders have normal readings. A cylinder leakage test is then conducted and it too shows normal conditions. The results of the power balance, compression, and cylinder leakage tests lead to the conclusion that the cause has to be in the valve train. Something is preventing a valve from opening.

Removing the cam cover for a visual inspection leads to the discovery of the fault: the intake lobe for cylinder 3 on the camshaft is severely worn. A replacement of the camshaft and matching lifter will correct the problem. The worn lobe only affects the opening of the valve and does not prevent it from sealing, which is why the compression and cylinder leakage test results were normal. Cylinder power and vacuum are affected by the valve not opening fully.

KEY TERMS

Bore	Glow plug
Cam	Horsepower
Combustion chamber	Lobe
Compression ratio	OHC
Crank throw	OHV
Cylinder power balance	Ping
Detonation	Rotary
Diesel	Stroke
Displacement	Torque
DOHC	VIN
Efficiency	Wankel
Firing order	

SUMMARY

◆ Automotive engines are classified by several different design features such as operational cycles, number of cylinders, cylinder arrangement, valve train type, valve arrangement, ignition type, cooling system, and fuel system.

◆ The basis of automotive gasoline engine operation is the four-stroke cycle. This includes the intake stroke, compression stroke, power stroke, and exhaust stroke. The four strokes require two full crankshaft revolutions.

◆ The most popular engine designs are the in-line (in which all the cylinders are placed in a single row) and V-type (which features two rows of cylinders). The slant design is much like the in-line, but the entire block is placed at a slant. Opposed cylinder engines use two rows of cylinders located opposite the crankshaft.

◆ The two basic valve and camshaft placement configurations currently in use on four-stroke engines are the overhead valve and overhead cam. A third type, the flathead or side valve, once was popular but is no longer in use.

◆ Bore is the diameter of a cylinder, and stroke is the length of piston travel between top dead center (TDC) and bottom dead center (BDC). Together these two measurements determine the displacement of the cylinder, which is the volume the cylinder holds between the TDC and BDC positions of the piston.

◆ Compression ratio is a measure of how much the air and fuel have been compressed. The higher the compression ratio is, the more power an engine can produce. The compression ratio of an engine must be suited to the fuel available. As compression ratio increases, the octane rating of the fuel must increase to prevent abnormal engine combustion.

◆ Horsepower is the rate at which torque is produced by an engine. The torque is then transmitted through the drivetrain to turn the driving wheels of the vehicle.

◆ The vehicle identification number, or VIN, is used to identify correct engine specifications. It is stamped on a metal tab, which is riveted to the instrument panel.

◆ An oil pressure test measures the pressure of the engine oil as it circulates throughout the engine. This test is very important because abnormal oil pressures can cause a host of problems, including poor performance and premature wear.

◆ The cylinder power balance test reveals if all the cylinders are doing an equal amount of work; if not, there is either a mechanical problem or trouble in the fuel or ignition system. This test is performed easiest on an engine analyzer. As each cylinder is shorted out, a noticeable drop in engine speed should occur.

◆ An engine malfunction often reveals itself as an unusual noise. When correctly interpreted, engine noise can be a very helpful diagnostic aid.

◆ Abnormal engine combustion can cause preignition and detonation noises. Detonation knock or ping is most noticeable during acceleration with the engine under load. Though this can be very harmful to the engine, it can usually be cured by removing carbon deposits from the combustion chambers and using a higher octane gasoline.

◆ Instead of relying on a spark for ignition, diesel engines use the heat produced by compressing air in the combustion chamber to ignite the fuel. Three types of combustion chambers are used in diesel engines: open, precombustion, and turbulence.

◆ Features of both the gasoline and diesel engine are found in the stratified charge engine. Its major advantages are good part-load fuel economy, low exhaust emissions, and an ability to operate on low-octane fuel.

◆ In addition to the diesel and stratified charge, other automotive engines that may figure prominently in the future include the rotary or Wankel, and the electric.

TECH MANUAL

The following procedures are included in Chapter 6 of the Tech Manual that accompanies this book:

1. Perform a cylinder compression test.

2. Perform cylinder leakage test.

3. Measure engine oil pressure.

REVIEW QUESTIONS

1. What occurs in the combustion chamber of a four-stroke engine?

2. Name the four strokes of a four-stroke cycle engine.

3. As an engine's compression ratio increases, what should happen to the octane rating of the gasoline?

4. What test can be performed to check the efficiency of individual cylinders?

5. Describe tappet noise.

6. Which of the following statements about engines is *not* true?

   a. The engine provides the rotating power to drive the wheels through the transmission and driving axle.
   b. Only gasoline engines are classified as internal combustion.
   c. The combustion chamber is the space between the top of the piston and the cylinder head.
   d. For the combustion in the cylinder to take place completely and efficiently, air and fuel must be combined in the right proportions.

7. Which stroke in the four-stroke cycle begins as the compressed fuel mixture is ignited in the combustion chamber?

   a. power stroke
   b. exhaust stroke
   c. intake stroke
   d. compression stroke

8. What is compression ratio?

   a. diameter of the cylinder
   b. cylinder arrangement
   c. the amount the air/fuel mixture is compressed
   d. none of the above

9. When a customer refers to the engine component that opens and closes the intake and exhaust valves, Technician A believes the customer is referring to the camshaft. Technician B thinks the component in question is the intake manifold. Who is correct?

   a. Technician A
   b. Technician B
   c. Both A and B
   d. Neither A nor B

10. A two-stroke engine is normally equipped with ____.

    a. a valve train
    b. a piston
    c. a reed valve
    d. all of the above

11. Technician A says if an engine had good results from a compression test, it will have good results from a cylinder leakage test. Technician B says if an engine had good results from a cylinder leakage test, it will have good results from a compression test. Who is correct?

    a. Technician A
    b. Technician B
    c. Both A and B
    d. Neither A nor B

12. What is piston slap?

    a. grooves on the side of the piston
    b. force applied to the piston
    c. noise made by the piston when it contacts the cylinder wall

    d. a high-pitched clicking that becomes louder during deceleration

13. Which engine system removes burned gases and limits noise produced by the engine?

    a. exhaust system
    b. emission control system
    c. ignition system
    d. air/fuel system

14. Technician A measures engine displacement in cubic centimeters, while Technician B measures it in cubic inches. Who is correct?

    a. Technician A
    b. Technician B
    c. Both A and B
    d. Neither A nor B

15. The stroke of an engine is ____ the crank throw.

    a. half
    b. twice
    c. four times
    d. equal to

16. Technician A calculates compression ratio with the following formula.

$$\frac{\text{volume above the piston at BDC}}{\text{volume above the piston at TDC}}$$

Technician B calculates compression ratio with the following formula.

$$\frac{\text{total cylinder volume}}{\text{total combustion chamber volume}}$$

Who is correct?

    a. Technician A
    b. Technician B
    c. Both A and B
    d. Neither A nor B

17. When performing a cylinder power balance test, Technician A says the push-button numbers on the engine analyzer refer to cylinder number designation. Technician B says they refer to cylinder firing order. Who is correct?

    a. Technician A
    b. Technician B
    c. Both A and B
    d. Neither A nor B

18. A vehicle is producing a sharp, metallic, rapping sound originating in the upper portion of the engine. It is most noticeable during idle. Technician A diagnoses the problem as piston pin knock, while Technician B says the problem is most likely a loose crankshaft thrust bearing. Who is correct?

    a. Technician A
    b. Technician B
    c. Both A and B
    d. Neither A nor B

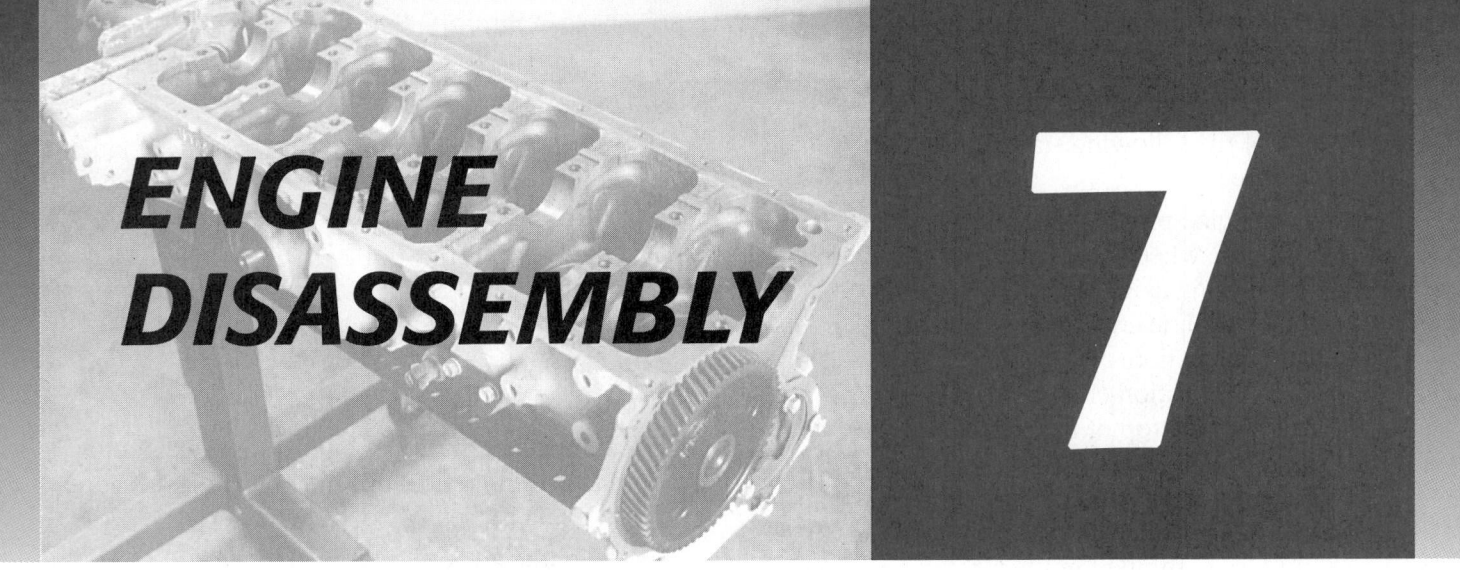

ENGINE DISASSEMBLY

7

OBJECTIVES

◆ *Prepare an engine for removal.* ◆ *Explain what is involved in lifting an engine.* ◆ *Describe how to disassemble and inspect an engine.* ◆ *Name the three basic cleaning processes.* ◆ *Identify the types of cleaning equipment.*

Careful diagnostics will determine if a starting or running problem is caused by the engine itself or by one of its systems, such as the ignition or air/fuel system. When the engine is the source of the problem, or its parts are broken or excessively worn, it normally needs to be rebuilt or overhauled. While some engine repairs can be made with the engine still in the vehicle, most require its removal.

Once an engine is removed from the vehicle, it must be disassembled and its parts properly cleaned using acceptable methods. Always refer to the service manual before beginning engine removal and disassembly. Procedures and safety precautions can vary greatly from model to model.

PREPARING THE ENGINE FOR REMOVAL

It is wise to clean the engine and engine compartment before beginning to remove the engine.

⚠ WARNING!

Be very careful not to damage electronic and fuel injection components while cleaning the engine. Cover any part that can be damaged with plastic bags and avoid spraying directly onto the bags. ∎

Once cleaned, begin to disconnect parts from the engine. All engine fluids should be drained, wires and hoses disconnected, linkages disconnected, and other things removed or disconnected before lifting the engine out of the vehicle. Always follow the specific steps given for engine removal in the vehicle's service manual. A typical procedure for preparing an engine for removal is outlined in the *Tech Manual* that accompanies this test.

🔒 CUSTOMER CARE

Make sure your hands, shoes, and clothing are clean before getting into a customer's car. Disposable seat and floor coverings should be used to help protect the interior. ∎

LIFTING AN ENGINE

To lift an engine out of its compartment, use either a canvas hoist and chain, which consists of gears that provide the necessary mechanical advantage to do the lifting, or a mobile crane, frequently called a **cherry picker**, which uses hydraulic power to do the lifting.

To lift an engine, attach a pulling sling or chain (Figure 7–1) to the engine. Some engines have eye

FIGURE 7–1 Lifting an engine out of its compartment. *Courtesy of OTC Tool and Equipment Division of SPX Corporation*

FIGURE 7-2 Transverse-mounted front-wheel-drive engine.

plates for use in lifting. If they are not available, the sling must be bolted to the engine. The sling attaching bolts must be large enough to support the engine and must thread into the block a minimum of 1-1/2 times the bolt diameter. Connect the chain hoist or mobile crane to the pulling cable. Check the engine to be sure everything is disconnected.

Raise the engine slightly and make certain the sling attachments are secure. Carefully lift the engine out of its compartment. Be sure the engine does not bind or damage any compartment component during this procedure.

Lower the engine close to the floor so it can be transported to the desired location. If you have not already disconnected the transmission and torque converter or clutch from the engine, do so now. The torque converter must remain with the transmission when the engine is removed. A C-clamp or bar clamp will prevent the converter from dropping out of the bell housing.

Raise the engine and position it next to an engine stand. Mount the engine to the engine stand with bolts. Most stands use a plate with several holes or adjustable arms. The engine must be supported by at least four bolts that fit solidly into the engine. The engine should be positioned so its center is in the middle of the engine's stand adapter plate. This will ensure that the engine is not too heavy when rotated on the engine stand. Once the pulling cable or chain is removed from the engine, the engine can be disassembled.

SHOP TALK

When lifting a transverse-mounted engine with front-wheel drive (Figure 7-2), some service manuals recommend removing the engine and transaxle assembly as a unit. The transaxle can be separat-

ed from the engine once it has been lifted out of the vehicle. In this case, the drive axles must be disconnected from the transaxle. It is wise to use a transverse engine support bar before attempting to remove this type of engine (Figure 7-3). ■

1. TOOL
2. THREAD ONTO STRUT ATTACHING BOLTS, ABOVE NUTS – 3 PER SIDE.

FIGURE 7-3 A transverse engine support bar provides the necessary support when removing the lower driveline cradle on a front-wheel-drive vehicle. *Courtesy of Chevrolet Motor Division, General Motors Corporation*

ENGINE DISASSEMBLY AND INSPECTION

Before engine disassembly, be sure the engine is securely bolted to an engine stand or sitting on blocks. Go slowly and visually inspect each part for any signs of damage. Look for excessive wear on the moving parts. Check all parts for signs of overheating, unusual wear, and chips. Look for signs of gasket and seal leakage. A disassembled engine is shown in Figure 7–4.

The following engine teardown of both cylinder head and block can be considered typical. Exact

FIGURE 7–4   Disassembled engine. *Courtesy of American Honda Motor Company, Inc.*

details will vary slightly depending on the style and type of engine. For instance, in some engines, the overhead camshaft is mounted directly in the cylinder head. In other engines, it is located in a separate housing that is mounted on the cylinder head. The camshaft housing is unbolted from the cylinder head. The bearing caps must be removed in order to remove a camshaft mounted to the cylinder head.

Although general methods of parts removal and procedures to inspect the various engine components are given in later chapters of this book, the vehicle's OEM service manual is always the final word.

USING SERVICE MANUALS

Look up the specific model car and engine prior to disassembling the engine. ∎

Cylinder Head Removal

The first step in disassembly of an engine is usually the removal of the intake and exhaust manifolds. On some in-line engines, the intake and exhaust manifolds are often removed as an assembly and are not disconnected from each other unless a problem exists that would require disassembly.

SHOP TALK

It is important to let an aluminum cylinder head cool completely before removing it. ∎

To start cylinder head removal, remove the valve cover or covers and disassemble the rocker arm components. When removing the rocker assembly, remember that each has a different assembly procedure. It is best to check the manufacturer's manual for specific procedures.

After removing the rocker arm and pushrods, check the rocker area for sludge. Excessive buildup can indicate a poor oil change schedule and is a signal to look for similar wear patterns on other components.

When removing the cylinder head, keep the pushrods and rocker arms or rocker arm assemblies in exact order (Figure 7–5). Use an organizing tray or label the parts with a felt-tipped marker to keep them together and labeled accurately. This type of organization greatly aids in diagnosing valve-related problems. Also, carefully check the lifters for a dished bottom or scratches, which indicate poor rotation.

FIGURE 7–5 Keep the rocker arm assemblies in exact order if they will be reused. *Courtesy of Perfect Circle/Dana*

The cylinder head bolts are loosened one or two turns each, working from the center of the cylinder head outward (Figure 7–6). This procedure prevents the distortion that can occur if bolts are all loosened at once. The bolts are then removed, again following the center-outward sequence. With the bolts removed, the cylinder head can be lifted off (Figure 7–7). The cylinder head gasket should be saved to compare with the new head gasket during reassembly.

FIGURE 7–6 Cylinder head bolts are loosened from the center outward.

FIGURE 7–7 Cylinder head removal. *Courtesy of Perfect Circle/Dana*

FIGURE 7–8 Using a special puller to remove the harmonic balancer or vibration damper.

FIGURE 7–10 Using a valve spring compressor. *Courtesy of Fel-Pro, Inc.*

On standard overhead valve engines, remove the timing cover. With certain engines, this may require removing the oil pan. The harmonic balancer of vibration damper usually must also be removed. This usually requires a special puller designed for the purpose (Figure 7–8).

The camshaft can now be carefully removed (Figure 7–9). Support the camshaft during removal to avoid dragging lobes over bearing surfaces, which would damage bearings and lobes. Do not bump cam lobe edges, which can cause chipping. Some engines might require the removal of the thrust plate before taking out the camshaft.

After the camshaft has been removed, visually examine it for any obvious defects—rounded lobes, edge wear, galling, and the like. If either the camshaft or lifters are worn at all, both should be replaced. Do not install old valve lifters with a new camshaft. Do not install new valve lifters on a used camshaft.

Cylinder Head Disassembly

On overhead cam engines, the camshaft must be removed before the cylinder head can be disassembled. Before tearing down the cam follower assembly, draw a diagram and use a felt-tipped marker to label the parts. Since the camshaft and followers are wear-mated parts, this will help ensure that each one is returned to the same position.

If the cam has springs beneath it, there is 60 to 80 psi pressure against any spot with the cam lobe against the follower. Random removal of bearing caps can cause the cam to break or spring up, possibly springing out and hitting you. Be sure to follow the service manual for the correct procedure because it is different for the bucket-type lifter design and lash adjuster design.

Next, use a valve spring compressor to begin disassembling the valve train. This compressor will allow the technician to compress the valve springs and remove the keepers (Figure 7–10). With the valves still in the cylinder head, use a valve stem height gauge to measure the stem height for each valve and record it (Figure 7–11). This measurement will be needed during reassembly to set the installed valve stem height.

Next, remove the valve oil seals and the valves. If a valve seems to be stuck in the guide, the tip might be peened over and have a ridge around it. If this is the case, do not drive the valve through the guide. It could score or crack the valve guide or head. Raise the stem and file off the excess metal until the stem slides through the guide easily (Figure 7–12).

While removing valves, look for signs of burning, pitting, cracks, grooves, scores, necking, or other signs

FIGURE 7–9 Removing the camshaft from the engine block. *Courtesy of Perfect Circle/Dana*

FIGURE 7–11 Using a valve stem height gauge. *Courtesy of Perfect Circle/Dana*

FIGURE 7–12 File away the excess metal until the valve stem slides easily through the guide. *Courtesy of Perfect Circle/Dana*

FIGURE 7–13 The oily buildup on the backside of the intake valves.

FIGURE 7–14 Tensioners and guides should be checked periodically for wear. *Courtesy of Perfect Circle/Dana*

component assemblies: the chain and sprocket, the gear, and the timing belt and sprocket.

Often the chain and sprocket assembly and the timing belt and sprocket assembly both have tensioners and guides (Figure 7–14). All three types of timing mechanisms should be replaced as complete assemblies during an engine overhaul. The tensioners and guides wear and should be replaced as well.

Some OHC engines have complicated drive systems; so if you are unsure of the removal process, consult the proper engine repair manual. Inspect the sprockets for wear, cracks, and broken teeth. Inspect the timing gears for excessive backlash. Check the chain for slackness and wear.

Carefully scrape the cylinder ridge with a ridge removing tool. Rotate the tool clockwise with a wrench to remove the ridge (Figure 7–15). Do not cut too deeply, because it will leave an indentation in the bore. Remove just enough metal to allow the piston assembly to slip out of the bore without causing damage to the surface of the bore. If the ridge is too large, the top rings will hit it and possibly break the ring lands.

The ridge is formed at the top of the cylinder. Because the top ring stops traveling before it reaches the top of the cylinder, a ridge of unworn metal is left. Carbon also builds up above this ridge, adding to the problem.

of wear. These wear patterns signal other problems in the engine. Valves that cannot be refaced without leaving at least a 1/32-inch valve margin must be discarded. Also, discard any valve that is badly burned, cracked, pitted, or shows signs of valve stem wear, bent valve stems, or damaged keeper grooves. Examine the backside of the intake valves. A black oily buildup in the neck and stem area indicates oil is entering the cylinder through the intake valve (Figure 7–13). Use this method to check for excessive oil consumption.

CUSTOMER CARE

When working on an engine, it is good practice to keep the customer informed of any unexpected problems. ∎

Cylinder Block Disassembly

After the cylinder head has been removed, the cylinder block can be torn down. First, remove the oil pan if it was not removed previously. Then, remove the oil pump as directed in the service manual.

Continue the disassembly by removing the timing components. There are three different types of timing

FIGURE 7–15 Remove the cylinder ridge with a ridge reamer. *Courtesy of Perfect Circle/Dana*

FIGURE 7–16   Stamping the bearing caps. *Courtesy of Perfect Circle/Dana*

After the ridge removing operation, wipe all the metal cuttings out of the cylinder. Use an oily rag to wipe the cylinder. The cuttings will stick to it.

Prior to removal of the piston and rod assembly, check all connecting rods and main bearing caps for correct position and numbering. If the numbers are not visible, use a center punch or number stamp to number them (Figure 7–16). Caps and rods should be stamped on the external flat surface. Remember, the caps and rods must remain as a set.

To remove the piston and rod assemblies, position the crankshaft throw at the bottom of its stroke. Remove the connecting rod nuts and cap. Tap the cap lightly with a soft hammer or wood block to aid in cap removal. Cover the rod bolts with protectors to avoid damage to the crankshaft journals (Figure 7–17). Carefully push the piston and rod assembly out with the wooden hammer handle or wooden drift and support the piston by hand as it comes out of the cylinder. Be sure the connecting rod does not damage the cylinder during removal. With bearing inserts in the rod and cap, replace the cap (numbers on same side) and install the nuts. Repeat the procedure for all other piston and rod assemblies.

Remove the flywheel or flex plate. Mark the position of the crankshaft and flywheel or flex plate. This aids the reassembly of the engine. Remove the main bearing cap bolts and main bearing cap.

After removing the main bearing caps, carefully take out the crankshaft by lifting both ends equally to

FIGURE 7–17   Install rod bolt protectors before removing the rod assembly from the block to prevent crankshaft damage. *Courtesy of Perfect Circle/Dana*

FIGURE 7–18   Lift the crankshaft out carefully. *Courtesy of Perfect Circle/Dana*

FIGURE 7–19   Inspect each crankshaft journal for damage and wear. *Courtesy of Perfect Circle/Dana*

avoid bending and damage (Figure 7–18). Store the crankshaft in a vertical position to avoid damage.

Remove the main bearings and rear main oil seal from the block and the main bearing caps. Examine the bearing inserts for signs of abnormal engine conditions such as embedded metal particles, lack of lubrication, antifreeze contamination, oil dilution, uneven wear, and wrong or undersized bearings. Remember that keeping the main bearing caps in order is very important. The location and position of each main bearing cap should be marked. Inspect them for any unusual wear signs, and inspect the main bearing inserts for indications that they are over- or under-sized. Also, carefully inspect the main journals on the crankshaft for damage (Figure 7–19).

The block cannot be thoroughly cleaned unless all core plugs and oil gallery plugs are removed. It is imperative that all plugs be removed to allow for a thorough cleaning. To remove cup-type free/core plugs, drive them in and then use a pair of channel lock pliers to pull them out. Flat-type plugs can be removed by drilling a hole near the center and then inserting a slide hammer to pull out the plug (Figure 7–20).

Sometimes removing threaded front and rear oil gallery plugs can be difficult. Using a drill and screw extractor can help. In some engines, the cup-type plug can be removed easily by using a slide hammer or by driving the plug out from the backside with a long rod.

FIGURE 7–20 Removing a flat-type core plug. *Courtesy of Perfect Circle/Dana*

FIGURE 7–21 From (A) grime to (B) shine.

SHOP TALK

Using heat to melt paraffin into the threads of oil plugs will make removal much easier. As the part is heated, it will expand and the paraffin will leak down between the threads. Because the paraffin provides a lubrication, you will be able to loosen the two parts. Hot paraffin burns, so wear gloves when handling it. ∎

After the teardown, the cylinder head and block and their parts must be visually checked for cracks or other damage before they are cleaned as described in the next section. While inspecting the parts, check to see if the engine has ever been torn down before. To do this, inspect the bearings for undersizes and check to see if the bearings are the original ones. For instance, Ford's bearings are date coded. If the engine has been previously torn down, use caution because a mistake could have been made during the last rebuild. Check for correct sizing before ordering any parts.

CLEANING ENGINE PARTS

When the block or cylinder head parts have been removed, they must be thoroughly cleaned (Figure 7–21). The cleaning method depends on the component to be cleaned and the type of equipment available. An incorrect cleaning method or agent can often be more harmful than no cleaning at all. For example, using caustic soda to clean aluminum parts will dissolve the part.

Only after all components have been thoroughly and properly cleaned can an effective inspection be made or proper machining be done.

Types of Soil Contaminants

Being able to recognize the type of dirt you are to clean will save you time and effort. Basically, there are four types of dirt.

WATER-SOLUBLE SOILS The easiest dirt to clean is **water-soluble** soil, which includes dirt, dust, and mud.

ORGANIC SOILS **Organic** soils contain carbon and cannot be effectively removed with plain water. There are three distinct groupings of organic soils:

◆ Petroleum by-products derived from crude oil including tar, road oil, engine oil, gasoline, diesel fuel, grease, and engine oil additives.
◆ By-products of combustion including carbon, varnish, gum, and sludge.
◆ Coatings including such items as rust-proofing materials, gasket sealers and cements, paints, waxes, and sound-deadener coatings.

RUST **Rust** is the result of a chemical reaction that takes place when iron and steel are exposed to oxygen and moisture. Corrosion, like rust, results from a similar chemical reaction between oxygen and metal containing aluminum. If left unchecked, both rust and corrosion can physically destroy metal parts quite rapidly. In addition to metal destruction, rust also acts to insulate and prevent proper heat transfer inside the cooling system.

SCALE When water containing mineral and deposits is heated, suspended minerals and impurities tend to dissolve, settle out, and attach to the surrounding hot metal surfaces. This buildup of minerals and deposits inside the cooling system is known as **scale**. Over a period of time, scale can accumulate to the extent that passages become blocked, cooling efficiency is compromised, and metal parts start to deteriorate.

Cleaning with Chemicals

There are three basic processes for cleaning automotive engine parts. The first process discussed is chemical cleaning.

This method of cleaning uses chemical action to remove dirt, grease, scale, paint, and/or rust.

⬤ CAUTION:

When working with any type of cleaning solvent or chemical, wear protective gloves and goggles and work in a well-ventilated area. Prolonged immersion of the hands in a solvent can cause a burning sensation. In some cases a skin rash might develop. There is one caution to mention about all manufactured cleaning materials that cannot be overemphasized: Read the labels carefully before mixing or using. Before using, learn how to operate the equipment. The best way to learn is from someone who already knows the equipment. The next best way is to study the equipment manufacturer's operating instructions. ◼

The most traditional line of defense against soils involves the use of cleaning chemicals. However, there is a major concern within the industry as to what chemicals to use. Chlorinated hydrocarbons and mineral spirits may have some health risks associated with their use through skin exposure and inhalation of vapors. Hydrocarbon cleaning solvents are also flammable. The use of water-based nontoxic chemicals can eliminate such risks. Those who prefer hydrocarbon solvents say solvents clean better than their water-based counterparts.

⚠ WARNING!

Prior to using any chemical, read through all the information given on the material safety data sheet (MSDS) or the Canadian workplace hazardous materials information systems sheets (WHMIS) for that chemical. Become aware of the health hazards presented by the various chemicals. ◼

Hydrocarbon solvents are labeled hazardous or toxic and require special handling and disposal procedures. The makers of many water-based cleaning solutions claim their products are biodegradable. Once the cleaning solution has become contaminated with grease and grime, it too becomes a hazardous or toxic waste that can be subject to the same disposal rules as a hydrocarbon solvent. Because there is so much latitude in local disposal rules, some municipalities allow neutralized water-based biodegradable cleaning solutions to be dumped down the sewer. Others do not.

Another alternative to the liquid waste disposal problem is recycling. Some manufacturers offer waste-handling services. The old solvent is recycled by a distillation process to separate the sludge and contaminants. The solvent is then returned to service and the contaminants disposed of. Independent services for maintaining hot tanks and spray washers are also available.

The choice of any cleaning system must take into consideration the types of chemicals and solvents required for the process involved. With more stringent EPA and OSHA regulations, some chemicals are becoming increasingly harder (and more expensive) to dispose of.

Parts Washers Parts washers (often called **solvent tanks**) are one of the most widely used and inexpensive methods of removing grease, oil, and dirt from the metal surfaces of a seemingly infinite variety of automotive components and engine parts. A typical washer setup (Figure 7–22) might consist of a tank to hold a given volume of solvent cleaner and some method of applying the solvent. These methods include soaking, soaking and agitation, solvent streams, and spray gun applicators. Because the solvent cleaners used in most parts washers are highly susceptible to evaporation and fuming, parts washers are restricted to operate only at cold or room temperatures.

Soak Tanks There are two types of soak tanks: cold and hot. Cold soak tanks are commonly used to clean carburetors, throttle bodies, and aluminum parts. A typical cold soak unit consists of a tank to hold the cleaner and a basket to hold the parts to be cleaned

FIGURE 7–22   Typical parts washer. *Courtesy of Kansas Instruments, Inc.*

FIGURE 7–23 Typical cold soak tank.

FIGURE 7–25 Hot spray tanks do a good job of initial post-machining cleanup. *Courtesy of Bayco, Inc.*

(Figure 7–23). After soaking with or without gentle agitation is complete, the parts are removed, flushed with water, and blown dry with compressed air.

Cleaning time is short, about 20 to 30 minutes, when the chemical cleaner is new. The time becomes progressively longer as the chemical ages. Agitation by raising and lowering the basket (usually done mechanically) will reduce the soak period to about 10 minutes. Some more elaborate tanks are agitated automatically.

Hot soak tanks are actually heated cold tanks. The source of heat is either electricity, natural gas, or propane. The electrical elements are inside the hot tank but are shielded from the solution. The gas heating elements are located outside and underneath the tank. The solution inside the hot tanks usually ranges from 160 to 200°F. Most tanks are generally large enough to hold an entire engine block and its related parts.

Hot tanks use a simple immersion process that relies on a heated chemical to lift the grease and grime off the surface. Liquid or parts agitation may also be used to speed up the job. Agitation helps shake the grime loose and also helps the liquid penetrate blind passageways and crevices in the part (Figure 7–24). Generally speaking, it takes one to several hours to soak most parts clean.

FIGURE 7–24 Hot soak tanks rely on agitating action to remove grime. *Courtesy of MAC Tools, Inc.*

Hot Spray Tanks Because of the Environmental Protection Agency (EPA) regulations against open steam cleaning, the spray tank has become more popular. The hot spray tank reassembles a large automatic dishwasher and is designed to remove organic and rust soils from a variety of automotive parts (Figure 7–25). In addition to parts being bathed and soaked as in the hot soak method, spray washers add the benefit of moderate pressure cleaning. In a typical spray cabinet, linear or circular configurations of spray nozzles apply the hot alkaline-based solution from all directions ensuring more effective cleaning. With some spray washers, the part sits on a turntable that rotates so liquid can be divided at every surface. As the soil is dislodged, it is washed away by the continuous streams of cleaner.

Using a hot jet spray washer can cut cleaning time to less than 10 minutes. Normally, a **caustic soda** or a strong soap solution is used as the cleaning agent. The speed of this system, along with lower operating costs, makes it popular with many machine shop owners.

SHOP TALK

Caustic soda, also known as sodium hydroxide, can be a very dangerous irritant to the eyes, skin, and mucous membranes. These chemicals should be used and handled with care. Because of the accumulation of heavy metals, it is considered a hazardous waste material and must be disposed of in accordance with EPA guidelines. ◼

Spray washers are often used to preclean engine parts prior to disassembly. A pass-through spray washer (Figure 7–26) is fully automatic once the parts have been loaded, and the cabinet prevents the runoff

FIGURE 7–26 Typical pass-through spray washer. *Courtesy of Peterson Machine Tool, Inc.*

FIGURE 7–27 Typical thermal cleaning oven.

FIGURE 7–28 Typical convection oven. *Courtesy of Bayco, Inc.*

from going down the drain or onto the ground (which is not permitted in many areas because of local waste disposal regulations). Spray washers are also useful for post-machining cleanup to remove machine oils and metal chips. Most use low-pressure (50 psi) spray nozzles to wash parts clean, although some spray washers (called power washers) use high pressure (80 to 180 psi or higher) to blast surfaces clean.

Regardless of the chemical cleaning method used, periodic cleaning or replacement of the chemicals and solid material filters is necessary. Failure to "sweeten" or maintain the proper chemical concentration of the cleaner not only reduces cleaning effectiveness but also increases operating costs and labor time as well. Also, the surface of the tank should be skimmed (preferably when cold) daily or weekly to remove any oil, grease, or scum that has accumulated at the surface.

Thermal Cleaning

The second basic process for cleaning engine parts is thermal cleaning. This process relies on heat to bake off or oxidize dirt and other contaminants.

Thermal cleaning ovens (Figure 7–27), especially the pyrolytic type, have become increasingly popular. The main advantage of thermal cleaning is a total reduction of all oils and grease on and in blocks, heads, and other parts. The high temperature inside the oven (generally 650 to 800°F) oxidizes all the grease and oil leaving behind a dry, powdery ash on the parts. The ash must then be removed by shot blasting or washing. The parts come out dry, which makes subsequent cleanup with shot blast or glass beads easier because the shot will not stick.

Ovens come in two basic varieties. A convection oven (Figure 7–28) is like a kiln. It uses indirect heat

to bake the parts. By heating the part all the way through, the inside and outside are baked clean. Cycle times for a convection oven can run from 2 to 6 hours or more depending on the size of the oven and the load. (Larger loads take longer to reach baking temperature.) Cleaning is still required afterward, which can be done by shot blasting or a hot spray washer.

Pyrolytic ovens (Figure 7–29) impinge a flame directly on the surface of the parts to sear off the con-

FIGURE 7–29 Pyrolytic ovens use a direct flame. *Courtesy of Am/Pro Machinery, Inc.*

taminants. These ovens are also called open- or direct-flame ovens. Pyrolytic ovens rotate the parts on a rotisserielike device to allow heat dissipation throughout the component, regardless of its configuration.

Pyrolytic oven action is similar to that of a self-cleaning kitchen oven. The cleaning cycle time is generally 1 to 4 hours, including cooling time. The smoke from the burning process is burnt in an afterburner, leaving carbon dioxide as the exhaust gas that is emitted.

SHOP TALK

A slow cooling rate is recommended to prevent distortion that could be caused by unequal cooling rates within complex castings. ■

One of the major attractions of cleaning ovens is that they offer a more environmentally acceptable process than chemical cleaning. But, although there is no solvent or sludge to worry about with an oven, the ash residue that comes off the cleaned parts must still be handled according to local disposal regulations. In some areas, steel shot can be thrown in the regular trash. In others, it must be treated as a hazardous waste if lead is present in the residue.

The maintenance procedure given in the owner's manual must be followed if the ovens are to operate properly.

Abrasive Cleaners

The third process used to clean engine parts involves the use of abrasives. Most abrasive cleaning machines are used in conjunction with other cleaning processes rather than as a primary cleaning process itself. Parts must be dry and grease-free when they go into an abrasive blast machine. Otherwise, the shot or beads will stick. Table 7–1 lists the media used in abrasive cleaners and the finishing results.

Abrasive Blaster

Airless shot and grit blasters are best used on parts that will be machined after they have been cleaned (Figure 7–30). Two basic types of media are available: shot and grit. Shot is round; grit is angular in shape (Figure 7–31). Steel shot and glass beads are used primarily for cleaning operations where etching or material removal is not desired. Steel shot and glass beads are also used for peening the surfaces of certain parts. Peening is a process of hammering on the surface of a part. This packs the molecules tightly, thereby increasing the part's resistance to fatigue and stress.

FIGURE 7–30 Typical airless shot blaster. *Courtesy of Am/Pro Machinery, Inc.*

A

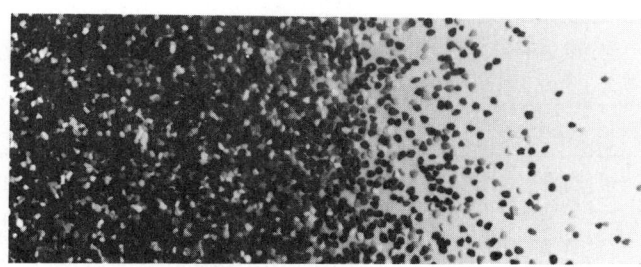

B

FIGURE 7–31 (A) Shot- and (B) grit-blasting media.

Stainless steel shot can be used for cleaning or peening parts where residual iron left on the surface is not wanted. Ceramic shot, which is very hard, is used primarily for peening heat-treated and hard alloy steels where maximum strength is desired. Ceramic is also clean in that it leaves no residue on the surface. Ceramic shot lasts about as long as steel shot, but like stainless it is expensive. Salt is a good and inexpensive cleaner that leaves no residue, but it can only be used once.

Aluminum shot, by comparison, is soft and is used primarily to clean aluminum surfaces where a bright or satin finish is desired. Plastic is the softest material of all and is used for cleaning soft metals and plastics and for jobs in which hot retention poses a serious problem, such as inside an engine.

Grit is used primarily for aggressive cleaning jobs or where the surface of the material needs to be etched

	TABLE 7–1 COMMON MEDIA USED AS ABRASIVE CLEANERS*	
Media	**Available Sizes**	**Use/Result**
Glass beads	8 to 10 sizes; from 30 to 440 mesh; also many special graduations	Blending, light deburring, peening, general cleaning, texturing. Non-contaminating. Peening media for nonmetal removal cleaning (holds tolerances). Retains critical part dimensions.
Aluminum oxide grit	10 to 12 sizes; from 16 to 325 mesh	Fast-cutting, matte finish. Do not use if etching is not wanted.
Aluminum shot	10 to 12 sizes; from 8 to 200 mesh	Primarily for cleaning aluminum. Gives bright or satin finish; expensive.
Stainless steel shot	6 to 8 sizes; from 16 to 325 mesh	Cleaning or peening parts where residual iron could be a problem; expensive.
Ceramic shot	6 to 10 sizes; from 12 to 320 mesh	Cleaning or peening hard metals.
Salt	10 to 60 mesh	Good cleaning for all soils. No residue, inexpensive, but it can only be used once.
Nut shells crushed	6 sizes; wide-band screening	Cleaning, very light deburring. Good for fragile parts.
Garnet	6 to 8 sizes; wide-band screening from 16 to 325 mesh	Noncritical cleaning, cutting, texturing. Noncontaminating for brazing steel and stainless steel.
Crushed glass	5 sizes; wide-band screening from 30 to 400 mesh	Fast-cutting, low-cost, short-life, abrasive. Noncontaminating.
Silicon carbide	36 to 220 mesh	Extremely fast cutting.
Steel shot	12 or more sizes; close graduation from 8 to 200 mesh	General-purpose, rough cleaning foundry operations, etc. Peening.
Steel grit	12 or more sizes; close graduation from 10 to 325 mesh	Rough cleaning, coarse textures.
Plastic chips	3 sizes; fine, medium, coarse definite size particles	Cleaning, light deburring.
Sand	10 to 50 mesh	General cleaning. Good for all soils.

*Courtesy of Zero Manufacturing Company

to improve paint adhesion. Steel grit and aluminum oxide are the two most common media for this purpose. Because grit cuts into the surface as it cleans, it removes dirt and scale faster than shot blasting or glass beading. But it also removes metal, leading to some change in tolerances. The beneficial effect of grit blasting is that it roughens the surface, leaving a matte finish to which paint or other surface treatments will stick better than a peened or polished surface. On the other hand, grit blasting is an abrasive process that chews out pits in the surface into which pollutants and blast residue can settle. This leads to stress corrosion unless the surface is painted or treated. The tiny crevices also focus surface stresses in the metal, which can lead to cracking in highly loaded parts. Because of that, grit should never be used for peening.

The type of media used for a given job depends on the job itself and the type of equipment. Steel shot is normally used with airless wheel blast equipment, which hurls the shot at the part with the centrifugal force of the spinning wheel. Used with air blast equipment, glass beads are blown through a nozzle by compressed air.

Parts Tumbler A cleaning alternative that can save considerable labor when cleaning small parts such as engine valves is a tumbler. Various cleaning media can be used in a tumbler to scrub the parts clean.

This saves considerable hand labor and eliminates dust. In some tumblers, all parts are rotated and tilted at the same time.

Vibratory Cleaning Shakers, as they are frequently called, use a vibrating tub filled with ceramic steel, porcelain, or aluminum abrasive to scrub parts clean. Most shakers flush the tub with solvent to help loosen and flush away the dirt and grime. The solvent drains out the bottom and is filtered to remove the sludge.

Cleaning by Hand Some manual cleaning must be done in every rebuilding job. Regardless of the cleaning process used, it is usually necessary to remove galley plugs and hand clean the oil galleries (Figure 7–32). Another often neglected area is between the heat shield and the bottom of the intake manifold, where carbon and oil deposits collect. This shield should be removed before cleaning the manifold. Any residual dirt left in the engine after cleaning can lead to failure. Therefore, proper cleaning of all engine components is vital in the rebuilding process. Remove any surface irregularities with very fine, abrasive paper (Figure 7–33). Make sure to keep any dirt out of the cylinder bores. The special power scraper pad shown in action in Figure 7–34 is guaranteed not to remove any metal.

Carbon can be removed from parts using a twist-type wire brush driven by an electric or air drill motor.

FIGURE 7–32 It is often necessary to remove the gallery plugs and hand clean the oil galleries.

FIGURE 7–33 Removing surface irregularities from the cylinder block with abrasive paper. *Courtesy of Perfect Circle/Dana*

FIGURE 7–34 Using a power scraper pad will prevent any metal from being removed. *Courtesy of Goodson Shop Supplies*

Using brushes can often be a time-consuming job. Some shops use a wire brush in addition to another cleaning method. Moving the drill motor in a light circular motion against the carbon helps to crack and dislodge the carbon for easier wire brush cleaning.

Alternative Cleaning Methods

In this age of material handling sheets, right-to-know laws, and concerns over hazardous waste generation and disposal, it is impossible to ignore the fact that cleaning equipment manufacturers and chemical producers are currently under much pressure to find alternatives to the cleaning chemicals commonly being used. Three of the most popular alternatives to traditional chemical cleaning systems are ultrasonic cleaning, citrus chemicals, and salt baths.

Ultrasonic Cleaning This cleaning process has been used for a number of years to clean small parts like jewelry, dentures, and medical instruments. Recently, however, the use of larger ultrasonic units has expanded into small engine parts cleaning (Figure 7–35). **Ultrasonic** cleaning utilizes high-frequency sound waves to create microscopic bubbles that burst into energy to loosen soil from parts. Because the tiny bubbles do all the work, the chemical content of the

FIGURE 7–35 Typical ultrasonic cleaning system. *Courtesy of Ramco Corporation*

FIGURE 7–36   The salt bath cleaning method is primarily used only by high-volume engine rebuilders. *Courtesy of Kolene Corporation*

FIGURE 7–37   Example of stress cracks.

cleaning solution is minimized, making waste disposal less of a problem. At the present time, however, the initial cost and handling capacity of ultrasonic equipment is its major disadvantage.

Citrus Chemicals Some chemical producers are starting to develop citrus-based cleaning chemicals as a replacement for the more hazardous solvent and alkaline-based chemicals currently used. Because of their citrus origin, these chemicals are safer to handle, easier to dispose of, and even smell good. As to their effectiveness, preliminary results show a great deal of promise; however, cost is a factor. At the present time, citrus-based cleaners cost more to produce than conventional chemicals.

Salt Bath The **salt bath** (Figure 7–36) is a unique process that uses high-temperature molten salt to dissolve organic materials including carbon, grease, oil, dirt, paint, and some gaskets. For cast iron and steel, the salt bath operates at about 700 to 850°F. For aluminum or combinations of aluminum and iron, a different salt solution is used at a lower temperature (about 600°F). The contaminants precipitate out of the solution and sink to the bottom of the tank where they must be removed periodically. The salt bath itself lasts indefinitely as long as the salt is maintained properly. Cycling times with a salt bath are fairly quick, averaging 20 to 30 minutes. Like a hot tank, the temperature of the salt bath is maintained continuously. Because of the high initial cost, the salt bath process is limited mainly to high-volume rebuilding shops. However, the disposal of contaminated salt waste can be as much of a problem as some caustics.

CRACK REPAIR

Once engine parts have been cleaned and given a thorough visual inspection, actual repair work begins. If cracks in the metal casting were discovered during the inspection, they should be repaired or the part replaced.

Cracks in metal castings are the result of stress or strain in a section of the casting. This stress or strain finds a weak point in that section of the casting and causes it to distort or separate at that point (Figure 7–37). Such stresses or strains in castings can develop from the following.

- Pressure or temperature changes during the casting procedure may cause internal material structure defects, inclusion, or voids.
- Fatigue may result from fluctuating or repeated stress cycles. It might begin as a small crack and progress to a larger one under the action of the stress.
- Flexing of the metal may result due to its lack of rigidity.
- Impact damage may occur by a solid, hard object hitting a component.
- Constant impacting of a valve against a hardened seat may produce vibrations that could possibly lead to fracturing a thin-walled casting.
- Chilling of a hot engine by a sudden rush of cold water or air over the surface may happen.
- Excessive overheating is possible due to improper operation of an engine system.

No matter what caused the crack, it is important to relieve the stress at the point of distortion or cracking and then add more metal and move it in such a way as to close the crack. This can be accomplished by the cold process of pinning or the hot process of welding.

Detecting Cracks

With either method of repair, detecting a crack in a metal casting means not only finding that a crack exists but also determining the exact location and extent of the crack.

The three most common methods of crack detection follow.

1. Use a magnet and magnetic powder (frequently referred to as the magna flux process).
2. Use penetrant dye (developed specially for non-magnetic castings such as aluminum heads and blocks).
3. Pressurize the head or block with a pressure tester.

Furnace Welding Crack Repairs

Furnace welding is considered by many people to be the best way to repair cracks in a cast-iron head. By preheating the entire casting, the problem of stress cracks forming during the cooling-off period is eliminated. Heat welding, however, requires a good heat source and proficient welding skills. As a rule, this repair is conducted only by a specialist.

Repairing Aluminum Heads

Aluminum heads have become popular in recent years, primarily because of the weight savings they offer. However, there are many problems associated with an aluminum cylinder head. The typical shop is most likely to encounter the following problems.

◆ Cracks in the aluminum between the valve seat rings (Figure 7–38). These cracks, usually quite small, require close inspection to find. They very seldom leak and can be closed by a light peening. Some shops make no repairs to them.
◆ Bottomside cracks coming from the coolant passages. These cracks can be repaired by veeing out the damaged area and welding with an aluminum filler rod.
◆ Topside cracks across the main oil artery. These cracks, although not too common, are usually very visible (Figure 7–39). Most authorities recommend replacing the head completely if such a crack is found. The length of time required to

FIGURE 7–39 The topside oil artery crack appeared when an oxyacetylene flame was passed over the casting. Carbon in the flame was trapped in the crack, highlighting it.

make the repair is not reasonable. The labor cost is not worth the risk of possible failure and is higher than the cost of purchasing an uncracked core.

◆ Detonation damage can occur on any cylinder (Figure 7–40). Repairs can be made by welding and freehand machining with a rotary burr in a die grinder.
◆ Meltdown damage is a somewhat common occurrence on the high-swirl combustion chamber heads (Figure 7–41). Again, repairs can be made by welding and freehand machining.

FIGURE 7–40 The effect of detonation on a combustion chamber.

FIGURE 7–38 Cracks between the center two valve seat rings are common with aluminum heads.

FIGURE 7–41 Typical combustion chamber meltdown damage.

◆ Coolant-related metal erosion. If damage around coolant passages is excessive, if the side of any valve seat has been exposed, or if the combustion chamber shows erosion, the head must be repaired or replaced (Figure 7–42). Coolant erosion such as shown in Figure 7–43 can be easily fixed by welding and resurfacing.

TIG welding is the preferred repair technique for aluminum heads (Figure 7–44). Welding aluminum is often considered difficult because it welds differently than iron or steel. When exposed to air, aluminum forms an oxide coating on the surface that helps protect the metal against further corrosion. The oxide layer makes welding difficult because it interferes with fusing and weakens the weld. Cleaning the surface can remove the oxide. However, as soon as the metal is heated, oxide re-forms (unless the weld is bathed in a constant supply of inert gas).

FIGURE 7–42 Severe coolant related damage can sometimes be repaired, but more often the head is replaced.

FIGURE 7–43 This type of coolant erosion damage can be fixed by welding and resurfacing.

FIGURE 7–44 TIG-welded aluminum head repair.

CASE STUDY

A four-cylinder engine is brought into the shop. The customer complains of excessive oil consumption and oil leaks. Compression and cylinder leakage tests indicate that the cylinders are sealing well and a power balance test indicates all of the cylinders are producing about the same amount of power. Based on these results, the technician assumes that the problem is leaking valve seals. The initial plan is to replace the seals and regasket the engine.

It is odd that the engine has both of these problems. It has less than 50,000 miles on it. Not really sure if the problems are related, the technician proceeds to disassemble the engine. Upon removing the valve cover, large amounts of sludge are evident throughout the valve train. This is normally a sign that the engine has been neglected. However, a review of the files indicates that the oil has recently been changed. In fact, the car has been well-maintained. Is the sludging related to the oil consumption and leaks?

The oil pan is removed and additional sludge is found. The cylinder head is then removed from the block. The piston tops and the combustion chamber are covered with a thick, black carbon coating. Is this buildup related to other problems?

The cylinder head is disassembled, and each of the valve seals is found to be deteriorated. What could cause the deterioration of rubber parts, leaking gaskets, sludging, and carbon buildup in the cylinders? After careful thought, the technician pays attention to the parts taken off the engine during initial disassembly. A thorough inspection is made of the PCV system, and it is discovered that the hose connecting the valve to the manifold is plugged solid. The valve is also found to be plugged.

The PCV system is designed to remove crankcase fumes and pressure from the crankcase. These fumes can cause rapid sludging of the oil and deterioration of rubber parts. Excessive crankcase pressure can cause leaks, as the pressure seeks to relieve itself. A faulty PCV valve can cause all of the problems exhibited by this engine. In fact, it is the cause of the problems.

The engine is resealed and new valve stem seals are installed. The engine is then installed with a new PCV valve and hose. Not only is the customer's complaint taken care of, but so is the cause of the problem.

KEY TERMS

Caustic soda	Scale
Cherry picker	Solvent tank
Organic	Ultrasonic
Rust	Water-soluble
Salt bath	

SUMMARY

◆ When preparing an engine for removal and disassembly, always follow the specific service manual procedures for the particular vehicle being worked on.

◆ A canvas hoist and chain or a cherry picker are needed to lift an engine out of its compartment. Mount the engine to an engine stand with a minimum of four bolts, or set it securely on blocks.

◆ While an engine teardown of both the cylinder head and block is a relatively standard procedure, exact details vary among engine types and styles. The vehicle's service manual should be considered as the final word.

◆ An understanding of specific soil types can save time and effort during the engine cleaning process. The main categories of contaminants include water-soluble and organic soils, rust, and scale.

◆ Protective gloves and goggles should be worn when working with any type of cleaning solvent or chemical. Read the label carefully before using, as well as all of the information provided on material safety data sheets.

◆ Parts washers, or solvent tanks, are a popular and inexpensive means of cleaning the metal surfaces of many automotive components and engine parts. Regardless of the type of solvent used, it usually requires some brushing, scraping, or agitation to increase the cleaning effectiveness.

◆ Cold soak tanks are used to clean carburetors, throttle bodies, and aluminum parts. Hot soak tanks, which can accommodate an entire engine block, use a heated cleaning solution to boil out dirt. Hot heat spray washers have the added benefit of moderate pressure cleaning.

◆ Alternatives to chemical cleaning have emerged in recent years, including ultrasonic cleaning, salt baths, and citrus chemical cleaning. These methods are all growing in popularity.

◆ The main advantage of thermal cleaning is its total reduction of all oils and grease. The high temperatures inside the oven leave a dry, powdery ash on the parts. This is removed by shot blasting or washing.

◆ Sheet shot and glass beads are used for cleaning operations in which etching or material removal are not desired. Grit, the other type of abrasive blaster, is used for more aggressive cleaning jobs.

◆ Some degree of manual cleaning is necessary in any engine rebuilding job. Very fine, abrasive paper should be used to remove surface irregularities. A twist-type wire brush driven by an electric or air drill motor is also helpful, though it can be time-consuming to work with.

◆ There are three common methods for detecting cracks in the metal casting of engine parts: using a magnet and magnetic powder, using penetrant dye (especially for aluminum heads and blocks), and pressuring with a pressure tester.

◆ TIG welding is the preferred repair technique for aluminum cylinder heads. Because it reacts differently to heat than iron or steel, aluminum is considered a challenge to repair by welding.

TECH MANUAL

The following procedures are included in Chapter 7 of the *Tech Manual* that accompanies this book:

1. Prepare engine for removal.

2. Remove and disassemble cylinder head.

3. Remove cylinder ring ridge.

REVIEW QUESTIONS

1. What precautions should be taken when cleaning an engine prior to its removal?

2. What should be worn when working with any type of cleaning solvent or chemical?

3. Name the two types of thermal cleaning ovens.

4. What is the best way to repair cracks in a cast-iron head?

5. What welding method is preferred for repairing aluminum heads?

6. When lifting a transverse-mounted engine on a front-wheel-drive vehicle, Technician A removes the engine and transaxle as a unit. Technician B uses a transverse engine support bar. Who is correct?
   - **a.** Technician A
   - **b.** Technician B
   - **c.** Both A and B
   - **d.** Neither A nor B

7. Technician A uses a cherry picker to remove an engine from its compartment. Technician B uses a canvas hoist and chain to remove an engine from its compartment. Who is correct?
   - **a.** Technician A
   - **b.** Technician B
   - **c.** Both A and B
   - **d.** Neither A nor B

8. Upon inspection of a camshaft, the valve lifters are found to be worn. Technician A replaces the lifters, while Technician B replaces the lifters and camshaft. Who is correct?
   - **a.** Technician A
   - **b.** Technician B
   - **c.** Both A and B
   - **d.** Neither A nor B

9. Technician A uses caustic soda to clean aluminum parts. Technician B uses caustic soda as the cleaning agent in a hot jet spray washer. Who is correct?
   - **a.** Technician A
   - **b.** Technician B
   - **c.** Both A and B
   - **d.** Neither A nor B

10. What do all organic soils contain?
    - **a.** oil
    - **b.** tar
    - **c.** carbon
    - **d.** nitrogen

11. Hydrocarbon solvents are ____.
    - **a.** flammable
    - **b.** toxic
    - **c.** both a and b
    - **d.** neither a nor b

12. Technician A operates parts washers at room temperatures. Technician B operates parts washers at cold temperatures. Who is correct?
    - **a.** Technician A
    - **b.** Technician B
    - **c.** Both A and B
    - **d.** Neither A nor B

13. Failure to "sweeten" the cleaner in a hot spray tank will ____.
    - **a.** reduce cleaning effectiveness
    - **b.** increase operating costs
    - **c.** increase labor time
    - **d.** all of the above

14. Which cleaning method uses high-frequency sound waves to create microscopic bubbles that loosen dirt from parts?
    - **a.** ultrasonic
    - **b.** salt bath
    - **c.** thermal
    - **d.** caustic

15. Technician A uses a fast cooling rate when working with thermal cleaning ovens. Technician B uses water to rinse off the parts after they have been cleaned in an oven. Who is correct?
    - **a.** Technician A
    - **b.** Technician B
    - **c.** Both A and B
    - **d.** Neither A nor B

16. Parts must be ____ when they go into an abrasive blast machine.
    - **a.** wet
    - **b.** dry
    - **c.** grease-free
    - **d.** both b and c

17. Technician A uses aluminum shot for peening heat-treated and hard alloy steels. Technician B uses ceramic shot for peening heat-treated and hard alloy steels. Who is correct?
    - **a.** Technician A
    - **b.** Technician B
    - **c.** Both A and B
    - **d.** Neither A nor B

18. Which of the following is best suited to cleaning small parts such as valves?
    - **a.** shaker
    - **b.** pyrolytic oven
    - **c.** tumbler
    - **d.** none of the above

19. Which method of crack detection is designed especially for aluminum heads and blocks?
    - **a.** penetrant dye
    - **b.** magna flux
    - **c.** pressurizing
    - **d.** both b and c

20. Technician A uses light peening to repair small cracks between aluminum head valve seat rings. Technician B repairs bottomside coolant passage cracks by welding. Who is correct?
    - **a.** Technician A
    - **b.** Technician B
    - **c.** Both A and B
    - **d.** Neither A nor B

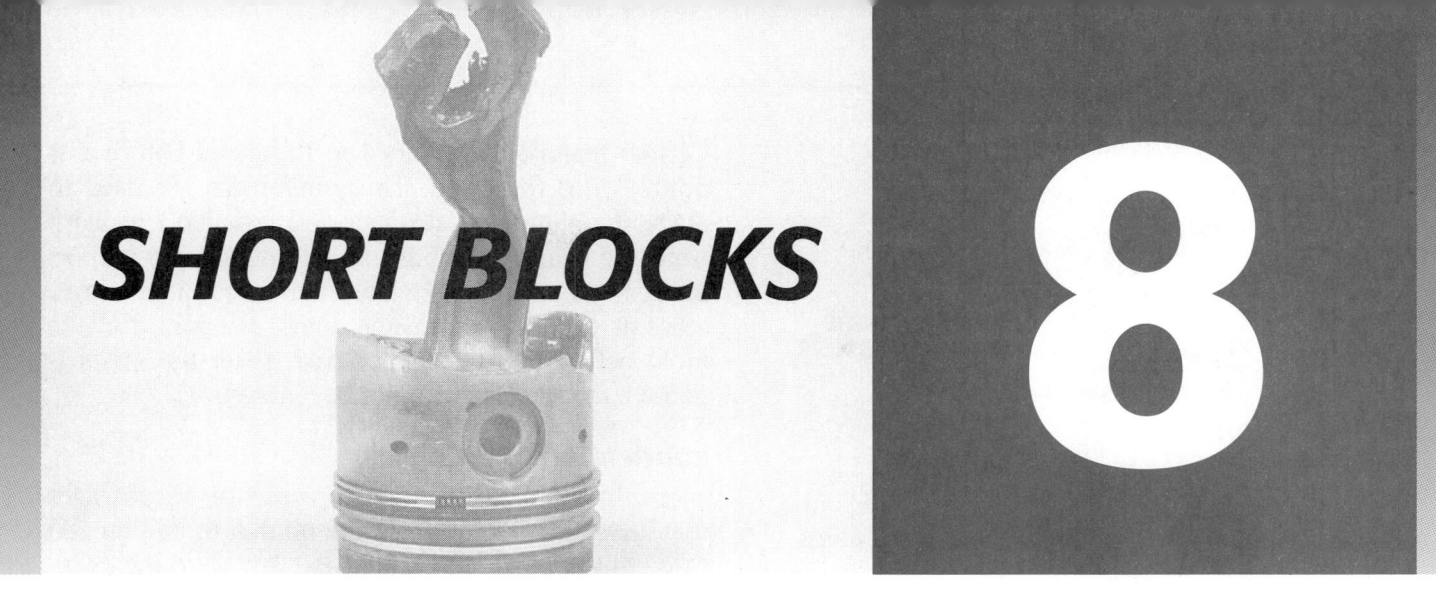

SHORT BLOCKS

8

OBJECTIVES

◆ *List the parts that make up a short block and briefly describe their operation.* ◆ *Describe the major service and rebuilding procedures performed on cylinder blocks.* ◆ *Explain crankshaft construction, inspection, and rebuilding procedures.* ◆ *Explain the function of engine bearings, flywheels, and harmonic balancers.* ◆ *Explain the common service and assembly techniques used in connecting rod and piston servicing.* ◆ *Explain the purpose and design of the different types of piston rings.* ◆ *Describe the procedure for installing pistons in their cylinder bores.*

An engine is made up of many parts, each with its own purpose and service procedure. When there is a major engine failure, shops either rebuild or replace the engine. Most often the **short block** is repaired or replaced as an assembly. A **long block** is basically a short block with cylinder heads.

A basic short block assembly consists of a cylinder block, crankshaft, crankshaft bearings, connecting rods, pistons and rings, and oil galley and core plugs (Figure 8–1). Parts that are related to the short block but not necessarily included are the engine's flywheel and **harmonic balancer**. A short block may also include the engine's camshaft and timing gear. These, however, are discussed in a later chapter.

CYLINDER BLOCK

The cylinder block makes up the lower section of the engine. It houses the areas where compression, ignition, and combustion of the air/fuel mixture take place (Figure 8–2). The upper section of the engine, known as the cylinder head, bolts on top of the cylinder block. In addition to covering the tops of the cylinder block bores, the head forms part of the combustion chamber and often contains the valve train components.

The cylinder block (Figure 8–3) is normally one piece, cast, and machined so all the parts contained in it fit properly. Blocks may be cast from several different materials: iron, aluminum, or possibly, in the future, plastic.

The word **cast** refers to how the block is made. To cast is to form molten metal into a particular shape by pouring or pressing it into a mold. This molded piece must then undergo a number of machining operations to make sure all the working surfaces are smooth and

FIGURE 8–1 Basic short block assembly. *Courtesy of Jasper Engine and Transmission Exchange, Inc.*

FIGURE 8–2 V-6 cylinder block.

OHC
(4 CYL. SHOWN)

CAMSHAFT

CAM FOLLOWERS
& LASH ADJUSTORS

VALVES & SPRINGS

CAMSHAFT
DRIVE
BELT

VALVE
GUIDES

ROCKER ARMS

PUSHRODS

OHV
(6 CYL. SHOWN)

VALVES

TYPICAL HEADS

VALVE LIFTERS

PISTON &
RINGS

CYLINDER BLOCK

CAMSHAFT
(OHV ONLY)

CRANKSHAFT

OIL PAN

OIL PUMP

TYPICAL BLOCK (6 CYL. SHOWN)

FIGURE 8–3 An engine can be divided into two main assemblies: the engine or cylinder block and the cylinder head. *Courtesy of Ford Motor Company*

true. The top of the block must be perfectly smooth because the cylinder head will later be attached at this point. The base or bottom of the block must also be machined because the oil pan attaches here. All block sealing areas are also machined. The cylinder bores must be smooth and have the correct diameter to accept the pistons.

The main bearing area of the block must be align bored to a diameter that will accept the crankshaft. Camshaft bearing surfaces must also be bored. The word **bore** means to drill or machine a hole. Align boring is a series of holes in a straight line.

Cast-iron blocks offer great strength and controlled warpage due to heat. With the increased concern for improved gasoline mileage however, car manufacturers are trying to make the vehicle lighter. One way to do this is to reduce the weight of the block. Aluminum is used for this purpose because it is a very light metal.

Certain materials are added to the metal before it is poured into the mold. These materials are used to make the aluminum stronger and less likely to warp from the heat of combustion. Aluminum blocks normally have a sleeve or steel liner placed in them to serve as cylinder walls. Steel liners are placed in the mold before the metal is poured. After the metal is poured, the steel liner cannot be removed.

Lubrication and Cooling

The cylinder block contains a series of oil passages that allows engine oil from the oil pan to be pumped through the block and crankshaft and onto the cylinder head. The oil lubricates, cools, and cleans engine components (Figure 8–4).

ENGINE BLOCK   CYLINDER   COOLANT PASSAGES

OIL PUMP MOUNTING

WATER PUMP MOUNTING

CRANKCASE   LUBRICANT PASSAGES

ENGINE BLOCK UPSIDE DOWN TO SHOW CRANKCASE

COOLANT FLOW

FIGURE 8–4 Oil and coolant passages in in-line and V-type engine blocks.

FIGURE 8–5 Typical core plug locations

FIGURE 8–6 A cylinder sleeve is fitted into the bore to serve as a wear surface for the piston rings.

Because engines are not 100 percent efficient, some of the heat they generate is absorbed by the block and cylinder heads. This absorbed heat is wasted power and must be removed from the engine parts before it damages the engine. This is the job of the cooling system. Water jackets are cast in the cylinder block around the cylinder bores. As shown in Figure 8–4, coolant circulates through these jackets to transfer heat away from these areas.

Core Plugs

All cast-iron cylinder blocks use **core plugs**. These are also called freeze-out or expansion plugs. During the manufacturing process, sand cores are used. These cores are partly broken and dissolved when the hot metal is poured into the mold. However, holes have to be placed in the block to get the sand out of the internal passageways. These are called core holes. The holes are machined and core plugs are placed into these holes to seal them (Figure 8–5).

Core plugs are made of soft metal. They can also protect the block from cracking. If the coolant in the block freezes, it will expand, putting an extreme amount of pressure on the passages inside the block. This pressure can easily crack the block. When the coolant freezes, the core plugs may pop out to allow the coolant to expand before the block cracks.

Cylinder Sleeves

Some automobile manufacturers use **cylinder sleeves** (Figure 8–6). Rather than casting the cylinder bores directly into the block, they insert a machined sleeve after the block has been machined. The purpose of using a sleeve is that if the cylinder is damaged, the sleeve can be removed and replaced rather easily. Cylinders without sleeves must be bored out to remove any damage. After boring, larger pistons are needed or standard-sized sleeves are added.

There are two types of sleeves: wet and dry. Both types are pressed into the block. The dry sleeve is

supported from top to bottom by the block. The wet sleeve is supported only at the top and bottom. Coolant touches the center part of the sleeve.

CYLINDER BLOCK RECONDITIONING

Before any reconditioning or rebuilding work is started, threaded holes should be cleaned with the correct size tap to remove any and all burrs or dirt to allow for proper bolt torquing (Figure 8–7). Use a bottoming tap in any blind holes. **Chamfering** or counterboring will eliminate thread pulls and jagged edges. All burrs and casting slag should be removed from inside the block with a high-speed grinder.

Deck Flatness

The top of the engine block where the cylinder head mounts, is called the **deck**. To check deck warpage, use a precision straightedge and feeler gauge (Figure 8–8) to measure the deck in each direction. With the straightedge positioned diagonally across the deck, the amount of warpage is determined by the size of feeler gauge that fits into the gap between the deck and the straightedge.

FIGURE 8–7 All threaded bores in the engine block should be cleaned with the correct size tap. *Courtesy of Perfect Circle/Dana*

FIGURE 8–8 Checking for deck warpage with a straight-edge and feeler gauge.

SHOP TALK

Instead of using a straightedge and feeler gauge, many technicians prefer to check for warpage with an arbor and gauge. Roll the dial indicator along the arbor and across the surface of the block. It can also be used to check a cylinder head for warpage (Figure 8–9). ∎

Some engines have special sealing surface flatness requirements. Always refer to the manufacturer's specifications. If specifications are not available, use 0.003 inch per 6 inches, and no more than 0.006-inch maximum on any length. In most cases if the block has more than one deck surface (such as a V-type engine), each deck should be machined to the same height. This allows for uniform compression and manifold alignment. If the gasket surface of the block is warped and not corrected, valve seat distortion will occur when the head is tightened to the block. Coolant and combustion leakage can also occur.

Two other reasons a technician might elect to resurface are to blend the sleeves into the deck surface after sleeving or to obtain uniform cylinder length for performance or blueprint work. Blocks can be refinished by broaching, milling, or grinding. Any of these methods is acceptable as long as the proper surface finish is obtained.

FIGURE 8–9 A dial indicator and arbor can also be used to check for deck warpage. *Courtesy of Goodson Shop Supplies*

Cylinder Walls

Inspect the cylinder walls for scoring, roughness, or other signs of wear. Ring and cylinder wall wear can be accelerated by an abrasive environment. Abrasive particles that get between mated moving parts grind away at the adjoining surfaces and remove material from the parts. Abrasive particles can include metallic debris in the engine, which is a result of wear and nonmetallic dirt particles that entered the engine during operation or maintenance. The source of contamination should be located and corrected to avoid a recurrence of the problem.

CUSTOMER CARE

If the cause of an engine problem is customer neglect, inform the customer of this. Do so in an understanding way. Never make the customer feel stupid. ∎

Piston ring, piston, and cylinder wall damage can also be caused by scuffing and scoring. Grooves cut in these parts act as passages for oil to bypass the rings and enter the combustion chamber. Scuffing and scoring occur when the oil film on the cylinder wall is ruptured, allowing metal-to-metal contact of the piston and rings on the cylinder wall. The heat generated causes momentary welding of the contacting parts. The reciprocating movement of the piston breaks these welds, cutting grooves in the ring faces, piston skirt, and cylinder wall. Cooling system hot spots, oil contamination, and fuel wash are significant causes of this problem.

A problem affecting the newer thin-wall engines is block distortion. Out-of-round cylinders break the face seal between the rings and cylinder wall permitting the passage of oil into the combustion chamber (Figure 8–10).

The cylinder heads and main bearing caps induce stresses in the block. These stresses must be duplicated when the cylinders are being bored, particularly if the block is of the thin-wall design. To accomplish

CYLINDER BLOCK

FIGURE 8–10 Checking for oil leakage past the piston rings.

FIGURE 8–11 Cross section of a worn cylinder.

FIGURE 8–13 Cylinder taper is determined by measuring the diameter of the bore at the top of ring travel and comparing it to the diameter at the bottom of ring travel. *Courtesy of Goodson Shop Supplies*

this, the main bearing caps should be installed and torqued to specifications. Torque or deck plates should be bolted to the block to simulate the weight and structure of the cylinder heads so the bores will be round when the engine is assembled. Failure to follow these steps can result in block distortion, which causes oil consumption.

Cylinder Bore Inspection

Normally cylinder bore wear is not uniform (Figure 8–11). The maximum amount of wear occurs at the top of the ring travel area. Pressure on the top ring is at a peak and lubrication at a minimum when the piston is at the top of its stroke. Shallow depressions form at the top of the cylinder on the thrust faces, giving the cylinder an oval shape at the top. A ridge of unworn material will remain above the upper limit of ring travel. Below the ring travel area, wear is negligible because only the piston skirt contacts the cylinder wall (Figure 8–12).

There are several requirements for a properly reconditioned cylinder. It must be the correct diameter, have no taper or out-of-roundness, and the surface finish must be such that the piston rings will seat to form a seal that will control oil and minimize blowby.

Taper is the difference in diameter between the cylinder bore at the bottom of the hole and the bore at the top of the hole, just below the ridge (Figure 8–13). Subtracting the smaller diameter from the larger one gives the cylinder taper. Some taper is permissible, but normally not more than 0.006 inch. If taper is less than 0.006 inch, it is possible to get by with just a re-ring job as opposed to reboring.

Cylinder out-of-roundness is the difference of the cylinder's diameter when measured parallel with the crank and perpendicular to the crank (Figure 8–14). Out-of-roundness is measured at the top of the cylinder just below the ridge. Typically the maximum allowable out-of-roundness is 0.0015 inch. Normally a cylinder bore is checked for out-of-roundness with a dial bore gauge. However, a telescoping gauge (Figure 8–15) can also be used.

Cylinder Bore Surface Finish

The surface finish on a properly prepared cylinder wall acts as a reservoir for oil to lubricate the piston rings and prevent piston and ring scuffing primarily during break-in. Piston ring faces can be damaged and experience premature wear if the cylinder wall is too rough. A surface that is too smooth will not allow

FIGURE 8–12 When piston slap occurs, the cylinder bore wears most at the top.

FIGURE 8–14 Measuring out-of-roundness with a dial bore gauge. *Courtesy of Atlas Engineering and Manufacturing, Inc.*

FIGURE 8–15 After the telescoping gauge has been expanded to fit the bore, it is measured with a micrometer. *Courtesy of Perfect Circle/Dana*

the rings to seat properly. Obtaining the correct cylinder wall finish is important. The finish should allow for good sealing and oil control.

CYLINDER DEGLAZING If the inspection and measurements of the cylinder wall show that surface conditions, taper, and out-of-roundness are within acceptable limits, the cylinder walls only need to be deglazed. Combustion heat, engine oil, and piston movement combine to form a thin residue on the cylinder walls that is commonly called **glaze**.

CAUTION:

Always wear eye protection when operating deglazing, honing, or boring equipment. ■

The two most common types of glaze breakers are shown in Figure 8–16. With either type, use an abrasive with about 220 or 280 grit. The driver end of the glaze breaker is installed in a slow-moving electric drill that operates at 300 to 500 rpm or in a

FIGURE 8–16 Two types of glaze breakers. *Courtesy of K-Line Industries*

FIGURE 8–17 Using a resilient-based, hone-type brush, commonly called a ball hone.

FIGURE 8–18 After honing, clean with soapy water and a soft, lint-free cloth. *Courtesy of TRW, Inc.*

honing machine. Various sizes of resilient-based hone-type brushes are available for honing and deglazing (Figure 8–17).

Deglazing residue and metal fragments adhering to the cylinder walls are abrasive and will quickly damage the rings, pistons, and cylinders if not removed. Using plenty of hot, soapy water, a stiff bristle brush, and a soft, lint-free cloth is the best way to clean the residue (Figure 8–18). Then rinse the block with clear water and dry thoroughly. Lightly coat all machined areas of the engine with clean, light engine oil to prevent rust. Cylinder cleanliness can be checked by wiping them with a clean white cloth after oiling. The cylinder walls can be considered free of abrasive residue when the cloth remains clean.

SHOP TALK

If the cylinders have varnish deposits, they can be swabbed with lacquer thinner to remove the varnish. Should the cylinders be lightly scuffed or scratched, light honing is recommended. Also, remember to adhere to the engine manufacturer's instructions. ■

FIGURE 8–19 Typical bore pattern created by a boring bar.

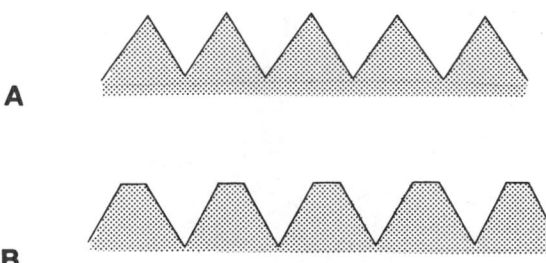

FIGURE 8–21 Comparison of (A) ridges and (B) plateaus on a honed cylinder surface.

CYLINDER BORING When cylinder surfaces are badly worn or excessively scored or when a perfectly straight cylinder is desired, a **boring bar** is used to cut the cylinders for oversize pistons or sleeves. A boring bar leaves a pattern on the cylinder wall similar to uneven screw threads (Figure 8–19). This makes it necessary to hone the bore to the correct finish after it has been bored to the proper size. This size is determined by the size of the replacement pistons and rings.

As shown in Figure 8–20, there are two types of boring machines: (A) stationary and (B) portable.

A

B

FIGURE 8–20 (A) Stationary and (B) portable boring machines. *Courtesy of Sunnen Products Company*

CYLINDER HONING It is necessary to **hone** the cylinder after boring to obtain proper ring and cylinder seating. Normally a minimum of 0.003 inch needs to be removed from the bore to smooth the marks left by the boring bar's cutter. These marks can slow down the piston ring seating process, which will cause poor oil control, blowby, and a dissatisfied customer. Honing will leave the cylinder with the proper surface so it will distribute oil, serve as an oil reservoir, and provide a place for worn metal and abrasive particles. A proper finish will provide for flat areas or plateaus in the surface. These act as bearing surfaces on which an oil film can form to separate the rings from the wall (Figure 8–21).

A rigid hone usually consists of two stones mounted opposite each other on a holder with guides located at right angles between them (Figure 8–22). The hone rotates at a selected speed. It is also manually or automatically reciprocated within the cylinder bore. The stones have an outward pressure on them and they remove some metal from the bore as they rotate within it. Honing oil flows over the stones and onto the cylinder wall to control the temperature and flush out any metallic and abrasive residue. The proper stones should be selected to ensure the walls will have the correct surface finish. Honing stones are classified by grit size, although honing equipment manufacturers can also have their own designation. The lower the grit number, the coarser the stone.

FIGURE 8–22 Using a rigid hone. *Courtesy of Sealed Power Corporation*

115° TO 135° REFERENCE
125° PREFERRED

22-1/2° TO 32-1/2°
27-1/2° PREFERRED

HORIZONTAL

VERTICAL

FIGURE 8–24 Automatic cylinder hone machine. *Courtesy of Kwik-Way Manufacturing Company*

FIGURE 8–23 Ideal cylinder honing pattern. *Courtesy of Sealed Power Corporation*

FIGURE 8–25 Torquing plates are fastened to the block during cylinder boring to prevent distortion. *Courtesy of Atlas Engineering and Manufacturing, Inc.*

A honing stone has thousands of tiny cutting edges that leave a multitude of crisscross grooves in the cylinder wall (Figure 8–23). These cutting edges continually break away from a properly operated hone to expose new, sharp cutting edges. Millions of tiny diamond-shaped areas are generated during the honing process, which serve as lubricant reservoirs to maintain the oil film on which the piston rings ride. Ideally, these grooves cross at 50 degree angles, although anything in the 20- to 60-degree range is acceptable.

Cylinder hone machines are available in manual and automatic models (Figure 8–24). The major advantage of the automatic type is that it allows the machine operator to dial in the exact crosshatch angle required in both the upper and lower stops of the bore.

Torquing plates are usually fastened to the cylinder block to equalize or prevent twist and distortion, while honing or boring a cylinder (Figure 8–25). When honing, be sure to keep a good flow of honing oil.

Engines with cylinder walls too thin for boring, engines with oversize pistons, and engines with only one damaged cylinder can be reconditioned by sleeving. Sleeving involves boring the cylinder oversize, then installing a thin metal liner. The inside diameter of the sleeve is then bored, usually to the original or standard piston size. This procedure can be used in one or all of the engine's cylinders. Figure 8–26 shows two methods used to install a cylinder sleeve.

INSTALLING CORE PLUGS

Old core and oil galley plugs are normally removed and replaced as part of cylinder block reconditioning. To install new core or soft plugs in the block, always use a nonhardening gasket sealer and the proper installation tool (Figure 8–27). It is important that the proper size and type of plug is used. Check a service manual for the proper replacement numbers. Brass core plugs are often recommended because they will not rust.

Prior to installing a core plug, the plug bore should be inspected for any damage that would inter-

A

B

FIGURE 8–26 Two methods used to install sleeves: (A) driving and (B) pressing. *Courtesy of Goodson Shop Supplies*

FIGURE 8–27 Steps in installing core plugs. *Courtesy of Goodson Shop Supplies*

fere with the proper sealing of the plug. If the bore is damaged, it will be necessary to true the surface by boring for the next specified oversize plug. Oversize (OS) plugs are identified by the OS stamped in the flat located on the cup side of the plug.

Coat the plug or bore lightly with an oil-resistant (oil galley) or water-resistant (cooling jacket) sealer. The three basic core plugs are installed as follows.

DISC- OR DISHED-TYPE This type fits in a recess in the engine casting with the dished side facing out (Figure 8–28A). With a hammer, hit the disc in the center of the crown and drive the plug into the bore until just the crown becomes flat. In this way the plug will expand properly and give a good, tight fit.

CUP-TYPE This type of plug is installed with the flanged edge outward (Figure 8–28B). The maximum diameter of this plug is located at the outer edge of the flange. The flange on cup-type plugs flares outward with the largest diameter at the outer (sealing) edge. The flanged (trailing) edge must be below the chamfered edge of the bore to effectively seal the

A

B

C

FIGURE 8–28 Core plug installation methods: (A) dished, (B) cup, and (C) expansion.

plugged bore. If the core plug replacing tool has a depth seating surface, do not seat the tool against a nonmachined (casting) surface.

EXPANSION-TYPE This type of plug is installed with the flanged edge inward (Figure 8–28C). The maximum diameter of this plug is located at the base of the flange with the flange flaring inward. When installed, the trailing (maximum) diameter must be below the chamfered edge of the bore to effectively seal the plugged bore. As was the case with a cup-type, if the core plug replacing tool has a depth seating surface, do not seat the tool against a nonmachined (casting) surface.

CRANKSHAFT

Crankshafts (Figure 8–29) are generally made of cast iron, forged cast steel, or nodular iron, and then machined. At the centerline of the crankshaft are the main bearing journals (Figure 8–30). These journals must be machined to a very close tolerance because the weight and movement of the crankshaft will be supported at these points. The number of main bearings is determined by the design of the engine. V-block engines generally have fewer main bearings than an in-line engine with the same number of cylinders. This is because the V-block engine uses a shorter crankshaft.

FIGURE 8–29   Typical crankshaft.

FIGURE 8–30   Crankshaft bearing and journal locations.

FIGURE 8–31   The crankshaft rotates on oil film between the bearing and journal.

Offset from the crankshaft centerline are the connecting rod bearing journals. The degree of offset and the number of journals are determined by engine design. An in-line six cylinder engine will have six connecting rod journals. A V-8 engine will have only four. Each journal will be connected to two connecting rods, one from each side of the V. The connecting rod journal is also called the crank pin. This area is machined to a very close tolerance just like the main bearing journal. The machining of the main and rod bearing journals must have a very smooth surface at the bearing area. The bearings must fit tightly enough to eliminate noise but must also have a clearance between them and their bearings for an oil film of 0.0015 inch and 0.002 inch to form. This is usually checked with plastigage.

The crankshaft does not turn directly on the bearings. It turns on a film of oil trapped between the bearing surface and the journal surface (Figure 8–31). This oil is supplied by the engine's oil pump. If the crankshaft journals become out of round, tapered, or scored, the oil film will not form properly and the journal will contact the bearing surface. This causes early bearing or crankshaft failure. The main and rod bearings are generally made of lead-coated copper or tin and aluminum. Both of these are softer material than that used to form the crankshaft. By using the soft material, any wear will appear first on the bearings. Early diagnosis of bearing failure most often will spare the crankshaft and only the bearings will need to be replaced.

As mentioned, the connecting rod journals are offset from the centerline of the crankshaft. This puts weight and piston pressure off center on the crankshaft. To balance this for smooth engine operation, counterweights must be added to the crankshaft. These weights are cast as part of the crankshaft and are positioned opposite the connecting rod journals.

Bearings surround each journal and are fed oil under pressure (Figure 8–32). For the oil to reach

FIGURE 8–34 A crankshaft has two distinct ends: drive belt and flywheel.

FIGURE 8–32 Bearings surround the journals in a crankshaft assembly. *Courtesy of Ford Motor Company*

In this way, all bearing journals receive oil under pressure to protect both the bearing and the journal. The crankshaft configuration determines the engine block design, or the positioning of the connecting rod journals around the centerline of the crankshaft (Figure 8–33).

The crankshaft has two distinct ends (Figure 8–34). One is called the flywheel end and, as its name implies, this is where the flywheel is connected. The front end or belt drive end of the crankshaft contains a threaded snout or is drilled and tapped for attaching a vibration damper.

WARNING!

Never lay a crankshaft down. It can warp or become bent. It should be stored standing up and with proper support in the middle. Remember that all engine parts must be carefully stored. ■

these bearings, oil passages must be drilled into the crankshaft. Each main bearing receives oil under pressure from the pump. Each main bearing journal will have a hole drilled into it with a connecting hole or holes leading to one or more rod bearing journals.

FIGURE 8–33 Various crankshaft configurations.

FIGURE 8–35 Typical vibration damper.

Vibration Damper

The purpose of the vibration damper is to dampen crankshaft vibration. The crankshaft experiences a back-and-forth or twisting motion each time a cylinder fires. The force applied to the crankshaft can be more than two tons. This causes the crank to momentarily twist and snap back. The vibration damper (Figure 8–35) consists of a center section, which is attached to the crankshaft. Surrounding the center section is a strip of rubberlike material. Attached to the material is a grooved counterweight. As the crankshaft twists, the enter section (A) applies a force to the material. The material must then apply this force to the counterweight (C). The weight is snapped in the direction of the crankshaft rotation to counterbalance the crankshaft connecting rod journal snapping back against the force due to ignition (B). The back-and-forth movement of the crankshaft is counterbalanced by the back-and-forth movement of the vibration damper, and the engine runs smoothly.

Flywheel

The **flywheel** also adds to the smooth running of the engine by applying a constant moving force to carry the crankshaft from one firing stroke to the next. This is called **inertia**. Because of its large diameter, the flywheel makes a convenient point for the starter to connect to the engine. The large diameter supplies good gear reduction for the starter, making it easy for the starter to turn the engine against its compression. The surface of a flywheel may be used as part of the clutch. On an engine that drives an automatic transmission, a **flex plate** is used. The automatic transmis-

sion torque converter provides the weight required to attain flywheel functions.

Balancer Shafts

The crankshaft is one of the main sources of engine vibration because its shape makes it inherently out of balance as it rotates. On some engines a balancer shaft (Figure 8–36) is employed to reduce vibration.

In its basic form, the balancer shaft is fitted with counterweights designed to mirror the throws on the crankshaft. It is driven directly by the crankshaft but in the opposite direction. As the engine turns, the two out-of-balance shafts mutually cancel out any vibrations.

CRANKSHAFT INSPECTION AND REBUILDING

Examine the crankshaft carefully. Check for the following.

◆ Are the vibration damper and flywheel mounting surfaces eroded or fretted?
◆ Are there indications of damage from previous engine failures?
◆ Do any of the journal diameters show signs of heat checking or discoloration from high operating temperatures?
◆ Are any of the sealing surfaces deeply worn, sharply ridged, or scored?
◆ Are there any signs of surface cracks or hardness distress?

If any or all of these conditions are present, document the area(s) of concern on the repair order and mark the areas for further evaluation.

To measure the rod journal (often called a throw or crank pin) diameter, use an outside micrometer (Figure 8–37). A micrometer can also be used to measure the journals for out-of-roundness and taper (Figure 8–38). Taper is measured from one side of the journals to the other. The maximum taper is 0.001 inch.

Compare these measurements to specifications and establish wear limits to determine the undersize to which the crankshaft is to be reground. Mark the repair order and the crankshaft to indicate the undersizing requirements and reference source for making these determinations. Generally, rebuilt crankshafts are used for replacement. Be sure they meet specifications.

USING SERVICE MANUALS

Crankshaft specifications can be found in the engine specification section of a service manual. ■

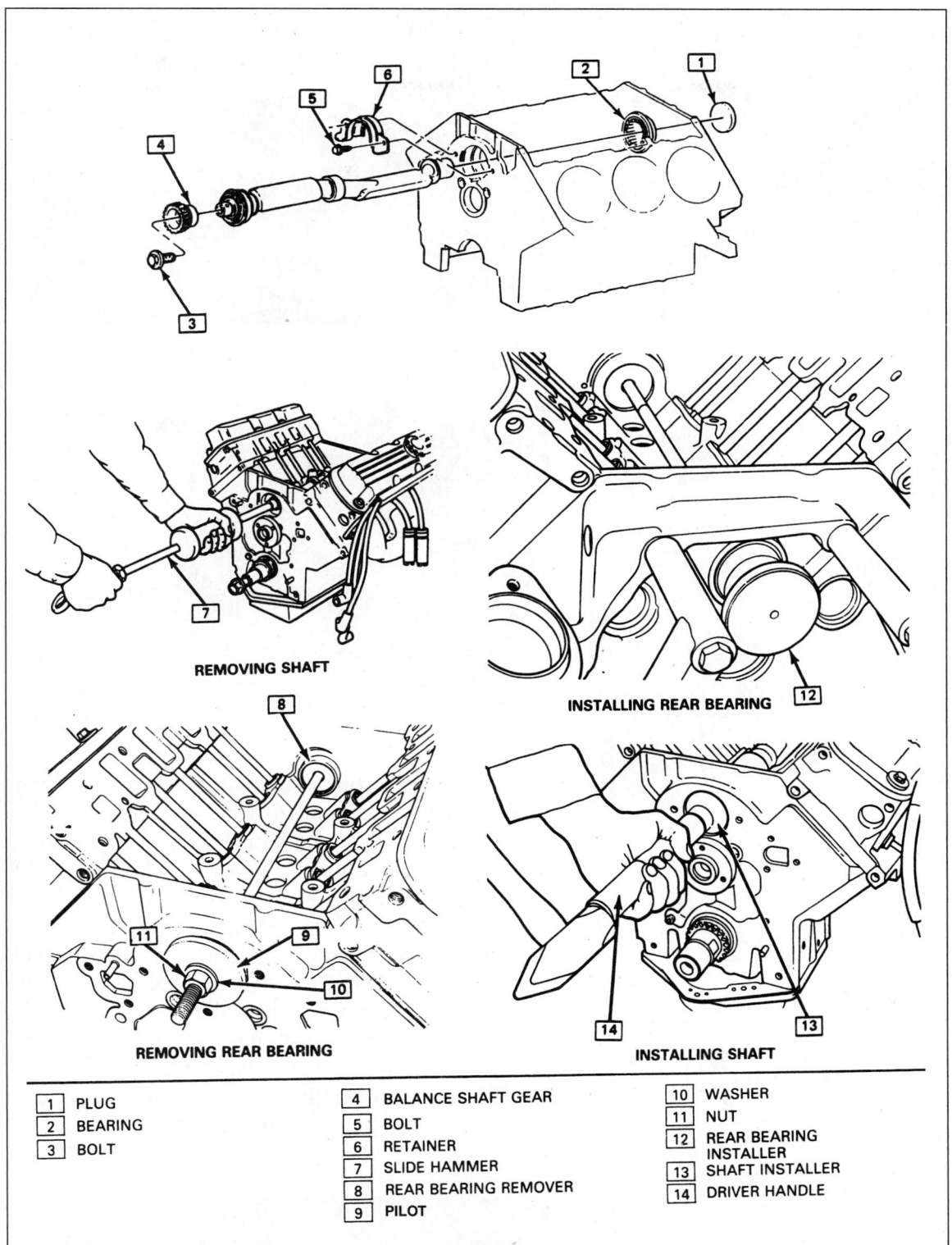

FIGURE 8–36 Balancer shaft assembly and location. *Courtesy of Buick Motor Division, General Motors Corporation*

Checking Crankshaft Saddle Alignment

Figure 8–39 is an exaggerated illustration of crankcase housing bores out of alignment. If the engine is operated with a warped housing centerline, the crankshaft will inflect heavy false loads on one side of the main bearings. Depending on the direction of the bowing or warpage of the main bearing housing bores, any side of the main bearings can become distressed. Engine blocks that are not severely warped can be repaired by an operation called **line boring**, a machining operation in which the main bearing housing bores are rebored to standard size and in perfect alignment.

To check the alignment of the crankshaft saddle bore, place an accurately ground arbor into the sad-

FIGURE 8–37 Measuring the connecting rod journal with a micrometer.

A VS B = VERTICAL TAPER
C VS D = HORIZONTAL TAPER
A VS C = OUT-OF-ROUND
B VS D = OUT-OF-ROUND

CHECK FOR OUT-OF-ROUND AT EACH END OF JOURNAL.

FIGURE 8–38 Checking for out-of-roundness and taper. *Courtesy of Perfect Circle/Dana*

CENTERLINE OF WARPED CRANKCASE

TRUE CENTERLINE OF CRANKCASE

FIGURE 8–39 Exaggerated view of crankcase housing misalignment.

dles (Figure 8–40). It should be 0.001 inch less in diameter than the low limit of the saddle bore specification and a little longer than the crankshaft. After the arbor is in position, assemble the main bearing caps without their bearings and tighten the cap bolts to the recommended torque specification. Rotate the arbor using a bar approximately 1 foot long. If it will not turn, one or more of the bores might be out-of-round. The condition must be corrected before the engine is assembled.

FIGURE 8–40 Checking crankshaft saddle bore alignment. *Courtesy of AE Clevite Engine Parts*

FIGURE 8–41 Checking bore alignment with a straight-edge and feeler gauge. *Courtesy of TRW, Inc.*

If a proper arbor is not available, saddle alignment can be checked with a metal straightedge (Figure 8–41). Place the straightedge in the saddles as shown. Using a feeler gauge that is half the maximum specified oil clearance, try to slide the feeler under the straightedge. If this can be done at any saddle, the saddles are out of alignment and the block must be line-bored. Repeat this procedure at two other parallel positions in the saddles.

Out-of-roundness of the saddles can also be checked by bolting on the main bearing caps and checking each bore with a dial bore gauge or an out-of-roundness indicator (Figure 8–42).

FIGURE 8–42 Main bearing saddles can be checked for out-of-roundness with a dial bore gauge. *Courtesy of Perfect Circle/Dana*

Checking Crankshaft Straightness

To evaluate the alignment or straightness of the crankshaft, the check should be made with the shaft supported on the main bearing journals, not on the centers of the crankshaft. The recommended location for supporting the crankshaft is on the end main bearing journals.

The journal supports should be a matched pair of well-maintained V-blocks. V-blocks made with roller bearings can introduce erroneous values due to bearing tolerances and clearances. Consequently, the best practice is to avoid the roller type of V-blocks unless they are a calibrated set. Once the crankshaft is located in the V-blocks, select and position the indicator for measuring the alignment/bow of the crankshaft. The selected indicator should have an accuracy of no less than 0.001 inch per full scale deflection. Position the indicator at the 3 o'clock position on the center main bearing journal (Figure 8–43).

Set the indicator at 0 (zero) and turn the crankshaft through one complete 360-degree rotation. The total deflection of the indicator, the amount greater than zero plus the amount less than zero, is the total indicator reading (**TIR**). Bow is 50 percent of the TIR (Figure 8–44). The bow indication at this bearing establishes the bow of the crankshaft. Compare the bow of the crankshaft to the acceptable alignment/bow specifications. Accept or reject as appropriate.

Checking Crankshaft Clearance and End Play

Clearance and end play should be checked before teardown is completed. The clearance check is made with a feeler gauge (Figure 8–45). The end play is checked with a dial gauge (Figure 8–46). Both checks should be within the specified limits given in the service manual.

FIGURE 8–44 Evaluating alignment bow.

FIGURE 8–45 Checking crankshaft clearance with a feeler gauge. *Courtesy of Federal-Mogul Corporation*

FIGURE 8–46 Checking crankshaft end play with a dial indicator. *Courtesy of Perfect Circle/Dana*

Flywheel Inspection

Check the runout of the flywheel and carefully inspect its surface. Replacement or resurfacing may be required. When checking the flywheel in a vehicle with automatic transmission, it must be done with the torque converter bolted to the flex plate.

With both manual shift or automatic transmissions, inspect the flywheel for a damaged or worn ring gear. Remember that improper flywheel runout can cause vibrations, poor clutch action, and clutch slippage.

USING SERVICE MANUALS

Procedures and specifications for checking a flywheel or flex plate will be found in the engine or transmission section of most service manuals. ∎

FIGURE 8–43 Checking the crankshaft for straightness. *Courtesy of Storm Vulcan, Inc.*

Crankshaft Bearings

Bearings are used to carry the critical loads created by crankshaft movement. They are a major wear item in the engine and require close inspection. Main bearings support the crankshaft journals that rest in the cylinder block. Connecting rod bearings are installed between the crankshaft and connecting rods.

The great majority of modern bearings are known as insert bearings. This name is derived from the fact that the bearing is made as a self-contained part and then inserted into the bearing housing. This type provides many advantages, including relative ease of replacement, greater variety of bearing materials, controlled lining thickness, and improved structure. Bearing thickness can be measured with a micrometer.

There are two types of insert bearings. Precision insert bearings are manufactured to close tolerances so that no further sizing is required at the time of assembly into the engine. Resizable insert bearings are manufactured with an extra-thick lining of bearing material on the inside diameter. This permits the bearing to be machined to any desired size up to and including standard size.

There are two basic designs of insert bearings (Figure 8–47). A **full round** (one piece) **bearing** is used in bores that allow the shaft's journals to be inserted into the bearing, such as with a camshaft. A **split** (two halves) **bearing** is used where the bearing must be assembled around the journal with the bearing housing being of two parts also, including a cap that holds the assembly together. Connecting rod bearings are split type.

The straight shell bearing and the flanged thrust bearing are two other configurations found in an automotive engine. The flanged thrust bearing provides the same support as the straight shell bearing, but also controls any horizontal movement or end play of the shaft. The connecting rod and most main bearings utilize the straight shell design. The flange bearing is used in the thrust position of the block. Most thrust main bearings are doubled flanged.

FIGURE 8–47 Full-round and split insert bearings.

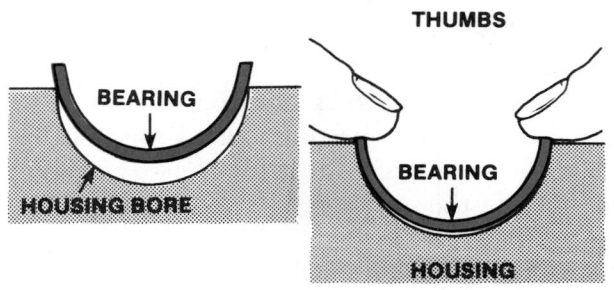

FIGURE 8–48 Spread requires a bearing to be lightly snapped into place.

Bearing Spread

Most main and connecting rod bearings are manufactured with spread. Bearing spread means the distance across the outside parting edges of the bearing insert is slightly greater than the diameter of the housing bore. To position a bearing half that has spread, it must be snapped into place by a light forcing action (Figure 8–48). This ensures positive positioning against the total bore and assists in subsequent assembly work by keeping the bearing halves in place.

Bearing Crush

Each half of a split bearing is made so it is slightly greater than an exact half. This can be seen quite easily when a half is snapped into place in its housing. The parting faces extend a little beyond the seat (Figure 8–49). This extension (as little as 0.001 inch) is called **crush**.

When the two bearing halves are assembled and the housing cap tightened, the crush sets up a radial pressure on the bearing halves so they are forced tightly into the housing bore. Bearing crush also helps to transfer heat from the crankshaft to the engine block.

Bearing Locating Devices

Engine bearings must be provided with some means to keep them from rotating or shifting sideways in their housings. There are a number of approaches to the problem with the specific design utilized being established by the original equipment manufacturer. The most common design is the locating lug. As shown in Figure 8–50, this consists of a protruding lug at the parting face of the bearing that nests into a slot in the housing that has been machined out to receive it.

Another approach is the locating dowel illustrated in Figure 8–51. The dowel can be located on the

FIGURE 8–49 Crush ensures good contact between the bearing and the housing.

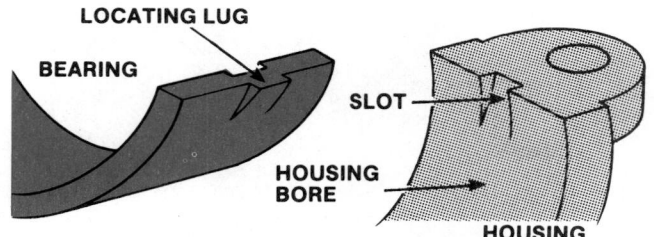

FIGURE 8–50 The locating lug fits into the slot in the housing.

FIGURE 8–51 The locating dowel fits into the corresponding hole in the mating part.

FULL ANNULAR GROOVE   PARTIAL GROOVE

SPREADER GROOVE

FIGURE 8–52 Typical bearing oil grooves.

housing or on the back of the bearing, with the dowel hole located in the mating part. In some cases, there is a dowel hole in both parts, with the dowel inserted as a separate piece.

A third design, which is not commonly used, utilizes a flathead screw secured to the housing through a hole in the crown of the bearing.

Oil Grooves

Providing an adequate oil supply to all parts of the bearing surface, particularly in the load area, is an absolute necessity. In many cases, this is accomplished by the oil flow through the bearing oil clearance. In other cases, however, engine operating conditions are such that this oil distribution method is inadequate. When this occurs, some type of oil groove must be added to the bearing. Some oil grooves are used to assure an adequate supply of oil to adjacent engine parts by means of oil throw-off.

Although oil grooves vary in size and shape, it has been found that a single groove works the best. A few typical oil grooves are shown in Figure 8–52.

Oil Holes

Oil holes are designed to allow the oil flowing through the engine block galleries to enter the bearing oil clearance space. Connecting rod bearings receive oil from the main bearings by means of rifled oilways in the crankshaft. Oil holes are also used to meter the amount of oil supplied to other parts of the engine. For example, oil spurt holes in connecting rods are often used to direct oil for the purpose of lubricating the cylinder walls. Oil spurt holes are also sometimes used in the bearing caps of the crankshaft main bearing (Figure 8–53). When the bearing is

FIGURE 8–53 Oil holes are often used in the main bearing cap to lubricate crankshaft.

equipped with an oil groove, the oil hole normally is in line with the groove.

The size and location of oil holes is critical. Thus, when replacement bearings are installed, care must be exercised to be sure that the oil hole matches the original equipment specifications. In addition to oil inlet holes, crankshafts are drilled with all the necessary passages (Figure 8–54) for lubrication.

Oil Clearance

Maintaining a specific oil clearance is critical to proper bearing operation. Many times, when wear on internal engine components such as the crankshaft is

OIL ENTERS AT THE
MAIN BEARING JOURNAL.

OIL COMES
OUT TO
LUBRICATE
THE CONNECT-
ING ROD
JOURNALS.

OIL
GALLERY

FIGURE 8–54 Crankshaft lubrication.

FIGURE 8–55 Polishing the journals will help determine if grinding is needed. *Courtesy of Perfect Circle/Dana*

then grinding is probably not necessary. If the crankshaft does not have to be reground, check it for straightness. ∎

negligible, the proper oil clearance specifications can be restored with the installation of standard size replacement bearings. However, if the crankshaft is worn to the point where the installation of standard size bearings will result in excessive oil clearance space, a bearing with a thicker wall must be used to compensate. Although these bearings are thicker, they are known as undersize because the journals and crank pins of the crankshaft are smaller in diameter. In other words, they are under the standard size.

SHOP TALK

Worn crankshaft journals have the same effect on oil pressure as worn bearings. When they are worn, there can not be uniform oil clearances. Excessive oil clearances will eventually lead to failures in other areas of the engine if they are not corrected. ∎

Undersize bearings are available in 0.001-inch or 0.002-inch sizes for shafts that are uniformly worn by that amount. Undersize bearings are also available in thicker sizes, such as 0.010 inch, 0.020 inch, and 0.030 inch, for use with crankshafts that have been refinished (or reground) to one of these standard undersizes.

SHOP TALK

If the journals measure within specifications but pitting and gouges exist, polish the worst journal to determine whether or not grinding is necessary (Figure 8–55). If polishing the journal achieves smoothness,

Bearing Failure and Inspection

As shown in Figure 8–56, bearings can fail due to a wide variety of reasons. Dirt infiltration and oil starvation are the major reasons for bearing failure. Insufficient or excessive crush is also a common cause. Problems in other engine components, such as bent or twisted crankshafts or connecting rods, or out-of-shape journals, can also cause bearings to wear irregularly.

A complete listing of bearing related problems, their symptoms, probable causes, and remedies is given in the *Tech Manual* that accompanies this textbook.

INSTALLING MAIN BEARINGS AND CRANKSHAFT

When selecting a new main bearing, remember that it must match the crankshaft journal diameter and main bearing housing size. If the crankshaft has been ground undersize, the main bearings will also have to be undersize. Similarly, if the housing bores have been machined oversize by align boring or align honing, the bearings must take up this space. Bearing size is usually marked on the bearing box and on the back of the bearing.

Consult the engine manufacturer's service literature for the exact engine buildup procedures. When the bearings are ready to be installed in the main bearing bores, make sure the bore is clean and dry before installing the bearing halves into place (Figure 8–57). Use a clean, lint-free cloth to wipe the bearing back and bore surface. Be certain that nothing is placed between the bearing back and the surface of the housing bore.

Put the new main bearing inserts into each of the main bearing caps and into the cylinder block hous-

DIRT

OUT-OF-ROUND BORE

HOURGLASS-SHAPED JOURNAL

INSUFFICIENT CRUSH

EXCESSIVE CRUSH

BARREL-SHAPED JOURNAL

OIL STARVATION

DIRT ON BEARING BACK

FILLET RIDE

SURFACE FATIGUE

TAPERED JOURNAL

BENT OR TWISTED CONNECTING ROD

SHIFTED BEARING CAP

DISTORTED CRANKCASE

BENT CRANKSHAFT

FIGURE 8–56 Common forms of bearing distress. *Courtesy of AE Clevite Engine Parts*

ings. Be sure to wipe the caps and housings perfectly clean and dry first. Make sure all holes align (Figure 8–58). The backs of the main bearing inserts should never be oiled or greased. Place the crankshaft in the block on the new main bearing inserts and arrange the main bearing caps in the correct order and direction over the crankshaft. Follow the factory markings or use those made during disassembly.

The next step is to measure the oil clearance between the crankshaft and the main bearing inserts. Proper lubrication and cooling of the bearing depend on correct crankshaft oil clearances. Scored bearings, worn crankshaft, excessive cylinder wear, stuck piston rings, and worn pistons can result from too small an oil clearance. If the oil clearance is too great, the crankshaft might pound up and down, overheat, and weld itself to the insert bearings.

Plastigage is fine, plastic string used to measure the oil clearance between the insert bearing and the

FIGURE 8–57 Crankshaft in main bearing saddles with the main bearings installed.

FIGURE 8–58 Align the oil holes in the bearings with those in the saddle. *Courtesy of Federal-Mogul Corporation*

crankshaft. The soft plastic string is relatively long and has a small diameter. The procedure for checking bearing clearance with plastigage is outlined in Photo Sequence 4.

One side of the plastigage has clearance stripes for U.S. standard measurements. The other side has stripes for measuring clearance in metric measurements. The string can be purchased to measure different clearance ranges. Usually, only the smallest clearance range is necessary for reassembly work. Plastigage designed to measure wide clearances can be used for troubleshooting worn engines.

Crankshaft end play should be measured with a feeler gauge by prying the crankshaft rearward and measuring the clearance between the cap and the counterweight with a blade. Insert the feeler gauge at several locations around the rear thrust bearing face. If end play is uniform at all locations and the measurements are within specifications, the end play is correct.

If the end play is within the specified limits, the job is done. If the end play is too large or too small, the main bearing with the thrust surface must be exchanged for one with a thicker or thinner thrust surface. If the engine has thrust washers or shims, thicker or thinner washers or shims must be used.

Most engines require the installation of main bearing seals during the final installation of the crankshaft. Always follow the recommended procedures for installing these seals, as given in the service manual. More details about these seals will be given in a later chapter.

Connecting Rod

The connecting rod is used to transmit the pressure applied on the piston to the crankshaft (Figure 8–59). The rod must be very strong and at the same time be kept as light as possible. Connecting rods are generally forged from high-strength steel or made of nodular steel or cast iron. The center section is made in the form of an I for maximum strength with minimum weight. The small end or piston pin end is made to accept the piston pin, which connects the piston to the connecting rod. The rod must be free to move back and forth as the crankshaft rotates. The piston pin can be a pressed fit in the piston and free fit in the rod. When this is the case, the small end of the rod will be fitted with a bushing. The pin can also be a free fit in the piston and pressed fit in the rod. In this case no bushings are used. The pin simply moves in the piston using the piston hole as a bearing surface. A third mounting allows the pin to move freely in both the piston and the rod. This design requires the use of clips or caps to prevent the pin from moving out against the cylinder walls.

FIGURE 8–59   Typical connecting rod.

The larger end of the rod is used to attach the connecting rod to the crankshaft. This end is made in two pieces. The upper half is part of the rod. The lower half is called the rod cap and is bolted to the rod. The connecting rod and its cap are manufactured as a unit and must always be kept together. During production, the rod caps are either machined off the rod or are scribed and broken off. The large crankshaft end of the rod is fitted with bearing half shells made of the same material as the main bearings (Figure 8–60). As mentioned earlier in the chapter, the crankshaft has oil passages that lead to the crank pins for lubricating the rod bearings. Some connecting rods have a hole drilled through the big end to the bearing area. The bearing insert might have a hole, which will align with this drilling. This

FIGURE 8–60   Connecting rod assembly with an insert bearing.

CHECKING MAIN BEARING CLEARANCE WITH PLASTIGAGE

P4–1 Checking main bearing clearance begins with mounting the engine block upside down on an engine stand.

P4–4 Wipe the crankshaft journals with a clean rag.

P4–2 Install main bearings into bores, being careful to properly seat them.

P4–5 Carefully install the crankshaft into the bearings. Try to not allow the crankshaft to move on the bearing surfaces.

P4–3 Wipe the bearings with a clean lint-free rag.

P4–6 Place a piece of plastigage on the journal. The piece should fit between the radii of the journal.

(continued)

P4–7   Install the main caps in their proper locations and directions. Wipe the threads of the cap bolts with a clean rag.

P4–8   Install the cap bolts and tighten them according to the manufacturer's recommendations.

P4–9   Remove the main caps and observe the spread of the plastigage. If the gage did not spread, try again with a larger gage.

P4–10   Compare the spread of the gage with the scale given on the plastigage container. Compare the clearance with the specifications.

P4–11   Carefully scrape the plastigage off the journal surface.

P4–12   Wipe the journal clean with a rag.

P4–13   If the clearance was within the specifications, remove the crankshaft and apply a good coat of fresh engine oil to the bearings.

P4–14   Reinstall the crankshaft and apply a coat of oil to the journal surfaces.

P4–15   Reinstall the main caps and tighten according to specifications.

hole is used to supply oil for lubricating and cooling the piston skirt. When the rod is properly installed, the oil hole should be pointing to the major thrust area of the cylinder wall.

PISTON AND PISTON RINGS

The piston forms the lower portion of the combustion chamber. The force of the expanding air/fuel mixture at the time of ignition is exerted against the head or dome of the piston. This force then pushes the piston down in the cylinder. The force applied to the piston can be as high as 2-1/2 tons. Therefore, the piston must be very strong.

In the past, pistons were made primarily of cast iron or a mixture of iron and steel. They were strong, but also heavy. Due to advances in aluminum technology, most modern pistons are made of lighter-weight aluminum or aluminum alloys.

Hypereutectic pistons are cast from an aluminum alloy containing up to 20 percent silicon. The silicon adds exceptional strength and durability to the metal. Higher strength means thinner side walls can be used, reducing piston weight. Hypereutectic pistons are very scuff resistant and less prone to ring groove, skirt, and pin bore wear. They offer excellent heat resistance and reduce thermal expansion so they can be installed to tight tolerances. This improves cold sealing and reduces operating noise. Hypereutectic pistons are now OEM equipment on many engines and are recommended replacement equipment for engines with scuffing and/or detonation problems. Passenger cars and light trucks with turbochargers or high output or severe duty operation also benefit from hypereutectic pistons.

The top of the piston is called the **head** or **dome**. Just below the dome on the side of the piston is a series of grooves. The grooves are used to contain the piston rings. The high parts between the grooves are called **ring lands**. Below the grooves, as shown in Figure 8–61, there is a bore, or hole, which is used for the **piston pin**, sometimes called the **wrist pin**. This hole is not always centered in the piston. It can be offset to one side. Piston pin offset is toward the major thrust side of the piston, the side that will contact the cylinder wall during the power stroke. By offsetting the pin, piston slap caused by the piston changing direction in the cylinder is eliminated.

SHOP TALK

The term piston slap or bang is used to describe the noises made by the piston when it contacts the cylinder wall. This noise is usually heard

FIGURE 8–61 Piston and connecting rod assembly.

only in older, high-mileage engines that have worn pistons or cylinder walls. The noise is most noticeable when the engine is cold or under a load. ◼

To ensure that the piston is installed correctly and the offset is on the proper side, the top of the piston will have a mark. The most common mark is a notch, machined into the top edge of the piston. This mark must always face the timing chain end of the engine when the piston is installed. The base of the piston, the area below the piston pin, is called the piston skirt. The area from just below the bottom ring groove to the tip of the skirt is the piston thrust surface.

There are two basic types of piston skirts: the slipper type and the full skirt. The full skirt is used primarily in truck and commercial engines. The slipper type is used for automobile engines. The slipper type allows the piston enough thrust surface for normal operation and has the advantage of allowing the piston to be lighter. This design also cuts down on piston expansion because there is less material to hold heat.

When an engine is designed, piston expansion determines how much piston clearance will be needed in the cylinder bore. Too little clearance will cause the piston to bind at operating temperatures. Too much will cause piston slap. The normal piston clearance for an engine, using slipper skirted pistons, is about 0.001 to 0.002 inch. This clearance is measured cold between the piston skirt and the cylinder wall. The piston clearance also supplies a space for piston lubrication.

USING SERVICE MANUALS

Piston clearance is normally found in the engine specifications table at the beginning of the engine section in a service manual. ■

Piston Rings

Piston rings are used to fill the expansion gap between the piston and cylinder wall. It is the piston rings that seal the combustion chamber at the piston.

Piston rings, which are available in several coatings, must serve three functions. They must seal the combustion chamber at the piston. They must remove oil from the cylinder walls to keep oil from reaching the upper cylinder where it will be burned. They must also carry heat from the piston to the cylinder walls to help cool the piston.

There are two basic ring families: compression rings and oil control rings. In most modern automobile engines, pistons are fitted with two compression rings and one oil control ring (Figure 8–62). The compression rings are found in the two upper grooves closest to the piston head. The oil ring is fitted to the groove just above the wrist pin.

Compression Rings The compression rings form the seal between the piston and cylinder walls (Figure 8–63). They are designed to use combustion pressure to force the ring against the cylinder wall and against the bottom edge of the ring groove. The top ring is the primary seal with the second ring used to seal any small amount of pressure that may reach it.

During the power stroke, the pressure caused by the expanding air/fuel mixture is applied between the inside of the ring and the piston groove. This forces the ring into full contact with the cylinder walls. The same force is applied to the top of the ring forcing it against the bottom of the ring groove. The combination of combustion pressure and the compression ring join together to form a tight ring seal.

FIGURE 8–62 Piston fitted into the cylinder bore.

FIGURE 8–63 The combustion rings use combustion pressure to push themselves against the cylinder walls and form a better seal.

Compression rings are generally made of cast iron. They come in a number of variations in cross section design. Most compression rings have a coating on their face, which aids the wear-in process. Wear-in is the time needed for the rings to conform to the shape and surface of the cylinder wall. Typical soft coatings are graphite, phosphate, iron oxide, and molybdenum. Some compression rings have a hard coating, such as chromium.

Oil Control Rings Oil is constantly being applied to the cylinder walls. The oil is used for lubrication as well as to clean the cylinder wall of carbon and dirt particles. This oil bath also aids in cooling the piston. Controlling this oil is the primary function of the oil ring. The two most common types of oil rings are the segmented oil ring and the cast-iron oil ring. Both types of rings are slotted so excess oil from the cylinder wall can pass through the ring. The oil ring groove of the piston is also slotted. After the oil passes through the ring, it can then pass through the slots in the piston and return to the oil sump through the open section of the piston.

Segmented oil rings are made of three pieces: an upper and lower scraper rail and an expander. The scrapers and expanders are made of spring steel. Segmented oil rings are a free-fit design. This means the expander is larger than the diameter of the cylinder. They must be carefully compressed when installed. The expander is used to form a tight seal of the scrapers at the cylinder walls.

INSTALLING PISTONS AND CONNECTING RODS

Once the crankshaft is in place, the piston and connecting rod assemblies are installed. First, lay out the piston assemblies in order from the front to the rear of the engine. Check the marks on the connecting rod

FIGURE 8–66 When fitting a bearing into the connecting rod, make sure the bearing tang is fully seated in the notch of the rod.

FIGURE 8–64 Common piston and connecting rod identification marks.

caps to make sure they are matched. Check the pistons to make sure they are installed on the connecting rods in the correct direction. Various markings are used to identify the positioning of pistons and connecting rods. Some of the more common markings are shown in Figure 8–64. Always check the manufacturer's service manual for exact component directions.

The insert bearings for the connecting rods, like those for the main bearings, must be the correct size. If the crankshaft has been machined undersize, matching rod bearing inserts must be installed. The size of the bearing inserts is printed on the box they come in and is stamped on the backs of the bearings (Figure 8–65).

Snap the new connecting rod bearing inserts into the connecting rods and rod caps. Make sure the tang on the bearing fits snugly into the matching notch

(Figure 8–66). Also make certain the con-rod and piston move freely (Figure 8–67).

The piston and rod can be assembled in the block in the following manner. Insert a new piston ring into the cylinder. Use the head of the piston to position the ring so it is square with the cylinder wall. In slightly worn cylinders that will not be resized, posi-

FIGURE 8–65 The connecting rod bearing size is marked on the back of the bearing.

FIGURE 8–67 Prior to installing the piston and rod assembly, make sure the piston moves freely on its wrist pin.

FIGURE 8–68   Steps in installing the piston and rod assembly in the block.

tion the ring below the ring travel area. When the cylinders have been refinished and have zero taper, the location of the ring is not critical. Next, use a feeler gauge to check the end gap (Figure 8–68A). Compose the end-gap specifications with the measured gap.

Correct as needed. Check the instructions on the piston ring box for correct installation. Normally, the gaps of the piston rings are staggered to prevent them from being in line with each other. Piston rings are installed easily with a ring expander.

Before attempting to install the piston and rod assembly into the cylinder bore, place rubber or aluminum protectors or boots over the threaded section of the rod bolts (Figure 8–68B). This will help to prevent bore and crank pin damage.

Lightly coat the piston, rings, rod bearings, cylinder wall, and crank pin with an approved assembly lubricant or a light engine oil (Figure 8–68C). Some technicians submerge the piston in a large can of clean engine oil before it is installed. Also, be sure to coat the cylinder wall with oil.

Fit the piston and ring into the cylinder bore by using a ring compressor tool (Figure 8–68D). This tool is expanded to fit around the piston rings. The steps on the tool are positioned downward. It is tightened with an Allen wrench to compress the piston rings. When the rings are fully compressed, the tool will not compress any further. The piston will fit snugly, but not tightly.

Rotate the crankshaft until the crank pin is at its lowest level (BDC). Then place the piston/rod assembly into the cylinder bore until the steps on the ring compressor contact the cylinder block deck (Figure 8–68E). Make sure the piston reference mark is in correct relation to the front of the engine. Also, when installing the assembly, make certain the rod threads do not touch or damage the crank pin.

Lightly tap on the head of the piston with a mallet handle (Figure 8–68F) or block of wood until the piston enters the cylinder bore. Push the piston down the bore while making sure the connecting rod fits into place on the crank pin. Remove the protective covering from the rod bolts.

Check the bearing clearances with plastigage, then assemble the connecting rod on the crank pin. A drop of anaerobic thread-locking compound is good insurance against a loose rod cap nut (Figure 8–68G). Position the matching connecting rod cap (Figure 8–68H) and finger tighten the rod nuts. Make sure the connecting rod blade and cap markings are on the same side. Gently tap each cap with a plastic mallet as it is being installed to properly position and seat it.

Torque the rod nuts to the specifications given in the service manual. When torquing the nuts, make sure the socket does not interfere with any part of the bearing cap. This can result in false readings. Lifting the socket slightly should alleviate this problem. Rotate the crankshaft to check for binding after each connecting rod is tightened to the crankshaft. Repeat the piston/rod assembly procedure for each assembly. Remember that connecting rods are numbered for easy identification and proper assembly (Figure 8–69).

FIGURE 8–69 Typical markings used to match a connecting rod cap with a rod.

FIGURE 8–70 Measuring connecting rod side clearance.

When all the pistons and rods have been installed, the connecting rod side clearance can be measured (Figure 8–70). The side clearance is the amount of clearance between the crankshaft and the side of the connecting rod. Side clearance is measured by inserting a feeler gauge between the crankshaft and connecting rod side or between the two connecting rods. The clearance determines the amount of oil throw-off from the connecting rod bearings. The clearance can be increased by removing the connecting rod and grinding material off the sides. If the clearance is too great, the connecting rods might have to be replaced.

Be sure to coat the crankshaft assembly with clean bearing lubricant or clean engine oil (Figure 8–71).

FIGURE 8–71 Lubricate the crankshaft both during and after assembly.

SHOP TALK

Most experts recommend that the bearing oil clearance of the connecting rod be checked against specifications. To do this, put a small strip of plasti-gage on the rod cap insert and hold it in place while positioning the insert on the connecting rod. Install the rod cap nuts and torque them to specifications. Remove the nuts and remove the cap. Compare the flattened plastic string to the plastigage package just as was done for the main bearings. ■

CASE STUDY

A car is brought into the shop just 2,000 miles after the owner rebuilt the engine. The shop is asked to diagnose the cause of excessive blue exhaust smoke and oil consumption and fouled spark plugs. Responding to questions, the customer indicates that she has rebuilt many engines before and never had this problem. She also has receipts for the parts she installed and the machining she had done to the engine. All of the parts were high-quality, and the machining was done by a reputable machine shop.

To verify the problem, a cylinder leakage test is conducted. The results indicate excessive leakage past the piston rings. To determine what went wrong during the rebuild, further questioning is needed. Assembly procedures are reviewed. Apparently no steps were missed. New piston rings were sized to the freshly honed cylinder walls and the resultant ring end gap is within specifications. The ring gaps were also staggered in the way recommended by the manufacturer. The work order from the machine shop showed that the cylinders were honed to a 30 RMS surface finish and the resultant size was 3.751 inches. The pistons are measured to be approximately 3.749 inches. The 0.002-inch clearance is within specifications.

Further examination of the receipts reveal the problem. The customer had originally intended to install cast-iron piston rings. But while the block was in the machine shop, she bought a set of molybdenum rings. Although these rings have advantages over cast rings, they are not best for this block. Molybdenum rings require a smooth cylinder wall finish; typically, a finish of 10 to 15 RMS is recommended. The rougher cylinder wall finish intended for cast-iron rings wore off the molybdenum coating, allowing oil to leak past the rings. This is the cause of the smoke, oil consumption, and spark plug fouling.

KEY TERMS

Boring bar	
Cast	Honing
Chamfering	Inertia
Core plug	Line boring
Crush	Long block
Cylinder sleeve	Piston pin
Deck	Piston rings
Dome	Plastigage
Flex plate	Ring lands
Flywheel	Short block
Full round bearing	Split bearing
Glaze	Taper
Harmonic balancer	TIR
Head	Wrist pin

SUMMARY

◆ The basic short block assembly consists of the cylinder block, crankshaft, crankshaft bearings, connecting rods, pistons and rings, and oil galley and core plugs. Related items include the flywheel and harmonic balancer.

◆ The cylinder block houses the areas where compression, ignition, and combustion occur. To protect the block from cracking due to expansion, core plugs are inserted during the manufacturing process.

◆ Cylinder bore wear is not uniform. Maximum wear occurs at the top of the ring travel area. A properly reconditioned cylinder must be of the correct diameter, have no taper or runout, and have a surface finish such that the piston rings will seat to form a seal that minimizes blowby and controls oil.

◆ Glaze is the thin residue that forms on cylinder walls due to a combination of heat, engine oil, and piston movement. Eye protection is a must when deglazing, as well as when honing and boring a cylinder.

◆ Freeze plugs and oil galley plugs are normally removed and replaced as part of cylinder block reconditioning. The three basic core plugs are the disc- or dished-type, cup-type, and expansion-type.

◆ The crankshaft turns on a film of oil trapped between the bearing surface and the journal surface. The journals must be smooth and highly polished.

◆ The flywheel adds to an engine's smooth running by applying a constant moving force to carry the crankshaft from one firing stroke to the next. The flywheel surface may be used as part of the clutch.

◆ Important crankshaft checks include saddle alignment, straightness, clearance, and end play. When replacement is necessary, a rebuilt crankshaft can be used as long as it meets specifications.

◆ Bearings carry the critical loads created by crankshaft movement. Most bearings used today are insert bearings, which are self-contained parts inserted into the bearing housing.

◆ Maintaining a specific oil clearance is critical to proper bearing operation. If the crankshaft is so worn that using standard size bearings will result in excessive oil clearance space, then so-called undersize bearings are needed.

◆ Today's aluminum pistons are lightweight, yet strong enough to withstand combustion pressure. Because of the tendency of aluminum to expand, steel struts are cast into aluminum pistons to help hold the heat and control expansion.

◆ Piston rings are used to fill the expansion gap between the piston and cylinder wall. Most of today's vehicle engines are fitted with two compression rings and one oil control ring.

◆ When installing a piston and connecting rod assembly, various markings can be used to make sure the installation is correct. Always check the service manual for exact locations.

◆ Connecting rod side clearance, the amount of clearance between the crankshaft and the side of the connecting rod, is an important measurement. It determines the amount of oil throw-off from the bearings. It is measured with a feeler gauge.

TECH MANUAL

The following procedures are included in Chapter 8 of the *Tech Manual* that accompanies this book:

1. Measure cylinder bore.

2. Measure crankshaft journals.

3. Check crankshaft end play.

4. Install pistons and connecting rods.

REVIEW QUESTIONS

1. Rather than casting the cylinder bores directly into the block, what technique is followed by some manufacturers?

2. What is the deck?

3. Where does maximum cylinder bore wear occur?

4. What type of insert bearing is manufactured with an extra-thick lining of bearing material on the inside diameter?

5. What is the function of compression rings?

6. Most pistons used today are made from ____.
   a. cast iron   c. ceramic
   b. aluminum   d. none of the above

7. Core plugs ____.
   a. are also called expansion plugs
   b. are used in all cast-iron cylinder blocks
   c. protect the block from cracking
   d. all of the above

8. Technician A says the maximum amount of cylinder out-of-roundness allowed in most cases is 0.0015 inch. Technician B says a cylinder can

have a taper of up to 0.010 inch and be acceptable. Who is correct?

a. Technician A   c. Both A and B
b. Technician B   d. Neither A nor B

9. The maximum amount of cylinder taper normally allowed is ____.

a. 0.0015 inch   c. 0.015 inch
b. 0.006 inch   d. 0.06 inch

10. Technician A says a cylinder wall with too smooth a surface will prevent the piston rings from seating properly. Technician B says a cylinder wall should have a crosshatch honing pattern. Who is correct?

a. Technician A   c. Both A and B
b. Technician B   d. Neither A nor B

11. Technician A says cylinder deglazing is not necessary if the cylinder out-of-roundness is within acceptable limits. Technician B says cylinders should always be honed before installing new pistons. Who is correct?

a. Technician A   c. Both A and B
b. Technician B   d. Neither A nor B

12. Technician A installs a cup-type core plug with its flanged edge outward. Technician B installs a dish-type core plug with the dished side facing inward. Who is correct?

a. Technician A   c. Both A and B
b. Technician B   d. Neither A nor B

13. Each half of a split bearing is made so it is slightly greater than an exact half. What is this extension called?

a. spread   c. both a and b
b. crush   d. neither a nor b

14. The connecting rod journal is also called the ____.

a. balancer shaft   c. plastigage
b. vibration damper   d. crank pin

15. Technician A uses a micrometer to measure the connecting rod journal for taper. Technician B uses a micrometer to measure the connecting rod journal for out-of-roundness. Who is correct?

a. Technician A   c. Both A and B
b. Technician B   d. Neither A nor B

16. Technician A uses line boring to service engine blocks that are not severely warped. Technician B uses line boring to service engine blocks that are severely warped. Who is correct?

a. Technician A   c. Both A and B
b. Technician B   d. Neither A nor B

17. Technician A checks crankshaft end play or end clearance with a feeler gauge, while Technician B uses a dial indicator. Who is correct?

a. Technician A   c. Both A and B
b. Technician B   d. Neither A nor B

18. ____ main and connecting rod bearings are manufactured with spread.

a. All   c. Very few
b. Most   d. No

19. Technician A says the size and location of engine oil holes is unimportant, provided there are a sufficient number of them. Technician B says the size and location of engine oil holes is critical. Who is correct?

a. Technician A   c. Both A and B
b. Technician B   d. Neither A nor B

20. Which type of oil ring is slotted so excess oil can pass through it?

a. cast-iron
b. segmented
c. both a and b
d. neither a nor b

CYLINDER HEADS AND VALVES

9

OBJECTIVES

◆ *Describe the purpose of an engine's cylinder head, valves, and related valve parts.* ◆ *Describe the types of combustion chamber shapes found on modern engines.* ◆ *Explain the procedures involved in reconditioning cylinder heads, valve guides, valve seats, and valve faces.* ◆ *Explain the steps in cylinder head and valve reassembly.*

The cylinder head mounts on top of the cylinder block to form the top portion of the engine. The cylinder head (Figure 9–1) is made of cast iron or aluminum. On overhead valve engines, the cylinder head contains the valves, valve seats, valve guides, valve springs, rocker arm supports, and a recessed area that makes up the top portion of the combustion chamber. On overhead cam engines, the cylinder head contains these items, plus the supports for the camshaft and camshaft bearings.

Both overhead valve and overhead cam cylinder heads contain passages that match passages in the cylinder block. These passages allow coolant to circulate in the head and to allow oil to drain back into the oil pan. The cylinder head also contains tapped holes in the combustion chamber to accept the spark plugs.

The sealing surface of the head must be flat and smooth. However, if the surface is too smooth, the gasket may be able move. The ideal surface for a cylinder head has a slight texture to it. This finish will grip the gasket and stop it from shifting around. This area must form a tight seal and contain the pressures formed during combustion. To aid in the sealing, a gasket is placed between the head and block. This gasket is called the head gasket. It is made of special material that can withstand high temperatures, high pressures, and the expansion of the metals around it. The head also serves as the mounting point for the intake and exhaust manifolds and contains the intake and exhaust ports.

Intake and exhaust ports are cast into the cylinder head. These ports are made so the air and fuel can pass through the cylinder head into the combustion chamber. One port is normally used for each valve. However, ports are sometimes combined because of space. These ports are called **siamese ports** (Figure 9–2). Siamese ports can be used because each cylinder uses the port at a different time. **Cross-flow ports**

FIGURE 9–1 Most of the other engine parts attach to the cylinder head.

FIGURE 9–2 With siamese ports, two cylinders feed the same exhaust port.

FIGURE 9–3 Coolant passages are cast into the cylinder head.

FIGURE 9–4 Typical wedge combustion chamber.

are used on some engines and have the intake and exhaust ports on the opposite sides. Heads of this design are called cross-flow heads.

Large openings in the cylinder head allow coolant to pass through the head (Figure 9–3). Coolant must circulate throughout the cylinder head to remove excess heat. The coolant flows from passages in the cylinder block through the head gasket and into the cylinder head. The coolant then passes back to other parts of the cooling system.

COMBUSTION CHAMBER

The performance of an engine, its fuel efficiency, and the level of pollutants in the exhaust all depend to a large extent on the shape of the combustion chamber. An efficient combustion chamber must be compact to minimize the surface area of the walls through which heat is lost to the engine's cooling system. The point of ignition (the nose of the spark plug) should be at the center of the combustion chamber. This minimizes the flame path, or the distance from the spark to the furthermost point in the chamber. The shorter the flame path, the more evenly the air/fuel mixture will burn.

Manufacturers have designed several different shapes of combustion chambers. Before looking at the popular combustion chamber designs, there are two terms that should be defined.

1. **Turbulence** is a very rapid movement of gases. Turbulence causes better combustion because the air and fuel are mixed better.
2. **Quenching** is the cooling of gases by pressing them into a thin area. The area in which gases are thinned is called the quench area.

Wedge Chamber

In the **wedge-type combustion chamber,** the spark plug is located at the wide part of the wedge (Figure 9–4). As the piston comes up on the compression stroke, the air/fuel mixture is squashed in the quench area. The **quench area** causes the air and fuel to be

mixed thoroughly before combustion. This helps to improve the combustion efficiency of the engine. Spark plugs are positioned to allow for rapid and even combustion. When the spark occurs, a flame front moves from the spark plug outward. The wedge-shaped combustion chamber is also called a turbulence-type combustion chamber. On newer model cars, the quench area has been reduced, which helps reduce exhaust emissions.

Hemispherical Chamber

The **hemispherical combustion chamber** gets its name from its basic shape. Hemi is defined as half, and spherical means circle. The combustion chamber is shaped like a half circle. This type of cylinder head is also called the **hemi-head**. The piston top forms the base of the hemisphere, and the valves are inclined at an angle of 60 to 90 degrees to each other with the spark plug positioned between them (Figure 9–5).

This design has several advantages. The flame path from the spark plug to the piston head is short, which gives efficient burning. The cross-flow arrangement of the inlet and exhaust valves allows for a relatively free flow of gases in and out of the chamber. Yet, the shape of the chamber also creates some tur-

FIGURE 9–5 Typical hemispherical combustion chamber.

FIGURE 9–6 Shrouding is a restriction in the flow of intake gases caused by the shape of the combustion chamber.

FIGURE 9–7 Domed pistons improve turbulence by producing a quench area.

bulence to ensure a thorough mixing of the fuel and air. The result is that the engine can breathe deeply, meaning that it can draw in a large volume of mixture for the space available and give a high power output.

The hemispherical combustion chamber is considered a nonturbulence-type combustion chamber. Little turbulence is produced in this type chamber. The air/fuel mixture is compressed evenly on the compression stroke. The spark plug is located directly between the valves. Combustion radiates evenly from the spark plug, completely burning the air/fuel mixture.

One of the more important advantages of the hemispherical combustion chamber is that air and fuel can enter the chamber very easily. The wedge combustion chamber restricts the flow of air and fuel to a certain extent. This is called **shrouding**. Figure 9–6 shows the valve very close to the side of the combustion chamber, which causes the air and fuel to be restricted. Volumetric efficiency is reduced. Hemispherical combustion chambers do not have this restriction. Hemispherical combustion chambers are used on many high-performance applications. This is especially true when large quantities of air and fuel are needed in the cylinder.

Some engines use a dome piston. This type of piston has a quench area to improve turbulence (Figure 9–7). Several variations of this design are used today.

Swirl Chamber

A **swirl combustion chamber** uses a compound curve port design to cause the air/fuel mixture to swirl in a corkscrew pattern to improve combustion. The swirl effect is the result of the intake port design, port location in the combustion chamber, and shape of the chamber itself. As the piston comes up on the compression stroke, this agitation of the air/fuel mixture continues and is compounded by compression. (Figure 9–8). This swirl action provides better fuel

FIGURE 9–8 Typical swirl combustion chamber. *Courtesy of Ford Motor Company*

FIGURE 9–9 (A) Swirl and (B) hemispherical combustion chambers.

FIGURE 9–11 (A) Standard uniform flow and (B) fast-burn, tangential-flow combustion chambers.

economy and lower exhaust emissions since fewer unburned hydrocarbons enter the exhaust system. A comparison of the swirl and hemispherical combustion chambers is shown in Figure 9–9.

Chamber-In-Piston

In this design, the valves are positioned vertically in the top of the cylinder head and are generally set flush with the face of the head (Figure 9–10). The spark plug is set to one side, midway between the inlet and exhaust valves. It is sometimes inclined a little away from the vertical.

In some designs, the inlet valve is well recessed into the inlet port and may even have a shroud on the head. Opening the inlet valve ensures a strong swirl and thorough mixing of the incoming charge of gases. The rim of the bowl in the piston head creates some squish. As the piston reaches the top of its stroke, some of the combustion gases around the rim are forced into the bowl itself, producing enough turbulence to minimize knocking.

An advantage of this shape is that because the combustion chamber lies in the piston itself, it remains hot. This helps to ensure the complete vaporization of combustion gases under light load, which, in turn, ensures smooth combustion.

Fast-Burn Combustion Chamber

A fast-burn combustion chamber is used on some four-cylinder engines to improve their efficiency (Figure 9–11). Faster combustion is achieved by directing airflow at angles through the intake valves to create turbulence. Fast-burn combustion chambers also decrease the potential for engine knock. With less potential for knock, compression ratios can be increased without increasing fuel octane requirements.

INTAKE AND EXHAUST VALVES

Every cylinder of a four-stroke cycle engine contains at least one intake valve to permit the air/fuel mixture to enter the cylinder and one exhaust valve to allow the burned exhaust gases to escape. The intake and exhaust valves, along with the cylinder head gasket, must also seal the combustion chamber (Figure 9–12).

The type of valve used in automotive engines is called a **poppet**. This is derived from the popping action of the valve as it opens and closes. A poppet valve has a round head with a tapered face, a stem that is used to guide the valve, and a slot that is machined at the top of the stem for the valve spring retainers.

FIGURE 9–10 Typical chamber-in-piston combustion chamber.

FIGURE 9–12 Sealing points of a typical engine.

The head of the valve is the large diameter end and is used to seal the intake or exhaust port. This seal is made by the **valve face** contacting the valve seat. The valve face is the tapered area machined on the head of the valve. The angle of this taper is determined by the design and manufacturer of the engine. The taper will vary from one engine family to another and may vary between intake and exhaust valves in the same engine. The area between the valve face and the head of the valve is called the **margin**. The margin allows for some machining of the valve face, which is sometimes necessary to restore its finish, and allows the valve an extra capacity to hold heat.

The intake and exhaust valve heads are different diameters. The intake valve is the larger of the two (Figure 9–13). The size or diameter of the valves is determined by the engine design. The exhaust valve does not need to be as large as the intake because the exhaust gases are compressed and the intake charge is not.

As mentioned, the stem guides the valve during its up-and-down movement and serves to connect the valve to its spring through its valve spring retainers and keepers. The stem rides in a guide that is either machined into the head (integral type) or pressed into the head (insert type) as a separate replaceable part.

The valve seat is the area of the cylinder head contacted by the face of the valve. The seat may be machined in the head (integral type) or it may be pressed in (insert type) like the valve guide. The valves found in today's engines are made from special high-strength steel or ceramic that is highly heat resistant. Heat resistance is very critical for exhaust valves because they must withstand working temperatures of between 1,500 to 4,000°F. Heat resistance is much less of a problem for intake valves because they receive extra cooling from the fuel mixture during the intake stroke.

There are two ways for the exhaust valve to cool. First, when the valve face is in contact with its seat,

FIGURE 9–14   (A) Sodium-filled valve and (B) hard-faced valve.

the heat from the valve will be transferred to the cylinder head, which is liquid cooled. The second is through the valve stem to the valve guide and again to the cylinder head. To aid in this second method of heat transfer, some exhaust valve stems are hollow. This hollow section is filled with sodium (Figure 9–14). Sodium is a silver-white alkaline metallic chemical element that transfers heat much better than steel.

⚠️ *WARNING!*

Never cut open any sodium-filled valves. Sodium will burn violently when it contacts water. ■

The valve seat area must be hard enough to withstand the constant closing of the valve and supply good heat transfer. Due to corrosive products found in the exhaust gas, the seats must be highly resistant to corrosion. When the cylinder head material meets these requirements, the seats are machined directly into it. When it does not, the seats are then made of material that will meet the requirements and the seats are pressed into the head.

The following are the important valve components found in a four-stroke engine.

VALVE GUIDES   Valve guides are the parts that support the valves in the head. They are machined to a fit of a few thousandths of an inch clearance with the valve stem. This close clearance is important for the following reasons.

- It keeps the lubricating oil from being drawn into the combustion chamber past the intake valve stem during the intake stroke.
- It keeps exhaust gases from leaking into the crankcase area past the exhaust valve stems during the exhaust stroke.
- It keeps the valve face in perfect alignment with the valve seat.

FIGURE 9–13   Valve nomenclature.

FIGURE 9–15 (A) Integral and (B) removable valve guides.

FIGURE 9–17 (A) Release and (B) positive valve rotators.

Valve guides can be cast integrally with the head (Figure 9–15A), or they can be removable (Figure 9–15B). Removable valve guides usually are press-fit into the head.

VALVE SPRINGS, RETAINERS, AND SEALS

The valve assembly is completed by the spring, retainer, and seal. Before the spring and the retainer fit into place, a seal is placed over the valve stem. The seal acts like an umbrella to keep oil from running down the valve stem and into the combustion chamber. The spring, which keeps the valve in a normally closed position, is held in place by the retainer. The retainer locks onto the valve stem with two wedge-shaped parts that are called **valve keepers**. Some engines utilize a single valve spring per valve (Figure 9–16A). Others use two or three springs (Figure 9–16B). Often the second or third spring is a flat spring called a **damper spring**, which is designed to control vibrations.

VALVE ROTATORS Many engines are equipped with mechanisms that cause the exhaust valves to rotate. Their purpose is to keep carbon from building up between the valve face and seat. Carbon buildup can hold the valve partially open, causing it to burn. The release-type rotator (Figure 9–17A) releases the

spring tension from the valve while it is open. The valve will then rotate from engine vibration. The positive rotator (Figure 9–17B) is a two-piece valve retainer that has a flexible washer between the two pieces. A series of balls, between the retainer pieces, roll on a machined ramp as pressure is applied and released from the opening and the closing of the valve. The movement of the balls up and down the ramps causes the valve to rotate.

Multivalve Engines

Many newer engines use multivalve arrangements. Automotive engineers have long been obsessed with the idea of additional valves in the cylinder head. It all started in 1918 with the dual-valve Pierce Arrow. This was one of the first cars to use four valves per cylinder as a way to enhance gas flow and increase horsepower.

Multivalve can be three valves per cylinder (Figure 9–18) or four valves (Figure 9–19) per cylinder. The most common arrangement is four valves per cylinder. A few four-cylinder engines have 12 valves. However, most multivalve four-cylinder engines have 16 valves. To aid in combustion, some multivalve arrangements feature a jet valve (Figure 9–20). Air from the carburetor throttle plate is directed to the jet valve (a smaller intake valve) at lower engine

FIGURE 9–16 Two types of valve spring assemblies: (A) single spring and (B) reverse wound secondary spring.

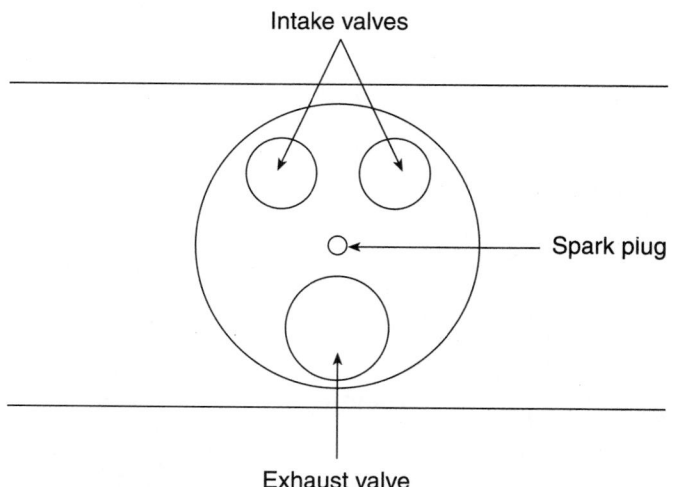

FIGURE 9–18 Arrangement of two intake valves and one exhaust valve in a cylinder head.

FIGURE 9–19 Cutaway view of a multivalve arrangement with four valves per cylinder.

FIGURE 9–21 Typical cross-flow pattern used in multivalve engines.

speeds. This results in a swirling action in the combustion chamber and increased turbulence. The location of the air inlet above the throttle plate allows very little air to enter the passage to the jet valve at higher engine speeds and greater throttle openings. In all multivalve engines, the heads are of the cross-flow design (Figure 9–21).

Replacing the conventional single intake and single exhaust valve with two intake and one or two exhaust valves increases the area of the intake and exhaust ports. More mixture can enter the cylinders. Thus, multivalve engines have a more complete combustion, which reduces the chances of misfire and detonation. This results in enhanced fuel efficiency, cleaner exhaust, and increased power output. The velocity of the intake air is higher with small multiple ports than a large single passage. This fast-moving intake charge promotes good torque production during low- and mid-range rpm operation. The smaller valves naturally have less mass than big ones, so mechanical inertia is reduced, making a higher engine

speed possible before valve float occurs. The more times the cylinder can be filled and evacuated per second, the more horsepower can be obtained.

Because increased gas velocity is the main benefit of a four-valve cylinder head, the technology works best at high engine speeds. Unfortunately, multiple-valve technology is also inhibited by manifold constructions and exhaust back pressure. This is the reason some manufacturers are researching new engine blocks that feature a one-piece cast cylinder head and block. The lack of cylinder head bolts allows a highly efficient manifold that maximizes the effect of multivalve design.

The benefits of multivalves are offset to some extent, however, by a more complicated camshaft arrangement. The easiest way to actuate four valves per cylinder is with dual overhead camshafts (Figure 9–22). These are sometimes difficult to lubricate. The cam drive is even more complicated with V-power plants. Most are using a single overhead cam per cylinder bank, with some kind of lever arm actuating the opposite bank of valves.

FIGURE 9–20 How a jet valve operates in a multivalve engine.

FIGURE 9–22 Typical dual overhead camshaft (DOHC) configuration. *Courtesy of Nissan Motor Company*

The high revolution rate inherent to multivalve engine design puts a premium on balancing techniques. Four-cylinder engines without balance shafts tend to be prone to high shaking forces. To overcome this problem, some multivalve engines use relatively long connecting rods to reduce angular changes during a piston stroke, a solution that has only been partially successful in the past. Using lightweight materials in the manufacturing of the piston rod assembly also contributes to the solution.

ALUMINUM CYLINDER HEADS

Aluminum heads have become popular primarily because a typical aluminum head weighs roughly half as much as a cast-iron head. Eliminating anywhere from 20 to 40 pounds of weight is a plus for fuel economy, but it has its drawbacks.

Attempts to lower overall engine weight have resulted in many lightweight cylinder head designs. One major problem with thin-walled, lightweight heads is cracking (Figure 9–23). These heads have also created head gasket sealing problems in the spark plug cooling port area (Figure 9–24). Head resurfacing when there is an existing core shift causes the narrow land area to move inward toward the combustion chamber and reduce gasket contact. Coolant can then leak into the cylinder. Before installing a lightweight head, carefully check this area for proper head gasket fit and possible hairline cracks. Aluminum expands

FIGURE 9–23   Lightweight heads are prone to cracking. This can lead to a recessed exhaust valve seat.

COMBUSTION CHAMBER   **NARROW LAND AREA**

COOLING PORT FOR SPARK PLUG

FIGURE 9–24   Before installing a rebuilt lightweight head, check the gasket-to-casting fit around the cooling port areas.

ALUMINUM

CAST IRON

FIGURE 9–25   Aluminum expands and contracts almost twice as much as cast iron.

and contracts almost twice as much as cast iron in response to temperature changes (Figure 9–25). This creates a number of problems. When an aluminum head is mated to an iron block (which most are), the difference in thermal expansion between head and block creates a great deal of scrubbing stress on the head gasket. Unless the gasket is engineered to take such punishment, leakage, and premature gasket failure can result.

Increased thermal expansion and stress can also lead to cracking. The most crack-prone areas in the head are usually the areas around the valve seats. High combustion temperatures and the constant pounding of the valve against its seat often cause cracking between the intake and exhaust seats or just under the exhaust seat. If the seats are not machined to very close tolerances and installed properly, cracking is virtually guaranteed.

The difference in thermal expansion between aluminum and iron creates a lot of stress throughout the head. The head wants to expand in all directions at once as it heats up, but the head bolts keep it from going sideways or lengthwise. The only place left to go is up, so the head tends to bow up in the middle.

Lack of rigidity in the head itself is another factor to consider and one that can contribute to other problems in an engine. Aluminum is not as strong as cast iron. Consequently, the head provides less top end support for the block. This can allow more distortion in the upper cylinder bore area, affecting combustion sealing, blowby, and ring life. Using deck plates when boring the block can help minimize some of the distortion that will occur after the head is torqued down. Aluminum cylinder head bolts should never be loosened or tightened when the metal is hot. Doing so may cause the cylinder head to warp due to the torque changes.

In engines with overhead cams and aluminum heads, the cam journals often run in machined bores in the head itself. Aluminum makes a fairly good bearing material. It is soft and provides good imbedability to foreign particles. But it lacks the support and rigidity of a conventional steel-backed bearing in an iron saddle. Because of this, overhead cam bores in such heads typically experience more flex than their cast-iron counterparts. The result is usually accelerated wear and egg-shaped bores. If the head overheats and warps, alignment through the cam bores is destroyed. In some instances, the misalignment can be so bad the cam will not turn once the head is unbolted from the engine. Since many aluminum heads lack serviceable cam bearings and, in many instances, enough metal for boring and sleeving (repair sleeves are generally unavailable anyway), the only cure short of replacing the head is to machine out the cam bores and install a cam with oversized journals.

Aluminum has another drawback—**porosity**. The casting process sometimes leaves microscopic pores in the metal, which can weep oil or coolant. In most instances, the problem is cosmetic only in that it does no real harm. But the customer may not agree. To him or her a wet spot on the outside of a cylinder head looks like a leak.

Reconditioning Aluminum Cylinder Heads

Warpage in an aluminum cylinder head is usually the result of overheating (low coolant, uneven coolant circulation within the head, a too-lean fuel mixture, and incorrect ignition timing).

Alignment of the cam bores in an overhead cam head must be checked with either a straightedge and feeler gauge (Figure 9–26) or with a dial indicator. If off by more than 0.002 to 0.003 inch, corrective action is required.

CUSTOMER CARE

Explain to the customer the reasons why a cylinder head will warp. An informed customer is more likely to be a satisfied one.   ∎

FIGURE 9–26   Checking cam bore alignment with a straightedge and feeler gauge.

SHOP TALK

Although specifications for the maximum amount of cylinder head surface warpage vary, traditionally, the maximum acceptable limit for cast-iron heads is 0.005 inch. Aluminum is not as forgiving, so 0.002 inch to 0.003 inch is a more realistic upper limit.   ∎

Although align boring and the installation of oversized cam bearings in the head or a cam with oversized journals might restore alignment in the cam bores, a badly warped head might be too far gone to allow the face to be resurfaced. Removing metal from the face of the head also alters the valve train geometry, which limits the amount of aluminum that can be removed.

Aluminum cylinder heads can be straightened through the use of heat and special clamping fixtures. Some manufacturers recommend that warped heads not be straightened, and instead should be replaced. Always follow the recommendations of the manufacturer.

SHOP TALK

Some engine rebuilding shops have ovens that can be used to straighten aluminum heads. Do not attempt to straighten a head without using an oven or without proper guidance.   ∎

RESURFACING CYLINDER HEADS

There are three reasons for resurfacing the deck surface of a cylinder head.

1. To make the surface flat so the gasket seals properly
2. To raise the compression ratio
3. To square the deck to the main bores

As engines undergo heating and cooling cycles over their life span, certain components tend to warp. This is especially true of cylinder heads. By using a precision straightedge or flatness bar and feeler gauge, the amount of warpage can be easily measured. While the manufacturers' specifications should always be checked, maximum head warpage for cast-iron limits are generally recognized as follows.

◆ In-line 6-cylinder—0.006 inch
◆ In-line 4-cylinder—0.004 inch
◆ V-6—0.003 inch
◆ V-8—0.004 inch
◆ Aluminum heads—0.002 to 0.003 inch

Some manufacturers allow aluminum heads to warp more than cast iron before recommending replacement. ■

The deck surface should be checked both across the head as well as lengthwise. Be sure to also check flatness of the intake and exhaust manifold mounting surface on the head. In general, maximum deformation allowed here is 0.004 inch.

In addition to warpage inspection, check for dents, scratches, and corrosion around water passages. This is especially important on aluminum heads. Heads that are deformed beyond specifications must be surfaced. The finished surface, however, should not be too smooth. It must be rough enough to provide "bite," but not enough to cause a poor seal and leakage.

Surface Finish

No cylinder head surface, no matter how it appears, is perfectly smooth. When viewed in cross section (Figure 9–27), a surface consists of a series of peaks and valleys. A special instrument, called a profilometer, incorporates a stylus that moves across the area to be checked. It is used to check surface roughness and to measure the distance between the peaks and valleys (Figure 9–28). It calculates the average value, which is about one-third of the peak-to-valley depth.

The unit of measurement used when checking surface finish is the microinch. One microinch is equal to one-millionth (0.000001) inch. Average surface finish can be expressed using either the **RMS** (root mean square) or **AA** (arithmetic average) methods. RMS

FIGURE 9–27   Cross section of a cylinder head surface.

FIGURE 9–28   Measuring head surface roughness with a profilometer.

readings are approximately 11 percent higher than AA readings. For all practical purposes this difference is negligible when checking machine finish.

A profilometer is the ideal instrument to measure cylinder head surface finish; however, it is expensive. Another way to measure surface finish is to use a specimen block kit. This kit contains a set of blocks that have various microinch roughnesses. By using a fingernail to compare the finish on the head with the many blocks in the kit, it is possible to estimate the head surface smoothness. ■

For proper head gasket seating, a cylinder head surface finish range of 60 to 120 microinches is generally recommended. This finish consists of shallow scratches and small projections that allow for gasket support and sealing of voids. A surface finish greater than 120 microinches is too rough. Such a finish has scratches and projections that allow only the gasket to be supported at a few points. Even with the head bolts torqued to proper specifications, there is improper loading on the gasket bore flange leading to leaking combustion gases.

Four different types of machines—belt surfacer, milling, broaching, and grinding—can be used in resurfacing operations.

WARNING!

Before attempting to operate any surfacing machine, be sure to become familiar with and follow all the cautions and warnings given in the machine's operation manual. Also, when operating these machines, you must wear safety glasses, goggles, or a face shield. ■

Belt Surfacers   Belt surfacers resemble belt sanders. These machines are easy to set up and operate. An operator merely places the part to be surfaced on the belt. A restraint rail helps keep the part positioned (Figure 9–29). Some machines have air-operated holddown fixtures.

Resurfacing quality depends on operator skill and factors such as belt condition, machine horsepower, and the holddown pressure applied.

Milling Machines   **Milling** machines (Figure 9–30) cut away thin layers of metal to create a level, properly

A

B

FIGURE 9–29 (A) Typical belt surfacer and (B) how it is used.

FIGURE 9–30 Typical milling machine. *Courtesy of Storm Vulcan, Inc.*

FIGURE 9–31 Milling an aluminum cylinder head.

FIGURE 9–32
Typical broaching machine. *Courtesy of Winona Van Norman Machine Company*

Surface Grinders Surface grinders use a grinding wheel to remove metal stock (Figure 9–33). They set up and operate similarly to milling machines. Grinding wheels must be sharp. A dull wheel will simply polish, not cut, the surface.

Stock Removal Guidelines

The amount of stock removed from the head gasket surface must be limited. Excessive surfacing can lead to problems in the following areas.

Engine's Clearance Volumes It might be necessary to measure and adjust the size of an engine's clearance volumes. Clearance volume is the volume of the combustion chamber plus the volume of the cylinder when the piston is at TDC.

Measuring the clearance volume is called **cc-ing** the cylinder head. This is done with the valves and

FIGURE 9–33 Typical surface grinder.

finished surface (Figure 9–31). Cutters remove up to 0.050 inch per pass. Both rough and finish cuts are usually made to create the desired finish. Milling requires operator skill. However, machine maintenance is low. A good variety of surface finishes is possible.

Broaching Machines **Broaching** machines use an underside rotary cutter or broach (Figure 9–32). A block, cylinder head, or intake manifold is held in an inverted position as the broach passes underneath. A mirror setup is needed to inspect the work in progress.

FIGURE 9–34 Cc-ing a cylinder head to find the combustion volume.

spark plugs installed. The cylinder head is mounted upside down, and a glass or plastic plate is installed over the combustion chamber. A graduated container called a burette is used to fill the combustion chamber with thin oil. The oil is poured through a hole in the plate, as shown in Figure 9–34. The amount of oil that enters the combustion chamber is noted by observing the cubic centimeter (cc) markings on the burette. The number of cc's used is equal to the clearance volume (in cubic centimeters) for this cylinder.

The clearance volumes for an engine can be adjusted in several ways. They may be reduced by surfacing the cylinder head. This, of course, reduces all the clearance volumes for that cylinder head. Individual clearance volumes can be increased by grinding the valve seats to sink the valves and by grinding and polishing metal from the combustion chamber surface. Either method can be employed to equalize all the clearance volumes and adjust them to the manufacturer's specifications.

Compression Ratio Standard engine rebuilding procedures can affect the engine's compression ratio in a number of ways.

Boring the block oversize changes the swept volume and the compression ratio. Generally speaking, the compression ratio increases at the same percentage the displacement increased. Boring an engine 0.060 inch oversize will increase the displacement 9 cubic inches or slightly more than 3 percent. Assuming the replacement piston has the same compression height as the original, the initial 9.0:1 compression ratio will be increased by 3.0 percent to 9.27:1. As a rule of thumb, there is a 2 percent increase at 0.030 inch oversize, a 4 percent increase at 0.060 inch, and a 6 percent increase at 0.125 inch. With today's gas, anything more than 9.0:1 is suspect without a detonation sensor.

Decking the block changes the compression ratio. Removing 0.010 inch from the deck surface of an engine with a 4-inch bore, 76-cc head, 0.060-inch head gasket, 0.080-inch deck height would raise the compression ratio by 0.14:1.

Resurfacing the head also increases the compression ratio. Though the effect varies for every type and size of chamber, a good rule of thumb is that when a head is surfaced 0.010 inch, the chamber is reduced by 1.50 cc for a 60-cc head and by 2.50 cc for a 90-cc head. This will increase the compression ratio by about 0.141:1 to 0.20:1, depending on the specific head configuration and actual swept volume.

Variations in head gasket thicknesses affect the compression ratio. There can be as much as 0.040-inch difference between various types and brands of gaskets. For instance, changing from a soft-faced to a steel or copper shim gasket can increase the compression ratio by as much as 0.50:1.

The piston itself can have an effect on the compression ratio. Replacing a dished piston with a flat top will increase the compression ratio significantly. Using the wrong piston with a particular chamber will raise or lower the compression ratio. The difference of 10 cc in chamber size can have a dramatic effect on the compression ratio and might require the use of a different piston.

Fortunately, most aftermarket suppliers either deck or destroke their oversize pistons to enable the technician to reduce or maintain the compression ratio instead of increasing it. These pistons should be used whenever available.

Piston/Valve Interference and Misalignment When the block or head is surfaced, the piston-to-valve clearance during the overlap period becomes less. To prevent the valves from making contact with the piston, a minimum of 0.070 inch piston-to-valve clearance is recommended.

Surfacing can also cause valve tips, rocker arms, and pushrods to be dimensioned closer to the camshaft. This causes a change in rocker arm geometry and can also cause hydraulic lifters to bottom out.

When metal is removed from the block or heads on a V-type OHV engine, the heads will be positioned closer to the crankshaft. This downward movement will cause the intake manifold to fit differently between the heads. As a result, ports might be mismatched and manifold bolts might not line up. In order to return the intake manifold to its original alignment, corrective machining on the manifold is required.

GRINDING VALVES

Valve grinding or refacing is done by machining a fresh, smooth surface on the valve faces and stem tips. Valve faces suffer from burning, pitting, and wear caused by opening and closing millions of times

FIGURE 9–35 Grinder-type valve resurfacer. *Courtesy of Sunnen Products Company*

during the life of an engine. Valve stem tips wear because of friction from the rocker arms.

Before grinding, inspect each valve face for burning and each stem tip for wear. Replace any valves that are badly burned or worn. Reusable valves are cleaned by soaking them in solvent, which will soften the carbon deposits. The deposits are then removed with a wire buffing wheel. Once the deposits are removed, the valve can be resurfaced. The face is reconditioned prior to grinding the valve tip.

Valves can be refaced on either grinding (Figure 9–35) or cutting (Figure 9–36) machines. Although both can reface valves and smooth and chamfer valve stem ends, the traditional grinding method of refacing is still the most popular. Larger valve grinder machines are capable of doing valve train reconditioning tasks such as refacing certain types of rocker arms and other repair jobs described in this chapter. There are also computerized valve refacing grinder machines.

FIGURE 9–36 Cutter-type valve resurfacer. *Courtesy of Neway Manufacturing, Inc.*

USING SERVICE MANUALS

Specifications for valve angles are normally listed in the engine specifications section of a service manual. ∎

To start the valve grinding operation, chuck the valve as close as possible to the valve head to eliminate stem flexing from wheel pressure (Figure 9–37). Set the grinding angle according to the desired angle. Take light cuts using the full grinding wheel width (Figure 9–38). Make sure coolant is striking the contact point between the valve face and grinding wheel. Remove only enough metal to clean up the valve face. A knifelike edge will burn easily or might cause pre-ignition (Figure 9–39). As a general rule, it is not

FIGURE 9–37 Once the grinder is set up, the valve is secured in the chuck, the correct angle is set, and the proper stroke is set. Be sure there is clearance between the edge of the stone and the valve.

FIGURE 9–38 Light cutting on a valve. *Courtesy of Sioux Tools, Inc.*

FIGURE 9–39 A sharp edge on the valve face is not recommended.

advisable to grind a valve face to a point where the margin is reduced by more than 25 percent or to where it is less than 0.045 inch on the exhaust and 0.030 inch on the intake valves.

After grinding, check valve head runout. Use a dial indicator on the valve margin and rotate the valve while it is still in the chuck. Valve runout should not exceed 0.002 inch total indicated reading (TIR). The face should not show any chatter marks or unground areas. After grinding, examine the valve face for cracks. Sometimes fine cracks are visible only after grinding. Sometimes they occur during grinding due to inadequate coolant flow or excessive wheel pressure.

CAUTION:

Always wear eye protection when operating any type of grinding equipment. ∎

If an interference angle is to be used, the grinder is set 1/2 to 1 degree less than the standard 30- or 45-degree face angle. Always consult the manufacturer's specifications to determine whether an interference angle is to be used. Grinding an interference angle produces a face angle close to 29 or 44 degrees. For the valve to seat properly, the face angle cannot be less than 29 or 44 degrees (Figure 9–40).

Once the face is ground, the valve tip might also need to be ground. This is best determined by placing

FIGURE 9–41 Grinding a valve tip. *Courtesy of Sioux Tools, Inc.*

the valve in the cylinder head to check the stem height. Using the manufacturer's specifications, determine whether and to what extent the tip must be ground. As shown in Figure 9–41, the tip is ground using a stemming stone that has been dressed. Just like the facing stone, the stemming stone is dressed with a diamond tool. The valve is secured in a V-holder and clamp, and a coolant is used to cool the valve tip and remove grit during grinding.

The valve tip is ground so that it is exactly square with the stem. Because valve tips have hardened surfaces up to 0.030 inch in depth, only 0.010 inch can be removed during grinding. If more than 0.010 inch is removed from the tip, the valve must be replaced. Also, if too much material is removed from the valve tip, there might be interference between the rocker arm and spring retainer or valve rotator. Follow the manufacturer's specifications for the allowable limits.

There is little basic difference in the refacing procedures for a grinder and cutter machine. In fact, most of the guidelines given for grinding a valve face are the same for cutting. Actually, the only difference is what is used to cut the valve: a grinding stone or a cutting tool such as shown in Figure 9–42.

SHOP TALK

Some valve refacing equipment requires a procedure that is the reverse of the one just given in the text. That is, the valve tip is dressed and chamfered before it is refaced. If this is not done on this type of equipment, the valve face will be ground off center. Follow the equipment manufacturer's instructions for procedures and sequences. ∎

Material removed from the valve face and valve seat increases the amount of valve stem length on the spring side of the cylinder head when the valve is seated. If excessive, this could cause the hydraulic lifter plunger to bottom out and prevent the valve from being fully seated when it is closed.

VALVE FACE → ← VALVE SEAT

1/2°–1° INTERFERENCE ANGLE

44°

INTAKE VALVE FACE ANGLE

45°

INTAKE VALVE SEAT ANGLE

30°

EXHAUST VALVE FACE ANGLE

31°

EXHAUST VALVE SEAT ANGLE

FIGURE 9–40 The difference between the seat angle and the valve face angle is known as the interference angle.

FIGURE 9–42 Cutting to reface a valve. *Courtesy of Neway Manufacturing, Inc.*

FIGURE 9–43 (A) Worn intake guides allow the intake vacuum to suck oil down the guide, and (B) worn exhaust guides can do the same.

Grinding material from the stem tip will generally correct any stem height problems and will center the hydraulic lifter plunger. Do not remove more material from the valve stem than the maximum allowed in the vehicle's service manual. If the valve stem height is greater than the acceptable amount plus the maximum amount allowed to be ground off the stem, this indicates the valve or seat should be replaced.

VALVE GUIDE RECONDITIONING

Valve guide problems can be lumped into one of three basic categories: inadequate lubrication, valve geometry problems, and wrong valve stem-to-guide clearance.

Inadequate lubrication can be caused by oil starvation in the upper valve train due to low oil pressure, obstructed oil passages, improper operation of pushrods, and using the wrong type of valve seal. Insufficient lubrication results in stem scuffing, rapid stem and guide wear, possible valve sticking, and ultimately valve failure due to poor seating and overheating.

Geometry problems include an incorrectly installed valve height, off-square springs, and rocker arm tappet screws or rocker arms that push the valve sideways every time it opens. This causes uneven guide wear, leaving an egg-shaped hole. The wear leads to increased stem-to-guide clearance, poor valve seating, and premature valve failure.

As for valve stem-to-guide clearance, a certain minimum amount is needed for lubrication and thermal expansion of the valve stem. Exhaust valves require more clearance than intakes because they run hotter. Clearance should also be close enough to prevent a buildup of varnish and carbon deposits on the stems, which could cause sticking. Insufficient clearance, however, can lead to rapid stem and guide wear, scuffing, and sticking, which prevents the valve from seating fully. This, in turn, causes the valve to run hot and burn.

If the clearance is too great, oil control will be a serious problem. Contrary to what some technicians might think, oil can be drawn past both the intake and exhaust guides. Though oil consumption is more of a problem with sloppy or worn intake guides because the guides are constantly exposed to vacuum, oil can also be pulled down the exhaust guides by suction created in the exhaust port. The outflow of hot exhaust creates a venturi effect as it exits the exhaust port, creating enough vacuum to draw oil down a worn guide (Figure 9–43).

Some guides might have internal rifling or spiral grooves to improve oil retention. These are usually used with exhaust valves and on diesel engines or dry fuel engines, such as those built to run on propane.

The antiseize and antiwear characteristics of bronze generally enable a bronze guide to last two to five times longer than a cast-iron guide. Unfortunately, bronze guides are more expensive so their use in original equipment applications is limited. Bronze is also a more difficult material to machine so tooling does not last as long with bronze as it does with cast iron. Because of these drawbacks, bronze guides are commonly used only as aftermarket replacements.

Bronze inserts provide better thermal conductivity than cast iron, allowing the valves to run cooler and last longer. Bronze also has a lower coefficient of friction and retains oil better than cast iron. This allows closer stem-to-guide clearances for improved valve stem cooling and reduced oil consumption.

Knurling

Knurling is one of the fastest techniques for restoring the inside diameter (ID) dimensions of a worn valve guide. The process raises the surface of the guide ID by plowing tiny furrows through the surface of the metal (Figure 9–44). As the knurling tool cuts into the guide, metal is raised or pushed up on either side of the indentation. This effectively decreases the ID of the guide hole. A burnisher is used to press the

FIGURE 9–44 (A) Typical tap-type knurling tool tip and (B) the cut it makes. *Courtesy of Goodson Shop Supplies*

ridges flat and is then used to shave off the peaks of these ridges to produce the proper-sized hole and restore the correct guide-to-stem clearance.

Knurling can be done with either a tap-type knurling tool or a wheel-type or roller knurler (Figure 9–45).

One of the main advantages of knurling is that it does not change the centerline of the valve stem appreciably, so it reduces the amount of work necessary to reseat the valve. Knurling also allows a rebuilder to reuse the old valve if wear is within acceptable limits, helping to reduce rebuilding costs. In spite of its speed and simplicity, knurling is not a cure for restoring badly worn guides to their original condition.

Opinions vary as to how much wear is acceptable for knurling. Most automotive experts seem to agree that the maximum amount of acceptable wear ranges from 0.004 to 0.007 inch.

Knurling is not considered a long-term repair because it restores only a portion of the original surface. As the raised ridges are worn, wear accelerates, and clearances become excessive. This occurs long before it would have if the entire ID of the guide had been restored.

Another consideration with knurling is that guides do not wear evenly from top to bottom. They wear the least in the middle and the most toward either end. The tapered wear pattern means a knurling tool will do the least where it is needed the most—toward the ends. Knurling a bell-mouthed guide, therefore, only succeeds in restoring the middle section of the guide. Excessive clearance might remain at either end. This has the same effect as shortening the valve guide: it decreases stem cooling and can encourage wobbling.

Reaming and Oversized Valves

Reaming is used to repair worn guides by increasing the guide hold size to take an oversize valve stem or by restoring the guide to its original diameter after installing inserts or knurling. Standard oversizes are 0.003, 0.005, 0.006, 0.010, 0.013, and 0.015. In some cases, other sizes also may be available. Be sure to check their availability before doing any machining.

When reaming (Figure 9–46), limit the amount of metal removed per pass to 0.005 inch. Always reface the valve seat after the valve guide has been reamed and use a suitable scraper to break the sharp corner (ID) at the top and bottom of the valve guide.

The advantage of reaming for an oversized valve is that the finished product is totally new. The guide is straight, the valve is new, and the clearance is accurate. The use of oversized valve stems is generally considered to be superior to knurling. Yet, like knurling, it is relatively quick and easy. The only tool that is required is a reamer. The valve centerline is maintained so the work required to finish the seat is reduced. However, since reaming requires the use of new valves, it can be more expensive on an engine with many worn guides. Its use is also limited to heads where the guides are not worn beyond the limits of the maximum oversize valve that is available. Because of these limitations, many technicians prefer more cost-effective alternatives such as guide liners, inserts, or replacement guides.

Thin-Wall Guide Liners

The thin-wall guide liners repair technique offers a number of important advantages and is also popular with many production engine rebuilders, as well as smaller shops. It provides the benefits of a bronze guide surface (better lubricity, wear, and tighter clearances). It can be used with either integral or replaceable guides. It is faster, easier, and cheaper than

FIGURE 9–45 Wheel-type or roller knurling tool. *Courtesy of Sunnen Products Company*

FIGURE 9–46 Reaming valve guides. *Courtesy of Goodson Shop Supplies*

FIGURE 9–47 Two setups for boring out old and worn guides. *Courtesy of Hall-Toledo, Inc.*

FIGURE 9–48 Bronze guide liner installation; (A) boring the guide to oversize; (B) installing the liner; and (C) trimming the liner.

FIGURE 9–49 ID finishes used for guides: (A) ball broach; (B) ream; and (C) spiral.

installing new guides in heads with replaceable or integral guides, and it maintains guide centering with respect to the seats.

Thin-wall guide liners are manufactured from a phosphor-bronze or silicon-aluminum-bronze material. The popular liner size is the 0.502-inch universal guide. This liner has a 0.502-inch outside diameter (OD), and its ID varies from 0.312 to 0.374 inch. These liners can be cut to almost any length. They are designed for a 0.002- to 0.0025-inch press fit. A tight fit is essential for proper heat transfer to the head and to prevent the liner from working loose.

The liners are installed by first boring out (Figure 9–47) the original guides to 0.030-inch oversize with a special piloted boring tool (Figure 9–48A) pressed into the guide using a driver and air hammer (Figure 9–48B). On guides not precut to length, the excess must be milled off before finishing (Figure 9–48C). The liner is then wedged in place and sized in a single operation by passing a ball broach down through it (Figure 9–49A). This eliminates the need to ream it to size and ensures a tight fit between the liner and guide. If a ream finish is desired (Figure 9–49B), it

can be obtained by lubricating the reamer with a bronze-lube and then running it through the guide. For closer than normal stem-to-guide clearance, spiraling or knurling is suggested for added lubrication (Figure 9–49C).

The only trick to using liners is to make sure the hole is round and the correct size. If the hole is distorted excessively or if it is too large, the liner will not fit properly and will cause problems. Running a ball broach or a roller burnishing tool down the liner helps compensate for hole distortion and presses the liner for a tight fit.

Valve Guide Replacement

Replacing the entire valve guide is another repair option possible on cylinder heads with replaceable guides. However, pressing out the old guides and installing new ones can be difficult with some aluminum heads where the interference fit is considerable. Cracking the head or galling the guide hole is always a risk. One recommendation is to preheat the heads in an oven prior to guide removal and to lubricate dry liners before driving them out.

SHOP TALK

An oven should be used to bring the head to 250°F. Guides can be difficult to remove after heating to 500 degrees. A torch should never be used because it can burn through the head. Localized heating can also induce considerable distortion. ∎

INTEGRAL GUIDES To replace integral guides, bore (Figure 9–50) or drive (Figure 9–51) the old guide out and drive a thin-wall replacement guide into the hole. Many shops use a seat and guide machine for this process (Figure 9–52), although it can be done with portable equipment. Drive the replacement guides in cold with approximately 0.002-inch press fit. Use an assembly lube to prevent galling. It is necessary to keep the centerline of the guide concentric with the valve seat so that the rocker arm-to-valve stem contact area is not disturbed (Figure 9–53).

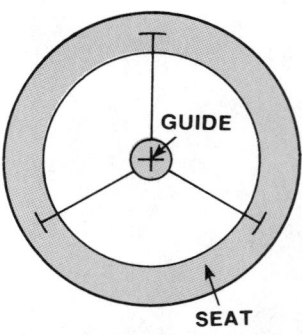

FIGURE 9–53 The centerline of the guide should be concentric with the seat.

Occasionally, a new guide will not be concentric with the valve seat. Install a new seat to correct the problem and check the concentricity of the valve seat with a concentricity gauge (Figure 9–54).

INSERT GUIDES To press out an old valve guide, place a proper-sized driver so that its end fits snugly into the guide. The shoulder on the driver must also be slightly smaller than the OD of the guide, so it will go through the cylinder head. Use a heavy ball peen hammer to drive the pressed guide out of the cylinder head.

Pressing or driving out and installing new guides is not difficult, but there is always the danger of breaking the guide or tearing up the guide hole in the head. Cast-iron guides in particular have a tendency to gall aluminum heads. Once the hole is damaged, it must be bored out and an oversized guide installed—assuming one is available to fit the application. New guides should be chilled prior to installation because of the needed interference fit between the guide and head. Chilling them in a freezer or with dry ice works well. Lubricant also helps to prevent galling.

FIGURE 9–50 Boring out an integral guide.

FIGURE 9–51 Driving out an integral guide.

FIGURE 9–52 Valve seat and guide machine. *Courtesy of Kwik-Way Manufacturing Company*

FIGURE 9–54 Checking valve seat concentricity.

A   **B**

FIGURE 9–55   Installing new guides (A) with a press and driver and (B) with an air hammer. *Courtesy of TRW, Inc. and Goodson Shop Supplies*

FIGURE 9–56
Measuring guide protrusion.
Courtesy of TRW, Inc.

When installing new guides, be careful not to damage them. Use a press and the same driver that was used to remove the old guide. Align the new guide and press straight down (Figure 9–55A), not at an angle. An air hammer (Figure 9–55B) and special driver can also be used to install new guides.

At least one engine manufacturer uses guides that are cut off at an angle on the combustion chamber end. Others may also be found to have guides cut at an angle at one end or the other. No attempt should be made to press or drive against the angled end.

Find the correct amount of guide protrusion. Guide height is important to avoid interference with the valve spring retainer. The guide must also fit the hole tightly or it can work loose. The manufacturer's specifications give the correct valve guide installed height, but it is good practice to measure how far the old guides stick out of the cylinder head and to use this measurement as a reference. As each guide is installed, the technician should measure the installed height with a scale (Figure 9–56). After the new guides have been installed, insert a valve. Check for any stem interference.

Valve guide honing is ideal for sizing both integral and insert guides. Very close tolerances, ± 0.002 inch, can be obtained with this process. With reaming, for example, it is difficult to have any clearance closer than 0.005 inch. These close tolerances give better oil control and heat dissipation.

One of the main drawbacks of replacing guides is that it changes the valve centerline, particularly when drilling out heads with integral guides. This can sometimes lead to seat refinishing problems if the centerline has moved too far off center.

RECONDITIONING VALVE SEATS

The most critical sealing surface in the valve train assembly is between the face of the valve and its seat in the cylinder head when the valve is closed. Leakage between these surfaces reduces the engine's compression and power and can lead to valve burning. To ensure proper seating of the valve, the valve seat must be the correct width (Figure 9–57), correct location on the valve face, and concentric with the guide (less than 0.002-inch runout).

The ideal seat width for automotive engines is 1/16 inch for intake valves and 3/32 inch for exhaust valves. Maintaining this width is important to ensure proper sealing and heat transfer. However, when an existing seat is refinished to make it smooth and concentric, it also becomes wider.

Wide seats cause problems. Seating pressure drops as seat width increases. Less force is available to crush carbon particles that stick to the seats, and seats run cooler, allowing deposits to build up on them.

The seat should contact the valve face 1/32 inch from the margin of the valve. When the engine reach-

SEAT WIDTH SCALE

FIGURE 9–57   Checking valve seat width.

FIGURE 9–58 Checking the seat for cracks.

es operating temperature, the valve expands slightly more than the seat. This moves the contact area down the valve face. Seats that make too low a contact with the valve face might lose partial contact at normal operating temperatures.

Like valve guides, there are two types of valve seats—integral and insert. Integral seats are part of the casting. Insert seats are pressed into the head and are always used in aluminum cylinder heads.

Valve seats can be reconditioned or repaired by one of two methods, depending on the seat type—machining a counterbore to install an insert seat, or grinding, cutting, or machining an integral seat.

Before starting seat work, carefully check the seats for cracks (Figure 9–58). Cracked integral seats sometimes can be repaired by installing inserts, if the crack is not too deep. Cracked insert seats must be replaced. Check insert seats for looseness with a small pry bar (Figure 9–59). Replace them if any movement is noted.

Installing Valve Seat Inserts

The following steps outline a typical insert valve seat removal and replacement.

FIGURE 9–59 Use a small pry bar to check insert seats for looseness. *Courtesy of TRW, Inc.*

PROCEDURES
Insert Valve Seat Removal and Replacement

1. To remove the damaged insert, use a puller (Figure 9–60) or a pry bar (Figure 9–61).
2. After removal, clean up the counterbore or recut it to accommodate oversized inserts (Figure 9–62).
3. Insert the counterboring pilot into the valve guide. Then mount the base and ball shaft assembly to the gasket face angle of the cylinder head (Figure 9–63).
4. Use an outside micrometer to accurately expand the cutterhead to a predetermined size of the counterbore (Figure 9–64). Remember that the counterbore should have a slightly smaller ID than the OD of the insert to provide for an interface fit.
5. Place the valve insert counterboring tool over the pilot and ball-shaft assembly. Preset the depth of the valve seat insert at the feed screw. A magnetic ring is often used to trap the dust created when counterboring valve seats (Figure 9–65).
6. Cut the insert by turning the stop-collar until it reaches the present depth (Figure 9–66). Use a lubricant on the cutters for a smoother finish.
7. To install the insert, heat it in a parts cleaning oven to approximately 350 to 400°F. Chill the insert in a freezer or with dry ice before installation.
8. Press the seat with the proper interference fit using a driver (Figure 9–67).
9. When the installation is complete, the edge around the outside of the insert is staked as shown in Figure 9–68. By doing so, the insert will be secured more effectively in the counterbore.

 CAUTION:

Wear the proper gloves when handling dry ice. ■

Reconditioning Integral Seats

The average valve seat width is 0.060 inch and the average seat begins 0.030 inch from the valve margin. A properly reconditioned seat has three angles: top, 30 or 15 degrees; seat, 45 or 30 degrees; and throat, 60 degrees. Typically, 45-degree angle wedges

FIGURE 9–60 Using a puller to remove a damaged insert seat. *Courtesy of TRW, Inc.*

FIGURE 9–61 Using a pry bar to remove a damaged insert seat.

FIGURE 9–62 Counterbores can be cleaned or recut to accommodate oversized inserts. *Courtesy of TRW, Inc.*

FIGURE 9–63 Mounting the base and ball shaft assembly to the gasket face angle of the head. *Courtesy of Hall-Toledo, Inc.*

FIGURE 9–64 Using an outside micrometer to expand a cutterhead. *Courtesy of Hall-Toledo, Inc.*

FIGURE 9–65 A magnetic ring is ideal for collecting grinding dust. *Courtesy of Goodson Shop Supplies*

FIGURE 9–66 Cutting the insert. *Courtesy of Hall-Toledo, Inc.*

FIGURE 9–67 Seat the insert firmly in the cylinder head. *Courtesy of Sunnen Products Company*

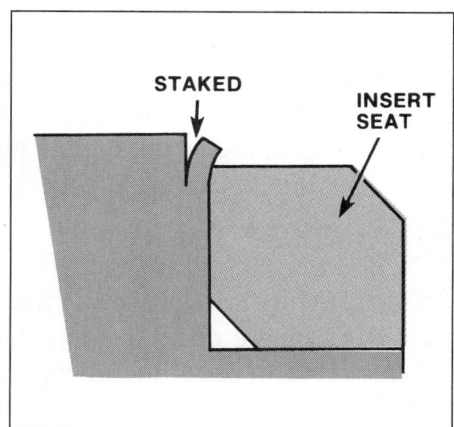

FIGURE 9–68 Staking can be done with a sharp chisel.

FIGURE 9–69   The three angles of a properly finished seat.

FIGURE 9–70   Proper valve overhang.

FIGURE 9–71   Inserting a pilot shaft into the valve guide in preparation for grinding.

tighter than the 30-degree seat, so it is used more often. Using three angles maintains the correct seat width and sealing position on the valve face (Figure 9–69). Correct sealing pressure and heat transfer from the valve through the seat are also affected. Always check service manual specifications for valve seat angles and valve face-to-seat contact amounts. As stated earlier, contact is usually 1/16 inch for intake valves and 3/32 inch for exhaust valves (Figure 9–70). Maintaining proper seat overhang is also required. This overhang is usually 1/64 inch for all valves.

Integral valve seats can be reconditioned by grinding, cutting, or machining.

Grinding Valve Seats

When grinding a valve seat, it is very important to select and use the correct size pilot and grind stone. Hard seats use a soft stone and soft seats (cast iron) use a harder stone. The stone must be properly dressed and cutting oil used to aid in grinding.

🔧 SHOP TALK

Before grinding, many technicians clean the seats by placing a piece of fine emery cloth between the stone and the seat and giving the surface a hard rub. This will help prevent contamination of the seat grinding stone with any oil or carbon residue that might be present on the valve seat. Such contamination could cause glazing.   ∎

The grinding wheel is positioned and centered by inserting a properly sized pilot shaft into the valve guide (Figure 9–71). All valve guide service must be completed before installing the pilot.

The seat is ground by continually raising and lowering the grinder unit on and off the seat at a rate of approximately 120 times per minute (Figure 9–72). Grinding should only continue until the seat is clean and free of defects.

After the seat is ground, valve fit is checked using machinist dye. The valve face is coated with dye, installed in its seat, and slightly rotated. The valve is then removed and the dye pattern on the valve face and valve seat inspected.

If the valve face and seat are not contacting each other evenly, or if the contact line is too high, the seat must be reground with the same stone used initially to correct the condition. If the line is too low or the width is not correct, the seat must be reground with stones of different angles (Figure 9–73).

FIGURE 9–72   Grinding the seat. *Courtesy of Hall-Toledo, Inc.*

| CORRECT | SEAT TOO NARROW | SEAT TOO WIDE | SEAT TOO HIGH | SEAT TOO LOW |

FIGURE 9–73 The fit of the valve in the seat should be checked carefully.

Cutting Valve Seats Cutting valve seats differs from grinding only in the equipment used (Figure 9–74). Hardened valve seat cutters replace grinding wheels for seat finishing. The basic seat cutting procedures are the same as those for grinding.

Machining Valve Seats As stated earlier in this chapter, a valve system rebuilding machine such as the one shown in Figure 9–75 can be used to install valve guides and to machine valve seats. Some have optional seat cutters that make three-angle cuts. The cutters are set to the proper diameter. Once set, they machine the seat as well as the top and throat angles. Two primary advantages of these cutters over other methods are high speed and precision.

VALVE STEM SEALS

Valve stem seals (Figure 9–76) are used on many engines to control the amount of oil allowed between the valve stem and guide. The stems and guides will scuff and wear excessively if they do not have enough lubrication. Too much oil produces heavy deposits that build up on the intake valve and hard deposits at the head end of the exhaust valve stem. Worn valve stem seals can increase the oil consumption by as much as 70 percent.

There are basically three types of seals. **Positive seals** fit tightly around the top of the stem and scrape

FIGURE 9–75 Typical valve system rebuilding machine. *Courtesy of Peterson Machine Tool, Inc.*

oil off the valve as it moves up and down. Deflector, splash, or **umbrella-type seals** ride up and down on the valve stems to deflect oil away from the guides. O-ring seals installed over the valve stem are also used to prevent oil from moving into the guide when the valve is open.

The ultimate effectiveness of the valve stem seal depends entirely on the way it is secured to the guide. Many guides require machining to accept the stem seals. This must be done using the proper tools. A special valve guide machining tool is available for valve seal cutting (Figure 9–77). Such a tool is made up of a cutter and pilot, with sizes that vary according to the valve stem diameter and desired guide OD.

FIGURE 9–74 Cutting a valve seat. *Courtesy of Neway Manufacturing, Inc.*

FIGURE 9–76 Valve stem seal fit over a guide.

FIGURE 9–77 Typical valve guide machining tool. *Courtesy of Goodson Shop Supplies*

TEFLON

TEFLON AND RUBBER

RUBBER TWO RING

FIGURE 9–78 Positive valve seal designs. *Courtesy of Goodson Shop Supplies*

The pilot is inserted into the guide, and the cutting tool machines the top of the guide.

Installing Positive Valve Seals

To install a positive valve seal (Figure 9–78), place the plastic sleeve in the kit over the end of the valve stem (Figure 9–79). This will protect the seal as it slides over the keeper grooves. Lightly lubricate the sleeve. If it extends more than 1/16 inch below the lower keeper groove, you might want to remove the sleeve and cut off the excess length for easier removal. Carefully place the seal on the cap over the valve stem and push the seal down until it touches the top of the valve guide (Figure 9–80). At this point, the installation cap can be removed and placed

FIGURE 9–79 The plastic sleeve goes over the end of the valve stem before the seal is slipped over the guide. *Courtesy of Fel-Pro, Inc.*

FIGURE 9–80 Push the seal down until it touches the top of the valve guide. *Courtesy of Fel-Pro, Inc.*

FIGURE 9–81 Installing an umbrella valve seal. *Courtesy of Fel-Pro, Inc.*

on the next valve. A special installation tool can be used to finish pushing the seal over the guide until the seal is flush with the top of the guide.

Installing Umbrella-Type Valve Seals

An umbrella-type seal is installed on the valve stem before the spring is installed. It is pushed down on the valve stem until it touches the valve guide boss (Figure 9–81). It will be positioned correctly when the valve first opens.

Installing O-Rings

When installing O-rings, use engine oil to lightly lubricate the O-ring. Then install it in the lower groove of the lock section of the valve stem (Figure 9–82). Make sure the O-ring is not twisted.

Valve Spring

The valve spring performs two functions. It closes the valve and maintains valve train contact during the opening and closing of the valve. Insufficient spring pressure can lead to valve bounce and breakage. Too much pressure will cause premature camshaft lobe wear and can also lead to valve breakage. Figure 9–83 shows the components that make up a valve spring assembly.

FIGURE 9–82 Installing an O-ring. *Courtesy of Fel-Pro, Inc.*

FIGURE 9–83 The valve spring is compressed between the valve spring seat on the cylinder head and the spring retainer.

The common designs of valve springs are illustrated in Figure 9–84. A problem that valve springs might have is **spring surge**. As the name implies, spring surge is the violent extending motion of the coils resulting in abnormal oscillation. The uniform pitch type is used when surge is usually not encountered. The other designs represent different approaches to surge control. Mechanical spring surge dampers depend on friction to control surge. Therefore, it is advisable to replace them at the same time the springs are replaced. Always install the closely wound coils of a basket coil-type spring toward the head end of the valve. Mechanical surge and vibration dampers should also be installed toward the head end of the

FIGURE 9–84 Common valve spring designs.

valve. To dampen spring vibrations and increase total spring pressure, some engine manufacturers use a reverse wound secondary spring inside the main spring.

Spring surge can occur when the springs are weak, the installed spring height is improper, or engine speeds are excessive. Whatever the cause, the occurrence of spring surge is visually apparent. The ends of the springs will look smooth or polished due to their rotation during operation. If left alone and not corrected, spring surge can cause damage to the valve train. For example, the self-rotation of the valve springs causes a grinding action between the valve face and seat. As a result, the face will wear down and the seat will recess. Continued operation with spring surge can also cause the springs to break.

The high stresses and temperatures imposed on valve springs during operation cause them to weaken and sometimes break. Rust pits will also cause valve spring breakage. To determine if the spring can be reused, the following tests should be performed.

FREESTANDING HEIGHT TEST Line up all the springs on a flat surface and place a straightedge across the tops (Figure 9–85). Free length should be within 1/16 inch of OE specifications. Throw away any spring that is not within specifications.

SPRING SQUARENESS TEST A spring that is not square will cause side pressure on the valve stem and abnormal wear. To check squareness, set a spring upright against a square (Figure 9–86). Turn the spring until a gap appears between the spring and the square. Measure the gap with a feeler gauge. If the gap is more than 0.060 inch, the spring should be replaced.

FIGURE 9–85 Freestanding spring height test. *Courtesy of Perfect Circle/Dana*

FIGURE 9–86 Spring squareness test. *Courtesy of Perfect Circle/Dana*

OPEN/CLOSE SPRING PRESSURE TEST Use a spring tester to check for open and close spring pressure. Close pressure guarantees a tight seal. The open pressure overcomes valve train inertia and closes the valve when it should close. Service manuals list spring pressure specifications according to spring height (Figure 9–87). The proper procedure for testing valve spring tension is given in Photo Sequence 5. Low spring pressure may allow the valve to float during high speed operation. Excessive spring tension may cause premature valve train wear. Any spring that does not meet specifications should be replaced.

Valve Spring Retainers and Keepers

Valve spring retainers and valve keepers hold the valve spring and valve in place. The retainer holds the spring in line with the valve stem. A worn retainer will allow the spring to move away from the centerline of the valve. This will affect valve operation because spring tension on the valve will not be evenly distributed. Each retainer should be carefully inspected for cracks, since a cracked retainer may result in serious damage to the engine. The inside shape of most retainers is a cone that matches the outside shape of the keepers. This must be a good fit, so the keepers will stay in their grooves on the valve stem.

The valve stem grooves should match the inside shape of the keepers. Some valves have multiple

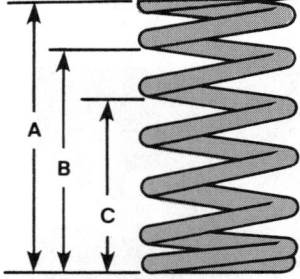

FIGURE 9–87 Valve spring height terminology: (A) free height, (B) valve closed spring height, and (C) valve open spring height.

FIGURE 9–88 (A) An even pattern means the rotator is functioning properly, while (B) no pattern and (C) a partial pattern means the rotator should be replaced and the rotation checked.

keeper grooves. Others have only one. All of the valve stem grooves should be inspected for damage and fit by inserting a keeper in them. Both the retainers and keepers should be carefully inspected for damage. If a defect is found, they should be replaced.

Valve Rotators

Most rotators impart positive rotation to the valve during each valve cycle and improve valve life two to five times, and in some cases, even more. In normal operation, rotators will continue to function for more than 100,000 miles and require no maintenance. However, when valves are refaced or replaced at high mileage, the rotators should be replaced because they cannot be visually inspected accurately. Whether or not they rotate when held in the hand is no indication of their function in the engine. While rotation can only be checked in a running engine, uneven wear patterns (Figure 9–88) develop at the valve stem tip if the rotators are not functioning properly.

Several types of rotators are available, but the most commonly used are the following.

◆ Ball type. This employs two small balls and slight ramp. Each ball moves down its ramp to turn the rotator sections in a positive direction as the valve opens (Figure 9–89).
◆ Spring-loaded type. In this design, the spring starts to move down as the valve opens. The spring-loaded rotator can rotate the valve in either direction (Figure 9–89).
◆ Free type. This rotator permits a momentary release of the spring tension from the valve during opening so the valve is free to rotate (Figure 9–90).

BALL TYPE

SPRING TYPE

FIGURE 9–89 Ball-type and spring-loaded type valve rotators.

PHOTO SEQUENCE 5

MEASURING AND FITTING VALVE SPRINGS

P5–1 Prior to installing the valve and fitting valve springs, all other head work should be completed.

P5–4 While pulling up on the retainer, measure the distance between the bottom of the retainer and the spring pad on the cylinder head with a divider.

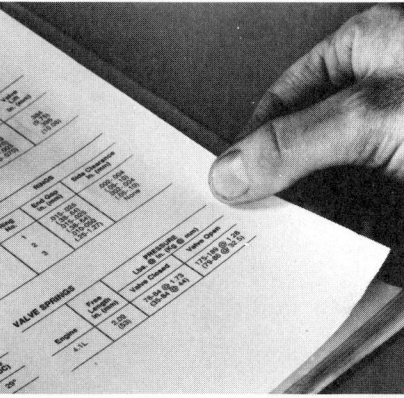

P5–6 Compare this measurement with the specifications given in the service manual for installed spring height.

P5–2 Install the valve into its proper valve guide.

P5–5 Use a scale to determine the measurement expressed by the divider.

P5–7 If measured installed height is greater than the specifications, a valve shim must be placed under the spring to correct the difference.

P5–3 Install the valve retainer and keepers. Without the spring, these must be held in place.

(continued)

P5-8 Spring tension must be checked at the installed spring height; therefore, if a shim is to be used, insert it under the spring on the valve spring tension gauge.

P5-9 Compress the spring into the installed height by pressing down on the tester's lever.

P5-10 The tension gauge will reflect the pressure of the spring when compressed to the installed or valve closed height. Compare this reading to the specifications.

P5-11 Now compress the spring to the open height specification. Use the rule on the gauge or a scale to measure the compressed height.

P5-12 Compare this reading to specifications. Any pressure outside the pressure range given in the specifications indicates the spring should be replaced. After the tension and height have been checked, the spring can be installed on the valve stem.

FIGURE 9–90 Free-type valve rotator.

The action does not cause positive valve rotation. Engine vibration and turbulence of gases contribute to valve rotation during the time the valve is free to rotate.

ASSEMBLING THE CYLINDER HEAD

Before a cleaned or reconditioned cylinder head is reassembled and installed, there are two critical measurements that must be carefully checked: the installed stem height and the installed spring height.

Installed stem height is determined by measuring the distance between the spring seat and stem tip. Since this measurement directly influences rocker arm geometry and installed spring height, accuracy and precision are important. This is especially true when the valve or valve seat has been ground. There are a number of tools that can be used to obtain an accurate stem height reading. These include a depth micrometer, vernier caliper, and telescoping gauge (Figure 9–91). There are several specially designed stem height gauges available (Figure 9–92). Use these as directed by their manufacturers.

USING SERVICE MANUALS

Stem height specifications are often not available in service manuals. As a guide for assembly, record the stem heights for all valves during disassembly. ■

Another specification can be used that corresponds directly to installed stem height and that is installed spring height. Installed spring height is measured from the spring seat to the underside of the retainer when it is assembled with keepers and held in place. This measurement, which can be made by using a set of dividers or scales, telescoping gauge, or spring height gauge, should be taken only after valve

A

B

C

FIGURE 9–91 Stem height can be measured using (A) a depth micrometer, (B) a vernier caliper, or (C) a telescoping gauge. *Courtesy of TRW, Inc.*

FIGURE 9–92 Special stem height gauges. *Courtesy of Goodson Shop Supplies*

and seat work is completed, valves are installed in their guides, and retainers and keepers are assembled.

By comparing the measurement to factory specs, it is possible to determine the needed increase in installed stem height. For example, if the installed spring height for an exhaust valve is 1.600 inches, and the measurement is 1.677 inches, the increase in spring height is 0.077 inch. This means installed stem height also has been increased by 0.077 inch.

Adjustments to valve spring height can be made with the aid of valve spring inserts, otherwise known as spring shims. Even though valve shims come in only three standard thicknesses—0.060, 0.030, and 0.015 inch—using combinations of different shims gives the correct amount of compensation (within 0.005 or 0.010 inch).

SHOP TALK

A 0.060-inch shim may increase spring pressure by 12 pounds, whereas 0.030-inch and 0.015-inch shims increase pressure by 6 and 3 pounds. ■

By comparing spring height to specifications, the desired amount of spring tension correction can be easily determined. For example, if spring height is 0.180 inch and the specifications call for 0.149 inch, a 0.030 shim (0.149 + 0.030 = 0.179) would be needed. If more than one shim is required, place the thickest one next to the spring, not the head. If one side of the shim is serrated or dimpled, place that side over the valve stem and onto the spring seat. There are two words of caution.

1. If the springs have close-spaced coils, the close end should be placed next to the head.
2. If the spring has an OD that is slightly tapered, the end with the greater diameter should be face down.

SHOP TALK

Valve keepers should be replaced in pairs. If a new keeper is mated with a used one, the spring retainer may cock and break off the valve tip or allow the assembly to come apart. ■

With the valve inserted into its guide, position the valve spring inserts, valve spring, and retainer over the valve stem. Using a valve spring compressor, compress the spring just enough to install the valve keepers into their grooves (Figure 9–93). Excess pressure may cause the retainer to damage the oil seal. Release the spring compressor and tap the valve stem with a rubber mallet to seat the keepers. When doing this, the valve will open slightly. To prevent damage to the valves, never tap the stems with the cylinder head lying flat on the bench. Turn the head on its side or raise it off the bench.

CAUTION:

If the keepers are not fully seated, the spring assembly could fly apart and cause personal injury (or serious damage to the engine if it occurs while the engine is running). For these reasons, it is good practice to assemble the valves with the retainers facing a wall and to wear eye protection. ■

Valve spring compressors are available in different designs for different applications. The most commonly used compressor is hand-operated. There are two different hand-operated designs: a universal tool with interchangeable jaws and a compressor specifically

FIGURE 9–93 Compress the spring just enough to install the keepers.

designed for OHC engines. This compressor allows for positive contact on the retainer without removing the camshaft. Another type of spring compressor is air-operated. Air-operated spring compressors are typically found in high-volume engine rebuilding shops.

CASE STUDY

While traveling in a late-model car, a family's car engine overheats. Water is added to the radiator. Then the car is taken to a service station to be diagnosed and repaired. Simple tests reveal a heater hose has split and is leaking coolant. The hose is replaced and new coolant added to the system. With the car repaired, the family continues on their trip.

After driving only a short time, smoke is noticed coming out of the tailpipe. The engine shakes violently whenever it is placed in a load condition. The driver turns the car around and heads back to the shop that fixed the leak. Upon arrival, the driver says the technician must have knocked something loose or broken something while replacing the hose. The technician doubts this, but agrees to take another look.

A cylinder power balance test would verify this, but it cannot be conducted because of the erratic idle. Instead, the spark plugs are removed and inspected. All look normal except for plug #2, which looks newer than the rest. A comparison test is taken and cylinder #2 has very low dry and wet readings. Then a cylinder leakage test is conducted. Cylinder #2 has excessive leakage and air can be felt leaving the exhaust pipe.

These test results lead to the conclusion that the engine is running on one less cylinder because an exhaust valve is not sealing. The customer still feels the technician did something wrong but agrees to allow the technician to remove the cylinder head for further diagnosis. As soon as the head is off the block, the problem is identified. The exhaust valve seat for cylinder #2 came loose from the head and is preventing the valve from closing. The technician then explains that this undoubtedly happened when the engine overheated, due to the expansion of the metal. The customer is satisfied with the explanation and allows the technician to correct the problem. The family is then able to continue their trip.

KEY TERMS

AA	Quenching
Broaching	Reaming
CC-ing	RMS
Cross-flow ports	Shrouding
Damper spring	Siamese ports
Hemi-head	Spring surge
Hemispherical	Swirl combustion
combustion chamber	chamber
Knurling	Turbulence
Margin	Umbrella-type seal
Milling	Valve face
Poppet	Valve keeper
Porosity	Wedge-type combustion
Positive seal	chamber
Quench area	

SUMMARY

◆ Aluminum cylinder heads have grown in popularity recently due to their light weight. However, the thermal expansion characteristics of aluminum can lead to problems such as leaking and cracking. The natural porosity of aluminum is another negative factor.

◆ An efficient combustion chamber must be compact in order to minimize heat loss. Popular combustion chamber designs include the wedge, hemispherical, swirl, chamber-in-piston, and fast-burn varieties.

◆ Every cylinder of a four-stroke engine contains at least one intake valve and one exhaust valve. The type of valve used in automotive engines is known as a poppet, which is characterized by a popping action as the valve opens and closes.

◆ Multivalve engines feature either three or four valves per cylinder, which means better combustion and reduced misfire and detonation. These benefits are offset to some extent by a more complicated camshaft arrangement.

◆ The means of resurfacing the deck of a cylinder head include grinding, milling, belt surfacing, and broaching.

◆ The amount of stock removed from the cylinder head gasket surface must be limited. Excessive surfacing can create problems in the engine's clearance volume and compression ratio, not to mention piston/valve interference and misalignment.

◆ The two surfaces of a valve reconditioned by grinding are the face and the tip. Valves can be refaced on grinding or cutting machines, with the traditional grinding method still the most popular. In general, do not grind a valve face to the point where the margin is reduced by more than 25 percent, or to where it is less than 0.045 inch on the exhaust and 0.030 inch on the intake valves.

◆ One of the fastest methods for restoring the inside diameter dimensions of a worn valve guide is knurling. This process does not change the centerline of the valve stem very much, so it reduces the work needed to reseat the valve. Reaming repairs worn guides by increasing the guide hole size to take an oversize valve stem or by restoring the guide to its original dimension after knurling or installing inserts.

◆ Pressing out an old valve guide to install a new one can be difficult on some aluminum heads where the interference fit is considerable. Preheating the head in an oven prior to guide removal and lubricating the liners before driving them out can make the job easier.

◆ To ensure proper seating of a valve, the seat must be the correct width, in the correct location on the valve face, and concentric with the guide. The ideal seat width for automotive engines is 1/16 inch for intake valves and 3/32 inch for exhaust valves.

◆ When grinding a valve seat, choosing the correct size pilot and stone is important. For soft seats such as cast iron, use a hard stone. For hard seats, a soft stone is needed. An overhang (the area of the face between the contact area and the margin) of 1/64 inch is required for both the intake and exhaust valves.

◆ Valve stem seals are used to control the amount of oil between the valve stem and guide. Too much produces deposits, while insufficient lubrication leads to excessive wear. The effectiveness of a valve stem seal depends on the way it is secured to the guide.

◆ The valve spring closes the valve and also maintains the valve train contact during the opening and closing of the valve. To determine if a spring needs to be replaced, three tests are valuable: free-standing height, spring squareness, and open/close spring pressure.

◆ Two critical measurements that must be made before a cylinder head is reassembled and installed are installed stem height and installed spring height. The first of these is determined by measuring the distance between the spring seat and stem tip. The latter is measured by the spring seat to the underside of the retainer when it is assembled with keepers and held in place.

TECH MANUAL
The following procedures are included in Chapter 9 of the *Tech Manual* that accompanies this book:

1. Inspect cylinder head for wear.

2. Inspect and test valve springs for squareness, pressure, and free height comparison.

3. Inspect valve spring retainers, locks, and valve lock grooves.

4. Replace valve stem seals, in vehicle.

5. Recondition valve faces.

REVIEW QUESTIONS

1. Why have auto manufacturers switched from cast iron to aluminum cylinder heads?

2. Define valve margin.

3. What usually causes warpage in an aluminum cylinder head?

4. What is one microinch equal to?

5. Why do some technicians not consider knurling a long-term repair?

6. Which of the following can be reconditioned by grinding?
   - **a.** valve face
   - **b.** valve tip
   - **c.** both a and b
   - **d.** neither a nor b

7. Which of the following is *not* true of knurling?
   - **a.** It is one of the fastest techniques for restoring the ID dimensions of a worn valve guide.
   - **b.** It reduces the amount of work necessary to reseat the valve.
   - **c.** It is useful for restoring badly worn guides to their original condition.
   - **d.** None of the above.

8. According to most experts, what is the maximum amount of acceptable wear for knurling?
   a. 0.005 to 0.009 inch
   b. 0.006 to 0.008 inch
   c. 0.004 to 0.007 inch
   d. 0.003 to 0.006 inch

9. To ensure proper seating of the valve, the valve seat must be ____.
   a. correct width
   b. correct location on the valve face
   c. concentric with the guide
   d. all the above

10. When grinding valve seats, ____.
    a. a pilot shaft is inserted into the valve guide
    b. a hard stone should be used on a hard seat
    c. a soft stone should be used on a soft seat
    d. all of the above

11. If the valve face and valve seat do not contact each other evenly after grindings, ____.
    a. regrind with the same stone
    b. regrind with stones of different angles
    c. discard cylinder head
    d. none of the above

12. Technician A says bronze valve guides retain oil better than cast-iron ones. Technician B says cast-iron valve guides are easier to machine than bronze guides. Who is correct?
    a. Technician A   c. Both A and B
    b. Technician B   d. Neither A nor B

13. Technician A says positive valve stem seals fit tightly around the top of the stem. Technician B says positive stem seals scrape oil off the valve as it moves up and down. Who is correct?
    a. Technician A   c. Both A and B
    b. Technician B   d. Neither A nor B

14. When adjusting spring height, Technician A places the thickest shim next to the spring. Technician B places the thickest shim below the retainer. Who is correct?
    a. Technician A   c. Both A and B
    b. Technician B   d. Neither A nor B

15. Which type of combustion chamber is considered to be nonturbulent?
    a. wedge   c. both and b
    b. hemispherical   d. neither a nor b

16. Technician A uses a profilometer to measure cylinder head surface finish. Technician B uses a specimen block kit to measure the finish of a cylinder head's sealing surface. Who is correct?
    a. Technician A   c. Both A and B
    b. Technician B   d. Neither A nor B

17. Which type of surfacing machine uses underside rotary cutters?
    a. milling
    b. broaching
    c. belt
    d. grinding

18. Technician A says it is not necessary to measure valve stem height unless the valves have been replaced. Technician B says the valve stem height can be adjusted with shims. Who is correct?
    a. Technician A   c. Both A and B
    b. Technician B   d. Neither A nor B

19. ____ is the cooling of gases by pressing them into a thin area.
    a. Turbulence
    b. Shrouding
    c. Reaming
    d. Quenching

20. Technician A uses a 30-degree stone for topping a 45-degree valve seat. Technician B uses a 60-degree stone to lower a 45-degree valve seat. Who is correct?
    a. Technician A   c. Both A and B
    b. Technician B   d. Neither A nor B

CAMSHAFTS AND VALVE TRAINS

10

OBJECTIVES

◆ **Describe the purpose, operation, and location of the camshaft.** ◆ **Identify the parts of the valve train and the purpose of each.** ◆ **Inspect the camshaft, valve train, and timing components.** ◆ **Describe the four types of camshafts.** ◆ **Describe how to install a camshaft and its bearings.** ◆ **Explain the factors involved in camshaft/crankshaft timing.**

The camshaft and valve train work together to open and close the intake and exhaust valve of the engine. This interaction must be precisely timed for the engine to breathe properly and burn fuel efficiently. Although the camshaft does not directly close the valves, its lobes move away and allow the valve springs to close them. Camshaft timing and the valve springs work together to close the valves at the correct time.

CAMSHAFT

A camshaft is a shaft (Figure 10–1) with a cam for each exhaust and intake valve, each one placed to allow for the proper timing of each valve. A cam is a device that changes rotary motion into reciprocating motion. Each cam has a high spot or cam lobe that controls the opening of the valves. The height of the lobe is proportional to the amount the valve will open. Some camshafts may also be equipped with an eccentric to operate the fuel pump and a gear to

drive the distributor and oil pump. Some diesel engines utilize lobes for fuel injectors, fuel injection pumps, or air starting valves.

The camshaft can be located in either the cylinder block or in the cylinder head. If the camshaft is in the block (Figure 10–2), it is positioned above the crankshaft, and the valves are opened through lifters, pushrods, and rocker arms. As the cam lobe rotates, it pushes up on the lifter, which lifts up the pushrod, moving one end of the rocker arm up while the other end pushes the valve down to open it. As the cam rotates, the valve spring forces the valve to close and maintains the contact between the valve and the rocker arm, thereby keeping the pushrod and the lifter in contact with the rotating cam.

Overhead camshaft engines have the camshaft mounted in or on the cylinder head (Figure 10–3). OHC engines have no need for pushrods. As the camshaft rotates, the cams ride directly above the valves. The lobes open the valves by either directly de-

FIGURE 10–1   Parts of a camshaft.

CAMSHAFT

CRANKSHAFT

FIGURE 10–2 The camshaft may be located in the cylinder block. *Courtesy of Ford Motor Company*

pressing the valve or by depressing the valve through the use of a cam follower, rocker arm, or bucket-type tappet. The closing of the valves is still the responsibility of the valve springs.

An advantage of the overhead camshaft engine is that through the elimination of the pushrod and, on some engines, the valve lifter, the inertia of the valve train is lower and there is less deflection in the system. Valve float is less likely to occur in OHC engines because they have fewer valve train parts and, therefore, less inertia. Inertia is best defined as the tendency of an object to continue moving in the same direc-

OVERHEAD CAMSHAFT

FIGURE 10–3 On OHC engines, the camshaft is located in or on the cylinder head. *Courtesy of Ford Motor Company*

FIGURE 10–4 The typical camshaft bearing is a full round design.

tion without a direct force applied to it. The heavier the object is and the greater its speed, the higher the inertia force will be. The OHC arrangement also allows for more precise control of valve opening and closing times.

Camshaft Bearings

The camshaft is supported by several friction-type bearings, or bushings. They are designed as one piece and are typically pressed into the camshaft bore in the cylinder head or block (Figure 10–4). Some OHC engines use split bearings to support the camshaft. Camshaft bearings are normally replaced during engine rebuilding. The old bearings should be inspected for signs of unusual wear that may indicate an oiling or bore alignment problem.

Cam bearings are normally press fit into the block or head using a bushing driver and hammer (Figure 10–5). This procedure is illustrated in the *Tech Manual* that accompanies this textbook.

Some overhead camshafts do not have bearing inserts. The bores in the aluminum casting serve as a bearing surface. On others, the camshaft bearings might be split two-piece inserts or the full-round type. When installing full-round bearings, a special type of puller tool such as the one shown in Figure 10–6 is required. Using this tool, it is possible to pull out the old bearings and push in new ones. Be sure to follow the manufacturer's directions when using this tool.

FIGURE 10–5 Installing a cam bearing using a hammer and driving tool. *Courtesy of Sealed Power Corporation*

FIGURE 10–6   A puller is needed to install split-type bearings.

FIGURE 10–7   Hydraulic valve lifter.

FIGURE 10–8   Solid valve lifter.

⚠️ **WARNING!**

The use of a standard bushing driver and hammer is not recommended because aluminum bearing supports are very easily damaged or broken. This can result in expensive head replacement. ■

After the cam bearings have been installed, the oil hole in the bearings should be checked for proper alignment with those in the block or head. This will ensure correct lubrication and oil supply in vital engine areas. Proper alignment can be checked by inserting a wire through the holes or by squirting oil into the holes. If the oil does not run out, the holes are misaligned. This procedure should be repeated with each bearing.

Valve Lifters

Valve lifters, sometimes called **cam followers** or tappets, follow the contour or shape of the cam lobe. Lifters are either mechanical (solid) or hydraulic. Solid valve lifters provide for a rigid connection between the camshaft and the valves. Hydraulic valve lifters provide for the same connection but use oil to absorb the shock that results from the movement of the valve train. Although both types function the same, solid lifters have certain disadvantages when compared to hydraulic lifters.

Hydraulic lifters (Figure 10–7) are designed to automatically compensate for the effects of engine temperature. Changes in temperature cause valve train components to expand and contract. Hydraulic lifters are designed to automatically maintain a direct connection between valve train parts.

Solid lifters (Figure 10–8) do not have this built-in feature and require a clearance between the parts of the valve train. This clearance allows for expansion of the components as the engine gets hot. Periodic adjustment of this clearance must be made. Excessive clearance might cause a clicking noise.

This clicking noise is also an indication of the hammering of valve train parts against one another, which will result in reduced camshaft and lifter life.

In an effort to reduce the friction—and the resulting power loss—from the lifter rubbing against the cam lobes, engine manufacturers often use roller-type hydraulic lifters. Roller lifters (Figure 10–9) are manufactured with a large roller on the camshaft end of the lifter. The roller acts like a wheel and allows the lifter to follow the cam lobe contour better than a flat-type lifter with reduced friction between the two contacting surfaces. Friction is reduced because the lifter rolls along the surface of the cam lobe as opposed to rubbing against it.

FIGURE 10–9   Typical roller lifter.

FIGURE 10–10 Exploded view of hydraulic valve lifter.

Operation of Hydraulic Lifter A typical hydraulic lifter contains ten parts. There is a plunger, oil metering valve disc, pushrod seat, retaining ring, valve disc or ball, check valve retainer, check valve spring, retainer clip, and plunger return spring all housed in a hardened iron body (Figure 10–10).

When the lifter is resting on the base circle of the cam (not on the lobe), the valve is closed and the plunger spring inside the lifter maintains a zero clearance in the valve train. Oil is pumped by the oil pump to the oil filter, main bearings, camshaft bearings, and to the oil feed holes of the valve lifter bore. Pressurized oil enters the lifter and flows through the plunger. Oil flow continues through the lifter until it is filled. The pressure of the oil seals the oil in the lifter by forcing down the check valve inside the lifter (Figure 10–11). The oil between the plunger and the check valve forms a rigid connection between the lifter and the pushrod. The position of the plunger inside the lifter is determined by the force of the pushrod on the plunger.

As the valve train grows from heat, clearance is reduced so the plunger is held lower in the lifter. As the cam lobe turns, the lifter's oil feed hole is no longer lined up with the feed in the block. New supplies of oil are not available until the lifter returns to the lower part of its bore. Also, the amount of force on the plunger increases as new forces result from the opening of the valve against the pressure of the valve spring. This new pressure causes the plunger to depress slightly. This allows a small amount of oil to leak out. This leaking out of oil is called leakdown.

Leakdown is defined as the relative movement of the plunger with respect to the lifter body after the check valve is seated by the pressurized oil. When the cam rotates and the lifter returns to the base of the cam, oil can again enter the lifter. At this point, the oil fills the lifter, and the lifter is ready to open the valve again.

If the lifter is unable to fill with oil or if it does not leak down the proper amount, a noise will be heard when the engine is running. Quite often light tapping noises are referred to as lifter noises. The lifter is not always at fault. There are other causes for similar sounding engine noises, such as worn cam lobes, stuck valves, broken valve springs, insufficient lubrication between the rocker arms and the pushrods or valves, or loose rocker arms. All of these problems relate to the opening and closing of the valves and will take on the rhythm of valve operation. Careful troubleshooting will help determine if the cause of the noise is a lifter or one of the other possible problems.

Pushrods

Pushrods are designed to be the connecting link between the rocker arm and the valve lifter; they are either solid or hollow. On certain engines, the pushrods have a hole in the center to allow oil to pass from the hydraulic lifter to the upper portion of the cylinder head. Some are designed to have small convex balls on both ends. These balls ride inside the lifter and the rocker arm.

Rather than having a convex ball, the end of the pushrod on solid lifters is concave. This end then fits into a ball on the rocker arm. Figure 10–12 shows examples of different types of pushrod ends. Pushrods are used only on engines that have the camshaft placed within the block.

FIGURE 10–11 Hydraulic roller-type valve lifter with the valve closed and the valve open.

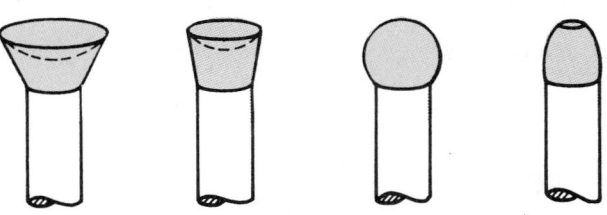

FIGURE 10–12 Several types of ends are used on pushrods.

PUSHROD GUIDE PLATES In some engines, pushrod **guide plates** are used to limit side movement of the pushrods. The guides hold the pushrods in alignment with the rocker arms. When the pushrods pass through holes in the cylinder head or intake manifold, guide plates are not needed. This is true only when the holes for the pushrods are small enough to limit the sideways movement of the pushrod.

Rocker Arms

Rocker arms are designed to do two things. They change the direction of the cam's lifting force and provide a certain mechanical advantage during valve lifting. As the lifter and pushrod move upward, the rocker arm pivots at the center point (Figure 10–13). This causes a change in direction on the valve side. This change in direction causes the valve to move downward and open.

On some engines, it may be important to open the valve more than the actual lift of the cam lobe. This can be done by changing the distance from the pivot point to the ends of the rocker arm. The difference in length from the valve end of the rocker arm and the center of the pivot point (shaft or stud) compared to the pushrod or cam end of the rocker arm and the pivot point (shaft or stud) is expressed as a ratio. Usually, rocker arm ratios range from 1:1 to 1:1.75. A ratio larger than 1:1 results in the valve opening farther than the actual lift of the cam lobe (Figure 10–14).

Rocker arms are designed and mounted in several ways (Figure 10–15). Springs, washers, individual rocker arms, and bolts are used in this type of assembly. Other rocker arms are placed on studs that are mounted directly in the cylinder head.

Some overhead camshaft engines use rocker arms in such a way that the camshaft rides directly on top

FIGURE 10–14 Rocker arm ratio is determined by the distance from (A) the rocker pivot to (B) the contact points of the pushrod and (C) the valve stem tip.

of the rocker arm. Other overhead camshaft engines do not use rocker arms and the camshaft rides directly on top of the valves.

Rocker arms are made of steel, aluminum, or cast iron. The most common for current use are the stamped steel variety (Figure 10–16). They are lightweight, strong, and inexpensive to manufacture. They usually pivot on a stud and ball.

Cast-iron rockers are used in large, low-speed engines. They almost always pivot on a common shaft. Aluminum rockers, on the other hand, are generally used on high-performance applications and frequently pivot on needle bearings. The use of needle bearings reduces the friction at the pivot.

Timing Mechanisms

On a four-stroke cycle engine, the camshaft is driven by the crankshaft at half its speed. This is accomplished through the use of a camshaft drive gear or drive sprocket that is twice as large as the crankshaft sprocket. For every two complete turns of the crankshaft, the camshaft turns once. Because the camshaft rotates at half the speed of the crankshaft and because the exhaust and intake valves are each opened only once during the four strokes, there is a cam lobe for each exhaust valve and a lobe for each intake valve on the camshaft.

SHOP TALK

The cam sprocket or gear has twice as many teeth as the crankshaft sprocket or gear. ∎

The following are the basic configurations for driving the camshaft.

GEAR DRIVE A gear on the crankshaft meshes directly with another gear on the camshaft (Figure 10–17A). The gear on the crankshaft is usually made of steel. The gear on the camshaft may be steel for

FIGURE 10–13 Rocker arms change the direction of the valve operating mechanism.

RETAINER SCREW

ROCKER ARM SHAFT

ROCKER ARM

SPACER

PLUG

A

SHAFT-MOUNTED NON-ADJUSTABLE ROCKER ARM

ROCKER ARM STUD NUT

ROCKER ARM

FULCRUM SEAT (BALL PIVOT)

HOLLOW STUD

OIL HOLE

B

STUD-MOUNTED ROCKER ARM

ROCKER ARM SHAFT

OIL HOLE

RETAINER

ROCKER ARM

ADJUSTING SCREW

LOCKNUT

COMPRESSION SPRING

CONICAL SPRING

ROCKER SUPPORT

C

SHAFT-MOUNTED ADJUSTABLE ROCKER ARM

ATTACHING BOLT

FULCRUM

OIL HOLE

ROCKER ARM

FULCRUM GUIDE

THREADED PEDESTAL

D

PEDESTAL-MOUNTED ROCKER ARM

FIGURE 10–15 Various rocker arm mountings: (A) shaft-mounted nonadjustable; (B) stud-mounted; (C) shaft-mounted adjustable; and (D) pedestal-mounted.

FIGURE 10–16 Stamped steel rocker arms.

heavy-duty applications, or it may be made of aluminum or pressed fiber when quiet operation is a major consideration. The gears are helical in design. Helical gears are used because they are stronger and also tend to push the camshaft backward during operation to help prevent the camshaft from walking out of the block.

CHAIN DRIVE Sprockets on the camshaft and the crankshaft are linked by a continuous chain (Figure 10–17B). The sprocket on the crankshaft is usually made of steel. The sprocket on the camshaft may be steel for heavy-duty applications. When quiet operation is a major consideration, an aluminum sprocket with nylon covering on the teeth is used. There are two common types of timing chains. One is a silent link-type chain that is used in standard and light-duty applications. The other is a roller link chain, which is used in heavy-duty applications. The roller link chain may have a single or double row of links.

BELT DRIVE Sprockets on the crankshaft and the camshaft are linked by a continuous neoprene belt (Figure 10–17C). The belt has square-shaped internal teeth that mesh with teeth on the sprockets. Some drive belts have slightly rounded teeth to reduce noise. However, don't assume that rounded teeth are

A OHC ENGINE WITH BELT DRIVEN CAMSHAFT   **B** OHV ENGINE WITH TIMING CHAIN AND GEARS   **C** OHV ENGINE WITH GEAR DRIVEN CAMSHAFT

FIGURE 10–17 Different timing drive mechanisms used today: (A) belt drive; (B) chain drive; (C) gear drive. *Courtesy of Ford Motor Company*

normal. Check to see if the rounding is caused by wear. If the belt is worn, replace it. Most technicians replace the belt anytime it has been removed. The timing belt is reinforced with nylon or fiberglass to give it strength and prevent stretching. This drive configuration is limited to overhead camshaft engines.

TIMING BELT AND CHAIN TENSIONERS Many engines with chain-driven and all engines with belt-driven camshafts use a tensioner. The tensioner pushes against the belt or chain to keep it tight. This serves to keep it from slipping on the sprockets, provide more precise valve timing, and compensate for component stretch and wear. The tensioner may have provisions for adjustment or may be self-adjusting. Check the service manual to identify the adjustment procedures.

TIMING MARKS The camshaft and the crankshaft must always remain in the same relative position to each other. They must also be in the proper initial relation to each other. This initial position between the two shafts is designated by marks called timing marks. To obtain the correct initial relationship of the components, the corresponding marks are aligned at the time of assembly (Figure 10–18).

AUXILIARY CAMSHAFT FUNCTIONS The camshaft, driven by the crankshaft, may be used to drive other engine components. On gasoline engines, the oil pump and the distributor are usually driven from a common gear that is machined into the camshaft. The fuel pump can also be driven by the camshaft. This is usually accomplished by machining an extra lobe or eccentric on the camshaft to operate the pump.

USING SERVICE MANUALS

Normally, camshaft timing marks are shown in the engine section of a service manual, under the heading of Timing Belt or Chain R&R. ∎

Variable Valve Timing

The absolute best valve timing for an engine varies with engine rpm and the load on the engine. This means valve timing set to produce smooth idling may not deliver top performance at high engine speeds. And an engine timed to produce maximum horsepower at higher speeds will idle poorly, if at all.

For this reason, the valve timing in most vehicles is a compromise between these two extremes. For most vehicles, this does not pose a problem. On high-performance vehicles, however, some top end performance is lost in order to maintain a workable idle speed.

Automotive manufacturers are now developing systems that vary valve timing, depending on engine speed.

In one system a computer monitors engine speed. At high speeds it activates a solenoid. This solenoid activates a special hydraulic device that allows the camshaft to rotate on its drive sprocket. As the camshaft rotates, valve timing is advanced.

CAM SPROCKET TIMING MARK

CRANK SPROCKET TIMING MARK

FIGURE 10–18 Timing mark alignment.

When engine speed drops, the device allows the camshaft to return to its normal position.

In a second system, the intake camshafts are not solidly mounted to their drive sprockets. Instead, a special spiral sleeve allows the camshaft and sprocket to move in relation to each other. As the camshaft and sprocket rotate against each other on the sleeve, the camshaft timing is either advanced or delayed.

Oil pressure is used to manipulate the position of the sleeve to provide the proper relationship between the camshaft and crankshaft. A computer-controlled solenoid determines what this relationship should be based on engine speed and other operating factors.

A third system operates on an entirely different principle. In this system, computer-controlled solenoids are used to bring the rocker arms into contact with a second set of high-performance camshaft lobes. At low speed the valves are opened and closed by the standard lobes on the camshaft.

At high speeds, the solenoids are activated, raising the rocker arms slightly. This brings them into contact with the second set of performance lobes on the camshaft. These lobes are machined to increase valve lift, duration, and overlap. The result is more power.

Although not presently in widespread use, variable valve timing will become more common, particularly on high-performance engines.

CAMSHAFT AND VALVE TRAIN INSPECTION

A valve will operate only as well as its actuating parts. This includes the timing gears, chain or belt, sprockets, camshaft, lifters, pushrods, and rocker arm assemblies. For good valve life, each of these must be checked and replaced if worn or damaged.

When making an inspection, each valve train component should be carefully checked. Use the following guidelines when inspecting the components.

1. Individually mounted rocker arm assemblies
   - Check for loose mounting stud and nut or bolt.
   - Check for plugged oil feed in the rocker arm.
2. Pushrods: Check for bent pushrods.
3. Valve spring assembly—with or without damper spring: Check for broken or damaged parts.
4. Retainer and keepers—both two-piece and one piece: Check for proper seating of keeper in the stem grooves and in the retainer.
5. Overhead cam follower arm and lash adjuster assemblies
   - Check for broken or severely damaged parts.
   - Check for a soft lash adjuster (adjusting shim) by using hand pressure on the rocker arm while it is on the base circle of the camshaft.

6. Camshaft
   - Check for plugged oil feed.
   - Check for correct cam lift.
   - Check for broken or severely worn areas.
7. Check the timing belt, sprockets, and related components.

Camshaft

After the camshaft has been cleaned and a visual inspection has been made, check each lobe for scoring, scuffing, fractured surface, pitting, and signs of abnormal wear (Figure 10–19).

Premature lobe and lifter wear is generally caused by metal-to-metal contact between the cam lobe and lifter bottom due to inadequate lubrication (Figure 10–20). The nose will be worn from the cam lobes, and the lifter bottoms will be worn to a concave shape

A

B

FIGURE 10–19 (A) Steel camshaft and roller followers in good condition; (B) badly burned and worn camshaft bearing bores.

FIGURE 10–20 Badly worn camshaft.

or may be worn completely away. This type of failure usually begins within the first few minutes of operation. It is the result of insufficient lubrication or use of an oil that does not meet the engine manufacturer's requirements for viscosity and API service grade.

There are several methods of measuring cam lobes for wear, but the two most popular are the dial indicator and outside micrometer.

The dial indicator test for worn cam lobes should be conducted with the camshaft in the engine. Check the lift of each cam lobe (Figure 10–21) in consecutive order and make a note of the readings. Be sure

FIGURE 10–22 Checking camshaft lobe using a dial indicator. *Courtesy of Ford Motor Company*

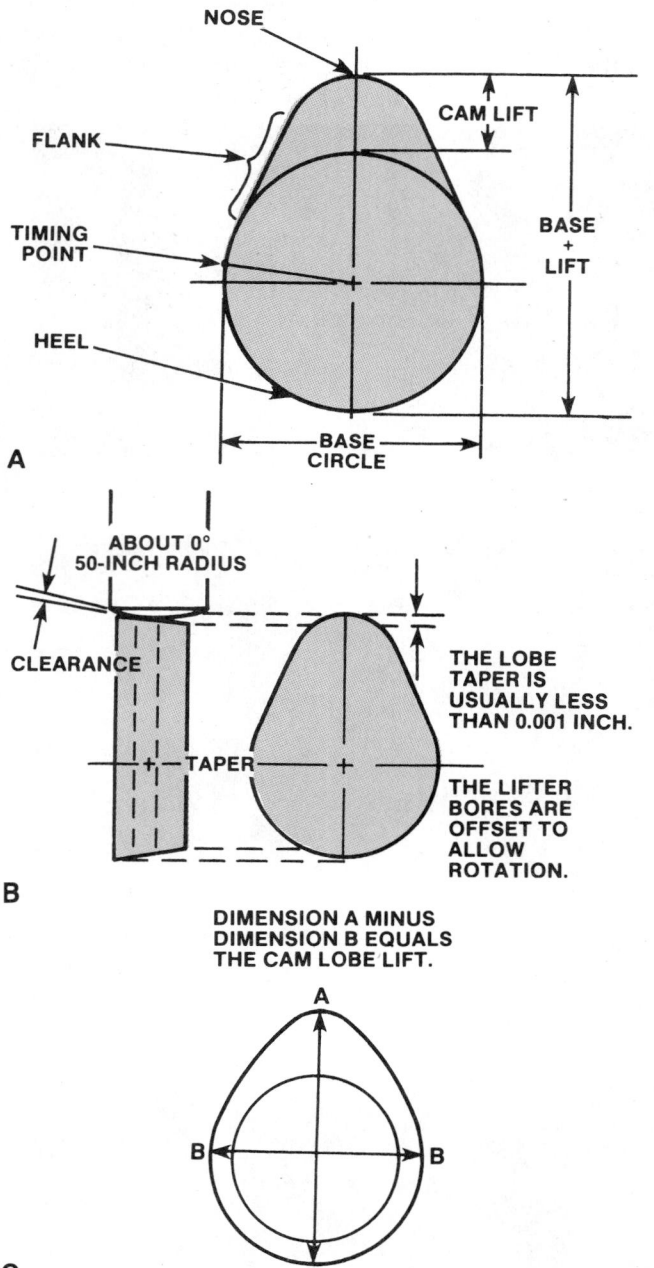

FIGURE 10–21 (A) Cam lobe nomenclature; (B) correct camshaft pattern; (C) determining cam lobe lift.

the pushrod is in the valve lifter socket. Install the dial indicator so the cup-shaped adapter fits into the end of the pushrod and is in the same plane as the pushrod movement (Figure 10–22). Connect a remote starter switch into the starting circuit. With the ignition switch off, bump the crankshaft over until the lifter is on the base circle of the camshaft lobe. At this point, the pushrod will be in its lowest position. Put the dial indicator at zero. Continue to rotate the crankshaft slowly until the pushrod is in its fully raised position (highest indicator reading). Compare the total lift recorded on the indicator with specifications. If the lift on the lobe is below the specified service limits, the camshaft and lifters operating on the worn lobe(s) must be replaced. Any lifter showing pitting or having its contact face worn flat or concave must also be replaced. To be safe, most manufacturers recommend all lifters be replaced when the camshaft is replaced.

To compare the cam lobe height with an outside micrometer, the camshaft must be removed from the engine. Place the micrometer in position to measure from the heel to the nose of the lobe and again 90 degrees from the original measurement. Record the measurement for each intake and exhaust lobe. Any variation in heights indicates wear. Also, check the measurements taken against the manufacturer's cam lobe heights.

Measure each camshaft journal in several places with a micrometer to determine if it is worn excessively. If any journal is 0.001 inch or more below the manufacturer's prescribed specifications, it should be replaced.

The camshaft should also be checked for straightness with a dial indicator. Place the camshaft on V-blocks. Position the dial indicator on the center bearing journal and slowly rotate the camshaft (Figure 10–23). If the dial indicator shows runout (a 0.002-

FIGURE 10–23 Checking camshaft straightness using a dial indicator on the camshaft journals. *Courtesy of Chevrolet Motor Division, General Motors Corporation*

FIGURE 10–24 Ideal contact between the crowned lifter bottom and the tapered cam lobe.

inch deviation), the camshaft is not straight. A bent camshaft must be replaced.

Valve Lifters

All engines that have mechanical lifters use some method of adjustment to bring valve lash (clearance) back into specification. There are four basic methods for lash adjustment: rocker arm with adjustable pivots, adjustable pushrods, rocker arm with adjustable screws, and adjustable cam follower (using some type of adjustable screw or replaceable shim).

Of these four adjustment types, the first two methods are typically associated with OHV engines. The other two adjustment procedures—rocker arms with adjustment screws and adjustable cam followers—are commonly found on OHC designs.

When inspecting mechanical lifters, carefully check their bottoms and pushrod sockets. Wear, scoring, or pitting makes their replacement necessary.

Technically, the normal wear of the valve lifters is referred to as adhesive or galling wear. This is a result of two solid surfaces (camshaft lobe and lifter face) that are in rubbing contact. The two surfaces tend to weld together. This process is considered normal wear between the cam lobe and lifter. Fortunately, proper lubrication retards this process. However, excessive loading will negate the beneficial effects of the lubricant and accelerate the wear process. Examples of excessive loading would be incorrectly matched valve springs (too much spring pressure), old lifters on a new camshaft, or new lifters on an old camshaft.

If a camshaft and lifters are going to be reused, the lifters must remain with their respective lobes. Worn valve lifters and improper camshaft installation are common causes of camshaft/lifter failure. Figure 10–24 shows the ideal contact between the crowned lifter bottom and the tapered cam lobe.

The normal wear path is off center with no edge contact between the lifter and the lobe. The taper on

the cam lobe and the spherical radius of the lifter bottom are specifically designed to result in an offset contact pattern causing the lifter to rotate. The spinning lifter reduces the sliding friction and also equalizes the load around the lifter bottom.

Interference occurs primarily in engines originally equipped with a separate cam sprocket spacer (used to control end clearance). Lifter damage develops when a replacement sprocket with a built-in spacer is installed without removing the original spacer. This forces the camshaft rearward, allowing the lobes to strike adjacent lifters, chipping the edges of both (Figure 10–25). Interference will also develop if sprocket bolts are not tightened properly or if the cam sprocket/engine block thrust surfaces are worn excessively.

Edge wear on cam lobes occurs when used lifters are installed with a new camshaft (Figure 10–26). The bottoms of used lifters are often flat or slightly concave due to previous wear. As a consequence, the lifters will contact the lobe along a narrow band at the lobe's edge. This tends to create high contact forces and rapid wear results. The cam shown in the right portion of the illustration displays a normal wear pattern.

FIGURE 10–25 Example of lobe and lifter interference. *Courtesy of TRW, Inc.*

FIGURE 10–26 Example of cam lobe edge wear. *Courtesy of TRW, Inc.*

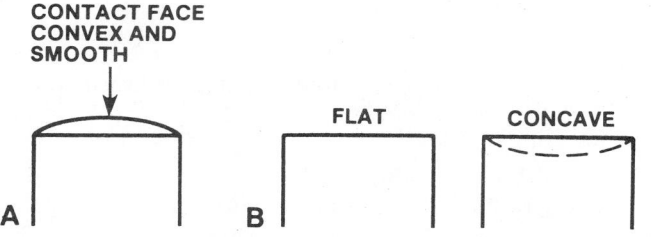

FIGURE 10–27 (A) Acceptable and (B) unacceptable valve lifter bottoms.

FIGURE 10–28 The hydraulic tappet leakdown tester uses a special fluid to check lifter leakdown rate. *Courtesy of Kent-Moore Corporation*

Malfunctioning hydraulic lifters can cause valves to burn or break. Whenever the valve train is disturbed, the hydraulic lifters should be removed, disassembled, cleaned, and checked. They should be kept in sequence during removal so they can be put back in the same place. Lifters should be replaced if the bottoms are worn or pitted or if a new camshaft is installed. Lifter bottoms, generally, are spherical (Figure 10–27).

To inspect, disassemble each lifter separately, but make sure not to intermix any parts because they are selectively fitted. Any time hydraulic lifters are removed, the varnish and deposits should be carefully removed from the lifter bores in the engine block, and the galleries should be flushed with pressurized oil to clear any dirt from the holes that feed the lifters. This latter step is of utmost importance because the act of removing the lifters will normally deposit some dirt right where the feed holes break into the bores. If this is not flushed out, the first oil fed to the newly installed lifter will contain this dirt, and trouble might develop immediately.

After cleaning, check the lifter's leakdown with a leakdown tester (Figure 10–28). Lifter (tappet) leakdown rate is important. If the tappets leak down too quickly, noisy operation will result. When diagnosis indicates no cause for noisy tappet operation, the condition can sometimes be remedied by checking the lifter leakdown rate and replacing all lifters that are outside specifications.

Pushrods

The pushrod fits between the valve lifter and the rocker arm to transmit cam action to the valves. During inspection, some pushrods may be found to have a groove worn in the area in which they pass through the cylinder head, and some may have tip wear. Also, the ends of the pushrods should be checked for nicks, grooves, roughness, or signs of excessive wear.

Bent pushrods can be the result of valve timing, valve sticking, or improper valve adjustment. Bent or broken pushrods indicate interference in the valve train. Common causes are the use of incorrect valve springs or an installed height less than specified, which can cause coil bind. Also, insufficient valve-to-piston clearance can cause a collision between the valve and piston at high engine speeds.

The pushrods can be visually checked for straightness while they are installed in the engine by rotating them with the valve closed. With the pushrods out of the engine, they can be checked for straightness by rolling them over a flat surface such as a surface plate. If a pushrod is not straight, it will appear to hop as it is rolled. However, the most accurate way to check for straightness is by using a dial indicator (Figure 10–29). If more than 0.003 TIR is found, the pushrod is not straight and should be replaced.

Rocker Arms

The rocker arm converts the upward movement of the valve lifter into a downward motion that opens the valve. Rocker arms also permit valves to be angled.

FIGURE 10–29 Checking pushrod straightness with a dial indicator.

FIGURE 10–30 The rocker arm shaft is lubricated by the oil supply drilled into the rocker arm bracket.

FIGURE 10–31 Some pushrods are hollow to carry oil to the upper reaches of the valve train. *Courtesy of Oldsmobile Division, General Motors Corporation*

FIGURE 10–32 Three types of rocker arm studs.

Rocker arms are lubricated in various ways. In some, engine oil is forced up around the outside of the cap screw that holds the bracket in place. On some overhead valve V-type engines, oil reaches the rocker arm assembly through a drilled passage in the cylinder head and rocker arm shaft bracket (Figure 10–30).

Possibly the most common way of supplying oil to the rocker arms is through the pushrods. Some pushrods are hollow and function as part of the lubricating system for the rocker arm assembly (Figure 10–31). Oil flows under pressure from the block through a hole in the valve lifter and up through the pushrod to the rocker arm. No oil will get to the rocker arms if these pushrods are plugged. Look through each pushrod to make sure the oil flow passage is clear.

Rocker arms are made of cast iron, cast aluminum, or stamped steel. Cast adjustable rocker arms are attached to a rocker arm shaft that is mounted on the head by rocker arm brackets. Although a cast rocker arm can be resurfaced, a stamped nonadjustable rocker arm that is worn must be replaced.

Even though some cast rocker arms are still in use, most domestic engines are equipped with an independent stamped rocker arm assembly for each valve and no rocker arm shaft is used. Rather, the rocker arm is mounted to a stud, which is either pressed or threaded into the cylinder head (Figure 10–32) and must be replaced if worn, bent, broken,

or loose. On some engines, the studs are drilled for an oil passage to the rocker arms. Make sure oil can pass through before installing the cylinder head on the block. Replacement press-in studs are available in standard sizes and oversizes. The standard size is used to replace damaged or worn studs, and the oversizes are used for loose studs.

Inspect the rocker shaft assembly for wear, especially at points that contact the valve stem and pushrod. The fit between the cast rocker arm and the rocker shaft is checked by measuring the outside diameter of the shaft and comparing it to the inside diameter of the rocker arm. Excessive clearance requires replacement of the rocker arm or the rocker shaft, or both. Another wear point that should be checked is the pivot area of the rocker arm to rocker shaft (Figure 10–33). Other rocker arm wear points are shown in Figure 10–34.

Excessive wear on the valve pad occurs when the rocker arm repeatedly strikes the valve tip in a hammerlike fashion. It is able to strike the valve tip in this way when valve train clearance, or lash, is exces-

FIGURE 10–33 A common area of wear is the rocker arm to rocker shaft pivot point.

FIGURE 10–34 Rocker arm wear spots.

A

B

C

D

E

sive. Excessive valve lash can occur in several ways. For example, it occurs when mechanical lifters are not adjusted properly or when hydraulic lifters are not working properly. In addition, worn rocker arm valve pads can result when there is insufficient lubrication. Proper lubrication transfers heat away from the valve pad and reduces the metal-to-metal contact. This will keep valve pad wear to a minimum.

Another problem associated with rocker arms is breakage due to interference in the valve train. Other rocker problems are shown in Figure 10–35.

Timing Components

The timing belt (or chain) and crankshaft/camshaft sprockets should be inspected or replaced if damaged or worn. This inspection should include a timing chain deflection check. To conduct this test, simply depress the chain at its midway point between the gears and measure the amount that the chain can be deflected. If the deflection measurement exceeds specifications, the timing chain and gears should be replaced.

Timing Gear Backlash A gear with cracks, spalling, or excessive wear on the tooth surface is an indication of improper **backlash** (either insufficient or excessive). With excessive backlash, operation will be noisy because the teeth will make violent impact contact. This overloading when coupled with the normal valve train loads causes accelerated tooth wear and often breakage. Insufficient backlash places a bind on the gears. Also, it generates high contact forces that can rupture the lubrication film between the teeth, causing spalling and wear.

FIGURE 10–35 Common rocker arm and pushrod problems: (A) broken rocker arm; (B) broken valve spring; (C) broken or bent pushrod; (D) worn pushrod end/ball socket; (E) worn rocker arm pad.

FIGURE 10–36 Checking timing gear backlash. *Courtesy of TRW, Inc.*

To determine gear backlash, install a dial indicator and bracketry on the cylinder block (Figure 10–36). Check the backlash between the camshaft gear and the crankshaft gear with a dial indicator at six equally-spaced teeth. Hold the gear firmly against the block while making the check. Refer to specifications in the vehicle's service manual for the backlash limits.

Rubber Timing Belt Stripped/broken rubber belt failure is commonly due to insufficient tensioning, extended service life, abusive operation, or worn tensioners. Most manufacturers recommend that a timing belt be replaced every 60,000 miles. Replacing them at this interval can prevent belt breakage. Loose timing belts will jump across the teeth of the timing sprockets causing shearing of the belt teeth. Localized tensile overloads from over-revving and engine can lead to belt breakage. Also, belts on those engines equipped with adjustable tensioners should be checked for wear whenever a belt is retensioned. Check the condition and operation of the tensioner. In addition, check for cord separation and cracks on all surfaces (Figure 10–37). If the belts are damaged, they should be replaced. It is wise to replace the belt anytime the engine is overhauled.

SHOP TALK

The condition of a rubber timing belt can frequently be checked by the fingernail test. Press your fingernail into the hardened backside of the belt. If no impression is left, the belt is too hard, caused by overheating and aging. ∎

Camshaft/Crankshaft Timing For the valves to open and close in correct relation to the position of the crankshaft, the camshaft must be timed to the crankshaft. This means the two shafts must be assembled so the cam lobes open the values at a precise time in relation to the position of the piston and crankshaft. In the typical valve timing diagram shown in Figure 10–38, which shows the relation to crankshaft rotation, the intake valve starts to open at

FIGURE 10–37 Various forms of timing belt wear.

FIGURE 10–38 Typical valve timing diagram.

21 degrees when the piston has reached top dead center (TDC) and remains open until it has traveled 51 degrees past bottom dead center (BDC). The number of degrees between the valve's opening and closing is called intake valve duration time.

The exhaust stroke begins at 53 degrees before BDC and continues until 15 degrees after TDC, or a total exhaust valve duration time of 200 degrees of crankshaft rotation. Although both power and compression time are approximately the same, there is a period of time when both the exhaust and intake valves are open, which is known as the valve **overlap**.

Overlap is critical to exhaust gas scavenging and the development of proper cylinder pressure. A camshaft with a lot of overlap helps scavenge the cylinders at high engine speeds for improved efficiency. However, since both valves are open for a longer period of time, low rpm cylinder pressure tends to drop. The amount of overlap, since it has an effect on cylinder pressure, is also a factor in determining overall engine efficiency and exhaust emissions. Valve timing and overlap vary from one engine to another. Valve overlap also helps get the intake mixture moving into the cylinder. As the exhaust gases move out of the cylinder, a low pressure is present in the cylinder. This low pressure causes atmospheric pressure to push the intake charge into the cylinder.

INSTALLING THE CAMSHAFT

To install the camshaft, wipe off each cam bearing with a lint-free cloth, then spread clean oil on the bearings. Also, coat the camshaft and lifters with an oil that meets or exceeds the engine manufacturer's specification (Figure 10–39). Current grades of oil that meet manufacturer's specifications are SF/SG for gasoline engines and CC/CD for automotive diesels. Most premature cam wear develops within the first few minutes of operation. Prelubrication helps to prevent this when the engine is started the first time. Special prelubricants can be used only if specifically recommended by the manufacturer.

FIGURE 10–39 Coating the camshaft with oil. *Courtesy of TRW, Inc.*

CUSTOMER CARE

Inform the customer about the benefits of using the correct grade of engine oil, as well as the hazards of using the wrong type. ■

The camshaft should be carefully installed to avoid damaging the bearings with the edge of a cam lobe or journal. Be especially careful to keep it straight to prevent it from cutting or grooving the bearings. A threaded bolt in the front of the camshaft can be helpful in guiding the cam in place. An alternative is to install the camshaft while the block rests on its end (Figure 10–40). When the camshaft is in place, install the thrust plate and the timing gear.

A camshaft timing gear may need to be pressed off and a replacement pressed on the camshaft (Figure 10–41). This is done prior to installing the camshaft into the block. Be sure to align the thrust plate with the woodruff key during removal to prevent damage to the thrust plate. Both the thrust plate and timing gear must then be aligned with the

FIGURE 10–40 Installing the camshaft with the block on end. *Courtesy of TRW, Inc.*

FIGURE 10–41 When pressing a camshaft timing gear on or off the shaft, always use the correct size sleeve.

FIGURE 10-42 Hand scraping a journal with a bearing scraper. *Courtesy of Perfect Circle/Dana*

woodruff key for assembly. Never hammer a gear or sprocket into the shaft. Heat all metal and aluminum gears on a hot plate 200 to 300°F. Be sure to install the gear while it is still hot to ensure ease of installation. This step does not apply to fiber gears. These gears should be carefully installed. Press the camshaft into the gear and be sure to keep the gear square and aligned with the keyway at all times.

Once the shaft is completely in the block, the shaft should be able to be turned by hand. If the cam does not turn, binding might be the cause. Binding is the result of a damaged bearing, a nick on the cam's journal, or a slight misalignment of the block journals. When the problem is determined as well as which bearings are right, hand scraping the journal might be necessary to clear up the problem (Figure 10-42). This can be done with an old camshaft when the end journal is cut for scraper grooves, a broken piston ring, or a bearing scraper.

Camshaft End Play

Before proceeding to the next step in the reassembly, check to be sure the clearance between the camshaft boss (or gear) and the backing plate is within manufacturer's specifications. Check with a feeler gauge. Install shims behind the thrust plate or reposition the camshaft gear and retest the end play. In some cases, adjustment is made by replacing the thrust plate. To check end play, use a dial indicator setup. Be sure the camshaft end play is not more than recommended in the service manual.

INSTALLING THE CYLINDER HEAD AND VALVE TRAIN

As mentioned several times, the valve train includes everything between the camshaft and valve. In the majority of domestic engines, it includes the lifter, pushrod, rocker arm, and rocker support. Once the basic assembly procedure is complete, the lower and upper portions of the engine can be reassembled. The first step in doing this is to sort out the cylinder head

bolts. Many engines use head bolts of different lengths (Figure 10-43). The service manual usually identifies where the long and short bolts go. The threads of the bolts should be thoroughly cleaned and then lightly lubricated with oil or antiseize compound.

The head gasket should be positioned on the block and checked for fit. The cylinder head is then placed in position on the block. The bolts are inserted into the bolt holes.

Cylinder head bolts must be tightened in the correct order and to the proper amount of torque. A typical tightening sequence (Figure 10-44) is usually provided in the service manual. The chart shows which bolt should be tightened first, second, and third. Most cylinder heads are tightened in a sequence that starts in the middle then moves out to the ends. The bolts are generally tightened in two or three stages. If the final torque is 100 foot-pounds, the bolts may first be tightened at 35 foot-pounds. Some manufacturers recommend that the head bolts be retorqued after the engine has been run and warmed up. NOTE: Some manufacturers use torque-to-yield bolts that cannot be reused and must be replaced.

When assembling the block and head, make sure the dowel pins are in place and the head and block are properly aligned. Threaded bolts entering the coolant jackets should be coated with nonhardening gasket sealant.

FIGURE 10-43 Head bolts are different lengths in some engines. *Courtesy of Ford Motor Company*

FIGURE 10–44 Examples of head bolt tightening sequences. *Courtesy of Chrysler Corporation*

24	DOWEL PIN	154	PUSHROD
143	HEAD GASKET	155	LIFTER GUIDE RETAINER
149	VALVE LIFTER	201	BOLT
150	PUSHROD GUIDE	202	BOLT
151	ROCKER ARM	203	HEAD BOLT

FIGURE 10–45 Typical rocker arm assembly. *Courtesy of General Motors Corporation*

Before inserting the pushrods, apply a small drop of prelube to eliminate any metal-to-metal contact on start-up. Liberally coat the rocker arms with clean SF/SG grade oil. Then insert the rods and the rocker arms (Figure 10–45). Most modern domestic engines use positive stop rocker arm adjustments. This means that when torquing the rocker arms to spec, the plunger of the hydraulic lifter is properly positioned, giving the correct lifter adjustment. This cannot happen if the lifter has been hand primed before installation. Therefore, it is not recommended that new lifters be primed before installation. This can damage valve train components.

SHOP TALK

Some engines have rocker arms designated for right- or left-hand positions. They must be installed in the correct locations for proper pushrod alignment. Note the location of the pushrod socket to determine position. ∎

If the metal was removed from the sealing surface of either the block or head, the geometry of the valve train will be affected. On engines with nonadjustable rocker arms, removal of more than 0.010 inch of material must be compensated for by shimming up the rocker arm assembly supports or by using shorter pushrods.

Adjustable tappets, or cam followers, have been on the automotive scene for years. An early design featured the tappet setting on top of the cam lobe with a threaded adjusting device directly under the valve tip.

Many of today's overhead cam engines utilize an adjustment screw. One side of the screw is flat and rests against the valve tip, and the other side is tapered and fits underneath the follower (Figure 10–46). By threading the screw in or out of the follower, the gap between the cam lobe surface and the top of the follower is made larger or smaller. The screw must be adjusted one complete turn at a time to keep the flat side against the valve tip. If necessary, install a different size adjustment screw to get proper clearance for turning.

Valve lash, on some engines, is adjusted with an adjusting nut on the valve tip end of the rocker arm. The lash or clearance is checked by inserting a feeler gauge between the valve tip and the adjusting nut (Figure 10–47). Installed valve stem height is critical to avoid incorrect valve train geometry and to correctly set valve lash.

Some overhead cam engines have an adjustment disc or shim between the cam lobe surface and the follower. To adjust clearance, a special tool and magnet must be used. To correct excessive clearance, a thicker disc or shim is added. If reduced clearance is needed, a thinner disc or shim must be installed.

FIGURE 10–46 Some overhead cam engines feature a cam follower with an adjustment screw.

FIGURE 10–47 Checking clearance with a feeler gauge.

FIGURE 10–48 Always adjust the lifters according to the engine manufacturer's specifications. *Courtesy of TRW, Inc.*

①	Oil filler cap	⑥	Shim	⑪	Spring seat
②	Rocker cover	⑦	Valve lifter	⑫	Intake valve
③	Camshaft bracket	⑧	Valve cotter	⑬	Exhaust valve
④	Intake camshaft	⑨	Spring retainer	⑭	Cylinder head
⑤	Exhaust camshaft	⑩	Valve spring	⑮	Cylinder head bolt

FIGURE 10–49 Dual overhead camshaft and four-valve per cylinder head design. *Courtesy of Nissan Motors*

Static valve adjustment is required after an engine has been rebuilt to ensure proper engine starting and prevent damage to the valves caused by the pistons hitting the valves. Normally, if the valves are adjusted accurately, no further valve adjustment is required unless the cylinder heads are re-tightened. All valve adjustments should be made only within the limits prescribed in the manufacturer's vehicle service manual (Figure 10–48). The service manual is the best source of information for servicing the latest cylinder head designs (Figure 10–49).

INSTALLING THE TIMING COMPONENTS

During most engine rebuilds, a completely new timing assembly is usually installed. If wear exists on any component, replacement of the entire assembly is necessary. Wear in the chain, gears, or sprockets means a timing lag, which results in poor engine performance.

If the camshaft is mounted in the cylinder block, it can be installed after the piston assemblies have been put in place. Each camshaft lobe and each bearing journal is lubricated with assembly lubricant. The camshaft is then carefully pushed into the cylinder block, as discussed earlier in this chapter. Next, the lifters are lubricated and installed in their bores on top of the camshaft lobes.

With either a cylinder block or cylinder head mounted camshaft, the camshaft drive must be installed so the camshaft and crankshaft are in time with each other. Both sprockets are held in position by a key or possibly a pin. There are factory timing marks on the crankshaft gear or sprocket and on the camshaft gear or sprocket (Figure 10–50). In some timing arrangements, the timing adjustment is on the crankshaft pulley damper. An overhead cam drive, which is belt-driven, can have several idler gears or pulleys with timing marks (Figure 10–51). The timing marks on all the gears must be positioned according to the manufacturer's instructions. The timing chain or belt is generally installed with the gears in their correct positions.

The chain is installed on the crankshaft sprocket first, then around the camshaft sprocket. Never wind a chain onto the sprockets. Also, a screwdriver, pry bar, or hammer should never be used to force a chain into position. Prying or pounding on the chain will damage the links, causing the chain to stretch and fail. Carefully place the chain on the sprockets and install the entire assembly as a unit by pressing both sprockets on evenly, keeping the keyways aligned. Use a sleeve and tap gently into place keeping the sprockets parallel and aligned.

When installing a timing belt, be sure to align the sprocket timing marks properly and adjust belt tension to the manufacturer's specifications. For more information, see Photo Sequence 6.

FIGURE 10–51 Many overhead cam engines use several idler gears or pulleys. *Courtesy of Chrysler Corporation*

FIGURE 10–52 Crankshaft and camshaft timing belt installation for a dual overhead cam engine. *Courtesy of Nissan Motors*

SHOP TALK

As the valve train and timing system become more and more complex, the service manual becomes a must. This can be noted in Figure 10–52, which shows the crankshaft and camshaft timing belt installation for the dual overhead camshaft (DOHC) and four valves per cylinder design. ■

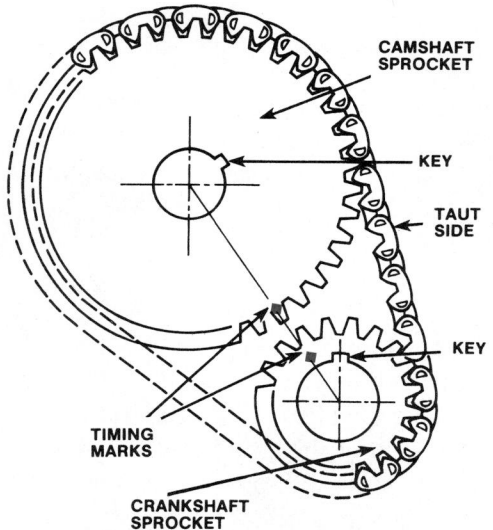

FIGURE 10–50 Factory timing marks can be found on the camshaft and crankshaft sprockets.

REPLACING A TIMING BELT ON AN OHC ENGINE

P6–1 Disconnect the negative cable from the battery prior to removing and replacing the timing belt.

P6–2 Carefully remove the timing cover. Be careful not to distort or damage it while pulling it up. With the cover removed, check the immediate area around the belt for wires and other obstacles. If some are found, move them out of the way.

P6–3 Align the timing marks on the camshaft's sprocket with the mark on the cylinder head. If the marks are not obvious, use a paint stick or chalk to clearly mark them.

P6–4 Carefully remove the crankshaft timing sensor and probe holder.

P6–5 Loosen the adjustment bolt on the belt tensioner pulley. It is normally not necessary to remove the tensioner assembly.

P6–6 Slide the belt off the crankshaft sprocket. Be careful not to allow the crankshaft pulley to rotate while doing this.

(continued)

P6–7   To remove the belt from the engine, the crankshaft pulley must be removed. Then the belt can be slipped off the crankshaft sprocket.

P6–8   After the belt has been removed, inspect it for cracks and other damage. Cracks will become more obvious if the belt is twisted slightly. Any defects in the belt indicate it must be replaced.

P6–9   To begin reassembly, place the belt around the crankshaft sprocket. Then reinstall the crankshaft pulley.

P6–10   Make sure the timing marks on the crankshaft pulley are lined up with the marks on the engine block. If they are not, carefully rock the crankshaft until the marks are lined up.

P6–11   With the timing belt fitted onto the crankshaft sprocket and the crankshaft pulley tightened in place, the crankshaft timing sensor and probe can be reinstalled.

P6–12   Align the camshaft sprocket with the timing marks on the cylinder head. Then wrap the timing belt around the camshaft sprocket and allow the belt tensioner to put a slight amount of pressure on the belt.

P6–13   Adjust the tension as described in the service manual. Then rotate the engine two complete turns. Recheck the tension.

P6–14   Rotate the engine through two complete turns again, then check the alignment marks on the camshaft and the crankshaft. Any deviation needs to be corrected before the timing cover is reinstalled.

CASE STUDY

A *four-cylinder DOHC engine has just been rebuilt. During the initial running of the engine, it runs quite rough. This is normal until everything gets seated. However, the condition becomes worse the more the engine runs. Slight adjustments to the ignition timing do not help the condition. A visual inspection reveals nothing loose or disconnected. Each hose and wire is traced to make sure it is connected to the proper fitting and terminal.*

Because it seems that the engine is running on only three cylinders, a cylinder leakage test is performed. The results indicate excessive leakage past the #4 intake valve. In an attempt to visually locate the problem, the intake cam cover is removed. A look at the camshaft reveals that the #4 intake lobe is worn. This was a new camshaft. Was it defective? Was it hardened properly? Did something else cause this?

Further visual inspection reveals that the shim used to set valve lash was not fully seated in its cup. The edge of the shim was working like a knife, cutting off the metal from the lobe. The initial rough running of the engine was caused by the shim preventing the valve from fully closing. The condition worsened as the lobe was cut away.

The oil was changed and a new camshaft and shim were installed to correct the problem.

KEY TERMS

Backlash
Cam follower
Guide plate
Leakdown

Overlap
Pushrod
Valve lash
Valve lifter

SUMMARY

- A cam changes rotary motion into reciprocating motion. The part of the cam that controls the opening of the valves is the cam lobe. The closing of the valves is the responsibility of the valve springs.
- The camshaft is supported in the cylinder block by friction-type bearings, or bushings, which are typically pressed into the camshaft bore in the block or head. Camshaft bearings are normally replaced during engine rebuilding.
- Solid valve lifters provide for a rigid connection between the camshaft and the valves. Hydraulic valve lifters do the same but use oil to absorb the shock resulting from movement of the valve train. Roller lifters are used to reduce friction and power loss.

- Lifter noises do not necessarily mean the lifter is at fault. Other causes for light tapping noise in the engine include worn cam lobes, a stuck valve, a broken valve spring, insufficient lubrication between the rocker arm and the pushrod or valve, or a loose rocker arm assembly. Careful troubleshooting is required to determine the source of the noise.

- Pushrods are the connecting link between the rocker arm and the valve lifter. They can be either solid or hollow. Pushrods are used only on engines that have the camshaft in the block.

- On a four-stroke cycle engine, the camshaft is driven by the crankshaft at half the engine speed. This is accomplished by a camshaft drive gear or drive sprocket that is twice as large as the crankshaft sprocket.

- A valve will operate only as well as its actuating parts, including the timing gears, chain or belt and sprockets, camshaft, lifters, pushrods, and rocker arm assemblies. When making an inspection, each valve train component should be carefully checked.

- The two most common ways of measuring cam lobes for wear are the dial indicator and outside micrometer. The dial indicator test should be conducted with the camshaft in the engine. When using an outside micrometer, the camshaft must be out of the engine.

- All engines with mechanical lifters have some method of adjustment to bring valve lash (clearance) back into specification. Rocker arms with adjustable pivots and adjustable pushrods are found on OHV engines. Rocker arms with adjustable screws and adjustable cam followers are part of OHC engines.

- The rocker arm converts the upward movement of the valve lifter into a downward motion to open the valve. It also permits the valves to be angled. Most domestic engines have an independent stamped rocker arm assembly for each valve, rather than a cast rocker arm.

- The timing belt or chain and crankshaft/camshaft sprockets should be inspected and replaced if damaged or worn. This inspection should include a timing chain deflection check.

- For the valves to open and close in correct relation to the crankshaft position, the camshaft must be timed to the crankshaft. The number of degrees between the intake valve's opening and closing is known as intake valve duration time.

◆ The period of time when both the exhaust valve and intake valve are open is known as valve overlap. Overlap is critical to exhaust gas scavenging and proper cylinder pressure. It is also a factor in determining overall engine efficiency and exhaust emission.

◆ Most premature cam wear develops within the first few minutes of operation. Prelubrication with the proper oil (SF/SG for gasoline engines and CC/CD for diesel) or approved assembly lubricant can help prevent this from occurring.

◆ During most engine rebuilds, a completely new timing assembly is installed. When installing a timing belt, be sure to align the sprocket timing marks properly and adjust the belt tension to the manufacturer's specifications.

TECH MANUAL

The following procedures are included in Chapter 10 of the *Tech Manual* that accompanies this book:

1. Install camshaft bearings.

2. Inspect and replace camshaft drives.

3. Test for worn cam lobes.

4. Inspect and recondition valve lifters, pushrods, and rocker arms.

REVIEW QUESTIONS

1. Where and how is the camshaft mounted on overhead camshaft engines?

2. What is used in some engines to limit the side movement of the pushrods?

3. Name the two most common ways to measure cam lobe wear.

4. Define galling wear.

5. How can pushrods be visually checked for straightness while they are installed in the engine?

6. What device in the valve train changes rotary motion into reciprocating motion?
   - **a.** eccentric
   - **b.** cam
   - **c.** bushing
   - **d.** mandrel

7. Technician A says valve float is less likely to occur in OHC engines. Technician B says valve float is caused by the valves staying open when they should be closed. Who is correct?
   - **a.** Technician A
   - **b.** Technician B
   - **c.** Both A and B
   - **d.** Neither A nor B

8. After installing cam bearings. Technician A checks that the oil holes in the bearings are properly aligned with those in the block by squirting oil into the holes. Technician B checks for proper alignment by inserting a wire through the holes. Who is correct?
   - **a.** Technician A
   - **b.** Technician B
   - **c.** Both A and B
   - **d.** Neither A nor B

9. What type of valve lifter automatically compensates for the effects of engine temperature?
   - **a.** hydraulic
   - **b.** solid
   - **c.** roller
   - **d.** all of the above

10. Technician A conducts the dial indicator test for worn cam lobes with the camshaft in the engine. Technician B checks cam lobe wear with a micrometer. Who is correct?
   - **a.** Technician A
   - **b.** Technician B
   - **c.** Both A and B
   - **d.** Neither A nor B

11. Technician A says a bent camshaft must be replaced. Technician B says a worn camshaft can be used if new lifters are installed. Who is correct?
   - **a.** Technician A
   - **b.** Technician B
   - **c.** Both A and B
   - **d.** Neither A nor B

12. What converts the upward movement of the valve lifter into a downward motion to open the valve?
   - **a.** pushrod
   - **b.** tappet
   - **c.** rocker arm
   - **d.** cam lobe

13. If the timing chain deflection measurement exceeds specifications, what should be done?
   - **a.** replace the timing chain
   - **b.** replace the timing gears
   - **c.** both a and b
   - **d.** neither a nor b

14. Timing gear backlash is determined by means of a dial indicator and ____.
    a. outside micrometer
    b. inside micrometer
    c. vernier caliper
    d. bracketry

15. A camshaft with ____ overlap helps scavenge the cylinders at high engine speeds for improved efficiency.
    a. no
    b. very little
    c. half the normal amount of
    d. a lot of

16. Technician A says the engine must be removed to replace a timing belt on a transversely mounted engine. Technician B says the procedures given in a service manual should be followed whenever a timing belt is being replaced. Who is correct?
    a. Technician A   c. Both A and B
    b. Technician B   d. Neither A nor B

17. Technician A uses SF/SG oil to coat the camshaft and lifters on a gasoline engine. Technician B uses CC/CD oil to coat the camshaft and lifters on all engines. Who is correct?
    a. Technician A   c. Both A and B
    b. Technician B   d. Neither A nor B

18. Which of the following statements is incorrect?
    a. Cylinder head bolts must be tightened to the proper amount of torque.
    b. Most cylinder head bolts are tightened in a sequence that starts on one end.
    c. On some engines, the head bolts are retorqued after the engine has been run and is hot.
    d. Many engines use head bolts of different lengths.

19. On engines with nonadjustable rocker arms, removal of more than ____ inch of metal from the gasket surface of either the block or head must be compensated for by shimming up the rocker arm assembly supports.
    a. 0.10   c. 0.001
    b. 0.010   d. 0.50

20. Technician A uses a pry bar to stretch the timing chain onto its sprockets. Technician B cools the timing sprockets so the timing chain will slip over the teeth. Who is correct?
    a. Technician A   c. Both A and B
    b. Technician B   d. Neither A nor B

LUBRICATING AND COOLING SYSTEMS

11

OBJECTIVES

◆ *Name and describe the components of a typical lubricating system.* ◆ *Inspect, service, and install an oil pump.* ◆ *Describe the purpose of a crankcase ventilation system.* ◆ *Explain oil service and viscosity ratings.* ◆ *List and describe the major components of the cooling system.* ◆ *Describe the operation of the cooling system.* ◆ *Describe the function of the water pump, radiator, radiator cap, and thermostat in the cooling system.* ◆ *Test and service the cooling system.*

The life of an engine depends largely on its lubricating and cooling systems. If an engine does not have a supply of oil or does not cool itself, the engine will quickly be destroyed.

LUBRICATION

An engine's lubricating system does several important things. It holds an adequate supply of oil to cool, clean, lubricate, and seal the engine. It also removes contaminants from the oil and delivers oil to all necessary areas of the engine.

Oil Types

Engine oil is a clean or refined form of **crude oil**. Crude oil, when taken out of the ground, is dirty and does not work well as a lubricant for engines. Crude oil must be refined to meet industry standards. Engine oil (often called motor oil) is just one of the many products that comes from crude oil. Engine oil is specially formulated so it has the following properties.

◆ Prompt circulation through the engine's lubrication system
◆ The ability to lubricate without foaming
◆ The ability to reduce friction and wear
◆ The ability to prevent the formation of rust and corrosion
◆ The ability to cool the engine parts it flows on
◆ The ability to keep internal engine parts clean

To provide these properties, engine oil contains many additives. Because of these additives, choosing the correct oil for each engine application can be a difficult task. However, the American Petroleum Institute (**API**) has developed service ratings for motor oil that greatly simplifies oil selection.

The API classifies engine oil as standard or S-class for passenger cars and light trucks and as commercial or C-class for heavy-duty commercial applications. Additionally, various grades of oil within each class are further classified alphabetically according to their ability to meet the engine manufacturers' warranty specifications (Table 11–1).

SHOP TALK

Among lubrication engineers, the designations *S* and *C* do not stand for standard and commercial vehicles, respectively. The letters refer to the type of ignition that each engine utilizes. *S* is for gasoline engines that use spark ignition. *C* is for compression ignition systems utilized by diesels. ■

In addition to oil additives, oil **viscosity** is equally important in selecting an engine oil. The ability of an oil to flow is its viscosity. Viscosity is affected by temperature. For example, hot oil flows faster than cold oil. The rate of oil flow is important to the life of an engine. Because an engine operates under a wide range of temperatures, selecting the correct viscosity becomes even more important.

To standardize oil viscosity ratings, the Society of Automotive Engineers (**SAE**) has established an oil

TABLE 11–1 API GASOLINE ENGINE DESIGNATION	
SC	Service typical of gasoline engines in 1964 through 1967. Oil designed for this service provides control of high and low temperature deposits, wear, dust, and corrosion in gasoline engines.
SD	Service typical of gasoline engines in 1968 through 1970. Oils designed for this service provide more protection against high and low temperature deposits, wear, rust, and corrosion in gasoline engines. SD oil can be used in engines requiring SC oil.
SE	Service typical of gasoline engines in automobiles and some trucks beginning in 1972. Oil designed for this service provides more protection against oil oxidation, high temperature engine deposits, rust, and corrosion in gasoline engines. SE oil can be used in engines requiring SC or SD oil.
SF	Service typical of gasoline engines in automobiles and some trucks beginning with 1980. SF oils provide increased oxidation stability and improved antiwear performance over oils that meet API designation SE. It also provides protection against engine deposits, rust, and corrosion. SF oils can be used in engines requiring SC, SD, or SE oils.
SG	Service typical of gasoline automobiles and lightduty trucks, plus CC classification diesel engines beginning in the late 1980s. SG oils provide the best protection against engine wear, oxidation, engine deposits, rust, and corrosion. It can be used in engines requiring SC, SD, or SF oils.

viscosity classification system that is accepted throughout the industry. This system is a numeric rating in which the higher viscosity, or heavier weight oils, receive the higher numbers. For example, an oil classified as an SAE 50 weight oil is heavier and flows slower than SAE 10 weight oil. Heavyweight oils are best suited for use in high-temperature regions. Low-weight oils work best in low temperature operations.

To meet the needs of the average motorist who might not want to change oils seasonally, oil manufacturers have developed **multiviscosity** oils. These oils carry a combined classification such as 10W-30. This classification means the oil has a weight of 10 at ambient air temperature. Once the engine builds up heat, the oil warms up to the viscosity of the 30-weight oil. This type of oil allows easy starting in cold weather and adequate protection at higher temperatures.

The SAE classification (Table 11–2) and the API rating are usually indicated on the top of an oil can (Figure 11–1). Selecting oils that specifically meet or exceed the manufacturer's recommendations and changing the oil on a regular basis will allow the owner to get the maximum service life from an engine.

SHOP TALK

Using the incorrect grade or type of oil can cause a variety of problems. For example, the wrong viscosity can cause either an oil consumption prob-

FIGURE 11–1 API designation and SAE rating. *Courtesy of Quaker State Corporation*

TABLE 11–2 SAE GRADES OF MOTOR OIL		
Lowest Atmospheric Temperature Expected	**Single-Grade Oils**	**Multigrade Oils**
32°F (0°C)	20, 20W, 30	10W-30, 10W-40, 15W-40, 20W-40, 20W-50
0°F (–18°C)	10W	5W-30, 10W-30, 10W-40, 15W-40
–15°F (–26°C)	10W	10W-30, 10W-40, 5W-30
Below –15°F (–26°C)	5W*	*5W-20, 5W-30

*SAE 5W and 5W-20 grade oils are not recommended for sustained high-speed driving.

lem or a low oil pressure problem, depending on the weather and driving conditions. Using an oil with the incorrect service rating can result in poor protection for engine bearings and other moving engine parts. This is especially true of oil for today's engines. Because of computerized controls, these engines start quickly. Oil for these engines must be able to circulate through the engine very quickly. This is why manufacturers recommend lower viscosity oils for these engines. Always consult the engine manufacturer's recommendations to make sure the engine is using the correct grade and type of oil.   ■

Engine oils can be classified as **energy-conserving** (fuel-saving) **oils**. These are designed to reduce friction, which in turn reduces fuel consumption. Friction modifiers and other additives are used to achieve this. Energy-conserving oil is identified as such on the top of the oil can.

The introduction of synthetic motor oils dates back to World War II. It is often described as the oil of the future. Synthetic oils are manufactured in a laboratory rather than pumped out of the ground. They offer a variety of advantages over natural oils including better fuel economy, stability over a wide range of temperatures and operating conditions, and longevity. They are more costly than natural oil.

CUSTOMER CARE

When changing oil or doing any work on an automobile, use fender covers and do not leave fingerprints on the exterior of the car. If oil or grease gets on the car, clean it off.   ■

Oil Consumption

Excessive oil consumption can result from external and internal leaks, faulty accessories, piston rings, and valve guides. Internal leaks (Figure 11–2), which usually result in oil burning, are more difficult to diagnose.

To diagnose an engine that seems to use too much oil, begin by checking the engine for external leaks. These leaks can occur at the valve cover gasket, camshaft expansion plug, oil filter, front and rear oil seals, oil pan gasket, fuel pump gasket, and timing gear cover.

Even the smallest oil leak can cause excessive oil consumption. Losing three drops of oil every 100 feet equals 3 quarts of oil lost every thousand miles. External leaks can occur under normal and abnormal crankcase pressures.

Normal crankcase pressure will cause oil leaks at gaskets or metal-to-metal joints that are in direct contact with oil. Worn seals, faulty gaskets, and loose cover or housing bolts could also cause the problem. Fresh oil on the clutch housing, oil pan (Figure 11–3), fuel pump, edges of valve covers, external oil lines, distributor shaft housing, base or crankcase filler tube, or at the bottom of the timing gear or chain cover usually indicates that the leak is close to or above that point.

As shown in Figure 11–4, oil pressure is checked at the sending unit passage with an externally mounted mechanical oil pressure gauge. To get accurate test results, follow the manufacturer's recommendations and compare your readings to the oil pressure specifications listed in the service manual. Low oil pressure readings can be caused by internal component wear, pump-related problems, a low oil level, contaminated

FIGURE 11–2   Indication of internal oil leak condition. *Courtesy of Perfect Circle/Dana*

FIGURE 11–3   Fresh oil on the clutch housing or oil pan usually indicates a leak. *Courtesy of Perfect Circle/Dana*

FIGURE 11–4   Typical mechanical oil pressure gauge. *Courtesy of Snap-on Tools Corporation*

oil, or oil viscosity that is too low. A high pressure reading can be caused by an overfilled crankcase, too high an oil viscosity, the wrong oil pump (remote but possible, especially if the pump has been replaced), or a faulty pressure relief valve.

When crankcase pressure is abnormally high, oil is forced out through joints that normally would not leak. Pressure develops when blowby becomes excessive or when a positive crankcase ventilation (PVC) system is not working properly. Blowby is a term used to describe the gases that escape the combustion chamber and enter the crankcase. These gases leak between the piston rings and the cylinder walls when a total seal is not there. Blowby gases are normally pressurized air/fuel mixture and/or pressurized exhaust gases. The PCV system provides a continuous flow of fresh air through the crankcase to relieve the pressure and prevent the formation of corrosive contaminants (Figure 11–5). It is important that the correct PCV valve be installed. PCV valves are designed for a particular engine's operating characteristics. Using the wrong valve can cause oil consumption, as well as other problems. If the PCV valve or connecting hoses become clogged, excessive pressure will develop in the crankcase. This might force oil into the air cleaner or cause it to be drawn into the intake manifold.

SHOP TALK

Internal leaks are frequently the result of aluminum intake manifolds on V-6 and V-8 engines because aluminum may warp due to heat. If an unacceptable amount of warpage is found, removing and milling the manifold is necessary to get it to seal. ■

Most oil consumption problems, as shown in Figure 11–6, can be corrected by proper servicing of the engine.

FIGURE 11–5 Operation of a PCV system.

LUBRICATING SYSTEMS

The main components of a typical lubricating system (Figure 11–7) are described here.

OIL PUMP The oil pump is the heart of the lubricating system. Just as the heart in a human body circulates blood through veins, an engine's oil pump circulates oil through passages in the engine.

OIL PUMP PICKUP The **oil pump pickup** is a line from the oil pump to the oil stored in the oil pan (Figure 11–8). It usually contains a filter screen, which is submerged in the oil at all times. The screen serves to keep large particles from reaching the oil pump. This screen should be cleaned any time the oil pan is removed.

FIGURE 11–6
Common oil consumption problems and their causes.

FRONT TIMING
BALANCER BELT
DRIVEN PULLEY

BALANCER DRIVEN
GEAR

THRUST
WASHER

OIL PUMP

O-RINGS

OIL CONTROL ORIFICE

O-RING

ENGINE OIL PRESSURE SWITCH

BALANCER
GEAR CASE

KNOCK SENSOR

O-RING

DOWEL
PIN

DOWEL PIN

GASKET

ENGINE OIL COOLER

OIL SCREEN

OIL FILTER

ENGINE OIL PRESSURE SWITCH

OIL PAN GASKET

WASHER

OIL PAN

DRAIN BOLT

FIGURE 11–7   Components of a typical lubricating system. *Courtesy of American Honda Motor Company, Inc.*

OIL PAN OR SUMP The oil pan attaches to the crankcase or block. It serves as the reservoir for the engine's oil. It is designed to hold the amount of oil that is needed to lubricate the engine when it is running, plus a reserve. The oil pan helps to cool the oil through its contact with the outside air.

PRESSURE RELIEF VALVE Since the oil pump is a **positive displacement pump**, an oil **pressure relief valve** (Figure 11–9) is included in the system to prevent excessively high system pressures from occurring as engine speed is increased. Once oil pressure exceeds a preset limit, the spring-loaded pressure relief valve opens and allows the excess oil to bypass the rest of the system and return directly to the sump.

OIL FILTER Under pressure from the oil pump, oil flows through a filter (Figure 11–10) to remove any

OIL PUMP
CASE

CRANKSHAFT

OUTER ROTOR

INNER ROTOR

PICK-UP
TUBE

OIL SCREEN

RELIEF VALVE

OIL PAN

FIGURE 11–8   Oil pump pickup. *Courtesy of Chrysler Corporation*

FIGURE 11–9 Oil pressure relief valve. *Courtesy of Toyota Motor Corporation*

impurities that might have become suspended in the oil. This prevents impurities from circulating through the engine, which can cause premature wear. Filtering also increases the usable life of the oil. Oil filters are equipped with a by-pass valve to allow oil to bypass the filter, if the filter is clogged.

ENGINE OIL PASSAGES OR GALLERIES From the filter, the oil flows into the engine oil galleries (Figure 11–11). These galleries consist of interconnecting passages that have been drilled completely through the engine block during manufacturing. The outside ends of the passages are blocked off so the oil can be routed through these galleries to various parts of the engine. The crankshaft also contains oil passages (oilways) to route the oil from the main bearings to the connecting rod bearing surfaces (Figure 11–12).

ENGINE BEARINGS Since oil is delivered to the engine bearings by an oil gallery, an oil hole is ma-

FIGURE 11–10 Typical oil filter circuit.

FIGURE 11–11 Oil galleries. *Courtesy of Nissan Motors*

FIGURE 11–12 Oil passages in block and crankshaft.

chined in the bearing for alignment with the oil gallery in the engine block. Many engine bearings are manufactured with an oil groove to help distribute the oil over the surface of the bearing. Oil grooving the main bearing also aids the flow of oil to the connecting rod bearings in the engine. Once the oil has been used by the bearing, it flows out of the oil clearance space and is replenished with a fresh supply of oil under pressure from the oil pump. This oil is then splashed or thrown off the bearing surface by the spinning motion of the crankshaft. The splashed oil then lubricates other parts of the engine, such as the cylinder walls and pistons.

CRANKCASE VENTILATION Crankcase ventilation is necessary because pressure can build in the crankcase due to combustion pressure. This pressure passes by the piston rings. Piston rings do not provide a total seal of the combustion area and some combustion gases are able to reach the oil pan. These gases contaminate the oil and apply unwanted pressure on gaskets and seals.

OIL PRESSURE INDICATOR The driver can monitor oil pressure by looking at a gauge, which indicates the engine oil pressure at all times, or it can be a warning light that will come on whenever the engine is running with insufficient oil pressure. The warning light is the most common oil pressure indicator.

OIL SEALS AND GASKETS These are used throughout the engine to prevent both external and internal oil leaks. The most common materials used for sealing are synthetic rubber, soft plastics, fiber, and cork. In critical areas, these materials might be bonded to a metal.

DIPSTICK The dipstick is used to measure the level of oil in the oil pan. The end of the stick is marked to indicate when the engine oil level is correct. It also has a mark to indicate the need to add oil to the system.

OIL COOLER Some engines, such as diesel engines or turbocharged engines, use an external oil cooler. This typically looks like a small radiator mounted near the front of the engine. Heat is removed from the oil as air flows through the cooler. Normal maximum engine oil temperature is considered to be 250°F. Hot oil mixed with oxygen breaks down (oxidizes) and forms carbon and varnish. The higher the temperature, the faster these deposits build. An oil cooler helps keep the oil at its normal operating temperature.

Oil Pump

The oil pump is usually located in the oil pan. Its purpose is to supply oil to the various moving parts in the engine. To make sure the parts are lubricated, an adequate amount of oil must be delivered to the parts. To get the oil to move through the engine and into the various parts, the oil must be pressurized. Oil pumps are designed to move a certain volume of oil and pressurize it to a certain amount. The amount of oil flow through the engine depends on the volume of oil available, the pressure of the oil, and the clearance or space through which the oil must flow. Engine bearing clearances have a great effect on oil flow.

Increased clearances reduce the resistance to oil flow and, consequently, increase the volume of oil circulating through the engine. This decreased resistance and increased volume lowers the pressure of the oil. The ability of an oil pump to deliver more than the required volume of oil is a safety measure to ensure lubrication of vital parts as the engine wears. Too much oil pressure is seldom a problem. Too little oil pressure can cause poor oil circulation. Poor circulation can result in poor lubrication of some vital parts.

An engine's oil pressure is also determined by the viscosity of the oil and the temperature of the oil. A high-viscosity oil has more flow resistance than a low-viscosity oil. As already mentioned, viscosity decreases as the temperature increases. For this reason, oil pressure is higher in a cold engine than it is when the engine reaches its normal operating temperature.

Types of Oil Pumps
The most commonly used oil pumps are the rotor and gear types. Both are positive displacement pumps. That is, a fixed volume of oil passes through the pump with each revolution of its drive shaft. This is because the gears or rotors form a near perfect mechanical seal as they mesh. They trap fixed volumes of oil inside the pump and push it out. Output volume is proportional to pump speed. As engine rpm increases, pump output also increases. Oil pumps are driven, directly or indirect-

ly, by the camshaft or by a gear at the front of the crankshaft.

A typical **rotor-type oil pump** (Figure 11–13) has a four-lobe inner rotor and a five-lobe outer rotor, which is driven by the inner rotor. When the rotors turn and the rotors' lobes unmesh, oil is drawn into the space. As the rotors continue to turn, the oil becomes trapped between the lobes, cover plate, and top of the pump cavity. Then it is forced out of the pump body by the meshing of the lobes. The meshing of the lobes squeezes the oil out and directs it through the engine. The rate and amount of oil forced out of the pump depends on the diameter and thickness of the pump's rotors.

Gear-type pumps (Figure 11–14) use a drive gear connected to the input shaft and a driven gear. The drive gear turns the driven gear. Both gears trap oil between their teeth and the pump cavity wall. As the gears rotate, the oil is forced out as the gear teeth unmesh. The output volume per revolution depends on the length and depth of the gear teeth. Another style of gear-type oil pump uses an idler gear with internal teeth that spins around the drive gear. In this style of pump, often called a crescent or trochoidal type, the gears are eccentric. That is, as the larger gear turns, it walks around the smaller, moving the oil in the space between.

The rotor type moves a greater volume of oil than a gear type because the space in the open lobe of the outer rotor is greater than the space between the teeth of the gears of a gear-type pump.

Oil pumps are often driven by the camshaft through the use of an intermediate shaft connected to the distributor (Figure 11–15). On other engines, the oil pump housing is an integral part of the timing gear cover. This type of pump is typically driven directly by the camshaft or crankshaft.

FIGURE 11–14 Two popular types of gear-driven oil pumps.

FIGURE 11–13 Rotor oil pump.

FIGURE 11–15 The gear on the end of this camshaft drives the distributor.

Pressure Regulation The faster an oil pump turns, the greater its output pressure becomes. Therefore, a pressure-regulating valve is needed to control the maximum oil pressure from the pump. Excessive oil

FIGURE 11–16 Cutaway of an oil pump showing the pressure-relief regulating valve in the (A) closed position and (B) open position. *Courtesy of TRW, Inc.*

FIGURE 11–17 Schematic of an electric oil pressure indicator.

pressure can lead to poor lubrication due to the oil blowing past parts rather than flowing over them. A pressure regulator valve is loaded with a closely calibrated spring that allows oil to bleed off at a given pressure. If the engine's manufacturer decides that 50 psi of oil pressure is desirable in the engine, the pressure-regulating valve will not allow the pressure to go beyond 50 psi. When the pressure on the output side of the pump reaches this point, it presses against either a check valve, a ball, or a plunger, forcing it to unseat and allow oil to bypass and return to either the inlet side of the pump or to the crankcase.

Figure 11–16A is a cutaway of an oil pump showing the pressure-regulating valve in the closed position. Figure 11–16B is the same pump with the valve in the open position. Note how the oil can flow through the end of the plunger to the by-pass and return to the inlet side of the pump. The plunger works within its bore with very little clearance. Therefore, it can be seen that foreign material entering this area can jam or hinder the operation of the pressure-regulating valve.

All automotive engines are fitted with an oil filtering system. This filter is located somewhere on the output side of the pump, either attached directly to the pump or at a remote point away from the pump.

Oil Pressure Indicators Vehicles are equipped with either an oil pressure gauge and/or a low-pressure indicator light. Oil gauges are either mechanically or electrically operated and display the actual oil pressure of the engine. The indicator light only warns the driver of low oil pressure.

In a mechanical gauge, oil travels up to the back of the gauge where a springy, flexible, hollow tube, called a Bourdon tube, uncoils as the pressure increases. A needle attached to the Bourdon tube moves over a scale to indicate the oil pressure.

Most pressure gauges are electrically controlled (Figure 11–17). An oil pressure sensor or sending unit is screwed into an oil gallery. As oil passes through an oil pressure sender (Figure 11–18), it

moves a diaphragm, which is connected to a variable resistor. This resistor changes the amount of current passing through the circuit. A gauge on the dashboard reacts to the current and moves a needle over a scale to indicate the oil pressure. Or, the current is translated into a digital reading on the gauge.

Warning light systems are basically simple electrical circuits. The indicator light comes on when the circuit is completed by a sensor. This sensor has a diaphragm connected to a switch inside the sensor. Under normal conditions, the sender switch is open. When oil pressure falls below a certain level, the reduction of pressure causes the diaphragm to move and close the sender switch (Figure 11–19), which completes the electrical circuit. When this happens, electricity flows and turns on the warning light on the dashboard.

Some late-model vehicles are equipped with an electronic oil level indicator. When the oil level in the

FIGURE 11–18 Oil pressure gauge sender.

FIGURE 11–19 Oil pressure sender switch.

oil pan drops below a predetermined level, a sensor completes the warning lamp circuit and the lamp lights.

Oil Filters

All of the oil that leaves the oil pump is directed to the oil filter. This ensures that very small particles of

FIGURE 11–21 The oil filter is usually mounted on an adapter that bolts to the engine block.

dirt and metal carried by the oil will not reach the close-fitting engine parts. The filter element and container are made as a unit. The assembly threads directly onto the main oil gallery tube. The oil from the pump enters the filter and passes through the element of the filter. From the element, the oil flows back into the engine's main oil gallery (Figure 11–20).

An oil filter assembly is a disposable metal container filled with a special type of treated paper or other filter substance (cotton, felt, or the like) that catches and holds impurities in the oil. It is usually mounted on and sealed to an adapter that bolts to the engine block (Figure 11–21). Oil filters are fitted with a check valve that prevents the oil from draining out of the filter when the engine is not running. This allows oil to flow through the engine upon engine start-up. There are several designs of oil filters. Always use the type of filter that is recommended for the vehicle on which you are working.

The oil filtration system used on today's vehicles is commonly referred to as a full-flow system (Figure 11–22). All of the oil going to the engine bearings goes through the filter first. However, should the filter become plugged, a relief valve in the filter will open and allow oil to bypass and go directly to the bearings. This provides the bearings and the rest of the engine with necessary, though unfiltered, lubrication.

FIGURE 11–20 Oil flow through the filter. *Courtesy of Ford Motor Company*

FIGURE 11–22 Full flow filtration system.

FIGURE 11-23 By-pass filtration system.

FIGURE 11-25 Plugged oil pickup screen.

FIGURE 11-26 Sludge and dirt buildup.

A few engines have been equipped with a by-pass oil filtration system (Figure 11-23). In this system the oil is not filtered before it is sent to the bearings. Filtered oil is sent to the oil pan.

OIL PUMP INSPECTION AND SERVICE

Many technicians install a new or rebuilt oil pump on each engine they rebuild. Integral pumps must be rebuilt. Bolt-on or nonintegral pumps can be rebuilt or replaced. Whenever an engine is being overhauled, the oil pump should be carefully inspected and thoroughly cleaned.

If the oil pressure of an engine is low, any number of problems could be the cause. Some examples follow.

- Worn or damaged oil pump
- Defective sending unit (Figure 11-24)
- Weak or damaged pressure relief valve spring
- Plugged oil pickup screen (Figure 11-25)
- Relief valve stuck in the open position
- Excessive oil dilution
- Buildup of sludge and dirt (Figure 11-26)
- Excess bearing clearances (crankshaft and camshaft)

FIGURE 11-27 Air leak on the oil pump's suction side.

- Air leak on the suction side of the oil pump (Figure 11-27). Since the air is compressible, it will cause the indicator to fluctuate and, in some cases, cause the pressure-regulator valve to hammer back and forth. Under prolonged operation, this can cause the valve to fail. It can also cause oil aeration, foaming, marginal lubrication, and failure of engine parts. Care should be taken to make sure all parts on the suction side of the pump fit tightly and there is no place for air leakage. Air leakage often comes from cracked seams in the pickup tube.

Although the oil pump is probably the best lubricated part of the engine, it is lubricated before the oil

FIGURE 11-24 Defective sending unit.

passes through the filter. Therefore, it can experience premature failure because of dirt or other materials entering the pump. Foreign particles can cause three kinds of trouble in a pump.

1. Fine abrasive particles gradually wear the surfaces, causing a reduction in efficiency.
2. Hard particles larger than the clearances can cause scoring and raising of metal as they pass through, finally resulting in seizure.
3. Large particles that cannot pass through will physically lock up the pump.

Of course, when the pump seizes or locks up, the intermediate or drive shaft will also be twisted or sheared off (Figure 11–28).

During normal operation the pickup by-pass valve seats on the supporting cross strap (Figure 11–29). When there is a demand for a large amount of oil and the oil is cold and thick, the valve will unseat and allow the oil to bypass the screen and go directly into the pump. Of course, if the screen becomes plugged, the by-pass valve will be open during most of the time the engine is running. As the oil rushes through the by-pass valve, it can cause a swirling motion or vortex in the oil pan. This could draw

FIGURE 11–28 Sheared drive shaft.

FIGURE 11–29 Pickup screen with cross strap bent out of position to show the by-pass valve.

FIGURE 11–30 Remove pressure relief valve and note direction in which it is pointing.

FIGURE 11–31 Mark the gear teeth so they can be reassembled with the same indexing.

up dirt that is either floating in the oil or lying in the bottom of the pan.

To thoroughly inspect the oil pump, it must be disassembled. Carefully remove the pressure relief valve and note the direction in which it is pointing so it can be reinstalled in its proper position (Figure 11–30). If the relief valve is installed backwards, the pump will not be able to build up pressure.

Before disassembling the pump, mark the gear teeth so they can be reassembled with the same tooth indexing (Figure 11–31). Some pumps have the gears or rotors marked when they are manufactured. Once all the serviceable parts have been removed, clean them and dry them off with compressed air.

USING SERVICE MANUALS

Correct oil pump disassembly instructions are given in the oil pump unit of the engines section of a service manual. ∎

After the pump has been disassembled and cleaned, inspect the pump gears or rotors for chipping, galling, pitting, or signs of abnormal wear. Examine the housing bores for similar signs of wear. If any part of the housing is scored or noticeably worn, replace the pump as an entire assembly.

Check the mating surface of the pump cover for wear. If it is worn, scored, or grooved, replace the pump. Use a feeler gauge and straightedge to check the flatness of the cover. The service manual gives the maximum and minimum acceptable feeler gauge thicknesses for the cover. If the cover is excessively worn, grooved, or scratched, it should be replaced.

Use an outside micrometer to measure the diameter and thickness of the outer rotor (Figure 11–32). The inner rotor's thickness should also be checked. If these dimensions are less than the specified amount, the rotors must be replaced.

With rotor pumps, assemble the rotors back into the pump body. Use a feeler gauge to check the clearance between the outer rotor and pump body (Figure 11–33). If the manufacturer's specifications are not available, replace the pump or rotors if the measured clearance is greater than 0.012 inch.

After checking the outer rotor-to-pump housing clearance, position the inner and outer rotor lobes so they face each other. Measure the clearance between them with a feeler gauge (Figure 11–34). A clearance of more than 0.010 inch is unacceptable.

FIGURE 11–34 Measuring clearance between the inner and outer rotor lobes.

FIGURE 11–35 Taking several measurements around the housing.

On a gear-type pump, it is important to measure the clearance between the gear teeth and pump housing. Take several measurements at various locations around the housing (Figure 11–35) and compare the readings. If the clearance at any point exceeds 0.005 inch, replace the pump as an assembly.

On both gear or rotor oil pumps, place a straightedge across the pump housing and measure the clearance between the straightedge and gears (Figure 11–36). To ensure an accurate reading, make sure the housing surface is clean and free of residual gasket material and that the gears are bottomed in the bore. The desired end play clearance should not exceed 0.003 inch.

If the pump uses a hexagonal drive shaft, inspect the pump drive and shaft to make sure the corners

FIGURE 11–32 Measuring the outer rotor with an outside micrometer.

FIGURE 11–33 Checking clearance between the outer rotor and pump body.

FIGURE 11–36 Measuring clearance between a straightedge and gears.

are not rounded. Check the drive shaft-to-housing bearing clearance by measuring the OD of the shaft and the ID of the housing bearing.

The gasket used to seal the end housing is also designed to provide the proper clearance between the gears and end plate. Consequently, do not substitute another gasket or make a gasket to replace the original one. If a precut gasket was not originally used, seal the end housing with a thin bead of anaerobic sealing material.

Inspect the relief valve spring for signs of collapsing or wear. Check the relief valve spring tension according to specifications. Also, check the relief valve piston for scores and free operation in its bore.

The pickup screen and pump drive (Figure 11–37) should be replaced when an engine is rebuilt. The screen and drive must be properly positioned. This is important to avoid oil pan interference and to ensure that the pickup is always submerged in oil. To make the oil pump pickup tube installation easier, there are several types of drivers available that are suitable for use with air-powered equipment or with a light mallet (Figure 11–38).

On integral pumps, the timing case and gear thrust plate might be worn also. Wear here will limit pump efficiency due to excess clearance. Replace them as necessary.

FIGURE 11–37 Pickup screen and pump drive.

FIGURE 11–38 Manual installation of pump pickup tube. *Courtesy of Goodson Shop Supplies*

INSTALLING THE OIL PUMP

Whether the pump is an integral or nonintegral type, it can be driven by a gear on the camshaft or by an extension shaft from the distributor. Care must be taken to make sure the gear or extension is engaged properly. Also, regardless of the type of pump, both should be primed before assembly. This can be done by submerging the pump in oil or by packing the pump with lightweight assembly lube, petroleum jelly, or oil. Rotate the pump shaft to distribute the oil within the pump body. In the case of a typical distributor-driven oil pump, the installation should be performed in the following manner.

1. Position the intermediate drive shaft into the distributor socket. With the shaft firmly seated, the stop on the shaft should touch the roof of the crankcase. Remove the shaft and position the stop as necessary.
2. With the stop properly positioned, insert the intermediate drive shaft into the oil pump. Install the pump and shaft as an assembly. Do not attempt to force the pump into position if it will not seat readily. The drive shaft hex might be misaligned with the distributor shaft. To align, rotate the intermediate drive shaft into a new position. Tighten the oil pump attaching screws to torque specifications.
3. Clean and install the oil pump inlet tube and screen assembly.

The installation of a typical camshaft-driven oil pump is as follows (Figure 11–39).

1. Apply a suitable sealant to the pump and block.
2. Install the pump to its full depth and rotate it back and forth slightly to ensure proper positioning and alignment through the full surface of the pump and the block machined interface surfaces.
3. Once installed, tighten the bolts or screws. The pump must be held in a fully seated position while installing bolts or screws (Figure 11–40).

SHOP TALK

The instructions here for the installation of either type of pump are general. Specific installation directions, as well as oil priming instructions (if necessary), can be found in the service manual. ■

There are some components that can be considered part of the lubrication system that help to increase engine performance. In newer engines, the baffle assembly (Figure 11–41) is one of these com-

1	BOLT
2	OIL PUMP
3	SHAFT WITH WHITE PAINT ID
4	LOCATING PIN
5	REAR MAIN CAP
6	ENGINE BLOCK
7	BOLT
8	CLAMP
9	OIL PUMP DRIVE
10	GREASE

FIGURE 11–39 Camshaft-driven oil pump installed. *Courtesy of Chevrolet Motor Division, General Motors Corporation*

FIGURE 11–40 Position and align the pump on the block. Tighten the mounting bolts uniformly. *Courtesy of TRW, Inc.*

ponents. It is used to restrict oil movement in the oil sump. Uncontrolled movement of the oil can allow the oil to mix with air.

FIGURE 11–41 Oil pan assembly with baffle plate.

COOLING SYSTEMS

Today's internal combustion engines generate a tremendous amount of heat. This heat is created when the air/fuel mixture is ignited and expands inside the engine combustion chamber. Metal temperatures around the combustion chamber can run as high as 1,000°F. To prevent the overheating of cylinder walls, pistons, valves, and other engine parts, it is necessary to dispose of this heat.

Two basic types of cooling systems are utilized by automotive manufacturers: liquid-cooled and air-cooled systems.

Liquid-Cooled System

By far, the most popular and efficient method of engine cooling is the liquid-cooled system (Figure 11–42). In this system, heat is removed from around the combustion chambers by a heat-absorbing liquid

FROM
HEATER
TO HEATER

DATA LINK
CONNECTOR

FILLER CAP

1. Engine coolant
2. Radiator cap
3. Radiator
4. Thermostat
5. Water pump
6. Electric coolant fan system
7. Fan motor
8. Engine coolant temperature sensor
9. Fan relay

FIGURE 11–42 Major components of a typical liquid-cooling system. Arrows indicate the coolant flow. *Courtesy of Mazda*

(coolant) circulating inside the engine. This liquid is pumped through the engine and, after absorbing the heat of combustion, flows into the radiator, where the heat is transferred to the atmosphere. The cooled liquid is then returned to the engine to repeat the cycle. These systems are designed to keep engine temperatures within a range in which they provide peak performance.

The technical definition of a thermostat is a temperature-responsive coolant flow control valve. The engine's thermostat controls the temperature and amount of coolant entering the radiator. While the engine is cold, the thermostat remains closed, allowing coolant to circulate only inside the engine. This allows the engine to warm up uniformly and eliminates hot spots. When the coolant reaches the opening temperature of the thermostat, the thermostat begins to open and allows the flow of coolant to the radiator. The hotter the coolant gets, the more the thermostat opens, allowing more coolant to flow through the radiator. Once the coolant has passed through the radiator and has given up its heat, it reenters the water pump. Here it is pushed through the passages surrounding the combustion chambers again to pick up heat and start the cycle.

The thermostat also maintains proper engine temperatures to keep the emission control systems working properly. Many vehicles fail the emissions

test because they are operating at too low a temperature.

Coolant Coolant is actually a mixture of water and ethylene glycol-based antifreeze/coolant. Water alone has a boiling point of 212°F and a freezing point of 32°F at sea level. A mixture of 67 percent antifreeze and 33 percent water will raise the boiling point of the mixture to 235°F and lower the freezing point to –92°F. As can be seen in Figure 11–43, antifreeze in excess of 67 percent will actually raise the freezing point of the mixture. This chart also indicates why antifreeze that is stored outside a service station might be very hard to pour at temperatures below 0°F. The typical recommended mixture is a 50/50 solution of water and antifreeze/coolant.

CUSTOMER CARE

Customers ought to be told that although ethylene glycol-based antifreeze is advertised as permanent, this simply means it should not boil away like earlier nonpermanent (alcohol) types. By no means does permanent mean that it should not be replaced. The antifreeze/coolant contains various rust and foam inhibitors that wear out. A system should be drained, flushed, and filled every two years to keep it intact. ∎

FIGURE 11–43   The relationship of the percentage of antifreeze in the coolant to the coolant's freezing and boiling points.

Most cooling systems today use an **expansion** or **recovery tank**. Cooling systems with expansion tanks are called closed-cooling systems. They are designed to catch and hold any coolant that passes through the pressure cap when the engine is hot. As the engine warms up, the coolant expands. This eventually causes the pressure cap to release. The coolant passes to an expansion tank. When the engine is shut down, the coolant begins to shrink. Eventually, the vacuum spring inside the pressure cap opens and the coolant in the expansion tank is drawn back into the cooling system.

There are marks on most recovery tanks that show where coolant levels should be when the car is running and when it is not (Figure 11–44). To check coolant levels on a car without a recovery tank, remove the radiator cap (when the engine is cold) and see if the coolant is up to where it should be. If there are no markings, make sure the coolant is covering the radiator core. If the coolant level is low after repeated filling, there is probably a leak in the cooling system.

CAUTION:

When working on the cooling system, remember that at operating temperature the coolant is extremely hot. Touching the coolant or spilling the coolant can cause serious body burns. Never remove the radiator cap when the engine is hot.   ■

Water Pump   The heart of the cooling system is the water pump. Its job is to move the coolant through the cooling system. Typically, the water pump is driven by the crankshaft through pulleys and a drive V-belt. The pump on some may be driven off the camshaft or the gear train. No matter how these units are driven, they all basically work the same way. The pumps are centrifugal-type pumps (Figure 11–45), with a rotating paddlewheel-type impeller to move the coolant. The shaft is mounted in the water pump housing and rotates on bearings. The pump contains a seal to keep the coolant from passing through it. At the drive end, the exposed end, a pulley is mounted to accept the belt. The pulley is driven by the crank-

FIGURE 11–44   Coolant recovery system with coolant levels marked on recovery tank.

FIGURE 11–45   Impeller-type water pump.

FIGURE 11–46 Two radiator designs: (A) cross flow and (B) down flow.

FIGURE 11–47 Two types of radiator core construction: (A) honeycomb or cellular and (B) tube and fin. *Courtesy of Ford Motor Company*

shaft. The pump housing usually includes the mounting point for the lower radiator hose.

When the engine is started, the pump impeller pushes the water from its pumping cavity into the engine block. When the engine is cold, the thermostat is closed. This stops the coolant from reaching the top of the radiator. For the water pump to circulate the coolant through the engine during warm-up, a by-pass passage is added below the thermostat, which leads back to the water pump. This passage must be kept free to eliminate hot spots in the engine during warm-up. It also allows hot coolant to pass through the valve, which will open the thermostat when it reaches the proper temperature.

Radiator The radiator is basically a heat exchanger, transferring heat from the engine to the air passing through it. The radiator itself is a series of tubes and fins that expose the heat from the coolant to as much surface area as possible. This maximizes the potential of heat being transferred to the passing air. The inlet tank on the radiator contains a baffle to distribute and de-aerate the coolant.

Factors influencing the efficiency of the radiator are the basic design of the radiator, the area and thickness of the radiator core, the amount of coolant going through the radiator, and the temperature of the cooling air.

A radiator's efficiency can be greatly increased by increasing the difference between the temperature of the coolant and the outside air flowing through it. This can be done only by raising the temperature of the coolant. Doing this permits the use of a smaller radiator or the use of the same size radiator to cool a larger engine. This is the primary reason manufacturers have been specifying higher start-to-open temperatures for thermostats and higher pressure ratings for radiator pressure caps.

The radiator is usually based on one of these two designs: cross flow or down flow. In a cross-flow radiator (Figure 11–46A), coolant enters on one side, travels through tubes, and collects on the opposite side. In

a down-flow radiator (Figure 11–46B), coolant enters the top of the radiator and is drawn downward by gravity. Cross-flow radiators are seen most often on large-engine or late-model cars because all the coolant flows through the fan air stream, which provides maximum cooling.

There are two types or radiator core construction: honeycomb or cellular type (Figure 11–47A), and tube and fin (Figure 11–47B). There are also two radiator core construction materials used—the copper/brass, soft solder coolers (Figure 11–48) and the vacuum-brazed, aluminum cores cinched to nylon tanks.

The aluminum type is thin, lightweight, and less costly. (The initial price of aluminum is below that of copper.) For these reasons, aluminum core radiators are being used more and more on newer-model vehicles.

Most radiators feature petcocks or plugs that allow a technician to drain coolant from the system. Coolant is added to the system at the radiator cap or the recovery tank depending on the type of system being used.

FIGURE 11–48   Different types of radiator construction. *Courtesy of Harrison Radiator, Division of General Motors Corporation*

RADIATOR PRESSURE CAP   At one time, the radiator cap was simply designed to keep the coolant (water and alcohol combination in the early days of motoring) from splashing out of the radiator. Today, it still serves that purpose, but it also does much more. Today, radiator caps are equipped with pressure springs and atmospheric vents. The cap allows for an increase in pressure in the radiator, which raises the boiling point of the coolant. For every pound of pressure put on the coolant, the boiling point is raised about 3-1/4°F. Today's caps are normally designed to hold between 14 and 17 pounds per square inch (psi). When pressures exceed this, the seal between the cap and the radiator filler neck opens and allows the excessive pressure to vent into a coolant recovery tank or out onto the ground via an overflow tube.

The three basic pressure cap designs are:

1. Constant pressure type (Figure 11–49A). The lower seal or pressure valve is held closed by a spring until the coolant gets hot enough to build enough pressure to open it within the preset pressure range. Pressure builds gradually as the coolant becomes hot.

2. Pressure vent type (Figure 11–49B). The lower seal or pressure valve is held closed as with the constant pressure type. The vacuum-release valve installed in the pressure valve is held open by a weight. The cap is open to atmospheric pressure through the vacuum-release valve until the coolant gets hot enough to cause a surge of coolant or steam to hit it, causing it to close to atmospheric pressure. From this point, the pressure vent cap works in the same way as the constant pressure cap.

3. Closed system type (Figure 11–49C). These caps operate in the same manner as the constant pressure caps except that they are designed for a closed system. The closed design keeps the cooling system full at all times without losing coolant due to expansion or overflow. On closed systems, coolant is added to the reservoir instead of to the radiator. The radiator caps are not designed to be

FIGURE 11–49 Radiator pressure cap designs: (A) constant pressure type; (B) pressure vent type; and (C) closed system type.

removed. Late-model cars use this type of radiator cap, and accessory kits are available to install them in other cars.

All radiator caps are designed to meet SAE standards for safety. This standard specifies that there shall be a detent or safety stop position allowing pressure to escape from the system without allowing the hot coolant to blow out of the radiator's neck into the person opening the cap. Only after all pressure has been relieved should the cap be removed from the filler neck (Figure 11–50). A lever or push button in the cap may be used to relieve the pressure prior to removal.

Cap specifications require that the cap must not leak below the low limit of the pressure range and must open above the high limit. Pressure caps should always be tested for the proper pressure release level and checked for gasket cracking, brittleness, or deterioration each time the antifreeze is changed or when any routine cooling system maintenance is performed.

SHOP TALK

Always refer to application charts or a service manual when replacing a pressure cap to make sure the new cap has the same pressure range as the original cap. ∎

WATER OUTLET The water outlet is the connection between the engine and the upper radiator hose through which hot coolant from the engine is pumped back into the radiator. The water outlet has been called a gooseneck, elbow, inlet, outlet, or thermostat housing. Generally, it covers and seals the ther-

FIGURE 11–50 Parts of a radiator pressure cap assembly. *Courtesy of Chrysler Corporation*

mostat and, in some cases, includes the thermostat by-pass.

Most water outlets are made of cast iron, cast aluminum, or stamped steel. Internal corrosion contributes to the failure of water outlets. Cast iron water outlets are more resistant to this type of corrosion than stamped steel or cast aluminum outlets. A more common cause of failure for a water outlet is the uneven torquing down of the water outlet mounting bolts, which can cause a mounting ear to break off.

When this happens, the outlet will not seal and must be replaced.

HOSES As already mentioned, the primary function of a cooling system hose is to carry the coolant between different elements of the system. Nearly all automobiles have an upper and lower radiator hose and two heater hoses. Some may also have a by-pass hose. The majority of cooling system hoses are made of butyl or neoprene rubber. Many hoses are wire reinforced, and some are used to connect metal tubing between the engine and the radiator. Normally, radiator hoses are designed with expansion bends to protect radiator connections from excessive engine motion and vibration.

The upper radiator hose is subjected to the roughest service life of any hose in the cooling system. It must absorb more engine motion than any of the other hoses. It is exposed to the coolant at its hottest stage, plus it is insulated by the hood during hot soak periods. These conditions make the upper hose the most probable to fail.

Normally, hoses begin to deteriorate from the inside. Pieces of deteriorated hose will circulate through the system until they find a place to rest. This place is usually the radiator core, causing clogging. Any external bulging or cracking of hoses is a definite sign of failure. Hoses will become either very soft and spongy or very hard and brittle when their life is near the end. When one hose fails, all of the others should be carefully inspected.

Nearly all original equipment radiator hose is of the molded, curved design. Aftermarket products may be of this type or of a wire inserted flex type. This flex-type hose allows greater vehicle coverage per part number, but may not be designed for some cars that require radical bends and shapes. Lower radiator hoses are normally wire reinforced to prevent collapse due to the suction of the water pump.

All cooling system hoses are basically installed the same way. The hose is clamped onto inlet-outlet nipples on the radiator, water pump, and heater. Figure 11–51 illustrates the four most common types of hose clamps.

Most new cars come from the factory equipped with clamps that are simply spring steel wires that exert the pressure necessary to seal a connection after being stretched over the joint.

Twin wire clamps use a bolt to tighten a metal band or wire. The bolt sometimes tends to be unnecessarily strong and can be difficult to remove. Perhaps the best clamp, overall, is the worm-drive clamp, which uses a simple screwdriver for tightening and loosening. The notched band will not cut the hose as

FIGURE 11–51 Common types of hose clamps: (A) twin wire; (B) worm-drive; (C) spring; and (D) screw tower.

a wire can. A worm-drive also will not distort the pressure applied to the hose end when it is tightened.

Thermostat An automotive thermostat works somewhat like a typical home thermostat. It attempts to control the engine's operating temperature by routing the coolant either to the radiator or through the by-pass or sometimes by a combination of both.

Today's thermostat is composed of a specially formulated wax and powdered metal pellet, which is tightly contained in a heat-conducting copper cup equipped with a piston inside a rubber boot. Heat causes the wax pellet to expand, forcing the piston outward, which opens the valve of the thermostat. The pellet senses temperature changes and opens and closes the valve to control coolant temperature and flow. Today's thermostats are also designed to slow down coolant flow when they are open. This helps to prevent overheating, which can result from the coolant moving too quickly, through the engine, to absorb enough heat.

While the thermostat might be situated in several locations, the most common spot is at the front of the engine on top of the engine block (Figure 11–52). The heat element fits into a recess in the block where it will be exposed to hot coolant. The top of the thermostat is then covered by the water outlet housing, which holds it in place and provides a connection to the upper radiator hose.

There are two basic types of thermostats on the market today. Both function in the same manner, but each has distinct differences.

The reverse poppet thermostat (Figure 11–53A) opens against the flow of the coolant from the water pump. The coolant, under water pump pressure, is used to help the reverse poppet thermostat stay closed

FIGURE 11–52 Parts of a thermostat.

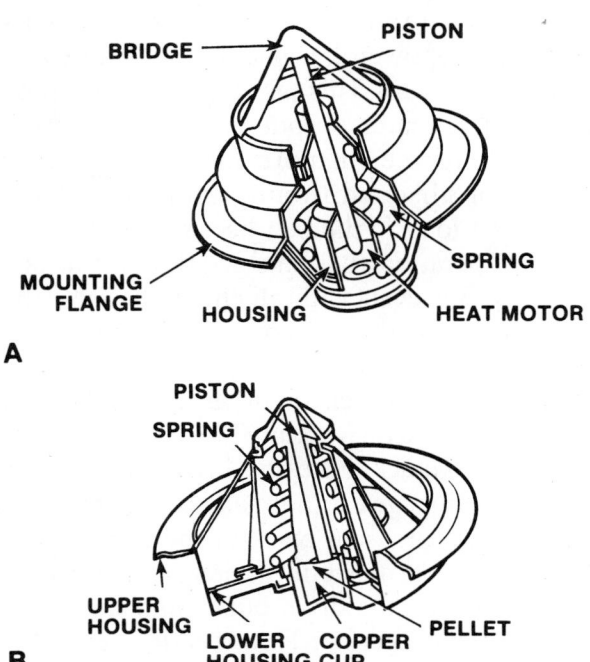

FIGURE 11–53 Types of thermostats: (A) reverse poppet; (B) balanced sleeve.

FIGURE 11–54 (A) Thermostat closed; (B) thermostat open.

when it is cool. The valve is self-aligning and also self-cleaning.

The balanced sleeve thermostat (Figure 11–53B) eliminates pressure shocks by allowing pressurized coolant to circulate around all of its working parts. By reducing pressure shocks, it provides coolant temperature stability during the most difficult operating conditions.

The thermostat permits fast warm-up of the engine after it has been started (Figure 11–54A). Slow warm-up causes moisture condensation in the combustion chambers, which finds its way into the crankcase and causes sludge formation. The thermostat keeps the coolant above a designated minimum temperature required for efficient engine performance. Most engines are equipped with a coolant by-pass, either outside the engine block or built into the casting. Some thermostat models are equipped with a by-pass valve that shuts off the engine by-pass after warm-up, forcing all coolant to flow to the radiator.

Thermostats must start to open at a specified temperature (Figure 11–54B)—normally 3°F above or below its temperature rating. It must be fully opened at about 20°F above the "start to open" temperature. It must also permit the passage of a specified amount of coolant when fully open and leak no more than a specified amount when fully closed.

When replacing the thermostat, be sure to use the same temperature thermostat as was used for original equipment. The thermostat should always be checked when performing routine cooling system maintenance.

Some cooling systems employ a two-stage thermostat. This thermostat is designed to control engine temperature more precisely by reducing peak temperatures during the critical warm-up periods. This type of thermostat contains two valves: a main valve and a subvalve (Figure 11–55). The subvalve begins to open at above 175°F and permits a limited amount of cooling during warm-up. This prevents peak temperature hot spots. The main valve begins to open at 192 or 195°F. Both valves remain open up to 212°F and both close at about 175°F.

FIGURE 11–55   Two-stage thermostat. *Courtesy of Ford Motor Company*

Belt Drives Belt drives (Figure 11–56) have been used for many years. V-belts and serpentine belts are used to drive water pumps, power steering pumps, air-conditioning compressors, alternators, and emission control pumps (Figure 11–57). The flexibility of belt drives has allowed many inexpensive improvements in the modern automobile.

FIGURE 11–56   V-belt. *Courtesy of Chrysler Corporation*

FIGURE 11–57   Single belts can drive many components. *Courtesy of Chrysler Corporation*

The belt system is popular for a number of reasons. It is very inexpensive and quiet when compared to chains and gears. It is also very easy to repair. Because the belts are flexible, they will absorb some shock loads and cushion shaft bearings from excessive loads.

The biggest problem with belt drives is that they are neglected. Typically, no one makes an effort to check these vital links until they begin to make noise or break. Additional requirements have been put on these belts and have tended to cause a few more problems with them. As engines began developing more horsepower, heavy-duty fans and water pumps were necessary. This placed more tension on the drive belt. Greater output requirements from charging systems meant more load on the belts. The advent of air-conditioning units added the greatest impact load to the belt because of the magnetic clutch operation that engages the unit at any engine speed. But even with all these changes, the belt continues to be the primary method for power take-offs.

Heat has adverse effects on drive belts. Belts tend to overcure due to excessive heat. This causes the rubber to harden and crack. Excessive heat usually comes from slippage. Slippage can normally be attributed to lack of proper belt tension or oily conditions. When slippage occurs, heat not only overcures the belt, it also travels through the drive pulley and down the shaft to the support bearing. These bearings might be damaged if the slippage is allowed to continue. As a V-belt wears, it begins to ride deeper in the pulley groove. This reduces its tension and promotes slippage. As this is a normal occurrence, periodic adjustment of belt tensions should be expected.

Serpentine belts are kept under constant tension by an idler pulley or tensioner. This pulley is designed to compensate for belt stretch and to keep a proper amount of tension on the belt.

Many drive units consist of two matched belts that run over parallel pulleys. If one pulley or belt should wear excessively, the belts will run at slightly different speeds, thus one will be constantly slipping. Matched belts should always be replaced in pairs so they wear together, thus maintaining the same length to prevent slippage and problems.

USING SERVICE MANUALS

Proper belt tightening procedures and specifications are given in the specification section of most service manuals. ∎

Fans and Fan Clutches As mentioned earlier, the efficiency of the cooling system is based on the amount of heat that can be removed from the system and transferred to the air. The system needs air. At highway speeds, the ram air through the radiator should be sufficient to maintain proper cooling. At low speeds and idle, the system needs additional air. This air is delivered by a fan.

The design of fans varies with the air requirements of the engine's cooling system. Diameter, pitch, and the number of blades can be varied to attain the needed flow. Fans are usually shrouded to maintain efficiency by causing all of the flow to pass through the radiator. This shrouding also allows the fan to be placed relatively far from the radiator, thus allowing the engine to be set back in the car while the radiator is left near the front of the vehicle.

Five- or six-blade fans are usually found on today's cars. Fans may be made of steel, nylon, or fiberglass, and are precisely balanced to prevent water pump bearing and seal damage. Since fan air is usually only necessary at idle and low speed operation, various design concepts are used to limit the fan's operation at higher speeds. Horsepower is required to turn the fan. Therefore, the operation of a cooling fan reduces the available horsepower to the drive wheels, as well as the fuel economy of the vehicle. Fans are also very noisy at high speeds, adding to driver fatigue and total vehicle noise.

In an effort to overcome these problems, some vehicle manufacturers use flexible blades or **flex blades** (Figure 11–58) that bend or change pitch based on engine speed. That is, at slower speeds the blade pitch is at the maximum (Figure 11–59A). As engine speed increases (Figure 11–59B), the blade pitch decreases as does the horsepower loss and noise level.

In most late-model applications, to save power and reduce the noise level, the conventional belt-driven, water-pump-mounted engine coolant fan has been replaced with an electrically driven fan (Figure 11–60). The fan and motor are mounted to the radiator shroud and are not connected mechanically or physically to the engine. The 12-volt, motor-driven fan is electrically controlled by either, or both, of two methods: an engine coolant temperature switch or sensor and the air-conditioner switch.

Following the schematic in (Figure 11–61A), the cooling fan motor is connected to the 12-volt battery supply through a normally open (NO) set of contacts (points) in the cooling fan relay. Protection for this circuit is provided by a fusible link (F/L). During normal operation, with the air conditioner off and the engine coolant below a predetermined temperature of approximately 215°F, the relay contacts are open and the fan motor does not operate.

Should the engine coolant temperature exceed approximately 230°F, the engine coolant temperature switch closes (Figure 11–61B). This energizes the fan

FIGURE 11–58 Flexible fan features.

FIGURE 11–59 Flex fan: (A) extreme pitch at low speed; (B) reduced pitch at high speed.

FIGURE 11–60 Electrically driven fan. *Courtesy of American Honda Motor Company, Inc.*

FIGURE 11–61 (A) Electric engine cooling fan schematic; (B) with the temperature sensor closed, the relay will be energized, completing the circuit to the fan motor.

relay coil, which in turn closes the relay contacts. The contacts provide 12 volts to the fan motor if the ignition switch is in the on position. The 12-volt supply for the relay coil circuit is independent of the 12-volt supply for the fan motor circuit. The coil circuit is from the on terminal of the ignition switch, through a fuse in the fuse panel, and to ground through the relay coil and temperature sensor.

Should the air-conditioner select switch be turned to any cool position, regardless of engine temperature, a circuit is completed through the relay coil to ground through the select switch. This action closes the relay contacts to provide 12 volts to the fan motor. The fan then operates as long as the air-conditioner and ignition switches are on.

There are many variations of electric cooling fan operation. Some provide a cool-down period whereby the fan continues to operate after the engine has been stopped and the ignition switch is turned off. The fan

stops only when the engine coolant falls to a predetermined safe temperature, usually about 210°F. In some systems, the fan does not start when the air-conditioner select switch is turned on unless the high side of the air-conditioning (A/C) system is above a predetermined safe temperature.

Some late-model cars control the cooling fan by completing the ground through the engine control computer. Check the service manual to see how an electric cooling fan is controlled before working with it.

CAUTION:

The engine electric cooling fan can come on at any time without warning even if the engine is not running. For this reason, it is always wise to remove the negative terminal from the battery or the electric cooling fan connector while working around an electric fan. Make sure you reconnect the connector before giving the car back to the customer. ∎

Another way of controlling fan noise and horsepower loss is by using a fan clutch. This unit connects the fan to the drive pulley (usually on the water pump shaft). The clutch slips at high speeds; therefore, it is not turning at full engine speed.

Cooling fan clutches may be speed-controlled or temperature-controlled. The obvious advantage of the temperature-controlled unit is the fact that it knows when air is needed to cool the system. A silicone fluid couples the fan blade drive plate to a driven disc via a series of annular grooves in the two pieces (Figure 11–62). The fluid fills these grooves and drives the fan until the differential torque between the fan and the drive disc causes the fluid to shear or slip. The unit has a bimetallic element that senses the air temperature behind the radiator. This bimetal is calibrated to open and close a valve in the clutch that dispenses the silicone at particular temperatures. When the fluid is returned to its reservoir, the unit freewheels the fan until more cooling is required. Tests

FIGURE 11–62 Parts of a fluid coupling temperature-controlled fan drive. *Courtesy of Chrysler Corporation*

FIGURE 11–63 Cooling system circulates coolant through the engine.

have proven that maximum cooling is necessary less than 10 percent of the time. Therefore, a temperature-controlled fan clutch saves fuel and reduces noise 90 percent of the time.

Water Jackets Hollow passages in the block and cylinder heads surround the areas closest to the cylinders and combustion chambers (Figure 11–63). Coolant flow through the block and head can be in one of the following ways.

SERIES FLOW SYSTEM In this system (Figure 11–64A), the coolant flows around all the cylinders on each bank as it flows to the rear of the block. Large main coolant passages at the rear of the block direct the coolant through the head gasket and to the head.

PARALLEL FLOW SYSTEM In this system (Figure 11–64B), coolant flows into the block under pressure, then crosses the gasket to the head through main coolant passage openings beside each cylinder.

SERIES-PARALLEL FLOW SYSTEM This system (Figure 11–64C) uses a combination of series and parallel flow systems. The cooling passages inside the engine are designed so the whole system can be drained and there are no pockets in which steam can form. Any steam that develops must be able to go directly to the top of the radiator, for the cooling system to function properly.

REVERSE FLOW SYSTEM This system is on a few high-performance engines. In it, the coolant flows through the cylinder heads first then it flows through the block. With the coolant flowing around the combustion chamber first, chamber temperatures are better maintained.

FIGURE 11–64 Coolant flow through the engine block and cylinder head: (A) series flow system; (B) parallel flow system; (C) series parallel flow system.

Included in the water jackets are soft (core) plugs and a block drain plug. The soft plugs and drain are usually removed during engine teardown. New ones are installed during reassembly. Core plugs are prone to rust and corrosion, and, therefore, will weep coolant or rust through completely. When this happens, the core plugs should be replaced.

Temperature Indicator Coolant temperature indicators are mounted in the dashboard to alert the driver of an overheating condition. It consists of a temperature gauge and/or a light. A temperature sensor is screwed into a threaded hole in the water jacket

FIGURE 11–65 Coolant temperature sender or sensor.

(Figure 11–65). A schematic of an electric temperature gauge including a voltage limiter is shown in Figure 11–66. Besides indicating coolant temperatures to the driver, temperature sensors supply some important information to today's computer-controlled engine control systems.

Heater System A hot liquid passenger compartment heater is part of the engine's cooling system. Heated coolant flows from the engine through heater hoses and a heater control valve to a smaller heater core, or radiator, located in a hollow container on either side of the fire wall. Air is directed or blown over the hot heater core, and the heated air flows into the passenger compartment. Movable doors can be controlled to blend cool air with heated air for more or less heat.

FIGURE 11–66 Schematic of an electric temperature gauge. *Courtesy of Ford Motor Company*

FIGURE 11–67 Cross section of a V-type air-cooled engine.

Oil Cooler Radiators used in vehicles with automatic transmissions have a sealed heat exchanger, or form of radiator, located in the coolant outlet tank of the regular radiator. Metal or rubber hoses carry hot automatic transmission fluid to the heat exchanger. The coolant passing over the sealed heat exchanger cools the fluid, which is then returned to the transmission. Cooling the transmission fluid is essential to the efficiency and durability of an automatic transmission.

Air-Cooled System

As mentioned at the beginning of this chapter, a few engines (such as the Porsche 911 and 930 models) use a cooling system that relies on air rather than a liquid to transfer heat from the engine to the atmosphere (Figure 11–67). Cylinders and heads have fins that are enclosed in a shroud to control airflow. The fins expose more of the surface area to airflow for improved heat dissipation. Ducts and shrouds direct the airflow over the engine components, especially over the hotter cylinder head area. A belt-driven or electric blower provides for airflow. Fresh air is taken in and heated air expelled into the atmosphere. A thermostat connected to a control valve or door regulates airflow to control engine temperature.

COOLING SYSTEM SERVICING

The cooling system must operate, be inspected, and be serviced as a system. Replacing one damaged part while leaving others dirty or clogged will not increase system efficiency. Service the entire system to ensure good results.

Service involves both a visual inspection of the parts and connections and pressure testing. Pressure testing is used to detect internal or external leaks. Guidelines for inspection and pressure testing of the cooling system are given in the *Tech Manual* that accompanies this textbook.

The following is a list of places to check for a suspected leak in the cooling system. Although this is not a complete list, it does present the most common areas where a leak can occur.

External Leakage

- ◆ Radiator
- ◆ Loose hose clamp
- ◆ Hose
- ◆ Faulty radiator cap
- ◆ Dented radiator hose connector for the inlet or outlet hose
- ◆ Heater connection
- ◆ Water pump, through weep hole
- ◆ Cracked or porous water pump housing
- ◆ Water core
- ◆ Loose core hole plug in cylinder block
- ◆ Cracked thermostat housing
- ◆ Water temperature sending unit
- ◆ Cylinder head bolts loose or tightened unevenly
- ◆ Warped or cracked cylinder head
- ◆ Heater control valve
- ◆ Cracked cylinder block
- ◆ Damaged gasket or dry gasket if engine has been stored
- ◆ Coolant reservoir or hose

Internal Leakage

- ◆ Faulty head gasket
- ◆ Cracked head
- ◆ Cracked block
- ◆ Transmission fluid cooler

Repairing Radiators

Most radiator leak repairs require the removal of the radiator from the vehicle. The coolant must be drained and all hoses and oil cooler lines disconnected. Bolts holding the radiator are then loosened and removed.

The actual radiator repair procedures depend on the material from which it is made and the type of damage. Most radiator repairs are made by radiator specialty shops that employ technicians with knowledge of such work. If the radiator is badly damaged, it should be replaced and the installation of a new one should be done as directed by the manufacturer.

Testing the Radiator Pressure Cap

Apply the proper cap testing adapter and radiator pressure cap to the tester head. Pump the tester (Figure 11–68) until the pressure valve of the cap releases pressure. The cap should hold pressure in its range as indicated on the tester gauge dial for one

FIGURE 11–68 Testing a radiator cap with radiator leaks.

FIGURE 11–69 Testing a thermostat's opening temperature by submerging it into water.

minute. If it doesn't, replace it. Remove the cap from the tester and visually inspect the condition of the cap's pressure valve and upper and lower sealing gaskets. If the gaskets are hard, brittle, or deteriorated, the cap may leak when exposed to hot, pressurized coolant. It should be replaced with a new cap in the same pressure range.

CAUTION:

The radiator cap should never be removed when the cap or radiator is hot to the touch. When the pressure in the radiator is suddenly released, the coolant's boiling temperature is reduced. This causes the coolant to immediately boil. Because coolant is a thick liquid, it will stick to your skin and cause severe burns if it is hot. The radiator should first be allowed to cool, or force cool it by lightly spraying water on the radiator core. When the cap is cool to the touch and the engine is shut off, release the pressure with the safety level or push button (if the cap is so equipped) or use a cloth over the cap and turn it counterclockwise one-quarter turn to the filler neck safety stop. Carefully watch for any liquid or steam loss around the ring of the cap and from the radiator overflow tube. Let the cap remain in this position until all pressure subsides. In this position, the pressure valve is lifted from the bottom sealing seat in the filler neck. When all evidence of discharge ends, use a cloth to cover the cap, press it down to pass the cap's ears over the safety stops, and continue to turn counterclockwise to remove the cap.

Testing the Thermostat

There are several ways to test the opening temperature of a thermostat. The first method does not require that the thermostat be removed from the engine. Remove the radiator pressure cap from a cool radiator and insert a thermometer into the coolant. Start the engine and let it warm up. Watch the thermometer and the surface of the coolant. When the coolant begins to flow, this indicates the thermostat has started to open. The reading on the thermometer indicates the opening temperature of the thermostat. If the engine is cold and coolant circulates, this indicates the thermostat is stuck open and must be replaced.

The other way to test a thermostat is to remove it. Suspend the thermostat completely submerged in a small container of water so it does not touch the bottom (Figure 11–69). Place a thermometer in the water so it does not touch the container and only measures water temperature. Heat the water. When the thermostat valve barely begins to open, read the thermometer. This is the opening temperature of this particular thermostat. If the valve stays open after the thermostat is removed from the water, the thermostat is defective and must be replaced.

Several types of commercial testers are available. When using such a tester, be sure to follow the manufacturer's instructions.

SHOP TALK

If a vehicle overheats and there is no evidence of previous water loss and the radiator pressure cap is holding the proper pressure, chances are very good that the thermostat is defective. ∎

If a thermostat is more than two years old, or if there is any doubt about its operation, replace it. Markings on the thermostat normally indicate which end should face toward the radiator. Regardless of the markings, the sensored end must always be installed toward the engine.

When replacing the thermostat, also replace the gasket that seals the thermostat in place and is positioned between the water outlet casting and the engine block. Generally, these gaskets are made of a composition fiber material and are die-cut to match the thermostat opening and mounting bolt configuration of the water outlet. Thermostat gaskets generally come with or without an adhesive backing. The adhesive backing of gaskets holds the thermostat securely centered in the mounting flange, leaving both hands of the technician free to align and bolt the thermostat securely in place. With the adhesive-backed gasket holding the thermostat in place, it will not drop out or become misaligned. This provides for a tight seal and also prevents breaking the mounting flange of the water outlet during installation.

Checking and Replacing Hoses

Carefully check all cooling hoses for leakage, swelling, and chafing. Also change any hose that feels mushy or extremely brittle when squeezed firmly (Figure 11–70). Be especially watchful for signs of splits when hoses are squeezed. These splits have a habit of bursting wide open under pressure. Also look for rust stains around the clamps. Rust stains indicate the hose is leaking, possibly because the clamp has eaten into the hose. Loosen the clamp, slide it back, and check for cuts.

Do not overlook the small by-pass hose on some models. It is located between the water pump and engine block. Also, check the lower radiator hose very carefully. This hose contains a coiled wire lining to keep it from collapsing during operation. If the

wire loses tension, the hose can partially collapse at high speed and restrict coolant flow. This results in a very elusive overheating problem.

CUSTOMER CARE

Technicians should do their customers a favor and remind them that all cooling hoses should be replaced every two to four years to prevent breakdowns. ■

When replacing a hose, drain the coolant system below the level that is being worked on. Use a knife to cut off the old hose (Figure 11–71) and loosen or cut the old clamp. Slide the old hose off the fitting. If the hose is stuck, do not pry it off. You could possibly damage the inlet/outlet nipple or the attachment between the end of the hose and the bead. Carefully cut the stuck hose off its fitting.

Clean off any remaining hose particles with a wire brush or emery cloth. The fitting should be clean when installing the new hose. Burrs or sharp edges could cut into the hose tube and lead to premature failure.

Coat the surface with a sealing compound (Figure 11–72). Place the new clamps on each end of the hose before positioning the hose. Do not reuse old spring-type clamps, even if they look good. Slide the clamps to about 1/4 inch from the end of the hose after it is

FIGURE 11–71 Cutting off an old hose.

FIGURE 11–70 Defects in hoses.

FIGURE 11–72 Applying sealing compound.

FIGURE 11–73 New clamps should be placed immediately after the bead of the fitting.

properly positioned on the fitting (Figure 11–73). Tighten the clamp securely. Do not overtighten.

It is a good idea to readjust the clamp of a newly installed coolant hose after a brief run-in period. The hose end does not contract and expand at the same rate as the metal of the inlet/outlet nipple to which it is attached. Rubber coolant hose, warmed by the hot coolant and hot engine, will expand. The clamp compresses the rubber around the hose end and sets it. When the engine cools, the fitting contracts more than the rubber, and the hose will not be as secure. This can result in cold leaks of coolant at the inlet/outlet nipple when the engine is cool. Retightening the clamp eliminates the problem.

Water Pump Service

The majority of water pump failures are attributed to leaks of some sort. When the pump seat fails, coolant will begin to seep out of the weep hole in the casting. This is an early indicator of trouble. The seals may simply wear out due to abrasives in the cooling system, or some types of seals crack due to thermal shock such as adding cold water to an overheated engine. This could also cause other internal parts to fail.

Other failures can be attributed to bearing and shaft problems and an occasional cracked casting. Water pump bearing or seal failure can be caused by surprisingly small out-of-balance conditions that are difficult to spot. Look for the following.

- A bent fan. A single bent blade will cause problems.
- A piece of fan missing.
- A cracked fan blade. Even a small crack will prevent proper flexing.
- Fan mounting surfaces that are not clean or flush.
- A worn fan clutch.

To check a water pump, start the engine and listen for a bad bearing, using a mechanic's stethoscope or rubber tubing. Place the stethoscope or hose on the bearing or pump shaft. If a louder than normal noise is heard, the bearing is defective.

CAUTION:

Whenever working near a running engine, keep your hands and clothing away from the moving fan, pulleys, and belts. Do not allow the stethoscope or rubber tubing to be caught by the moving parts. ■

There is another test that can be performed with the engine off and the fan belt and shroud removed. Grasp the fan and attempt to move it in and out and up and down (Figure 11–74). More than 1/16 inch of movement indicates worn bearings that require water pump replacement.

To determine whether the water pump is allowing for good circulation, warm up the engine and run it at idle speed. Squeeze the upper hose connection with one hand and accelerate the engine with the other hand. If a surge on the hose is felt, the pump is working.

Any air being sucked into the cooling system is certain to have a detrimental effect. It cuts down pumping efficiency and causes both rusting and wear at a rate approximately three times above normal. To test for aeration, have the engine fully warmed up, all hose connections tight, and the coolant level up to normal. Attach one end of a small hose to the radiator overflow pipe and put the other end into a jar of water. Run the engine at a fast idle. If a steady stream of bubbles appears in the jar of water, air is getting into the cooling system.

Check first for a cylinder gasket leak by running a compression test. If two adjacent cylinders test low, the gasket is bad. Otherwise, there is an air leak somewhere else in the cooling system.

Replacing the Water Pump When replacing a water pump, it is necessary to drain the cooling system. Any components—belts, fan, fan shroud, shaft

FIGURE 11–74 Checking water pump bearings. *Courtesy of Chrysler Corporation*

spacers, or viscous drive clutch—should be removed to make the pump accessible. Most pumps are attached to the cylinder block as shown in Figure 11–75. Loosen and remove the bolts in a crisscross pattern from the center outward. Insert a rag into the block opening and scrape off any remains of the old gasket.

⬤ CAUTION:

When working on the coolant system (for example, replacing the water pump or thermostat), a certain amount of coolant will spill on the floor. The antifreeze in the coolant causes it to be very slippery. Always immediately wipe up any coolant that spills to reduce or eliminate the chance of injury. ■

When replacing a water pump, always follow the procedures recommended by the manufacturer. Most often a coating of good waterproof sealer should be applied to a new gasket before it is placed into position on the water pump. Coat the other side of the gasket with sealer, and position the pump against the engine block until it is properly seated. Install the mounting bolts and tighten them evenly in a staggered sequence to the torque specifications with a torque wrench. Careless tightening could cause the pump housing to crack. Check the pump to make sure it rotates freely.

Checking Fans and Fan Clutches

Fan operation can be checked by spinning the fan by hand. A noticeable wobble or any blade that is not in the same plane as the rest indicates that replacement is in order. The fan can also be checked by removing it and laying it on a flat surface. If it is straight, all the blades should touch the surface. Never attempt to

FIGURE 11–75 Installing a water pump. *Courtesy of Perfect Circle/Dana*

straighten a damaged cooling fan. Bending it back into shape might seem easier (and cheaper) than replacing it, but doing so is risky. Whenever metal is bent, it is weakened. Bending creates microscopic stress cracks that spread throughout the metal. Repeated bending or stress eventually leads to fatigue failure. Cooling fans are especially vulnerable to this type of failure. Their vulnerability is due to the high rotational speeds at which they operate and the centrifugal forces and loading they experience.

Any condition that causes the fan blades to run untrue can produce enough vibration and overload to knock out the water pump bearing and break the shaft. Obviously, the farther out from the pump bearing the fan blade is located, the more severe will be the effect of the blade being mounted in a crooked position. Almost all cars equipped with an air conditioner also have a fan clutch, which locates the fan blades several inches out from the flange on the pump shaft. This amounts to an outboard weight of approximately 6 pounds and creates a terrific strain on the pump shaft if it is not running in perfect alignment and balance.

Both types of fan clutches—torque drive or thermostat and controlled viscous drive—use a fluid-filled chamber (usually silicone) to turn the fan. Obviously, loss of the drive fluid will render the fan useless. In thermostat-type units, a defective thermostat spring or binding in the clutch plates will also cause problems and prevent the fan from speeding up as the engine gets hotter. The result is overheating and boiling over.

One of the simplest checks is to visually inspect the fan clutch for signs of fluid loss. Oily streaks radiating outward from the hub shaft mean fluid has leaked out past the bearing seal.

Most fan clutches offer a slight amount of resistance if turned by hand when the engine is cold. They offer drag when the engine is hot. If the fan freewheels easily hot or cold, replace the clutch.

Another check that should be made is to push the tip of a fan blade in and out. Any visible looseness in the shaft bearing means the fan clutch should be replaced.

Fan blades are balanced at the time of manufacture but can be bent if handled carelessly. Likewise, fan clutches are machined very accurately to run true. However, rough handling at the time of pump replacement causes nicks and dents on the mounting faces. This can cause the fan blade to be installed crookedly. Serious trouble might follow soon after the car is back in service. Therefore, technicians should be cautioned to handle fan clutches and blade with care and to file away any nicks, burrs, or dents someone else might have caused. Obviously, if any fins have been broken off the fan clutch, it must be replaced.

FIGURE 11–77 Adjusting tension of a drive belt. *Courtesy of Chrysler Corporation*

SHOP TALK

Damaged fan shrouds can usually be repaired if the damage is not severe. Polyethylene and polypropylene plastics can be hot-air or airless welded. Fiberglass can be glued with epoxy. The important rule here is never leave a fan shroud off. The shroud is needed to help the fan work at peak efficiency and leaving it off will affect the fan's efficiency. ∎

Checking Belts

If a belt breaks, at best the fan stops spinning and the coolant does not cool down efficiently. At worst, the water pump stops, the coolant does not circulate, and, eventually, the engine overheats.

Belts, like hoses, are made of elastic rubber compounds. Although they are extremely sturdy, they are primarily designed for transmitting power. Even the best belts last only an average of four years. Advise the customer to replace all belts every four years, regardless of how they look.

Fortunately, belt problems are easily discovered either by visual inspection for cracks, splits, glazing, or oil soakage (Figure 11–76), or by the screech of slippage. As stated earlier in the chapter, the coolant fan belt is part of a multibelt arrangement. In servicing a multibelt setup, it is very important to replace all of the belts when one set is bad.

The mounting brackets on alternators, power-steering pumps, and air compressors are designed to be adjustable so proper tension can be maintained on these belts. Some of these brackets have a hole or slot to allow the use of a pry bar or wrench when adjusting. Some automobiles require the fan, fan pul-

FIGURE 11–78 Checking fan belt tension. *Courtesy of TRW, Inc.*

ley, and other accessory drive belts to be removed to gain access to belts needing replacement. After replacing a belt, make sure it is adjusted properly. To do so, use a pry bar, where possible, to move the accessory so there is tension on the belt (Figure 11–77). Be careful not to damage the part you are prying against while tightening the belt. Tighten all bolts and nuts to keep the tension. Then check the belt's tension with a belt tension gauge (Figure 11–78). Make sure the tension meets the manufacturer's recommendations.

CRACKED   OIL-SOAKED   GLAZED   TORN OR SPLIT

FIGURE 11–76 Drive belt defects. *Courtesy of Chrysler Corporation*

SHOP TALK

It is never advisable to pry a belt onto a pulley. Obtain enough slack so the belt can be slipped on without damaging either the V-belts or a pulley.

Some power-steering pumps have a 1/2-inch drive socket to aid in adjusting belts to the proper tension without prying against any accessory. ■

After installation of the new belts, the engine should be run for 10 to 15 minutes to allow belts to seat and reach their initial stretch condition. Modern steel-strengthened V-belts do not stretch much after the initial run-in, so the re-tensioning should be done very carefully with an accurate gauge. Recheck the tension again after 5,000 miles.

Misalignment of the V-pulleys reduces the belt's service life and brings about rapid V-pulley wear, which causes thrown belts and screech. Undesirable side or end thrust loads can also be imposed on pulley or pump shaft bearings. The more wrap a belt has around a pulley, the easier it is to transmit full power. A small pulley causes more belt flexing; therefore, it will crack and be ruined sooner.

It is important to check alignment by using a straightedge. Pulleys should be in alignment within 1/16 inch per foot of the distance across the face of the pulleys.

Flushing Cooling Systems

Rust and scale will inevitably form in any cooling system. When they do, there are a few vulnerable places they can attack. One happens to be the main seal in the water pump, which keeps coolant away from the bearing and its lubricant. If grit is allowed to erode the seal, the bearing will be the next item to go. Coolant leaking from the water pump's vent hole is evidence of seal failure.

Whenever coolant is changed, and especially before a water pump is replaced, a thorough reverse flushing or back flushing should be performed. Before this flushing is done, chemical cleaners can be added to the cooling system to help dissolve rust and scale deposits. Two types of cleaners are commonly used for this purpose.

Heavy-duty cooling system cleaners consist of powdered phosphoric acid. The thermostat must be removed to prevent damage before heavy-duty cleaners are used. After use, a chemical neutralizer (baking soda) is put into the system to neutralize any remaining phosphoric acid before flushing.

It is important that whenever you drain or flush out a cooling system, the fluid should not be allowed to enter into a normal sewage line or drain. The chemicals used in engine coolant and the flushing chemicals are harmful to our environment. They should be captured in a holding tank. These holding tanks should be drained by certified waste disposers.

CAUTION:

Always wear proper clothing and eye protection when using coolant additives to remove silicate and calcium deposits. They might be very corrosive. Be careful not to inhale fumes when pouring the powdered cleaner into the radiator. If powder gets on your skin, wash the area immediately. ■

Liquid-cooling system cleaners consist of a milder solution of phosphoric acid dissolved in water and mixed with detergent. Liquid cleaners can be used without removing the thermostat. The flushing procedure removes the cleaning solution.

Reverse flushing is the procedure of forcing clean liquid backwards through the cooling system. This carries away rust, scale, corrosion, and other contaminants. A flushing gun that operates on compressed air is used to force clean water and air through the system (Figure 11–79).

Refilling and Bleeding

After the cooling system has been cleaned, refill the system with new coolant mixed to the recommended strength. Be sure all the flushing water is out of the radiator and evacuated from the engine block before refilling.

The cooling system must be bled to ensure there are no air pockets in the coolant. Air in the system

FIGURE 11–79 (A) Reverse flushing the radiator with shop air and water with a special flushing gun; (B) reverse flushing head and block. *Courtesy of Chrysler Corporation*

can reduce cooling ability and lead to water pump and other component damage.

Each vehicle has its own specific bleeding procedure. In many cases, the system is filled and the radiator cap is left off. The engine is then run until the thermostat opens and the coolant circulates. Trapped air bubbles escape through the opened radiator.

Other bleeding procedures are more involved. They may require the connection of special bleeder hoses to air bleed valves located on the radiator or other components. Air is bled through the valves as the system is filled. Always follow the bleeding steps outlined in the vehicle's service manual.

CUSTOMER CARE

Many additives, inhibitors, and quick-fix remedies are available for use in the automotive cooling system. These include, but are not limited to, stop leak, water pump lubricant, engine flush, and acid neutralizers. Explain to your customers that extreme caution should be exercised when using any additive in the cooling system. Tell them to read the label directions and precautions in order to know in advance the end results of any additive used. For example, caustic solutions must never be used in aluminum radiators. Alcohol-based remedies should never be used in any cooling system. ∎

CASE STUDY

A late-model minivan's engine overheats while going up a mountain road. It is a very hot day so water is added to the radiator and the trip continues. After driving 30 miles, the engine overheats again. Again, water is added. The engine is allowed to cool for an hour while the owner eats. After about 30 miles of driving, the engine overheats again. This time the van is taken to a service station to be diagnosed and repaired. It is late in the day and the owner agrees to stay overnight at a local motel. A fresh supply of water is added to the radiator and the owner drives about a mile to the motel.

In the morning the owner adds water to the system. The van is brought back to the service station for diagnosis. It is obvious that the engine is overheating and there is a loss of fluid. There is no need to verify the customer's complaint. A visual inspection shows little

water in the radiator, but no signs of external leakage is found. The oil level is found to be a little high and the oil appears to be thin.

A radiator tester is attached to the system and there is no sign of pressure or coolant leakage. The operation of the water pump is to be checked next. However, this test cannot be done because the engine will not start. The starter cannot turn the engine over. A quick check of the battery reveals it is fully charged. Careful thought suggests the problem is hydrostatic lock-up. This is a condition in which a fluid fills the cylinder. Since a liquid cannot be compressed, the liquid prevents the piston from moving up.

To verify this, the spark plugs are removed. All plugs looked normal except cylinder #5. It is wet with water. With the plugs out, the engine is cranked by the starter motor and water comes gushing out of the cylinder. The exact cause of the internal leak will be best identified by tearing down the engine. During disassembly, a crack in the engine block is found. This crack allowed the coolant to pass from a coolant passage in the block into the cylinder.

This leak is not detected by the radiator pressure test because when the engine is cold, little, if any, coolant leaks through the crack. The crack grows larger as the engine becomes hotter, allowing the cylinder to rapidly fill when it is hot. A new short block is put in the van and the problem is corrected.

KEY TERMS

API	Oil pump pickup
Coolant	Positive displacement
Crude oil	pump
Energy-conserving oil	Pressure relief valve
Expansion tank	Recovery tank
Flex blades	Rotor-type oil pump
Gear-type pump	SAE
Multiviscosity	Viscosity

SUMMARY

◆ An engine's lubrication system has several important purposes: hold an adequate supply of oil to cool, clean, lubricate, and seal the engine; remove contaminants from the oil; and deliver oil to all necessary areas of the engine. The API has developed two basic classifications for engine oils: S class for passenger cars and light trucks and C class for heavy-duty commercial applications. The SAE has standardized oil viscosity ratings. API and SAE classifications are stamped on top of the oil can.

◆ Excessive oil consumption can be a result of external and internal leaks, faulty accessories, piston rings, and valve guides. Internal leaks, which usually result in oil burning, are usually more difficult to diagnose.

◆ The main components of a typical lubrication system are: an oil pump, oil pump pickup, oil pan, pressure relief valve, oil filter, engine oil passages, engine bearings, crankcase ventilation, oil pressure indicator, oil seals and gaskets, dipstick, and oil coolers.

◆ The purpose of the oil pump is to supply oil to the various moving parts in the engine. The most commonly used stock pumps are the rotor and gear type. Both are positive displacement pumps. Because the faster the pump turns the greater the pressure becomes, a pressure-regulating valve is installed to control the maximum oil pressure. All automotive vehicles are equipped with either an oil pressure gauge or a low-pressure indicator light. The gauges are either mechanically or electrically operated.

◆ All oil leaving the oil pump is directed to the oil filter. The filter is a disposable metal container filled with a special type of treated paper or other filter substance that catches and holds the oil's impurities. Two types of oil filtration systems are commonly used: full flow and by-pass.

◆ After an engine is rebuilt, a new or rebuilt oil pump is often installed. Integral pumps must be rebuilt. Bolt-on or nonintegral pumps can be rebuilt or replaced. If the old pump is to be reused, it should be carefully inspected for wear and thoroughly cleaned.

◆ Two basic types of cooling systems are utilized by automotive manufacturers: liquid-cooled systems and air-cooled systems. The most popular and efficient method of engine cooling is the liquid-cooled system.

◆ The fluid used as coolant today is a mixture of water and ethylene glycol-based antifreeze/coolant. Closed-cooling systems are cooling systems with an expansion or recovery tank. The function of the water pump is to move the coolant efficiently through the system. The radiator transfers heat from the engine to the air passing through it. The radiator is usually one of two designs: cross flow or down flow. The thermostat attempts to control the engine's operating temperature by routing the coolant either to the radiator or through the by-pass, or sometimes a combination of both.

◆ V-belts and multiple-ribbed belts (called serpentine belts) are used to drive water pumps and to

power steering pumps, air-conditioning compressors, alternators, and emission control pumps. The fan delivers additional air to the radiator to maintain proper cooling at low speeds and idle. Since fan air is usually only necessary at idle and low speed operation, various design concepts are used to limit the fan's operation at higher speeds.

◆ The hollow passages in the block and cylinder heads through which coolant flows may be arranged as a series flow system, a parallel flow system, or a series-parallel flow system. Included in the water jackets are soft plugs and a block drain plug. A temperature indicator is mounted in the dashboard to alert the driver to an overheating condition. A hot liquid passenger heater is part of the engine cooling system. Radiators for vehicles with automatic transmissions have a sealed heat exchanger located in the coolant outlet tank.

◆ The basic procedure for testing a vehicle's cooling system includes inspecting the radiator filler neck, inspecting the overflow tube for dents and other obstructions, testing for external leaks, and testing for internal leaks. Most radiator leak repairs require removing the radiator from the vehicle.

◆ The pressure cap should hold pressure in its range, as indicated on the tester gauge dial, for one minute. A thermostat can be tested in the engine or after it is removed.

◆ Hoses should be checked for leakage, swelling, and chafing. Any hose that feels mushy or extremely brittle or shows signs of splitting when it is squeezed should be replaced. The majority of water pump failures are attributed to leaks of some sort. Other failures can be attributed to bearing and shaft problems and an occasional cracked casting.

◆ Fan operation can be checked by spinning the fan by hand. A noticeable wobble or any blade that is not in the same plane as the rest indicates replacement is in order. The fan can also be checked by removing it and laying it on a flat surface. If it is straight, all the blades will touch the surface. Never attempt to repair a damaged fan; replace it. One of the simplest ways to check a fan clutch is to visually inspect it for signs of fluid loss.

◆ Belt problems are easily discovered by visual inspection or by the screech of slippage. When a new belt is installed, it should be properly adjusted.

◆ Whenever coolant is changed, a thorough reverse flushing or back flushing should be performed. The old coolant should be captured and recycled.

TECH MANUAL

The following procedures are included in Chapter 11 of the *Tech Manual* that accompanies this book:

1. *Service and install oil pump and oil pan.*
2. *Inspect, replace, and adjust drive belts and pulleys.*
3. *Clean, inspect, test, and replace electric cooling fans and cooling system-related temperature sensors.*
4. *Test cooling system.*

 REVIEW QUESTIONS

1. What is the most efficient way to increase a radiator's efficiency?

2. What is indicated by an abnormal amount of water being emitted from the exhaust?

3. Describe the simple test used to determine whether the water pump is causing good circulation.

4. How is the oil pump driven?

5. What is the name of the component in the lubrication system that prevents excessively high system pressures from occurring as engine speed increases?

6. Which of the following is a function of the engine's lubrication system?
   a. Hold an adequate supply of oil
   b. Remove contaminants from the oil
   c. Deliver oil to all necessary areas of the engine
   d. All of the above

7. Technician A says the gear pump pumps a greater volume of oil than a rotor pump. Technician B says engine oil pressure is dependent upon oil viscosity. Who is correct?
   a. Technician A   c. Both A and B
   b. Technician B   d. Neither A nor B

8. Technician A says most pressure indicators found in vehicles today are electronically controlled. Technician B says most engines made in recent years have an oil filtering system somewhere on the input side of the pump. Who is correct?
   a. Technician A   c. Both A and B
   b. Technician B   d. Neither A nor B

9. Which type of oil filtration system is used on most engines today?
   a. by-pass   c. full flow
   b. independent   d. shunt

10. Which of the following could cause low oil pressure during diagnostic checks?
    a. plugged oil pickup screen
    b. excessive oil dilution
    c. both a and b
    d. neither a nor b

11. Technician A uses a feeler gauge and straightedge to determine the pump cover flatness. Technician B uses an outside micrometer to measure the diameter and thickness of the outer rotor. Who is correct?
    a. Technician A   c. Both A and B
    b. Technician B   d. Neither A nor B

12. Technician A says the API classification *S* stands for standard passenger cars. Technician B says that the API classification *C* stands for vehicles with compression ignition. Who is correct?
    a. Technician A   c. Both A and B
    b. Technician B   d. Neither A nor B

13. Technician A says the American Petroleum Institute has established an oil viscosity classification system. Technician B says higher viscosity oils receive the higher rating numbers. Who is correct?
    a. Technician A   c. Both A and B
    b. Technician B   d. Neither A nor B

14. Which of the following is designed to greatly reduce friction?
    a. SE oil
    b. CC oil
    c. energy-conserving oil
    d. synthetic oil

15. In most automotive applications, the water pump is driven by the ____.
    a. gear train   c. crankshaft
    b. belt   d. impeller

16. Which of the following statements is incorrect?
    a. When replacing a hose, drain the coolant system below the level that is being worked on.

b. A thermostat that is more than two years old should be replaced.

c. Spring-type hose clamps should not be reused, even if they look good.

d. It is not possible to tell if a coolant hose is working correctly simply by starting the engine and feeling the hose.

17. Technician A says if a vehicle overheats, but there is no evidence of previous water loss and the radiator pressure cap is holding the proper pressure, chances are very good that there is a defective water pump. Technician B replaces matched drive belts in pairs. Who is correct?

    a. Technician A   **c.** Both A and B

    b. Technician B   **d.** Neither A nor B

18. When must a thermostat be fully opened?

    a. 3°F above its temperature rating

    b. 3°F above or below its temperature rating

    c. 20°F above the start to open temperature

    d. 20°F below the start to open temperature

19. In which type of system does coolant flow into the engine block under pressure, then cross the head gasket to the head through the main coolant passage openings beside each cylinder?

    a. parallel flow   **c.** series flow

    b. balanced flow   **d.** all of the above

20. Most fan clutches offer a lot of drag when the engine is ____.

    a. cold   **c.** turned by hand

    b. hot   **d.** both a and c

INTAKE AND EXHAUST SYSTEMS

12

OBJECTIVES

◆ *Explain the operation of the components in the air induction system, including ductwork, air cleaner/filters, and intake manifolds.* ◆ *Describe how the engine creates vacuum and how vacuum is used to operate and control many automotive devices.* ◆ *Inspect and troubleshoot vacuum and air induction systems.* ◆ *Explain the operation of exhaust system components, including exhaust manifold, gaskets, exhaust pipe and seal, catalytic converter, muffler, resonator, tailpipe, and clamps, brackets, and hangers.* ◆ *Properly perform an exhaust system inspection, and service and replace exhaust system components.* ◆ *Explain the purpose and operation of a turbocharger.* ◆ *Inspect a turbocharger, and describe some common turbocharger problems.* ◆ *Explain supercharger operation, and identify common supercharger problems.*

An internal combustion engine requires air to operate. This air supply is drawn into the engine by the vacuum created during the intake stroke of the pistons. The air is mixed with fuel and delivered to the combustion chambers. Controlling the flow of air and the air/fuel mixture is the job of the induction system.

THE AIR INDUCTION SYSTEM

Prior to the introduction of emission control devices, the induction system was quite simple. It consisted of an air cleaner housing mounted on top of the engine with a filter inside the housing. Its function was to filter dust and grit from the air being drawn into the carburetor.

Modern air induction systems filter the air and do much more. The introduction of emission standards and fuel economy standards encouraged the development of intake air temperature controls. Figure 12–1 shows a typical thermostatic air cleaner housing with a vacuum motor and temperature sensor. These components draw air warmed by the exhaust manifold into the engine during cold start-up and warm-up.

The air intake system on a modern fuel injected engine is much more complicated (Figure 12–2). Ducts channel cool air from outside the engine compartment to the throttle plate assembly. The air filter has been moved to a position below the top of the

FIGURE 12–1 Typical air cleaner assembly. *Courtesy of Chrysler Corporation*

engine to allow for aerodynamic body designs. Electronic meters measure airflow, temperature, and density. Heat riser tubes warm the intake air during cold weather warm-up. Pulse air systems provide fresh air to the exhaust stream to oxidize unburned hydrocarbons in the exhaust. These components allow the air induction system to perform the following functions.

FIGURE 12–2 Typical air induction system for engines equipped with fuel injection. *Courtesy of Ford Motor Company*

◆ Provide the air the engine needs to operate
◆ Filter the air to protect the engine from wear
◆ Monitor airflow temperature and density for more efficient combustion and a reduction of hydrocarbon (HC) and carbon monoxide (CO) emissions
◆ Operate with the PCV system to burn the crankcase fumes in the engine
◆ Provide air for some air injection systems

Air Intake Ductwork

Figure 12–3 shows a typical air intake system. Cool air is drawn through the fresh air tube from the leading edge of the engine compartment and routed through a preheat assembly, the air cleaner, and into the carburetor. In a fuel injection system, air usually passes through an air filter and airflow meter before entering a throttle body.

Be sure that the intake ductwork is properly installed and all connections are airtight—especially those between an airflow sensor or remote air cleaner and the carburetor or fuel injection throttle plate assembly. Generally, metal or plastic air ducts are used when engine heat is not a problem. Special paper-metal ducts are used when they will be exposed to high engine temperatures.

Air Cleaner/Filter

The primary function of the air filter is to prevent airborne contaminants and abrasives from entering into the engine with the air/fuel mixture. Without proper filtration, these contaminants can cause serious damage and appreciably shorten engine life. All incoming air should pass through the filter element before entering the engine.

Most air filter assemblies are located inside the air cleaner housing, which is mounted directly to a flange on the carburetor air horn, the fuel injection throttle plate assembly, the intake manifold (on diesel engines), the engine, or the engine compartment (Figure 12–4). In such cases, the air cleaner unit is connected to the air horn, throttle plate assembly, or manifold by an air transfer tube or duct.

The air cleaner assembly also helps muffle noise caused by the airflow through the throttle plates. The air cleaner also provides filtered air to the PCV system and provides engine compartment fire protection in the event of backfire.

Air Filter Design Air filters are available in two basic designs. Light-duty (standard) air filters, which are

FIGURE 12–3 Typical air induction system for carburetor-equipped engines. *Courtesy of Ford Motor Company*

FIGURE 12–4 Ducts are used on remote air cleaners. *Courtesy of Ford Motor Company*

CLEAN AIR FILTER ALLOWS THE REQUIRED AMOUNT OF AIR TO ENTER THE ENGINE.

DIRTY AIR FILTER PREVENTS THE REQUIRED AMOUNT OF AIR FROM ENTERING THE ENGINE.

FIGURE 12–6 Restricted airflow within the induction system caused by a dirty air filter.

usually made of pleated paper or oil-wetted polyurethane. Heavy-duty air filters have an oil-wetted polyurethane outer cover over a dry paper element. The polyurethane effectively traps larger dirt particles on its surface. The finer particles that pass through the polyurethane are trapped by the paper media. The polyurethane outer cover can be removed, cleaned, and reinstalled. This extends filter life.

When selecting a new air filter, keep these design features in mind (Figure 12–5).

◆ Fine mesh screen on the inside reduces the possibility of fire hazards caused by engine backfire.
◆ Heat-resistant plastisol on the top and bottom with special sealing beads provides a positive dust seal.
◆ Oil-wetted resin-impregnated paper provides long-lasting filter efficiency.
◆ Wire or expanded metal outer screen adds construction strength and protects against accidental paper damage during handling and shipping.

Air Filter Servicing If the air filter becomes very dirty, the dirt can block the flow of air into the fuel

charging assembly (Figure 12–6). Without enough air, the engine will constantly receive a rich air/fuel mixture. The use of extra fuel means poor fuel economy and a lack of power.

The manufacturer's recommended air filter replacement interval is usually specified in the vehicle owner's manual. However, replacement of the air filter might be required on a more frequent schedule if the vehicle is subjected to continuous operation in an extremely dusty or severe off-the-road environment.

Certain types of heavy-duty air filters can be cleaned and reused. These filters have a heavy paper media encased in an element with metal end caps. Generally, reusable heavy-duty air filter elements should be replaced with a new element after six cleanings, or once a year.

Thermostatic Air Cleaner Thermostatic air cleaners are used on carbureted and throttle body fuel injection engines to heat the intake air when needed. Warm combustion air improves fuel evaporation leading to cleaner burning and, therefore, lower emissions.

These systems mix air that has been heated by a

FIGURE 12–5 Automotive air filter design features.

FIGURE 12–7 Heated air intake system operation.

FIGURE 12–8 (A) Typical intake manifold design used on in-line engines; (B) typical design used on V-type engines.

heat stove (shroud) on the exhaust manifold with cooler outside air to warm the intake air to a temperature ideal for combustion (Figure 12–7).

If the heated air inlet door sticks open, heated air cannot reach the engine. The cold air that enters the engine will not allow the fuel to vaporize completely. Liquid fuel will not ignite as easily as fuel that is vaporized.

A bimetal temperature sensor is used to monitor air temperature within the air cleaner housing. When the temperature is low, the sensor signals a vacuum motor to close a door in the cold air intake snorkel and route warm air from the exhaust manifold stove into the assembly. If the intake air becomes too warm, the sensor signals the vacuum motor to reopen the door and introduce cold outside air into the system. Complete details on the operation of heated air inlet systems are given in a later chapter.

Intake Manifold

The intake manifold distributes the clean air or air/fuel mixture as evenly as possible to each cylinder of the engine.

On carbureted and throttle body (central) fuel injection systems, the intake manifold delivers an air/fuel mixture. The air and fuel are mixed in the carburetor or throttle body and then enter the intake manifold. The design of the intake manifold helps to prevent condensation and assists in the vaporization of the air/fuel mixture (Figure 12–8). Smooth and efficient engine performance depends on mixtures that are uniform in strength, quality, and degree of vaporization. This is partly the job of the intake manifold. Ideally, the fuel is completely vaporized when it goes into the combustion chamber. Complete vapor-

ization requires high temperature, but high temperatures decrease the volumetric efficiency of the engine. Therefore, the best alternative is to deliver an air/fuel mixture that is vaporized above the point where fuel particles will be deposited on the manifold and below the point where excess heat results in power losses.

On port fuel injection and diesel injection systems the intake manifold delivers only clean air to the cylinders. Fuel is introduced into the combustion chamber by the individual fuel injectors. There are many new intake manifold designs for ported gasoline fuel injection. They are often referred to as tuned intake manifolds because they have been redesigned to deliver equal amounts of airflow to each cylinder (Figure 12–9).

Intake manifolds are made of cast-iron or die-cast aluminum. Aluminum manifolds reduce engine weight. A few are cast integrally with the cylinder head.

Manifolds can be either wet or dry. Wet manifolds have coolant passages cast directly into them. Dry manifolds do not have cooling passages. Some intake manifolds have an integrally cast water cross-

FIGURE 12–9 This type of tuned intake manifold, used with ported fuel injection, gives a more equal amount of air to each cylinder. *Courtesy of Ford Motor Company*

FIGURE 12–10 An intake manifold for an in-line four-cylinder engine.

FIGURE 12–11 V-8 engine intake manifold. Note how cylinders are fed from carburetor bores. Exhaust crossover passage provides heat for improved fuel vaporization and prevents carburetor icing.

over passage. This allows coolant to flow through a passage below the carburetor and warm the incoming air/fuel mixture.

Manifold design varies with the different engine types. For example, on four-cylinder engines, the intake manifold has either four runners or two runners that break into four near the cylinder head (Figure 12–10). On in-line six-cylinder engines, there are either six runners or three that branch off into six near the cylinder head. On V-configuration engines (V-6 and V-8), both open and closed intake manifolds are used. Open intake manifolds have an open space between the bottom of the manifold and the valve lifter valley. Closed intake manifolds act as the cover to the lifter valley.

On some manifolds, there is an exhaust crossover passage (Figure 12–11). This passage allows the exhaust from one side of the engine to cross over through the intake manifold to the other side to be exhausted. The exhaust crossover provides heat to the base of the carburetor to improve the vaporization of the fuel while the engine is warming up. On many engines, the exhaust crossover is also used to provide automatic choke heat. On in-line engines the heat riser valve also directs heat to the base of the carburetor. Some engines use an electric grid or heater located under the carburetor to improve vaporization (Figure 12–12).

Intake manifolds for V-type engines may include coolant connecting passages between cylinder heads. Some include a provision for mounting the thermostat and thermostat housing. In addition, connections to the intake manifold on some vehicles provide a vacuum source for exhaust gas recirculation (EGR) valves, automatic transmission vacuum modulators, distributor vacuum advance units, thermostatic air cleaners, power brakes, and/or heater and air-conditioning airflow control doors. Other devices located

FIGURE 12–12 Intake manifold with an electric heater for an in-line engine.

on or connected to the intake manifold include manifold absolute pressure (MAP) sensors, manifold air temperature (MAT) sensors, knock sensors, and EGR passages.

Vacuum System

The vacuum in the intake manifold is used to operate many systems, such as emission controls, brake boosters, parking brake releases, headlight doors, heater/air conditioners, and cruise controls. Vacuum is applied to these systems through a system of hoses and tubes, which can become quite elaborate.

Vacuum Basics Vacuum refers to any pressure that is lower than the earth's atmospheric pressure at any given altitude. The higher the altitude, the lower the atmospheric pressure.

Vacuum is measured in relation to atmospheric pressure. Atmospheric pressure is the pressure exerted on every object on earth and is caused by the weight of the surrounding air. At sea level, the pressure exerted by the atmosphere is 14.7 psi. Most pressure gauges ignore atmospheric pressure and read zero under normal conditions. The normal measure of vacuum is in inches of mercury (in. Hg) instead of psi. Other units of measurement for vacuum are kilopascals and bars. Normal atmospheric pressure at sea level is about 1 bar or 100 kilopascals.

Vacuum in any four-stroke engine is created by the downward movement of the piston during the intake stroke. With the intake valve open and the piston moving downward, a partial vacuum is created within the cylinder and intake manifold. The air passing the intake valve does not move fast enough to fill the cylinder, thereby causing the lower pressure. This partial vacuum is continuous in a multi-cylinder engine, since at least one cylinder is always at some stage of its intake stroke.

The amount of vacuum created is partially related to the positioning of the choke (on carbureted vehicles) and to the throttle plates. The throttle plate not only admits air or air/fuel into the intake manifold, it also helps to control the amount of vacuum available during engine operation. At closed throttle idle, the vacuum available is usually between 15 to 22 inches. At a wide-open throttle acceleration, the vacuum can drop to zero.

Increased Vacuum Controls The intake manifold on early engines simply connected the carburetor to the engine. It did not have any auxiliary vacuum plugs or connections.

From the 1920s to the early 1970s, a single vacuum line was normally found. It either operated the vacuum advance of the distributor or the windshield wipers.

Since the 1970s, many systems rely on vacuum controls. The use of electronic engine controls have further complicated the vacuum system. Where once a vacuum line may have run from a carburetor to the EGR valve, it now goes from the carburetor to a computer-controlled vacuum relay solenoid and then to the valve.

In addition to being used to draw filtered air into the engine, vacuum is typically used to control these systems.

- Fuel Induction System. Certain vacuum-operated devices are added to carburetors and some central fuel-injection throttle bodies to ease engine start-up, warm-and-cold engine driveaway, and to compensate for air-conditioner load on the engine.
- Emission Control System. While some emission control output devices are solenoid or linkage controlled, many operate on vacuum. This vacuum is usually controlled by solenoids that are opened or closed, depending on electrical signals received from the Powertrain Control Module (**PCM**). Other systems use switches that are controlled by engine coolant temperature, such as a ported vacuum switch (**PVS**) or by ambient air such as a temperature vacuum switch (**TVS**).
- Accessory Controls. Engine vacuum is used to control operation of certain accessories, such as air conditioner/heater systems, power brake boosters, speed-control components, automatic transmission vacuum modulators, and so on.

Vacuum Schematic An engine emissions vacuum schematic is required to be on all domestic and import vehicles. It is located on an underhood decal. This schematic shows the vacuum hose routings and vacuum source for all emissions-related equipment. The vacuum schematic shown in Figure 12–13A is a new-style line-drawing schematic that shows the relationship and position of components as they are mounted on the engine. This new type of schematic is easier to understand than the flat-plane road-map vacuum schematics used in the past (Figure 12–13B). It is important to remember that these schematics only show the vacuum controlled parts of the emission system. Hose routing and positions for vacuum devices not related to the emissions control system can be found in the service manual.

Diagnosis and Troubleshooting Vacuum system problems can produce or contribute to the following driveability symptoms.

- Stalls
- No start (cold)
- Hard start (hot soak)
- Backfire (deceleration)
- Rough idle
- Poor acceleration
- Rich or lean stumble
- Overheating
- Detonation, or knock or pinging

A

B

FIGURE 12–13   (A) New style line-drawn vacuum schematic; (B) old style vacuum schematic.

◆ Rotten eggs exhaust odor
◆ Poor fuel economy

As a routine part of problem diagnosis, a technician suspecting a vacuum problem should first

◆ Inspect vacuum hoses for improper routing or disconnections (engine decal identifies hose routing).

◆ Look for kinks, tears, or cuts in vacuum lines.
◆ Check for vacuum hose routing and wear near hot spots, such as exhaust manifold or the EGR tubes.
◆ Make sure there is no evidence of oil or transmission fluid in vacuum hose connections. (Valves can become contaminated by oil getting inside.)
◆ Inspect vacuum system devices for damage (dents

in cans; by-pass valves; broken nipples on VCV or PVS valves; broken "tees" in vacuum lines, and so on).

Broken or disconnected hoses allow vacuum leaks that admit more air into the intake manifold than the engine is calibrated for. The most common result is a rough running engine due to the leaner air/fuel mixture created by the excess air.

Kinked hoses can cut off vacuum to a component, thereby disabling it. For example, if the vacuum hose to the EGR valve is kinked, vacuum cannot be used to move the diaphragm. Therefore, the valve will not open.

To check vacuum controls, refer to the service manual for the correct location and identification of the components. Typical locations of vacuum-controlled components are shown in Figure 12–14.

Tears and kinks in any vacuum line can affect engine operation. Any defective hoses should be replaced one at a time to avoid misrouting. OEM vacuum lines are installed in a harness consisting of 1/8-inch or larger outer diameter and 1/16-inch inner diameter nylon hose with bonded nylon or rubber connectors. Occasionally, a rubber hose might be connected to the harness. The nylon connectors have rubber inserts to provide a seal between the nylon connector and the component connection (nipple). In recent years, many domestic car manufacturers have been using ganged steel vacuum lines.

Vacuum Test Equipment The vacuum gauge is one of the most important engine diagnostic tools used by technicians. With the gauge connected to the intake manifold and the engine warm and idling, watch the action of the gauge's needle. A healthy engine will give a steady, constant vacuum reading between 17 and 22 in. Hg. On some four- and six-cylinder engines, however, a reading of 15 inches is considered acceptable. With high-performance engines, a slight flicker of the needle can also be expected. Keep in mind that the gauge reading will drop about 1 inch for each 1,000 feet above sea level. Figure 12–15 shows some of the common readings and what engine malfunctions they indicate.

As shown in Figure 12–16, a hand-held vacuum pump/gauge is used to test vacuum-actuated valves and motors. If the component does not operate when the proper amount of vacuum is applied, it should be serviced or replaced.

EXHAUST SYSTEM COMPONENTS

The various components of the typical exhaust system include the following.

FIGURE 12–14 Typical vacuum devices and controls. *Courtesy of Chrysler Corporation*

FIGURE 12–15 Common vacuum gauge readings and the conditions they indicate.

- Exhaust manifold
- Exhaust pipe and seal
- Catalytic converter
- Muffler
- Resonator
- Tailpipe
- Heat shields
- Clamps, brackets, and hangers

All the parts of the system are designed to confirm to the available space of the vehicle's undercarriage and yet be a safe distance above the road.

CONNECT AN EXTERNAL VACUUM SOURCE OF 16 IN. HG TO THE VACUUM MOTOR. THE DUCT DOOR SHOULD MOVE TO THE CLOSED (HEAT ON) POSITION.

DISCONNECT THE VACUUM HOSE FROM THE VACUUM MOTOR CONNECTOR. THE DUCT DOOR SHOULD BE OPEN (HEAT OFF).

A

TRAP VACUUM AND MAKE SURE DOOR REMAINS CLOSED FOR 60 SECONDS. IF NOT, REPLACE VACUUM MOTOR.

B

FIGURE 12–16 (A) Hand-operated vacuum pump being used to test an air cleaner vacuum motor; (B) two-port/four-port VCV or PVS test.

CAUTION:

When inspecting or working on the exhaust system, remember that its components get very hot when the engine is running. Contact with them could cause a severe burn. Also, always wear safety glasses or goggles when working under a vehicle. ■

Exhaust Manifold

The exhaust manifold (Figure 12–17) collects the burnt gases as they are expelled from the cylinders and directs them to the exhaust pipe. Exhaust manifolds for most vehicles are made of cast- or nodular-iron. Some newer vehicles have stamped, heavy-gauge sheet metal or stainless steel units.

In-line engines have one exhaust manifold. V-type engines have an exhaust manifold on each side of the engine. An exhaust manifold will have either three, four, or six passages, depending on the type of engine. These passages blend into a single passage at the other end, which connects to an exhaust pipe. From here, the flow of exhaust gases continues to the rear of the car.

FIGURE 12–17 Exhaust manifold designs for an in-line engine.

V-type engines may be equipped with a dual exhaust system that consists of two almost identical, but individual systems in the same vehicle (Figure 12–18).

Exhaust systems are designed for particular engine-chassis combinations. Exhaust system length, pipe size, and silencer size are used to tune the flow of gases within the exhaust system. Proper tuning of the exhaust manifold tubes can actually create a vacuum that helps draw exhaust gases out of the cylinder, improving volumetric efficiency. Separate, tuned exhaust headers (Figure 12–19) can also improve efficiency by preventing the exhaust flow of one cylinder from interfering with the exhaust flow of another cylinder. Cylinders next to one another may release exhaust gas at about the same time. When this happens, the pressure of the exhaust gas from one cylinder can interfere with the flow from the other cylinder (Figure 12–20). With separate headers, the cylinders are isolated from one another, inter-

FIGURE 12–19 Efficiency can be improved with tuned exhaust headers. *Courtesy of Ford Motor Company*

ference is eliminated, and the engine breathes better. The problem of interference is especially common with V-8 engines. However, exhaust headers tend to improve the performance of all engines.

Exhaust Pipe and Seal

The exhaust pipe is metal pipe—either aluminized steel, stainless steel, or zinc-plated heavy-gauge steel—that runs under the vehicle between the exhaust manifold.

FIGURE 12–18 Dual exhaust system.

FIGURE 12–20 Tuned exhaust headers in a four-cylinder engine designed to prevent flow interference.

Some types of emission control, such as an EGR valve, early fuel evaporation (EFE) valve, or a heat riser valve is usually mounted between the exhaust manifold and the exhaust pipe. In electronic engine-control systems, an oxygen sensor is installed in the exhaust pipe. This device is used to sense the amount of oxygen in the exhaust and sends signals to the electronic control unit. This information is used to control the mixture of air and fuel being delivered to the engine.

Intermediate, or connecting, **pipes** are used at any point past the exhaust pipe to join the exhaust system components (Figure 12–21).

SHOP TALK

The exhaust manifold gasket seals the joint between the head and exhaust manifold. Many new engines are assembled without exhaust manifold gaskets. This is possible because new manifolds are flat and fit tightly against the head without leaks. Exhaust manifolds go through many heating/cooling cycles. This causes stress and some corrosion in the exhaust manifold. Removing the manifold will usually distort the manifold slightly so it is no longer flat enough to

seal without a gasket. Exhaust manifold gaskets are normally used to eliminate leaks when exhaust manifolds are reinstalled.   ■

Catalytic Converters

The **catalytic converter** has been the biggest change in exhaust systems over the years. It was added in the mid-1970s to reduce emissions, but car makers quickly discovered that it also silenced the exhaust. As a result, mufflers have become lighter and simpler.

The catalytic converter is located ahead of the muffler in the exhaust system. The extreme heat in the converter oxidizes the exhaust that flows out of the engine. A catalyst is a substance that causes a chemical reaction in other elements without actually becoming a part of the chemical change itself and without being used up or consumed in the process. A catalytic converter uses catalysts to cause a change in the elements of the exhaust gases as they pass through the exhaust system.

The catalyst elements used in catalytic converters are platinum, palladium, and rhodium. These elements are used alone or in combination with each other to change the undesirable CO, HC, and NO_x into harmless water vapor, CO_2, N, and O_2 (Figure 12–22).

There are several types of catalytic converters. The most common follow.

PELLET CATALYTIC CONVERTER Uses hundreds of small beads that act as the catalyst agent (Figure 12–23A).

MONOLITHIC CATALYTIC CONVERTER Uses a ceramic block (made of substrate material called alumina) that is shaped like a honeycomb and is coated with a special chemical that helps the converter act on the exhaust gases (Figure 12–23B).

THREE-WAY CONVERTER The dual-bed type (Figure 12–24) treats all three controlled emission gases. It oxidizes HC and CO by adding oxygen and reduces NO_x by removing oxygen from the nitrogen oxides.

FIGURE 12–21 Exhaust pipe coupling connecting the exhaust pipe with the intermediate pipe.

FIGURE 12–22 How a conventional catalytic converter works.

FIGURE 12-23 (A) Pellet catalytic converter; (B) monolithic catalytic converter.

FIGURE 12-26 Particulate catalytic converter.

FIGURE 12-24 Three-way or dual-bed converter.

up. These converters are commonly called warm-up converters or preheaters.

PARTICULATE OXIDIZER CATALYTIC CONVERTER Uses a monolithic element, located between the exhaust manifold and turbocharger, to react to the particulates of a diesel engine (Figure 12-26). Particulates are solid particles of carbon-like soot that are emitted from a diesel engine as black smoke.

SHOP TALK

Because of constant change in EPA catalytic converter removal and installation requirements, check with the manufacturer or EPA for the latest data regarding replacement. ∎

MINICATALYTIC CONVERTER Provides a close coupled converter that is either built in the exhaust manifold or located next to it (Figure 12-25). It is primarily used to clean the exhaust during engine warm-

FIGURE 12-25 Mini- or pre-catalytic converter.

The converter is normally a trouble-free emission control device, but two things can damage it. One is leaded gasoline. Lead coats the catalyst and renders it useless. The difficulty of obtaining leaded gasoline has reduced this problem. The other is overheating. If raw fuel enters the exhaust because of a fouled spark plug or other problem, the temperature of the converter quickly increases. The heat can melt the ceramic honeycomb or pellets inside, causing a major restriction to the flow of exhaust.

![seatbelt icon] CUSTOMER CARE

To avoid converter overheating, advise customers to avoid prolonged idling (20 minutes or more). Running the engine with very low fuel levels may also cause a misfire that can overload the converter.

As a technician, you should also follow these guidelines in the shop and during test drives. In addition, avoid prolonged engine compression measurement or spark jump testing. They can allow fuel to collect in the converter. When you need to conduct these tests, do them as rapidly as possible. ∎

A plugged converter or any exhaust restriction can cause: loss of power at high speeds, stalling after starting (if totally blocked), a drop in engine vacuum as engine rpm increases, or sometimes popping or backfiring at the carburetor.

The best way to determine if a catalytic converter is working, is to check the quality of the exhaust. This is done with a four-gas exhaust analyzer. The results of this test should show low emission levels if the converter is working properly.

Another way to test a converter is to use a hand-held digital **pyrometer**, an electronic device that measures heat. By touching the pyrometer probe to the exhaust pipe just ahead of and just behind the converter, it is possible to read an increase of at least 100 degrees as the exhaust gases pass through the converter. If the outlet temperature is the same or lower, nothing is happening inside the converter. Do not be quick to condemn the converter. To do its job efficiently, the converter needs a steady supply of oxygen from the air pump. A bad pump, faulty diverter valve or control valve, leaky air connections, or faulty computer control over the air injection system could be preventing the needed oxygen from reaching the converter.

![wrench icon] SHOP TALK

The new OBD-II law that goes into effect in 1997 (with a phase-in starting in 1995) has a clause that mandates the manufacturers to provide a way to warn the driver of a problem with the catalytic converter. This is accomplished by placing an oxygen sensor upstream and downstream of the converter. The computer will compare both sensor voltages. If the readings are the same, there is a problem with the

FIGURE 12–27   Catalytic converter installation kit.

FIGURE 12–28   Direct fit catalytic converter replaces original equipment with no modification to the exhaust system.

converter or with the engine. This will light the malfunction indicator light (MIL). ∎

If a catalytic converter is found to be bad, it is replaced. There are two types of replacement. Installation kits (Figure 12–27) include all necessary components for the installation. There are also direct-fit catalytic converters (Figure 12–28).

![wrench icon] SHOP TALK

Under no circumstances should the converter be removed and replaced with a straight piece of pipe (a test pipe). This practice is illegal for the professional auto technician. ∎

Mufflers

The **muffler** is a cylindrical or oval-shaped component, generally about 2 feet long, mounted in the exhaust system about midway or toward the rear of the car. Inside the muffler is a series of baffles, chambers, tubes, and holes to break up, cancel out, or silence the pressure pulsations that occur each time an exhaust valve opens.

Two types of mufflers are commonly used on passenger vehicles (Figure 12–29). Reverse-flow mufflers change the direction of the exhaust gas flow through the inside of the unit. This is the most common type of automotive muffler. Straight-through mufflers permit exhaust gases to pass through a single tube. The tube has perforations that tend to break

FIGURE 12–29 (A) Reverse-flow muffler; (B) straight-through muffler.

FIGURE 12–30 (A) An electronic muffler might seem far-fetched, but the production of a mirror image, out-of-phase waveform can cancel out sound. (B) Schematic shows how sensors, microphones, and speakers are teamed up to alternate noise.

up pressure pulsations. They are not as quiet as the reverse-flow type.

There have been several important changes in recent years in the design of mufflers. Most of these changes have been centered at reducing weight and emissions, improving fuel economy, and simplifying assembly. These changes include the following.

NEW MATERIALS More and more mufflers are being made of aluminized and stainless steel. Using these materials reduces the weight of the units as well as extending their life.

DOUBLE-WALL DESIGN Retarded engine ignition timing that is used on many small cars tends to make the exhaust pulses sharper. Many small cars now use a double-wall exhaust pipe to better contain the sound and reduce pipe ring.

REAR-MOUNTED MUFFLER More and more often, the only space left under the car for the muffler is at the very rear. This means the muffler runs cooler than before and is more easily damaged by condensation in the exhaust system. This moisture, combined with nitrogen and sulfur oxides in the exhaust gas, forms acids that rot the muffler from the inside out. Many mufflers are being produced with drain holes drilled into them.

CUSTOMER CARE

Many customers do not always like the drain holes because they allow a small amount of gas and noise to escape, but they are one of the cheapest and most effective ways to fight corrosion. Explain this to your customers and let them make the choice. Do not plug the drain holes with a sheet metal screw. ■

BACK PRESSURE Even a well-designed muffler will produce some **back pressure** in the system. Back pressure reduces an engine's volumetric efficiency, or ability to "breathe." Excessive back pressure caused by defects in a muffler or other exhaust system part can slow or stop the engine. However, a small amount of back pressure can be used intentionally to allow a slower passage of exhaust gases through the catalytic converter. This slower passage results in more complete conversion to less harmful gases.

ELECTRONIC MUFFLER Basically, sensors and microphones pick up the pattern of the pressure waves an engine emits from its exhaust pipe (Figure 12–30). This data is analyzed by a computer. A mirror-image pattern of pulses is instantly produced and sent to speakers mounted near the exhaust outlet. Contra-waves are created that cancel out the noise. Noise is removed without creating back pressure in the muffler. Electronic mufflers can be designed to emit certain sounds, or no sound at all.

Resonator

On some vehicles, there is an additional muffler, known as a **resonator** or silencer. This unit is designed to further reduce the sound level of the exhaust. It is located toward the end of the system and generally looks like a smaller, rounder version of a muffler. The resonator is constructed like a straight-through muffler and is connected to the muffler by an intermediate pipe. The resonator on some cars is an integral part of the tailpipe, forming a one-piece unit. Resonators have been eliminated on nearly all late-model cars as manufacturers attempt to reduce production costs and weight.

Tailpipe

The **tailpipe** is the last pipe in the exhaust system. It releases the exhaust fumes into the atmosphere beyond the back end of the car.

Heat Shields

Heat shields are used to protect other parts from the heat of the exhaust system and the catalytic converter (Figure 12–31). They are usually made of pressed or perforated sheet metal.

Clamps, Brackets, and Hangers

Clamps, brackets, and hangers are used to properly join and support the various parts of the exhaust system. These parts also help to isolate exhaust noise by preventing its transfer through the frame or body to the passenger compartment. Clamps help to secure

FIGURE 12–32   (A) One pipe slides inside the other. (B) Clamps secure exhaust system parts to each other.

exhaust system parts to one another. The pipes are formed in such a way that one slips inside the other (Figure 12–32). This design makes a close fit. A U-type clamp usually holds this connection tight. Another important job of clamps and brackets is to hold pipes to the bottom of the vehicle. Clamps and brackets must be designed to allow the exhaust system to vibrate without transferring the vibrations through the car.

There are many different types of hangers available. Each is designed for a particular application. Some exhaust systems are supported by doughnut-shaped rubber rings between hooks on the exhaust component and on the frame or car body. Others are supported at the exhaust pipe and tailpipe connections by a combination of metal and reinforced fabric hanger (Figure 12–33). Both the doughnuts and the reinforced fabric allow the exhaust system to vibrate without breakage that could be caused by direct physical connection to the vehicle's frame.

Exhaust system pipes can be welded together. Welding, of course, is a process in which heat is used to melt metal and allow the molten portions to flow together. When cooled, a welded joint is as strong as, or sometimes stronger than, a single piece of metal. A welding torch can also be used to cut exhaust system pipes.

CAUTION:

Do not attempt to use welding equipment without proper training and safety equipment. The light caused by welding can cause permanent eye damage or even blindness. Furthermore, the heat from welding can ignite fuel vapors or damage parts. ■

Some exhaust systems are a single unit in which the pieces are welded together by the factory. By welding instead of clamping the assembly together, car makers save the weight of overlapping joints as well as that of clamps.

FIGURE 12–31   Location of heat shields.

FIGURE 12-33 Various exhaust clamp assemblies.

EXHAUST SYSTEM SERVICE

Exhaust system components are subject to both physical and chemical damage. Any physical damage to an exhaust system part that causes a partially restricted or blocked exhaust system usually results in loss of power or backfire up through the throttle plate(s). In addition to improper engine operation, a blocked or restricted exhaust system causes increased noise and air pollution. Leaks in the exhaust system caused by either physical or chemical (rust) damage could result in illness, asphyxiation, or even death. Remember that vehicle exhaust fumes can be very dangerous to one's health.

Exhaust System Inspection

Most parts of the exhaust system, particularly the exhaust pipe, muffler, and tailpipe, are subject to rust, corrosion, and cracking. Broken or loose clamps and hangers can allow parts to separate or hit the road as the car moves.

⚫ CAUTION:

During all exhaust inspection and repair work, wear safety glasses or equivalent eye protection. ■

Complete exhaust system inspection and testing procedures are given in the *Tech Manual* that accompanies this textbook. Any inspection should include listening for hissing or rumbling that would result from a leak in the system. An on-lift inspection should pinpoint any of the following types of damage.

- Holes, road damage, separated connections, and bulging muffler seams
- Kinks and dents

- Discoloration, rust, soft corroded metal, etc.
- Torn, broken, or missing hangers and clamps
- Loose tailpipes or other components
- Bluish or brownish catalytic converter shell indicating overheating.

The system should also be tested for blockage and restrictions using a vacuum gauge and tachometer.

Before beginning work on the system, be sure it is cool to the touch. Some technicians disconnect the battery ground to avoid short-circuiting the electrical system. Soak all rusted nuts, bolts, etc., in a good quality penetrating oil. Finally, check the system for critical clearance points so they can be maintained when new components are installed.

Replacing Exhaust System Components

Most exhaust system servicing involves the replacement of parts. When replacing exhaust system components, it is important that original equipment parts (or their equivalent) are used to ensure proper alignment with other parts in the system and provide acceptable exhaust noise levels. When replacing only one component in an exhaust system, it is not always necessary to take off the parts behind it.

Exhaust system component replacement might require the use of special tools (Figure 12-34) and welding equipment.

Exhaust Manifold and Exhaust Pipe Servicing As mentioned, the manifold itself rarely causes any problems. On occasion, an exhaust manifold will warp because of excess heat. A straightedge and feeler gauge can be used to check the machined surface of the manifold.

Another problem—also the result of high temperatures generated by the engine—is a cracked manifold. This usually occurs after the car passes through a large

FIGURE 12–34   Special tools required for exhaust work.

puddle and cold water splashes on the manifold's hot surface. If the manifold is warped beyond manufacturer's specifications or is cracked, it must be replaced. Also, check the exhaust pipe for signs of collapse. If there is damage, repair it. These repairs should be done as directed in the vehicle's service manual.

REPLACING LEAKING GASKETS AND SEALS
The most likely spots for leaking gaskets and seals are between the exhaust manifold and the cylinder head, and between the exhaust pipe and the exhaust manifold (Figure 12–35).

When installing exhaust gaskets, carefully follow the recommendations on the gasket package label and instruction forms. Read through all installation steps before beginning. Take note of any of the original equipment manufacturer's recommendations in service manuals that could affect engine sealing. This is especially important when working with aluminum components. Manifolds warp more easily if an attempt is made to remove them while still hot.

FIGURE 12–35   Leaking gaskets and seals are often found between the exhaust manifold and pipe.

Remember, heat expands metal, making assembly bolts more difficult to remove and easier to break.

Follow the torque sequence in reverse to loosen each bolt. Repeat the process to remove the bolts. This minimizes the chance of components warping.

Any debris left on the sealing surfaces increases the chance of leaks. A good gasket remover will quickly soften the old gasket debris and adhesive for quick removal. Carefully remove the softened pieces with a scraper and a wire brush. Be sure to use a nonmetallic scraper when attempting to remove gasket material from aluminum surfaces.

Inspect the manifold for irregularities that might cause leaks, such as gouges, scratches, or cracks. Replace any parts that are cracked or badly warped. This will ensure proper sealing of the manifold.

Due to high heat conditions, it is important to retap and redie all threaded bolt holes, studs, and mounting bolts. This procedure ensures tight, balanced clamping forces on the gasket. Lubricate the threads with a good high-temperature antiseize lubricant. Use a small amount of contact adhesive to hold the gasket in place. Align the gasket properly before the adhesive dries. Allow the adhesive to dry completely before proceeding with manifold installation.

Install the bolts finger-tight. Tighten the bolts in three steps—one-half, three-quarters, and full torque—following the torque tables in the service manual or gasket manufacturer's instructions. Torquing is usually begun in the center of the manifold, working outward in an X pattern.

To replace a damaged exhaust pipe, begin by supporting the converter to keep it from falling. Carefully remove the oxygen sensor if there is one.

Remove any hangers or clamps holding the exhaust pipe to the frame. Unbolt the flange holding the exhaust pipe to the exhaust manifold. When removing the exhaust pipe, check to see if there is a gasket. If so, discard it and replace it with a new one. Once the joint has been taken apart, the gasket loses its effectiveness. Disconnect the pipe from the converter and pull the front exhaust pipe loose and remove it.

🔧 SHOP TALK

An easy way to break off rusted nuts is to tighten them instead of loosening them. Sometimes a badly rusted clamp or hanger strap will snap off with ease. Sometimes the old exhaust system will not drop free of the body because a large part is in the way, such as the rear end or the transmission support. Use a large cold chisel, pipe cutter, hacksaw, muffler cutter, or chain cutter to cut the old system at convenient points to make the exhaust assembly smaller. ■

Although most exhaust systems use a slip joint and clamps to fasten the pipe to the muffler, a few use a welded connection. If the vehicle's system is welded, cut the pipe at the joint with a hacksaw or pipe cutter (Figure 12–36). The new pipe need not be welded to the muffler. An adapter, available with the pipe, can be used instead. When measuring the length for the new pipe, allow at least 2 inches for the adapter to enter the muffler.

● CAUTION:

Be sure to wear work gloves to prevent cutting your hands on rusted metal parts. ■

The old exhaust pipe might be rusted into the muffler or converter opening. Attempt to collapse the old pipe by using a cold chisel or slitting tool and a

FIGURE 12–36 Cutting an exhaust pipe with a pipe cutter.

FIGURE 12–37 Removing a rusted-on muffler.

hammer (Figure 12–37). While freeing the pipe, try not to damage the muffler inlet. It must be perfectly round to accept the new pipe.

Slide the new pipe into the muffler (some lubricant might be helpful). Attach the front end to the manifold. The pipe must fit at least 1-1/2 inches into the converter or muffler. A new gasket must be used at the manifold. Before tightening the connectors, check the system for alignment. When it is properly aligned, tighten the clamps.

If the vehicle is equipped with a mechanical heat riser valve, it should be sprayed with graphite oil. Also, be sure the counterweight is in balance (Figure 12–38). To do this, use pliers to move the counterweight and valve shaft slowly and carefully. Graphite oil is applied liberally during this process until the shaft moves freely and easily.

FIGURE 12–38 Mechanical heat riser valve.

SHOP TALK

Graphite oil is a thin lubricant containing graphite particles. After the engine starts, the oil will burn off. The graphite, an excellent dry lubricant, will remain. ■

CAUTION:

Be sure no exhaust part comes into direct contact with any section of the body, fuel lines, fuel tank, or brake lines. ■

TURBOCHARGERS AND SUPERCHARGERS

The power generated by the internal combustion engine is directly related to the amount of air that is compressed in the cylinders. In other words, the greater the compression (within reason), the greater the output of the engine.

Two approaches can be used to increase engine compression. One is to modify the engine to increase the compression ratio. This has been done in many ways including the use of such things as domes or high top pistons, altered crankshaft strokes, or changes in the shape and structure of the combustion chamber.

Another, less expensive way to increase compression (and engine power) without physically changing the shape of the combustion chamber is to simply increase the intake charge. By pressurizing the intake mixture before it enters the cylinder, more air and fuel molecules can be packed into the combustion chamber.

The two processes of artificially increasing the amount of airflow into the engine are known as turbocharging and supercharging.

Turbocharger Operation

Turbochargers are used to increase engine power by compressing the air that goes into the engine's combustion chambers. They do not require a mechanical connection between the engine and the pressurizing pump to compress the intake gases. Instead, they rely on the rapid expansion of hot exhaust gases exiting the cylinders. These gases spin the turbine blades (hence the name turbocharger) of the pump. Because exhaust gas is a waste product, the energy developed by the turbine is said to be free since it theoretically does not use any of the engine's power it helps to produce.

A typical turbocharger, usually called a turbo, consists of the following components (Figure 12–39).

FIGURE 12–39 Cross section of a turbocharger shows the turbine wheel, the compressor wheel, and their connecting shaft. *Courtesy of Toyota Motor Corporation*

- Turbine or hot wheel
- Shaft
- Compressor or cold wheel
- Waste gate valve
- Actuator
- Center housing and rotating assembly (CHRA). This component contains the bearings, shaft, turbine seal assembly, and compressor seal assembly.

The turbocharger is normally located close to the exhaust manifold. An exhaust pipe runs between the exhaust manifold and the turbine housing to carry the exhaust flow to the turbine wheel (Figure 12–40). Another pipe connects the compressor housing intake to an injector throttle plate assembly or a carburetor.

Inside the turbocharger, the turbine wheel (hot wheel) is attached via a shaft to the intake compressor wheel (cold wheel). Each wheel is encased in its own spiral-shaped housing that serves to control and direct the flow of exhaust and intake gases. The shaft that joins the two wheels rides on bearings.

The air compressing process typically starts when the engine's speed is above 2,000 rpm. The force of the exhaust flow is directed through a nozzle against the side of the turbine wheel. As the hot gases hit the turbine wheel causing it to spin, the specially curved turbine fins direct the air toward the center of the

FIGURE 12–40 Exhaust gas and airflow in a typical turbocharger system. *Courtesy of Toyota Motor Corporation*

housing where it exits. This action creates a flow called a vortex. Once the turbine starts to spin, the compressor wheel (shaped like a turbine wheel in reverse) also starts to spin. This causes air to be drawn into the center where it is caught by the whirling blades of the compressor and thrown outward by centrifugal force. From there, the air exits under pressure through the remainder of the induction system on its way to the cylinder.

Air is typically drawn into the cylinders by the difference in pressure between the atmosphere and engine vacuum. A turbocharger, however, is capable of pressurizing the intake charge above normal atmospheric pressure. Turbo boost is the term used to describe the positive pressure increase created by a turbocharger. For example, 10 psi of boost means the air is being fed into the engine at 24.7 psi (14.7 psi atmospheric plus 10 pounds of boost).

WASTE GATE VALVE If the turbocharged air pressure becomes too high, knocking occurs and engine output actually decreases. To prevent this, the turbocharger uses a **waste gate** valve. This valve allows a certain amount of exhaust gas to bypass the turbine once the ideal boost is exceeded. The waste gate is usually operated by an actuator that senses the air pressure in the induction system. When the pressure becomes too high, the actuator opens the waste gate valve. The flow of exhaust gas reaching the turbine decreases. This reduces turbine and compressor wheel speed. The result is a drop in turbocharged air pressure.

INTERCOOLER The **intercooler** cools the turbocharged air before it reaches the combustion cham-

ber. Cooling the air makes it denser. It also lowers the temperature produced in the combustion chamber. These factors help reduce engine knock and increase engine output. Intercoolers are like radiators in that heat from the air passing through them is removed and dissipated to the atmosphere. Intercoolers can be air or water cooled.

LUBRICATING SYSTEM Most turbochargers are lubricated by pressurized and filtered engine oil that is line-fed to the unit's oil inlet. The oil drains back to the engine (by gravity) through a separate line. The lubrication system is critical to the center bearing of a turbocharger. This bearing has the high heat of the exhaust on one side of it and the oil tends to keep it cool as well as lubricate it.

⚠️ WARNING!

Lack of lubrication and oil lag are major causes of turbocharger failure. ∎

A turbocharger should never be operated under load if the engine has less than 30 psi oil pressure. A turbocharger is much more sensitive to a limited oil supply than an engine, due to the high rotational speed of the shaft and the relatively small area of the bearing surfaces. Low oil pressure and slow oil delivery during engine starting can destroy the bearings in a turbocharger. During normal engine starting, this should not be a problem. There are, of course, abnormal starting conditions. Oil lag conditions will most often occur during the first engine start after an engine oil and filter change. Before the engine is put under load and the turbo activated, the engine should be run for 3 to 5 minutes at idle to prevent oil starvation to the turbo. Similar conditions can also exist if an engine has not been operated for a long period of time. Engine lube systems have a tendency to bleed down. Before allowing the engine to start, the engine should be cranked over until a steady oil pressure reading is observed. This is called priming the lubricating system. The same starting procedure should be followed in cold weather. The thick engine oil will take a longer period of time to flow.

SHOP TALK

When oil leakage is noted at the turbine end of the turbocharger, always check the turbocharger oil drain tube and the engine crankcase breathers for restrictions. When sludged engine oil is found, the engine's oil and oil filter must be changed. ■

CUSTOMER CARE

Explain to customers the oiling needs of a turbocharger and the need for special attention during starting and turning off the engine. ■

SPARK-RETARD SYSTEM Retarding spark timing is an often used method of controlling detonation on turbocharged engine systems. Unfortunately, any time the ignition is permanently retarded to prevent detonation, power is lost, fuel economy suffers, and the engine tends to run hotter. Because of these trade-offs, most systems use knock-sensing devices to retard timing only when detonation is detected.

COMPUTER-CONTROLLED SYSTEM Control devices limit the amount of boost to prevent detonation and engine damage. In fact, some turbocharging systems on computer-controlled vehicles use an electronic control unit to operate the waste gate control valve through sensor signals.

USING SERVICE MANUALS

General service procedures for turbocharger systems are normally in a separate section of service manuals. Individual inputs and outputs that are part of the electronic control system are covered in the engine control or performance section of the manual. ■

Turbocharger Inspection To inspect a turbocharger, start the engine and listen to the sound the turbo system makes. As a technician becomes more familiar with this characteristic sound, it will be easier to identify an air leak between the compressor outlet and engine or an exhaust leak between engine and turbo by the presence of a higher pitched sound. If the turbo sound cycles or changes in intensity, the likely causes are a plugged air cleaner or loose material in the compressor inlet ducts or dirt buildup on the compressor wheel and housing.

SHOP TALK

This chapter covers typical units to explain the basic procedures for inspection, troubleshooting, and service. Use the appropriate service manual for the unit on which you are working. ■

After listening, check the air cleaner and remove the ducting from the air cleaner to turbo and look for dirt buildup or damage from foreign objects. Check for loose clamps on the compressor outlet connections and check the engine intake system for loose bolts or leaking gaskets. Then, disconnect the exhaust pipe and look for restrictions or loose material. Examine the exhaust system for cracks, loose nuts, or blown gaskets. Rotate the turbo shaft assembly. Does it rotate freely? Are there signs of rubbing or wheel impact damage?

Visually inspect all hoses, gaskets, and tubing for proper fit, damage, and wear. Check the low pressure, or air cleaner, side of the intake system for vacuum leaks.

On the pressure side of the system you can check for leaks using soapy water. After applying the soap mixture, look for bubbles to pinpoint the source of the leak.

Leakage in the exhaust system upstream from the turbine housing will also affect turbo operation. If exhaust gases are allowed to escape prior to entering the turbine housing, the reduced temperature and pressure will cause a proportionate reduction in boost and an accompanying loss of power. If the waste gate does not appear to be operating properly (too much or too little boost), check to make sure the connecting linkage is operating smoothly and not binding. Also, check to make sure the pressure sensing hose is clear and properly connected.

SHOP TALK

Specialty shops normally rebuild turbochargers. Because of the needed balance and sealing of the units, automotive technicians do not rebuild the units. Most repair shops do not have the equipment needed. ■

WASTE GATE SERVICE Waste gate malfunctions can usually be traced to carbon buildup, which keeps the unit from closing or causes it to bind. A defective diaphragm or leaking vacuum hose can result in an inoperative waste gate. But, before condemning the waste gate, check the ignition timing, the spark-retard system, vacuum hoses, knock sensor, oxygen sensor, and computer to be sure each is operating properly.

WARNING!

When removing carbon deposits from turbine and waste gate parts, never use a hard metal tool or sandpaper. Remember that any gouges or scratches on these metal parts can cause severe vibration or damage to the turbocharger. To clean these parts, use a soft brush and a solvent. ■

Common Turbocharger Problems The turbocharger with proper care and servicing, will provide years of reliable service. Most turbocharger failures are caused by lack of lubricant, ingestion of foreign objects, or contamination of lubricant.

Refer to Table 12–1 and the service manual for the symptoms of turbocharger failures, a summary of causes, and recommended remedies.

Turbo-Lag Increases in horsepower are normally evidenced by an engine's response to a quick opening of the throttle. The lack of throttle response is felt with some turbocharged systems. This delay or turbo-lag occurs because exhaust gas requires a little time to build enough energy to spin the blower up to speed.

The variable nozzle turbine (**VNT**) has greatly improved the turbo-lag traditionally associated with turbochargers. **Turbo lag** occurs when the turbocharger is unable to meet the immediate demands of the engine. This causes the power from the engine to temporarily lag behind the need. VNT units allow the turbine to accelerate more quickly than the conventional turbos thereby reducing the lag time.

Replacing a Turbocharger If the turbocharger is faulty, it can be replaced with a new or rebuilt unit.

Always follow the procedure given in the service manual.

Once the new or rebuilt unit is installed, the turbo should be started up as described in the following section.

TURBO START-UP AND SHUTDOWN After replacement of a turbocharger, or after an engine has been unused or stored, there can be a considerable lag after engine start-up before the oil pressure is sufficient to deliver oil to the turbo's bearings. To prevent this problem, follow these simple steps.

1. When installing a new or remanufactured turbocharger, make certain the oil inlet and drain lines are clean before connecting them.
2. Be sure the engine oil is clean and at the proper level.
3. Fill the oil filter with clean oil.
4. Leave the oil drain line disconnected at the turbo and crank the engine without starting it until oil flows out of the turbo drain port.
5. Connect the drain line, start the engine, and operate it at low idle for a few minutes before running it at higher speeds.

CUSTOMER CARE

Remind your customer not to immediately stop a turbocharged engine after pulling a trailer or driving at a high speed or uphill. Idle the engine for 20 to 120 seconds. The turbocharger will continue to rotate after the engine oil pressure has dropped to zero, which can cause bearing damage. Also, remind the owner of the proper starting procedures and the importance of proper maintenance. ■

Contaminated oil can cause sludge buildups within the turbo. Check the oil drain outlet for sludge buildup with the oil drain line removed. Failure to follow these steps can result in bearing failure on the turbo's main shaft. Remember, shaft rotation speed in modern turbochargers can easily exceed 2,000 revolutions per second.

Superchargers

Supercharging fascinated auto engineers even before they decided to steer with a wheel instead of a tiller. The 1906 American Chadwick had a supercharger. Since then, many manufacturers have equipped engines with superchargers. Supercharged Dusenbergs, Hispano-Suizas, and Mercedes-Benzes were giants among luxury-car marques, as well as winners

TABLE 12–1 TURBOCHARGER TROUBLESHOOTING GUIDE

Condition	Possible Causes Code Numbers	Remedy Description by Code Numbers
Engine lacks power	1, 4, 5, 6, 7, 8, 9, 10, 11, 18, 20, 21, 22, 25, 26, 27, 28, 29, 30, 37, 38, 39, 40, 41, 42, 43	1. Dirty air cleaner element 2. Plugged crankcase breathers 3. Air cleaner element missing, leaking, not sealing correctly; loose connections to turbocharger 4. Collapsed or restricted air tube before turbocharger 5. Restricted-damaged crossover pipe, turbocharger to inlet manifold
Black smoke	1, 4, 5, 6, 7, 8, 9, 10, 11, 18, 20, 21, 22, 25, 26, 27, 28, 29, 30, 37, 38, 39, 40, 41, 43	6. Foreign object between air cleaner and turbocharger 7. Foreign object in exhaust system (from engine, check engine) 8. Turbocharger flanges, clamps, or bolts loose. 9. Inlet manifold cracked; gaskets loose or missing; connections loose
Blue smoke	1, 2, 4, 6, 8, 9, 17, 19, 20, 21, 22, 32, 33, 34, 37, 45	10. Exhaust manifold cracked, burned; gaskets loose, blown, or missing 11. Restricted exhaust system
Excessive oil consumption	2, 8, 15, 17, 19, 20, 29, 30, 31, 33, 34, 37, 45	12. Oil lag (oil delay to turbocharger at start-up) 13. Insufficient lubrication 14. Lubricating oil contaminated with dirt or other material 15. Improper type lubricating oil used
Excessive oil turbine end	2, 7, 8, 17, 19, 20, 22, 29, 30, 32, 33, 34, 45	16. Restricted oil feed line 17. Restricted oil drain line 18. Turbine housing damaged or restricted 19. Turbocharger seal leakage
Excessive oil compressor end	1, 2, 4, 5, 6, 8, 19, 20, 21, 29, 30, 33, 34, 45	20. Worn journal bearings 21. Excessive dirt buildup in compressor housing 22. Excessive carbon buildup behind turbine wheel
Insufficient lubrication	8, 12, 14, 15, 16, 23, 24, 31, 34, 35, 36, 44, 46	23. Too fast acceleration at initial start (oil lag) 24. Too little warm-up time 25. Fuel pump malfunction 26. Worn or damaged injectors 27. Valve timing
Oil in exhaust manifold	2, 7, 17, 18, 19, 20, 22, 29, 30, 33, 34, 45	28. Burned valves 29. Worn piston rings 30. Burned pistons 31. Leaking oil feed line
Damaged compressor wheel	3, 4, 6, 8, 12, 15, 16, 20, 21, 23, 24, 31, 34, 35, 36, 44, 46	32. Excessive engine pre-oil 33. Excessive engine idle 34. Coked or sludged center housing 35. Oil pump malfunction 36. Oil filter plugged

Damaged turbine wheel	7, 8, 12, 13, 14, 15, 16, 18, 20, 22, 23, 24, 25, 28, 30, 31, 34, 35, 36, 44, 46	37. Oil-bath-type air cleaner:
		  ◆ Air inlet screen restricted
		  ◆ Oil pullover
		  ◆ Dirty air cleaner
		  ◆ Oil viscosity low
		  ◆ Oil viscosity high

Drag or bind in rotating assembly	3, 6, 7, 8, 12, 13, 14, 15, 16, 18, 20, 21, 22, 23, 24, 31, 34, 35, 36, 44, 46	38. Actuator damaged or defective 39. Waste gate binding 40. Electronic control module or connector(s) defective 41. Waste gate actuator solenoid or connector defective
Worn bearings, journals, bearing bores	6, 7, 8, 12, 13, 14, 15, 16, 23, 24, 31, 35, 36, 44, 46	42. EGR valve defective 43. Alternator voltage incorrect
Noisy	1, 3, 4, 5, 6, 7, 8, 9, 10, 11, 12, 13, 14, 15, 16, 18, 20, 21, 22, 23, 24, 31, 34, 35, 36, 37, 44, 46	44. Engine shut off without adequate cool-down time 45. Leaking valve guide seals 46. Low oil level
Sludged or coked center housing	2, 11, 13, 14, 15, 17, 18, 24, 31, 35, 36, 44, 46	

FIGURE 12–41 Supercharger installed on a V-6 engine.

on the race tracks in the 1920s and 1930s. Then, after World War II, supercharging started to fade, although both Ford and American Motors sold supercharged passenger cars into the late 1950s. However, after being displaced first by larger V-8 engines, then by turbochargers, the supercharger started to make a comeback with 1989 models. Some automobile manufacturers are offering superchargers as an alternative to the turbo (Figure 12–41).

USING SERVICE MANUALS

Service procedures for supercharger systems are normally in a separate unit of a service manual. ∎

Supercharger Operation **Superchargers** are air pumps directly driven by the engine's crankshaft by a belt. They improve horsepower and torque by pumping extra air into the engine in direct relationship to crankshaft speed. This positive connection provides for instant power response.

Figure 12–42 illustrates the flow of the air through the supercharger. The air comes in through the remote-mounted air cleaner and the mass airflow meter, which are not shown. It goes through the air intake charge throttle plate assembly, then passes through the supercharger inlet plenum assembly, which is bolted to the back of the supercharger.

The air is inducted into the bottom of the supercharger, pressurized by the spinning rotors, and exits through the top of the supercharger by way of the air outlet adapter. As the air is compressed by the super-

charger, its temperature increases. Since cooler, denser air is desired for increased power, the heated air is routed through the air-to-air intercooler. The upper tube assembly carries the air into the top of the intercooler, and it exits through the outlet tube assembly at the bottom. The intercooler is quite efficient and can decrease the temperature of the air by 150°F.

This cooled air then passes through to the intake manifold adapter assembly, which is bolted to the rear of the intake manifold (Figure 12–43). When the intake valves open, the air is forced into the combustion chambers where it is mixed with fuel delivered by the fuel injectors.

Notice that the system also incorporates a bypass, which branches off from the upper portion of the air cooler to the intake manifold adapter assembly. This by-pass (Figure 12–44) is designed to allow the supercharger to idle when the extra power is not needed. The by-pass routes any excess air in the intake manifold back through the supercharger inlet plenum assembly, allowing the engine to run, in effect, normally aspirated.

The by-pass incorporates a simple vacuum motor that regulates the amount of air to be by-passed according to the power demands placed upon the engine. As the engine's power demands increase, the vacuum motor modulates a butterfly valve to progressively close off the by-pass and route more of the air to the intake manifold, thereby increasing boost. With the by-pass completely closed, boost can reach about 12 psi. In a typical system, the engine control computer controls a valve that allows air to by-pass the supercharger when boost is not needed.

Unlike a turbocharger, the supercharger does not require a waste gate to limit boost and prevent a potentially damaging overboost condition. Since the speed of the supercharger is directly linked to the engine speed, its pumping power is limited by the rpm of the engine itself rather than revolutions produced by exhaust gases. Supercharger boost is, therefore, directly controlled through the opening and closing of the throttle.

Supercharger Designs While there have been a number of supercharger designs on the market over the years, the most popular is the **Roots** type. The pair of three lobed rotor vanes in the Roots supercharger is driven by the crankshaft. The lobes force air into the intake manifold.

The key to the supercharger's operation, of course, is primarily the design of the rotors. Some Roots-type superchargers use straight-lobe rotors that result in uneven pressure pulses and, consequently, relatively high noise levels. Therefore, the supercharger used

FIGURE 12–42   Airflow through a supercharger assembly into the intake manifold. *Courtesy of Ford Motor Company*

with most of today's engines uses a helical design for the two rotors. The helical design evens out the pressure pulses in the blower and reduces noise. It was found that a 60-degree helical twist works best for equalizing the inlet and outlet volumes.

Another benefit of the helical rotor design is it reduces carryback volumes—air that is carried back to the inlet side of the supercharger because of the unavoidable spaces between the meshing rotors—which represents a loss of efficiency.

The rotors are held in a proper relationship to each other by timing gears. They are supported by ball bearings in the front and needle roller bearings in the back. The needle bearings are greased for life. The ball bearings are generally lubricated by gear oil, and a plug is provided for periodic checks of the oil level at the ball bearings. The oil is a synthetic base specifically produced for high-speed use. When servicing the gear case, it is very important to keep out dirt and moisture.

The intercooler (Figure 12–45) in the supercharging system extracts excess heat from the air. By cooling the air in this manner, its density and, consequently, its oxygen content, result in increased power output for a

1 SUPERCHARGER
2 GASKET, SUPERCHARGER
3 LOWER INTAKE MANIFOLD
4 BOLTS, SUPERCHARGER (8)
5 LOCATOR PINS
6 O-RINGS, COOLANT PASSAGE (2)
7 STUD, TENSIONER BRACKET TO SUPERCHARGER

FIGURE 12–43 The supercharger and throttle plate assembly are mounted to the intake manifold. *Courtesy of General Motors Corporation*

given boost pressure. The air-to-air intercooler is located next to the conventional cooling radiator.

To handle the higher operating temperatures imposed by supercharging, an engine oil cooler is usually built into the engine system. This water-to-oil cooler is generally mounted between the engine front cover and oil filter.

Superchargers can be enhanced with electrically operated clutches and by-pass valves. These allow the same computer that controls fuel and ignition to kick the boost on and off precisely as needed. This results in far greater efficiency than a full-time supercharger.

Another popular supercharger design, especially in Europe, is the **G-Lader** supercharger, which is based on a 1905 French design. As shown in Figure 12–46, spiral ramps in both sides of the rotor intermesh with similar ramps in the housing. Unlike most superchargers, the rotor of the G-Lader does not spin on its axis, rather it moves around an eccentric shaft. This motion draws in air, squeezes it inward through the spiral,

FIGURE 12–44 Supercharger by-pass hose and intake elbow.

FIGURE 12–45 A typical intercooler system.

FIGURE 12–46   Operation of a G-Lader type supercharger.

which compresses it, then forces it through ducts in the center into the engine. Airflow is essentially constant, so intake noise is lower than that of a Roots blower. Because there is only a slight wiping motion between the spiral and housing, wear is minimal.

A comparison of supercharger and turbocharger operations is given in Table 12–2.

Supercharger Problems   Many of the problems and their remedies given for turbochargers hold good for superchargers. There are also problems associated specifically with the supercharger. Refer to the service manual for the symptoms of supercharger failure, and a summary of the causes and the recommended repairs.

CASE STUDY

A customer's high-mileage, mid-1980s car has a tendency to run hotter than it used to. It seems to be using more gas and has less power. There are no service records for the car and based on its overall condition, it is determined that the car was not well-maintained. A visual inspection is performed and nothing abnormal is found. However, when the technician removes the air-filter assembly to visually check the action of the carburetor, the smell of raw fuel is evident. Careful inspection reveals no fuel leaks. The engine is started so the carburetor and fuel lines can be observed. A small amount of fuel sprays out the top of the carburetor each time the throttle is opened. This is probably the cause for the gas smell. But what is causing the fuel to spray out? Is this related to the original complaint?

Diagnosis continues with a vacuum test. At idle, the engine has 17 in. Hg. When the engine speed is raised to 1,500 rpm and held there, the vacuum gauge climbs to 19 in. Hg then starts to drop. This normally indicates excessive exhaust back pressure. A collapsed exhaust pipe or plugged converter could be the problem. A plugged exhaust will cause fuel to spray out of the carburetor, and it will cause poor gas mileage and poor overall performance.

	TABLE 12–2 COMPARISON OF SUPERCHARGER VS TURBOCHARGER	
	Supercharger	**Turbocharger**
Efficiency loss	Mechanical friction and power to rotate	Increased exhaust back pressure
Packaging	Belt driven	Major revisions required to package—new exhaust manifold
Lube system	Self-contained	Uses engine oil and coolant
System noise	Pressure pulsation and gear noise	High frequency whine and waste gate
Durability	In use by OEMs, seems to be durable	In use by OEMs, improvements have been made and durability has increased
Performance	30% to 40% power increase over naturally aspirated Better low end torque No lag—dramatic improvement in start-up and passing acceleration, particularly with automatic transmission	30% to 40% power increase over naturally aspirated No loss of horsepower to operate
Temperatures	No change from naturally aspirated	Increased underhood temperatures

To determine the location of the exhaust restriction, the catalytic converter is removed and the same vacuum test performed. This time the gauge reacts normally. The restriction in the exhaust is the converter. It is plugged. Replacing the converter will correct the problem. However, the cause of the plugging is still unknown.

A look at the fuel filler assembly reveals the cause of the problem. The owner has enlarged the nozzle opening to accommodate leaded fuel nozzles. The lead in this type fuel will clog a converter. This is explained to the customer and a new fuel filler neck and converter is installed.

KEY TERMS

Back pressure
Catalytic converter
G-Lader
Intercooler
Intermediate pipe
Muffler
PCM
PVS
Pyrometer
Resonator
Roots
Supercharger
Tailpipe
Turbocharger
Turbo lag
TVS
VNT
Waste gate

SUMMARY

◆ The air induction system allows a controlled amount of clean, filtered air to enter the engine. Cool air is drawn in through a fresh air tube. It passes through a preheater and air cleaner before entering the carburetor or fuel injection throttle.

◆ The intake manifold distributes the air or air/fuel mixture as evenly as possible to each cylinder, helps to prevent condensation, and assists in the vaporization of the air/fuel mixture. Intake manifolds are made of cast iron or die-cast aluminum. They can be either wet or dry. That is, they may or may not have coolant passages cast in them. Some manifolds have an exhaust crossover passage.

◆ The vacuum in the intake manifold operates many systems such as emission controls, brake boosters, heater/air conditioners, cruise controls, and more. Vacuum is applied through an elaborate system of hoses, tubes, and relays. A diagram of emission system vacuum hose routing is located on the underhood decal. Loss of vacuum can create many driveability problems.

◆ A vehicle's exhaust system carries away gases from the passenger compartment, cleans the exhaust emissions, and muffles the sound of the engine. Its components include the exhaust manifold, exhaust pipe, catalytic converter, muffler, resonator, tailpipe, heat shields, clamps, brackets, and hangers.

◆ The exhaust manifold is a bank of pipes that collects the burned gases as they are expelled from the cylinders and directs them to the exhaust pipe. Engines with all the cylinders in a row have one exhaust manifold. V-type engines have an exhaust manifold on each side of the engine. The exhaust pipe runs between the exhaust manifold and the catalytic converter.

◆ The catalytic converter uses the catalysts to change CO, HC, and NO_x into water vapor, CO_2, N, and O_2. The most common types of converters are the pellet, monolythic, three-way, particulate oxidizer catalytic converter, and the minicatalytic converter.

◆ The muffler consists of a series of baffles, chambers, tubes, and holes to break up, cancel out, and silence pressure pulsations. Two types commonly used are the reverse-flow and the straight-through mufflers.

◆ Some vehicles have an additional muffler called a resonator to further reduce the sound level of the exhaust. The tailpipe is the end of the pipeline carrying exhaust fumes to the atmosphere beyond the back end of the car. Heat shields protect vehicle parts from exhaust system heat. Clamps, brackets, and hangers join and support exhaust system components.

◆ Exhaust system components are subject to both physical and chemical damage. The exhaust can be checked by listening for leaks and by visual inspection. Most exhaust system servicing involves the replacement of parts.

◆ Two approaches can be used to increase engine compression. One is to modify the internal configuration of the engine to increase the basic compression ratio. The less expensive way is to increase the quantity of the intake charge. The two processes of artificially increasing the amount of airflow into the engine are known as turbocharging and supercharging.

◆ The turbocharger does not require a mechanical connection between the engine and pressurizing pump to compress the intake gases. Instead, it relies on the rapid expansion of hot exhaust gases exiting the cylinder to spin turbine blades.

◆ A typical turbocharger consists of a turbine (or hot wheel), shaft, compressor (or cold wheel), turbine housing, compressor housing, and center housing and rotating assembly. A waste gate manages turbo output by controlling the amount of exhaust gas that is allowed to enter the turbine housing. Turbo boost is the positive pressure increase created by a turbocharger.

◆ Most turbochargers are lubricated by pressurized and filtered engine oil that is line-fed to the unit's oil inlet. Some turbocharged engines are equipped with an intercooler, which is designed to cool the compressed air from the turbocharger.

◆ Retarding spark timing is an often-used method of controlling detonation on turbocharged engine systems. Most systems use knock-sensing devices to retard timing only when detonation is detected. Some systems use an electronic control unit to operate the waste gate control valve through sensor signals.

◆ If the turbo sound cycles or changes in intensity, the likely causes are a plugged air cleaner or loose material in the compressor inlet ducts of dirt build-up on the compressor wheel and housing. Most turbocharger failures are caused by one of the following reasons: lack of lubricant, ingestion of foreign objects, or contamination of lubricant. Turbo lag occurs when the turbocharger is unable to meet the immediate demands of the engine.

◆ Superchargers are air pumps connected directly to the crankshaft by a belt. The positive connection yields instant response and pumps air into the engine in direct relationship to crankshaft speed.

◆ The most popular supercharger design is the Roots type. Another supercharger design is the G-Lader supercharger.

TECH MANUAL

The following procedure is included in Chapter 12 of the *Tech Manual* that accompanies this book:

1. Inspect exhaust system.

REVIEW QUESTIONS

1. What can be used to check for leaks on the pressure side of a turbocharger system?

2. What advantages are there to preheating intake air?

3. Name three purposes of the intake manifold.

4. How can the effectiveness of a catalytic converter be checked?

5. Name two likely spots for leaking gaskets and seals.

6. Which of the following statements is *not* a basic function of a vehicle's exhaust system?
   a. carries away poisonous gases from the passenger compartment
   b. muffles the sound of the engine
   c. enhances carburetor performance
   d. cleans exhaust emissions

7. Which of the following are functions of an air cleaner assembly?
   a. provides filtered air to the PCV emission control system
   b. provides engine compartment fire protection in the event of a backfire
   c. meters, mixes, and warms incoming air
   d. all of the above

8. Technician A says a vacuum leak results in less air entering the engine, which causes a richer air/fuel mixture. Technician B says a vacuum leak anywhere in the system can cause the engine to run poorly. Who is correct?
   a. Technician A   c. Both A and B
   b. Technician B   d. Neither A nor B

9. Technician A says vacuum hose routing for the entire vehicle is illustrated on the underhood decal. Technician B says this decal illustrates emission system vacuum hose routing. Who is correct?
   a. Technician A   c. Both A and B
   b. Technician B   d. Neither A nor B

10. Before replacing any exhaust system component, Technician A soaks all old connections with a penetrating oil. Technician B checks the old system's routing for critical clearance points. Who is correct?
    a. Technician A   c. Both A and B
    b. Technician B   d. Neither A nor B

11. A vehicle's manifold is warped beyond the manufacturer's specifications. Technician A replaces it. Technician B cuts the surface flat. Who is correct?
    a. Technician A   c. Both A and B
    b. Technician B   d. Neither A nor B

12. Technician A says the exhaust manifold gasket seals the joint between the exhaust manifold and the exhaust pipe. Technician B says a resonator helps to reduce exhaust noise. Who is correct?
    a. Technician A
    b. Technician B
    c. Both A and B
    d. Neither A nor B

13. Technician A says a catalytic converter breaks down HC and CO to relatively harmless by-products. Technician B says using leaded gasoline or allowing the converter to overheat can destroy its usefulness. Who is correct?
    a. Technician A
    b. Technician B
    c. Both A and B
    d. Neither A nor B

14. Which of the following is *not* characteristic of a turbocharger?
    a. used to increase engine power by compressing the air that goes into the combustion chambers
    b. usually located close to the exhaust manifold
    c. utilizes an exhaust-driven turbine wheel
    d. requires a mechanical connection between the engine and the pressurizing pump to compress the intake gases

15. Ten psi of turbo boost means air is being fed into the engine at _____ when the engine is operating at sea level.
    a. 4.7 psi
    b. 10 psi
    c. 14.7 psi
    d. 24.7 psi

16. What manages turbo output by controlling the amount of exhaust gas entering the turbine housing?
    a. waste gate
    b. turbine seal assembly
    c. hot wheel
    d. cold wheel

17. Technician A says a turbocharger has its own, self-contained, lubrication system. Technician B says a turbocharger should not be operated at an engine oil pressure any lower than 30 psi. Who is correct?
    a. Technician A
    b. Technician B
    c. Both A and B
    d. Neither A nor B

18. What is the first step in turbocharger inspection?
    a. Check the air cleaner for a dirty element.
    b. Open the turbine housing at both ends.
    c. Start the engine and listen to the system.
    d. Remove the ducting from the air cleaner to turbo and examine the area.

19. Which of the following statements concerning superchargers is incorrect?
    a. Superchargers must overcome inertia and spin up to speed as the flow of exhaust gas increases.
    b. Superchargers do not require a waste gate to limit boost.
    c. A by-pass is designed into the system to allow the supercharger to idle along when extra power is not needed.
    d. Superchargers improve horsepower and torque.

20. Technician A uses sandpaper to remove carbon deposits from turbocharger waste gate parts. Technician B scrapes off heavy deposits before attempting to clean the unit. Who is correct?
    a. Technician A
    b. Technician B
    c. Both A and B
    d. Neither A nor B

ENGINE SEALING AND REASSEMBLY

13

OBJECTIVES

◆ *Explain the principles and precautions of working with various automotive fasteners.* ◆ *Explain the purpose of the various gaskets used to seal an engine.* ◆ *Identify the major gasket types and their uses.* ◆ *Explain general gasket installation procedures.* ◆ *Describe the methods used to seal the timing cover and rear main bearing.* ◆ *Reassemble an engine including core plugs, bearings, crankshaft, camshaft, pistons, connecting rods, timing components, cylinder head, valvetrain components, oil pump, oil pan, and timing covers.* ◆ *Explain the ways to prelubricate a rebuilt engine.* • *Reinstall an engine and observe the correct starting and break-in procedures.*

Proper sealing of an engine keeps the low-pressure liquids in the cooling system away from the cylinders and lubricating oil. It also keeps the high pressure of combustion in the cylinders. It prevents both internal and external oil leaks and suppresses and muffles noise.

FASTENERS

Many types and sizes of fasteners are used in the automotive industry. Each fastener is designed for a specific purpose and condition. One of the most commonly used type of fastener is the threaded fastener. Threaded fasteners include bolts, nuts, screws, and similar items that allow a technician to install or remove parts easily (Figure 13–1).

When replacing fasteners, you should observe the following precautions.

◆ Always use the same number of fasteners as originally used by the OEM.
◆ Always use the same diameter, length, number of threads, type, and grade of fastener as used by the OEM.
◆ Always observe the OEM's recommendation for tightening sequence, tightening steps (increments), and torque values given in the service manual.
◆ Never reuse a cotter pin.
◆ Always replace stretched fasteners or fasteners with damaged threads.
◆ Always use the correct washers and pins as specified by the OEM.

FIGURE 13–1 Many different threaded fasteners are used on the automobile engine. *Courtesy of Bolts Auto Parts Company*

Over the years, a number of terms have been used to identify the various types of threads. Some of these have been replaced with new terms. The terms most commonly used in the automotive trade—the United States Standard (USS), the American National Standard (ANS), and the Society of Automotive Engineers Standard (SAE)—have all been replaced by the Unified National Series. The Unified National Series consists of four basic classifications.

◆ Unified National Coarse (UNC or NC)
◆ Unified National Fine (UNF or NF) (SAE)
◆ Unified National Extrafine (UNEF or NEF)
◆ Unified National Pipe Thread (UNPT or NPT)

The two common metric threads are coarse and fine and can be identified by the letters SI (Systeme

H = HEAD
G = GRADE MARKING (BOLT STRENGTH)
L = LENGTH (INCHES)
T = THREAD PITCH (THREAD/INCH)
D = NOMINAL DIAMETER (INCHES)

A

H = HEAD
P = PROPERTY CLASS (BOLT STRENGTH)
L = LENGTH (MILLIMETERS)
T = THREAD PITCH (THREAD/MILLIMETER)
D = NOMINAL DIAMETER (MILLIMETER)

B

FIGURE 13–2 (A) English and (B) metric bolt terminology.

TABLE 13–1 STANDARD BOLT HEAD SIZES*	
Common English (U.S. Customary) Head Sizes	**Common Metric Head Sizes**
Wrench Size (inches)	Wrench Size (millimeters)
3/8	9
7/16	10
1/2	11
9/16	12
5/8	13
11/16	14
3/4	15
13/16	16
7/8	17
15/16	18
1	19
1-1/16	20
1-1/8	21
1-3/16	22
1-1/4	23
1-5/16	24
1-3/8	26
1-7/16	27
1-1/2	29
	30
	32

*This does not suggest equivalency.

International d'Unites or International System of Units) or ISO (International Standards Organization).

Bolt Usage

A bolt has several parts (Figure 13–2). The **bolt head** is used to torque or tighten the bolt. A socket or wrench fits over the head, which enables the bolt to be tightened. Common U.S. Customary (USC) and metric sizes for bolt heads includes those given in Table 13–1. The sizes are given in fractions of an inch and in millimeters.

⚠️ WARNING!

Although some of USC and metric head sizes are very close, never use a metric wrench or socket for USC bolts, or vice versa. Tool slippage may cause injury or may damage the bolt head. ∎

Bolt diameter is the measurement across the major diameter of the threaded area or across the **bolt shank**. The **thread pitch** of a bolt in the English system is determined by the number of threads that are in one inch of threaded bolt length and is expressed in number of threads per inch. The thread pitch in the metric system is determined by the distance in millimeters between two adjacent threads. To check the thread pitch of a bolt or stud, a thread **pitch gauge** is used. Gauges are available in both English and metric dimensions. Bolt length is the distance measured from the bottom of the head to the tip of the bolt. The bolt's tensile strength, or grade, is the amount of stress or stretch it is able to withstand. The type of bolt material and the diameter of the bolt determine its tensile strength. In the English system, the tensile strength of a bolt is identified by the number of radial lines (**grade marks**) on the bolt head. More lines mean higher tensile strength (Table 13–2). In the metric system, tensile strength of a bolt or stud can be identified by a property class number on the bolt head (Figure 13–3). The higher the number, the greater the tensile strength.

All bolts in the same connection must be of the same grade. Otherwise, they will not perform equally.

TABLE 13–2 STANDARD BOLT STRENGTH MARKINGS

SAE Grade Markings					
Definition	No lines;- unmarked indeterminate quality SAE grades 0-1-2	3 Lines: common commercial quality Automotive and AN bolts SAE grade 5	4 Lines: medium commercial quality Automotive and AN bolts SAE grade 6	5 Lines: rarely used SAE grade 7	6 Lines: best commercial quality NAS and aircraft screws SAE grade 8
Material	Low carbon steel	Med. carbon steel tempered	Med. carbon steel quenched and tempered	Med. carbon alloy steel	Med. carbon alloy steel quenched and tempered
Tensile Strength	65,000 psi	120,000 psi	140,000 psi	140,000 psi	150,000 psi

FIGURE 13–3   The grade of metric bolts and studs is marked by a property class number.

Likewise, nuts are graded to match their respective bolts (Table 13–3). For example, a grade 8 nut must go with a grade 8 bolt. If a grade 5 nut was used instead, a grade 5 connection would result. The grade 5 nut cannot carry the loads expected of the grade 8 bolt. Nut markings are usually located on one side. Grade 8 and critical applications require the use of fully hardened flat washers. They do not dish out like soft washers, which can cause a loss of clamp load.

Bolt heads can pop off because of **fillet** damage. The fillet is the smooth curve where the shank flows into the bolt head (Figure 13–4). Scratches in this area introduce stress to the bolt head, causing failure. The bolt head can be protected by removing any burrs around the edges of holes. Also, place flat washers with their rounded, punched side against the bolt head and their sharp side to the work surface.

Torque Principles

All metals are elastic. **Elasticity** means a bolt can be stretched and compressed up to a certain point. This

TABLE 13–3 STANDARD NUT STRENGTH MARKING

Inch System		Metric System	
Grade	**Identification**	**Class**	**Identification**
Hex Nut Grade 5	3 Dots	Hex Nut Property Class 9	Arabic 9
Hex Nut Grade 8	6 Dots	Hex Nut Property Class 10	Arabic 10
Increasing dots represent increasing strength.		Can also have blue finish or paint dab on hex flat. Increasing numbers represent increasing strength.	

FIGURE 13–4 Bolt fillet detail.

FIGURE 13–5 These bolts have been torqued past their yield points. Note the classic soda bottle effect.

elastic, spring-like property is what provides the clamping force when a bolt is threaded into a tapped hole or when a nut is tightened. As the bolt is stretched a few thousandths of an inch, clamping force or holding power is created due to the bolt's natural tendency to return to its original length.

Like a spring, the more a bolt is stretched, the tighter it becomes. However, a bolt can be stretched too far. This is obvious when the grip on the wrench feels "mushy." At this point, the bolt can no longer safely carry the load it was designed to support.

If a bolt is stretched into **yield**, it takes a permanent set and never returns to normal (Figure 13–5). The bolt will continue to stretch more each time it is used, just like a piece of taffy that is stretched until it breaks.

Proper use of torque will avoid this yield condition. Torque values are calculated with a 25 percent safety factor below the yield point. There are some fasteners, however, that are intentionally torqued just barely into a yield condition, although not far enough to distort the bolt. This type of fastener, known as a torque-to-yield (**T-T-Y**) bolt, will provide 100 percent of its intended strength, compared to 75 percent when torqued to normal values. These fasteners, however, should not be reused. Some aftermarket gasket manufacturers include new T-T-Y bolts in their gasket sets.

Table 13–4 gives standard bolt and nut torque specifications. If the manufacturer's torque specifications are available, follow them precisely. If a T-T-Y bolt is replaced with a new bolt of identical grade but torqued to a value found in a regular torque table, the clamping force produced will be at least 25 percent less. This is one reason many manufacturers are replacing OEM bolts with the next higher grade. As an example, a grade 8 bolt torqued properly to its 25 percent safety factor produces as much, if not more, clamping force than a grade 5 bolt at 100 percent with no safety factor.

The grade and surface condition, whether plated or nonplated, dry or lubricated, oil or antiseize, cut threads or rolled, straight shank or reduced, affects the torque/tension relationship and causes the performance of the connection to change. Because torque is actually a combination of both tension and torsion, it is also a function of friction. The bolt head or nut, whichever is being rotated, produces friction as it is turned, as do the threads when they gall together under the pressure of being in tension. Tests have proven that 90 percent of work energy is consumed by friction. Friction must first be overcome before any true work is done. To compensate for surface variations, the following formula may be used to approximate the required torque.

TABLE 13–4 STANDARD BOLT AND NUT TORQUE SPECIFICATIONS					
Size Nut or Bolt	Torque (foot-pounds)	Size Nut or Bolt	Torque (foot-pounds)	Size Nut or Bolt	Torque (foot-pounds)
1/4–20	7–9	7/16–20	57–61	3/4–10	240–250
1/4–28	8–10	1/2–13	71–75	3/4–16	290–300
5/16–18	13–17	1/2–20	83–93	7/8–9	410–420
5/16–24	15–19	9/16–12	90–100	7/8–14	475–485
3/8–16	30–35	9/16–18	107–117	1–8	580–590
3/8–24	35–39	5/8–11	137–147	1–14	685–695
7/16–14	46–50	5/8–18	168–178		

$$T = FDC \div 12$$

in which T = Torque in pound-feet
F = Friction factor (torque coefficient)
D = Bolt diameter in inches
C = Bolt tension required in pounds

Table 13–5 gives the friction factor (F) for various surfaces and the percentage of torque required.

Nonplated bolts have a rougher surface than plated finishes. Therefore, it takes more torque to produce the same clamping force as on a plated bolt, even with one-third less friction. Add a lubricant and the torque might be as much as two-thirds lower.

Most printed torque values are for dry, plated bolts. Lubricants are beneficial when working with engines. They provide smoother surfaces and more consistent and evenly loaded connections. They also help reduce thread galling.

Reusing a dry nut will produce a connection with decreasing clamp force each time it is used. Nut threads are designed to collapse slightly to carry the bolt load. If dry nuts are reused, increased thread galling will result each time the nuts are reused at the same torque.

Lubrication of fasteners is recommended for consistency (Table 13–6). However, be sure to lubricate all the bolts with the same lubricant. Some lubricants are more slippery than others, which affects torque values. Lubricate the bolt, never the hole. Otherwise, the bolt may merely be tightening against the oil in the hole.

If a bolt with a reduced shank diameter (for example, a connecting rod bolt) is specified by the OEM, never replace it with a standard, straight

TABLE 13–6 FRICTION FACTORS (F) AND TORQUE REDUCTIONS FOR LUBRICATED SURFACES ON ALLOY STEEL BOLTS

Lubricant	Friction Factor	Percentage of Torque Reduction Required
Collodial copper	0.11	Reduce standard torque 45%.
Never-seize	0.11	Reduce standard torque 45%.
Grease	0.12	Reduce standard torque 40%.
Moly-cote (molybdenum disulphite)	0.12	Reduce standard torque 40%.
Heavy oils	0.12	Reduce standard torque 40%.
Graphite	0.14	Reduce standard torque 30%.
White lead	0.15	Reduce standard torque 25%.

shank bolt. A reduced shank diameter bolt looks "dog-boned." Its function is to reduce the stress on the threads by transferring it to the shank. A standard bolt under similar conditions would break very quickly at the threads.

Rolled threads are 30 percent stronger than cut threads. They also offer better fatigue resistance because there are no sharp notches to create stress points.

Studs are used to prevent continued damage to tapped holes by remaining in place at one end while the other end does the remainder of the work for future use. If a bolt or stud breaks in a tapped hole, the threads will become damaged from the shock of the breakage. The hole must then be retapped to reshape the damaged threads and ensure even torque. Tapped holes in aluminum alloys should always be strengthened with thread inserts. Manufacturers do not add them during assembly because of cost and labor time. However, they are necessary for repeated maintenance.

Some manufacturers recommend a **torque-angle** method for cylinder head bolts. If the work thickness is no more than four times the bolt's diameter, snug the nut tightly against the work and rotate it one-third of a turn (120 degrees). If the work is between four to eight times the diameter, rotate the nut a half turn (180 degrees). This will produce a very reliable clamp load that is much higher than can be achieved by just torquing. Other variables will not affect the results.

Keep the following points in mind.

1. Visually inspect the bolts.
   ◆ Threads must be clean and undamaged. Discard all bolts that are not acceptable.
   ◆ Use liquid sealant or engine oil on the threads and seating face of the cylinder head bolts to

TABLE 13–5 COMPENSATION FOR VARIOUS SURFACES

Surface	Friction Factor	Percentage of Torque Change Required
Dry, unplated steel	0.20	Use standard torque value shown.
Cadmium plating	0.15	Reduce standard torque 25%.
Zinc plating	0.21	Increase standard torque 10%.
Aluminum	0.15	Reduce standard torque 25%.
Stainless steel	0.30	Increase torque 50%.
Supertanium Special alloy steel	0.20	Use standard torque value shown.

prevent seizure from rust and corrosion. This is particularly important for an aluminum block or head. Use sealant on those bolts that hold in coolant or oil.

♦ Install bolts in their proper holes.
♦ Run a nut over the bolt's threads by hand. Discard it if any binding occurs.
♦ Clean bolt and cylinder block threads with a thread chaser or tap (Figure 13–6).

2. Apply a light coat of 10W engine oil to threads and bottom face of bolt head. A sealer is required for a bolt that enters a water jacket (Figure 13–7). This will stop coolant seepage around the bolt threads. Seeping coolant could get in the oil or cause corrosion that might damage parts, resulting in engine failure.

3. Tighten bolts in the recommended sequence. This is important to prevent warpage of the cylinder head or other parts.
   ♦ Use an accurate torque wrench.
   ♦ Tighten bolts to the recommended torque in steps and proper sequence.

4. If bolt heads are not tight against the surface, the bolts should be removed and washers installed.

5. Make sure the bolt is the proper length (not too long).

Bolt hole threads in the engine block will often pull up, leaving a raised edge around the hole (Figure

FIGURE 13–6 Cleaning bolt holes with a tap. *Courtesy of AE Clevite Engine Parts*

FIGURE 13–7 If a bolt enters the coolant passages, coat it with a flexible sealer. *Courtesy of Fel-Pro, Inc.*

FIGURE 13–8 Bolt hole threads can pull up, leaving a raised edge. Also, if the block has been resurfaced, the threads might run up to the surface. In either case, the hole must be chamfered.

13–8). If the block has been resurfaced, the threads might run up to the surface. In either case, the bolt holes should be cleaned by chamfering and the threads cleaned with an appropriate size bottoming tap. Always repair damaged threads to ensure proper bolt performance.

Many different nuts are used by the automotive industry. Beware of hexagon (hex) nut rotation when using power wrenches. It is deceptively easy to place a bolt into a yield condition within seconds. Impact wrenches are the worst offenders. Friction is needed to prevent the nut from spinning. If the nut is lubricated, there is no friction left to stop the impact wrench from hammering the nut past the bolt's yield point or stripping the threads.

SHOP TALK

Impact wrenches should only be used to loosen nuts and bolts. Use other power or hand tools to tighten them. Final tightening should always be done with a torque wrench. ■

Smaller air-powered ratchets do not produce the severe force of impact wrenches and are much safer to use.

A rule of thumb about lock washers: If the connection did not come with one, do not add one. Lock washers are extremely hard and tend to break under severe pressure (Figure 13–9).

Thread Repair

A common fastening problem is threads stripping inside an engine block, cylinder head, or other structure. This problem is usually caused by over-torquing or by incorrectly threading the bolt into the hole. Rather than replacing the block or cylinder head, the

PLAIN   SPRING LOCK   EXTERNAL TOOTH LOCK   INTERNAL TOOTH LOCK

FIGURE 13–9 Types of lock washers.

FIGURE 13–10 Steps in the installation of a helically coiled threaded insert. (A) Drill the damaged threads and clean all metal chips out of the hole. (B) Tap new threads in the hole using the specified tap. The thread depth should exceed the length of the bolt. (C) Install the insert on the mandrel provided in the installation kit. Bottom it against the tang. (D) Lubricate the insert with oil and thread it into the hole until flush with the surface. Use a punch or side-cutters to break off the tang.

threads can be replaced by the use of threaded inserts. Several threaded inserts are available. The helically coiled insert is the most popular. Figure 13–10 shows the proper procedure for installing this type of threaded insert. Always follow the directions given with the insert kit.

GASKETS

Gaskets are used predominantly to prevent gas or liquid leakage between two parts that are bolted together (Figure 13–11). Gaskets also serve as spacers, wear insulators, and vibration dampers.

As a spacer, the gasket serves as a shim between two joined engine components, such as the fuel pump lever and cam. It also helps compensate for manufacturing or rebuilding tolerances in the cylinder head. In

1	Cap—Shrader Valve	
2	Shrader Valve	
3	Fuel Rail	
4	Seal "O" Ring	
5	Gasket, Fuel Pressure Regulator	
6	Fuel Pressure Regulator	
7	Screw	
8	Bolt, Att Rails to Lower Manifold	
9	Fuel Injector	
10	Fuel Rail Assy	

11	Cover, Upper Manifold
12	Screw
13	Bolt
14	Upper Intake Manifold (Plenum)
15	Plug-Cup 1.75 Inch Dia
17	Bolt
18	Gasket, Upper to Lower Manifold
19	Sensor, EEC Coolant Temp

20	Rocker Cover Assy
21	Cap, Oil Fill
22	Tube, Heater Water Supply and Return
23	Lower Intake Manifold
24	Gasket, Thermostat Housing
25	Thermostat
26	Connector Assy, Water Outlet
27	Bolt

28	Housing Assy, Distributor
29	Adapter, Distributor
30	Distributor and Control Assy
31	Bolt
32	Sensor, EEC Air Charge Temp Sensor
33	Clamp Distributor
34	PCV Valve
35	PCV Grommet
36	Element Crankcase Vent

37	Flywheel
38	Rear Cover
39	End Seal, Rear
40	End Seal, Front
41	Cylinder Block
42	Insert, Oil Filter Mounting
43	Oil Pressure Sender
44	Intake Manifold Gasket
45	Front Cover
46	Front Cover Gasket
47	Timing Pointer

48	Front Crankshaft Seal
49	Water Pump Gasket
50	Water Pump Assy
51	Water Pump Pulley
52	Bolt
53	Rocker Cover
54	Rocker Cover Gasket
55	Bolt
56	Spark Plug
57	Cylinder Head
58	Cylinder Head Gasket
59	Oil Filter
61	Gasket, Oil Pan
62	Oil Pan
63	Bolt
64	EGR Valve Assy
65	Gasket, EGR Valve
66	Gasket, EGR Spacer
67	EGR Spacer
68	Gasket, Throttle Body
69	Connector, TPS Sensor (PIATPS)
70	Sensor, Throttle Position
71	Screw
72	Gasket, Idle Speed Motor
73	Idle Air Bypass Motor
74	Throttle Body Assy
75	Clamp
76	Clean Air Tube
77	Clamp
78	Air Inlet Assy
79	Air Cleaner Tray Top
80	Air Cleaner Element
81	Air Cleaner Tray
82	Air Cleaner Tray Bracket
83	EGO Sensor
84	Exhaust Manifold RH
85	Exhaust Manifold LH
86	Dipstick—Oil Level Indicator
87	Tube, Oil Level Indicator

FIGURE 13–11 Typical engine gasket and seal locations. *Courtesy of Ford Motor Company*

the wear insulator function, the gasket material is softer than the separated components. This allows for alternating expansion and contraction with less friction, thus preventing fretting or brinelling of machined surfaces. Keep in mind that the shock absorberlike function does not apply to liquid sealants that are used without a gasket and allow a metal-to-metal seal.

There are four basic classifications of engine gaskets.

♦ Hard gaskets are steel, stainless steel, copper, or a combination metal enclosure with a compressible and heat-resistant clay/fiber compound sandwiched inside. Gaskets in this class are cylinder head gaskets, exhaust manifold gaskets, and some intake manifold gaskets.

♦ Soft gaskets consist of soft, flexible materials such as cork, rubber, a combination of cork/rubber, rubber-coated steel, paper, and other compressed fiber materials. Newer materials, sometimes called gaskets-in-a-tube, include silicone gaskets and anaerobics. Soft gaskets are often used on valve covers, oil pans, rocker covers, pushrod covers, water pumps, thermostat housing, timing covers, and inspection plates.

♦ **Silicone gasketing** is available in three grades. The black is for general purpose; blue is for special applications; and red is for high-temperature requirements. Most mechanics use silicone gasketing to aid sealing in corners, notches, or dovetails.

♦ **Sealants** and **adhesives** generally come in a liquid form to be applied to all metal gaskets such as beaded steel-type cylinder head gaskets and intake manifold gaskets. They dry to flexible, nonhardening sealants to help prevent oil, water, gasoline, air pressure, or vacuum leaks. They are also useful as an **antiseize** for threads on bolts, studs, and fittings.

Gasket Materials

Historically, with heavy-wall, all-cast-iron engines, most gasket materials and constructions were similar, if not identical. One key to the auto industry's success in achieving late-model engine performance goals has been the development of gaskets specifically designed to seal the new engines. This includes exhaust-flange gaskets as well as exhaust rings—areas most subject to severe stresses of temperature and pressure. These new sealing products have been highly engineered for virtually all critical areas of the different engine designs. Inappropriate substitution of non-OE-equivalent products while servicing an engine may lead to premature failure.

Another recent change in gasket technology is the elimination of **asbestos**. Although the industry had voluntarily reduced the use of asbestos, the EPA has

FIGURE 13–12 Molded silicone rubber gaskets designed for use with late-model engines. *Courtesy of Fel-Pro, Inc.*

banned its use in all manufactured products after 1994. Asbestos is an excellent gasket material. However, it poses a health threat and is considered a hazardous substance for those who work with it.

Most late-model engines are equipped with premium gaskets made of space-age materials, such as molded silicone rubber (Figure 13–12) and cut plastic gaskets with silicone sealing beads. Advanced gasketing technology incorporating flexible graphite cores, specialized surface coatings, new asbestos-free materials, elastomeric beading, reinforced cork products, wire-ring combustion seals, flat-plate hoop-strength constructions, and many other gasket design innovations all are different technological approaches by different OE suppliers to reach the same goal. That goal is long-term, leak-free joints. The new gaskets have entirely different properties than traditional gasketing materials (asbestos, rubber, cork, and the like) that influence many critical design features including gasket thickness, compressibility, no-retorque characteristics, near-zero creep, greatly improved corrosion resistance, and superior thermal properties in sealing at temperatures exceeding 1,000°F.

General Gasket Installation Procedures

The following general instructions will serve as a helpful guide for installing gaskets. Because there are many different gasket materials and designs, it is impossible to list in this chapter directions for every type of installation. Always follow any special directions provided on the instruction sheets packed with most gasket sets (Figure 13–13). These will give you additional tips on replacing the gaskets of an engine.

USING SERVICE MANUALS

Special procedures for installing gaskets are found in the section that covers the part to be fastened to the engine block or cylinder head. ■

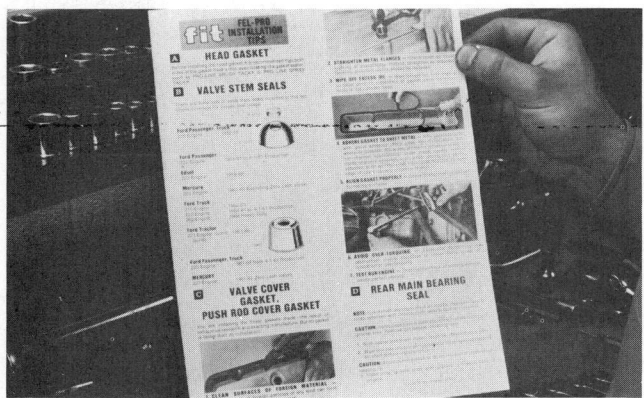

FIGURE 13–13 Follow the directions provided with the gasket set. *Courtesy of Fel-Pro, Inc.*

1. Never reuse old gaskets. Even if the old gasket appears to be in good condition, it will never seal as well as a new one. The old gasket has been exposed to high combustion temperatures and pressures, hot oil or coolant, and might have worn or damaged sealing surfaces. It also has been compressed by bolt torquing to fit the parts it has been sealing. It will not be able to re-form itself to create another good seat.

2. Handle new gaskets carefully. Be careful not to damage the new gaskets before placing them on the engine. Any bend or crease in the gasket material is a potential weak spot that might cause a leak after installation. This is especially true of the composition-type gaskets used on many cylinder heads and manifolds. If any attempt is made to straighten a bent or distorted gasket, it could fracture the gasket and create a weak spot. Protect the new gaskets by keeping them in their packages until installation.

USING SERVICE MANUALS

Always refer to the specific engine and engine part section of the service manual for the recommended procedures for using sealants. ■

3. Use gasket sealants only when they are absolutely necessary. The hot, oily environment of an engine can cause some chemical sealants to react adversely with the binding compound in composition-type gaskets, causing the gasket to deteriorate and leak.

SHOP TALK

Some technicians tend to use too much sealant on gaskets. Do not make this mistake. Be-

cause sealants have less strength than gasket materials, they create weaker joints. They can also prevent some gasket material from doing what it is supposed to do, which is to soak up oil and swell to make a tight seal. ■

4. Cleanliness is essential. New gaskets seal best when used on clean surfaces. Thoroughly clean all mating surfaces of dirt, oil deposits, rust, old sealer, and gasket material. If any foreign substances remain, they can create a path for leaks. Scraping away the old gasket is not an easy job, but it is essential to ensure a leak-free seal. When using a hand gasket scraper on aluminum parts, be very careful not to scratch the softer metal surfaces (Figure 13–14).

5. Use the right gasket in the right position. Always compare the new gasket to the component mating surfaces to make sure it is the right gasket (Figure 13–15). Comparing the new gasket with the original is another way to make sure you are using the correct part. Check that all bolt holes, dowel holes,

FIGURE 13–14 Use care when scraping off an old gasket, particularly on aluminum surfaces. *Courtesy of Victor/Dana*

FIGURE 13–15 Checking a head gasket for proper fit. *Courtesy of Fel-Pro, Inc.*

FIGURE 13–16 Some gaskets have installation directions stamped on them. *Courtesy AE Clevite Engine Parts*

FIGURE 13–17 Thermal growth characteristics of bimetal engines.

pushrod openings, coolant, and lubrication passages line up perfectly with the gasket. Some gaskets will have directions such as "top," "front," or "this side up" stamped on one surface (Figure 13–16). Follow these instructions exactly when putting the gasket in place. An upside-down or reversed gasket can easily cause loss of oil pressure, overheating, and engine failure.

Cylinder Head Gaskets

Cylinder head gaskets are the most sophisticated type of gasket. They also have the most demanding job. When first starting an engine in cold weather, parts near the combustion chamber are very cold. Then, after only a few minutes of engine operation, these same parts might reach 400°F. The inner edges of the cylinder head gasket are exposed to combustion flame temperatures from 2,000 to 3,000°F.

Pressures inside the combustion chamber also vary tremendously. On the intake stroke, a vacuum or low pressure exists in the cylinder. Then, after combustion, pressure peaks of approximately 1,000 psi occur. This extreme change from suction to high pressure happens in a fraction of a second.

Cylinder head gaskets, under these conditions, must simultaneously do the following.

◆ Seal intake stroke vacuum, combustion pressure, and the heat of combustion.
◆ Prevent coolant leakage, resist rust, corrosion and, in many cases, meter coolant flow.
◆ Seal oil passages through the block and head while resisting chemical action.
◆ Allow for lateral and vertical head movement as the engine heats and cools.
◆ Be flexible enough to seal minor surface warpage while being stiff enough to maintain adequate gasket compression.
◆ Fill small machining marks that could lead to serious gasket leakage and failure.
◆ Withstand forces produced by engine vibration.

Bimetal Engine Requirements Another problem that head gaskets must face is the differing expansion

rates of aluminum/cast-iron combination engines (Figure 13–17). Aluminum has a coefficient of thermal expansion two to three times greater than steel, depending on the alloy. This creates a scrubbing action on a head gasket as the engine goes from cold to hot and back again. If the surface of the aluminum head has been roughly machined, it can grab and tear the head gasket. To prevent this, slippery nonstick surface coatings and other materials are applied by the manufacturer to the gaskets. This coating provides the needed lubrication between the head and gasket. **Graphite** is a natural lubricant, so graphite-faced gaskets are not coated.

Today's **bimetal** engines with thin-wall castings experience more movement and flexing between the head, block, and cylinder bores, which means a more rigid gasket is often needed. This can be accomplished by using different facing materials, changing the design and loading of the combustion flanges, or using silicone beading to increase sealing loads in critical areas.

The latest generation of aftermarket gaskets includes a bead sealant that increases clamping pressure around troublesome areas. Another common and desirable gasket design today is the no-retorque type. Older gasket designs, such as the steel-faced sandwich and perforated core, require the cylinder head of an engine to be retorqued 300 to 500 miles after it has been rebuilt. These gaskets take a set after initial engine operation and relax to the point that retorquing is needed to restore the clamping force. The extra labor and expense of

FIGURE 13–18   Dim or weak lines on the carbon paper indicate poor surface gasket. *Courtesy of Victor/Dana*

retorquing a cylinder head gasket makes the repair more expensive than no-retorque designs in the long run. The no-retorque design retains a higher level of clamping force. Therefore, no retorquing is needed.

CUSTOMER CARE

If a head gasket that requires retorquing has been installed, explain the importance of doing this to the customer.   ■

Impression Testing   The carbon impression paper technique is growing in popularity as a means of checking the effectiveness of the head gasket seal. Start by cutting a piece of carbon impression paper to about the size of the gasket and follow these steps.

1. Place the paper on top of the old gasket installed on the engine block.
2. Reinstall the cylinder head.
3. Tighten the head bolts to the recommended torque and in the proper sequence.
4. Remove the cylinder head.
5. Inspect the impression left on the paper (Figure 13–18). Dim or weak lines indicate poor gasket contact due to a warped block or head.

Manifold Gaskets

There are three types of manifold gaskets—the intake manifold, exhaust manifold (Figure 13–19), and the

FIGURE 13–19   Typical exhaust manifold gaskets. *Courtesy of Fel-Pro, Inc.*

FIGURE 13–20   Combination intake/exhaust manifold gasket. *Courtesy of Fel-Pro, Inc.*

combination intake and exhaust (Figure 13–20). Each type of manifold gasket has its own sealing characteristics and problems. Therefore, be sure to follow the manufacturer's instructions when installing them.

USING SERVICE MANUALS

Refer to the manifold unit in the engine section of the service manual for specific instructions on the installation of manifold gaskets.   ■

Valve Cover Gaskets

Valve cover gaskets have an increasingly difficult job in today's high-temperature engines. They must seal between a steel or aluminum (or molded plastic) stamping and a cylinder head surface that might not be machined. The valve cover does not seal by pressure or tight bolts. The bolts that attach the cover to the cylinder head are usually widely spaced. It might appear that almost any gasket could do the job. But the gasket must be able to withstand high temperatures and the caustic action of acids in the oil.

To provide an effective seal, a valve cover gasket must conform to flange distortion. At the same time, it must provide good crush and split resistance to limit torque loss and provide chemical and heat resistance for long-term sealing. The most commonly used material is a blend of cork and rubber particles. The quality of the materials is crucial when using cork/rubber gaskets, because a low-quality cork/rubber mixture can develop leakage after a fairly short period of operation. Another popular valve cover material is made of synthetic rubber. Whether it is a cork/rubber or synthetic rubber gasket, it must be a perfect fit (Figure 13–21).

FIGURE 13–21 The two primary valve cover gasket materials are synthetic rubber and cork/rubber. *Courtesy of Fel-Pro, Inc.*

FIGURE 13–23 Applying adhesive to the oil pan flange will prevent the gasket from moving and will provide a positive seal. *Courtesy of Fel-Pro, Inc.*

FIGURE 13–22 Oil pan gaskets and seals.

Oil Pan Gaskets

An oil pan gasket seals the joint between the oil pan and the bottom of the block (Figure 13–22). The oil pan gasket might also seal the bottom of the timing cover and the lower section of the rear main bearing cap.

It is difficult to locate oil pan gasket leaks. They might be in areas not immediately seen, making the oil pan gasket one of the most ignored gaskets on an engine. Oil leaks might be blamed on other gaskets or seals rather than the oil pan gasket.

Like valve cover gaskets, the oil pan gasket must resist hot, thin engine oil. Oil pans are usually made of stamped steel, but with a stronger gasket flange. Because of the added weight and splash of crankcase oil, the pan has many assembly bolts closely spaced. As a result, the clamping force on the oil pan gasket is great. The gasket is thinner and must resist crushing.

Oil pan gaskets are made of several types of material. A commonly used material is synthetic rub-

ber, known for its long-term sealing ability. It is tough, durable, and resists hot engine oil. Synthetic rubber gaskets are easy to remove, so the sealing surfaces need less cleanup.

Carefully follow the recommendations from the gasket manufacturer. Read through all the installation steps before beginning. Take note of any of the original equipment manufacturer's recommendations that could affect engine sealing. Before installing the oil pan, make sure its flange is flat. The gasket should be mounted with a few dabs of quick-drying contact adhesive (Figure 13–23). Carefully align the gasket before the adhesive dries. Wait until the adhesive is dry before installing the pan. Tighten the oil pan bolts to the recommended torque specification and sequence given in the service manual.

ADHESIVES, SEALANTS, AND OTHER CHEMICAL SEALING MATERIALS

There are a number of chemicals that can be used to reduce labor and ensure a good seal. Many gasket sets include a label with the proper chemical recommendation for use with that gasket set. Some even include sealers in the sets when the original equipment manufacturer used a sealer to replace a gasket and a gasket cannot be manufactured for that application. They also include sealers in some sets when gasket unions need a sealant to ensure a good seal.

SHOP TALK

Chemical adhesives and sealants give added holding power and sealing ability where two parts are joined. Sealants usually are added to threads where fluid contact is frequent. Chemical thread retainers are either **aerobic** (cures in the presence of air) or **anaerobic** (cures in the absence of air). These chemical products are used in place of lock washers. ∎

Of course, there are numerous locations in an engine where precut or premolded gaskets can benefit from the services of a chemical sealant. For example, to seal the intake manifold on a V-type engine, it is important to place a dab of silicone in the corners. The same can be said about the front cover-to-oil-pan joint, rear bearing cap seals, and valley pan manifold installations.

Adhesives

Quick-drying contact adhesive is designed for bonding cork, rubber, fiber, and metal gaskets in place prior to assembly. Gasket adhesives form a tough bond when used on clean, dry surfaces. Adhesives do not aid the sealing ability of the gasket. They are meant only to hold gaskets in place during component assembly. Use small dabs; they will dry quicker for fast installation. Do not assemble components until the adhesive is completely dry. Most adhesives are ideal for use on gasket applications such as valve covers, pushrod covers, manifold and manifold end seals, and oil pan and oil pan end seals (Figure 13–24).

Sealants

General-Purpose Sealants General-purpose sealers (sometimes called chemical positioning agents) come in liquid form and are available in a brush type (known as brush tack) and an aerosol type (known as spray tack). General purpose sealers (Figure 13–25) form a tacky, flexible seal when applied in a thin, even coat that aids in gasket sealing by helping to position the

FIGURE 13–24 Holding an intake manifold gasket in place with contact adhesive. *Courtesy of Fel-Pro, Inc.*

A

B

FIGURE 13–25 Applying (A) brush-type and (B) aerosol-type general-purpose sealant. *Courtesy of Fel-Pro, Inc.*

gasket during assembly. The chemicals in a general-purpose sealant will not upset the designed performance of most mechanical gaskets. The possible exception to this is that sealant manufacturers do not recommend their use on rubber parts. These sealants are nonhardening and can cause rubber gaskets to slip.

⚠️ WARNING!

Never use a hard-drying sealant (such as shellac) on gaskets. It will make future disassembly extremely difficult and might damage the gasket material. ∎

Flexible Sealants Flexible sealants are most often used on threads of bolts that go into fluid passages. They are nonhardening sealers that fill voids, preventing the fluid from running up the threads. They resist the chemical attack of lubricants, synthetic oils, detergents, antifreeze, gasoline, and diesel fuel.

Silicone Formed-In-Place Sealants Silicone gasketing can be used to replace conventional paper, cork, and cork/rubber gaskets. It is generally for use on oil pans, valve covers, thermostat housing, timing covers, water pumps, and other such installations. Room temperature vulcanizing (**RTV**) silicone sealing products are the best known of the formed-in-place (FIP) gasket products.

⚠️ WARNING!

Be careful not to use excessive amounts of RTV. If too much is applied, it can loosen up and get into the oil system where it can clog up an oil passage and cause severe engine damage. ∎

Today's RTV aerobic silicone formulations are impervious to most automotive fluids, extremely resistant to oil, oxygen-sensor safe, exhibit outstanding flexibility (a necessary feature on modern bimetal engines), and adhere well to a broad range of materials that include plastics, metal, and glass.

To use RTV silicone, make sure the mating surfaces are free from dirt, grease, and oil. Apply a continuous 1/8-inch bead on one surface only (preferably the cover side). Make sure to circle all bolt holes. Adjust the shape before a skin forms (in about 10 minutes) as shown in Figure 13–26. Remove excess RTV silicone with a dry towel or paper towel. Press the parts together. Do not slide the parts together; this will disturb the bead. Tighten all retaining bolts to the manufacturer's specified torque. Cure time is approximately 1 hour for metal-to-metal joints and can take up to 24 hours for 1/8-inch gaps.

⬤ CAUTION:

The uncured rubber contained in RTV silicone gasketing irritates the eyes. If any gets in your eyes, immediately flush with clean water or eyewash. If the irritation continues, see a doctor. ∎

Anaerobic Formed-In-Place Sealants These formed-in-place materials are used for thread locking as well as gasketing (Figure 13–27). As a retaining compound, they are mostly used to hold sleeves, bearings, and locking screw nuts in place where there is a high exposure to vibration.

⚠️ WARNING!

Never use a sealant or formed-in-place gasket material on exhaust manifolds. ∎

FIGURE 13–26 When using RTV silicone, assemble the joint as soon as possible before the RTV begins to cure. *Courtesy of Fel-Pro, Inc.*

FIGURE 13–27 Anaerobic sealant is used as a formed-in-place gasket, as well as a retaining compound. *Courtesy of Fel-Pro, Inc.*

The major difference between aerobic and anaerobic sealants other than their method of curing is their gap-filling ability. Typically, 0.050 inch (3/64 inch) is the absolute limit of any anaerobic's gap-filling material. Some are only designed to seal 0.005- to 0.010-inch gaps. Anaerobic sealers are intended to be used between the machined surfaces of rigid castings, not on flexible stampings.

🔧 SHOP TALK

Once hardened, a good anaerobic bond is unbelievably tenacious and can withstand high temperatures. Therefore, care must be taken in selection. They tend to be highly specialized and not readily interchangeable. For example, there are various levels of thread-locking products that range from medium-strength antivibration agents to high-strength, weldlike retaining compounds. The inadvertent use of the wrong product could make future disassembly an impossibility. Check the label to be certain that anaerobic material will suit the purpose of the application. ∎

FIGURE 13–28 Using a high-temperature antiseize compound. *Courtesy of Fel-Pro, Inc.*

Hylomar Hylomar, which stands for high temperature (hy), low cost (lo), Marston (mar) product, is neither an RTV nor an anaerobic. It is a combination of polyurethene paste and silica (not silicone) flakes mixed with methylene chloride solvent. When Hylomar is clamped in a joint, the silica flakes interlock and encapsulate the plastic paste, effectively shielding it from heat, liquids, and contaminants that might otherwise dissolve it. Because Hylomar never hardens or cures, the center remains soft and pliable—like an armor-plated sponge.

As a sealing supplement, Hylomar sticks to virtually any surface, resists all fluids (including gasoline), and has a claimed temperature range of 50° to more than 600°F. In addition, if a Hylomar-coated gasket is set down wrong, it can be peeled off and reseated without damage.

Antiseize Compounds

Antiseize compounds prevent dissimilar metals from reacting with one another and seizing (Figure 13–28). This chemical-type material is used on many fasteners, especially those used with aluminum parts. Always follow the manufacturer's recommendations when using this compound.

OIL SEALS

The job of seals is to keep oil and other vital fluids from escaping around a rotating shaft. They are pressed into stationary bores in the crankshaft and timing gear cover and generally consist of a metal casing to which a synthetic rubber sealing element is bonded.

SHOP TALK

Whenever installing an oil seal, make sure its lip seal is lubricated with a light coating of grease. Also, make sure the lip portion of the seal is facing the direction that oil is coming against. ■

REPAIR SLEEVE

WORN GROOVE CAUSED BY OIL SEAL

HARMONIC BALANCER NECK, WHICH GOES THROUGH TIMING CHAIN COVER

FIGURE 13–29 Replacement sleeves are available for the harmonic balancer pulley hub.

Timing Cover Oil Seals

An oil seal prevents oil from leaking out around the crankshaft at the front of the engine. The seal is usually located in the timing cover. It seals on the shaft hub of the harmonic balancer pulley hub or on the crankshaft. Sometimes this seal will wear a groove in the shaft or hub. A replacement seal will not be reliable if it is installed on the worn shaft. It can only seal properly on a smooth surface.

If the balancer shaft or pulley hub has a groove, it might have to be replaced, a new sleeve installed, or welded and ground to its original size and finish. To replace the sleeve, use a rebuilder replacement set that includes a sleeve, new front seal, anaerobic sealant, and any other gasket components required to seal the timing cover assembly (Figure 13–29). The sleeve will cover the groove in the balancer shaft or pulley hub and provide a new sealing surface for the front oil seal.

To install the remaining oil cover seals, follow the gasket manufacturer's instructions.

Rear Main Bearing Seals

Always make it a practice to replace oil seals on re-ring or overhaul jobs to avoid the chance of costly do-overs. This is a simple, inexpensive operation when the engine is torn down, but a costly and time-consuming job when seals start to leak after assembly.

Rear main bearing seals keep oil from leaking at the crankshaft around the rear main bearing. There are two basic types of constructions: wick- or rope-type packing and molded synthetic rubber.

Wick- or rope-type packings are common on many older engines (Figure 13–30). Molded synthetic rubber lip-type seals are used on many newer engines. They do a good job of sealing even when there is some eccentricity in the shaft, as long as the surface of the shaft is very smooth. Synthetic rubber seals may sometimes be retrofitted to some older

FIGURE 13–30 Installing wick- or rope-type seals. *Courtesy of Fel-Pro, Inc.*

FIGURE 13–31 Installing a one-piece rubber crankshaft seal. *Courtesy of Chrysler Corporation*

FIGURE 13–32 Typical two-piece rubber seal.

engines that have wick seals, but only if the seals are offered as an option by the sealing manufacturer.

Three types of synthetic rubber are used for rear main bearing seals. **Polyacrylate** is commonly used because it is tough and abrasion resistant, with moderate temperature resistance to 350 degrees. Silicone synthetic rubber has a greater temperature range, but it has less resistance to abrasion and is more fragile than polyacrylate. Silicone seals must be handled carefully during installation to avoid damage. **Viton** has the abrasion resistance of polyacrylate and the temperature range of silicone, but it is the most expensive of the synthetic types. The synthetic rubber

seals may be one piece (Figure 13–31) or two pieces (Figure 13–32).

No matter what the construction of the seal is, always check the shaft for smoothness. Shafts should be free of nicks and burrs to ensure long oil seal life. Carefully remove any roughness with a very fine emery cloth and then clean the shaft thoroughly. The shaft should have a highly polished appearance and a smooth feel. Also, be sure to check and clean the oil slinger and oil return channel in the bearing cap.

Other Seals

Different parts of the engine have different sealing requirements. Some gaskets must seal pressure; others must seal vacuum. Some seal hot oil and others hot antifreeze. Some gaskets seal joints under flexible flanges; others seal joints between fairly rigid flanges

FIGURE 13–33 Typical OHC cover seals.

FIGURE 13–34 Intake manifold end strip seals.

FIGURE 13–35 Typical EGR valve gaskets. *Courtesy of Fel-Pro, Inc.*

held together with large mounting bolts. The construction of each gasket matches its sealing requirement. Choose the correct gasket or sealing material to ensure that proper sealing is achieved.

Some overhead cam engines, for example, have solid, one-piece cam bearings and cam bearing supports. It is necessary to have a semicircular notch in the front and back of the head for machining the cam bearing bore or saddle at the factory (Figure 13–33). The notch is sealed with molded synthetic rubber semicircular plugs. These plugs can deteriorate in time, taking a set. They should be replaced anytime a cam cover gasket is replaced.

Most gasket sets for V-type engines include manifold end strip seals. They seal the joint between the manifold ends and the block (Figure 13–34). Molded rubber and cork/rubber are materials often used for end strip seals. Some have self-adhesive backings to aid in installation. The corner joints where the end strip seals meet the intake manifold gaskets should be sealed with a small amount of RTV silicone. This ensures a complete seal all around the manifold.

The exhaust gas recirculation (EGR) valve recirculates some of the exhaust gases back into the engine, reducing NO_x emissions by lowering the combustion temperature. The EGR valve gasket (Figure 13–35) seals the valve and, in some applications, regulates the flow of exhaust by a specifically sized hole in the gasket. Choosing the correct gasket for this application is critical because a one-size-fits-all gasket could change the exhaust gas flow and, as a result, change the performance of the engine.

The carburetor mounting gasket, located between the carburetor and the manifold, prevents vacuum and fuel leaks. It also helps to insulate the carburetor from the heat of the engine. Most of these gaskets are equipped with ferrules at the bolt holes, which help

prevent carburetor base distortion. Distortion could damage the casting, as well as cause the throttle plates to bind or cause fuel leaks. Spacers are used in some engine applications for emission control systems or heat insulation for the carburetor. The carburetor spacer is located between the carburetor and the manifold, with the space gasket mounted underneath the spacer.

Many overhead cam (OHC) engine designs allow replacement of individual seals at the front of the engine. Figure 13–36 illustrates the typical timing sealing arrangement. Although it might save money to purchase only the parts that are needed, most technicians replace all of them.

FIGURE 13–36 Typical OHC timing cover gasket arrangement.

ENGINE REASSEMBLY

When reassembling an engine, the assembly sequence is essentially the reverse of the tear-down sequence outlined in a previous chapter. Details for assembling the major engine parts can be found in the chapters covering that part. It should be noted that some technicians prefer to install the camshaft before installing ▓▓▓haft in pushrod-type engines.

F▓▓ ▓eassembly Steps

T▓▓ ▓eps in final engine assembly involve installing va▓▓us engine covers and installing manifolds and related items that mount directly to the engine assembly.

IN▓TALL THE TIMING COVER When replacing the timing cover, remove the old gaskets and seals from the timing cover and engine block. If the timing cover extends over the front lip of the oil pan, the front portion of the oil pan gasket will be exposed. With a sharp knife or razor blade, carefully cut off the front exposed portion of the oil pan gasket.

Install the new seal using a press, seal driver, or hammer and a clean block of wood (Figure 13–37). When installing the seal, be sure to support the cover underneath to prevent damage. apply a light coating of adhesive on the timing cover and position the gasket on the cover. Some manufacturers recommend a sealant be used on both surfaces. Check the service manual and gasket instructions. Finally, mount the timing cover and torque the bolts to specifications.

INSTALL THE VIBRATION DAMPER Install the vibration damper (harmonic balancer) by carefully pounding on it, or using a special installation tool. In most cases, the damper is installed until it bottoms out against the oil slinger and the timing sprocket. If

FIGURE 13–38 When checking the valve cover for flatness, a hammer can be used to tap down any distorted bolt holes. *Courtesy of Fel-Pro, Inc.*

in doubt, install the water pump and pulley and pound the damper into place until its pulley aligns with the water pump pulley. It is advisable to use the installation tool, because pounding on the damper can cause stress on the crank thrust bearing surface. It is best to stand the engine block on end and support the crankshaft if the damper must be pounded on.

Some vibration dampers are not pressed-fit on the crankshaft. Be sure to install the large washer behind the damper-retaining bolt on these engines. Otherwise, the damper might fly off, causing damage and a safety hazard.

INSTALL THE VALVE COVER To install the valve cover, first make sure the cover's sealing flange is flat (Figure 13–38), then apply contact adhesive to the valve cover's sealing surfaces in small dabs. Mount the valve cover gasket on the valve cover and align it in position. If the gasket has mounting tabs, use them in tandem with the contact adhesive. Allow the adhesive to dry completely before mounting the valve cover on the cylinder head. Torque the mounting bolts to specifications.

SHOP TALK

Many technicians install the water pump at this point or wait until the engine is back in the vehicle. When installing a water pump, apply a coating of good waterproof sealer to a new gasket and place it in position on the water pump. Coat the other side of the gasket with sealer and position the pump against the engine block until it is properly seated. Install the mounting bolts and tighten them with a torque wrench in a staggered sequence to specifications. Careless tightening could cause the pump housing to crack. After tightening, check the pump to make sure it rotates freely. ■

FIGURE 13–37 Installing an oil seal into a timing cover. *Courtesy of Fel-Pro, Inc.*

FIGURE 13–39 Using an electric drill to prelubricate an engine. *Courtesy of Perfect Circle/Dana*

Prelubrication Check

There are several ways to prelubricate, or prime, an engine. One method is to drive the oil pump with an electric drill. With most engines, it is possible to make a drive that can be chucked in an electric drill motor to engage the drive on the oil pump. Insert the fabricated oil pump drive extension into the oil pump through the distributor drive hole. Drive the oil pump with the electric drill (Figure 13–39). To control oil splash, loosely set the valve cover(s) on the engine. After running the oil pump for several minutes, remove the valve cover and see whether there is any oil flow to the rocker arms. If oil reached the cylinder head, the engine's lubrication system is full of oil and is operating properly. If no oil reached the cylinder head, there is a problem either with the pump, with an alignment of an oil hole in a bearing, or perhaps a plugged gallery.

⚠ WARNING!

A great deal of care must be taken when using an electric drill to prime an engine. A speed that is too fast could damage the oil pump. ■

Using a **prelubricator** (Figure 13–40), which consists of an oil reservoir attached to a continuous air supply, is the best method of prelubricating an engine without running it. When the reservoir is attached to the engine and the air pressure turned on, the prelubricator will supply the engine's lubrication system with oil under pressure.

The engine prelubricator also checks the effectiveness of the engine repairs by showing the amount of leakage through the bearings. If the prelubrication check indicates the overhaul was performed properly, continue with final reassembly.

FIGURE 13–40 Priming an engine with a prelubricator. *Courtesy of Federal Mogul Corporation*

FIGURE 13–41 Straightening distorted oil pan flanges. *Courtesy of AE Clevite Engine Parts*

INSTALL OIL PAN Before installing the oil pan gasket, check the flanges for warpage. Use a straightedge or lay the pan, flange side down, on a flat surface with a flashlight underneath it to spot uneven edges. Carefully check the flange around bolt holes. Minor distortions can be corrected with a hammer and block of wood (Figure 13–41). If the flanges are too bent to be repaired in this manner, the pan should be replaced. Once it has been determined that the flanges are flat, install the oil pan with a new gasket. Finally, fill the engine with the proper grade oil.

INSTALL INTAKE MANIFOLD The intake manifold gasket seals the joint between the intake manifold and the cylinder head. To be sure the gasket will seal, check its fit (Figure 13–42). This will ensure proper sealing of the manifold. On steel shim-type gaskets, it is necessary to put a thin and even coat of positioning sealer around the vacuum port openings and a small bead of RTV silicone around the coolant openings. Install the intake manifold with a new gasket and tighten the fastening bolts to the recommended torque specification.

INSTALL THE THERMOSTAT AND WATER OUTLET HOUSING In frost-free areas of the country, some people neglect their cooling systems and do not use coolant. Many of today's automobiles have

FIGURE 13–42 Checking for proper fit of the intake manifold gasket. *Courtesy of Fel-Pro, Inc.*

aluminum heads and must be run with anticorrosion additives, like those found in coolant. Aluminum water outlet housings are not very durable when used with water alone. Install the thermostat with the temperature sensor facing into the block. If the thermostat is installed upside down, the engine will overheat.

CUSTOMER CARE

Advise the customer about the need to change coolant every two years. Stress the importance of the anticorrosion additives in coolant. ■

INSTALL THE FUEL PUMP Most engines are equipped with an electric fuel pump. However, many older engines use mechanical pumps. If the engine has a mechanical pump, install the pump with its gasket. Prior to installation, turn the engine over until the fuel pump eccentric is at its lowest position in relation to the pump. Failure to do this makes it difficult to install the pump. Then tighten the pump's attaching bolts.

PAINT THE ENGINE A good paint job is an important part of a professional engine overhaul. It is easier to paint the engine when it is completely assembled. Exhaust manifolds should not be painted, so paint the engine before they are installed. Apply a thin layer of grease to exhaust gasket surfaces and carburetor or throttle plate gasket surfaces. This makes it easier to remove the paint from these areas. Spray one light coat of paint. Wait until it becomes tacky to the touch, and then spray the second coat. Spraying the second coat after the first coat becomes tacky will prevent runs and give better paint coverage.

SPIN TEST THE ENGINE If one is available, use a run-on stand to spin test rebuilt engines following assembly. The engine is spun at 600 rpm with oil pressure. Major problems can be spotted using this tester. Compression and oil pressure can be checked. Cam, rod, and main bearings can be visually checked for excessive bearing oil leakage. Valve adjustment can be performed. And, lifter rotation can be checked.

When a dynamometer is used for spin testing, break in the engine at 10 percent load. When running an engine on a dyno at high rpm, a remote control should be used so the operator will not be injured if an engine part should fail.

INSTALL EXHAUST MANIFOLD After the block assembly is painted, install the exhaust manifold(s). Tighten the bolts in the center of the manifold first to prevent cracking it. If there are dowel holes in the exhaust manifold that align with dowels in the cylinder head, make sure these holes are larger than the dowels. If the dowels do not have enough clearance because of the buildup of foreign material, the manifold will not be able to expand properly, and may crack. Tighten the individual manifold-to-engine bolts first. Then, tighten the bolts where the two parts meet. Some in-line engines use a combined intake and exhaust manifold gasket.

INSTALL FLYWHEEL OR FLEX PLATE Reinstall the engine sling. Raise the engine into the air on a suitable lift, and remove the engine stand mounting head. Set the assembled engine on the floor and support it with blocks of wood while attaching the flywheel or flex plate. Be sure to use the right flywheel bolts and lock washers. These bolts have very thin heads and the lock washers are thin. If normal bolts or washers are used, they may cause interference with the clutch disc or the torque converter. Make sure the bolts are properly torqued.

INSTALL CLUTCH PARTS If the vehicle has a manual transmission, install the clutch. Make sure the transmission's pilot bushing or bearing is in place in the rear of the crankshaft and it is in good condition. If the bushing must be removed, use a puller. To remove a pilot bearing, pack the cavity behind the bearing with grease, then insert the largest bolt that will fit into the ID of the bearing. Pound on the bolt to force out the bearing.

Using a clutch-aligning tool, or an old transmission input shaft, align the clutch disc. Then, tighten the disc and clutch pressure plate to the flywheel. Make sure the disc is installed in the right direction. There should be a marking on it that says flywheel side. Then install the bell housing if it was removed from the transmission.

INSTALL TORQUE CONVERTER On cars equipped with automatic transmissions, it is a good practice to replace the transmission's front pump seal. If the transmission was removed from the car with the engine, reinstall it on the engine now.

Install the torque converter, making sure it is correctly engaged with the transmission's front pump. The drive lugs on the converter should be felt engaging the transmission front pump gear. Failure to correctly install the converter can result in damage to the transmission's front pump.

INSTALL MOTOR MOUNTS The motor mount bolts may now be installed loosely on the block. The bolts are left loose during engine installation so the mounts can be easily aligned with the front mount brackets. Make sure the mounts are in good condition.

INSTALLING THE ENGINE

Installing a computer-controlled engine into the engine compartment of a front-wheel-drive vehicle can be a complex task requiring special procedures. Very often engine system specialists may be needed to perform the various tasks involved in the installation of a rebuilt engine.

The *Tech Manual* that accompanies this textbook outlines the general procedures for engine installation. Referring to the vehicle's service manual is absolutely essential for this procedure.

Starting Procedure

Set the valves and ignition timing as accurately as possible before starting the engine. The engine can be fine-tuned after it has been started and goes through the **break-in** test by using an engine analyzer or diagnostic tester. However, it is wise to time the ignition distributor before attempting to start the engine even though it is not the final adjustment.

CAUTION:

An engine that is not in correct time might backfire when it is first started. If this happens when there is a fuel leak, a fire might start and cause burns. Also, be sure to connect the exhaust pipe's ventilation system to prevent a dangerous buildup of carbon monoxide when the engine is running. ■

To adjust the ignition distributor, mark the crankshaft pulley notch or TDC mark an the timing cover pointer on the TDC mark with a dab of white paint. Turn the crankshaft until the number 1 piston, coming up on the compression stroke, aligns the TDC

mark with the pulley or pointer. Watch the rocker arms or valves on the number 1 cylinder. TDC on the compression stroke is just after the intake valve closes and before the exhaust valve opens. Install the distributor with the rotor pointing to the mark on its body that indicates number 1 position. It might be necessary to turn the rotor about 15 degrees away from the mark and wiggle the rotor slightly to engage the intermediate drive shaft or oil pump drive. Once the distributor base slides into solid contact with the block or manifold mounting, align the reference marks and tighten the mounting bolt slightly. You will have to check the ignition timing later, so do not completely tighten at this time.

USING SERVICE MANUALS

Ignition timing specifications and the guidelines for setting timing are given in the tuneup specification section of the service manual. ■

When the engine is in time, fill the gasoline tank with several gallons of fresh gasoline. Have an associate crank the engine. It will take some time for fuel to be pumped from the tank to the engine if the car has a mechanical fuel pump. When the engine gets fuel, it will try to start. Once it does start, set the throttle to an engine speed of approximately 1,500 rpm. When the engine coolant reaches normal operating temperature, turn off the engine. Recheck all adjustments, ignition timing, and valve clearance. Look for signs of coolant or oil leaks. After these checks, run the engine at fast idle during the warm-up period to ensure adequate initial lubrication for the piston rings, pistons, and camshaft.

Break-In Procedure

To prevent engine damage after it has been rebuilt or completely overhauled and to ensure good initial oil control and long engine life, the proper break-in procedure must be followed. Make a test run at 30 mph and accelerate at full throttle to 50 mph. Repeat the acceleration cycle from 30 to 50 mph at least ten times. No further break-in is necessary. If traffic conditions will not permit this procedure, accelerate the engine rapidly several times through the intermediate gears during the road test. The objective is to apply a load to the engine for short periods of time and in rapid succession soon after the engine warms up. This action thrusts the piston rings against the cylinder wall with increased pressure and results in accelerated ring seating.

CUSTOMER CARE

After the engine has been totally checked over, return it to the owner with the following instructions:

1. Drive the vehicle normally but avoid sustained high speed during the first 500 miles (break-in period).
2. Check the oil level frequently during the break-in period. It is not unusual to use 1 or 2 quarts of oil during this time.
3. The oil and oil filter will need to be changed at the end of the break-in time.
4. The cylinder head and intake manifold bolts may need to be retorqued.
5. Some adjustments, such as valve adjustments and ignition timing, will also need to be checked. ■

CASE STUDY

A car with a four-cylinder OHC engine is towed back to the shop. It was recently in the shop because of overheating. The head was milled and a new head gasket installed. This time, the engine will not run. The technician attempts to start the engine and finds that it turns over faster than normal. Black powder is discovered on the timing belt cover and the front of the engine during a visual inspection. The powder is obviously from the timing belt. The timing belt cover is removed to examine the belt. More than half of the teeth are worn off.

A new belt was installed when the head gasket was replaced. Therefore, it is unlikely that the belt has failed on its own. To determine the cause of the failure, attempts are made to turn the camshaft. Only with a great amount of effort would the camshaft turn. This explains why the belt is worn. The worn belt explains why the engine turns over faster than normal with the starter motor.

To determine what has caused the camshaft to be so hard to turn, the cam cover is removed. There is no sign of oil around the camshaft or followers. Both the camshaft and followers have a blue tint to them, indicating they had been overheated. The technician remembers the oil pressure was checked after the head was reinstalled and it was good. Why is there no oil to the camshaft now? After removing the timing belt, oil pressure was

again checked by cranking the engine with the starter motor. Oil pressure is still good.

Still not sure of the cause of the problem, the technician removes the head to visually inspect the valve train and oil passages. During disassembly, the head gasket is inspected, and the cause of the problem is discovered. The gasket has been blocking off an oil feed hole from the engine block to the cylinder head. During the original repair, the technician failed to check the gasket against the block surface. Blocking this oil feed prevented oil from flowing into the cylinder head. This resulted in damage to the cam bearings and caused the problem.

The technician apologizes to the customer and explains what has gone wrong. The correct head gasket and new camshaft, cam bearings, followers, and timing belt are installed. This corrects the problem.

KEY TERMS

Adhesives	Graphite
Aerobic	Hylomar
Anaerobic	Pitch gauge
Antiseize	Polyacrylate
Asbestos	Prelubricator
Bimetal	RTV
Bolt diameter	Sealants
Bolt head	Silicone gasketing
Bolt shank	Thread pitch
Break-in	Torque-angle
Elasticity	T-T-Y
Fillet	Viton
Gasket	Yield
Grade marks	

SUMMARY

◆ Threaded fasteners, including bolts, nuts, and screws, allow easy installation and removal of parts. It is very important to be familiar with bolt sizes and markings. Likewise, nuts are graded to match their respective bolts.

◆ Elasticity means a bolt can be stretched a certain amount and, when the stretching load is reduced, return to its original size. Yield means a stretched bolt takes a permanent set and never returns to normal. Proper use of torque will prevent a yield condition.

◆ When threads inside a block or head are stripped, they can be replaced by the use of threaded inserts. While several types are available, the helically coiled insert is the most popular.

◆ Gaskets serve as sealers, spacers, wear insulators, and vibration dampeners. Engine gaskets are generally classified as either hard or soft. Today's gaskets are specifically designed to seal the new engine designs, and thus must cope with severe temperature and pressure stresses.

◆ General recommendations for installing gaskets include the following: never reuse old ones; handle new ones carefully, especially the composition-type; use sealants properly; thoroughly clean all mating surfaces; and use the right gasket in the right position.

◆ Cylinder head gaskets on today's bimetal engines have a demanding job. The no-retorque head gasket retains a high level of clamping force. A good way to check the effectiveness of a head gasket seal is with a carbon impression test.

◆ Contact adhesive bonds cork, rubber, fiber, and metal gaskets in place. It does not aid in sealing. Its only purpose is to hold the gasket securely during component assembly.

◆ General-purpose sealers aid in gasket sealing without upsetting the designed performance of most mechanical gaskets. Hard-drying sealants, such as shellac, should never be used on gaskets because they will make future disassembly very difficult.

◆ Flexible sealant is often used on bolt threads that go into fluid passages. Silicone gasketing, of which RTV is the best known, is used on oil pans, valve covers, thermostat housing, timing covers, and water pumps. Anaerobic formed-in-place sealants are used for both thread locking and gasketing.

◆ Oil seals keep oil and other vital fluids from escaping around a rotating shaft. Oil seals should always be replaced on re-ring or overhaul jobs to ensure against costly do-overs.

◆ The steps in final engine assembly involve installing various engine covers, prelubing the engine, and installing manifolds and related items that mount directly to the engine assembly. The best method of prelubricating an engine under pressure without running it is to use a prelubricator, which consists of an oil reservoir attached to a continuous air supply.

◆ Whenever possible, use a run-on stand to spin test a rebuilt engine following assembly. This can detect problems in major areas such as compression and oil pressure.

◆ Time the ignition before attempting to start a reassembled engine. This will prevent backfire. Be sure to connect the exhaust pipe's ventilation system to prevent a dangerous buildup of carbon monoxide.

◆ A proper break-in procedure is necessary to ensure good initial oil contact and long engine life. Make a test run at 30 mph and accelerate at full throttle to 50 mph. Repeat this acceleration cycle from 30 to 50 mph at least ten times to achieve accelerated ring seating.

TECH MANUAL

The following procedures are included in Chapter 13 of the *Tech Manual* that accompanies this book:

1. Apply RTV silicone sealant.
2. Adjust valves on an OHC engine.

REVIEW QUESTIONS

1. How is bolt length measured?

2. What does it mean when a bolt is stretched into yield?

3. Name some applications of hard gaskets.

4. Where are flexible sealers most often used?

5. What are the major differences between aerobic and anaerobic sealants?

6. Which of the following performs the vital task of sealing the engine?
   a. gaskets   **c.** fasteners
   b. seals   **d.** all of the above

7. Technician A uses an impact wrench to tighten all non-critical bolts. Technician B uses a torque wrench to tighten all bolts that have a torque specification. Who is correct?
   a. Technician A   **c.** Both A and B
   b. Technician B   **d.** Neither A nor B

8. Which of the following statements is incorrect?
   a. All metals are elastic.
   b. Proper use of torque will avoid a yield condition.
   c. Torque is a function of friction.
   d. Cut bolt threads are 30 percent stronger than rolled threads.

9. Technician A uses adhesives to hold gaskets in place while installing them. Technician B uses RTV sealant on all surfaces that are prone to leaks. Who is correct?
   a. Technician A   c. Both A and B
   b. Technician B   d. Neither A nor B

10. Technician A uses soft gaskets on valve covers. Technician B uses soft gaskets on water pumps. Who is correct?
    a. Technician A   c. Both A and B
    b. Technician B   d. Neither A nor B

11. Technician A says two extremely smooth surfaces do not require gaskets or sealants when they are fastened together. Technician B always uses new gaskets and never reuses old ones. Who is correct?
    a. Technician A   c. Both A and B
    b. Technician B   d. Neither A nor B

12. Which gasket is one of the most ignored on an engine?
    a. valve cover   c. exhaust manifold
    b. cylinder head   d. oil pan

13. Technician A uses chemical thread retainers on critical bolts and nuts. Technician B says chemical thread retainers cannot be used as a substitute for lock washers. Who is correct?
    a. Technician A   c. Both A and B
    b. Technician B   d. Neither A nor B

14. Hylomar is ____.
    a. an anaerobic   c. both a and b
    b. an RTV   d. neither a nor b

15. Which of the following statements is incorrect?
    a. In a pushrod-type engine, the camshaft can be installed prior to the crankshaft.
    b. Some vibration dampeners are not pressed-fit on the crankshaft.
    c. Most gasket sets for V-type engines include manifold end strip seals.
    d. Wick- or rope-type packing rear main bearing seals are common on late-model engines.

16. Coolant should be changed ____.
    a. once a year   c. every three years
    b. every two years   d. every five years

17. Technician A spray paints the engine assembly after it is completely assembled. Technician B puts grease on the exhaust and intake ports before painting the engine. Who is correct?
    a. Technician A   c. Both A and B
    b. Technician B   d. Neither A nor B

18. After assembling and installing an engine, when is it best to time the ignition distributor?
    a. after the engine has been run a few minutes
    b. after the vehicle has been driven a few miles
    c. immediately following proper break-in
    d. before starting the engine

19. When replacing fasteners. Technician A uses harder bolts and nuts than were used by the OEM. Technician B uses washers on all bolts and nuts. Who is correct?
    a. Technician A   c. Both A and B
    b. Technician B   d. Neither A nor B

20. The proper engine break-in procedure is a test run at ____.
    a. 30 mph
    b. 10 mph and acceleration to 30 mph
    c. highway speed
    d. 30 mph and acceleration to 50 mph

SECTION 3

ELECTRICITY

The electrical system is perhaps the most important support system of a car or truck. Without an electrical system, gasoline engines would not run. Electricity provides the needed spark for combustion, plus the power needed for starting, lighting and signaling, instrumentation, safety devices, and many other accessories. Advances made in the field of electronics and brought into the automotive industry have allowed our vehicles to be more efficient. Technicians need to be able to diagnose and service both electrical and electronic systems. Although test equipment can simplify working with these systems, understanding electrical principles, component operation, circuit design, and testing procedures is absolutely necessary to be successful as an automotive technician.

The material covered in Section 3 matches the content areas of the ASE certification test on Electrical Systems.

WE ENCOURAGE
PROFESSIONALISM

THROUGH TECHNICIAN
CERTIFICATION

BASICS OF ELECTRICAL SYSTEMS

14

OBJECTIVES

◆ **Define the terms normally used to describe electricity.** ◆ **Use Ohm's law to determine voltage, current, and resistance.** ◆ **List the basic types of electrical circuits.** ◆ **Describe the differences between a series and a parallel circuit.** ◆ **Name the various electrical components and their uses in electrical circuits.** ◆ **Describe the different kinds of automotive wiring.** ◆ **Read electrical automotive diagrams.** ◆ **Describe how each of the major types of electrical test equipment are connected and interpreted.** ◆ **Perform troubleshooting procedures using meters, testlights, and jumper wires.** ◆ **Explain the principles of magnetism and electromagnetism.**

Understanding electrical components and their operation is absolutely essential to properly servicing today's cars and trucks. Although some electrical basics were presented in an earlier chapter, these will be repeated and expanded upon. Repeating some of these facts emphasizes the importance of this knowledge.

BASICS OF ELECTRICITY

Perhaps the one reason why some people find it difficult to understand electricity is that they cannot see it. By actually knowing what it is and what it is *not*, you can easily understand it. Electricity is not magic! It is something that takes place or can take place in everything you know. It not only provides power for lights, TVs, stereos, and refrigerators, it is also the basis for the communications between our brain and the rest of our bodies. Although electricity cannot be seen, the effects of it can be seen, felt, heard, and smelled. One of the most common displays of electricity is a lightning bolt. Lightning is electricity, a large amount of electricity. The power of lightning is incredible. Using the power from much smaller amounts of electricity to perform some work is the basis for an automobile's electrical system. Electricity cannot be seen because it results from the movement of extremely small objects that move at the speed of light (669,600,000 miles per hour).

Flow of Electricity

All things are made up of atoms (Figure 14–1), which are extremely small particles. In the center of every atom is a nucleus. The nucleus contains positively charged particles called protons and particles called neutrons that have no charge. Negatively charged particles called electrons orbit around every nucleus. The electrons stay in orbit around the nucleus because they are naturally attracted to the protons. Every type of atom has a different number of protons and electrons, but the number of protons and electrons in each atom is equal. Therefore, the total electrical charge of an atom is zero, or neutral.

Electricity is the flow of electrons from one atom to another (Figure 14–2). The release of energy as one electron leaves the orbit of one atom and jumps into the orbit of another is electrical energy. The key

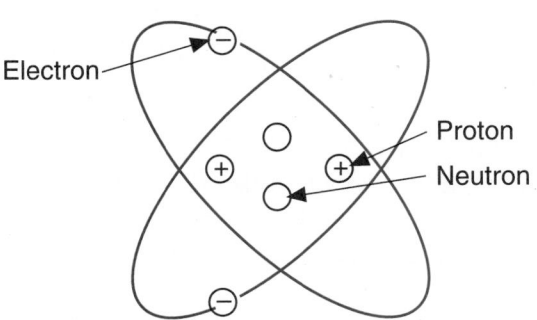

FIGURE 14–1 Basic structure of an atom.

Conductor

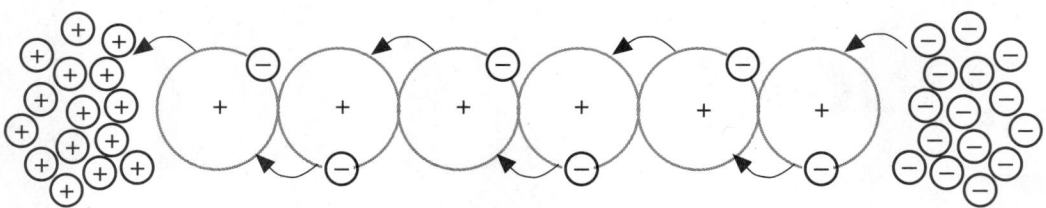

FIGURE 14–2   Electricity is the flow of electrons from one atom to another.

to creating electricity is to provide a reason for the electrons to move to another atom.

There is a natural attraction of electrons to protons. Electrons have a negative charge and are attracted to something with a positive charge. When an electron leaves the orbit of an atom, the atom then has a positive charge. An electron moves from one atom to another because the atom next to it appears to be more positive than the one it is orbiting around.

An electrical power source provides for a more positive charge and to allow for a continuous flow of electricity, it supplies free electrons. To have a continuous flow of electricity, three things must be present: an excess of electrons in one place, a lack of electrons in another place, and a path between the two places.

Two power or energy sources are used in an automobile's electrical system. These are based on a chemical reaction and magnetism. A car's battery is a source of chemical energy. A chemical reaction in the battery provides for an excess of electrons and a lack of electrons in another place. Batteries have two terminals, a positive and a negative. Basically, the negative terminal is the outlet for the electrons and the positive terminal is the inlet for the electrons to get to the protons. The chemical reaction in a battery causes a lack of electrons at the positive (+) terminal and an excess at the negative (–) terminal. This creates an electrical imbalance, causing the electrons to flow through the path provided by a wire.

The chemical process in the battery continues to provide electrons until the chemicals become weak. At that time, either the battery has run out of electrons or all the protons are matched with an electron. When this happens, there is no longer a reason for the electrons to want to move to the positive side of the battery. To the electrons, it no longer looks more positive. Fortunately, the vehicle's charging system restores the battery's supply of electrons. This allows the chemical reaction in the battery to continue indefinitely. In an electrical diagram, a battery is drawn as shown in Figure 14–3.

Electricity and magnetism are interrelated. One can be used to produce the other. Moving a wire (a

FIGURE 14–3   Symbol for a battery.

conductor) through an already existing magnetic field (such as a permanent magnet) can produce electricity. This process of producing electricity through magnetism is called induction. In a generator, a coil of wire is moved through a magnetic field. In an alternator, a magnetic field is moved through a coil of wire. In both cases, electricity is produced. The amount of electricity produced depends on a number of factors, including the strength of the magnetic field, the number of wires that pass through the field, and the speed at which the wire moves through the magnetic field.

ELECTRICAL TERMS

Electrical current describes the movement or flow of electricity. The greater the number of electrons flowing past a given point in a given amount of time, the more current the circuit has. The unit for measuring electrical current is the ampere, usually called an amp. The instrument used to measure electrical current flow in a circuit is called an ammeter.

In the flow of electricity, millions of electrons are moving past any given point at the speed of light. The electrical charge of any one electron is extremely small. It takes millions of electrons to make a charge that can be measured. For these reasons, 1 ampere of current means that 6.28 billion billion electrons are flowing past a given point in 1 second.

There are two types of current: direct current (DC) and alternating current (AC). In direct current, the electrons flow in one direction only. In alternating current, the electrons change direction at a fixed rate. Typically, an automobile uses DC while the current in homes and buildings is AC. Some components of the automobile generate or use AC. These will be discussed in later chapters.

Although there are many theories about current and the direction in which it flows, it is correct to base your understanding on current flowing from a

FIGURE 14–4 Current moves from a point of higher potential to a point of lower potential.

FIGURE 14–5 Common symbol for an ohm.

point of positive voltage to a point of less positive, or negative, voltage (Figure 14–4).

Voltage is electrical pressure. It is the force developed by the attraction of the electrons to protons. The more positive one side of the circuit is, the more voltage is present in the circuit. Voltage does not flow; it is the pressure that causes current flow. To have current flow, some force is needed to move the electrons between atoms. This force is the pressure that exists between a positive and negative point within an electrical circuit. This force, also called electromotive force (EMF), is measured in units called volts. One volt is the amount of pressure required to move 1 ampere of current through a resistance of 1 ohm. Voltage is measured by an instrument called a voltmeter.

When any substance flows, it meets resistance. The resistance to electrical flow can be measured. The resistance to current flow produces heat. This heat can be measured to determine the amount of resistance. A unit of measured resistance is called an ohm. The common symbol for an ohm is shown in Figure 14–5. Resistance can be measured by an instrument called an ohmmeter. Differing amounts of resistance are measured by changing scales (such as × 1, × 10, × 100) on the ohmmeter.

Circuit Terminology

An electrical circuit is considered complete when there is a path that connects the positive and negative terminals of the electrical power source. A completed circuit is called a **closed circuit**, whereas an incomplete circuit is called an **open circuit**. When a circuit is complete, it is said to have **continuity**. Conductors are drawn in electrical diagrams as a line connecting two points, as shown in Figure 14–6.

Most automotive electrical circuits use the chassis as the path from the negative side of the battery.

FIGURE 14–6 Conductors are drawn as lines from one point to another.

FIGURE 14–7 Symbols for grounds: (A) made through the component's mounting; (B) made by a remote wire.

Electrical components have a lead that connects them to the chassis. These are called the chassis ground connections. These connections can be made through a wire or through the mounting of the component. Chassis ground connections are drawn to show which type of connection is normal for that part (Figure 14–7). When the ground is made through the mounting of the component, the connection is represented with the drawing A. When the ground is made by a wire that connects to the chassis, the connection is shown as B.

In a complete circuit, the flow of electricity can be controlled and applied to do useful work, such as light a headlamp or turn over a starter motor. Components that use electrical power put a load on the circuit and consume electrical energy. These components are often referred to as electrical loads. Loads are drawn in electrical diagrams as a symbol representing the part or as a resistor. The typical drawing of a resistor is shown in Figure 14–8.

The amount of current that flows in a circuit is determined by the resistance in that circuit. As resistance goes up, the current goes down. The total resistance in a circuit determines how much current will flow through the circuit. The energy used by a load is measured in volts. Amperage stays constant in a circuit but the voltage is dropped as it powers a load. Measuring voltage drop tells how much energy is being consumed by the load.

Ohm's Law

Hundreds of years ago, a scientist studied electricity and the interrelationship of the key elements of electricity. He found it takes one volt of electrical pressure to push one ampere of electrical current through one ohm of resistance. This statement is the basic law of electricity. It is known as **Ohm's law**.

A simple electrical circuit is a load connected to a voltage source by conductors. The resistor could be a fog light, the voltage source could be a battery, and the conductor could be a copper wire (Figure 14–9).

In any electrical circuit, current (I), resistance (R), and voltage (E) work together in a mathematical relationship. This relationship is expressed in a mathematical statement of Ohm's law. Ohm's law can be applied to the entire circuit or to any part of a circuit.

FIGURE 14–8 Symbol for a resistor.

FIGURE 14–9 A simple circuit consists of a voltage source, conductors, and a resistance or load.

When any two factors are known, the third factor can be found by using Ohm's law. Using the circle shown in Figure 14–10, you can easily find the formula for calculating the unknown element. By covering the element you need to find, the necessary formula is shown in the circle.

To find voltage, cover the *E* (Figure 14–11). The voltage (E) in a circuit is equal to the current (I) in amperes multiplied by the resistance (R) in ohms.

To find current, cover the *I* (Figure 14–12). The current (amperage) in a circuit equals the voltage divided by the resistance (in ohms).

FIGURE 14–10 Ohm's law.

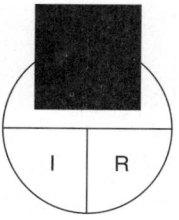

FIGURE 14–11 To find voltage, cover the *E* and use the exposed formula.

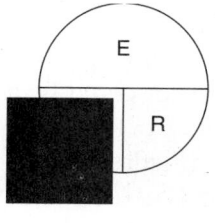

FIGURE 14–12 To find current, cover the *I* and use the exposed formula.

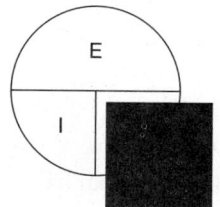

FIGURE 14–13 To find resistance, cover the *R* and use the exposed formula.

To find resistance, cover the *R* (Figure 14–13). The resistance of a circuit (in ohms) equals the voltage divided by the current (in amperes).

It is very important for technicians to understand Ohm's law. It explains how an increase or decrease in voltage, resistance, or current will affect a circuit.

For example, if the fog light in Figure 14–9 has a 6-ohm resistance, how many amperes does it use to operate? Since cars and light trucks have a 12-volt battery and you know two of the factors in the fog light circuit, it is simple to solve for the third.

$$I \text{ (unknown)} = \frac{E \text{ (12 volts)}}{R \text{ (6 ohms)}}$$

$$I = \frac{12}{6}$$

$$I = 2 \text{ amperes}$$

In a clean, well-wired circuit, the fog lights will draw 2 amperes of current. What would happen if resistance in the circuit increases due to corroded or damaged wire or connections? If the corroded connections add 2 ohms of resistance to the fog light circuit, the total resistance is 8 ohms (Figure 14–14). The amount of current flowing through the circuit for the lights decreases.

$$I = \frac{12}{6+2} = \frac{12}{8}$$

$$I = 1.5 \text{ amperes}$$

If the lights are designed to operate at 2 amperes, this decrease to 1.5 amperes will cause them to burn dimly. Cleaning the corrosion away or installing new wires and connectors will eliminate the unwanted resistance; the correct amount of current will flow through the circuit, allowing the lamp to burn as brightly as it should.

Power

Electrical power, or the rate of work, is found by multiplying the amount of electrical pressure by the amount of current flow (power = voltage × amperage). Power is measured in watts. Although power

FIGURE 14–14 This is the same circuit as Figure 14–9, but this one has a corroded wire, represented by the additional resistor.

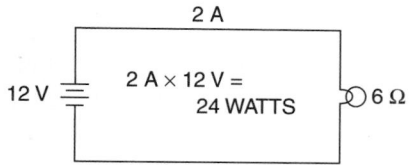

FIGURE 14–15 Electrical power is calculated by multiplying voltage by current.

measurements are rarely, if ever, needed in automotive service, knowing the power requirements of light bulbs, electric motors, and other components is sometimes useful when troubleshooting electrical systems.

Another useful formula is one used to find the power of an electrical circuit expressed in watts.

$$P = E \times I$$

That is, power (P) in watts equals the voltage (E) multiplied by the current (I) in amperes (Figure 14–15). This is known as Watt's law. Looking back at the example of the fog light circuit, we can calculate the amount of power used or heat generated by the fog light.

$$P = 12 \text{ volts} \times 2 \text{ amperes}$$
$$P = 24 \text{ watts}$$

The normal fog light generates 24 watts of power, while the corroded fog light circuit produces the following.

$$P = 12 \text{ volts} \times 1.5 \text{ amperes}$$
$$P = 18 \text{ watts}$$

This reduction in power or heat explains the decrease in bulb brightness.

CONDUCTORS AND INSULATORS

Controlling and routing the flow of electricity requires the use of materials known as conductors and insulators. **Conductors** are materials with a low resistance to the flow of current. If the number of electrons in the outer shell or ring of an atom is less than four, the force holding them in place is weak. The voltage needed to move these electrons and create current flow is relatively small. Most metals, such as copper, silver, and aluminum are excellent conductors.

When the number of electrons in the outer ring are greater than four, the force holding them in orbit is very strong and very high voltages are needed to move them. These materials are known as **insulators**. They resist the flow of current. Thermal plastics are the most common electrical insulators used today. They can resist heat, moisture, and corrosion without breaking down.

Wire insulation should always be in good condition. Broken, frayed, or damaged insulation that exposes live wires can allow current to flow to unwanted places. These conditions can also create a safety hazard. Replace all wires that have damaged insulation.

Copper wire is by far the most popular conductor used in automotive electrical systems. Wire wound inside electrical units, such as ignition coils and generators, usually has a very thin baked-on insulating coating. External wiring often is covered with a plastic-type insulating material that is highly resistant to environmental factors like heat, vibration, and moisture. Where flexibility is required, the copper wire will be made of a large number of very small strands of wire woven together.

The resistance of a uniform, circular copper wire depends on the length of the wire, the diameter of the wire, and the temperature of the wire. If the length is doubled, the resistance between the wire ends is doubled. The longer the wire, the greater the resistance. If the diameter of a wire is doubled, the resistance for any given length is cut in half. The larger the wire's diameter, the lower the resistance.

In any circuit, the smallest wire that will not cause excessive voltage drop is used to minimize cost.

The other important factor affecting the resistance of a copper wire is temperature. As the temperature increases, the resistance increases. The effects of temperature are very important in the design of electrical equipment. Excessive resistance caused by normal temperature increases can hurt the performance of the equipment.

Heat is developed in any wire carrying current because of the resistance in the wire. If the heat becomes excessive, the insulation will be damaged. Resistance occurs when electrons collide as current flows through the conductor. These collisions cause friction, which in turn generates heat.

Circuits

A complete electrical circuit exists when electrons flow along a path between two points. In a complete circuit, resistance must be low enough to allow the available voltage to push electrons between the two points. Most automotive circuits contain four basic parts.

1. Power sources, such as a battery or alternator that provides the energy needed to cause electron flow.
2. Conductors, such as copper wires that provide a path for current flow.
3. Loads, which are devices that use electricity to perform work, such as light bulbs, electric motors, or resistors.
4. Controllers, such as switches or relays that control or direct the flow of electrons.

There are also three basic types of circuits used in automotive electrical systems. They are series circuits, parallel circuits, and series-parallel circuits. Each circuit type has its own characteristics regarding amperage, voltage, and resistance.

Series Circuits A **series circuit** consists of one or more resistors connected to a voltage source with only one path for electron flow. For example, a simple series circuit consists of a resistor (2 ohms in this example) connected to a 12-volt battery (Figure 14–16A). The current can be determined by applying Ohm's law.

$$I = \frac{E}{R} = \frac{12}{2} = 6 \text{ amperes}$$

Another series circuit may contain a 2-ohm resistor and a 4-ohm resistor connected to a 12-volt battery (Figure 14–16B). The word *series* is given to a circuit in which the same amount of current is present throughout the circuit. The current that flows through one resistor also flows through other resistors in the circuit. As that amount of current leaves the battery, it flows through the conductor to the first resistor. At the resistor, some electrical energy or voltage is consumed as the current flows through it. The decreased amount of voltage is then applied to the next resistor as current flows to it. By the time the current is flowing in the conductor leading back to the battery, all voltage has been consumed. All of the source voltage available to the circuit is dropped by the resistors in the circuit.

In a series circuit, the total amount of resistance in the circuit is equal to the sum of all the individual resistors. In the circuit in Figure 14–16B, the total circuit resistance is 4 + 2 = 6 ohms. Based on Ohm's law, current is I = E/R = 12/6 = 2 amperes. In a series circuit, current is constant throughout the circuit. Therefore, 2 amps of current flows through the conductors and both resistors.

Ohm's law can be used to determine the voltage drop across parts of the circuit. For the 2-ohm resistor, E = IR = 2 × 2 = 4 volts. For the 4-ohm resistor, E = 2 x 4 = 8 volts. These values are called **voltage drops**. The sum of all voltage drops in a series circuit must equal the source voltage, or 4 + 8 = 12 volts.

An ammeter connected anywhere in this circuit will read 2 amperes, and a voltmeter connected across each of the resistors will read 4 volts and 8 volts, as shown in Figure 14–17.

All calculations for a series circuit work in the same way no matter how many resistors there are in series. Consider the circuit in Figure 14–18. This circuit has four resistors in series with each other. The total resistance is 12 ohms (5 ohms + 2 ohms + 4 ohms + 1 ohm). Using Ohm's law, we can see that the circuit current is 1 amp (I = E/R = 12/12 = 1 amp). We can also use Ohm's law to determine the voltage drop across each resistor in the circuit. For example, since the circuit current is 1 amp, 4 volts

FIGURE 14–17 Measuring the current and voltage drops in the circuit.

FIGURE 14–16 In a series circuit, the same amount of current flows through the entire circuit.

FIGURE 14–18 Values in the series circuit.

are dropped by the 4-ohm resistor (E = I × R = 1 amp × 4 ohms = 4 volts).

A series circuit is characterized by the following three facts.

1. The circuit's current is determined by the total amount of resistance in the circuit; it is constant throughout the circuit.
2. The voltage drops across each resistor are different if the resistance values are different.
3. The sum of the voltage drops equals the source voltage.

Parallel Circuits A **parallel circuit** provides two or more different paths for the current to flow through. Each path has separate resistors (loads) and can operate independently of the other paths. The different paths for current flow are commonly called the legs of a parallel circuit.

A parallel circuit is characterized by the following facts.

1. Total circuit resistance is always lower than the resistance of the leg with the lowest total resistance.
2. The current through each leg will be different if the resistance values are different.
3. The sum of the current on each leg equals the total circuit current.
4. The voltage applied to each leg of the circuit will be dropped across the legs if there are no loads in series with the parallel circuit.

Consider the circuit shown in Figure 14–19. Two 3-ohm resistors are connected to a 12-volt battery. The resistors are in parallel with each other, since the battery voltage (12 volts) is applied to each resistor and they have a common negative lead. The current through each resistor or leg, can be determined by applying Ohm's law. For the 3-ohm resistors, I = E/R = 12/3 = 4 amperes. Therefore, the total circuit current supplied by the battery is 4 + 4 = 8 amperes. Using Ohm's law, we find that 12 volts are dropped by both resistors (Figure 14–20).

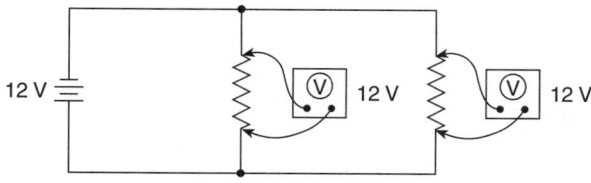

FIGURE 14–20 Parallel circuit with voltage drops shown.

Resistances are not added up to calculate the total resistance in a parallel circuit. Rather, they can be determined by dividing the product of their ohm value by the sum of their ohm values. This formula works when the circuit has two parallel legs.

$$\frac{3 \text{ ohms} \times 3 \text{ ohms}}{3 \text{ ohms} + 3 \text{ ohms}} = \frac{9}{6} = 1.5 \text{ ohms}$$

Total resistance can also be calculated by using Ohm's law if you know the total circuit current and the voltage (R = E/I = 12/8 = 1.5 ohms).

Consider another parallel circuit, Figure 14–21. In this circuit there are two legs and four resistors. Each leg has two resistors in series. One leg has a 4-ohm and a 2-ohm resistor. The total resistance on that leg is 6 ohms. The other leg has a 1-ohm and a 2-ohm resistor. The total resistance of that leg is 3 ohms. Therefore, we have 6 ohms in parallel with 3 ohms.

Current flow through the circuit can be calculated by different methods. Using Ohm's law, we know that I = E/R. If we take the total resistance of each leg and divide it into the voltage, we then know the current through that leg. Since total circuit current is equal to the sum of the current flows through each leg, we simply add the current across each leg together. This will give us total circuit current.

Leg #1: I = E/R = 12/6 = 2 amps
Leg #2: I = E/R = 12/3 = 4 amps
2 amps + 4 amps = 6 amps = total circuit current

Circuit current can also be determined by finding the total resistance of the circuit. To do this, the product-over-sum formula is used. By dividing this total into the voltage, total circuit current is known.

FIGURE 14–19 Simple parallel circuit.

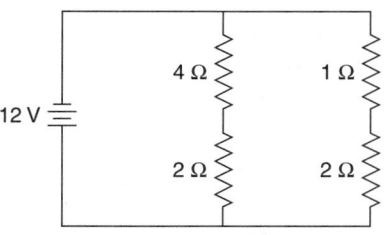

FIGURE 14–21 Series circuits within a parallel circuit.

$$\frac{\text{Leg \#1} \times \text{Leg \#2}}{\text{Leg \#1} + \text{Leg \#2}} = \frac{6 \times 3}{6 + 3} = \frac{18}{9} = 2 \text{ ohms}$$

since I = E/R, I = 12/2, I = 2 amps (total circuit current)

When a circuit has more than two legs, the reciprocal formula should be used to determine total circuit resistance. The formula follows.

$$\frac{1}{\dfrac{1}{R_1} + \dfrac{1}{R_2} + \dfrac{1}{R_3} + \dots \dfrac{1}{R_n}}$$

To demonstrate how to use this formula, consider the circuit in Figure 14–22. Here is a parallel circuit with four legs. The resistances across each leg are 4 ohms, 3 ohms, 6 ohms, and 4 ohms. Using the reciprocal formula, we will find that the total resistance of the circuit is 1 ohm. (Note that the total resistance is lower than the leg with the lowest resistance.)

$$\frac{1}{\dfrac{1}{4} + \dfrac{1}{3} + \dfrac{1}{6} + \dfrac{1}{4}} =$$

$$\frac{1}{\dfrac{3}{12} + \dfrac{4}{12} + \dfrac{2}{12} + \dfrac{3}{12}} = \frac{1}{\dfrac{12}{12}} = \frac{1}{1} = 1$$

The total of this circuit could also have been found by calculating the current across each leg then adding them together to get the total circuit current. Using Ohm's law, if you divide the voltage by the total circuit current, you will get total resistance.

Leg #1: I = E/R = 12/4 = 3 amps
Leg #2: I = E/R = 12/3 = 4 amps
Leg #3: I = E/R = 12/6 = 2 amps
Leg #4: I = E/R = 12/4 = 3 amps
Total circuit current = 3 + 4 + 2 + 3 = 12 amps

then,

R = E/I = 12/12 = 1 ohm

Series-Parallel Circuits In a **series-parallel circuit**, both series and parallel combinations exist in the same circuit.

FIGURE 14–22 Parallel circuit with four legs.

FIGURE 14–23 In a series-parallel circuit, the sum of the currents through the legs must equal the current through the series part of the circuit.

A series-parallel is illustrated in Figure 14–23. The 6- and 3-ohm resistors are in parallel with each other and together are in series with the 2-ohm resistor.

The total current in this circuit is equal to the voltage divided by the total resistance. The total resistance can be determined as follows. The 6- and 3-ohm parallel resistors in Figure 14–23 are equivalent to a 2-ohm resistor, since 6 × 3/6 + 3 = 2. This equivalent 2-ohm resistor is in series with the other 2-ohm resistor. To find the total resistance, add the two resistance values together. This gives a total circuit resistance of 4 ohms (2 + 2 = 4 ohms). The total current, therefore, is I = 12/4 = 3 amperes. This means that 3 amps of current is flowing through the 2-ohm resistor in series and 3 amps are divided between the resistors in parallel. In series-parallel circuits, the sum of the currents, flowing in the parallel legs, must equal that of the series resistors' current.

To find the current through each of the resistors in parallel, find the voltage drop across those resistors first. With 3 amperes flowing through the 2-ohm resistor, the voltage drop across this resistor is E = IR = 3 × 2 = 6 volts, leaving 6 volts across the 6- and 3-ohm resistors. The current through the 6-ohm resistor is I = E/R = 6/6 = 1 ampere, and through the 3-ohm resistor is I = 6/3 = 2 amperes. The sum of these two current values must equal the total circuit current and it does, 1 + 2 = 3 amperes (Figure 14–24). The sum of the voltage drops across the parallel part of the circuit and the series part must also equal source voltage.

FIGURE 14–24 The circuit in Figure 14–23 with voltage drops shown.

FIGURE 14–25 In most vehicles, the metal frame, engine block, or transmission case is used as a source of ground to complete the circuit back to the battery.

Grounding the Load

In the illustrations used to explain series, parallel, and series-parallel circuits, the return wire from the load or resistor connects directly to the negative terminal of the battery. If this were the case in an actual vehicle, there would be literally hundreds of wires connected to the negative battery terminal.

To avoid this, auto manufacturers use a wiring style that involves using the vehicle's metal frame components as part of the return circuit. Using the chassis as the negative wire is often referred to as **grounding**. The wire or metal mounting that serves as the contact to the chassis is commonly called the **ground wire** or lead. As shown in Figure 14–25, the load is grounded directly to the metal frame. The metal frame then acts as the return wire in the circuit. Current passes from the battery, through the load, and into the frame. The frame is connected to the negative terminal of the battery through the battery's ground wire.

An electrical component, such as an alternator, may be mounted directly to the engine block, transmission case, or frame. This direct mounting effectively grounds the component without the use of a separate ground wire. In other cases, however, a separate ground wire must be run from the component to the frame or another metal part to ensure a good connection for the return path. The increased use of plastics and other nonmetallic materials in body panels and engine parts has made electrical grounding more difficult. To ensure good grounding back to the battery, some manufacturers now use a network of common grounding terminals and wires (Figure 14–26).

LT LICENSE LAMP ASM

RT LICENSE LAMP ASM

CHMSL ASM

LEFT TAIL LAMP ASM

RIGHT TAIL LAMP ASM.

FUEL PUMP

CARGO LAMP — BLUB 906

RT BACK–UP LAMP ASM

LT BACK–UP LAMP ASM

155KK .50 BLK

155W .35 BLK

155V .35 BLK

155NN 1.0 BLK

155PP 2.0 BLK

155Z .80 BLK

155U .35 BLK

155XX .35 BLK

155WW .35 BLK

REAR BODY GROUND SPLICE PACK

155MM 2.0 BLK

FIGURE 14–26 Some vehicles use a network of grounding wires and terminals to ensure a good ground in all electrical circuits.

Circuit Components

Automotive electrical circuits contain a number of different types of electrical devices. The more common components are outlined in the following sections.

Resistors As shown in the explanation of simple circuit design, resistors are used to limit current flow (and thereby voltage) in circuits where full current flow and voltage are not needed or desired. Resistors are devices specially constructed to put a specific amount of resistance into a circuit. In addition, some other components use resistance to produce heat and even light. An electric window defroster is a specialized type of resistor that produces heat. Electric lights are resistors that get so hot they produce light.

Automotive circuits typically contain these types of resistors: fixed value, stepped or tapped, and variable.

Fixed value resistors are designed to have only one rating, which should not change. These resistors are used to decrease the amount of voltage applied to a component, such as an ignition coil. Often manufacturers use a special wire, called **resistor wire**, to limit current flow and voltage in a circuit. This wire looks much like normal wire but is not a good conductor and is marked as a resistor.

Tapped or **stepped resistors** are designed to have two or more fixed values, available by connecting wires to the several taps of the resistor. Heater motor resistor packs, which provide for different fan speeds, are an example of this type of resistor (Figure 14–27).

Variable resistors are designed to have a range of resistances available through two or more taps and a control. Two examples of this type of resistor are **rheostats** and **potentiometers**. Rheostats (Figure 14–28) have two connections, one to the fixed end of a resistor and one to a sliding contact with the resistor. Moving the control moves the sliding contact away from or toward the fixed end tap, increasing or decreasing the resistance. Potentiometers (Figure 14–29) have three connections, one at each end of the resistance and one connected to a sliding contact with the resistor. Moving the control moves the sliding contact away

FIGURE 14–27   Stepped resistor.

12 V   10 V   8 V   6 V   4 V

FIGURE 14–28   Rheostat.

FIGURE 14–29   Potentiometer.

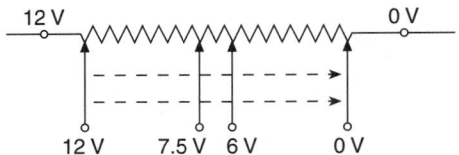

12 V   7.5 V   6 V   0 V

FIGURE 14–30   Voltage across a potentiometer.

from one end of the resistance but toward the other end. These are called potentiometers because different amounts of potential or voltage can be sent to another circuit. As the sliding contact moves, it picks up a voltage equal to the source voltage minus the amount dropped by the resistor, so far (Figure 14–30).

Another type of variable resistor is the **thermistor**. This type of resistor is designed to change its resistance value as its temperature changes. Although most resistors are carefully constructed to maintain their rating within a few ohms through a range of temperatures, the thermistor is designed to change its rating. Thermistors are used to provide compensating voltage in components or to determine temperature. As a temperature sensor, the thermistor is connected to a voltmeter calibrated in degrees. As the temperature rises or falls, the resistance also changes, and so does the voltage in the circuit. These changes are read on the temperature gauge. Thermistors are also commonly used to sense temperature and send a signal back to a control unit. The control unit interprets the signal as a temperature value (Figure 14–31).

Circuit Protective Devices When overloads or shorts in a circuit cause too much current to flow, the wiring in the circuit heats up, the insulation melts, and a fire can result, unless the circuit has some kind of protective device. Fuses, fuse links, maxi-fuses, and circuit breakers are designed to provide protection from high current. They may be used singularly or in combination. Typical symbols for protection devices are shown in Figure 14–32.

WARNING!

Fuses and other protection devices normally do not wear out. They go bad because something went wrong. Never replace a fuse or fusible link, or reset a circuit breaker, without finding out why it went bad. ■

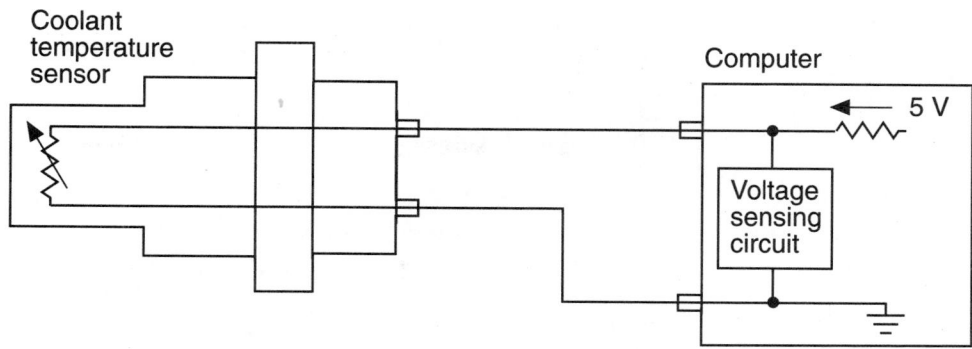

FIGURE 14-31 A thermistor is used to measure temperature. The sensing unit measures the change in resistance and translates this into a temperature value.

FUSES There are three basic types of fuses in automotive use: cartridge, blade, and ceramic (Figure 14–33). The **cartridge fuse** is found on most older domestic cars and a few imports. It is composed of a strip of low melting metal enclosed in a transparent glass or plastic tube. To check this type of fuse, look for a break in the internal metal strip. Discoloration of the glass cover or glue bubbling around the metal end caps is an indication of overheating. Late-model domestic vehicles and many imports use **blade** or **spade fuses**. To check the fuse, pull it from the fuse panel and look at the fuse element through the transparent plastic housing. Look for internal breaks and discoloration. The **ceramic fuse** is used on many European imports. The core is a ceramic insulator with a conductive metal strip along one side. To check this type of fuse, look for a break in the contact strip on the outside of the fuse. All types of fuses can be checked with an ohmmeter or testlight. If the fuse is good, there will be continuity through it.

Fuses are rated by the current at which they are

FUSE   CIRCUIT   FUSIBLE
        BREAKER   LINK

FIGURE 14-32 Electrical symbols for common circuit protection devices.

A   B   C

FIGURE 14-33 (A) Cartridge fuse, (B) ceramic fuse, and (C) blade fuse.

designed to blow. A three-letter code is used to indicate the type and size of fuses. Blade fuses have codes ATC or ATO. All glass SFE fuses have the same diameter, but the length varies with the current rating. Ceramic fuses are available in two sizes, code GBF (small) and the more common code GBC (large). The amperage rating is also embossed on the insulator. Codes, such as AGA, AGW, and AGC, indicate the length and diameter of the fuse. Fuse lengths in each of these series is the same, but the current rating can vary. The code and the current rating is usually stamped on the end cap.

The current rating for blade fuses is indicated by the color of the plastic case (Table 14–1). In addition, it is usually marked on the top. The insulator on ceramic fuses is color coded to indicate different current ratings.

CUSTOMER CARE

Advise your customers to carry an assortment of spare fuses in the car's glove compartment. It is difficult to know when one will blow. Also, show the customer how to borrow a fuse from a less critical circuit. For example, it is possible to do without power for the radio or air conditioner, if a fuse is needed for the headlights or brake lights. Make certain, however, that the fuse borrowed and later replaced has the same current rating. Remember that a blown fuse was caused by something going wrong. Inform the customer that replacing the fuse may or may not give a temporary solution to the problem. ∎

Fuses are located in a box or panel (Figure 14–34), usually under the dashboard, behind a panel in the foot well, or in the engine compartment. Fuses are generally numbered, and the main components abbreviated. On late-model cars, there may be icons or symbols indicating which circuits they serve. This identification system is covered in more detail in the owner's and service manuals.

TABLE 14–1 TYPICAL COLOR CODING OF PROTECTIVE DEVICES

Blade Fuse Color Coding

Ampere Rating	Housing Color
4	pink
5	tan
10	red
15	light blue
20	yellow
25	natural
30	light green

Fuse Link Color Coding

Wire Link Size	Insulation Color
20 GA	blue
18 GA	brown or red
16 GA	black or orange
14 GA	green
12 GA	gray

Maxi-Fuse Color Coding

Ampere Rating	Housing Color
20	yellow
30	light green
40	amber
50	red
60	blue

55 by the battery voltage (12 volts) to find out how much current the circuit has to carry. Since 55 ÷ 12 = 4.58, the current is approximately 5 amperes. To allow for current surges, the correct in-line fuse should be rated slightly higher than the normal current flow. In this case, an 8- or 10-ampere fuse would do the job. ■

FUSE LINKS Fuse or **fusible links** are used in circuits when limiting the maximum current is not extremely critical. They are often installed in the positive battery lead to the ignition switch and other circuits that have power with the key off. Fusible links

FIGURE 14–34   Typical fuse box or panel.

Sometimes it is necessary to protect a device in a portion of a circuit even though the entire circuit is protected by a fuse in the fuse panel. This is done by installing an **in-line fuse** in the wire that carries current to the device. In-line fuses are primarily used on accessories that are very sensitive to power surges, such as radios and compact disc players. They are also used with added-on units like driving lights and power antennas. Normally, these fuses are close to the units they protect.

There are several types of in-line fuse carriers. One of the most popular and easiest to install is shown in Figure 14–35.

SHOP TALK

To calculate the correct fuse rating, use Watt's law: watts ÷ volts = amperes. For example, if you are installing a 55-watt pair of fog lights, divide

1. CUT THE WIRE AND INSERT ONE WIRE IN EACH SIDE.

3. INSERT BLADE FUSE.

2. CLOSE EACH SIDE AND SQUEEZE WITH PLIERS TO LOCK.

FIGURE 14–35   In-line blade fuse carrier.

SMALL WIRE   SPLICE

FUSE LINK BURNS OUT IN THIS
AREA WHEN TOO MUCH CURRENT
FLOWS THROUGH.

CIRCUIT
CONDUCTOR

FIGURE 14–36   Typical fuse link.

are normally found in the engine compartment near the battery. Fusible links are also used when it would be awkward to run wiring from the battery to the fuse panel and back to the load.

A fuse link (Figure 14–36) is a short length of small gauge wire installed in a conductor. Because the fuse link is a lighter gauge of wire than the main conductor, it melts and opens the circuit before damage can occur in the rest of the circuit. Fuse link wire is covered with a special insulation that bubbles when it overheats, indicating that the link has melted. If the insulation appears good, pull lightly on the wire. If the link stretches, the wire has melted. Of course, when it is hard to determine if the fuse link is burned out, check for continuity through the link with a testlight or ohmmeter.

 WARNING!

Do not mistake a resistor wire for a fuse link. A resistor wire is generally longer and is clearly marked "Resistor—do not cut or splice." ■

To replace a fuse link, cut the protected wire where it is connected to the fuse link. Then, tightly crimp or solder a new fusible link of the same rating as the original link (Figure 14–37). Since the insulation on the manufacturer's fuse link is flameproof, never fabricate a fuse link from ordinary wire because the insulation may not be flameproof.

TAPE   FUSE
LINK   TAPE OR
STRAP

TYPICAL REPAIR FOR ANY IN-LINE FUSE LINK USING THE SPECIFIED GAUGE FUSE LINK FOR THE SPECIFIC CIRCUIT.

TAPE

TYPICAL REPAIR USING THE EYELET TERMINAL FUSE LINK OF THE SPECIFIED GAUGE FOR ATTACHMENT TO A CIRCUIT WIRE END.

FIGURE 14–37   Typical fuse link repair.

CAUTION:

Always disconnect the battery ground cable prior to servicing any fuse link.   ■

MAXI-FUSES Many late-model vehicles use **maxi-fuses** instead of fusible links. Maxi-fuses look and operate like two-prong, blade, or spade fuses, except they are much larger and can handle more current. (Typically, a maxi-fuse is four to five times larger.) Maxi-fuses are located in their own underhood fuse block.

Maxi-fuses are easier to inspect and replace than are fuse links. To check a maxi-fuse, look at the fuse element through the transparent plastic housing. If there is a break in the element, the maxi-fuse has blown. To replace it, pull it from its fuse box or panel. Always replace a blown maxi-fuse with a new one having the same ampere rating.

Maxi-fuses allow the vehicle's electrical system to be broken down into smaller circuits that are easy to diagnose and repair. For example, in some vehicles a single fusible link controls one-half or more of all circuitry. If it burns out, many electrical systems are lost. By replacing this single fusible link with several maxi-fuses, the number of systems lost due to a problem in one circuit is drastically reduced. This makes it easy to pinpoint the source of trouble.

CIRCUIT BREAKERS Some circuits are protected by **circuit breakers** (abbreviated c.b. in the fuse chart of a service manual). They can be fuse panel mounted or in-line. Like fuses, they are rated in amperes.

Each circuit breaker conducts current through an arm made of two types of metal bonded together (bimetal arm). If the arm starts to carry too much current, it heats up. As one metal expands faster than the other, the arm bends, opening the contacts. Current flow is broken. A circuit breaker can be cycling (Figure 14–38) or must be manually reset.

In the cycling type, the bimetal arm will begin to cool once the current to it is stopped. Once it returns to its original shape, the contacts are closed and

SIDE VIEW
(EXTERNAL)

SIDE VIEW
(INTERNAL)

BIMETAL ARM

CONTACTS

FIGURE 14–38   Cycling circuit breaker.

FIGURE 14-39   Resetting noncycling circuit breakers by (A) removing power from the circuit and (B) depressing a reset button.

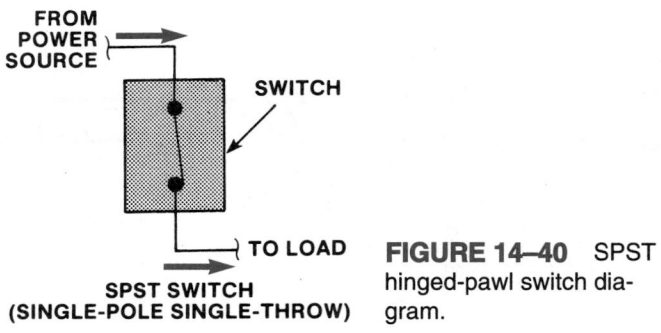

FIGURE 14-40   SPST hinged-pawl switch diagram.

power is restored. If the current is still too high, the cycle of breaking the circuit will be repeated.

Two types of noncycling or resettable circuit breakers are used. One is reset by removing the power from the circuit. There is a coil wrapped around a bimetal arm (Figure 14–39A). When there is excessive current and the contacts open, a small current passes through the coil. This current through the coil is not enough to operate a load, but it does heat up both the coil and the bimetal arm. This keeps the arm in the open position until power is removed. The other type is reset by depressing a reset button. A spring pushes the bimetal arm down and holds the contacts together (Figure 14–39B). When an over-current condition exists and the bimetal arm heats up, the bimetal arm bends enough to overcome the spring and the contacts snap open. The contacts stay open until the reset button is pushed, which snaps the contacts together again.

Voltage Limiter   Some instrument panel gauges are protected against voltage fluctuations that could damage the gauges or give erroneous readings. A **voltage limiter** restricts voltage to the gauges to a particular amount. The limiter contains a heating coil, a bimetal arm, and a set of contacts. When the ignition is in the on or accessory position, the heating coil heats the bimetal arm, causing it to bend and open the contacts. This action results in voltage from both the heating coil and the circuit. When the arm cools down to the point that the contacts close, the cycle is repeated. The rapid opening and closing of the contacts produces a pulsating voltage at the output terminal averaging about 5 volts.

Switches   Electrical circuits are usually controlled by some type of switch. Switches do two things. They turn the circuit on or off, or they direct the flow of current in a circuit. Switches can be under the control of the driver or can be self-operating through a condition of the circuit, the vehicle, or the environment.

Contacts in a switch can be of several types, each named for the job they do or the sequence in which they work. A hinged-pawl switch (Figure 14–40) is the simplest type of switch. It either makes (allows for) or breaks (opens) current flow in a single conductor or circuit. This type of switch is a single-pole, single-throw (**SPST**) switch. The **throw** refers to the number of output circuits, and the **pole** refers to the number of input circuits made by the switch.

Another type of SPST switch is a momentary contact switch (Figure 14–41). The spring-loaded contact on this switch keeps it from closing the circuit except when pressure is applied to the button. A horn switch is this type of switch. Because the spring holds the contacts open, the switch has a further designation: **normally open**. In the case where the contacts are held closed except when the button is pressed, the switch is designated **normally closed**. A normally closed momentary contact switch is the type of switch used to turn on the courtesy lights when one of the vehicle's doors is opened.

Single-pole, double-throw (**SPDT**) switches have one wire in and two wires out. Figure 14–42 shows an SPDT hinged-pawl switch that feeds either the high-beam or low-beam headlight circuit. The dotted

FIGURE 14-41   SPST momentary contact switch diagram.

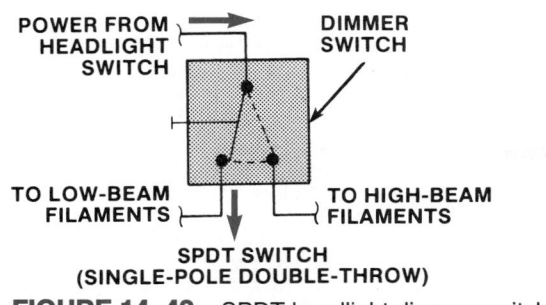

FIGURE 14–42 SPDT headlight dimmer switch.

FIGURE 14–43 MPMT neutral start safety switch.

FIGURE 14–44 Typical mercury switch.

FIGURE 14–45 Typical electrical relay design.

lines in the symbol show movement of the switch pawl from one contact to the other.

Switches can be designed with a great number of poles and throws. The transmission neutral start switch shown in Figure 14–43, for instance, has two poles and six throws and is referred to as a multiple-pole, multiple-throw (**MPMT**) switch. It contains two movable wipers that move in unison across two sets of terminals. The dotted line shows that the wipers are mechanically linked, or **ganged**. The switch closes a circuit to the starter in either P (park) or N (neutral) and to the back-up lights in R (reverse).

Most switches are combinations of hinged-pawl and push-pull switches, with different numbers of poles and throws. Some special switches are required, however, to satisfy the circuits of modern automobiles. A mercury switch is sometimes used to detect motion in a component, such as the one used in the engine compartment to turn on the compartment light.

Mercury is a very good conductor of electricity. In the mercury switch, a capsule is partially filled with mercury (Figure 14–44). In one end of the capsule are two electrical contacts. The switch is attached to the hood or luggage compartment lid. Normally, the mercury is in the end opposite to the contacts. When the lid is opened, the mercury flows to the contact end and provides a circuit between the electrical contacts.

A temperature-sensitive switch usually contains a bimetallic element heated either electrically or by some component where the switch is used as a **sensor**. When engine coolant is below or at normal operating temperature, the engine coolant temperature sensor is in its normally open condition. If the coolant exceeds the temperature limit, the bimetallic element bends the two contacts together and the switch is closed to the indicator or the instrument panel. Other applications for heat-sensitive switches are time-delay switches and flashers.

Relays A **relay** is an electric switch that allows a small amount of current to control a high current circuit (Figure 14–45). When the control circuit switch is open, no current flows to the coil of the relay, so the windings are de-energized. When the switch is closed, the coil is energized, turning the soft iron core into an electromagnet and drawing the armature down. This closes the power circuit contacts, connecting power to the load circuit. When the control switch is opened, current stops flowing in the coil and the electromagnet disappears. This releases the armature, which breaks the power circuit contacts.

Solenoids **Solenoids** are also electromagnets with movable cores used to change electrical current flow into mechanical movement. They can also close contacts, acting as a relay at the same time.

Capacitors (Condensers) **Capacitors** are constructed from two or more sheets of electrically conducting material with a nonconducting or **dielectric** (anti-electric) material placed between them. Conductors

FIGURE 14–46
Charging a capacitor.

BATTERY

TABLE 14–2 WIRE GAUGE SIZES		
Metric Size (mm²)	**Wire Size**	**Ampere Capacity**
0.5	20	4
0.8	18	6
1.0	16	8
2.0	14	15
3.0	12	20
5.0	10	30
8.0	8	40
13.0	6	50
19.0	4	60

are connected to the two sheets. Capacitors are devices that oppose a change of voltage.

If a battery is connected to a capacitor as shown in Figure 14–46, the capacitor will be charged when current flows from the battery to the plates. This current flow will continue until the plates have the same voltage as the battery. At this time, the capacitor is charged.

The capacitor remains charged until a circuit is completed between the two plates. If the charge is routed through a voltmeter, the capacitor will discharge with the same voltage as the battery that charged it. This statement explains why capacitors are commonly used to filter or clean up voltage signals, such as sound from a stereo. Current can only flow during the period of time that a capacitor is either charging or discharging.

Automotive capacitors are normally encased in metal. The grounded case provides a connection to one set of conductor plates and an insulated lead connects to the other set.

Variable capacitors are called **trimmers** or tuners and are rated very low in capacity because of the reduced size of their conducting plates. For this reason, they are only used in very sensitive circuits, such as radios and other electronic applications.

Wiring Electrical wires are used to conduct electricity to operate the electrical and electronic devices in a vehicle. There are two basic types of wires used: solid and stranded. **Solid wires** are single-strand conductors. **Stranded wires** are made up of a number of small solid wires twisted together to form a single conductor. Stranded wires are the most commonly used type of wire in an automobile. Electronic units, such as computers, use specially shielded, twisted cable for protection from unwanted induced voltages that can interfere with computer functions. In addition, some solid state components use printed circuits.

The current-carrying capacity and the amount of voltage drop in an electrical wire are determined by its length and gauge (size). The wire sizes are established by the Society of Automotive Engineers (SAE), which is the American wire gauge (**AWG**) system. Sizes are identified by a numbering system ranging

from number 0 to 20, with number 0 being the largest and number 20 the smallest in a cross-sectional area (Table 14–2). Most automotive wiring ranges from number 10 to 18 and the battery cables are normally at least number 4 gauge. Battery cables are large gauge wires capable of carrying the high currents for the starter motor.

Automotive wiring can also be classified as primary or secondary. Primary wiring carries low voltage to all the electrical systems of the vehicle except to secondary circuits of the ignition system. Secondary wire, also called **high-tension cable**, has extra thick insulation to carry high voltage from the ignition coil to the spark plugs. The conductor itself is designed for low currents.

The proper selection of the correct gauge wire is very important. The wire should be large enough to assure safe and reliable performance. However, overly large wires add weight and expense to the vehicle. If too small a wire is used, a voltage drop can occur due to electrical resistance. The two factors that should always be considered when the size of a wire is determined are the total amperage the circuit carries and the total length of wire used in each circuit, including the return. Allowance for the return circuits, including grounded returns, has been computed in Table 14–3. The length of cable should be determined by totaling both wires on a two-wire circuit.

Wires are commonly grouped together in harnesses. A single-plug harness connector may form the connections for four, six, or more circuits. Harnesses and harness connectors help organize the vehicle's electrical system and provide a convenient starting point for tracking and testing many circuits. Most major wiring harness connectors are located in a vehicle's dash or fire wall area (Figure 14–47).

Printed Circuits Many late-model vehicles use flexible printed circuits (Figure 14–48) and printed circuit boards. Both types of printed circuits allow for

TABLE 14-3 WIRE SIZE AND LENGTH									
Total Approximate Circuit Amperes	**Wire Gauge (for Length in Feet)**								
12V	**3**	**5**	**7**	**10**	**15**	**20**	**25**	**30**	**40**
1.0	18	18	18	18	18	18	18	18	18
1.5	18	18	18	18	18	18	18	18	18
2	18	18	18	18	18	18	18	18	18
3	18	18	18	18	18	18	18	18	18
4	18	18	18	18	18	18	18	16	16
5	18	18	18	18	18	18	18	16	16
6	18	18	18	18	18	18	16	16	16
7	18	18	18	18	18	18	16	16	14
8	18	18	18	18	18	16	16	16	14
10	18	18	18	18	16	16	16	14	12
11	18	18	18	18	16	16	14	14	12
12	18	18	18	18	16	16	14	14	12
15	18	18	18	18	14	14	12	12	12
18	18	18	16	16	14	14	12	12	10
20	18	18	16	16	14	12	10	10	10
22	18	18	16	16	12	12	10	10	10
24	18	18	16	16	12	12	10	10	10
30	18	16	16	14	10	10	10	10	10
40	18	16	14	12	10	10	8	8	6
50	16	14	12	12	10	10	8	8	6
100	12	12	10	10	6	6	4	4	4
150	10	10	8	8	4	4	2	2	2
200	10	8	8	6	4	4	2	2	1

Note: 18 AWG as indicated above this line could be 20 AWG electrically. 18 AWG is recommended for mechanical strength.

FIGURE 14–47 Typical front wiring harness.

complete circuits to many components without having to run dozens of wires. Printed circuit boards are typically contained in a housing, such as the engine control module. These boards are not serviceable and in some cases not visible. When these boards fail, the entire unit is replaced.

A flexible printed circuit saves weight and space. It is made of thin sheets of nonconductive plastic onto which conductive metal, such as copper, has been deposited. Parts of the metal are then etched or eaten away by acid. The remaining metal lines form the conductors for the various circuits on the board. The printed circuit is normally connected to the power supply or ground wiring through the use of plug-in connectors mounted on the circuit sheet.

FIGURE 14–48 Typical printed circuit board.

There are several precautions that should be observed when working on a printed circuit.

1. Never touch the surface of the board. Dirt, salts, and acids on your fingers can etch the surface and set up a resistive condition. It is possible to knock out an entire section of the dash with a fingerprint.
2. The copper conductors can be cleaned with a commercial cleaner or by lightly rubbing a pencil eraser across the surface.
3. A printed circuit board is easily damaged because it is very thin. Be careful not to tear the surface especially when plugging in connectors or bulbs.

Electrical Wiring Diagrams Wiring diagrams, sometimes called **schematics**, are used to show how circuits are constructed. A typical service manual contains dozens of wiring diagrams vital to the diagnosis and repair of the vehicle.

A wiring diagram does not show the actual position of the parts on the vehicle or their appearance, nor does it indicate the length of the wire that runs between components. It usually indicates the color of the wire's insulation and sometimes the wire gauge size. Typically, the primary wire insulation is color coded as shown in Table 14–4. The first letter in a combination of letters usually indicates the base color. The second letter usually refers to the strip color (if

any). Tracing a circuit through a vehicle is basically a matter of following the colored wires.

Many different symbols are also used to represent components such as resistors, batteries, switches, transistors, and many other items. Some of these symbols have already been shown earlier in the chapter. Other common symbols are shown in Figure 14–49. Part of a typical wiring diagram is shown in Figure 14–50, notice that the components are also labeled.

Wiring diagrams can become quite complex. To avoid this, most diagrams usually illustrate only one distinct system, such as the backup light circuit, oil pressure indicator light circuit, or wiper motor circuit. In more complex ignition, electronic fuel injection, and computer control systems, a diagram may be used to illustrate only part of the entire circuit.

USING SERVICE MANUALS

Keep in mind that electrical symbols are not standardized throughout the automotive industry. Different manufacturers may have different methods of representing certain components, particularly the less common ones. Always refer to the symbol reference charts, wire color code charts, and abbreviation tables listed in the vehicle's service manual to avoid confusion when reading wiring diagrams. Also, most diagrams are designed to be read from left to right, top to bottom, just as you would a book. ∎

TABLE 14–4 COMMON WIRE COLOR CODES			
Color	**Abbreviations**		
Aluminum	AL		
Black	BLK	BK	B
Blue (Dark)	BLU DK	DB	DK BLU
Blue (Light)	BLU LT	LB	LT BLU
Brown	BRN	BR	BN
Glazed	GLZ	GL	
Gray	GRA	GR	G
Green (Dark)	GRN DK	DG	DK GRN
Green (Light)	GRN LT	LG	LT GRN
Maroon	MAR	M	
Natural	NAT	N	
Orange	ORN	O	ORG
Pink	PNK	PK	P
Purple	PPL	PR	
Red	RED	R	RD
Tan	TAN	T	TN
Violet	VLT	V	
White	WHT	W	WH
Yellow	YEL	Y	YL

Electrical Problems All electrical problems can be classified into one of three categories: opens, shorts, or high-resistance problems. Identifying the type of problem allows you to identify the correct tests to perform when diagnosing an electrical problem. The different classifications of electrical problems follow.

An open occurs when a circuit has a break in the wire. Without a completed path, current cannot flow and the load or component cannot work. An open circuit can be caused by a disconnected wire, a broken wire, or a switch in the OFF position. Although voltage will be present up to the open point there is no current flow. Without current flow, there are no voltage drops across the various loads.

A short results from an unwanted path for current. Shorts cause an increase in current flow. This increased current flow can burn wires or components. Sometimes two circuits become shorted together. When this happens, one circuit powers another. This may result in strange happenings, such as the horn sounding every time the brake pedal is depressed. In

FIGURE 14–49 Common electrical symbols used on wiring diagrams.

FIGURE 14–50   One part of a large wiring diagram.

this case, the brake light circuit is shorted to the horn circuit. Improper wiring or damaged insulation are the two major causes of short circuits.

A short can also be an unwanted short to ground. This problem provides a low resistance path to ground. This problem causes extremely high current flow,

which will damage wires and electrical components. Some call this problem a grounded circuit.

High-resistance problems occur when there is unwanted resistance in the circuit. The higher-than-normal resistance causes the current flow to be lower than normal and the components in the circuit are

LEFT DOOR CONNECTOR AND WINDOW LIFT SWITCH FUNCTION			
B+ POLARITY	B- POLARITY	SWITCH SECTION	WINDOW MOVEMENT
WT	LB	4	LEFT FRONT UP
LB	WT	4	LEFT FRONT DOWN
VT/WT*	BR/WT*	3	RIGHT FRONT UP
BR/WT*	VT/WT*	3	RIGHT FRONT DOWN
RD/BK*	DB/WT*	2	LEFT REAR UP
DB/WT*	RD/BK*	2	LEFT REAR DOWN
DG/WT*	GY/BK*	1	RIGHT REAR UP
GY/BK*	DG/WT*	1	RIGHT REAR DOWN
—	BK	N/A	GROUND B-
TN	—	5	GROUND B+

FIGURE 14–50 *Continued*

unable to operate properly. A common cause of this type of problem is corrosion at a connector. The corrosion becomes an additional load in the circuit. This load uses some of the circuit's voltage, which prevents full voltage to the normal loads in the circuit.

With a basic understanding of electricity and simple circuits, it is easier to understand the operation and purpose of the various types of electrical test equipment described in the following sections.

Electrical Test Meters

Several meters are used to test and diagnose electrical systems. These are the voltmeter, ammeter, and ohmmeter. These should be used along with volt-

PREFIX	SYMBOL	RELATION TO BASIC UNIT
Mega	M	1,000,000
Kilo	k	1,000
Milli	m	.001 or $\frac{1}{1000}$
Micro	μ	.000001 or $\frac{1}{1000000}$
Nano	n	0.000000001
Pico	p	0.000000000001

FIGURE 14–51   Common prefixes used on meters.

FIGURE 14–52   Checking a circuit using a voltmeter.

FIGURE 14–53   Wire resistance results in a slight voltage drop in the circuit.

ohmmeters, test lights, jumper wires, and variable resistors (piles).

Meters have either an "auto range" feature, in which the appropriate scale is automatically selected by the meter or they must be set to a particular range. In either case, you should be familiar with the ranges and the different settings available on the meter you are using. To designate particular ranges and readings, meters display a prefix before the reading or range. For example, if the meter has a setting for mAmps, this means the readings will be given in milli-amps or 1/1000th of an amp. The common prefixes, their symbols, and their meaning are shown in Figure 14–51.

Voltmeter   A voltmeter measures the voltage available at any point in an electrical system. For example, it can be used to measure the voltage available at the battery. It can also be used to test the voltage available at the terminals of any component or connector. A voltmeter can also be used to test voltage drop across an electrical circuit, component, switch, or connector.

A voltmeter has two leads: a red positive lead and a black negative lead. The red lead should be connected to the positive side of the circuit or component. The black should be connected to ground or to the negative side of the component. Voltmeters should always be connected across the circuit being tested.

Consider a simple circuit (Figure 14–52). If there are 12 volts available at the battery and the switch is closed, there should also be 12 volts available at each light. If, for example, less than 12 volts is indicated, that would mean that some additional resistance is somewhere else in the circuit. The lights may light but not as brightly as they should.

The loss of voltage due to resistance in wires, connectors, and loads is called voltage drop. Voltage drop is checked using a voltmeter. The procedure for checking voltage is shown in Photo Sequence 7.

Figure 14–53 illustrates two headlights connected to a 12-volt battery using two wires. Each wire has a resistance of 0.05 ohm. Each headlight has a resistance of 2 ohms. As you can see, the two headlights are wired parallel so their effective resistance is

$$\frac{2 \text{ ohms} \times 2 \text{ ohms}}{2 \text{ ohms} + 2 \text{ ohms}} = 1 \text{ ohm}$$

The total circuit resistance is

$$1 \text{ ohm} + 0.05 \text{ ohm} + 0.05 \text{ ohm} = 1.1 \text{ ohms}$$

Therefore, the current in the circuit is

$$I = \frac{E}{R} = \frac{12}{1.1} = 10.9 \text{ amperes}$$

The voltage drop across each wire is

$$E = I \times R$$
$$E = 10.9 \times 0.05 = 0.54 \text{ V}$$

This means there is a total of 1.08 volts dropped across the wires. When the voltage drop of the wires is subtracted from the 12-volt source voltage, 10.92 volts remain for the headlights.

Without the resistance in the wires, the headlights receive 12 amperes. With the resistance, the current flow was reduced to 10.9 amperes.

All wiring must have resistance values low enough to allow enough voltage to the load for prop-

PERFORMING A VOLTAGE DROP TEST

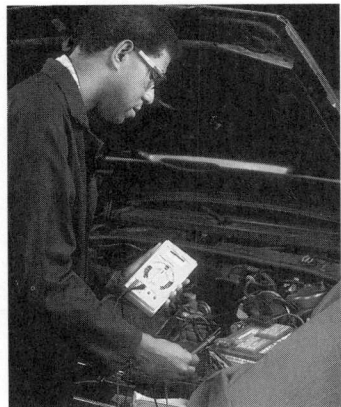

P7–1 Tools required to perform this task: voltmeter and fender covers.

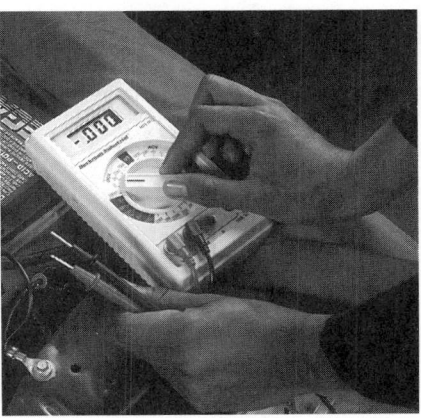

P7–2 Set the voltmeter on its lowest DC volt scale.

P7–3 To test the voltage drop of the entire headlamp system, connect the positive (red) lead to the battery positive (+) terminal.

P7–4 Connect the negative (black) lead to the low beam terminal of the headlight socket. Make sure you are connected to the input side of the headlight.

P7–5 Turn on the headlights (low beam) and look at the voltmeter reading. The voltmeter will show the amount of voltage dropped between the battery and the headlight. This reading should be very low

er operation. The maximum allowable voltage loss due to voltage drops across wires, connectors, and other conductors in an automotive circuit is 10 percent of the system voltage. So, in an automotive electrical system powered by a 12-volt battery, this maximum loss is 1.2 volts.

A voltmeter can also be used to check for proper circuit grounding. For example, consider the lighting circuit shown in Figure 14–52. If the voltmeter reading indicates full voltage at the lights, but no lighting is seen, the bulbs or sockets could be bad or the ground connection is faulty.

An easy way to check for a defective bulb is to replace it with one known to be good. You can also use an ohmmeter to check for electrical continuity through the bulb.

If the bulbs are not defective, the problem lies in either the light sockets or ground wires. Connect the voltmeter to the ground wire and a good ground as shown in Figure 14–54. If the light socket is defec-

FIGURE 14–54 Using a voltmeter to check for open grounds.

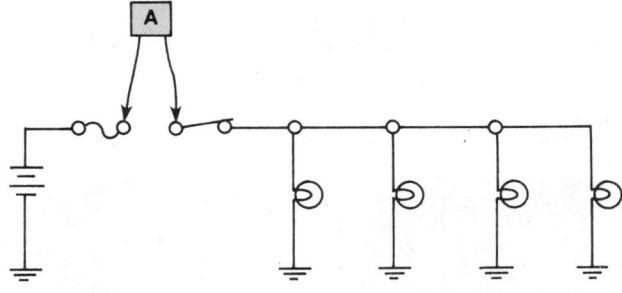

FIGURE 14–55 Checking a circuit using an ammeter.

tive, there would be no voltage through the lights and the voltmeter would read 0 volts. If the socket was not defective but the ground wire was broken or disconnected, the voltmeter would read very close to 12 volts. Any voltage reading would indicate a bad or poor ground circuit. The higher the voltage, the greater the problem.

Ammeter An ammeter measures current flow in a circuit. Current is measured in amperes. An ammeter must be placed into the circuit or in series with the circuit being tested. Normally, this requires disconnecting a wire or connector from a component and connecting the ammeter between the wire or connector and the component. The red lead of the ammeter should always be connected to the side of the connector closest to the positive side of the battery and the black lead should be connected to the other side.

WARNING!

Never place the leads of an ammeter across the battery or a load. This puts the meter in parallel with the circuit and will blow the fuse in the ammeter or possibly destroy the meter. ■

It is much easier to test current using an ammeter with an inductive pickup. The pickup clamps around the wire or cable being tested. The ammeter determines amperage based on the magnetic field created by the current flowing through the wire. This type of pickup eliminates the need to separate the circuit to insert the meter.

Because ammeters are built in very low internal resistance, connecting them in series does not add any appreciable resistance to the circuit. Therefore, an accurate measurement of the current flow can be taken.

For example, assume that a circuit normally draws 5 amps and is protected by a 6-amp fuse. If

the circuit constantly blows the 6-amp fuse, a short exists somewhere in the circuit (Figure 14–55). Mathematically, each light should draw 1.25 amperes (5 ÷ 4 = 1.25). To find the short, disconnect all lights by removing them from their sockets. Then, close the switch and read the ammeter. With the load disconnected, the meter should read 0 amperes. If there is any reading, the wire between the fuse block and the socket is shorted to ground.

If zero amps was measured, reconnect each light in sequence. The reading should increase 1.25 amperes with each bulb. If, when making any connection, the reading is higher than expected, the problem is in that part of the light circuit.

WARNING!

When testing for a short, always use a fuse. Never bypass the fuse with a wire. The fuse should be rated at no more than 50 percent higher capacity than specifications. This offers circuit protection and provides enough amperage for testing. After the problem is found and corrected, be sure to install the specified rating of fuse for circuit protection. ■

Ohmmeter An ohmmeter measures resistance to current flow in a circuit. The two leads of the ohmmeter are placed across or in parallel with the circuit or component being tested. The red lead is placed on the positive side of the circuit, and the black lead is placed on the negative side of the circuit. The meter sends current through the component and determines the amount of resistance based on the voltage dropped across the load. The scale of an ohmmeter reads from 0 to infinity (∞). A 0 reading means there is no resistance in the circuit and may indicate a short in a component that should show a specific resistance. An infinity reading indicates a number higher than the meter can measure. This usually is an indication of an open circuit.

FIGURE 14–56 Measuring resistance using an ohmmeter. Note that the circuit fuse is removed to de-energize the circuit.

FIGURE 14–57 (A) Testing a circuit using a nonpowered test light, and (B) testing with a powered test light. With powered test lights, the circuit must be de-energized.

Ohmmeters are used to test circuit continuity and resistance with no power applied. In other words, the circuit or component to be tested must first be disconnected from the power source (Figure 14–56). Connecting an ohmmeter into a live circuit usually results in damage to the meter.

Ohmmeters are also used to trace and check wires or cables. Assume that one wire of a four-wire cable is to be found. Connect one probe of the ohmmeter to the known wire at one end of the cable and touch the other probe to each wire at the other end of the cable. Any evidence of resistance, such as meter needle deflection, indicates the correct wire. Using this same method, you can check a suspected defective wire. If resistance is shown on the meter, the wire is sound. If no resistance is measured, the wire is defective (open). If the wire is okay, continue checking by connecting the probe to other leads. Any indication of resistance indicates that the wire is shorted to one of the other wires and that the harness is defective.

Volt-Ohmmeter This combination meter is very useful for all types of diagnostics. It is capable of measuring exact amounts of voltage and resistance at any point in a circuit. Basically, there are two types of volt-ohmmeters available: the analog and digital. Analog meters use a sweeping needle to indicate the measurement. This type of meter is commonly used on normal automotive electrical circuits. A digital volt-ohmmeter (DVOM) is used on electronic circuitry. This type meter displays the measurement in numerical or digital form. Most DVOMs are of high impedance, which is a requirement for use on most computerized and other sensitive electronic equipment.

Testlights There are two types of testlights commonly used in diagnosing electrical problems, the nonpowered and powered testlight. Nonpowered testlights are used to check for available voltage. With the

wire lead connected to ground and the tester's probe at a point of voltage, the light turns on with the presence of voltage (Figure 14–57A). The amount of voltage determines the brightness of the light. A self-powered testlight is used to check for continuity. Hooked across a circuit or component, the light turns on if the circuit is complete. A powered testlight should only be used if the power for the circuit or component has been disconnected (Figure 14–57B).

Jumper Wires Jumper wires are used to bypass individual wires, connectors, or components. Bypassing a component or wire helps to determine if that part is faulty (Figure 14–58). If the problem is no longer evident after the jumper wire is installed, the part by-

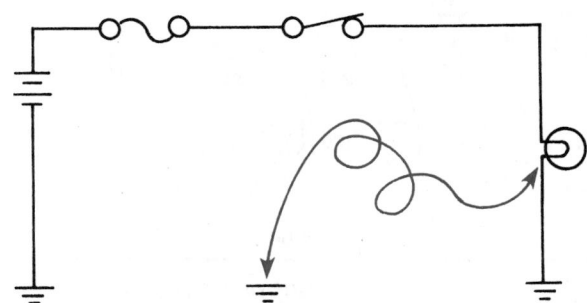

FIGURE 14–58 Using a jumper wire to test for an open ground.

passed is normally faulty. Technicians typically have jumper wires of various lengths, usually some of the wires have a fuse or circuit breaker in them to protect the circuits being tested.

Variable Resistors Variable resistors or piles are used to cause a certain amount of current to flow through a circuit. This type of test equipment is especially important when testing a battery and alternator. By causing current flow through the test equipment, the ability of the battery or alternator to react to the current draw is a precise way to check its efficiency. Most battery/starting/charging system testers are equipped with a carbon pile. The resistance of the carbon pile is either adjusted by the technician or is automatically adjusted by the tester.

Troubleshooting Circuits

Troubleshooting electrical problems involves using meters, testlights, and jumper wires to determine if any part of the circuit is open or shorted, or if there is unwanted resistance.

To troubleshoot a problem, always begin by verifying the customer's complaint. Operate the system and others to get a complete understanding of the problem. Often there are other problems that are not as evident or bothersome to the customer that will provide helpful information for diagnostics. Obtain the correct wiring diagram for the car and study the circuit that is affected. From the diagram, you should be able to identify testing points and probable problem areas. Test and use logic to identify the cause of the problem.

An ammeter and a voltmeter connected to a circuit at the different locations shown in Figure 14–59 should give readings as indicated when there are no problems in the circuit.

If there is an open anywhere in the circuit, the ammeter will read zero currents. If the open is in the 1-ohm resistor, a voltmeter connected from C to ground will read zero. However, if the resistor is open

and the voltmeter is connected to points B and C, the reading will be 12 volts. The reason is that the battery, ammeter, voltmeter, 2-ohm resistor, and 3-ohm resistor are all connected together to form a series circuit. Because of the open in the circuit, there is only current flow in the circuit through the meter, not the rest of the circuit. This current flow is very low because the meter has such high resistance. Therefore, the voltmeter will show a reading of 12 volts, indicating little, if any, voltage drop across the resistors.

To help you understand this concept, look at what happens if the 2-ohm resistor was open instead of the 1-ohm resistor. A voltmeter connected from point C to ground would indicate 12 volts. The 1-ohm resistor in series in the high resistance of the voltmeter would have little affect on the circuit. If an open should occur between point E and ground, a voltmeter connected from points B, C, D, or E to ground would read 12 volts. A voltmeter connected across any one of the resistors, from B to C, C to D, or D to E, would also read zero volts, because there will be no voltage drops if there is no current flow.

A short would be indicated by excessive current and/or abnormal voltage drops. These examples illustrate how a voltmeter and ammeter may be used to check for problems in a circuit. An ohmmeter also may be used to measure the values of each component and compared to specifications. If there is no continuity across a part, it is open. If there is more resistance than called for, there is high internal resistance. If there is less resistance than specified, the part is shorted.

Repairing Connecting and Wiring Many automotive electrical problems can be traced to faulty wiring. Loose or corroded terminals, frayed, broken, or oil-soaked wires, and faulty insulation are the most common causes. Wires, fuses, and connections should be checked carefully during troubleshooting. Keep in mind that the insulation does not always appear to be damaged when the wire inside is broken. Also, a terminal may be tight but still may be corroded.

Wire end terminals are connecting devices. They are generally made of tin-plated copper and come in many shapes and sizes. They may be either soldered or crimped in place.

When installing a terminal, select the appropriate size and type terminal. Be sure it is suitable for the unit connecting post or prongs and it has enough current carrying capacity for the circuit. Also, make sure it is heavy enough to endure normal wire flexing and vibration. Ring terminals should be used for critical applications or where heavy vibration occurs. Because they completely encircle the post, they will

FIGURE 14–59   Sample circuit being tested with voltmeter and ammeter.

FIGURE 14–60 Proper method of crimping a wire to a terminal.

not fall off if the connection loosens. Figure 14–60 shows how to crimp a terminal. Be sure to use the proper crimping tool and to follow the tool manufacturer's instructions.

⚠ WARNING!

Do not crimp a terminal with the cutting edge of a pair of pliers. While this method may crimp the terminal, it also weakens it. ∎

General procedures for crimping on a connector follows:

1. Use the correct size stripping opening on the crimping tool (Figure 14–61) and remove enough insulation to allow the wire to completely penetrate the connector.
2. Place the wire into the connector and crimp the connector (Figure 14–62). To get a proper crimp, place the open area of the connector facing toward the anvil. Make sure the wire is compressed under the crimp.
3. Insert the stripped end of the other wire into the connector, if connecting two wires, and crimp in the same manner.
4. Use electrical tape or heat shrink tubing to tightly seal the connection. This will provide good protection for the wire and connector.

The preferred way to connect wires or to install a connector is by soldering. Photo Sequence 8 demonstrates the proper procedure for soldering two copper wires together. Some car manufacturers use aluminum in their wiring. Aluminum cannot be soldered. Follow the manufacturer's guidelines and use the proper repair kits when repairing aluminum wiring.

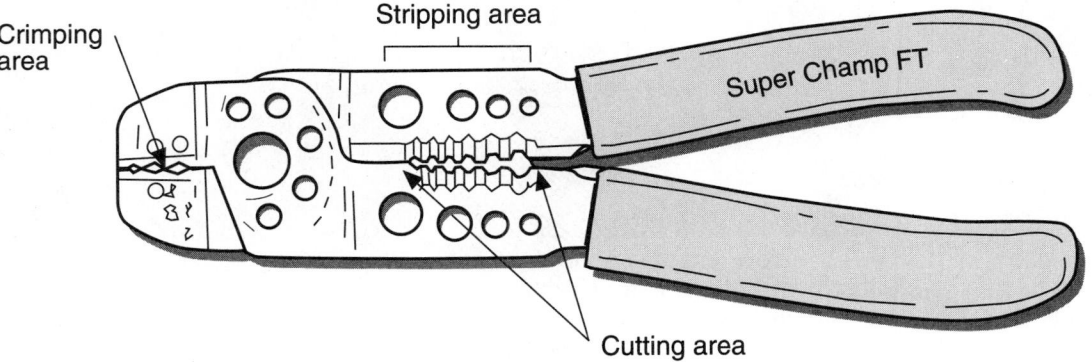

FIGURE 14–61 Typical crimping tool used for making electrical repairs.

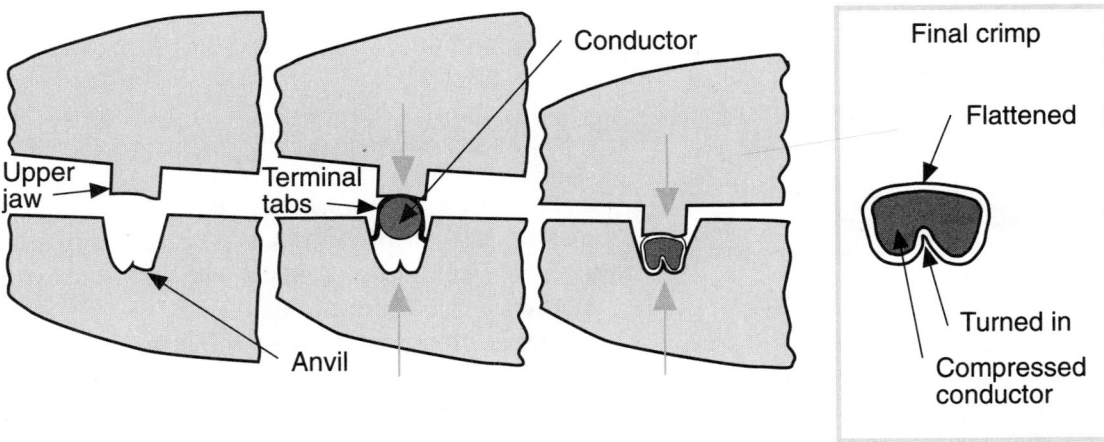

FIGURE 14–62 Crimping the connector properly.

PHOTO SEQUENCE 8

SOLDERING TWO COPPER WIRES TOGETHER

P8–1 Tools required to solder copper wire: 100-watt soldering iron, 60/40 rosin core solder, crimping tool, splice clip, heat shrink tube, heating gun, and safety glasses.

P8–2 Disconnect the fuse that powers the circuit being repaired. Note: If the circuit is not protected by a fuse, disconnect the ground lead of the battery.

P8–3 Cut out the damaged wire.

P8–4 Using the correct size stripper, remove about 1/2 inch of the insulation from both wires.

P8–5 Now remove about 1/2 inch of the insulation from both ends of the replacement wire. The length of the replacement wire should be slightly longer than the length of the wire removed.

P8–6 Select the proper size splice clip to hold the splice.

WARNING!

Never use acid core solder. It creates corrosion and can damage electronic components. ∎

When working with wiring and connectors, never pull on the wires to separate the connectors. This can create an intermittent contact and an intermittent problem that may be very difficult to find later. When required, always use the special tools designed for separating connectors.

Never reroute wires when making repairs. Rerouting wires can result in induced voltages in nearby components. These stray voltages can interfere with the function of electronic circuits.

Dielectric grease is used to moistureproof and protect connections from corrosion. Some car manufacturers suggest using petroleum jelly to protect connection points.

P8–7 Place the correct size and length of heat shrink tube over the two ends of the wire.

P8–8 Overlap the two splice ends and center the splice clip around the wires, making sure the wires extend beyond the splice clip in both directions.

P8–9 Crimp the splice clip firmly in place.

P8–10 Heat the splice clip with the soldering iron while applying solder to the opening of the clip. Do not apply solder to the iron. The iron should be 180 degrees away from the opening of the clip.

P8–11 After the solder cools, slide the heat shrink tube over the splice.

P8–12 Heat the tube with the hot air gun until it shrinks around the splice. Do not overheat the heat shrink tube

ELECTROMAGNETISM BASICS

Electricity and magnetism are related. One can be used to create the other. Current flowing through a wire creates a magnetic field around the wire. Moving a wire through a magnetic field creates current flow in the wire.

Many automotive components, such as alternators, ignition coils, starter solenoids, and magnetic pulse generators operate using these principles of **electromagnetism**.

Fundamentals of Magnetism

A substance is said to be a **magnet** if it has the property of magnetism—the ability to attract such substances as iron, steel, nickel, or cobalt. These are called magnetic materials.

A magnet has two points of maximum attraction, one at each end of the magnet. These points are called **poles**, with one being designated the North pole and the other the South pole (Figure 14–63A). When two magnets are brought together, opposite poles attract (Figure 14–63B), while similar poles repel each other (Figure 14–63C).

A magnetic field, called a **flux field** (Figure 14–64), exists around every magnet. The field consists of imaginary lines along which the magnetic force acts. These lines emerge from the North pole and enter the South pole, returning to the North pole

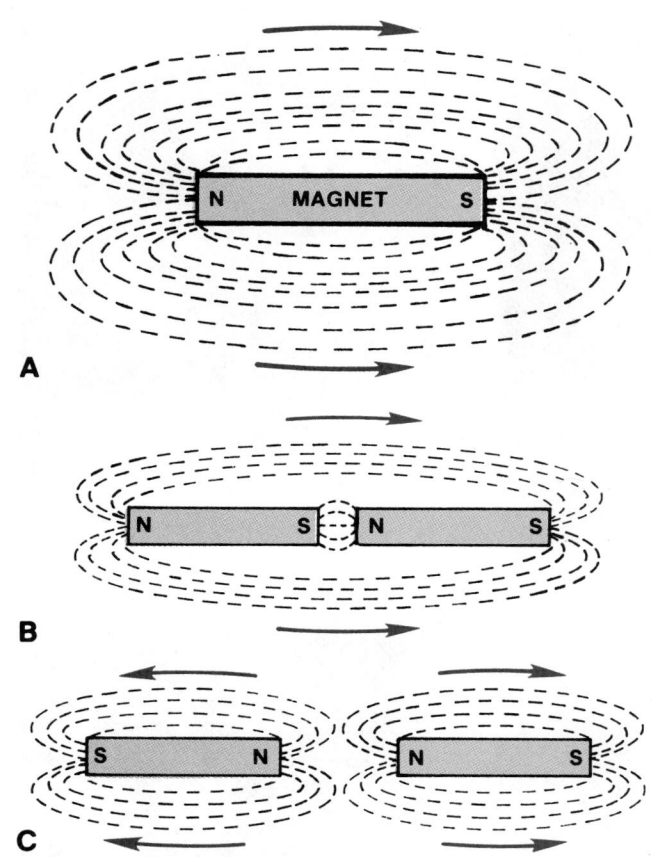

A

B

C

FIGURE 14–63   (A) In a magnet, lines of force emerge from the North pole and travel to the South pole before passing through the magnet back to the North pole. (B) Unlike poles attract, while (C) similar poles repel each other.

through the magnet itself. All lines of force leave the magnet at right angles to the magnet. None of the lines cross each other. All lines are complete.

Magnets can occur naturally in the form of a mineral called magnetite. Artificial magnets can also be made by inserting a bar of magnetic material inside a coil of insulated wire and passing direct current through the coil. This principle is very important in understanding certain automotive electrical components. Another way of creating a magnet is by stroking the magnetic material with a bar magnet. Both methods force the randomly arranged molecules of the magnetic material to align themselves along North and South poles (Figure 14–65).

Artificial magnets can be either temporary or permanent. Temporary magnets are usually made of soft iron. They are easy to magnetize but quickly lose their magnetism when the magnetizing force is removed. Permanent magnets are difficult to magnetize. However, once magnetized they retain this property for very long periods.

The earth is a very large magnet, having a North and South pole, with lines of magnetic force running between them. This is why a compass always aligns itself to straight north and south.

FIGURE 14–64   Iron filings show the lines of magnetic flux.

UNMAGNETIZED

MAGNETIZED

FIGURE 14–65   Molecular arrangement of unmagnetized and magnetized iron.

In 1820, a simple experiment discovered the existence of a magnetic field around a current-carrying wire. When a compass was held over the wire, its needle aligned itself at right angles to the wire (Figure 14–66). The lines of magnetic force are concentric circles around the wire. The density of these circular lines of force is very heavy near the wire and decreases farther away from the wire. As is also shown in the same figure, the polarity of a current-carrying wire's magnetic field changes depending on the direction the current is flowing through the wire.

Remember, these magnetic lines of force or flux lines do not move or flow around the wire. They simply have a direction as shown by their effect on a compass needle. These lines of force are always at right angles to the conducting wire.

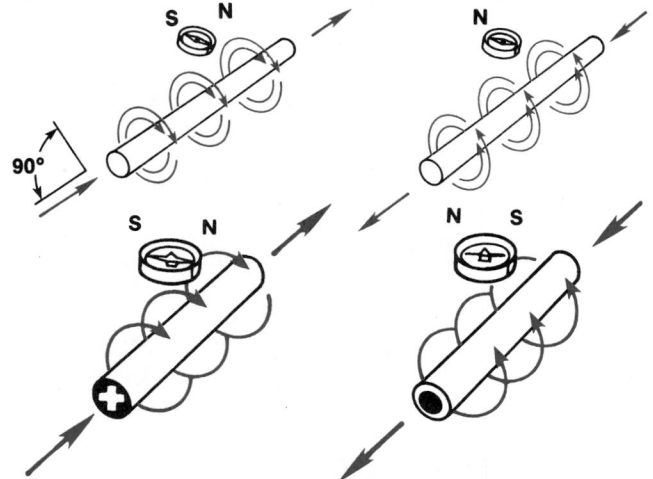

FIGURE 14–66   When current is passed through a conductor such as wire, magnetic lines of force are generated around the wire at right angles to the direction of the current flow.

MAGNETIC FIELDS ADD TOGETHER.

FIGURE 14–67 Increasing the number of conductors carrying current in the same direction increases the strength of the magnetic field around them.

FLUX DENSITY The more flux lines, the stronger the magnetic field at that point. Increasing current will increase **flux density**. Also, two conducting wires lying side by side carrying equal currents in the same direction create a magnetic field equal in strength to one conductor carrying twice the current. Adding more wires also increases the magnetic field (Figure 14–67).

COILS Looping a wire into a coil concentrates the lines of force inside the coil. The resulting magnetic field is the sum of all the single-loop magnetic fields added together (Figure 14–68). The overall effect is the same as placing many wires side by side, each carrying current in the same direction.

Magnetic Circuits and Reluctance

Just as current can only flow through a complete circuit, the lines of flux created by a magnet can only occupy a closed magnetic circuit. The resistance that a magnetic circuit offers to a line of flux is called **reluctance**. Magnetic reluctance can be compared to electrical resistance.

Reconsider the coil of wire shown in Figure 14–68. The air inside the coil has very high reluc-

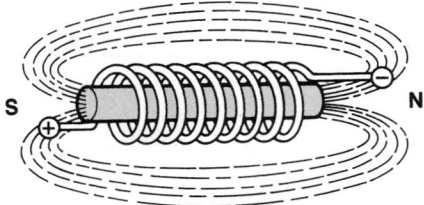

FIGURE 14–69 Placing a soft iron core inside a coil greatly reduces the reluctance of the coil and creates a usable electromagnet.

tance and limits the magnetic strength produced. However, if an iron core is placed inside the coil, magnetic strength increases tremendously. This is because the iron core has a very low reluctance (Figure 14–69).

When a coil is wound around an iron core in this manner, it becomes a usable electromagnet. The strength of the magnetic poles in an electromagnet is directly proportional to the number of turns of wire and the current flowing through them.

The equation for an electromagnetic circuit is similar to Ohm's law for electrical circuits. It states that the number of magnetic lines is proportional to the ampere-turns divided by the reluctance. To summarize:

- Field strength increases if current through the coil increases.
- Field strength increases if the number of coil turns increases.
- If reluctance increases, field strength decreases.

Induced Voltage

Now that we have explained how current can be used to generate a magnetic field, it is time to examine the opposite effect of how magnetic fields can produce electricity.

Figure 14–70 shows a straight piece of wire with the terminals of a voltmeter attached to both ends. If the wire is moved across a magnetic field, the voltmeter registers a small voltage reading. A voltage has been induced in the wire.

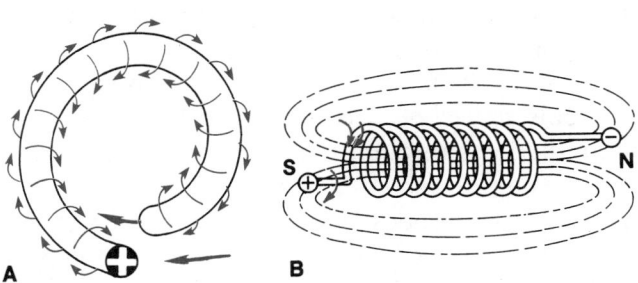

FIGURE 14–68 (A) Forming a wire loop concentrates the lines of force inside the loop. (B) The magnetic field of a wire coil is the sum of all the single-loop magnetic fields.

CONDUCTOR MOVEMENT

VOLTMETER READS VOLTAGE.

FIGURE 14–70 Moving a conductor so it cuts across the magnetic lines of force induces a voltage in the conductor.

FIGURE 14–71 The polarity of the induced voltage depends on the direction in which the conductor moves as it cuts across the magnetic field.

It is important to realize that the wire must cut across the flux lines to induce a voltage. Moving the wire parallel to the lines of flux does not induce voltage.

Voltage can also be induced by holding the wire still and moving the magnetic field at right angles to the wire. This is the exact setup used in a vehicle's alternator. A magnetic field is made to cut across stationary conductors to produce voltage.

The wire becomes a source of electricity and has a polarity or distinct positive and negative end. However, this polarity can be switched depending on the relative direction of movement between the wire and magnetic field (Figure 14–71). This is why charging devices produce alternating current.

The amount of voltage that is induced depends on four factors.

◆ The stronger the magnetic field, the stronger the induced voltage.
◆ The faster the field is being cut, the more lines of flux are cut and the stronger the voltage induced.
◆ The greater the number of conductors, the greater the voltage induced.
◆ The closer the conductor(s) and magnetic field are to right angles (perpendicular) to one another, the greater the induced voltage.

The importance of electromagnetism and induced voltage is clearly seen in chapters dealing with starting, charging, ignition, and electronic control systems.

KEY TERMS

AWG	Continuity
Blade fuse	Dielectric
Capacitor	Electromagnetism
Cartridge fuse	Fixed value resistors
Ceramic fuse	Flux density
Circuit breaker	Flux field
Closed circuit	Fusible link
Conductor	Ganged
Ground wire	Schematic
Grounding	Sensor
High-tension cable	Series circuit
In-line fuse	Series-parallel circuit
Insulator	Solenoid
Magnet	Solid wire
Maxi-fuse	Spade fuse
MPMT	SPDT
Normally closed	SPST
Normally open	Stepped resistor
Ohm's law	Stranded wire
Open circuit	Tapped resistor
Parallel circuit	Thermistor
Poles	Throw
Potentiometer	Trimmer
Relay	Variable resistor
Reluctance	Voltage drop
Resistor wire	Voltage limiter
Rheostat	

SUMMARY

◆ For electrical flow to occur there must be an excess of electrons in one place, a lack of electrons in another, and a path between the two places.
◆ Voltage is the force or pressure in an electrical circuit. A voltage drop across a load in a circuit indicates that work is being done.
◆ Current is measured in amps. This is a measurement of the actual flow rate of electrons in an electrical circuit.
◆ Resistance is measured in ohms. This is a measurement of the size of the restriction to current flow. The more resistance there is, the less current will be able flow through the circuit.
◆ The mathematical relationship between current, resistance, and voltage is expressed in Ohm's law, $E = IR$, where voltage is measured in volts, current in amperes, and resistance in ohms.
◆ The mathematical relationship between current, voltage, and power is expressed in Watt's law, $P = E \times I$. Power is measured in watts or kilowatts (1,000 watts).
◆ Three basic types of circuits are used in automobile wiring systems: series circuits, parallel circuits, and series-parallel circuits.
◆ Electrical schematics are diagrams with electrical symbols that show the parts and how electrical current flows through the vehicle's electrical circuits. They are used in troubleshooting.
◆ An open circuit does not have a complete path for the current to flow through. A shorted circuit is one that allows current to flow along an unwanted path. A high-resistance problem in a circuit decreases the power available for the load.

◆ The strength of an electromagnet depends on the number of current-carrying conductors and what is in the core of the coil. Inducing a voltage requires a magnetic field producing lines of force, conductors that can be moved, and movement between the conductors and the magnetic field so the lines of force are cut.

◆ Fuses, fuse links, maxi-fuses, and circuit breakers protect circuits against overloads. Switches control on/off and direct current flow in a circuit. A relay is an electric switch. A solenoid is an electromagnetic switch that translates current flow into mechanical movement. Resistors limit current flow.

TECH MANUAL

The following procedures are included in Chapter 14 of the *Tech Manual* that accompanies this book:

1. *Check continuity in a circuit with a test light.*
2. *Check applied voltages with a voltmeter.*
3. *Check voltage drop across connectors.*
4. *Inspect and check fuses, fusible links, and circuit breakers.*

REVIEW QUESTIONS

1. What is the name for the formula E = I × R?

2. In a series circuit, resistance is always ____.

3. What kind of diagram is used to troubleshoot an electrical circuit?

4. An ammeter is always connected ____ with the circuit, while a voltmeter is connected in ____ with the circuit.

5. Variable capacitors are called ____.

6. What is the process called in which a conductor cuts across a magnetic field and produces a voltage?

7. What happens in an electrical circuit when the resistance increases?

8. What is the difference between voltage and current?

9. What kind of solder is used to repair electrical wiring?

10. What is an SPST switch?

11. For electrical flow to occur, which of the following must be present?
    a. a difference in the quantity of electrons between two places
    b. a path between two places
    c. a battery
    d. both a and b

12. Technician A says magnetism is a source of electrical energy in an automobile. Technician B says chemical reaction is a source of electrical energy in an automobile. Who is correct?
    a. Technician A   c. Both A and B
    b. Technician B   d. Neither A nor B

13. Which of the following is *not* a circuit-protection device?
    a. a fuse   c. a mini-fuse
    b. a fusible link   d. a maxi-fuse

14. Technician A uses a test light to detect resistance. Technician B uses a jumper wire to test circuit breakers, relays, and lights. Who is correct?
    a. Technician A   c. Both A and B
    b. Technician B   d. Neither A nor B

15. Which type of resistor is commonly used in automotive circuits?
    a. fixed valve   c. variable
    b. stepped   d. all of the above

16. Technician A says the cross-sectional area in circular mms of a solid wire must be calculated to find its gauge. Technician B says the smaller the gauge number, the heavier the wire. Who is correct?
    a. Technician A   c. Both A and B
    b. Technician B   d. Neither A nor B

17. What is the current in a 12-volt circuit with two 6-ohm resistors connected in parallel?
    a. 2 amps   c. 6 amps
    b. 4 amps   d. 12 amps

18. While discussing a 12-volt circuit with three resistors (a 3-ohm, a 6-ohm, and a 2-ohm) in parallel: Technician A says the total resistance of the circuit is 1 ohm. Technician B says the current flow through the 6-ohm resistor is 12-amps. Who is correct?

   a. Technician A   **c.** Both A and B
   b. Technician B   **d.** Neither A nor B

19. Which of the following statements is untrue?

   a. A short causes increased current flow.
   b. An open causes unwanted voltage drops.

   c. High-resistance problems cause increased current flow.
   d. Both opens and high-resistance problems may cause a load not to work.

20. Technician A says a 12-volt light bulb that draws 12 amps has a power output of 1 watt. Technician B says a motor that has 1 ohm of resistance has a power rating of 144 watts if it is connected to a 12-volt battery. Who is correct?

   a. Technician A   **c.** Both A and B
   b. Technician B   **d.** Neither A nor B

15

BASICS OF ELECTRONICS

OBJECTIVES

◆ *Describe how semiconductors, diodes, and transistors work.* ◆ *Explain the principles of operation for common electronic circuits.* ◆ *Explain the principle of multiplexing.* ◆ *Describe the basic function of the central processing unit (CPU).* ◆ *List and describe the functions of the various sensors used by computers.* ◆ *Describe the principle of analog and digital signals.* ◆ *Explain the principle of computer communications.* ◆ *Summarize the function of a binary code.* ◆ *Name the various memory systems used in automotive microprocessors.* ◆ *List and describe the operation of output actuators.* ◆ *Identify the proper procedures to safeguard electronic systems.* ◆ *Describe the basic electronic logic circuits.* ◆ *Explain how to use an oscilloscope for diagnosing electronic systems.*

INTRODUCTION

Computerized engine controls and other features of today's cars would not be possible if it were not for electronics. For purposes of clarity, let us define **electronics** as the technology of controlling electricity. Electronics has become a special technology beyond electricity. Transistors, diodes, semiconductors, integrated circuits, and solid-state devices are all considered to be part of electronics rather than just electrical devices. Keep in mind that all the basic laws of electricity apply to all electronic controls.

Although it is not necessary to understand all of the concepts of computer operation to service the systems they control, a good knowledge will allow you to be more productive.

A **computer** is an electronic device that stores and processes data. It is also capable of operating other computers. The operation of a computer is divided into four basic functions:

1. **Input:** A voltage signal sent from an input device. The device can be a sensor or a button activated by the driver, technician, or mechanical part.
2. **Processing:** The computer uses the input information and compares it to programmed instructions. This information is processed by logic circuits in the computer.

3. **Storage:** The program instructions are stored in the computer's memory. Some of the input signals are also stored in memory for processing later.
4. **Output:** After the computer has processed the sensor input and checked its programmed instructions, it will put out control commands to various output devices. These output devices may be instrument panel displays or output actuators. The output of one computer may also be an input to another computer.

Semiconductors

A semiconductor is a material or device that can function as either a conductor or an insulator, depending on how its structure is arranged. Semiconductor materials have less resistance than an insulator but more resistance than a conductor. Some common semiconductor materials include silicon (Si) and germanium (Ge).

In semiconductor applications, materials have a crystal structure. This means that their atoms do not lose and gain electrons as the atoms in conductors do. Instead, the atoms in these semiconductor materials share outer electrons with each other. In this type of atomic structure, the electrons are tightly held and the element is stable.

Because the electrons are not free, crystals cannot conduct current. These materials are called **electri-**

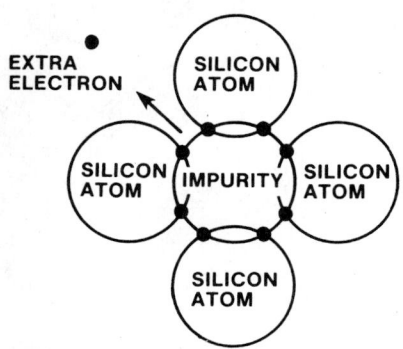

FIGURE 15–1   Atomic structure of N-type silicon semiconductor.

cally inert materials. To function as semiconductors, a small amount of trace element must be added. The addition of these traces, called **impurities**, allows the material to function as a semiconductor. The type of impurity added determines what type of semiconductor will be produced.

N-Type Semiconductors   N-type semiconductors have loose, or excess, electrons. They have a negative charge. This enables them to carry current. N-type semiconductors are produced by adding an impurity with five electrons in the outer ring (called pentavalent atoms). Four of these electrons fit into the crystal structure, but the fifth is free. This excess of electrons produces the negative charge. Figure 15–1 shows an example.

P-Type Semiconductors   P-type semiconductors are positively charged materials. This enables them to carry current. P-type semiconductors are produced by adding an impurity with three electrons in the outer ring (trivalent atoms). When this element is added to silicon or germanium, the three outer electrons fit into the pattern of the crystal, leaving a hole where a fourth electron would fit. This hole is actually a positively charged empty space that carries the current in the P-type semiconductor. Figure 15–2 shows an example of a P-type semiconductor.

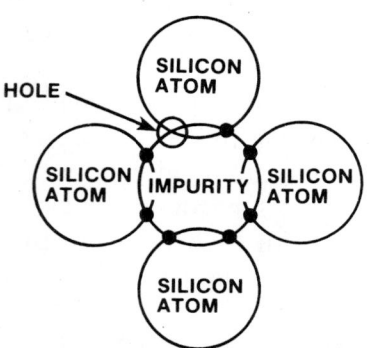

FIGURE 15–2   Atomic structure of P-type silicon semiconductor.

HOLE FLOW   Understanding how semiconductors carry current without losing electrons requires understanding the concept of hole flow. The holes in a P-type semiconductor, being positively charged, attract electrons. Although the electrons cannot be freed from their atom, they can rearrange their pattern and fill a hole in a nearby atom. Whenever this happens, the electron leaves a hole. This hole in turn is filled by another electron, and the process continues. The electrons move toward the positive side of the structure, and the holes move to the negative side. This is the principle by which semiconductors carry current.

Semiconductor Uses   Because semiconductors have no moving parts, they seldom wear out or need adjustment. Semiconductors, or solid-state devices, are also small, require little power to operate, are reliable, and generate very little heat. For all these reasons, semiconductors are being used in many applications.

Diodes and Transistors

Because a semiconductor can function as both a conductor and an insulator, it is very useful as a switching device. How a semiconductor functions depends on the way current flows (or tries to flow) through it. Two common semiconductor devices are diodes and transistors.

Diodes   The diode is the simplest semiconductor device. Basically there are three types of diodes used in automobiles: regular diodes, LEDs, and Zener diodes.

A **diode** allows current to flow in one direction (Figure 15–3) but not in the opposite direction. Therefore, it can function as a switch, acting as either conductor or insulator, depending on the direction of current flow. Diodes turn on when the polarity of the current is correct and turn off when the flow has the wrong polarity.

One application of diodes is in the alternator, where they function as one-way valves for current flow. All charging systems, whether alternators or generators, produce alternating current. In the generator, current was rectified (changed from AC to DC) by a rotating commutator and a set of brushes. In the alternator, current is rectified by the use of diodes. The diodes are arranged so that current can leave the alternator in one direction only (as direct current).

Inside a diode are small positive and negative areas, which are separated by a thin boundary area. The boundary area is called the **PN junction**. When a diode is placed in a circuit with the positive side of the circuit connected to the positive side of the diode and the negative side of the circuit connected to the negative side of the circuit, the diode is said to have **forward bias** (Figure 15–4).

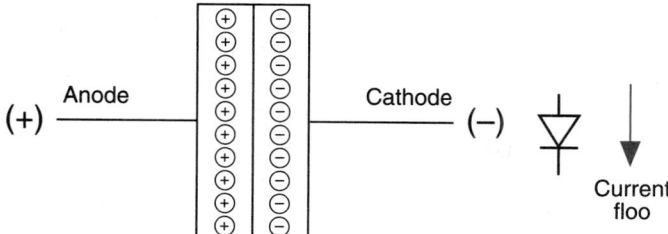

FIGURE 15–3 Diode and its schematical symbol.

Unlike electrical charges are attracted to each other and like charges repel each other. Therefore, the positive charge from the circuit's power supply is attracted to the negative side of the circuit. The voltage in the circuit is much stronger than the charges inside the diode and causes the charges inside the diode to move. The diode's P conductive material is repelled by the positive charge of the circuit and is pushed toward the N material and the N material is pushed toward the P. This causes the PN junction to become a conductor, allowing the circuit's current to flow.

When **reverse bias** is applied to the diode, the P and N areas of the diode are connected to opposite charges. Since opposites attract, the P material moves toward the negative part of the circuit whereas the N material moves toward the positive part of the circuit. This empties the PN junction and current flow stops.

Light-emitting Diodes (**LEDs**) are much the same as regular diodes (Figure 15–5). However, they emit light when they are forward biased. LEDs are very

current sensitive and can be damaged if they subjected to more than 50 mAmps. LEDs also require higher amounts of voltages to turn on than do regular diodes. Normally 1.5 to 2.5 volts are required to forward bias an LED enough to cause it to light up. LEDs also offer much less resistance to reverse bias voltages. High reverse bias voltages may cause the LED to light or cause it to burn up.

Zener diodes (Figure 15–6) are a more complex type of diode. They are used to regulate voltage in a circuit and are available in many voltage sizes, typically from 2 to 200 volts. Although Zener diodes work in the same way as a regular diode when forward biased, they are placed backwards in a circuit. When the Zener voltage is reached, the Zener diode begins to allow current flow but maintains a voltage drop across itself. This voltage drop is regulated at whatever voltage the diode is rated. A Zener diode functions just like a regular diode until a certain voltage is reached. When the voltage level reaches this point, the Zener diode allows current to flow in the reverse direction. Zener diodes are often used in electronic voltage regulators.

Transistor Another semiconductor commonly used in the automotive industry is the **transistor**. These devices are used in place of switches and relays in electronic circuits. They are used to turn an electrical circuit ON or OFF and are controlled by another electrical circuit. Perhaps the easiest way to describe the action of a transistor is to say it is a switch controlled by conditions. The conditions are the voltages present at the parts of the transistor.

A transistor is produced by joining three sections of semiconductor materials. Like the diode, it is very useful as a switching device, functioning as either a conductor or an insulator. Figure 15–7 shows two designs of transistors, which come in many different sizes and types.

A transistor resembles a diode with an extra side. It can consist of two P-type materials and one N-type material or two N-type materials and one P-type

FIGURE 15–4 Forward-biased voltage allows current flow through the diode.

FIGURE 15–5 (A) An LED uses a lens to emit the light generated by current flow. (B) Schematic symbol for an LED.

FIGURE 15–6 A simplified gauge circuit with a Zener diode used to maintain a constant supply voltage to the gauge.

FIGURE 15–7 Typical transistors.

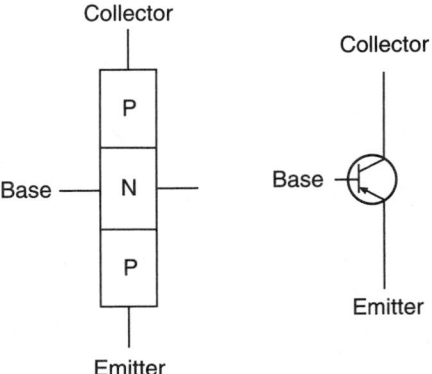

FIGURE 15–8 PNP transistor and its schematical symbol.

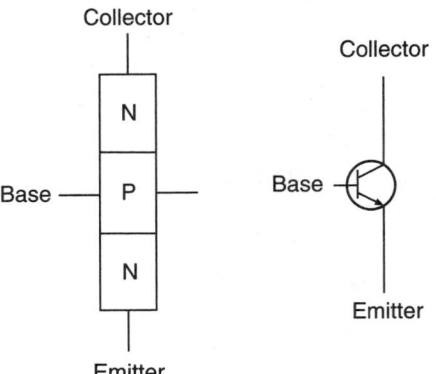

FIGURE 15–9 NPN transistor and its schematical symbol.

material. These are called **PNP** and **NPN** types. In both types, junctions occur where the materials are joined. Figure 15–8 shows a PNP junction transistor in a circuit, while Figure 15–9 shows an NPN transistor. Notice that each of the three sections has a lead connected to it. This allows any of the three sections to be connected to the circuit. The different names for the legs of the transistor are the **emitter**, **base**, and **collector**.

The center section is called the base and is the controlling part of the circuit or where the larger controlled part of the circuit is switched ON and OFF. The path to ground for the base circuit is through the emitter leg of the transistor. A resistor is normally in the base circuit to keep current flow low. This prevents damage to the transistor. The emitter and collector make up the controlled circuit. When a transistor is drawn in electrical schematics, the arrow on the emitter points to the direction of current flow. When positive voltage is applied to the base of an NPN transistor, the emitter to collector circuit is turned on (Figure 15–10).

The base of a PNP transistor is controlled by its ground. Current flows in from the emitter through the base, then to ground. A negative voltage or

ground must be applied to the base to turn on a PNP transistor. When this transistor is on, the circuit from the emitter to the collector is closed.

Transistors can also serve as variable switches. By varying the voltage applied to the base, the completeness of the emitter and collector circuit will also vary. This is done simply by the presence of a variable resistor in the base circuit. This type of arrangement is typically part of a light-dimming circuit.

Semiconductor Circuits

One transistor or diode is limited in its ability to do complex tasks. However, when many semiconductors

FIGURE 15–10 When positive voltage is applied to the base of an NPN transistor, current flows through the collector and the emitter.

are combined into a circuit, they can perform complex functions. An example of this is the electronic voltage regulator.

The heart of the electronic regulator is a Zener diode. As mentioned, the Zener diode has the ability to conduct in the reverse direction without damage.

The Zener diode used in regulators is doped, so it conducts in reverse once the maximum battery voltage has been achieved.

Figure 15–11 shows a typical transistorized regulator circuit in simplified form. When the voltage of the vehicle's system rises above the maximum battery

FIGURE 15–11 (A) Voltage regulator operation when battery is charging. (B) Voltage regulator operation when maximum battery voltage is exceeded.

voltage, the diode conducts and permits current to flow to the base of transistor 1. This turns the transistor on, which in turn switches off transistor 2. Transistor 2 is in control of field current for the alternator. With it off, no field current can flow, thus shutting off the alternator until the voltage level drops below specification. Transistor 2 is acting like a switch turning field current on then off as the system voltage rises and falls above and below the specified voltage. This occurs many times a second and cannot be measured with a standard voltmeter. The thermistor in the upper left of the diagram gives the temperature voltage change necessary to keep the battery charged in cold weather. An actual voltage regulator would have many additional parts, such as capacitors to protect the regulator from voltage surges. These systems can use conventional electronic components or integrated circuits.

INTEGRATED CIRCUITS

An **integrated circuit** is simply a large number of diodes, transistors, and other electronic components, such as resistors and capacitors, all mounted on a single piece of semiconductor material (Figure

15–12). These circuits are commonly called **ICs** or **chips**. These circuits are extremely small. Circuitry that used to take up entire rooms can now fit into a pocket. The principles of semiconductor operation remain the same in integrated circuits.

The size of chips is constantly becoming smaller. This means electronics is no longer confined to the simple tasks, such as rectifying alternator current. Enough transistors, diodes, and other solid-state components can be installed in a car to make logical decisions and issue commands to automobile systems, such as the ignition, fuel injection, transmission, brake, and suspension systems.

OPERATION OF MICROPROCESSORS

The microprocessor has taken over many of the tasks in cars and trucks that were formerly performed by vacuum, mechanical, or electromechanical devices. When properly programmed, they can carry out explicit instructions with blinding speed and almost flawless consistency.

A typical electronic control system is made up of sensors, actuators, and related wiring that is tied into

☒ P Type
☐ N Type
▨ Poly
☐☐ Contact
▨ Metal

FIGURE 15–12 Enlarged illustration of an IC with thousands of transistors, diodes, resistors, and capacitors. The actual size of this chip can be less than 1/4 inch square.

a central processor called a **microprocessor** or micro-computer (a smaller version of a computer).

The central processing unit (**CPU**) is the brain of a computer. The CPU is constructed of thousands of transistors placed on a small chip. The CPU brings information into and out of the computer's memory. The input information is processed in the CPU and checked against the program in the computer's memory. The CPU also checks the memory for any other information regarding programmed parameters. The information obtained by the CPU can be altered according to the instructions of the program. The CPU may be ordered to make logic decisions on the information received. Once these decisions, or calculations, are made, the CPU sends out commands to make the required corrections or adjustments to the system being controlled (Figure 15–13).

Sensors

The CPU receives inputs that it checks with programmed values. Depending on the input, the computer will control the actuator(s) until the programmed results are obtained. The inputs can come from other computers, the driver, the technician, or through a variety of sensors.

Driver input signals are usually provided by momentarily applying a ground through a switch. The computer receives this signal and performs the desired functions. For example, if the driver wishes to reset the trip odometer on a digital instrument panel, a reset button is depressed. This switch provides a momentary ground that the computer receives as an input and sets the trip odometer to zero.

Switches can be used as inputs for any operation that only requires a yes-no, or on-off, condition. Other inputs include those supplied by means of a sensor and those signals returned to the computer in the form of **feedback**. Feedback means that data concerning the effects of the computer's commands are fed back to the computer as an input signal.

If the computer sends a command signal to actuate an output device, a feedback signal may be sent back from the actuator to inform the computer that the task was performed. The feedback signal will

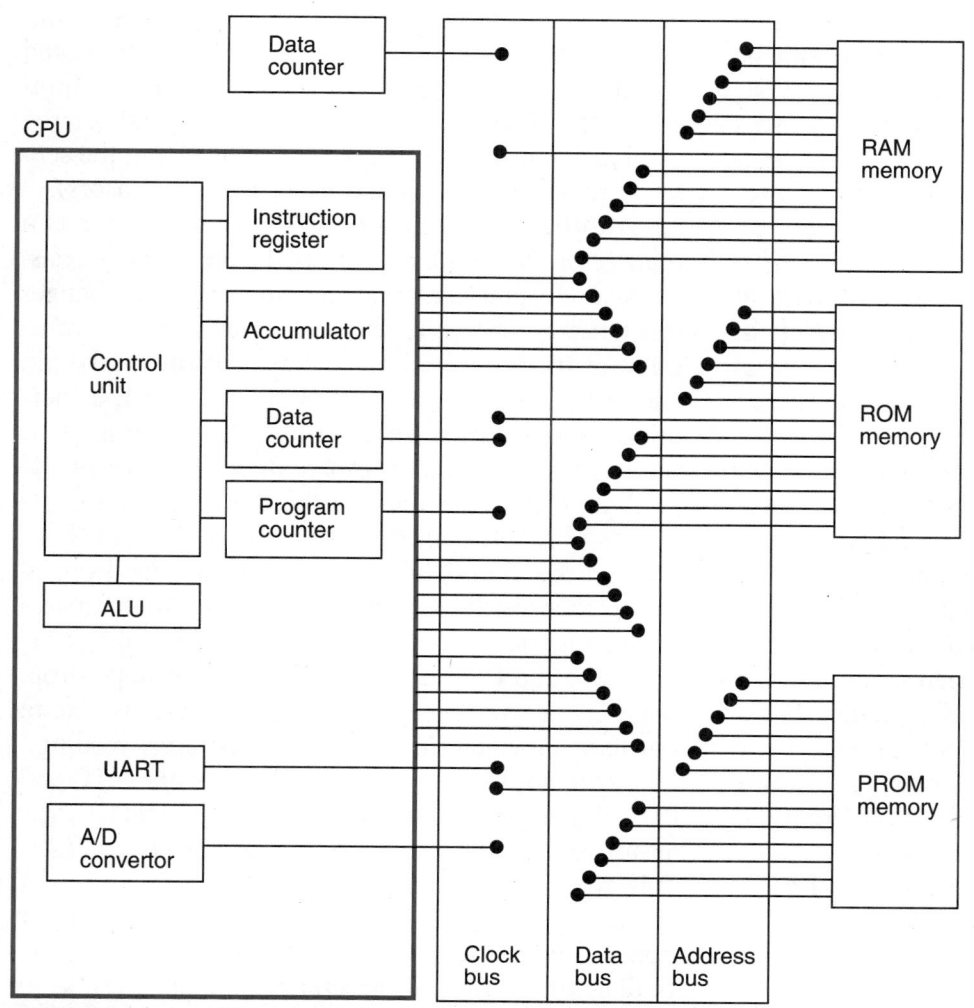

FIGURE 15–13 Main components of a computer and its CPU.

FIGURE 15–14   A potentiometer sensor circuit measures the amount of voltage drop to determine the position of the A/C mode door.

confirm both the position of the output device and the operation of the actuator. Another form of feedback is for the computer to monitor voltage as a switch, relay, or other actuator is activated. Changing positions of an actuator should result in predictable changes in the computer's voltage sensing circuit. The computer may set a diagnostic code if it does not receive the correct feedback signal.

All sensors perform the same basic function. They detect a mechanical condition (movement or position), chemical state, or temperature condition and change it into an electrical signal that can be used by the computer to make decisions. The CPU makes decisions based on information it receives from the sensors. Each sensor used in a particular system has a specific job to do (for example, monitor throttle position, vehicle speed, manifold pressure). Together these sensors provide enough information to help the computer form a complete picture of vehicle operation. Even though there are a variety of different sensor designs, they all fall under one of two operating categories: reference voltage sensors or voltage-generating sensors.

Reference voltage (**Vref**) sensors provide input to the computer by modifying or controlling a constant, predetermined voltage signal. This signal, which can have a reference value from 5 to 9 volts, is generated and sent out to each sensor by a reference voltage regulator located inside the CPU. Because the computer knows a certain voltage value has been sent out, it can indirectly interpret things like motion, temperature, and component position, based on what comes back. For example, consider the operation of the throttle position sensor (TPS). During acceleration (from idle to wide-open throttle), the computer monitors throttle plate movement based on the changing reference voltage signal returned by the TPS. (The TPS is a type of variable resistor known as a rotary potentiometer that changes circuit resistance based on throttle shaft rotation.) As TPS resistance varies, the computer is

programmed to respond in a specific manner (for example, increase fuel delivery or alter spark timing) to each corresponding voltage change.

Most sensors presently in use are variable resistors or potentiometers (Figure 15–14). They modify a voltage to or from the computer, indicating a constantly changing status that can be calculated, compensated for, and modified. That is, most sensors simply control a voltage signal from the computer. When varying internal resistance of the sensor allows more or less voltage to ground, the computer senses a voltage change on a monitored signal line. The monitored signal line may be the output signal from the computer to the sensor (one- and two-wire sensors), or the computer may use a separate return line from the sensor to monitor voltage changes (three-wire sensors).

Another commonly used variable resistor is a thermistor. A thermistor is a solid-state variable resistor made from a semiconductor material that changes resistance in relation to temperature changes. Thermistors are used to monitor engine coolant, intake air, and ambient temperatures. By monitoring the thermistor's resistance value, the CPU is capable of observing small changes in temperature. The CPU sends a reference voltage to the thermistor, normally 5 volts, through a fixed resistor. As the current flows through the thermistor to ground, voltage is dropped by the thermistor. A voltage-sensing circuit compares the voltage sent out by the CPU to the voltage returned to the CPU and determines the voltage drop. Using its programmed values, the computer is able to translate the voltage drop into a temperature reading.

There are two basic types of thermistors: NTC and PTC. A negative temperature coefficient (**NTC**) thermistor reduces its resistance as temperature increases. This type is the most commonly used thermistor. A positive temperature coefficient (**PTC**) thermistor increases its resistance with an increase in temperature. To diagnose thermistors accurately, you must be able to identify the type by looking at a wiring diagram.

FIGURE 15–15 Wheatstone bridge.

Wheatstone bridges (Figure 15–15) are also used as variable resistance sensors. These are typically constructed of four resistors, connected in series-parallel between an input terminal and a ground terminal. Three of the resistors are kept at the same value. The fourth resistor is a sensing resistor. When all four of the resistors have the same value, the bridge is balanced and the voltage sensor will have a value of 0 volts. If the sensing resistor changes value, a change will occur in the circuit's balance. The sensing circuit will receive a voltage reading proportional to the amount of resistance change. If the Wheatstone bridge is used to measure temperature, temperature changes will be indicated as a change in voltage by the sensing circuit. Wheatstone bridges are also used to measure pressure (**piezoresistive**) and mechanical strain.

In addition to variable resistors, another commonly used reference voltage sensor is a switch. By opening and closing a circuit, switches provide the necessary voltage information to the computer so vehicles can maintain the proper performance and driveability.

While most sensors are variable resistance/reference voltage, there is another category of sensors—the **voltage-generating devices**. These sensors include components like the magnetic pulse generators, Hall-effect switches, oxygen sensors (zirconium dioxide), and knock sensors (piezoelectric), which are capable of producing their own input voltage signal. This varying voltage signal, when received by the computer, enables the computer to monitor and adjust for changes in the computerized engine control system.

Magnetic pulse generators use the principle of magnetic induction to produce a voltage signal. They are also called permanent magnet (PM) generators. These sensors are commonly used to send data to the computer about the speed of the monitored component. This data provides information about vehicle speed, shaft speed, and wheel speed. The signals from speed sensors are used for instrumentation, cruise control systems, antilock brake systems, ignition systems, speed-sensitive steering systems, and automatic ride control systems. A magnetic pulse generator is

also used to inform the computer about the position of a monitored device. This is common in engine controls where the CPU needs to know the position of the crankshaft in relation to rotational degrees.

The major components of a pulse generator are a timing disc and a pick-up coil. The **timing disc** is attached to a rotating shaft or cable. The number of teeth on the timing disc is determined by the manufacturer and the application. If only the number of revolutions is required, the timing disc may have only one tooth. Whereas, if it is important to track quarter revolutions, the timing disc needs at least four teeth. The teeth will cause a voltage generation that is constant per revolution of the shaft. For example, a vehicle speed sensor may be designed to deliver 4,000 pulses per mile. The number of pulses per mile remains constant regardless of speed. The computer calculates how fast the vehicle is going based on the frequency of the signal. The timing disc is also known as an armature, reluctor, trigger wheel, pulse wheel, or timing core.

The **pick-up coil** is also known as a stator, sensor, or pole piece. It remains stationary while the timing disc rotates in front of it. The changes of magnetic lines of force generate a small voltage signal in the coil. A pick-up coil consists of a permanent magnet with fine wire wound around it.

An air gap is maintained between the timing disc and the pick-up coil. As the timing disc rotates in front of the pick-up coil, the generator sends a pulse signal (Figure 15–16). As a tooth on the timing disc aligns with the core of the pick-up coil, it repels the magnetic field. The magnetic field is forced to flow through the coil and pick-up core (Figure 15–17). When the tooth passes the core, the magnetic field is able to expand (Figure 15–18). This action is repeated every time a tooth passes the core. The moving lines of magnetic force cut across the coil windings and induce a voltage signal.

When a tooth approaches the core, a positive current is produced as the magnetic field begins to concentrate around the coil. When the tooth and

FIGURE 15–16　Pulse signal sine wave.

FIGURE 15–17　A strong magnetic field is produced in the pick-up coil as the teeth align with the core.

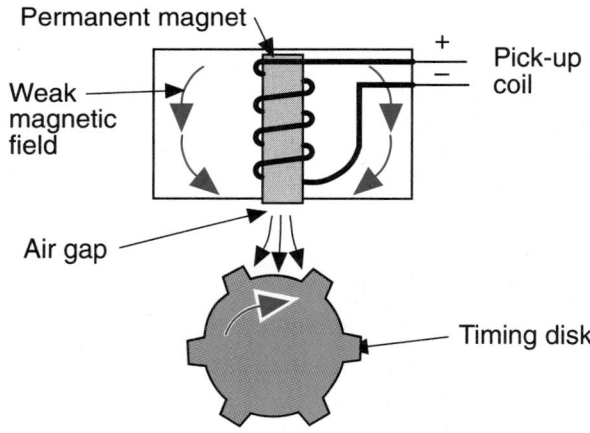

FIGURE 15–18　The magnetic field expands and weakens as the teeth pass the core.

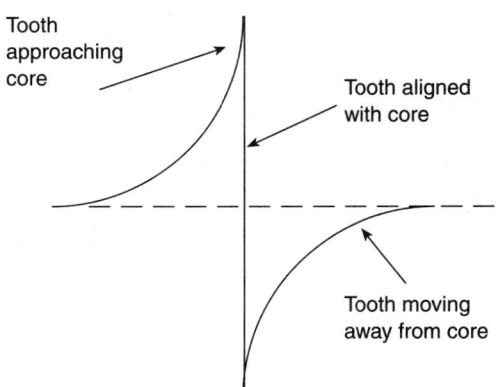

FIGURE 15–19　Waveform produced by a magnetic pulse generator.

core align, there is no more expansion or contraction of the magnetic field and the voltage drops to zero. When the tooth passes the core, the magnetic field expands and a negative current is produced (Figure 15–19). The resulting pulse signal is sent to the CPU.

The **Hall-effect switch** performs the same function as a magnetic pulse generator. It operates on the principle that if a current is allowed to flow through thin conducting material exposed to a magnetic field, another voltage is produced (Figure 15–20).

A Hall-effect switch contains a permanent magnet and a thin semiconductor layer made of Gallium arsenate crystal (Hall layer) and a shutter wheel (Figure 15–21). The Hall layer has a negative and a positive terminal connected to it. Two additional terminals located on either side of the Hall layer are used for the output circuit.

The permanent magnet is located directly across from the Hall layer so its lines of flux will bisect at right angles to the current flow. The permanent magnet is mounted; a small air gap is between it and the Hall layer.

A steady current is applied to the crystal of the Hall layer. This produces a signal voltage perpendicular to the direction of current flow and magnetic flux. The signal voltage produced is a result of the effect the magnetic field has on the electrons. When the magnetic field bisects the supply current flow, the electrons are deflected toward the Hall layer negative terminal (Figure 15–22, page 372). This results in a weak voltage potential being produced in Hall switch.

The shutter wheel consists of a series of alternating windows and vanes. It creates a magnetic shunt that changes the strength of the magnetic field from the permanent magnet. The shutter wheel is attached to a rotational component. As the wheel rotates, the

FIGURE 15–20 Hall-effect principles of voltage induction.

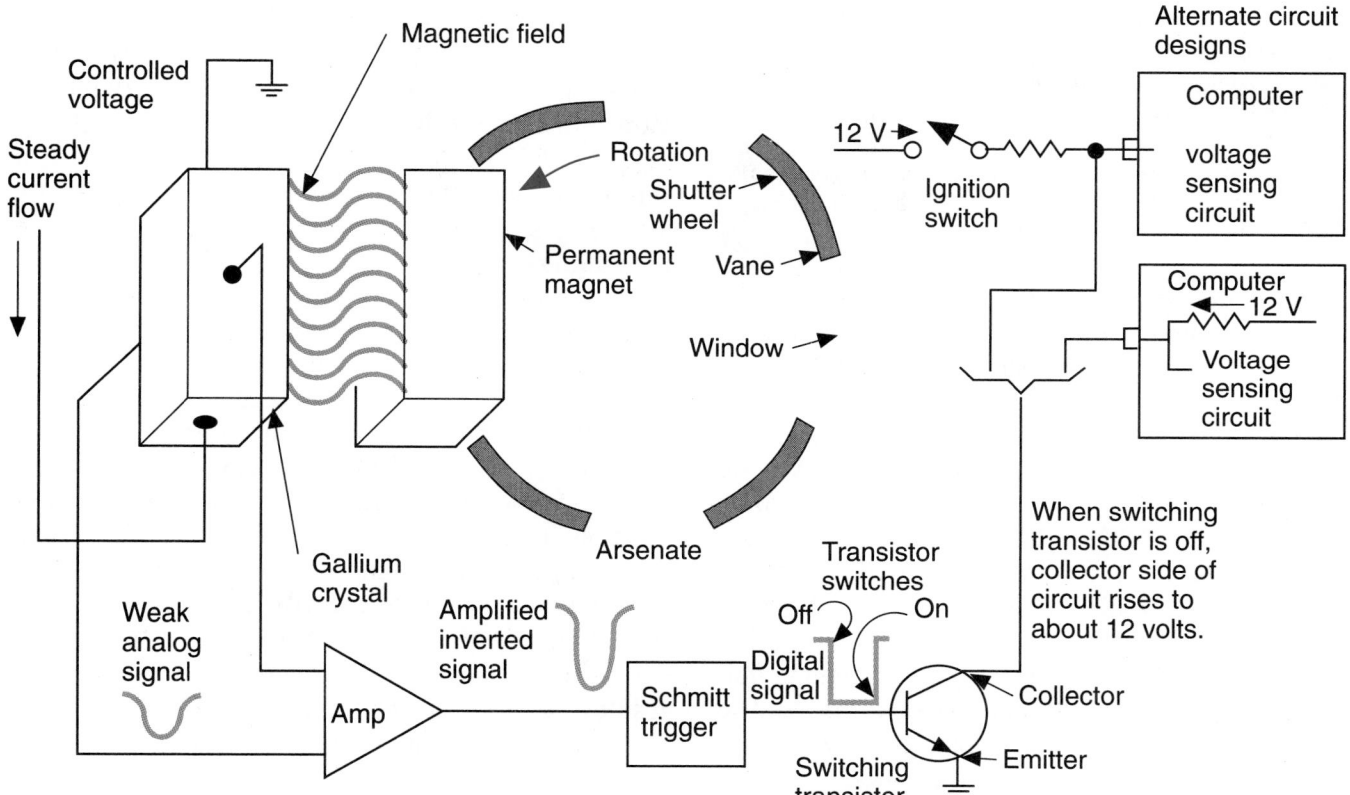

FIGURE 15–21 Typical circuit of a Hall-effect switch.

vanes pass through the air gap. When a shutter vane enters the gap, it intercepts the magnetic field and shields the Hall layer from its lines of force. The electrons in the supply current are no longer disrupted and return to a normal state. This results in low voltage potential in the signal circuit of the Hall switch.

The signal voltage leaves the Hall layer as a weak analog signal. To be used by the CPU, the signal must be conditioned. It is first amplified because it is too weak to produce a desirable result. The signal is also inverted; a low input signal is converted into a high output signal. It is then sent through a **Schmitt trigger**, which is a type of A/D converter, where it is digitized and conditioned into a clean square wave signal. The signal is finally sent to a switching transistor.

The computer senses the turning on and off of the switching transistor to determine the frequency of the signals and calculates speed.

Regardless of the type of sensors used in electronic control systems, the computer is incapable of functioning properly without input signal voltage from sensors.

Communication Signals

Voltage does not flow through a conductor, current flows while voltage is the pressure that pushes the current. However, voltage can be used as a **signal**, for example, difference in voltage levels, frequency of change, or switching from positive to negative values can be used as a signal.

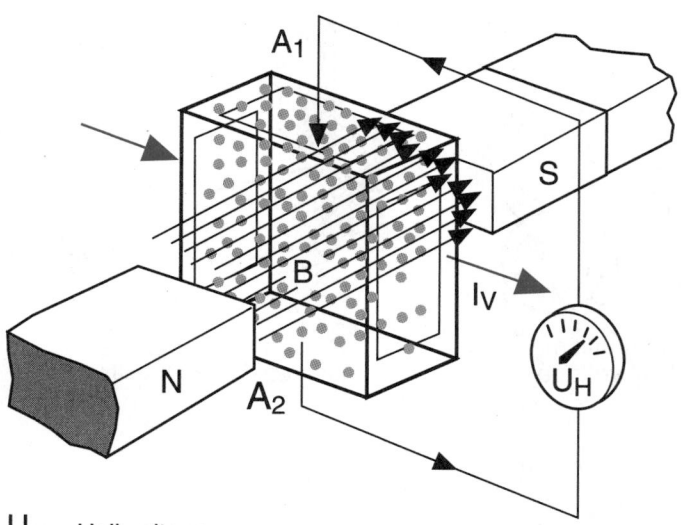

U_H = Hall voltage
B = Magnetic field (flux density)
I_V = Constant supply current
A_1, A_2 = Hall layer

FIGURE 15–22   The magnetic field causes the electrons from the supply current to gather at the Hall layer's negative terminal. This creates a voltage potential.

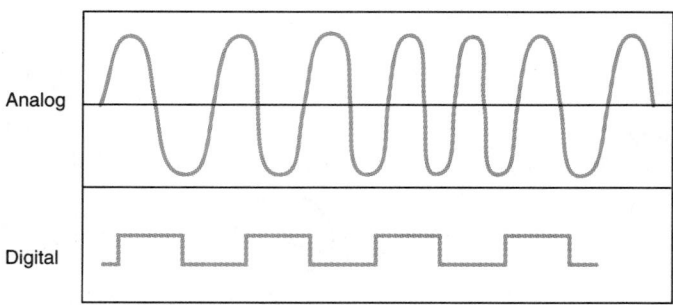

FIGURE 15–23   Analog signals can be constantly variable. Digital signals are either on-off or low-high.

A computer is capable of reading voltage signals. The programs used by the CPU are "burned" into IC chips using a series of numbers. These numbers represent various combinations of voltages that the computer can understand. The voltage signals to the computer can be either analog or digital. **Analog** means a voltage signal is infinitely variable, or can be changed, within a given range. **Digital** means a voltage signal that is one of two states—either on-off, yes-no, or high-low. Most input sensors are designed to produce a voltage signal that varies within a given range, which is an analog signal. For example, ambient temperature sensors do not change abruptly. The temperature varies in infinite steps from low to high.

The same is true for several other outputs, such as engine speed, vehicle speed, fuel flow, etc.

Compared to an analog voltage signal, digital voltage patterns are square-waved because the transition from one voltage to another is very abrupt (Figure 15–23). A digital signal is produced by an on-off or high-low voltage. In a digital signal, the voltage is represented by a series of digits, which create a **binary code**.

A computer can only read a digital binary signal. To overcome this communication problem, all analog voltage signals are converted to a digital format by a device known as an analog-to-digital converter (**A/D converter**). The A/D converter (Figure 15–24) is located in a section of the processor called the input signals. However, some sensors, such as the Hall-effect switch, produce a digital or square-wave signal that can go directly to the CPU as an input. The term **square wave** is used to describe the appearance of a digital circuit after it has been plotted on a graph. The abrupt changes in circuit condition (on and off) result in a series of horizontal and vertical lines that connect to form a square-shaped pattern.

FIGURE 15–24   The A/D converter prepares input signals for the CPU.

DIGITAL SIGNAL

BINARY TRANSLATION

FIGURE 15–25 Each zero (0) and one (1) represents a bit of information. When eight bits are combined in specific sequence, they form a byte or word that makes up the basis of a computer's language. *Courtesy of General Motors Corporation*

Decimal Number	Binary Number Code 8421	Binary to Decimal Conversion
TABLE 15–1 BINARY NUMBER CODE		
0	0000	= 0 + 0 = 0
1	0001	= 0 + 1 = 1
2	0010	= 2 + 0 = 2
3	0011	= 2 + 1 = 3
4	0100	= 4 + 0 = 4
5	0101	= 4 + 1 = 5
6	0110	= 4 + 2 = 6
7	0111	= 4 + 2 + 1 = 7
8	1000	= 8 + 0 = 8

The A/D converter changes a series of signals to a binary number made up of 1s and 0s. Voltage above a given value converts to 1, and zero voltage converts to 0 (Figure 15–25). Each 1 or 0 represents a **bit** of information. Eight bits equal a **byte** (sometimes referred to as a word). All communication between the CPU, the memories, and the interfaces is in binary code, with each information exchange in the form of a byte.

To get an idea of how binary coding works, let us see how signals from the coolant temperature sensor (CTS) are processed by the CPU. The CTS is a type of thermistor (negative coefficient to be exact) that controls a reference signal based on temperature changes. Upon receiving the CTS's analog signals, the input conditioner immediately groups each signal value into predetermined voltage range and assigns a numeric value to each range. In our example, use the following ranges and numeric values: 0 to 2 volts = 1, 2 to 4 volts = 2, and 4 to 5 volts = 3 (assuming a Vref of 5 volts). If you are wondering where these ranges and numeric values come from, they are written into the computer's memory by a human programmer at the time of the computer's development.

When the CTS is hot, its resistance is low and the modified voltage signal it sends back falls into the high range (4 to 5 volts). Upon entering the A/D converter, the voltage value is assigned a numeric value of 3 (based on the ranges previously cited) and is ready for further translation into a binary code format. Binary numbers are represented by the numbers 0 and 1. Any number and word can be translated into a combination of binary 1s and 0s.

Without going into the finer points of binary numbering, the number 3 in binary is expressed as

11. To the thousands of tiny transistors and diodes that act as the on-off switches inside digitally oriented microprocessors, 11 instructs the computer to turn on or apply voltage to a specific circuit for a predetermined length of time (based on its program). Table 15–1 illustrates how binary numbers can be converted into decimal or base ten numbers. Note how the right-hand binary number equals one and the left number equals eight.

In addition to A/D conversion, some voltage signals require amplification before they can be relayed to the CPU. To perform this task, an input conditioner known as an **amplifier** is used to strengthen weak voltage signals (Figure 15–26).

After input has been generated, conditioned, and passed along to the computer, it is ready to be processed for the purposes of performing work and displaying information. The computer contains a crystal oscillator or **clock** that delivers a constant time pulse. The clock is a crystal that electrically vibrates when subjected to current at certain voltage levels. As a result, the chip produces very regular series of voltage pulses. The clock maintains an orderly flow of information through the computer circuits by transmitting one bit of binary code for each pulse. In this manner, the computer is capable of distinguishing between the binary codes such as 101 and 1001. For the CPU to make the most informed decisions regarding system operation, sensor input is sent through different logic gates constructed within the CPU.

Logic Gates

Logic gates are the thousands of field-effect transistors (**FET**) incorporated into the computer's circuitry. The FETs use the incoming voltage patterns to determine the pattern of pulses leaving the gate. These circuits are called logic gates because they act as gates

FIGURE 15–26   Here is an example of how digital voltage signals relay information. After receiving the digital signal and converting it to a binary format, the information is then displayed in a numerical form that is easily understood by the CPU. *Courtesy of General Motors Corporation*

to output voltage signals depending on different combinations of input signals. The following are the most common logic gates and their operation. The symbols in the figures represent functions and not electronic construction.

Truth table	
Input	Output
0	1
1	0

FIGURE 15–27   NOT gate symbol and truth table. The NOT gate inverts the input signal.

1. **NOT gate:** A NOT gate simply reverses binary 1s and 0s and vice versa (Figure 15–27). A high input results in a low output, and a low input results in a high output.

2. **AND gate:** The AND gate will have at least two inputs and one output. The operation of the AND gate is similar to two switches in series with a load (Figure 15–28). The only way the light will turn on is if switches A and B are closed. The output of the gate will be high only if both inputs are high. Before current can be present at the output of the gate, current must be present at the base of both transistors (Figure 15–29).

Truth table		
A	B	Output
0	0	0
0	1	0
1	0	0
1	1	1

FIGURE 15–28   AND gate symbol and truth table. The AND gate operates similarly to switches in series.

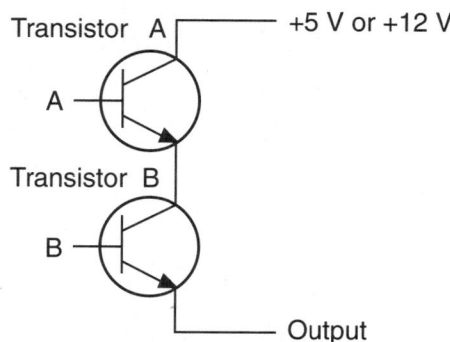

FIGURE 15–29 AND gate circuit.

3. OR gate: The OR gate operates similarly to two switches that are wired in parallel to a light (Figure 15–30). If switch A or B is closed, the light will turn on. A high signal to either input will result in a high output.

4. NAND and NOR gates: A NOT gate placed behind an OR or AND gate inverts the output signal (Figure 15–31).

5. Exclusive-OR (XOR) gate: A combination of gates that will produce a high output signal only if the inputs are different (Figure 15–32).

These different gates are combined to perform the processing function. The following are some of the most common combinations.

1. Decoder circuits: A combination of AND gates used to provide a certain output based on a given combination of inputs (Figure 15–33). When the correct bit pattern is received by the decoder, it will produce the high-voltage signal to activate the relay coil.

2. Multiplexer (MUX): The basic computer is not capable of looking at all of the inputs at the same time. A multiplexer is used to examine one of many inputs depending on a programmed priority rating (Figure 15–34).

3. Demultiplexer (DEMUX): Operates similar to the MUX except that it controls the order of the

Truth table		
A	B	Output
0	0	0
0	1	1
1	0	1
1	1	1

FIGURE 15–30 OR gate symbol and truth table. The OR gate is similar to parallel switches.

Truth table		
A	B	Output
0	0	1
0	1	1
1	0	1
1	1	0

Truth table		
A	B	Output
0	0	1
0	1	0
1	0	0
1	1	0

FIGURE 15–31 Symbols and truth tables for NAND and NOR gates. The small circle represents an inverted output on any logic gate symbol.

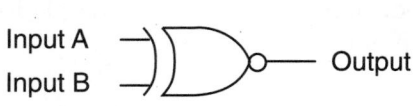

Truth table		
A	B	Output
0	0	0
0	1	1
1	0	1
1	1	0

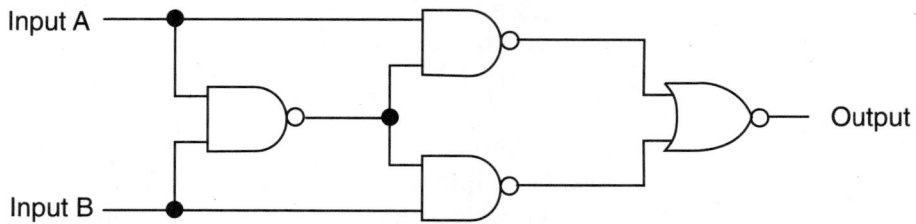

FIGURE 15–32 XOR gate symbol and truth table. An XOR gate is a combination of NAND and NOR gates.

FIGURE 15–33 Simplified temperature sensing circuit that will turn on the A/C compressor when the inside temperature reaches a predetermined level.

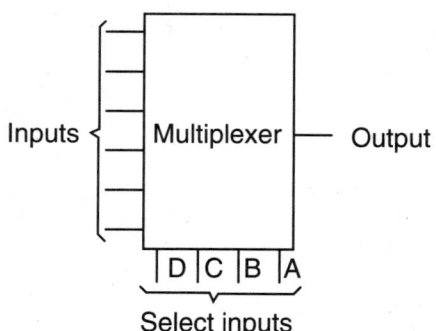

FIGURE 15–34 Selection at inputs DCBA will determine which data input will be processed.

outputs (Figure 15–35). The process that the MUX and DEMUX operate on is called **sequential sampling**. This means the computer will deal with all the sensors and actuators one at a time.

4. **RS and clocked RS flip-flop circuits:** Logic circuits that remember previous inputs and do not change their outputs until they receive new input signals. Figure 15–36 shows a basic RS flip-flop circuit. The clocked flip-flop circuit has an inverted clock signal as an input so circuit operations occur in the proper order (Figure 15–37). Flip-flop circuits are called **sequential logic circuits** because the output is determined by the sequence of inputs. A given input affects the output produced by the next input.

5. **Registers:** Used in the computer to temporarily store information. A register is a combination of flip-flops that transfers bits from one to another every time a clock pulse occurs (Figure 15–38, page 378).

6. **Accumulators:** Registers designed to store the results of logic operations that can become inputs to other computers or modules.

Logic gates process input information to command output devices. The order of this logic or the instructions to the computer are held in the computer's memory.

FIGURE 15–35 Block diagram representation of the MUX and DEMUX circuit.

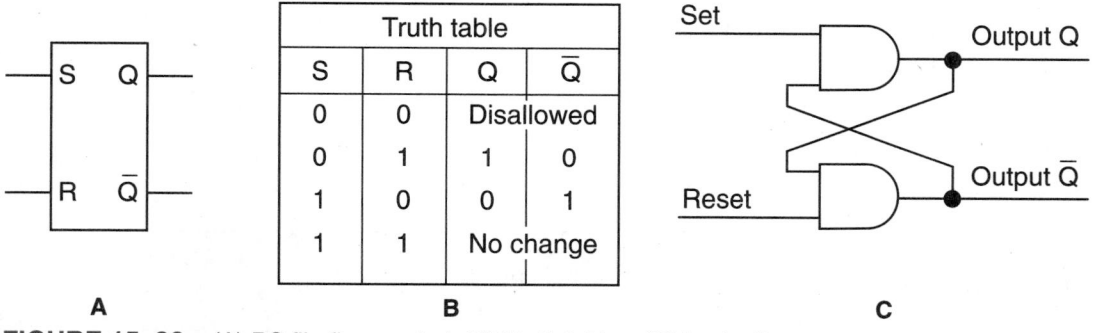

FIGURE 15–36 (A) RS flip-flop symbol. (B) Truth tables. (C) Logic diagram.

FIGURE 15–37 Clocked RS flip-flop symbol.

Memories

A computer's memory holds the programs and other data, such as vehicle calibrations, which the microprocessor refers to in performing calculations. To the CPU, the program is a set of instructions or procedures that it must follow. Included in the program is information that tells the microprocessor when to retrieve input (based on temperature, time, etc.), how to process the input, and what to do with it once it has been processed.

The microprocessor works with memory in two ways: it can read information from memory or change information in memory by writing in or storing new information (Figure 15–39). To write information in memory, each memory location is assigned a number (written in binary code also) called an address. These addresses are sequentially numbered, starting with zero, and are used by the microprocessor to retrieve data and write new information into memory. During processing, the CPU often receives more data than it can immediately handle. In these instances, some information has to be temporarily stored or written into memory until the microprocessor needs it.

When ready, the microprocessor accesses the appropriate memory location (address) and is sent a copy of what is stored. By sending a copy, the memory retains the original information for future use.

There are basically three types of memory used in automotive CPUs today (Figure 15–40, page 379). They are read only memory, programmable read only memory, and random access memory.

READ ONLY MEMORY (ROM) Permanent information is stored in read only memory (**ROM**). Information in ROM cannot be erased, even if the system is turned off or the CPU is disconnected from

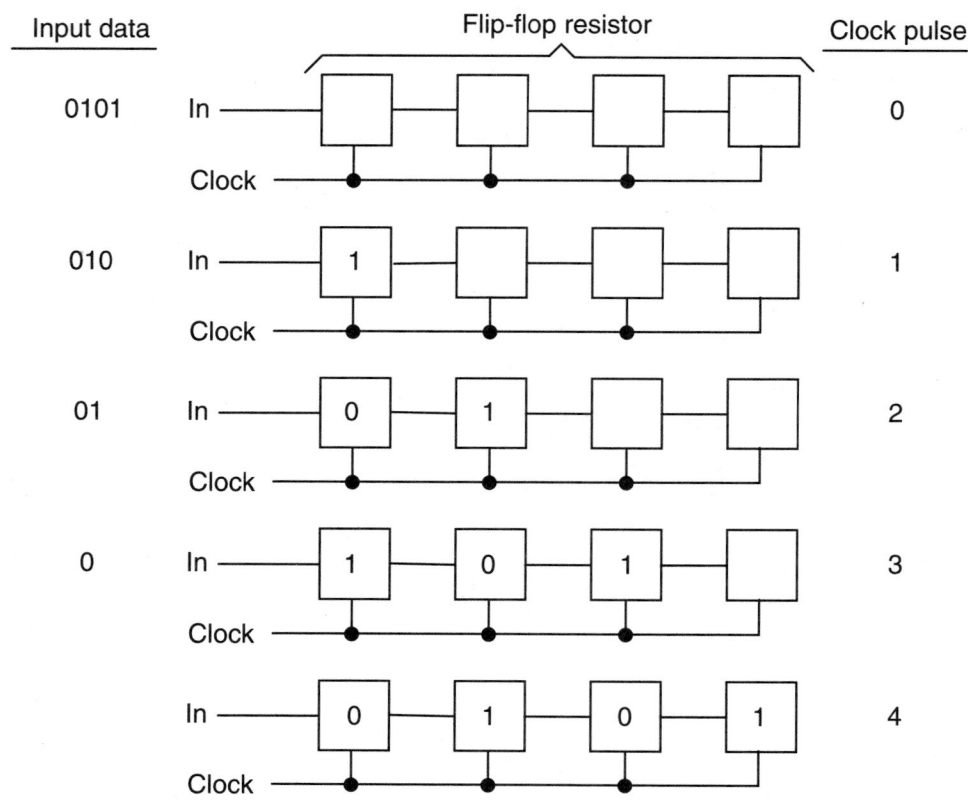

FIGURE 15–38 It takes four clock pulses to load four bits into the register.

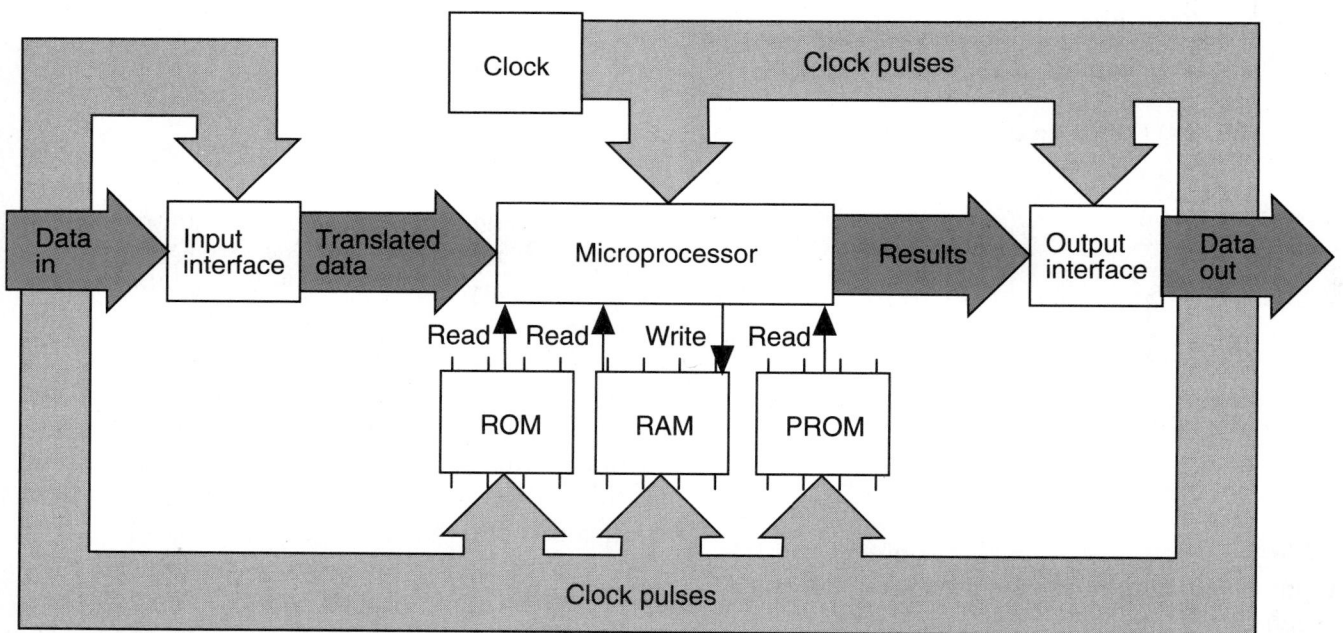

FIGURE 15–39 Interaction of the microprocessor and its support systems and memory banks. *Courtesy of General Motors Corporation*

the battery. As the name implies, information can only be read from ROM.

When making decisions, the microprocessor is constantly referring to the stored information and the input from sensors. By comparing information from these sources, the CPU makes informed decisions.

PROGRAMMABLE READ ONLY MEMORY (PROM)

The **PROM** differs from the ROM in that it plugs into the computer and is more easily removed and reprogrammed or replaced with one containing a revised program. It contains program information specific to different vehicle model calibrations.

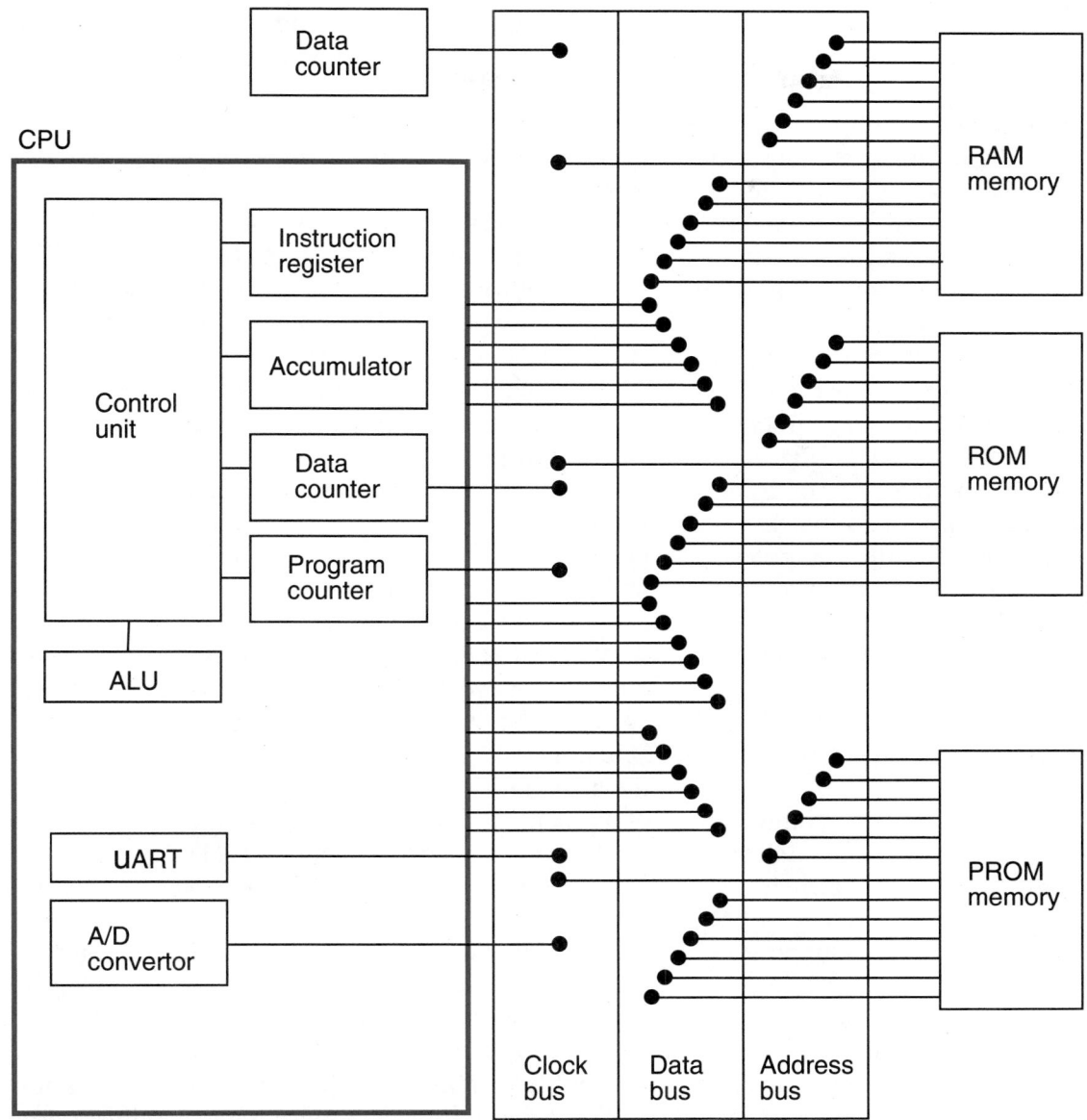

FIGURE 15–40 The three memories within a computer. *Courtesy of General Motors Corporation*

Erasable PROM (**EPROM**) is similar to PROM except that its contents can be erased to allow new data to be installed. A piece of Mylar tape covers a window. If the tape is removed, the memory circuit is exposed to ultraviolet light that erases its memory.

Electrically erasable PROM (**EEPROM**) allows changing the information electrically one bit at a time. Some manufacturers use this type of memory to store information concerning mileage, vehicle identification number, and options.

RANDOM ACCESS MEMORY (RAM) The **RAM** is used during computer operation to store temporary information. The CPU can write, read, and erase information from RAM in any order, which is why it is called random. One characteristic of RAM is that when the ignition key is turned off and the engine is

stopped, information in RAM is erased. RAM is used to store information from the sensors, the results of calculations, and other data that are subject to constant change.

There are currently two other versions of RAM in use: volatile and nonvolatile. A volatile RAM, usually called keep alive memory (**KAM**) has most of the features of RAM. Information can be written into KAM and can be read and erased from KAM. Unlike RAM, information in KAM is not erased when the ignition key is turned off and the engine is stopped. However, if battery power to the processor is disconnected, information in KAM is erased.

A nonvolatile RAM (**NVRAM**) does not lose its stored information if its power source is disconnected. Vehicles with digital display odometers usually store mileage information in nonvolatile RAM.

Actuators

Once the computer's programming instructs that a correction or adjustment must be made in the controlled system, an output signal is sent to control devices called **actuators**. These actuators, which are solenoids, switches, relays, or motors, physically act on or carry out the command sent by the computer.

Actually, actuators are electromechanical devices that convert an electrical current into mechanical action. This mechanical action can then be used to open and close valves, control vacuum to other components, or open and close switches. When the CPU receives an input signal indicating a change in one or more of the operating conditions, the CPU determines the best strategy for handling the conditions. The CPU then controls a set of actuators to achieve a desired effect or strategy goal. For the computer to control an actuator, it must rely on a component called an **output driver**.

The output driver usually applies the ground circuit of the actuator. The ground can be applied steadily if the actuator must be activated for a selected amount of time, or the ground can be pulsed to activate the actuator in pulses.

Output drivers operate by the digital commands issued by the CPU. Basically, the output driver is nothing more than an electronic on-off switch used to control a specific actuator.

To illustrate this relationship, let us suppose the computer wants to turn on the engine's cooling fan. Once it makes a decision, it sends a signal to the output driver that controls the cooling fan relay (actuator). In supplying the relay's ground, the output driver completes the power circuit between the battery and cooling fan motor and the fan operates. When the fan has run long enough, the computer signals the output driver to open the relay's control circuit (by removing its ground), thus opening the power circuit to the fan.

For actuators that cannot be controlled by a digital signal, the CPU must turn its digitally coded instructions back into an analog signal. This conversion is completed by the A/D converter.

Displays can be controlled directly by the CPU. They do not require digital-to-analog conversion or output drivers because they contain circuitry that decodes the microprocessor's digital signal. The decoded information is then used to indicate such things as vehicle speed, engine rpm, fuel level, or scan tool values. Common types of electronic readout devices used as displays include light-emitting diodes (LED), liquid crystal display (**LCD**), and vacuum fluorescent display (**VFD**).

Some systems require the actuator to either be turned on and off very rapidly or for a set amount of cycles per second. It is duty cycled if it is turned on and off a set amount of cycles per second. **Duty cycle** is the percentage of on-time to total cycle time. Most duty cycled actuators cycle ten times per second. To complete a cycle, it must go from off to on to off again. If the cycle rate is ten times per second, one actuator cycle is completed in 1/10th of a second. If the actuator is turned on for 30 percent of each tenth of a second and off for 70 percent, it is referred to as a 30 percent duty cycle (Figure 15–41).

If the actuator is cycled on and off very rapidly, the pulse width can be varied to provide the desired results. **Pulse width** is the length of time in milliseconds that an actuator is energized. For example, the computer program will select an illumination level of a digital instrument panel based on the intensity of the ambient light in the vehicle. The illumination level is achieved through pulse width modulation of the lights. If the lights need to be bright, the pulse width is increased, which increases the length of on-time. As light intensity needs to be reduced, the pulse width is decreased (Figure 15–42).

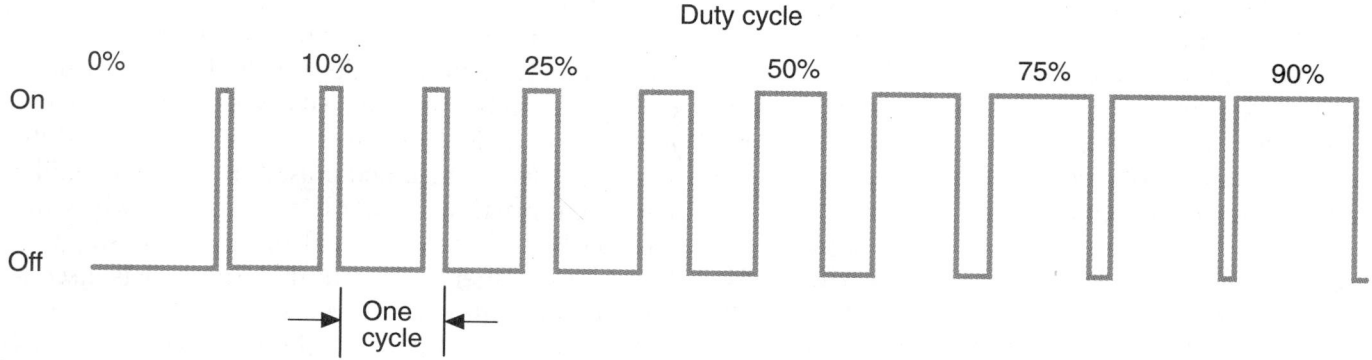

FIGURE 15–41 Duty cycle is the percentage of on-time per cycle. Duty cycle can be changed; however, total cycle time remains constant.

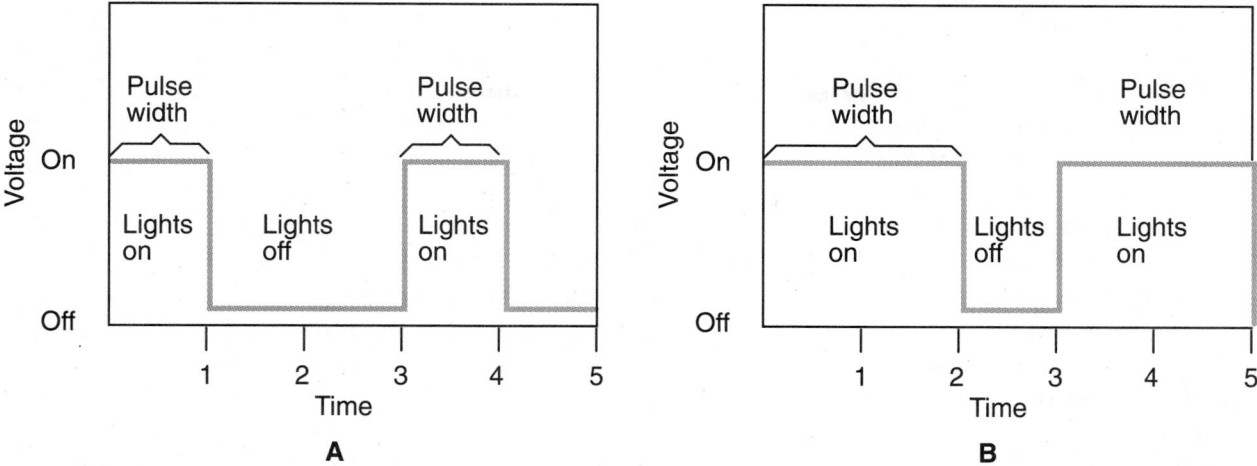

FIGURE 15–42 Pulse width is the duration of on-time: (A) pulse width modulation to achieve dimmer dash lights, (B) pulse width modulation to achieve brighter dash illumination.

Power Supply

The CPU also contains a power supply that provides the various voltages required by the microprocessor and internal clock that provides the clock pulse, which in turn controls the rate at which sensor readings and output changes are made. Also contained are protection circuits that safeguard the microprocessor from interference caused by other systems in the vehicle and diagnostic circuits that monitor all inputs and outputs and signal a warning light if any values go outside the specified parameters. This warning light is called the malfunction indicator lamp (MIL).

Complete specific information concerning the use of computers (microprocessors) in various automotive electronic systems is presented in later chapters.

MULTIPLEXING

To eliminate the necessity of adding wires and the subsequent weight to vehicles as more and more electronics are added, manufacturers are using **multiplexing**. A multiplex wiring system uses bus data links that connect different computers or control modules together. Each module can transmit and receive digital codes over the bus data links. This allows the module to share the same information with other modules. The signal sent from a sensor can go to any of the modules and can be used by any other module. This eliminates the need to have separate wires from each sensor to each of the modules, thereby eliminating many wires.

An IC or chip is used to prevent the digital codes from overlapping by allowing only one code to be transmitted at a time. Each digital signal is proceeded by an identification code that establishes its priority. If two modules attempt to send a message at the same time, the signal with the higher priority code is transmitted first.

PROTECTING ELECTRONIC SYSTEMS

The last thing a technician wants to do when a vehicle comes into the shop for repair is create problems. This is especially true when it comes to electronic components. It is a must to be aware of the proper ways to protect automotive electrical systems and electronic components during storage and repair.

The computer operates on a very low voltage, and there needs to be a word said on static electricity, which can generate up to 25,000 volts. Simply touching the computer case is not likely to damage the computer, but it is always a good idea to be careful. Never touch the electrical contacts on any other electrical part. Before touching a computer, whether removing or replacing it, always touch a good ground with your finger. This safely discharges any static electricity. Some technicians even attach a metal wire or chain around their wrist and connect the other end to a good ground. When parts inside a computer are being replaced, such as a PROM module, this is a good idea.

Avoid touching bare metal contacts. Oils from the skin can cause corrosion and poor contacts.

The sensor wires that connect to the computer should never be rerouted. Induction of voltage can occur and the resulting problems may be impossible to find. When replacing wiring, always check the service manual and follow the routing instructions.

Accidentally touching a metal slip lead or test probe between metal terminals can cause a short circuit. Expensive computer modules or sensors can be destroyed instantly, without warning, by incorrect testing procedures.

If the code indicates a problem with the oxygen sensor, extra caution is required. The oxygen sensor wire carries a very low voltage and must be isolated from other wires. If it is not, nearby wires could add more induced voltage. This gives false data to the computer and can result in a driveability problem. Some car makers use a foam sleeve around the oxygen sensor wire for this purpose. Do not allow grease, lubricants, or cleaning solvents of any kind to touch the sensor end or the electrical connector plug. Apply the manufacturer's special anti-seize compound to the threads before installing the sensor.

Avoid jump-starting whenever possible. The discharged battery can explode, or you can create voltage spikes that could damage electronic components. This is true of both the car you are trying to start and the car providing the jump. However, if you must jump-start a car, observe these safety precautions. Connect positive terminal to positive terminal on the batteries, connect the negative terminal of the good battery to a ground other than the ground terminal of the bad battery. If you use another car for the jump, make sure the two vehicles are not touching each other. Make sure every electrical device in the car, including the dome light, is turned off before connecting the batteries. Only after the hookups are properly made should you turn the key in the dead car to get it started. Once the dead car is running, remove all jumper connections before turning on any electrical devices.

Computer diagnostic tests can be performed using a scan tool. Connect the tool to the diagnostic connector. Follow the sequence given in the service manual or the scanning tool's instruction manual. The trouble codes are displayed on the scan tool readout.

Remove any computer module that could be affected by welding, hammering, grinding, sanding, or metal straightening. Be sure to protect the removed computer equipment by wrapping it in a plastic bag to shield it from moisture and dust.

Many test procedures require that electrical power or ground be supplied to the circuit being tested. Avoid grounding powered circuits with metal tools. Avoid touching live electrical leads to grounded metal parts of the automobile. Personal injury from sparks may result, or the unit being tested may be damaged or destroyed.

Be careful not to damage connectors and terminals when removing electronic components. Some may require special tools to remove them.

When procedures call for connecting test leads, or wires, to electrical connections, use extreme care and follow the manufacturer's instructions. Identify the correct test terminals before attempting to connect test leads.

The charging system, including the battery, must remain in good operating condition. If the electrical system falls below 12 volts, the computer may not work properly. However, low voltage does not damage the computer. If there are more than 15 volts, the computer may become damaged and must be replaced.

When checking a computerized ignition system, use a high-impedance digital meter. The computer may be damaged by using an analog (needle-type) meter. Do not connect the meter directly to the computer. Use part of the circuit. Do not connect jumper wires across a sensor unless the service manual tells you to do so. This could damage the computer.

TESTING ELECTRONIC CIRCUITS AND SYSTEMS

Most electronic circuits can be checked in the same way as other electrical circuits. However, only high-impedance meters should be used. Multimeters and oscilloscopes are the most commonly used diagnostic tools for these circuits.

A multimeter may have AC selection modes for voltage and amperage. These modes are used to measure voltages and amperages that change polarity or levels very quickly. Most meters display the average voltage or current in an AC circuit. Some meters display **RMS** (root-mean-square) readings. These readings are very close to being average readings; however, there may be slight differences as this scale compensates for extreme fluctuations in voltage and current flow.

RMS refers to the effective or useful value of an AC signal. To determine the RMS value, peak voltage readings are multiplied by the RMS constant (0.707). The effective value of AC is the amount of current or voltage that produces the same heating effect as an equal amount of DC current or voltage. The effective RMS value is calculated by squaring the instantaneous values of all the points on the sine wave, taking the average of these values and extracting the square root. Therefore, the effective value is the root of the mean (average) square of the values along the sine wave. The resulting answer from this mathematical formula is the root-mean-square (Figure 15–43).

Multimeters can also be used to check individual components, such as a diode. To test a diode, an

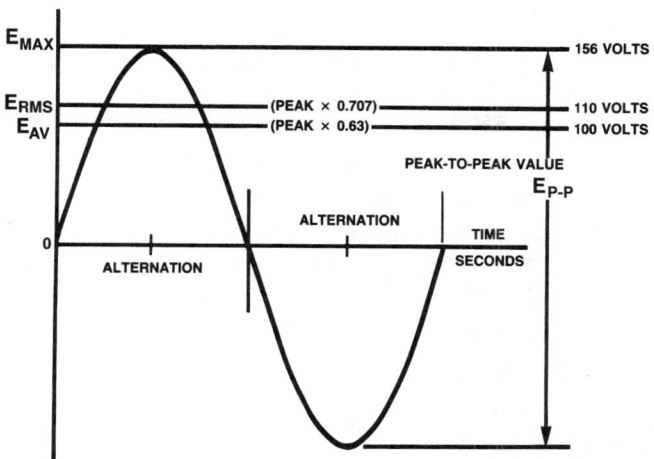

FIGURE 15–43 AC voltage: RMS. *Courtesy of Hydra-Matic Division of General Motors Corporation*

ohmmeter is normally used. There should be continuity in one direction only. By connecting the meter leads across the diode, the meter should show low or high resistance. When the leads across the diode are reversed, an opposite reading should be observed. If zero ohms of resistance is measured across the diode, the diode is shorted. If high or infinite resistance is measured across the diode, in both directions, the diode is open.

Some multimeters have a diode test mode that can be selected to check continuity through a diode. When using this function, remember that a good diode allows current flow in one direction only.

An oscilloscope is a valuable tool for understanding and diagnosing electronic circuits. The **scope** is primarily used to measure voltages. Scopes are relatively easy to use. Most have two leads which are connected to the circuit in the same way as a voltmeter.

The screen on the scope displays voltage over time; therefore, any change in voltage will be displayed. Changing the voltage scale on the scope changes how many volts or millivolts each horizontal line is worth. The vertical lines on the scope represent periods of time. The time control sets how long a time period each line represents. Normally these time periods are in parts of a second, such as **milliseconds** (1/1,000th of a second).

These time periods show the frequency of a voltage signal. **Frequency** is a term that describes how often a signal performs a complete cycle. A **cycle** is simply a description of the changes that a signal goes through without repeating itself. Frequency is measured in **Hertz**. Hertz is a measurement of cycles per second. To determine the frequency of something,

divide the length of time it takes to complete one cycle into 1.

Many scopes can display two signals at the same time. These are known as dual-trace scopes. They are used to compare the signals of two components or circuits.

Whenever using a scope on a circuit, always follow the meter's instruction manual for hookup and proper settings. Most service manuals have illustrations of the patterns that are expected from the different electronic components. If the patterns do not match those in the service manual, a problem is indicated. The problem may be in the component or in the circuit. Further testing is required to locate the exact cause of the problem.

SHOP TALK

It is very helpful to know if the component being tested with a scope is digital or analog based. With this knowledge, it is easier to recognize an incorrect pattern. Digital patterns should show a clear on-off signal, whereas analog signals should show steady voltage changes as conditions change. ■

CASE STUDY

A customer came in with her vehicle. Her complaint was basically that the car had poor performance, especially during acceleration. The technician road tested the car and found the customer's complaint was valid. He also noticed the engine's idle was not as smooth as it should be.

The car had electronic engine controls, but the technician did not have the proper scan tool to test the system. However, he did understand the system and knew the primary purposes of each of the components. He began to test the system with his multimeter and portable scope.

Going through the basics, he tested the primary inputs. One of these was the TPS. He knew this sensor was a potentiometer and the resistance and voltage output from the sensor should change with a change in throttle position. He connected his scope to the TPS and moved the throttle. When the analog signal on the scope did not change smoothly with a change in the throttle, he knew what the basic problem with the car was—a bad TPS.

KEY TERMS

Accumulator	Microprocessor
Actuators	Millisecond
A/D converter	Multiplexer (MUX)
Amplifier	Multiplexing
Analog	NAND gate
AND gate	NOR gate
Base	NOT gate
Binary code	NPN
Bit byte	NTC
Chip	NVRAM
Clock	OR gate
Collector	Output
Computer	Output driver
CPU	Pick-up coil
Cycle	Piezoresistive
Decoder circuit	PN junction
Demultiplexer	PNP
(DEMUX)	Processing
Digital	PROM
Diode	PTC
Duty cycle	Pulse width
EEPROM	RAM
Electrically inert	Register
Electronics	Reverse bias
Emitter	RMS
EPROM	ROM
Exclusive-OR (XOR)	RS flip-flop
gate	Schmitt trigger
Feedback	Scope
FET	Sequential logic circuits
Forward bias	Sequential sampling
Frequency	Signal
Hall-effect switch	Square wave
Hertz	Storage
IC	Timing disc
Impurities	Transistor
Input	VFD
Integrated circuit	Voltage-generating
KAM	devices
LCD	Vref
LED	Wheatstone bridge
Logic gate	Zener diode
Magnetic pulse generator	

SUMMARY

- A computer is an electronic device that stores and processes data.
- A semiconductor is a material or device that can function as either a conductor or an insulator.
- Some common semiconductor materials include silicon (Si) and germanium (Ge).

- N-type semiconductors have loose, or excess, electrons. They have a negative charge.
- P-type semiconductors are positively charged materials.
- A diode allows current to flow in one direction.
- When a diode is placed in a circuit with the positive side of the circuit connected to the positive side of the diode and the negative side of the circuit connected to the negative side of the circuit, the diode is said to have forward bias.
- Light-emitting diodes (LEDs) are much the same as regular diodes. They emit light when they are forward biased.
- Zener diodes are used to regulate voltage in a circuit.
- Transistors are used in place of switches and relays in electronic circuits.
- A transistor resembles a diode with an extra side. It can consist of two P-type materials and one N-type material or two N-type materials and one P-type material. These are called PNP and NPN types.
- The different names for the legs of the transistor are the emitter, base, and collector.
- A very small current applied to the base of the transistor controls a much larger current flowing through the entire transistor.
- An integrated circuit is simply a large number of diodes, transistors, and other electronic components, such as resistors and capacitors, all mounted on a single piece of semiconductor material.
- Computers are electronic decision-making centers. Input devices called sensors feed information to the computer. The computer processes this information and sends signals to controlling devices.
- A typical electronic control system is made of sensors, actuators, CPU, and related wiring.
- Most input sensors are variable resistance/reference types, switches, and thermistors.
- The central processing unit (CPU) is the brain of a computer. It brings information into and out of the computer's memory. The input information is processed in the CPU and checked against the program in the computer's memory.
- Feedback means that data concerning the effects of the computer's commands are fed back to the computer as an input signal.
- All sensors perform the same basic function. They detect a mechanical condition (movement or position), chemical state, or temperature condition and change it into an electrical signal that can be used by the computer to make decisions.
- Reference voltage (Vref) sensors provide input to the computer by modifying or controlling a constant, predetermined voltage signal.

◆ Most sensors presently in use are variable resistors or potentiometers. They modify a voltage to or from the computer, indicating a constantly changing status that can be calculated, compensated for, and modified.

◆ A thermistor is a solid-state variable resistor made from a semiconductor material that changes resistance in relation to temperature changes.

◆ There are two basic types of thermistors: NTC and PTC. A negative temperature coefficient (NTC) thermistor reduces its resistance as temperature increases. This type is the most commonly used thermistor. A positive temperature coefficient (PTC) thermistor increases its resistance with an increase in temperature.

◆ A Wheatstone bridge is also used as a variable resistance sensor. These are typically constructed of four resistors, connected in series-parallel between an input terminal and a ground terminal. Three of the resistors are kept at the same value. The fourth resistor is a sensing resistor.

◆ Voltage-generating sensors include components like the magnetic pulse generators, Hall-effect switches, oxygen sensors (zirconium dioxide), and knock sensors (piezoelectric), which are capable of producing their own input voltage signal.

◆ Magnetic pulse generators use the principle of magnetic induction to produce a voltage signal. These sensors are commonly used to send data to the computer about the speed of the monitored component.

◆ The major components of a pulse generator are a timing disc and a pick-up coil.

◆ The Hall-effect switch performs the same function as a magnetic pulse generator. It operates on the principle that if a current is allowed to flow through thin conducting material exposed to a magnetic field, another voltage is produced.

◆ A Hall-effect switch contains a permanent magnet, a thin semiconductor layer made of Gallium arsenate crystal (Hall layer), and a shutter wheel.

◆ Outputs or actuators are electromechanical devices that convert current into mechanical action.

◆ A computer is capable of reading voltage signals. The programs used by the CPU are "burned" into IC chips using a series of numbers. These numbers represent various combinations of voltages that the computer can understand. The voltage signals to the computer can be either analog or digital. Analog means a voltage signal is infinitely variable, or can be changed, within a given range. Digital means a voltage signal that is one of two states either on-off, yes-no, or high-low.

◆ A computer can only read a digital binary signal.

To overcome this communication problem, all analog voltage signals are converted to a digital format by a device known as an analog-to-digital converter (A/D converter).

◆ Logic gates are the thousands of field effect transistors (FET) incorporated into the computer's circuitry. The FETs use the incoming voltage patterns to determine the pattern of pulses leaving the gate. These circuits are called logic gates because they act as gates to output voltage signals depending on different combinations of input signals.

◆ The most common logic gates are NOT gates, AND gates, OR gates, NAND and NOR gates, and XOR gates.

◆ A computer's memory holds the programs and other data, such as vehicle calibrations, which the microprocessor refers to in performing calculations.

◆ The microprocessor works with memory in two ways: it can read information from memory or change information in memory by writing in or storing new information.

◆ There are basically three types of memory used in automotive CPUs today: read only memory, programmable read only memory, and random access memory.

◆ Permanent information is stored in read only memory (ROM).

◆ The PROM differs from the ROM in that it plugs into the computer and is more easily removed and reprogrammed or replaced with one containing a revised program. It contains program information specific to different vehicle model calibrations.

◆ The RAM is used during computer operation to store temporary information. The CPU can write, read, and erase information from RAM in any order, which is why it is called random.

◆ Once the computer's programming instructs that a correction or adjustment must be made in the controlled system, an output signal is sent to control devices called actuators. These actuators, which are solenoids, switchers, relays, or motors, physically act or carry out the command sent by the computer.

◆ For the computer to control an actuator, it must rely on a component called an output driver. These drivers usually apply the ground circuit of the actuator.

◆ Some systems require the actuator to either be turned on and off very rapidly or for a set amount of cycles per second. It is duty cycled if it is turned on and off a set amount of cycles per second. Duty cycle is the percentage of on-time to total cycle time.

◆ If the actuator is cycled on and off very rapidly, the pulse width can be varied to provide the desired results. Pulse width is the length of time in milliseconds an actuator is energized.

◆ A multiplex wiring system uses bus data links that connect different computers or control modules together. Each module can transmit and receive digital codes over the bus data links. This allows the module to share the same information with other modules.

◆ Most electronic circuits can be checked in the same way as other electrical circuits. However, only high-impedance meters should be used. Multimeters and oscilloscopes are the most commonly used diagnostic tools for these circuits.

◆ A multimeter may have AC selection modes for voltage and amperage. These modes are used to measure voltages and amperages that change polarity or levels very quickly. Most meters display the average voltage or current in an AC circuit. Some meters display root-mean-square (RMS) readings. These readings are very close to being average readings; however, there may be slight differences as this scale compensates for extreme fluctuations in voltage and current flow.

◆ The screen on an oscilloscope displays voltage over time; therefore, any change in voltage will be displayed.

◆ Frequency is a term that describes how often a signal performs a complete cycle. A cycle is simply a description of the changes a signal goes through without repeating itself. Frequency is measured in Hertz. Hertz is a measurement of cycles per second. To determine the frequency of something, divide the length of time it takes to complete one cycle into 1.

TECH MANUAL

The following procedures are included in Chapter 15 of the *Tech Manual* that accompanies this book:

1. Check continuity across electronic components and circuits with an ohmmeter.

2. Inspect and repair or replace wires and connectors.

REVIEW QUESTIONS

1. The three main types of memory in a computer are called ____, ____, and ____.

2. A device that stores and processes data is a ____.

3. ____ signals show any change in voltage.

4. Digital signals are typically called ____ ____ patterns.

5. ____ means that data concerning the effects of the computer's commands are fed back to the computer as an input signal.

6. The type of memory that contains specific information about the vehicle and can be removed and reprogrammed or replaced is called ____.

7. What are the major components of an electronic control system?

8. A ____ is the simplest type of semiconductor.

9. What is meant by the term *pulse width*?

10. What is the major difference between ROM and RAM memory in a microprocessor?

11. Most semiconductors are made of which of the following materials?
   a. gallium   **c.** copper
   b. silicone   **d.** all of the above

12. Technician A says when positive voltage is present at the base of an NPN transistor, the transistor is turned on. Technician B says when an NPN transistor is turned on, current flows through the collector and emitter of the transistor. Who is correct?
   a. Technician A   **c.** Both A and B
   b. Technician B   **d.** Neither A nor B

13. Which of the following is *not* a type of information stored in ROM?
   a. strategy   **c.** sensor input
   b. look-up tables   **d.** none of the above

14. Technician A uses an ohmmeter to test diodes. Technician B uses a low-impedance voltmeter to measure the effective value of the AC voltage present in a circuit. Who is correct?
   a. Technician A   **c.** Both A and B
   b. Technician B   **d.** Neither A nor B

15. Which of the following is *not* made of semiconductor material?

    a. Zener diodes
    b. thermistors
    c. PM generators
    d. Hall-effect switches

16. Technician A says knock sensors are basically Wheatstone bridges. Technician B says oxygen sensors are basically thermistors. Who is correct?

    a. Technician A
    b. Technician B
    c. Both A and B
    d. Neither A nor B

17. Which of the following is a basic function of a computer?

    a. store information
    b. process information
    c. send out commands
    d. all of the above

18. Technician A says some types of voltage sensors provide input to the computer by modifying or controlling a constant, predetermined voltage signal. Technician B says another type of voltage sensor is a voltage generating sensor. Who is correct?

    a. Technician A
    b. Technician B
    c. Both A and B
    d. Neither A nor B

19. Which of the following statements is untrue?

    a. A diode allows current flow in one direction only.
    b. A Zener diode can allow current flow in both directions if the correct amount of voltage is applied to it.
    c. LEDs light when voltage is applied to them.
    d. Zener diodes are used to regulate circuit voltage.

20. Technician A says when current is applied to the base, the transistor shuts off. Technician B says that alternator current applied to the P side of the diode makes it an excellent conductor. Who is correct?

    a. Technician A
    b. Technician B
    c. Both A and B
    d. Neither A nor B

BATTERIES: THEORY AND SERVICE

16

OBJECTIVES

◆ *Explain the purpose of a battery.* ◆ *Describe the basic parts of an automotive battery.* ◆ *Compare conventional and maintenance-free batteries.* ◆ *Explain the chemical reaction that occurs to produce current in a battery.* ◆ *Describe the differences, advantages, and disadvantages of the different types of batteries.* ◆ *Describe the different types of battery terminals used.* ◆ *Describe the different types of ratings used with batteries.* ◆ *Explain the effects of temperature on battery output.* ◆ *Demonstrate all safety precautions and rules associated with servicing batteries.* ◆ *Perform a visual inspection of a battery.* ◆ *Test a conventional battery's specific gravity.* ◆ *Perform open circuit tests.* ◆ *Test the capacity of a battery.* ◆ *Correctly slow and fast charge a battery.* ◆ *Jump start a vehicle by using a booster battery and jumper cables.* ◆ *Remove, clean, and reinstall a battery properly.*

An automotive battery is an **electrochemical** device that provides for and stores electrical energy. When the battery is connected to an external load, an energy conversion occurs that results in current flow through the circuit to operate the load. Electrical energy is produced in the battery by the chemical reaction that occurs between two dissimilar plates that are immersed in an electrolyte solution.

When discharging the battery, the battery changes chemical energy into electrical energy. It is through this change that the battery releases stored energy. During charging, electrical energy is converted into chemical energy. As a result, the battery can store energy until it is needed.

The storage battery is the heart of a vehicle's electrical and electronic systems. It plays an important role in the operation of the starting, charging, ignition, and accessory circuits. The largest demand placed on the battery occurs when it must supply current to operate the starter motor. The amperage requirements of a starter motor may be over several hundred amps.

After the engine has started, the vehicle's charging system recharges the battery. It also provides the power to run the electrical accessories.

If the charging system of the vehicle fails, the battery must supply all the current needed to run the vehicle. Most batteries can supply 25 amperes for

two hours before they become so low that they are unable to keep the engine running. The amount of time a battery can be discharged at a certain rate before the voltage drops to a specified level is referred to as the **reserve capacity** of the battery.

An automotive storage battery has three main functions. It provides voltage and serves as a source of current for starting, lighting, and ignition. It acts as a voltage stabilizer for the entire electrical system of the vehicle. And, finally, it provides current whenever the vehicle's electrical demands exceed the output of the charging system.

The battery must be able to maintain a good charge when the engine is off. The condition of the battery determines this capability, as does the electrical demands of the vehicle. When the engine is off, electrical power is still needed to maintain the memory in the various computers used in the vehicle and to keep clocks going. The electrical loads that are present when the ignition switch is off are called **parasitic loads**. At times the parasitic loads are so great that a battery will go dead if the vehicle has not been driven for a while.

There are six types of batteries in use today. They are the conventional battery, the low maintenance battery, the maintenance-free battery, the sealed maintenance-free battery, the hybrid battery, and the recombination battery.

CONVENTIONAL DESIGN BATTERY

The storage battery consists of grids, positive plates, negative plates, separators, elements, electrolyte, a container, cell covers, vent plugs, and cell containers (Figure 16–1). The **grids** form the basic framework of the battery **plates**. In a conventional battery, the grids are made of lead alloyed with approximately 5 percent **antimony** for strength. Each grid holds the active materials of the plate within its borders.

A positive plate consists of a grid filled with **lead peroxide** as its active material. Lead peroxide (PbO_2) is a dark brown, crystalline material. Its high degree of porosity allows the liquid electrolyte to penetrate freely.

The material pasted onto the grids of the negative plates is **sponge lead** (Pb). This porous gray lead allows the electrolyte to penetrate freely.

Elements and Cells

Each battery contains a number of elements. An **element** is a group of positive and negative plates. All of the positive plates are connected together, as are the negative plates. The plates are connected to each other by a **plate strap**. The positive and negative groups are then interlaced so the plates alternate. A **separator** is placed between groups to prevent contact between positive and negative plates, which would cause the plates to lose their stored energy. A further separator requirement is that the **electrolyte** must flow easily back and forth between the plates. Everything from wood to porous rubber has been used as a separator, but sheets of porous fiberglass or polyethylene are now most popular. The plate straps, sometimes called post straps, extend up to provide terminals for connecting one element of the battery to another.

FIGURE 16–1 Components of a typical conventional storage battery.

When the element is placed inside the battery case and immersed in electrolyte, it becomes a cell. A 12-volt battery has six cells, which are connected in series with each other. Each cell has an open circuit voltage of approximately 2.1 volts; therefore, a 12-volt storage battery has an actual open circuit voltage of 12.6 volts.

Electrolyte and Specific Gravity

As mentioned, the lead peroxide and sponge lead that fill the element plates are the active materials in the battery. However, these materials cannot become active until they are immersed in electrolyte, a liquid composed of water and sulfuric acid (H_2SO_4).

The sulfuric acid of the electrolyte supplies sulfate, which chemically reacts with both the lead and lead peroxide to release electrical energy. In addition, the sulfuric acid is the carrier for the electrons inside the battery between the positive and negative plates.

The electrolyte of a fully charged battery is usually about 64 percent water and 36 percent sulfuric acid. This corresponds to a specific gravity of 1.270. **Specific gravity** is the weight of a given volume of any liquid divided by the weight of an equal volume of water. Pure water has a specific gravity of 1.000, while battery electrolyte should have a specific gravity of 1.260 to 1.280 at 80°F (26.7°C). In other words, the electrolyte of the battery is 1.260 to 1.280 times as heavy as water.

CAUTION:

Electrolyte is very corrosive. It can cause severe injuries if it comes in contact with your skin or eyes. If electrolyte gets on you, immediately wash with baking soda and water. If the acid gets in your eyes, immediately flush them with cool water, then get medical help. ■

Discharging and Charging

Remember, a chemical reaction between active materials on the positive and negative plates and the acid in the electrolyte produces electrical energy. When a battery discharges (Figure 16–2), lead in the lead peroxide of the positive plate combines with the sulfate radical (SO_4) to form lead sulfate ($PbSO_4$).

A similar reaction takes place at the negative plate. In this plate, lead (Pb) of the negative active material combines with sulfate radical (SO_4) to also form lead sulfate ($PbSO_4$), a neutral and inactive material. Thus, lead sulfate forms at both types of plates as the battery discharges.

As the chemical reaction occurs, the oxygen from the lead peroxide and the hydrogen from the sulfuric

FIGURE 16–2 Chemical action that occurs inside a battery during a discharge cycle.

TABLE 16–1 ELECTROLYTE SPECIFIC GRAVITY AS RELATED TO CHARGE	
Specific Gravity	**Percent of Charge**
1.265	100%
1.225	75%
1.190	50%
1.155	25%
1.120 or lower	discharged

suring the specific gravity of the electrolyte with a tool known as a hydrometer can be a good indicator of how much charge a battery has lost. Table 16–1 lists specific gravity readings for cells in various stages of charge with respect to their ability to crank an engine over at a temperature of 80°F.

The recharging process (Figure 16–3) is the reverse of the discharging process. Electricity from an outside source, such as the vehicle's alternator, generator, or a battery recharger, is forced into the battery. The lead sulfate ($PbSO_4$) on both plates separates into lead (Pb) and sulfate (SO_4). As the sulfate (SO_4) leaves both plates, it combines with hydrogen in the electrolyte to form sulfuric acid (H_2SO_4). At the same time, the oxygen (O_2) in the electrolyte combines with the lead (Pb) at the positive plate to form lead peroxide (PbO_2). As a result, the negative plate returns to its original form of lead

acid combine to form water (H_2O). As discharging takes place, the acid in the electrolyte is used up and replaced with water.

Consequently, the specific gravity of the electrolyte decreases as it is discharged. This is why mea-

FIGURE 16–3 Chemical action that occurs inside a battery during the charge cycle.

(Pb), and the positive plate reverts to lead peroxide (PbO_2).

An unsealed battery gradually loses water due to its conversion into hydrogen and oxygen gases, which escape into the atmosphere through the **vent caps**. If the lost water is not replaced, the level of the electrolyte falls below the tops of the plates. This results in a high concentration of sulfuric acid in the electrolyte and also permits the exposed material of the plates to dry and harden. In this situation, premature failure of the battery is certain. The electrolyte level in the battery must be checked frequently.

Casing Design

The container or shell of the battery is usually a one-piece, molded assembly of polypropylene, hard rubber, or plastic. The case has a number of individual cell compartments. A number of cell connectors are used to join all cells of a battery in series.

The top of the battery is encased by a **cell cover**. The cover may be a one-piece design, or the cells might have their own individual covers or cell covers. On conventional-design batteries, the cover must have vents.

The vent holes provide access into the cells for servicing them with electrolyte or water and permit the escape of hydrogen and oxygen gases, which form during charging and discharging. Vent plugs or caps are used to close the openings in the cell cover.

CAUTION:

When lifting a plastic-cased battery, excessive pressure on the end walls could cause acid to spew through the vent caps, resulting in personal injury. Lift with a battery carrier or with your hands on opposite corners. ■

Terminals

The battery has two external terminals: a positive (+) and a negative (–). These terminals are either two tapered posts, "L" terminals, threaded studs on top of the case, or two internally threaded connectors on the side (Figure 16–4). Some batteries have top and side terminals so that one battery fits either application. The terminals connect, internally, to either end of the series of elements inside the battery and have either a positive (+) or a negative (–) marking, depending on which end of the series they represent.

Tapered terminals have a given dimension in accordance with standards agreed upon by the Battery Council International (**BCI**) and Society of Automotive Engineers (SAE). This ensures that all positive and negative cable clamp terminals would fit any corresponding battery terminal interchangeably, regardless of the battery's manufacturer. However, the positive terminal is slightly larger, usually around 11/16 inch in diameter at the top, while the negative terminal usually has a 5/8-inch diameter. This design minimizes the danger of installing the battery cables in reverse polarity.

Side terminals are positioned near the top of the battery case. These terminals are threaded and require a special bolt to connect the cables. Polarity identification is by positive and negative symbols. "L" terminals are on some specialty and imported batteries.

Battery Cables

Battery cables must be of sufficient capacity to carry the current required to meet all demands (Figure 16–5). Normal 12-volt cable size is 4 or 6 gauge. Various forms of clamps and terminals are used to ensure a good electrical connection at each end of the cable. Connections must be clean and tight to prevent arcing, corrosion, and high voltage drops.

The positive cable is normally red and the negative cable is black. The positive cable fastens to the battery and the starter solenoid or relay. The negative cable fastens to ground on the engine block. Some manufacturers use a negative cable with no insulation. Sometimes the negative battery cable may have a body grounding wire to help assure that the vehicle's body is properly grounded.

Side terminal   Post or top terminal   "L" terminal

Battery terminals

FIGURE 16–4 Most common types of automotive battery terminals. *Courtesy of Ford Motor Company*

FIGURE 16–5   The battery cable is designed to carry the high current required to start the engine and supply the vehicle's electrical systems.

FIGURE 16–7   Construction of a maintenance-free battery.

Battery Hold-Downs

All batteries must be secured in the vehicle to prevent damage and the possibility of shorting across the terminals. Normal vibrations cause the plates to shed their active materials. Hold-downs reduce the amount of vibration and help increase the life of the battery.

Heat Shields

Many late-model vehicles employ a heat shield made of plastic or other materials to protect the battery from high underhood temperatures (Figure 16–6). While heat shields need not be removed for most routine testing and inspection jobs, they must be removed and correctly installed during battery replacement.

LOW-MAINTENANCE AND MAINTENANCE-FREE BATTERIES

The majority of batteries sold and installed in today's vehicles are either low-maintenance or maintenance-free designs. Low-maintenance batteries are still equipped with vent holes and caps, which allow water to be added to the cells. A low-maintenance battery will require additional water substantially less often than a conventional battery.

Maintenance-free batteries were introduced in 1972. They do not have holes or caps. They are equipped with small gas vents that prevent gas-pressure buildup in the case (Figure 16–7). Water is never added to maintenance-free batteries.

Both maintenance-free and low-maintenance batteries differ from conventional battery designs in two important ways: plate design and water use.

The most important difference is the materials used for the plate grids. As mentioned under the section on conventional battery design, antimony strengthens the grid alloy. In low-maintenance batteries, the amount of antimony is reduced to about 3 percent. In maintenance-free batteries, the antimony is eliminated and replaced by calcium or strontium (Figure 16–8). Reducing the amount of antimony or replacing it with calcium or strontium alloy reduces both the battery's internal heat and the amount of **gassing** that occurs during charging. Gassing is the conversion of the battery water into hydrogen and oxygen gas. This process is also called electrolysis. Since heat and gassing are the principal reasons for battery water loss, these changes reduce or eliminate the need to periodically add water.

FIGURE 16–6   Many vehicles have a molded heat shield to protect the battery from high engine temperatures.

Maintenance Free Grid

Calcium or strontium alloy...
• Adds strength
• Cuts gassing up to 97%
• Resists overcharge

FIGURE 16–8   Maintenance-free battery grids with support bars give increased strength and faster electrical delivery. *Courtesy of Ford Motor Company*

Reduced water loss also reduces terminal corrosion since the major cause of this corrosion is condensation from normal battery gassing. Additionally, nonantimony lead alloys have better conductivity, so a maintenance-free battery has about a 20 percent higher cold-cranking power rating than a comparably sized conventional battery.

The calcium battery is also more resistant to overcharging and its self-discharge rate is 20 to 30 percent lower. The tradeoff, however, is that calcium grids are not as well suited for deep cycling. In other words, if a calcium battery is run completely dead several times, its ability to deliver current can be diminished with each subsequent recharge.

CUSTOMER CARE

One good piece of advice you can give a customer is that just because it says maintenance-free on the side of the battery does not mean it can be ignored for the next five years. The battery should still be checked occasionally, battery terminals and case kept clean and tight, and the battery kept firmly mounted. ∎

The advantages of maintenance-free batteries over conventional batteries include:

1. A larger reserve of electrolyte above the plates.
2. Increased resistance to overcharging.
3. Longer shelf life.
4. Ability to be shipped with electrolyte installed, reducing the possibility of accidents and injury to the technician.
5. Higher cold-cranking ampere ratings.

The major disadvantages of the maintenance-free battery include:

1. Grid growth when the battery is exposed to high temperatures. Grid growth is a condition in which the grid grows little metallic fingers that extend through the separators and short out the plates.
2. Inability to withstand deep cycling. Deep cycling means to discharge the battery completely before recharging it.
3. Low reserve capacity.
4. Faster discharge by parasitic loads.
5. Shorter life expectancy.

HYBRID BATTERIES

A **hybrid battery** is also called a **deep-cycle battery**. It combines the advantages of the low-maintenance and maintenance-free batteries. It can withstand six deep cycles and still retain 100 percent of its original reserve capacity. The grid construction of the hybrid battery consists of approximately 2.75 percent antimony alloy on the positive plates and a calcium alloy on the negative plates. This allows the battery to withstand deep cycling while retaining reserve capacity for improved cranking performance. Also, the use of antimony alloys reduces grid growth and corrosion. The lead calcium has less gassing than conventional batteries.

Grid construction differs from other batteries in that the plates have a lug located near the center of the grid. In addition, the vertical and horizontal grid bars are arranged in a radial design. **Radial** infers that the lines branch out from a common center (Figure 16–9). By locating the lug near the center of the grid and by using the radial design, the current has less resistance and a shorter path to follow to the lug (Figure 16–10). This means the battery is capable of providing more current at a faster rate.

The separators used are constructed of glass covered with a resin. Some batteries use fiberglass in place of the resin-covered glass. The glass separators

Grid with active material

100% glass separator

Grid only

FIGURE 16–9 Hybrid battery grid and separator construction. *Courtesy of Ford Motor Company*

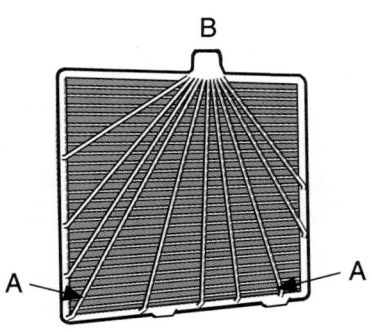

Hybrid grid radial design and center lug reduces the resistance for current that is produced at points "A" to reach point "B".

FIGURE 16–10   Hybrid battery grid construction allows for faster current delivery. Electrical energy at point "A" has a shorter distance to travel to get to the tab at point "B."

offer low electrical resistance with high resistance to chemical contamination. This type of construction provides for increased cranking performance and battery life.

RECOMBINATION BATTERIES

Recently, several manufacturers have introduced completely sealed maintenance-free or **recombination batteries**. These new batteries do not require the gas vent used on other maintenance-free designs. Although these batteries are basically lead-acid voltage cells, a slight change in place and electrolyte chemistry virtually eliminates hydrogen generation.

During charging, a conventional or maintenance-free battery releases hydrogen at the negative plates and oxygen at the positive plates. Most of the hydrogen is released through electrolysis of the water in the electrolyte near the negative plates as the battery reaches full charge. In recombination batteries, the negative plates never reach a fully charged condition and, therefore, cause little or no release of hydrogen. Oxygen is released at the positive plates, but it passes through the separators and recombines with the negative plates.

The end result is virtually no gassing from the battery. Because the oxygen released by the electrolyte is forced to recombine with the negative plate, these batteries are called recombination or recombinant electrolyte batteries.

Test and service requirements of recombination batteries are basically the same as for other maintenance-free, lead-acid batteries. Some manufacturers caution, however, fast charging at high current rates might overheat the battery and cause damage. Always check the manufacturer's instructions for test specifications and charging rates before servicing.

BATTERY VOLTAGE AND CAPACITY

The open-circuit voltage of a fully charged cell is roughly 2.1 volts in conventional batteries and 2.2 volts in some sealed maintenance-free batteries. The specific gravity of the electrolyte is roughly 1.270. A cell's voltage rating and specific gravity remain at these levels (when fully charged) regardless of the size of the cell. It is the fixed characteristics of the chemicals used in the battery and the strength of the electrolyte that determine this factor.

Cell size, state of charge, rate of discharge, battery condition and design, and electrolyte temperature all strongly influence the voltage of a cell during discharge. When cranking an engine over at 80°F, the voltage of an average battery may be about 11.5 to 12 volts. At 0°F, the voltage is significantly lower.

The concentration of acid in the electrolyte in the pores of the plates also affects battery voltage or discharge. As the acid chemically combines with the active materials in the plates and is used up, the voltage drops unless fresh acid from outside the plate moves in to take its place. As discharging continues, this outside acid becomes weaker, and sulfate saturates the plate material. It then becomes increasingly difficult for the chemical reaction to continue. As a result, voltage drops to a level no longer effective in delivering sufficient current to the electrical system.

Cold weather can create this same effect. Even the acid is not overly weak. At low temperatures, the viscosity of the electrolyte increases, making it more difficult for the acid to move freely into the plate pores and around the separators. This slows the rate of the chemical reaction and lowers battery voltage, limiting the output of the battery, especially at cranking rates.

Battery capacity is the ability to deliver a given amount of current over a period of time. It depends on the number and size of the plates used in the cells and the amount of acid used in the electrolyte.

BATTERY RATING METHODS

The Battery Council International (BCI) rates batteries according to reserve capacity and cold-cranking power. When replacing a battery, always refer to an application chart to select a battery with the correct BCI group number. Vehicle options, such as air conditioning and a number of major electrical accessories, may indicate the need for an optional heavy-duty battery with a higher rating. Remember, to handle cranking power and the vehicle's other electrical needs, the replacement unit should never have a lower rating than the original battery.

Reserve Capacity

A reserve capacity (RC) rating represents the approximate time in minutes it is possible to travel at night with battery ignition and minimum electrical load, but without a charging system in operation. The time in minutes is based on a current draw of 25 amperes while maintaining a minimum battery terminal voltage of 10.5 volts (12-volt batteries) at 80°F. This rating represents the electrical load that must be supplied by the battery in the event of a charging system failure.

Ampere-Hour Rating

The **ampere-hour** rating is the amount of steady current that a fully charged battery can supply for 20 hours at 80°F (26.7°C) without the cell voltage falling below 1.75 volts or 10.5 volts at the terminals. For example, if a battery can be discharged for 20 hours at a rate of 4.0 amperes before its terminal voltage reads 10.5 volts, it would have a rating of 80 ampere-hours.

Cold Cranking

A **cold-cranking amperes (CCA)** rating specifies the minimum amperes available at 0°F and at –20°F. This rating allows cranking capability to be related to such significant variables as engine displacement, compression ratio, temperature, cranking time, condition of engine and electrical system, and lowest practical voltage for cranking and ignition. This rating indicates the amperes that a fully charged battery will maintain for 30 seconds without the terminal voltage falling below 7.2 volts for a 12-volt battery. The cold-cranking rating is given in total amperage and is identified as 300 CCA, 400 CCA, and so on.

To provide enough starting power under adverse conditions, a 12-volt system generally requires 1 ampere for each cubic inch of engine displacement. In other words, a 350 cubic inch engine requires a battery with a cold-cranking rating of at least 350 amperes.

CUSTOMER CARE

An excellent service you can offer your customer is to help select the right type of battery based on the make of the vehicle and the customer's driving habits. In cold climates, putting in a larger battery with higher CCAs is a good idea, but do not get carried away. Reserve capacity and proper mounting are important, too. ■

BATTERY SIZE SELECTION

Besides selecting a battery based on its capacity and rating, the proper battery is also one that fits. The battery should fit the battery holding fixture and the hold-down must be able to be installed. It is also important that the height of the battery not allow the terminals to short across the vehicle's hood when it is closed. BCI group numbers are used to indicate the physical size and other features of the battery (Figure 16–11). The size of the battery does not always indicate the current capacity of a battery.

Grp. Size	Vlt.	Cold cranking power—amps for 30 secs. at 0°F*	No. of mo. warranted	Size of battery container in inches (incl. terminals)		
				Lgth.	Wd.	Ht.
17HF	6	400	24	7¼	6¾	9
21	12	450	60	8	6¾	8½
22F	12	430	60	9	6⅞	8⅛
	12	380	55	9	6⅞	8⅛
	12	330	40	9	6⅞	8⅛
22NF	12	330	24	9½	5½	8⅞
24	12	525	60	10¼	6⅞	8⅝
	12	450	55	10¼	6⅞	8⅝
	12	410	48	10¼	6⅞	8⅝
	12	380	40	10¼	6⅞	8⅝
	12	325	36	10¼	6⅞	8⅝
	12	290	30	10¼	6⅞	8⅝
24F	12	525	60	10¼	6⅞	8⅝
	12	450	55	10¼	6⅞	8⅝
	12	410	48	10¼	6⅞	8⅝
	12	380	40	10¼	6⅞	8⅝
	12	325	36	10¼	6⅞	8⅝
	12	290	30	10¼	6⅞	8⅝
27	12	560	60	12	6⅞	8⅝
27F	12	560	60	12	6⅞	9
41	12	525	60	11⁹⁄₁₆	6¹³⁄₁₆	6¹⁵⁄₁₆
42	12	450	60	9⅝	6⅞	6¾
	12	340	40	9⅝	6⅞	6¾
45	12	420	60	9½	5½	8⅞
46	12	460	60	10¼	6⅞	8⅝
48	12	440	60	12	6⅞	7½
49	12	600	60	14½	6⅞	7½
56	12	450	60	10	6	8⅜
	12	380	48	10	6	8⅜
58	12	425	60	9¼	7¼	6⅞
71	12	450	60	8	7¼	8½
	12	395	55	8	7¼	8½
	12	330	36	8	7¼	8½
72	12	490	60	9	7¼	8¼
	12	380	48	9	7¼	8¼
74	12	585	60	10¼	7¼	8¾
	12	525	60	10¼	7¼	8¾
	12	505	60	10¼	7¼	8¾
	12	450	55	10¼	7¼	8¾
	12	410	48	10¼	7¼	8¾
	12	380	40	10¼	7¼	8¾
	12	325	36	10¼	7¼	8¾

*Meets or exceeds Battery Council International rating standards.

FIGURE 16–11 BCI battery group numbers indicate the size and features of the battery.

FACTORS AFFECTING BATTERY LIFE

All storage batteries have a limited service life, but many conditions can decrease service life.

Improper Electrolyte Levels

With nonsealed batteries, water should be the only portion of the electrolyte lost due to evaporation during hot weather and gassing during charging. Maintaining an adequate electrolyte level is the basic step in extending battery life for these designs. When adding water to the cells, use distilled water when available or clean, soft water.

Fill each cell to just above the top of the plates. Underfilling causes a greater concentration of acid, which deteriorates the plates' grids more rapidly.

Overfilling weakens the concentration of sulfuric acid (reduces the electrolyte's specific gravity), which reduces the efficiency of the battery.

Corrosion

Battery corrosion is commonly caused by spilled electrolyte or electrolyte condensation from gassing. In either case, the sulfuric acid from the electrolyte corrodes, attacks, and can destroy not only connectors and terminals but hold-down straps and the carrier box as well.

Corroded connections increase resistance at the battery terminals, which reduces the applied voltage to the vehicle's electrical system. The corrosion in the battery cover can also create a path for current which can allow the battery to slowly discharge. Finally, corrosion can destroy the hold-down straps and carrier box, which can result in physical damage to the battery.

Overcharging

Batteries can be overcharged by either the vehicle's charging system or a battery charger. In either case, the result is a violent chemical reaction within the battery that causes a loss of water in the cells. This can push active materials off the plates permanently reducing the capacity of the battery. Overcharging can also cause excessive heat, which can oxidize the positive plate grid material and even buckle the plates, resulting in a loss of cell capacity and early battery failure.

Undercharge/Sulfation

The vehicle's charging system might not fully recharge the battery due to excessive battery output, stop-and-go driving, or a fault in the charging system. In all cases, the battery operates in a partially discharged condition. A battery in this condition will become sulfated when the sulfate normally formed in the plates becomes dense, hard, and chemically irreversible. This occurs because the sulfate has been allowed to remain in the plates for a long period.

Sulfation of the plates causes two problems. First, it lowers the specific gravity levels and increases the danger of freezing at low temperatures. Secondly, in cold weather, a sulfated battery often fails to crank the engine because of its lack of reserve power.

Poor Mounting

Loose hold-down straps or covers allow the battery to vibrate or bounce during vehicle operation. This can have several adverse effects. It can shake the active materials off the grid plates, severely shortening battery life. It can also loosen the plate connections to the plate strap, loosen cable connections, or even crack the battery case.

Cycling

Cycling is simply the discharging and recharging of the battery. Heavy and repeated cycling can cause the positive plate material to break away from its grids and fall into the sediment chambers at the base of the case. This problem reduces battery capacity and can lead to premature short circuiting between the plates. Fortunately, the new envelope design found in many batteries reduces this problem.

SAFETY PROCEDURES

The potential dangers caused by the sulfuric acid in the electrolyte and the explosive gases generated during battery charging require that battery service and troubleshooting be conducted under absolute safe working conditions. According to the National Society to Prevent Blindness, over 14,000 Americans suffered serious eye damage from acid in wet-cell batteries in a recent year.

CAUTION:

Always wear safety glasses or goggles when working with batteries no matter how small the job. ■

Sulfuric acid can also cause severe skin burns. If electrolyte contacts your skin or eyes, flush the area with water for several minutes. When eye contact occurs, force your eyelid open. Always have a bottle of neutralizing eyewash on hand and flush the affected areas with it. Do not rub your eyes or skin.

CAUTION:

Receive prompt medical attention if electrolyte contacts your skin or eyes. Call a doctor immediately. ∎

When a battery is charging or discharging, it gives off quantities of highly explosive hydrogen gas. Some hydrogen gas is present in the battery at all times. Any flame or spark can ignite this gas, causing the battery to explode violently, propelling the vent caps at a high velocity and spraying acid in a wide area. To prevent this dangerous situation, take these precautions.

◆ Do not smoke near the top of a battery, and never use a lighter or match as a flashlight.
◆ Remove wristwatches and rings before servicing any part of the electrical system. This helps to prevent the possibility of electrical arcing and burns.
◆ Even sealed, maintenance-free batteries have vents and can produce dangerous quantities of hydrogen if severely overcharged.
◆ Always disconnect the battery's ground cable when working on the electrical system or engine. This prevents sparks from short circuits and prevents accidental starting of the engine.
◆ Always operate charging equipment in well-ventilated areas. A battery that has been overworked should be allowed to cool down and let air circulate around it before attempting to jump-start the vehicle. Most batteries have flame arresters in the caps to help prevent explosions, so make sure that the caps are tightly in place.
◆ Never connect or disconnect charger leads when the charger is turned on. This generates a dangerous spark.
◆ Never lay metal tools or other objects on the battery because a short circuit across the terminals can result.

Other battery and electrical system safety precautions follow.

◆ Always disconnect the battery ground cable before fast-charging the battery on the vehicle. Improper connection of charger cables to the battery can reverse the current flow and damage the alternator.
◆ When removing a battery from a vehicle, always disconnect the battery ground cable first. When installing a battery, connect the ground cable last.
◆ Never reverse the polarity of the battery connections. Generally, all vehicles use a negative ground. Reversing this polarity damages the alternator and circuit wiring. Another common cause of explosions is reversal of jumper cables. Remember

FIGURE 16–12 Use a lifting strap or carrier when carrying batteries. *Courtesy (left) of Johnson Controls Inc.*

to connect negative to negative and positive to positive.
◆ Never attempt to use a fast charger as a boost to start the engine.
◆ As a battery gets closer to being fully discharged, the acidity of the electrolyte is reduced, and the electrolyte starts to behave more like pure water. A dead battery may freeze at temperatures near 0°F. Never try to charge a battery that has ice in the cells. Passing current through a frozen battery can cause it to rupture or explode. If ice or flush is visible or the electrolyte level cannot be seen, allow the battery to thaw at room temperature before servicing. Do not take chances with sealed batteries. If there is any doubt, allow them to warm to room temperature before servicing.
◆ As batteries get old, especially in warm climates and especially with lead-calcium cells, the grids start to grow. The chemistry is rather involved, but the point is that plates can grow to the point where they touch, producing a shorted cell. If you see a battery with normal fluid levels in five cells and one nearly dry cell, you are probably looking at a battery that has shorted one cell and turned its electrolyte into hydrogen gas.
◆ Always use a battery carrier or lifting strap (Figure 16–12) to make moving and handling batteries easier and safer.
◆ Acid from the battery damages a vehicle's paint and metal surfaces and harms shop equipment. Neutralize any electrolyte spills during servicing.

ROUTINE INSPECTIONS

As part of any tune-up procedure or electrical system work, always check the battery.

1. Visually inspect the battery cover and case for dirt and grease.
2. Check the electrolyte level.
3. Inspect the case for cracks, loose terminal posts, and other signs of physical damage.
4. Check for missing cell plug covers and caps.

FIGURE 16–13 Corroded battery terminals reduce the efficiency of the battery.

5. Inspect all cables for broken or corroded wires (Figure 16–13), frayed insulation, or loose or damaged connectors.
6. Visually check battery terminals, cable connectors, metal parts, hold-downs, and trays for corrosion damage or buildup.
7. Check the heat shield for proper installation on vehicles so equipped.

ROUTINE CLEANING

Before removing battery connectors or the battery itself for cleaning or other service, always neutralize accumulated corrosion on terminals, connectors, and other metal parts. Apply a solution of baking soda and water or ammonia and water (Figure 16–14).

Do not splash the corrosion onto the vehicle's paint, metal or rubber parts, or onto your hands and face. Be sure the solution cannot enter the battery cells. A stiff bristle brush is ideal for removing heavy buildup. Dirt and accumulated grease can be removed with a detergent solution or solvent.

After cleaning, rinse the battery and cable connections with clean water. Dry the components with a clean rag or low-pressure compressed air.

To clean the inside surfaces of the connectors and the battery terminals, remove the cables. Always

begin with the ground cable. Spring-type cable connectors are removed by squeezing the ends of their prongs together with wide-jaw, vise-gripping, channel lock, or battery pliers. This pressure expands the connector so it can be lifted off the terminal post.

🔧 SHOP TALK

It should be noted that disconnecting the battery on late-model cars removes some memory from the engine's computer and the car's accessories. Besides losing the correct time on its clock or the programmed stations on the radio, the car might run roughly. If this occurs, allow the engine to run for awhile before shutting it off.   ∎

For connectors tightened with nuts and bolts, loosen the nut using a box wrench or cable-clamp pliers. Using ordinary pliers or an open-end wrench can cause problems. These tools might slip off under pressure with enough force to break the cell cover or damage the casing.

Always grip the cable while loosening the nut. This eliminates unnecessary pressure on the terminal post that could break it or loosen its mounting in the battery. If the connector does not lift easily off the terminal when loosened, use a clamp puller to free it (Figure 16–15). Prying with a screwdriver or bar strains the terminal post and the plates attached to it. This can break the cell cover or pop the plates loose from the terminal post.

Once the connectors have been removed, open the connector using a connector-spreading tool. Neutralize any remaining corrosion by dipping it in a baking soda or ammonia solution. Next, clean the inside of the connectors and the posts using a wire brush with external and internal bristles (Figure 16–16).

Felt washers treated with corrosion-resistant compound can be installed over the terminals before reinstalling the cable connectors (Figure 16–17).

Begin reinstallation by correctly positioning the positive connector on its post. Do not overtighten

FIGURE 16–14 Cleaning and neutralizing acid corrosion using a solution of baking soda and water or water and ammonia.

FIGURE 16–15 Battery pullers remove cables without damaging the terminal posts.

FIGURE 16–16 Combination external/internal wire brushes clean both terminals and inside cable connector surfaces.

FIGURE 16–17 A protective pad prevents corrosion of the cable clamp and terminal.

any nuts or bolts since this could damage the post or connector. Finally, coat the connectors with petroleum jelly or battery anticorrosion paste or paint.

BATTERY TESTING

Testing batteries is an important part of electrical system service. Poor and inaccurate tests can lead to serious problems and expensive and unneeded repairs. Depending on the design of the battery, state of charge and capacity can be determined in several ways: specific gravity tests, visual inspection of batteries with a built-in hydrometer, open circuit voltage tests, and the capacity test.

Specific Gravity Tests

On unsealed battery designs, the specific gravity of the electrolyte can be measured to give a fairly good indication of the battery's state of charge. A **hydrometer** is used to perform this test. A basic battery hydrometer consists of a glass tube or barrel, rubber bulb, rubber tube, and a glass float or hydrometer with a scale built into its upper stem. The glass tube encases the float and forms a reservoir for the test electrolyte. Squeezing the bulb pulls electrolyte into the reservoir.

When filled with test electrolyte, the sealed hydrometer float bobs in the electrolyte. The depth to which the glass float sinks in the test electrolyte indicates its relative weight compared to water. The reading is taken off the scale by sighting along the level of the electrolyte.

FIGURE 16–18 (A) When the scale sinks in the electrolyte, the specific gravity is low; (B) when it floats high, the specific gravity is high.

If the hydrometer floats deep in the electrolyte, the specific gravity is low (Figure 16–18A). If the hydrometer floats shallow in the electrolyte, the specific gravity is high (Figure 16–18B).

Temperature Correction At extremely high and low electrolyte temperatures, it is necessary to correct the reading by adding or subtracting 4 points (0.004) for each 10°F above or below the standard of 80°F. Most hydrometers have a built-in thermometer to measure the temperature of the electrolyte (Figure 16–19). The hydrometer reading can be misleading if the hydrometer is not adjusted properly. For example, a reading of 1.260 taken at

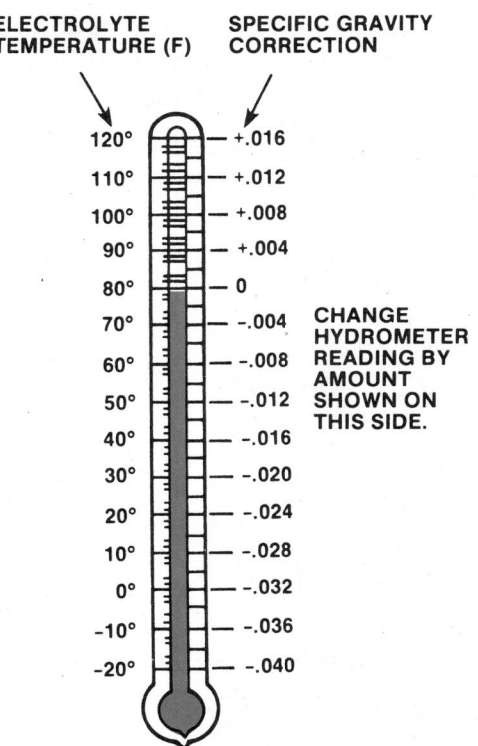

FIGURE 16–19 Hydrometers with thermometer correction scales make adjustment for electrolyte temperature easy.

20°F would be 1.260 − (6 × 0.004 or 0.024) = 1.236. This lower reading means the cell has less charge than indicated.

It is important to make these adjustments at high and low temperatures to determine the battery's true state of charge.

Interpreting Results The specific gravity of the cells of a fully charged battery should be near 1.265 when adjusted for electrolyte temperature. Table 16-1 shows the relationship between specific gravity and the state of charge of the cell.

Recharge any battery if the specific gravity drops below an average of 1.230. A specific gravity difference of more than 50 points between cells is a good indication of a defective battery in need of replacement.

Built-In Hydrometer

On many sealed maintenance-free batteries, a special temperature-compensated hydrometer is built into the battery cover. A quick visual check indicates the battery's state of charge. The hydrometer has a green ball within a cage that is attached to a clear plastic rod. The green ball floats at a predetermined specific gravity of the electrolyte that represents about a 65 percent state of charge. When the green ball floats, it rises within the cage and positions itself under the rod. Visually, a green dot then shows in the center of the hydrometer (Figure 16–20). The built-in hydrometer provides a guide for battery testing and charging.

In testing, the green dot means the battery is charged enough for testing. If the green dot is not visible and has a dark appearance, it means the bat-

GREEN DOT   DARK   CLEAR

65% OR ABOVE STATE OF CHARGE   BELOW 65% STATE OF CHARGE   LOW-LEVEL ELECTROLYTE

FIGURE 16–20 Design and operation of built-in hydrometers on maintenance-free sealed batteries.

tery must be charged before the test procedure is performed.

While charging, the appearance of the green dot means the battery is sufficiently charged. Charging can be stopped to prevent overcharging.

It is important when observing the hydrometer that the battery have a clean top in order to see the correct indication. A flashlight may be required in some poorly-lit areas. Always look straight down when viewing the hydrometer.

On some special applications, some hydrometers feature a red dot indication in addition to the green dot, dark, and clear appearances. The red dot means the battery is nearing complete discharge and must be charged before being used.

Some maintenance-free batteries do not have a built-in hydrometer. A voltage check is the only way to check this type of battery's state of charge. The specific gravity of these batteries cannot be checked because they are sealed. NEVER pry off the cell caps to check the electrolyte levels or condition on a sealed battery.

Complete hydrometer information on most batteries is printed on the label located on the top of the battery. By referring to this label, an accurate interpretation of the hydrometer appearance can be made.

Open Circuit Voltage Test

An open circuit voltage check can be used as a substitute for the hydrometer specific gravity test on maintenance-free sealed batteries with no built-in hydrometer. As the battery is charged or discharged, slight changes occur in the battery's voltage. So battery voltage with no load applied can give some indication of the state of charge.

The battery's temperature should be between 60 and 100°F. The voltage must be allowed to stabilize for at least 10 minutes with no load applied. On vehicles with high drains (computer controls, clocks, and accessories that always draw a small amount of current), it may be necessary to disconnect the battery ground cable. On batteries that have just been recharged, apply a heavy load for 15 seconds to remove the surface charge. Then allow the battery to stabilize. Once voltage has stabilized, use a digital voltmeter to measure the battery voltage to the nearest one-tenth of a volt (Figure 16–21). Use Table 16-2 to interpret the results. As you can see, minor changes in battery open circuit voltage can indicate major changes in state of charge.

If the open circuit voltage test indicates a charge of below 75 percent of full charge, recharge the battery and perform the capacity test to determine battery condition.

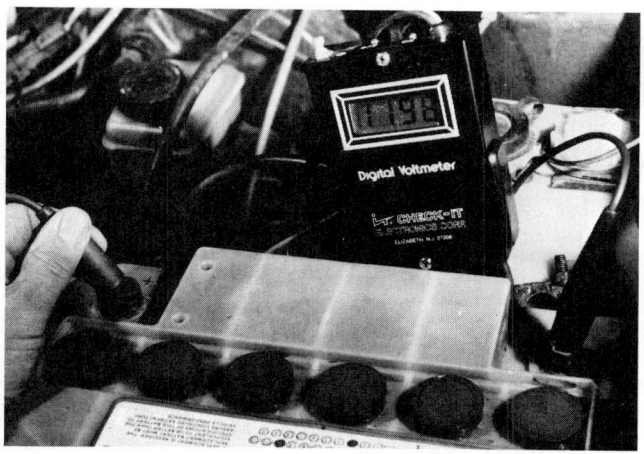

FIGURE 16–21 Measuring open circuit voltage across battery terminals using a voltmeter.

FIGURE 16–22 Performing a battery leakage test.

Battery Leakage Test

To perform a battery leakage test, set a voltmeter on a low DC volt range. Connect the negative test lead to the battery negative terminal. Then move the meter's positive lead across the top and sides of the battery case (Figure 16–22). If some voltage is read on the voltmeter, current is leaking out of the battery cells. The battery should be cleaned then rechecked. If the battery again has some leakage, it should be replaced as the case is excessively porous or is cracked.

Capacity Test

The load or **capacity test** determines how well any type of battery, sealed or unsealed, functions under a load. In other words, it determines the battery's ability to furnish starting current and still maintain sufficient voltage to operate the ignition system.

The load or capacity test can be performed with the battery either in or out of the vehicle. The battery must be at or very near a full state of charge. Use the specific gravity test or open circuit voltage test to determine charge, and recharge the battery if needed before proceeding. For best results, the electrolyte should be as close to 80°F as possible. Cold batteries

FIGURE 16–23 Adapters may be needed to test and charge batteries with side-mount terminals.

show considerably lower capacity. Never load test a sealed battery if its temperature is below 60°F.

On some batteries designed with side terminals, obtaining a sound connection can be a problem. The best solution is to screw in the appropriate manufacturer's adapter (Figure 16–23). If an adapter is not available, use a 3/8-inch coarse bolt with a nut on it. Bottom out the bolt. Back it off a turn. Then tighten the nut against the contact. Now, attach the lead to the nut.

⚠️ *WARNING!*

Simply turning in a bolt does not do the job. The thread contact area is too small to carry enough current for the load test (or for battery charging). ■

A battery tester with a carbon pile should be used to check the capacity of a battery. The typical connections for this type of meter are shown in Figure 16–24. When performing a battery load test, follow these guidelines.

1. An inductive pick-up must surround all the wires from the battery's negative terminal.
2. Observe the correct polarity and make sure the test leaks are making good contact with the battery posts.

TABLE 16–2 BATTERY OPEN CIRCUIT VOLTAGE AS AN INDICATOR OF STATE OF CHARGE	
Open Circuit Voltage	**State of Charge**
12.6 or greater	100%
12.4 to 12.6	75–100%
12.2 to 12.4	50–75%
12.0 to 12.2	25–50%
11.7 to 12.0	0–25%
11.7 or less	0%

FIGURE 16–24 Typical meter hookup for conducting a battery load test.

TABLE 16–3 MINIMUM LOAD TEST VOLTAGES AS AFFECTED BY TEMPERATURE	
Battery Temperature (F)	**Minimum Test Voltage**
70°	9.6 volts
60°	9.5 volts
50°	9.4 volts
40°	9.3 volts
30°	9.1 volts
20°	8.9 volts
10°	8.7 volts
0°	8.5 volts

3. If the tester is equipped with an adjustment for battery temperature, set it to the proper setting.
4. Turn the load control knob (if the tester is so equipped) to draw current at the rate of three times the battery's ampere-hour rating or one-half of its CCA rating.
5. Maintain the load for 15 seconds. Observe the tester's voltmeter.
6. Discontinue the load after 15 seconds of current draw.
7. At 70°F or above or on testers that are temperature connected, voltage at the end of 15 seconds should not fall below 9.6 volts. If the tester is not temperature corrected, use Table 16-3 to determine the adjusted minimum voltage reading for a particular temperature.

Interpreting Results If the voltage reading exceeds the specification by a volt or more, the battery is sup-

plying sufficient current with a good margin to safety. If the reading is right on the spec, the battery might not have the reserve necessary to handle cranking during low temperatures. If the battery was at 75 percent charge and fell right on the load specifications, it is probably in good shape.

If the voltage reads below the temperature corrected minimum, continue to observe the voltmeter of the tester after removing the load. If it rises above 12.4, the battery is bad. It can hold a charge but has insufficient cold-cranking amperes. The battery can be recharged and retested, but the results are likely to be the same.

If the voltage tests below the minimum and the voltmeter does not rise above 12.4 when the load is removed, the problem may only be a low state of charge. Recharge the battery and **load test** again.

If a volt-ampere tester is not available, the starter motor can be used as a loading device to conduct a capacity test. By observing a voltmeter before and after the starting motor has run, the condition of the battery can be determined. Connect the voltmeter across the battery. Make sure the ignition is disabled to prevent engine starting.

⚠️ *WARNING!*

Electronic ignition systems might sustain damage during prolonged engine cranking unless properly disconnected. Refer to the vehicle's specific instructions if needed. One-time popular single-cell checks, such as cadmium-probe tests and the three-minute charge tests, are seldom practiced today because they are not recommended for maintenance-free batteries. ■

BATTERY CHARGING

Both fast- and slow-charging units are used to recharge batteries (Figure 16–25). Each has its advantages. Fast chargers are the most popular. They charge batteries at a higher rate or charge—usually 40 amperes for 12-volt batteries and 70 amperes for 6-volt batteries. At this rate, fast chargers can recharge most batteries in about 1 hour. However, batteries must be in good condition to accept a fast charge. Sulfation on the plates of the battery can lead to excessive gassing, boiling, and heat buildup during fast charging. Never fast charge a battery that shows evidence of sulfation buildup or separator damage.

Trickle chargers provide low charging currents of about 5 to 15 amperes. Slow charging may require

SERIES CHARGING CONNECTIONS

VOLTMETER

CHARGER

BATTERIES

PARALLEL CHARGING CONNECTIONS

VOLTMETER

CHARGER

BUS BARS

BATTERIES

FIGURE 16–25 Battery charger connections. Always follow charger manufacturer directions.

Battery Capacity (Reserve Minutes)	Slow Charge
80 minutes or less	10 hrs. @ 5 amperes 5 hrs. @ 10 amperes
Above 80 to 125 minutes	15 hrs. @ 5 amperes 7.5 hrs. @ 10 amperes
Above 125 to 170 minutes	20 hrs. @ 5 amperes 10 hrs. @ 10 amperes
Above 170 to 250 minutes	30 hrs. @ 5 amperes 15 hrs. @ 10 amperes

Courtesy of Battery Council International

FIGURE 16–26 Table showing the rate and time of slow charging a battery according to reserve capacity.

Perform charging in a well-ventilated area away from sparks and open flames. Always be sure the charger is off before connecting or disconnecting the leads to the battery. Remember to wear eye protection, and never attempt to charge a frozen battery.

All battery chargers have manufacturer-specific characteristics and operating instructions that must be followed. When charging a battery in the vehicle, always disconnect the battery cables to avoid damaging the alternator or other electrical components. Complete details of charging procedures are given in the *Tech Manual*.

⚠️ *WARNING!*

Do not exceed the manufacturer's battery charging limits. Also, never charge the battery if the built-in hydrometer registers clear or light yellow. Replace the battery. ∎

JUMP-STARTING

When it is necessary to jump-start a car with a discharged battery using a booster battery and jumper cables, follow the instructions shown in Figure 16–27 to avoid damaging the charging system or creating a hazardous situation. Always wear eye protection when making or breaking jumper cable connections.

The following steps should be followed to safely jump-start most vehicles.

1. Make sure the two vehicles are not touching each other. The excessive current flow through the vehicle's bodies can damage the small ground

12 to 24 hours but is the only safe way of charging sulfated batteries. In general, almost any battery can be charged at any current rate as long as excessive electrolyte gassing does not occur and the electrolyte temperature does not exceed 125°F. However, when time is available, slow charging is the safest and easiest method to use. In fact, many fast chargers can be adjusted to provide slow charging. The basic rule of thumb for slow charging a battery is 1 ampere for each positive plate in one cell. Use the chart shown in Figure 16–26 to determine the rate of charge according to the reserve capacity of the battery.

Regardless of fast- or slow-charging rates, always begin by checking the electrolyte level when possible. Add water as needed to a conventional battery. Charging with electrolyte levels below the separators can damage the battery.

FIGURE 16–27 Proper setup and connections for jump-starting a vehicle with a low battery.

straps that attach the engine block to the frame. These small wires are designed to carry only 30 amperes. If the vehicles are touching, as much as 400 amperes may be carried through them.

2. For each vehicle, engage the parking brake and put the transmission in neutral or park.

3. Turn off the ignition switch and all accessories, on both vehicles.

4. Attach one end of the positive jumper cable to the disabled battery's positive terminal.

5. Connect the other end of the positive jumper cable to the booster battery's positive terminal.

6. Attach one end of the negative jumper cable to the booster battery's negative terminal.

7. Attach the other end of the negative jumper cable to an engine ground on the disabled vehicle.

8. Attempt to start the disabled vehicle. If the disabled vehicle does not readily start, start the jumper vehicle and run it at fast idle to prevent excessive current draw.

9. Once the disabled vehicle starts, disconnect the ground connected negative jumper cable from its engine block.

10. Disconnect the negative jumper cable from the booster battery.

11. Disconnect the positive jumper cable from the booster battery, then from the other battery.

⚠ WARNING!

Consult the manufacturer's service manual for procedures and precautions when jump-starting late-model vehicles with electronic control systems. Excessive battery voltages can damage sensitive electronic components. ■

CASE STUDY

A customer complains the vehicle will not start without having to jump the battery. The technician learns this happens every time the customer attempts to start the vehicle. The customer also says the voltmeter in the dash has been reading higher than normal.

The technician verifies the complaint. The engine turns over very slowly for a few seconds then does not turn. After jumping the battery to get the vehicle into the shop, the technician makes a visual inspection of the battery and cables. The open circuit voltage test shows a voltage of 12.5 volts across the terminals. When the battery is subjected to the capacity test, the voltage drops to 7.8 volts at 80 degrees. After 10 minutes, the open circuit voltage is back up to 12.5 volts. The technician determines that the battery is sulfated and calls the customer with an estimate of repair costs. The customer agrees to have the battery replaced. This cures the problem.

KEY TERMS

Ampere-hour	Hydrometer
Antimony	Lead peroxide
BCI	Load test
Capacity test	Parasitic load
CCA	Plate
Cell cover	Plate strap
Cold-cranking amperes	Radial
Cycling	Recombination battery
Deep-cycle battery	Reserve capacity
Electrochemical	Separator
Electrolyte	Specific gravity
Element	Sponge lead
Gassing	Trickle charger
Grid	Vent cap
Hybrid battery	

SUMMARY

◆ A conventional battery consists of grids, positive plates, negative plates, separators, elements, electrolyte, a container, cell covers, vent plugs, and cell containers. Maintenance-free batteries have no holes or caps, but they do have gas vents. Sealed maintenance-free batteries do not require the gas vents used on other maintenance-free designs.

- A battery's state of charge and capacity can be determined by several different test methods: specific gravity tests, built-in hydrometers, capacity test, and alternative capacity test.
- An automotive battery is an electrochemical device that provides for and stores electrical energy.
- A battery has three main functions: provides voltage and serves as a source of current, acts as a voltage stabilizer for the entire electrical system of the vehicle, and provides current whenever the electrical demands exceed the output of the charging system.
- The electrical loads that are present when the ignition switch is off are called parasitic loads.
- A battery's positive plate consists of a grid filled with lead peroxide as its active material. The material pasted onto the grids of the negative plates is sponge lead.
- Each battery contains a number of elements. An element is a group of positive and negative plates. All of the positive plates are connected together, as are the negative plates.
- A separator is placed between groups to prevent contact between positive and negative plates.
- A 12-volt battery has six cells that are connected in series with each other. Each cell has an open circuit voltage of approximately 2.1 volts; therefore, a 12-volt battery has an actual open circuit voltage of 12.6 volts.
- The lead peroxide and sponge lead that fill the element plates are the active materials in the battery. However, these materials cannot become active until they are immersed in electrolyte, a liquid composed of water and sulfuric acid (H_2SO_4).
- An unsealed battery gradually loses water due to its conversion into hydrogen and oxygen gases, which escape into the atmosphere through the vent caps.
- The container or shell of the battery is usually a one-piece, molded assembly of polypropylene, hard rubber, or plastic.
- The vent holes provide access into the cells for servicing them with electrolyte or water and permit the escape of hydrogen and oxygen gases. Vent plugs or caps are used to close the openings in the cell cover.
- The battery has two external terminals, either two tapered posts, "L" terminals, threaded studs on top of the case, or two internally threaded connectors on the side.
- Normal 12-volt battery cable size is 4 or 6 gauge.
- The positive cable is normally red and the negative cable is black. The positive cable fastens to the battery and the starter solenoid or relay. The

- negative cable fastens to ground on the engine block. Some manufacturers use a negative cable with no insulation.
- Low-maintenance batteries are still equipped with vent holes and caps, which allow water to be added to the cells. However, they will require additional water less often than a conventional battery.
- Maintenance-free batteries do not have holes or caps. They are equipped with small gas vents that prevent gas-pressure buildup in the case. Water is never added to maintenance-free batteries.
- In low-maintenance batteries, the amount of antimony is reduced to about 3 percent. In maintenance-free batteries, the antimony is eliminated and replaced by calcium or strontium. Reducing the amount of antimony reduces both the battery's internal heat and the amount of gassing that occurs during charging. Gassing is the conversion of water into hydrogen and oxygen gas.
- A hybrid battery is also called a deep-cycle battery. It combines the advantages of the low-maintenance and maintenance-free batteries.
- Completely sealed maintenance-free or recombination batteries do not require the gas vent used on other maintenance-free designs.
- The open-circuit voltage of a fully charged cell is roughly 2.1 volts in conventional batteries and 2.2 volts in some sealed maintenance-free batteries.
- Cell size, state of charge, rate of discharge, battery condition and design, and electrolyte temperature all strongly influence the voltage of a cell during discharge.
- The Battery Council International (BCI) rates batteries according to reserve capacity and cold-cranking power.
- A reserve capacity (RC) rating represents the approximate time in minutes it is possible to travel at night with battery ignition and minimum electrical load, without a charging system in operation.
- The ampere-hour rating is the amount of steady current a fully charged battery can supply for 20 hours at 80°F without the cell voltage falling below 1.75 volts.
- A cold-cranking amperes (CCA) rating specifies the minimum amperes available at 0°F and at −20°F.
- Battery selection should be based on capacity and size. A battery should fit its holding fixture, and the hold-down must be able to be installed. The height of the battery should not allow the terminals to short across the vehicle's hood when it is closed.
- Improper electrolyte levels, corrosion, overcharging, undercharge/sulfation, poor mounting, and cycling will affect the life of a battery.

◆ Sulfuric acid can cause severe skin burns. If electrolyte contacts your skin or eyes, flush the area with water for several minutes. When eye contact occurs, force your eyelid open. Do not rub your eyes or skin.

◆ When a battery is charging or discharging, it gives off quantities of highly explosive hydrogen gas. Some hydrogen gas is present in the battery at all times. Any flame or spark can ignite this gas, causing the battery to explode.

◆ On unsealed battery designs, the specific gravity of the electrolyte can be measured to give a fairly good indication of the battery's state of charge. A hydrometer is used to perform this test.

◆ At extremely high and low electrolyte temperatures, it is necessary to correct the reading on a hydrometer. Most hydrometers have a built-in thermometer to measure the temperature of the electrolyte.

◆ On many sealed maintenance-free batteries, a special temperature-compensated hydrometer is built into the battery cover.

◆ In testing, the green dot means the battery is charged enough for testing. If the green dot is not visible and has a dark appearance, it means the battery must be charged before the test procedure is performed.

◆ An open circuit voltage check can be used as a substitute for the hydrometer specific gravity test on maintenance-free sealed batteries with no built-in hydrometer.

◆ The load or capacity test determines how well any type of battery, sealed or unsealed, functions under a load. It determines the battery's ability to furnish starting current and still maintain sufficient voltage to operate the ignition system.

◆ To charge a battery, a given charging current is passed through the battery for a period of time. Fast chargers are more popular, but slow charging is the only safe way to charge a sulfated battery.

TECH MANUAL

The following procedures are included in Chapter 16 of the *Tech Manual* that accompanies this book:

1. Remove, clean, and replace a battery.

2. Inspection of a battery.

3. Test a battery's state of charge.

4. Test a battery's capacity.

5. Charge a maintenance-free battery.

6. Inspect, clean, and replace battery terminals and cables.

REVIEW QUESTIONS

1. What is a parasitic load?

2. What design characteristics determines the current capacity of a battery?

3. How is a battery leakage test conducted?

4. _____ and _____ batteries have removable vent caps.

5. Battery corrosion is commonly caused by spilled _____ and electrolyte condensation from _____.

6. A _____ battery is also called a deep-cycling battery.

7. What causes gassing in a battery?

8. List five things that shorten the life of a battery.

9. How many volts are present in a fully charged 12-volt battery?

10. What is meant by the term *specific gravity*?

11. Which of the following purposes does an automotive battery have?

   a. It provides voltage and serves as a source for current flow.

   b. It serves as a voltage stabilizer.

   c. It supplies the power needed when the vehicle's charging system fails.

   d. All of these statements are true.

12. Technician A says larger batteries have higher current capacities. Technician B says BCI group numbers identify the features of the battery. Who is correct?

   a. Technician A   c. Both A and B

   b. Technician B   d. Neither A nor B

13. Which of the following is *not* a common cause for premature battery failure?
    a. cycling
    b. sulfation
    c. gassing
    d. overcharging

14. Technician A uses a voltmeter to test the open circuit voltage of a battery. Technician B uses the results of an open circuit voltage test to determine the battery's state of charge. Who is correct?
    a. Technician A
    b. Technician B
    c. Both A and B
    d. Neither A nor B

15. Which of these statements is *not* a true conclusion from a battery load test?
    a. The battery needs to be replaced if the voltage dropped below 9.6 volts while under a load but rose above 12.4 volts when the load was removed.
    b. The battery should be charged then retested because it dropped below 9.6 volts and didn't rise above 12.4 volts when the load was removed.
    c. The battery should be charged then retested because it dropped below 9.6 volts and rose above 12.4 volts when the load was removed.
    d. The battery is good because the voltage dropped only to 10.3 volts while under load.

16. Technician A says baking soda can be used to neutralize battery corrosion. Technician B says baking soda should be used to clean batteries. Who is correct?
    a. Technician A
    b. Technician B
    c. Both A and B
    d. Neither A nor B

17. What is the first step when removing an old battery?
    a. Disconnect the ground cable.
    b. Remove the battery hold-down straps and cover.
    c. Inspect and clean the area.
    d. Remove the heat shield.

18. Technician A says the reserve rating of battery is the amount of steady current that a fully charged battery can supply for 20 hours without the voltage dropping below 10.5 volts. Technician B says ampere-hour ratings state how many hours the battery is capable of supplying 25 amperes. Who is correct?
    a. Technician A
    b. Technician B
    c. Both A and B
    d. Neither A nor B

19. Which of the following is *not* part of routine battery inspections and maintenance?
    a. Visual check of the cables and terminals.
    b. Check the case for cracks.
    c. Refill the electrolyte level with clean electrolyte.
    d. Clean all dirt from the battery case and tray.

20. Technician A says battery straps should be used whenever a battery is lifted. Technician B says when a battery is removed, the positive cable should be disconnected first. Who is correct?
    a. Technician A
    b. Technician B
    c. Both A and B
    d. Neither A nor B

STARTING SYSTEMS

17

OBJECTIVES

◆ *Explain the purpose of the starting system.* ◆ *List the components of the starting system, starter circuit, and control circuit.* ◆ *Explain the different types of magnetic switches and starter drive mechanisms.* ◆ *Explain how a starter motor operates.* ◆ *Describe the operation of the different types of starter motors.* ◆ *Perform basic tests to determine the problem areas in a starting system.* ◆ *Perform and accurately interpret the results of a current draw test.* ◆ *Disassemble, clean, inspect, repair, and reassemble a starter motor.*

The vehicle's starting system is designed to turn or crank the engine over until it can operate under its own power. To do this, the starter motor receives electrical power from the battery. The starter motor then converts this energy into mechanical energy, which it transmits through the drive mechanism to the engine's flywheel.

The only function of the starting system is to crank the engine fast enough to run. The vehicle's ignition and fuel systems provide the spark and fuel for engine operation, but they are not considered components of the basic starting system.

STARTING SYSTEM—DESIGN AND COMPONENTS

A typical starting system has six basic components and two distinct electrical circuits. The components are the battery, ignition switch, battery cables, magnetic switch (either an electrical relay or a solenoid), starter motor, and the starter safety switch.

The starter motor draws a great deal of current from the battery. A large starter motor might require 250 or more amperes of current. This current flows through the large cables that connect the battery to the starter and ground.

The driver controls the flow of this current using the ignition switch normally mounted on the steering column. The battery cables are not connected to the switch, rather the system has two separate circuits: the starter circuit and the control circuit. The starter circuit, indicated by the solid lines in Figure 17–1,

carries the heavy current from the battery to the starter motor through a magnetic switch in a relay or solenoid. The control circuit, shown by the dashed lines in Figure 17–1, connects battery power at the ignition switch to the magnetic switch, which controls the high current to the starter motor.

Starter Circuit

The starter circuit carries the high current flow within the system and supplies power for the actual engine cranking. Components of the starter circuit are the battery, battery cables, magnetic switch or solenoid, and the starter motor.

Battery and Cables Many problems associated with the starting system can be solved by troubleshooting the battery and its related components.

FIGURE 17–1   Major components and circuits of a typical starting system. The starter circuit is shown in a solid line. The control circuit is indicated by a dashed line.

FIGURE 17–2 Basic battery cable and wiring connections in a typical starting system.

FUSIBLE LINK BEFORE SHORT CIRCUIT

FUSIBLE LINK AFTER SHORT CIRCUIT

FIGURE 17–3 Example of a good and a burnt fusible link.

The starting circuit requires two or more heavy-gauge cables (Figure 17–2). Two of these cables attach directly to the battery. One of these cables connects between the battery's negative terminal and an excellent ground. The other cable connects the battery's positive terminal with the solenoid. On vehicles equipped with a **starter relay**, two positive cables are needed. One runs from the positive battery terminal to the relay and the second from the relay to the starter motor terminal. In any case, these cables carry the required heavy current from the battery to the starter and from the starter back to the battery.

All cables must be in good condition. Corrosion at the cable terminals acts as a resistor and causes a voltage drop. Cable terminals become corroded from battery acid fumes and the oxidation of the metals at the connectors. The cable itself may become corroded and weakened if the cable has contact with engine parts and other metal surfaces that can fray the insulation of the cable. Frayed insulation can also cause a dead short that can seriously damage some of the electrical units of the vehicle. A short to ground is the cause of many dead batteries and can result in fire.

Cables must also be heavy enough to comfortably carry the required current load. Cranking problems can be created when undersized cables are installed. Some replacement cables use smaller-gauge wire encased in thick insulation, so the small gauge cables can look as heavy as the original equipment. In warm weather, with good connections and no extra current drawn from lights or accessories, an engine can start well with smaller cables. But many starts must be done under conditions that are less than ideal. With undersized cables, the starter motor does not develop

its greatest turning effort and even a fully charged battery might be unable to start the engine. Always check cable size during the general inspection of the system.

When checking cables and wiring, always check any fusible links in the wiring. Many vehicles are equipped with fusible links to protect the wiring from overloading. These links are different in construction than a fuse, but they operate in much the same way (Figure 17–3). The most common type is made of a wire with a special nonflammable insulation. The wire used to make fusible links is typically two gauge sizes smaller than the wire used in the circuits they are designed to protect. Often, when a fusible link is subjected to excessive current, the insulation will become charred and give the appearance of a failed link. This is not always a true indication. The best way to check a fusible link is to disconnect the battery cables and connect an ohmmeter across the link to check for continuity.

The largest fusible link is usually located at the starter solenoid battery terminal. From this terminal, current is distributed to all parts of the vehicle. Another large fusible link joins this battery terminal to the main body harness and protects the complete wiring of the vehicle. It may be located in its own special holder or be attached directly to the starter relay terminal. When a link has failed, always troubleshoot the system and locate the cause before replacing the link. Many late-model vehicles are equipped with maxi-fuses in place of the fusible links. These should be checked during any routine starting system inspection.

Magnetic Switches Every starting system contains some type of magnetic switch that enables the control circuit to open and close the starter circuit. This magnetic switch can be one of several designs.

SOLENOID The solenoid-actuated starter is by far the most common starter system used. A **solenoid** is an electromechanical device that uses the movement

1 CONTACT, STARTER SOLENOID SWITCH
2 PLUNGER, STARTER SOLENOID SWITCH
3 SWITCH, STARTER SOLENOID
4 SPRING, STARTER SOLENOID SWITCH PLUNGER
5 LEVER, STARTER SHIFT
6 BUSHING, STARTER DRIVE
7 COLLAR, STARTER DRIVE STOP
8 DRIVE, STARTER
9 COIL, STARTER FIELD
10 ARMATURE, STARTER
11 BRUSH, STARTER
12 TERMINAL, STARTER SOLENOID

FIGURE 17–4 Example of a solenoid-actuated starter in which the solenoid mounts directly to the starter motor.

of a plunger to exert a pulling or holding force. As shown in the starter in Figure 17–4, the solenoid mounts directly on top of the starter motor.

In this type of starting system, the solenoid uses the electromagnetic field generated by its coil to perform two distinct jobs.

The first is to push the drive pinion of the starter motor into mesh with the engine's flywheel. This is the solenoid's mechanical function. The second job is to act as an electrical relay switch to energize the motor once the drive pinion is engaged. Once the contact points of the solenoid are closed, full battery current flows to the starter motor.

The solenoid assembly has two separate windings: a **pull-in winding** and a **hold-in winding**. The two windings have approximately the same number of turns but are wound from different size wire. Together these windings produce the electromagnetic force needed to pull the plunger into the solenoid coil. The heavier pull-in windings draw the plunger into the solenoid, while the lighter gauge windings produce enough magnetic force to hold the plunger in this position.

Both windings are energized when the ignition switch is turned to the start position. When the plunger disc makes contact with this solenoid terminal, the pull-in winding is deactivated. At the same time, the plunger contact disc makes the motor feed connection between the battery and the starting motor, directing full battery current to the field coils and starter motor armature for cranking power (Figure 17–5).

As the solenoid plunger moves, the shift fork also pivots on the pivot pin end pushes the starter drive pinion into mesh with the flywheel ring gear. When the starter motor receives current, its armature starts

FIGURE 17–5 Solenoids operate using a heavy-gauge pull-in winding, and a light-gauge hold-in winding. The heavy-gauge pull-in winding generates a strong magnetic field to move the plunger. A light-gauge hold-in winding generates a weaker magnetic field to hold the plunger in position after it has moved and completed the starter circuit.

to turn. This motion is transferred through an overrunning clutch and pinion gear to the engine flywheel and the engine is cranked.

With this type of solenoid-actuated direct drive starting system, teeth on the **pinion gear** may not immediately mesh with the flywheel ring gear. If this occurs, a spring located behind the pinion compresses so the solenoid plunger can complete its stroke. When the starter motor armature begins to turn, the pinion teeth quickly line up with the flywheel teeth and the spring pressure forces them to mesh.

STARTER RELAY Relays are the second major type of magnetic switch used. All **positive engagement starters** (described later in this chapter) use a relay in

FIGURE 17–6 Cross-sectional view of a starter relay, which is actually a solenoid that is used to close an electrical circuit.

FIGURE 17–7 (A) Solenoid shift and (B) solenoid shift with starter relay starting systems.

series with the battery cables to deliver the high current necessary through the shortest possible battery cables. Figure 17–6 shows a typical starter relay. It is very similar to the solenoid. However, it is not used to move the drive pinion into mesh. It is strictly an electrical relay or switch. When current from the ignition switch arrives at the ignition switch terminal of the relay, a strong magnetic field is generated in the coil of the relay. This magnetic force pulls the plunger contact disc up against the battery terminal and the starter terminal of the relay, allowing full current flow to the starter motor.

A secondary function of the starter relay is to provide an alternate electrical path to the ignition coil during cranking. This current flow bypasses the resistance wire (or ballast resistor) in the ignition primary circuit. This is done when the plunger disc contacts the ignition by-pass terminal on the relay. Not all systems have an ignition by-pass setup.

Some vehicles use both a starter relay and a starter motor mounted solenoid. The relay controls current flow to the solenoid, which in turn controls current flow to the starter motor. This reduces the amount of current flowing through the ignition switch. In other words, it takes less current to activate the relay than to activate the solenoid.

Basically, all the different starting systems in use today fit into one of three categories: the solenoid shift, solenoid shift with relay, or positive engagement with relay. Typical wiring diagrams for each type of system are shown in Figures 17-7 and 17-8.

Starter Motor The starting motor (Figure 17–4) converts the electrical energy from the battery into mechanical energy for cranking the engine. The starter is a special type of electric motor designed to

operate under great electrical overloads and to produce very high horsepower.

Because of these design features, the starter can only operate for short periods of time without rest. The high current needed to operate the starter creates considerable heat, and continuous operation for any length of time causes serious heat damage to the unit. The starter must never operate for more than 30 seconds at a time and should rest for 2 minutes between these extended crankings. This permits the heat to dissipate without damage to the unit.

All starting motors are generally the same in design and operation. Basically, the starter motor consists of a housing, field coils, an armature, a commutator and brushes, and end frames. The main difference between designs is in the drive mechanism used to engage the flywheel.

The **starter housing** or **starter frame** encloses the internal starter components and protects them from damage, moisture, and foreign materials. The housing supports the field coils and forms a path for the magnetism produced by the current passing through the coils.

FIGURE 17–8   Schematic of a positive-engagement starter.

The **field coils** and their **pole shoes** (Figure 17–9) are securely attached to the inside of the iron housing (Figure 17–10). The field coils are insulated from the housing but are connected to a terminal that protrudes through the outer surface of the housing.

The field coils and pole shoes are designed to produce strong stationary electromagnetic fields within the starter body as current is passed through the starter. These magnetic fields are concentrated at the pole shoe. Fields have an N or S magnetic polarity depending on the direction of current flow. The coils are wound around respective pole shoes in opposite directions to generate opposing magnetic fields.

The field coils connect in series with the armature winding through the starter **brushes**. This design permits all current passing through the field coil circuit to also pass through the armature windings.

The **armature** is the only rotating component of the starter. It is located between the drive and commutator end frames and the field windings. When the starter operates, the current passing through the armature produces a magnetic field in each of its conductors. The reaction between the armature's magnetic field and the magnetic fields produced by the field coils causes the armature to rotate. This is the mechanical energy that is then used to crank the engine.

The armature has two main components: the armature windings and the **commutator**. Both mount

FIGURE 17–9   Example of a field coil and pole shoe.

FIGURE 17–10   Cross-sectional view of a motor housing with field coils mounted to the inner housing walls.

FIGURE 17-11 The armature's two main components, the commutator and the armature windings, are mounted to the armature shaft.

to the armature shaft (Figure 17-11). The armature windings are not made of wire. Instead, heavy flat copper strips are used that can handle the heavy current flow. The windings are made of several coils of a single loop each. The sides of these loops fit into slots in the armature core or shaft, but they are insulated from it.

The coils connect to each other and to the commutator so current from the field coils flows through all of the armature windings at the same time. This action generates a magnetic field around each armature winding, resulting in a repulsion force all around the conductor. This repulsion force causes the armature to turn.

The commutator assembly presses onto the armature shaft. It is made up of heavy copper segments separated from each other and the armature shaft by insulation. The commutator segments connect to the ends of the armature windings.

Most starter motors have two to six brushes that ride on the commutator segments and carry the heavy current flow from the stationary field coils to the rotating armature windings via the commutator segments.

The brushes mount on and operate in some type of holder, which may be a pivoting arm design inside

the starter housing or frame (Figure 17-12). However, in many starters the brush holders are secured to the commutator end frame. In both cases, the brush holder supports the brushes in position. Springs hold the brushes against the commutator with the correct pressure. Finally, alternate brush holders are insulated from the housing or end frame. Those in between the insulated holders are grounded.

The commutator end frame consists of a metal plate that bolts to the commutator end of the starter housing. It supports the commutator end of the armature with a bushing and often contains the brush holders that support the brushes.

Operating Principle The starter motor converts electric current into torque or twisting force through the interaction of magnetic fields. It has a stationary magnetic field, the field windings, and a current-carrying conductor, the armature windings (Figure 17-13). When the armature windings are placed in this stationary magnetic field and current is passed through the windings, a second magnetic field is generated with its lines of force wrapping around the wire (Figure 17-14). Since the lines of force in the stationary magnetic field flow in one direction across the winding, they combine on one side of the wire increasing the field strength but are opposed on the other side, weakening the field strength. This creates an unbalanced magnetic force, pushing the wire in the direction of the weaker field (Figure 17-15).

Since the armature windings are formed in loops or coils, current flows outward in one direction and returns in the opposite direction. Because of this, the magnetic lines of force are oriented in opposite directions in each of the two segments of the loop. When placed in the stationary magnetic field of the field coils, one part of the armature coil is pushed in one

FIGURE 17-12 Location of the starter motor brushes and commutator. *Courtesy of General Motors Corporation*

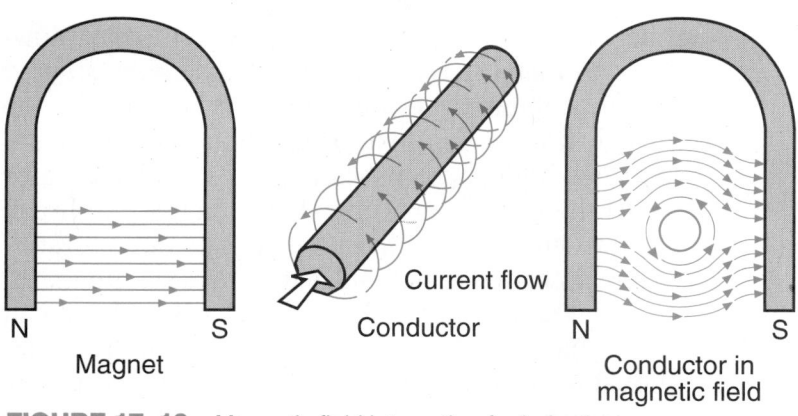

FIGURE 17–13   Magnetic field interaction for induction.

FIGURE 17–14   Simple DC motor.

direction. The other part is pushed in the opposite direction. This causes the coil and the shaft to which it is mounted to rotate.

Each end of the armature windings is connected to one segment of the commutator (Figure 17–16). Carbon brushes are connected to one terminal of the power supply. The brushes contact the commutator segments conducting current to and from the armature coils.

As the armature coil turns through a half revolution, the contact of the brushes on the commutator causes the current flow to reverse in the coil. The

FIGURE 17–16   Armature of a starter.

commutator segment attached to each coil end has traveled past one brush and is now in contact with the other. In this way, current flow is maintained constantly in one direction, while allowing the segment of the rotating armature coils to reverse polarity as they rotate.

In a starter motor, many armature segments must be used. As one segment rotates past the secondary magnetic field pole, another segment immediately takes its place. The turning motion is made uniform and the torque needed to turn the flywheel is constant rather than fluctuating as it would be if only a few armature coils were used.

The number of coils and brushes may differ between starter motor models. The armature may be wired in series with the field coils (**series motor**); the

FIGURE 17–15   Rotation of the conductor is in the direction of the weaker magnetic field.

A

B

SERIES COIL

C

SHUNT COIL

FIGURE 17–17 Starter motors are grouped according to how they are wired: (A) in series, (B) in parallel (shunt), or (c) a compound motor using both series and shunt coils.

field coils may be wired parallel or shunted across the armature (**shunt motors**); or a combination of series and shunt wiring may be used (**compound motors**) (Figure 17–17).

The amount of turning torque from a starter motor depends on a number of factors. One of the most important factors is current draw. The more current a starter draws, the more torque it is able to apply. Also, the slower the motor turns, the more current it will draw. This is why a starter motor will draw excessive amounts of current when the engine is very difficult to turn over or crank. A motor needs more torque to crank a difficult-to-turn engine. The relationship between current draw and motor speed is explained by the principles of **counter EMF (CEMF)**.

When the armature rotates within the field windings of a motor, conditions exist to induce a voltage in the armature. Voltage is induced any time a wire is passed through a magnetic field. When the armature, which is a structure with many loops of wire, rotates past the field windings, a small amount of voltage is induced. This voltage opposes the voltage supplied by the battery to energize the armature. As a result, less current is able to flow through the armature.

The faster the armature spins, the more induced voltage is present in the armature. The more voltage in the armature, the more opposition there is to normal current flow to the armature. The induced voltage in the armature opposes or is counter to the battery's voltage. This is why the induced voltage is called CEMF.

The effects of CEMF are quite predictable. When the armature of the motor turns slowly, low amounts of voltage are induced and, therefore, low amounts of CEMF are present. The low amount of CEMF allows a high amount of current draw. In fact, the

only time a starter motor draws its maximum amount of current is when the armature is not rotating.

A series-wound motor develops its maximum torque at start-up and develops less torque as speed increases. It is ideal for application involving heavy starting loads.

Shunt or parallel-wound motors develop considerably less start-up torque but maintain a constant speed at all operating loads. Compound motors combine the characteristics of good starting torque with constant speed. The compound design is particularly useful for applications in which heavy loads are suddenly applied. In a starter motor, a shunt coil is frequently used to limit the maximum free speed at which the starter can operate.

Drive Mechanisms

The area in which starters differ most is in their drive mechanisms used to crank the engine. The solenoid-actuated direct drive system has been explained earlier in this chapter.

Positive Engagement Movable Pole Shoe Drive

Positive engagement movable pole shoe drive starters (Figure 17–18) are mostly used by Ford. In this design, the drive mechanism is an integral part of the motor, and the drive pinion is engaged with the flywheel before the motor is energized.

When the ignition switch is moved to the start position, the system's starter relay closes, and full battery current is delivered to the starter. This current runs through the winding of the movable pole shoe and through a set of contacts to ground. This generates a magnetic force that pulls down the movable pole shoe. It also forces the drive pinion to engage the flywheel ring gear using a lever action and opens the contacts. A small holding coil helps keep the movable shoe and lever assembly engaged during cranking. When the engine starts, an overrunning clutch prevents the engine's flywheel from spinning the armature of the motor.

When the ignition switch is released from the start position, both the pole shoe and lever return to their original positions.

Solenoid-Actuated Gear Reduction Drive
Solenoid-actuated **gear reduction-drive starters** use a solenoid to engage the pinion with the flywheel and to close the motor circuit (Figure 17–19). The starter armature does not drive the pinion directly. Instead, it drives a small gear that is permanently meshed with a larger gear having a reduction ratio of 2:1 to 3.5:1, depending on the engine size. This design allows a small, high-speed motor to develop increased turning torque at a satisfactory cranking rpm. The solenoid

COVER SCREW

COVER ASSY

LEVER ASSY

SPRING

GROMMET

FIELD COILS

SCREW POLE

BRUSH

BRUSH
HOLDER

INSULATOR
BRUSH
HOLDER

BOLT

BRUSH

PIN

BRUSH

SPRING
BRUSH

PLATE ASSY
BRUSH END

HOUSING ASSY

FLANGE

SLEEVE

CORE ASSY

POLE

FIGURE 17–18   Typical positive engagement movable pole shoe starter. *Courtesy of Ford Motor Company*

and starter drive operation is basically the same as in solenoid-actuated direct drive systems.

While reduction starters are designed to deliver more cranking power using fewer amperes than ordinary starters, the reverse may be true if the gears wear or otherwise go bad. Increased starter noise is a sign that worn reduction gears may be a problem.

Permanent Magnet Starting Motor The most recent change in starting motors has been in the use of permanent magnets rather than electromagnets as field coils. Electrically, this starter motor is simpler. It does not require current for field coils. Current is delivered directly to the armature through the com-

POLE
SHOE

SOLENOID

SHIFT
LEVER

FIELD
COIL

ARMATURE

REDUCTION
GEARS

OVERRUNNING
CLUTCH

FIGURE 17–19   Typical gear reduction starter design.

FIGURE 17–20 (A) Permanent magnet, planetary drive starter and (B) planetary gear construction details.

mutator and brushes. Figure 17–20 shows this starter motor. With the exception of no electromagnets for the fields, this unit functions exactly as the other styles considered. Increased use of this style is expected in the future as production costs are greatly reduced. Maintenance and testing procedures are the same as for other designs. Notice the use of a planetary gear reduction assembly on the front of the armature. This allows the armature to spin with increased torque, resulting in improved starter cold-cranking performance. The starter design also results in reduced size and weight. Consequently, overall vehicle weight is lighter and fuel efficiency is enhanced. Reducing the overall size while keeping the torque high improves the adaptability of the unit in certain vehicles where space is at a premium. The unit still requires the use of a starting solenoid. It should also be noted that these units require special handling since the permanent magnet material is quite brittle and can be destroyed with a sharp blow or if the starter is dropped.

STARTER DRIVE

A **starter drive** includes a pinion gear set that meshes with the flywheel on the engine's crankshaft (Figure 17–21). To prevent damage to the pinion gear or the flywheel's ring gear, the pinion gear must mesh with the ring gear before the starter motor rotates. To help ensure smooth engagement, the end of the pinion gear is tapered (Figure 17–22). Also, the movement of the armature must always be caused by the action

FIGURE 17–21 Starter drive pinion gear is used to turn the engine's flywheel.

FIGURE 17–22 The pinion gear teeth are tapered to allow for smooth engagement.

of the motor, not the engine. For this reason, starter drive assemblies include an overrunning clutch.

Overrunning Clutch The **overrunning clutch** performs a very important job in protecting the starter

FIGURE 17–23 Sectional view of a typical overriding clutch.

FIGURE 17–25 When the engine starts, the flywheel spins the pinion gear faster, which releases the rollers from the wedge.

motor. When the engine starts and runs, its speed increases. If the starter motor remained connected to the engine through the flywheel, the starter motor would spin at very high speeds, destroying the armature winding.

To prevent this, the starter must be disengaged from the engine as soon as the engine turns more rapidly than the starter has cranked it. However, with most starter designs the pinion remains engaged until electricity stops flowing to the starter. In these cases, an overrunning clutch is used to disengage the starter. A typical overrunning clutch is shown in Figure 17–23.

The clutch housing is internally splined to the starting motor armature shaft. The drive pinion turns freely on the armature shaft within the clutch housing. When the clutch housing is driven by the armature, the spring-loaded rollers are forced into the small ends of their tapered slots and wedged tightly against the pinion barrel (Figure 17–24). This locks

the pinion and clutch housing solidly together, permitting the pinion to turn the flywheel and, thus, crank the engine.

When the engine starts (Figure 17–25) the flywheel spins the pinion faster than the armature. This releases the rollers, unlocking the pinion gear from the armature shaft. The pinion then overruns the armature shaft freely until being pulled out of the mesh without stressing the starter motor. Note that the overrunning clutch is moved in and out of mesh by the starter drive linkage.

CONTROL CIRCUIT

The control circuit allows the driver to use a small amount of battery current to control the flow of a large amount of current in the starting circuit.

The entire circuit usually consists of an ignition switch connected through normal gauge wire to the battery and the magnetic switch (solenoid or relay). When the ignition switch is turned to the start position, a small amount of current flows through the coil of the magnetic switch, closing it and allowing full current to flow directly to the starter motor. The ignition switch performs other jobs besides controlling the starting circuit. It normally has at least four separate positions: accessory, off, on (run), and start.

Starting Safety Switch

The **starting safety switch**, often called the **neutral safety switch**, is a normally open switch that prevents the starting system from operating when the transmission is in gear. This eliminates the possibility of a situation that could make the vehicle lurch unexpectedly forward or backward. Safety switches are more commonly used with automatic transmissions but are also used on manual transmissions.

FIGURE 17–24 When the armature turns, it locks the rollers into the tapered notch. *Courtesy of Robert Bosch Corporation*

FIGURE 17–26 This starter safety switch must be closed before battery current can reach the starter relay.

Starting safety switches can be located in either of two places within the control circuit. One location is between the ignition switch and the relay or solenoid. In this position, the safety switch must be closed before current can flow to the relay or solenoid. A second location for the safety switch is between the relay and ground. The switch must be closed before current can flow from the relay to ground.

The safety switch used with an automatic transmission can be either an electrical switch or a mechanical device. Contact points on the electrical switch are closed only when the shift selector is in park or neutral (Figure 17–26). The switch can be mounted near the shift selector (Figure 17–27) or on the transmission housing. The switch contacts are wired in series with the control circuit so that no current can flow through the relay or solenoid unless the transmission is in neutral or park.

Mechanical safety switches for automatic transmissions are simply devices that physically block the movement of the ignition key when the transmission is in a gear (Figure 17–28). The ignition key can only be turned when the shift selector is in park or neutral.

The safety switches used with manual transmissions are usually electrical switches mounted near the gear-shift lever or on the transmission housing. A clutch switch is a second type of safety switch used

A-Locking washer
B-Switch attaching nut
C-Switch adjusting bolt
D-Neutral safety switch

FIGURE 17–27 Neutral safety switch attached to the shift lever on the console.

with manual transmissions. This electrical switch mounts on the floor or fire wall. Its contacts are closed only when the clutch pedal is fully depressed (Figure 17–29).

FIGURE 17–28 Mechanical linkage used to prevent starting the engine while the transmission is in gear. *Courtesy of Cadillac Motor Car Division, General Motors Corporation*

FIGURE 17–29 The clutch pedal must be fully depressed to close the clutch switch and complete the control circuit.

STARTING SYSTEM TESTING

As mentioned earlier, the starter motor is a special type of electrical motor designed for intermittent use only. During testing, it should never be operated for more than 30 seconds without resting for 2 minutes in between operation cycles to allow it to cool.

Preliminary Checks

The cranking output obtained from the motor is also affected by the condition and charge of the battery, the circuit's wiring, and the engine's cranking requirement.

The battery should be checked and charged as needed before testing. Be sure the battery is rated to meet or exceed the vehicle manufacturer's recommendations. The voltage rating of the battery must also match the voltage rating of the starter motor.

Check the wiring for clean, tight connections. The starter motor may draw several hundred amperes or more during cranking. Loose or dirty connections will cause excessive voltage drop. Cables should also be checked for correct gauge size. These cables should also be inspected to see if they are too long. Excessive length causes excessive resistance.

Make certain the engine is filled with proper weight oil as recommended by the vehicle manufacturer. Heavier-than-specified oil when coupled with low operating temperatures can drastically lower cranking speed to the point where the engine does not start and excessively high current is drawn by the starter.

Check the ignition switch for loose mounting, damaged wiring, sticking contacts, and loose connections. Check the wiring and mounting of the safety switch, if so equipped, and make certain the switch is properly adjusted. Check the mounting, wiring, and connections of the magnetic switch and starter motor. Also, be sure the starter pinion is properly adjusted.

Safety Precautions

Almost all starting system tests must be performed while the starter motor is cranking the engine. However, the engine must not start and run during the test or the readings will be inaccurate.

To prevent the engine from starting, the ignition switch can be bypassed with a remote starter switch that allows current to flow to the starting system but not to the ignition system. On vehicles with the ignition starting by-pass in the ignition switch or the starter relay, the ignition must be disabled.

On standard ignition systems, disable the ignition by removing the secondary lead from the center of the distributor cap and grounding the lead. With electronic systems or engine control systems, disconnect the wiring harness connector from the distributor.

During testing, be sure the transmission is out of gear during cranking and the parking brake is set. When servicing the battery, always follow safety precautions. Always disconnect the battery ground cable before making or breaking connections at the system's relay, solenoid, or starter motor.

Troubleshooting Procedures

A systematic troubleshooting procedure is essential when servicing the starting system. Consider the fact that nearly 80 percent of defective starters returned on warranty claims work perfectly when tested. This is often the result of poor or incomplete diagnosis of the starting and related charging systems. A summary of a systematic approach to starting system diagnosis is found in the *Tech Manual* that accompanies this textbook. Testing the starting system can be divided into area tests, which check voltage and current in the entire system, and more detailed pinpoint tests, which target one particular component or segment of the wiring circuit.

Battery Load Test (Area Test)

An engine that turns sluggishly when cranked is often not receiving sufficient voltage from the battery. The battery must be able to crank the engine under all load conditions while maintaining enough voltage to supply ignition current for starting. Perform a battery load test before performing any starting systems tests.

Cranking Voltage Test (Area Test)

The **cranking voltage test** measures the available voltage to the starter during cranking. To perform the test, disable the ignition or use a remote starter switch to bypass the ignition switch. Normally, the remote starter switch is connected to the positive side of the battery and the starter terminal of the solenoid or relay (Figure 17–30). Refer to the service manual for specif-

FIGURE 17–30 Using a remote starter switch to bypass the control circuit and ignition system.

ic instructions on the model car being tested. Connect the voltmeter's negative lead to a good chassis ground. Connect the positive lead to starter motor feed at the starter relay or solenoid. Activate the starter motor and observe the voltage reading. Compare the reading to the specifications given in the service manual. Normally, 9.6 volts is the minimum required.

Test Conclusions If the reading is above specifications but the starter motor still cranks poorly, the starter motor is faulty. If the voltage reading is lower than specifications, a cranking current test and circuit resistance test should be performed to determine if the problem is caused by high resistance in the starter circuit or an engine problem.

Cranking Current Test (Area Test)

The **cranking current test** measures the amount of current the starter circuit draws to crank the engine. Knowing the amount of current draw helps to identify the cause of starter system problems. Photo Sequence 9 outlines the procedure for conducting this test.

Nearly all starter current testers use an inductive pick-up (Figure 17–31) to measure the current draw. However, some earlier models were equipped with an ammeter that needed to be connected in series with the battery.

To conduct the cranking current test, disable the ignition prior to testing (Figure 17–32, page 424). Follow the instructions given with the tester when connecting the test leads. Crank the engine for no more than 15 seconds. Observe the voltmeter. If the voltage drops

FIGURE 17–31 Connecting the test leads of a typical CSB tester. *Courtesy of Sun Electric Corporation*

below 9.6 volts, a problem is indicated. Also, watch the ammeter and compare the reading to specifications.

Test Conclusions Normally, the expected current draw is approximately equal to the cubic inch displacement of the engine. Table 17–1 (page 424) summarizes the most probable causes of too low or high starter motor current draw. If the problem appears to be caused by excessive resistance in the system, conduct an insulated circuit resistance test.

Insulated Circuit Resistance Test

The complete starter circuit is made up of the insulated circuit and the bare ground circuit. The insulated circuit includes all of the high current cables and connections from the battery to the starter motor.

To test the insulated circuit for high resistance, disable the ignition or bypass the ignition switch with

USING A VOLT AND AMP TESTER TO TEST THE BATTERY AND THE STARTING SYSTEM

P9–1   Testing the battery and starting system begins with a visual inspection of the battery and its cables. Make sure they are clean and free of corrosion.

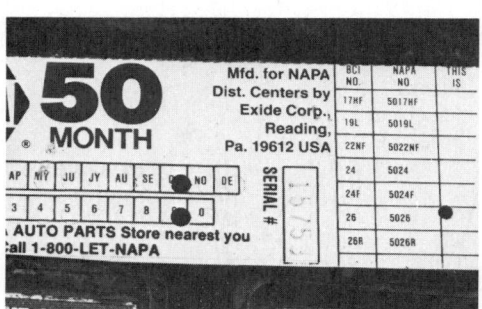

P9–2   The battery's label normally contains all of the information needed to test it. The part number can be used to determine the CCA rating of the battery.

P9–3   A typical battery and starting and charging system tester.

P9–4   Testing begins with connecting the positive and negative tester leads to the battery.

P9–5   When testing the battery, the tester's ampere pick-up probe must be installed around the tester's negative cable. If the inductive clamp is directional, point the arrow away from the battery.

P9–6   The first test will measure the battery's capacity. For this test (known as the battery load test) the voltage is observed during and after the load test.

P9–7   The tester puts a load or causes a current drain on the battery. The amount of load is determined by the battery's CCA rating. Some machines require the technician to manually set the load to an amount that draws one-half of the CCA rating. This tester automatically sets the load after the CCA is programmed into the tester and the load activation button is depressed.

P9—8 This battery checked out fine. Its voltage decreased to an amount above 9.6 volts while under a load of 156 amperes for 15 seconds.

P9—9 To test the starting system, the ampere pick-up probe must be repositioned around the battery's negative cable. Make sure the arrow on the clamp is pointing away from the battery.

P9—10 To observe the tester's meters during this test, the tester should be placed where it can be seen easily from the driver's seat.

P9—11 Prior to testing the starting system, disable the ignition system.

P9—12 Turn the ignition key to allow the starter to rotate. Observe the readings on the tester. This starter drew 170 amperes and dropped voltage to 9.82 volts. These readings should be compared to the specifications given in the service manual

FIGURE 17–32 (A) Grounding the secondary coil wire to disable the ignition. (B) To disable an HEI ignition system, disconnect the BAT wire from the coil connector.

TABLE 17–1 RESULT OF CRANKING CURRENT TESTING	
Problem	**Possible Cause**
Low current draw	Undercharged or defective battery. Excessive resistance in circuit due to faulty components or connections.
High current draw	Short in starter motor. Mechanical resistance due to binding engine or starter system component failure or misalignment.

a remote starter switch. Connect the positive (+) lead of the voltmeter to the battery's positive (+) terminal post or nut. By connecting the lead to the cable, the point of high resistance (cable-to-post connection) may be bypassed. Connect the negative (–) lead to the voltmeter to the starter terminal at the solenoid or

relay (Figure 17–33). Crank the engine and record the voltmeter reading. If the reading is within specifications (usually 0.2 to 0.6 voltage drop), the insulated circuit does not have excessive resistance. Proceed to the ground circuit resistance test outlined in the next section. If the reading indicates a voltage loss above specifications, move the negative lead of the tester progressively toward the battery, cranking the engine at each test point. Normally, a voltage drop of 0.1 volt is the maximum allowed across a length of cable.

Test Conclusions When an excessive amount of voltage drop is observed, the trouble is located between that point and the preceding point tested. It is either a damaged cable or poor connection, an undersized wire, or possibly a bad contact assembly within the solenoid. Repair or replace any damaged wiring or faulty connections. Refer to Table 17–2 to find the maximum allowable voltage drops for the starter circuit.

FIGURE 17–33 (A) Test lead connections for starter-mounted solenoids. (B) Test lead connections for relay controlled systems. *Courtesy of Sun Electric Corporation*

TABLE 17–2 MAXIMUM VOLTAGE DROPS		
	6-volt	**12-volt**
Each cable	0.1	0.2
Each connection	0.1	0.1
Starter solenoid switch	0.3	0.3

Starter Relay By-Pass Test

The starter relay by-pass test is a simple way to determine if the relay is operational. First, disable the ignition. Connect a heavy jumper cable between the battery's positive (+) terminal and the starter relay's starter terminal. This bypasses the relay. When the connection is made, the engine should crank.

Test Conclusions If the engine cranks with the jumper installed and did not before the relay was bypassed, the starter relay is defective and should be replaced.

Ground Circuit Resistance Test

The ground circuit provides the return path to the battery for the current supplied to the starter by the insulated circuit. This circuit includes the starter-to-engine, engine-to-chassis, and chassis-to-battery ground terminal connections.

To test the ground circuit for high resistance, disable the ignition, or bypass the ignition switch with a remote starter switch. Refer to Figure 17–34 for the proper test connection. Crank the engine and record the voltmeter reading.

Test Conclusions Good results would be less than 0.2 voltage drop for a 12-volt system. Voltages in excess of these indicate the presence of a poor ground

FIGURE 17–34 Setup for checking voltage drop across the ground circuit. This tests for high resistance in the circuit.

circuit connection, resulting from a loose starter motor bolt, a poor battery ground terminal post connector, or a damaged or undersized ground system wire from the battery to the engine block. Isolate the cause of excessive voltage drop in the same manner as recommended in the insulated circuit resistance test by moving the positive (+) voltmeter lead progressively back toward the battery. If the ground circuit tests out satisfactorily and a starter problem exists, move on to the control circuit test.

Control Circuit Test

The control circuit test examines all the wiring and components used to control the magnetic switch, whether it is a relay, a solenoid acting as a relay, or a starter motor-mounted solenoid.

High resistance in the solenoid switch circuit reduces the current flow through the solenoid windings, which can cause improper functioning of the solenoid. In some cases of high resistance, it may not function at all. Improper functioning of the solenoid switch generally results in the burning of the solenoid switch contacts, causing high resistance in the starter motor circuit.

Check the vehicle wiring diagram, if possible, to identify all control circuit components. These normally include the ignition switch, safety switch, the starter solenoid winding, or a separate relay.

To perform the test, disable the ignition system. Connect the positive meter lead to the battery's positive terminal and the negative meter lead to the starter switch terminal on the solenoid or relay. Crank the engine and record the voltmeter reading.

Test Conclusions Generally, good results would be less than 0.5 volt, indicating that the circuit condition is good. If voltage reads more than 0.5 volt, it is usually an indication of excessive resistance. However, on certain vehicles, a slightly higher voltage loss may be normal.

Identify the point of high resistance by moving the negative test lead back toward the battery's positive lead, eliminating one wire or component at a time (Figure 17–35).

A reading of more than 0.1 volt across any one wire or switch is usually an indication of trouble. If a high reading is obtained across the safety switch used on automatic transmission, check the adjustment of the switch according to the manufacturer's service manual. Clutch-operated safety switches cannot be adjusted. They must be replaced.

Test Starter Drive Components

This test detects a slipping starter drive without removing the starter from the vehicle. First, disable

VOLTMETER

BATTERY

GROUND

FIGURE 17-35 Typical test points to use when checking voltage drops to determine control circuit resistance.

the ignition or bypass the ignition switch with a remote starter switch. Turn the ignition switch to start and hold it in this position for several seconds. Repeat the procedure at least three times to detect an intermittent condition.

Test Conclusions If the starter cranks the engine smoothly, this is an indication of acceptable starter drive. If the engine stops cranking and the starter spins noisily at high speed, the drive is slipping and should be replaced.

If the drive is not slipping, but the engine is not being cranked, inspect the flywheel for missing or damaged teeth. Remove the starter from the vehicle and check its drive components. Inspect the pinion gear teeth for wear and damage. Test the overrunning clutch mechanism. If good, the overrunning clutch should turn freely in one direction, but not in the other. A bad clutch turns freely in the overrun direction or not at all. If a drive locks up, it can destroy the starter by allowing the starter to spin at more than 15 times engine speed.

The weak point in the movable pole starter is the pole shoe that pulls in toward the armature to engage the starter. This starter requires a minimum of 10.5 volts and about 300 to 400 amperes to operate. Otherwise, it simply clicks and does not engage.

As a movable pole starter wears, the pivot bushing sometimes hangs up and prevents the movable pole shoe from being pulled down. When this happens, the starter motor will not spin and the drive will not engage with the flywheel.

A similar problem can occur on solenoid-actuated starters. If the solenoid is too weak to overcome the force of the return springs, the starter does not operate.

CASE STUDY

A vehicle equipped with a solenoid-actuated direct-drive starting system is towed into the shop. The owner complains that the starter does not crank the engine when the ignition switch is turned to the start position.

The technician performs a battery load test to confirm that the battery is in good working order. It is. The technician then tests for voltage to the M or motor terminal on the solenoid using a voltmeter. Voltage reading at the M terminal is 12.5 volts.

Because there is voltage at the M terminal of the solenoid, inspection of individual connections and components, such as the starter safety switch, are not needed at this time. They are obviously allowing current to pass through the insulated circuit.

The technician then performs a ground circuit check to verify that the ground return path is okay. It is. Since the insulated and ground circuits have checked out okay, the only other source of an open circuit is the starter motor. The technician can now confidently pull the starter motor from the vehicle for rebuilding or replacement.

KEY TERMS

Armature	Pinion gear
Brushes	Pole shoes
Commutator	Positive engagement
Compound motor	starter
Counter EMF (CEMF)	Pull-in winding
Cranking current test	Series motor
Cranking voltage test	Shunt motor
Field coil	Solenoid
Gear reduction-drive	Starter drive
starter	Starter frame
Hold-in winding	Starter housing
Neutral safety switch	Starter relay
Overrunning clutch	Starting safety switch

SUMMARY

◆ The starting system turns the engine over until it can operate under its own power. The system has two distinct electrical circuits: the starter circuit and the control circuit.

◆ The starter circuit carries high current flow from the battery, through heavy cables, to the starter motor.

◆ The control circuit uses a small amount of current to operate a magnetic switch that opens and closes the starter circuit.

◆ The ignition switch is used to control current flow in the control circuit.

◆ Solenoids and relays are the two types of magnetic switches used in starting systems. Solenoids use electromagnetic force to pull a plunger into a coil to close the contact points. Relays use a hinged armature to open and close the circuit.

◆ The starter motor is an electric motor capable of producing very high horsepower for very short periods.

◆ The drive mechanism of the starter motor engages and turns the flywheel to crank the engine for starting.

◆ An override clutch protects the starter motor from spinning too fast once the vehicle engine starts.

◆ Starting safety switches prevent the starting system from operating when the transmission is engaged.

◆ All starting system wiring must have clean, tight connections.

◆ During starter system testing, the ignition system must be bypassed or disabled so the vehicle does not start during cranking.

◆ Battery load, cranking voltage, cranking current, insulated circuit resistance, starter relay by-pass, ground circuit resistance, control circuit, and drive component tests are all used to troubleshoot the starting system.

TECH MANUAL

The following procedures are included in Chapter 17 of the *Tech Manual* that accompanies this book:

1. Remove, inspect, and replace a starter motor.

2. Test cranking voltage.

3. Test cranking current.

4. Test the resistance of the starting control circuit.

REVIEW QUESTIONS

1. Why does proper starter operation depend on good battery cables and connectors?

2. Which of the following is *not* part of the starter circuit?

 a. battery
 b. starting safety switch
 c. starter motor
 d. relay solenoid

3. Which of the following could result in a hard starting condition?

 a. corroded battery cables
 b. excessive CCA capacity
 c. heavy-gauge battery cables
 d. all of the above

4. Which of the following is *not* a member of the control circuit?

 a. ignition switch
 b. starter relay

 c. ballast resistor
 d. starting safety switch

5. Which of the following tests would be performed to check for high resistance in the battery cables?

 a. cranking voltage test
 b. insulated circuit resistance test
 c. starter relay by-pass test
 d. ground circuit resistance test

6. When the starter spins but does not engage the flywheel, which of the following may be true?

 a. defective starter drive
 b. excessive resistance in the control circuit
 c. a faulty starter relay
 d. all of the above

7. The usual cranking voltage specification is approximately _____ volts.

 a. 9.6
 b. 10.5
 c. 11.0
 d. 12.65

8. A cranking current test is performed, and the amperage is found to be less than specification. Technician A says the starter is bad and it should be replaced. Technical B insists on testing the resistance of the cables, grounds, and connections. Who is correct?

   a. Technician A   **c.** Both A and B
   b. Technician B   **d.** Neither A nor B

9. A control circuit test may uncover which of the following conditions?

   a. high resistance in the solenoid switch circuit
   b. defective starter relay
   c. loose battery cable connection
   d. short in the starter armature windings

10. An engine cranks slowly. Technician A says a possible cause of the problem is poor starter circuit connections. Technician B says a possible cause is incorrectly set ignition timing.

    a. Technician A   **c.** Both A and B
    b. Technician B   **d.** Neither A nor B

11. If a ground circuit test reveals a voltage drop of more than 0.2 volt, the problem may be ____.

    a. a loose starter motor mounting bolt
    b. a poor battery ground terminal post connector
    c. a damaged batter ground cable
    d. all of the above

12. Which of the following components protects the starter motor from excessive turning speeds?

    a. sun gear   **c.** override clutch
    b. drive pinion   **d.** none of the above

13. What controls the amount of current drawn by a starter motor?

14. Which of the following is produced when the armature rotates within the field windings?

    a. magnetism   **c.** CEMF
    b. resistance   **d.** all of the above

15. Which of the following would *not* cause excessive current draw by the starter motor?

    a. a short in the motor
    b. high resistance in the circuit
    c. using oil that is too heavy in the engine
    d. very cold weather

16. There are three basic types of DC motors. They are the combination-type, ____-type, and ____-type.

17. The device that prevents the engine from turning the armature of the starter motor is the ____.

    a. overrunning clutch   **c.** flywheel
    b. pinion gear   **d.** pole shoe

18. The part of the armature that the brushes ride on is called the ____.

19. Technician A says the purpose of the starter relay is to complete the circuit from the battery to the starter motor. Technician B says the purpose of the solenoid is to complete the circuit from the battery to the starter motor. Who is correct?

    a. Technician A   **c.** Both A and B
    b. Technician B   **d.** Neither A nor B

20. When checking for excessive resistance in the starting circuit, Technician A connects a voltmeter across the ground cable from the battery to the ground connection of the cable. Technician B connects an ohmmeter across the positive battery cable after it has been removed from the vehicle. Who is correct?

    a. Technician A   **c.** Both A and B
    b. Technician B   **d.** Neither A nor B

CHARGING SYSTEMS

18

OBJECTIVES

◆ *Explain the purpose of the charging system.* ◆ *Identify the major components of the charging system.* ◆ *Explain the purposes of the major parts of an alternator.* ◆ *Explain half- and full-wave rectification, and how they relate to alternator operation.* ◆ *Identify the different types of AC voltage regulators.* ◆ *Describe the two types of stator windings.* ◆ *Perform charging system inspection and testing procedures using electrical test equipment.*

The primary purpose of a charging system is to recharge the battery. After the battery has supplied the high current needed to start the engine, the battery, even a good battery, has a low charge. The charging system recharges the battery by supplying a constant and relatively low charge to the battery. Charging systems work on the principles of magnetism to change mechanical energy into electrical energy. This is done by inducing voltage.

INDUCED VOLTAGE

Figure 18–1 shows a straight piece of conducting wire with the terminals of a voltmeter attached to both ends. If the wire is moved across a magnetic field, the voltmeter registers a small voltage reading. A voltage has been induced in the wire.

It is important to remember that the conducting wire must cut across the flux lines to induce a voltage. Moving the wire parallel to the lines of flux does not induce voltage.

The wire need not be the moving component in this setup. Holding the conducting wire still and moving the magnetic field at right angles to it also induces voltage in the wire. In fact, this is the exact setup used in a vehicle's alternator. A magnetic field is made to cut across stationary conductors to produce voltage and current.

The wire or conductor becomes a source of electricity and has a polarity or distinct positive and negative end. However, this polarity can be switched depending on the relative direction of movement between the wire and magnetic field (Figure 18–2). This is why an alternator produces alternating current.

The amount or **magnitude** of the induced voltage depends on four factors.

1. The stronger the magnetic field, the stronger the induced voltage.
2. The faster the field is being cut, the more lines of flux are cut and the stronger the voltage induced.

CONDUCTOR MOVEMENT

VOLTMETER READS VOLTAGE.

FIGURE 18–1 Moving a conductor so it cuts across the magnetic lines of force induces a voltage in the conductor.

CURRENT FLOW   CURRENT FLOW

FIGURE 18–2 The polarity of the induced voltage depends on the direction in which the conductor moves as it cuts across the magnetic field.

3. The greater the number of conductors, the greater the voltage induced.

4. The closer the conductor(s) and magnetic field are to right angles (perpendicular) to one another, the greater the induced voltage.

ALTERNATING CURRENT CHARGING SYSTEMS

During cranking, the battery supplies all of the vehicle's electrical energy. However, once the engine is running, the charging system is responsible for producing enough energy to meet the demands of all the loads in the electrical system, while also recharging the battery (Figure 18–3). With all of the electronic and electrical devices used on cars today, the demands on the charging system are great.

During the early days of the automobile, the automotive charging system produced direct current, or DC, using a belt-driven generator that operated like a typical electrical motor. In a DC generator, a conductor (armature) spins inside a stationary magnetic field (Figure 18–4A). This induces an output voltage in the conductors. Although these generators are called **DC generators**, they produced AC but the output was purely DC. The conversion of AC to DC was accomplished internally through the position and polarity of the armature's brushes.

These DC charging systems offered limited current output, particularly at low speeds or idle. For this reason, AC charging systems, called **alternators**, were developed and are now universally used. Unlike the generators they replaced, alternators are compact, lightweight, and efficient at all engine speeds.

Alternators use a design that is basically the reverse of a generator. In an alternator, a spinning

FIGURE 18–4   (A) DC generator and (B) AC alternator construction.

magnetic field rotates inside stationary conductors (Figure 18–4B). As the spinning north and south poles of the magnetic field pass the conducting wires, they induce voltage that first flows in one direction and then in the opposite direction. Because automotive electrical systems operate on direct current, this alternating current must be changed or rectified into direct current. This is done using an arrangement of diodes that will be explained later in the chapter.

Alternator Construction

Figure 18–5 illustrates the major parts of an alternator.

Rotor   The rotor assembly consists of a drive shaft, coil, and two pole pieces (Figure 18–6). A pulley mounted on one end of the shaft allows the rotor to be spun by a belt driven by the crankshaft pulley.

The **rotor** is a rotating magnetic field inside the alternator. The coil is simply a series of conductive windings wrapped around an iron core. The core is located between the two sets of **pole pieces**. A magnetic field is formed by a small amount (4.0 to 6.5 amperes) of current passing through the coil windings. As current flows through the coil, the core is magnetized and the pole pieces assume the magnetic polarity of the end of the core that they touch. Thus, one pole piece has a north polarity and the other has a south polarity. The extensions of the pole pieces, known as **fingers**, form the actual magnetic poles. A typical rotor has fourteen poles, seven north and seven south, with the magnetic field between the pole pieces moving from the N poles to the adjacent S poles (Figure 18–7).

Slip Rings and Brushes   Current to create the magnetic field is supplied to the coil from one of two sources, the battery, or the alternator itself. In either

FIGURE 18–3   Component and current flow in an AC charging system.

FIGURE 18–5 Components of a typical alternator. *Courtesy of Ford Motor Company*

FIGURE 18–6 The rotor is made up of a coil, pole pieces, and a shaft.

FIGURE 18–7 The magnetic field moves from the N poles, or fingers, to the S poles.

case, the current is passed through the alternator's voltage regulator before it is applied to the coil. The voltage regulator varies the amount of current supplied. Increasing field current through the coil increases the strength of the magnetic field. This, in turn, increases alternator voltage output. Decreasing the field voltage to the coil has the opposite effect. Output voltage decreases.

Slip rings and brushes conduct current to the rotor. Most alternators have two slip rings mounted directly on the rotor shaft. They are insulated from the shaft and each other. Each end of the **field coil** connects to one of the slip rings. A carbon brush (Figure 18–8) located on each slip ring carries the current to and from the field coil. Current is transmitted from the field terminal of the voltage regulator through the first brush and slip ring to the field coil. Current passes through the field coil and the second slip ring and brush before returning to ground (Figure 18–9).

Stator The **stator** is the stationary member of the alternator. It is made up of a number of conductors, or wires, into which the voltage is induced by the rotating magnetic field. Most alternators use three windings to generate the required amperage output. They are placed in slightly different positions so their electrical pulses are staggered in either a **delta** config-

FIGURE 18–8 Brushes are the stationary electrical contact to the rotor's slip rings.

FIGURE 18–9 Current is carried by the brushes to the rotor windings via the slip rings.

uration or a **wye** configuration (Figure 18–10). The delta winding received its name because its shape resembles the Greek letter delta, Δ. The wye winding resembles the letter *Y*. Alternators use one or the other. Usually, a wye winding is used in applications where high charging voltage at low engine speeds is required. Alternators with delta windings are capable of putting out higher amperages.

The rotor rotates inside the stator (Figure 18–11). A small air gap between the two allows the rotor to turn without making contact with the stator. The

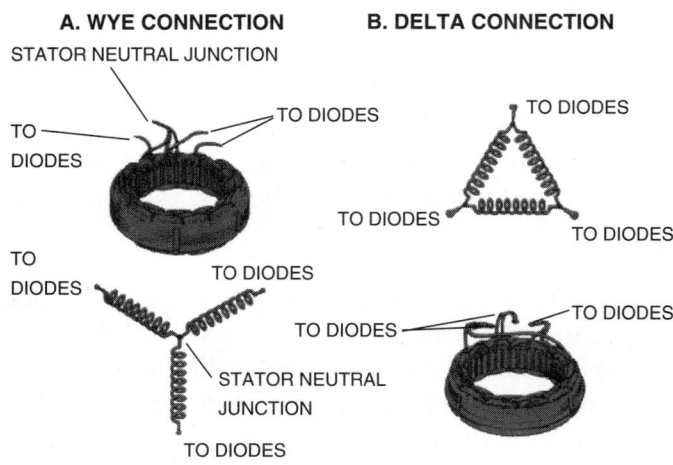

FIGURE 18–10 (A) Wye wound and (B) delta stators. *Courtesy of Ford Motor Company*

FIGURE 18–11 A small air gap exists between the spinning rotor and the stationary stator.

magnetic field of the rotor is able to energize all of the stator windings at the same time. Therefore, the generation of AC can be quite high if needed.

Alternating current produces a positive pulse and then a negative pulse. The resultant waveform is known as a sine wave, This **sine wave** can be seen on an oscilloscope (Figure 18–12). Notice that the complete waveform starts at zero, goes positive, then drops back to zero before turning negative. The angle and polarity of the field coil fingers are what cause this sine wave in the stator. When the north pole magnetic field cuts across the stator wire, it generates a positive voltage within the wire. When the south polarity magnetic field cuts across the stator wire, a negative voltage is induced in the wire. A single loop of wire energized by a single north then a south results in a single-phase voltage. Remember that there are three stator windings overlapped. This produces the overlapping sine wave (Figure 18–13). This voltage, since it was produced by three windings, is called **three-phase voltage**.

FIGURE 18–12 Sine wave from a stator, as displayed on an oscilloscope.

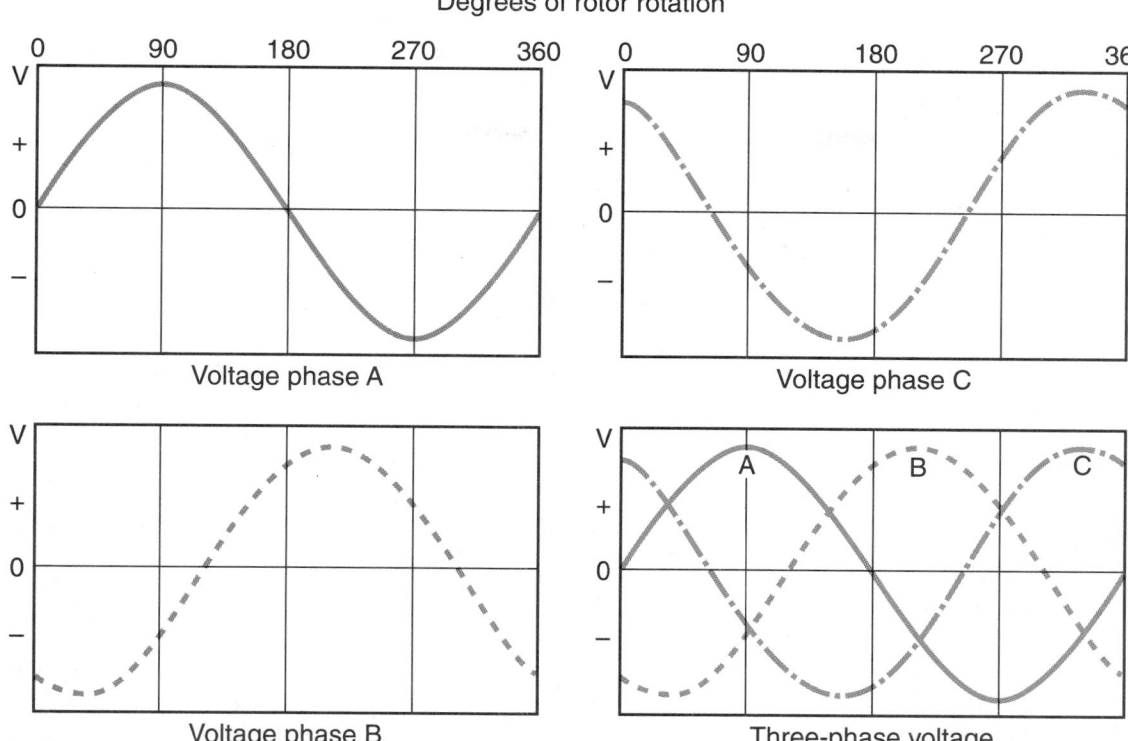

Degrees of rotor rotation

Voltage phase A

Voltage phase C

Voltage phase B

Three-phase voltage

FIGURE 18–13 The voltage produced in each stator winding is added together to create a three-phase voltage.

FIGURE 18–14 Bridge rectifier.

FIGURE 18–15 AC current rectified to a pulsating DC current after passing through a positive-biased diode.

End Frame Assembly The end frame assembly, or housing, is made of two pieces of cast aluminum. It contains the bearings for the end of the rotor shaft where the drive pulley is mounted. Each end frame also has built-in ducts so the air from the rotor shaft fan can pass through the alternator. Normally, a heat sink containing three positive rectifier diodes is attached to the rear end frame. Heat can pass easily from these diodes to the moving air (Figure 18–14). Three negative rectifier diodes are contained in the end frame itself (Figure 18–15). Because the end frames are bolted together and then bolted directly to the engine, the end frame assembly is part of the electrical ground path. This means that anything connected to the housing that is not insulated from the housing is grounded.

Alternator Operation

As mentioned earlier, alternators produce alternating current that must be converted, or rectified, to DC. This is accomplished by passing the AC through diodes.

DC Rectification

Figure 18–16 shows that if AC runs through the diode, the negative pulses are blocked off to produce the scope pattern shown. If the diode is reversed, it blocks off current during the positive pulse and

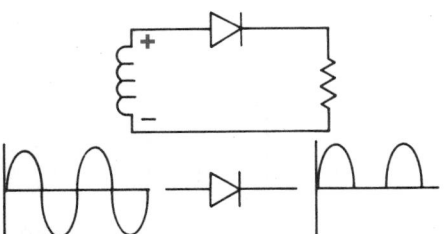

FIGURE 18–16 Half-wave rectification, diode positively biased.

FIGURE 18–17 Half-wave rectification, diode negatively biased.

allows the negative pulse to flow (Figure 18–17). Because only half of the AC current pulses (either the positive or the negative) is able to pass, this is called **half-wave rectification**.

By adding more diodes to the circuit, more of the AC is rectified. When all of the AC is rectified, **full-wave rectification** occurs.

Full-wave rectification for stator windings requires another circuit with similar characteristics. Figure 18–18 shows a wye stator having two diodes attached to each winding. One diode is insulated, or positive, and the other is grounded, or negative. The center of the *Y* contains a common point for all windings. It can have a connection attached to it. It is called the stator neutral junction. At any time during the rotor movement, two windings are in series and the third coil is neutral and inactive. As the rotor revolves, it energizes the different sets of windings in different directions. However, the uniform result is

FIGURE 18–18 Wye stator wired to six diodes.

FIGURE 18–19 Delta stator wired to six diodes.

that current in any direction through two windings in series produces the required DC for the battery.

The diode action does not change when the stator and diodes are wired into a delta pattern. Figure 18–19 shows the major difference. Instead of having two windings in series, the windings are in parallel. Thus, more current is available from a delta wound alternator because the parallel paths allow more current to flow through the diodes. Nevertheless, the action of the diodes remains the same.

Some alternators have additional diodes, which connect the stator windings to the rotor coil (Figure 18–20).

Voltage Regulation

A **voltage regulator** controls the amount of voltage produced by the alternator and thus the voltage level in the charging circuit. Without a voltage regulator, the battery would be overcharged and the voltage level in the electrical systems would rise to the point where lights would burn out and fuses and fusible links would blow. Controlling the voltage is particularly important for on-board computers and other digital equipment. Microprocessors and electronic sensors and switches are easily damaged by voltage spikes and high-voltage levels.

The regulation of the charging circuit is accomplished by varying the amount of field current flowing through the rotor. Output is high when the field current is high and low when the field current is low. The operation of the regulator is comparable to that of a variable resistor in series with the field coil (Figure 18–21). If the resistance the regulator offers is low, the field current is high and if the resistance is high, the field current is low. The amount of resistance in series with the field coil determines the amount of field current, the strength of the rotor's magnetic field, and thus the amount of alternator output. The resistance offered by the regulator varies

FIGURE 18–20 Wiring diagram of a charging circuit with a diode trio.

FIGURE 18–21 The voltage regulator acts like a variable resistor to control voltage.

according to charging system demands or needs. These needs are determined by the regulator as it interprets voltage and temperature inputs.

Many newer electronic voltage regulators turn the current flow to the rotor on and off to control an alternator's output. When more charge is needed, current flows for a longer period of time.

Voltage Input

Charging voltage is critically important to the process of fully charging the battery. If the charging voltage is only 12.5 volts, the battery never comes all the way up on charge. Not only does the entire vehicle operate at 12.5 volts, but current is being drawn from the battery instead of charging it. By raising the voltage of the alternator about 2 volts above the voltage of the battery, the alternator now becomes the source of current for the vehicle and of current to charge the battery. Most regulators are set for a system voltage between 14.0 and 14.7 volts so the charging voltage is higher than the 12.6 volts of the battery. A full charge is ensured.

To regulate the charging system, the regulator must have system voltage as an input. This voltage is also called sensing system voltage because the regulator is sensing system voltage. The regulator determines the need for charging current according to the level of the sensing voltage. When the sensing voltage is less than the regulator setting, the regulator increases the field current to increase the charging current. As sensing voltage rises, a corresponding decrease in field current and system output occurs. Thus, the regulator responds to changes in system voltage by increasing or decreasing charging current. For example, if a car is running down the road with no accessories on and a fully charged battery, the regulator senses a high system voltage because the battery is fully charged. So it maintains the charging voltage at a level sufficient enough to run the ignition system and to supply a 2- to 4-ampere trickle charge to the battery. If the headlights are turned on, the additional draw drops or loads the system voltage down. When the regulator senses this reduced voltage through the sensing circuit, it reduces the field circuit resistance to increase the field current and, as a result, the charging current. This adjustment takes place in less than a second. Of course, turning off accessories reverses the process. In response to a system voltage rise, the regulator reduces field current and alternator output.

Temperature Input

Temperature is the second input to the regulator. All regulators are temperature compensated (Table 18-1) because the battery is less willing to accept a charge if it is cold. So, as the temperature goes down, the regulator raises the system voltage until it is at a level that the battery readily accepts. In this way, the bat-

TABLE 18–1 REGULATOR TEMPERATURE VS. VOLTAGE

Temperature	Volts	
	Minimum	**Maximum**
20°F	14.3	15.3
80°F	13.8	14.4
140°F	13.3	14.0
Over 140°F	Less than 13.8	—

FIGURE 18–24 This chart shows the relationship between rotor speed, current in field windings, and output voltage. As the rotor speed increases, field current is reduced to keep the regulated voltage controlled.

tery can be brought up on charge quickly, even in very cold climates.

Regulator Circuit

There are basically two ways the regulator circuit is connected to the alternator. The A-circuit has the regulator wired between the field terminal of the alternator and ground. Field current is regulated by changing the resistance in the ground path as shown in Figure 18–22. This circuit is commonly used with solid-state regulators. A B-circuit has the regulator between the B+ feed and the field coil as shown in Figure 18–23. The field coil is grounded inside the alternator. The result is the same as it was in the A-circuit. B-circuits are often used with older electromagnetic voltage regulators.

Voltage Regulator Design

All voltage regulators are designed to control the amount of current flowing through the field windings. The relationship between rotor speed, field current, and the regulated voltage is shown in Figure 18–24. To keep the regulated voltage con-

FIGURE 18–25 Alternator with an internally mounted voltage regulator.

FIGURE 18–22 A-circuit.

FIGURE 18–23 B-circuit.

trolled, the field current is reduced as the rotor speed increases.

Integrated circuit voltage regulators are used on most late-model vehicles. This is the most compact regulator design. All of the control circuitry and components are located on a single silicon chip. The chip is sealed in a plastic module and mounted either inside or on the back of the alternator (Figure 18–25). Integrated circuit regulators are also nonserviceable and must be replaced if defective.

Figure 18–26 illustrates a solid-state integrated regulator. It mounts inside the alternator slip ring end frame along with the brush holder assembly. All voltage regulator parts are enclosed in a solid mold. The rectifier bridge contains the six diodes needed to

FIGURE 18–26 Component locations of an alternator with an internally mounted voltage regulator. *Courtesy of General Motors Corporation*

change AC to DC, which is then available at the output battery terminal. Field current is supplied through a diode trio, which is connected to the stator windings.

FAIL-SAFE CIRCUITS To prevent simple electrical problems from causing high-voltage outputs that can damage delicate electronic components, many voltage regulators contain **fail-safe circuits**.

A detailed explanation of how these circuits operate can be quite confusing. All you need to know is what a fail-safe circuit does, not how it does it. If wire connections to the alternator become corroded or accidently disconnected, the regulator's fail-safe circuits may limit voltage output that might rise to dangerous levels. Under certain conditions, the fail-safe circuits may prevent the alternator from charging at all. A fusible line in the fail-safe circuitry confines damage to the alternator. Delicate electronic components in other vehicle systems are not damaged.

Computer Regulation

On a growing number of late-model vehicles, a separate voltage regulator is no longer used. Instead, the voltage regulation circuitry is located in the vehicle's electronic control module or unit (Figure 18–27).

FIGURE 18–27
Wiring diagram of a charging system that uses the on-board computer system for voltage regulation control. *Courtesy of Chrysler Corporation*

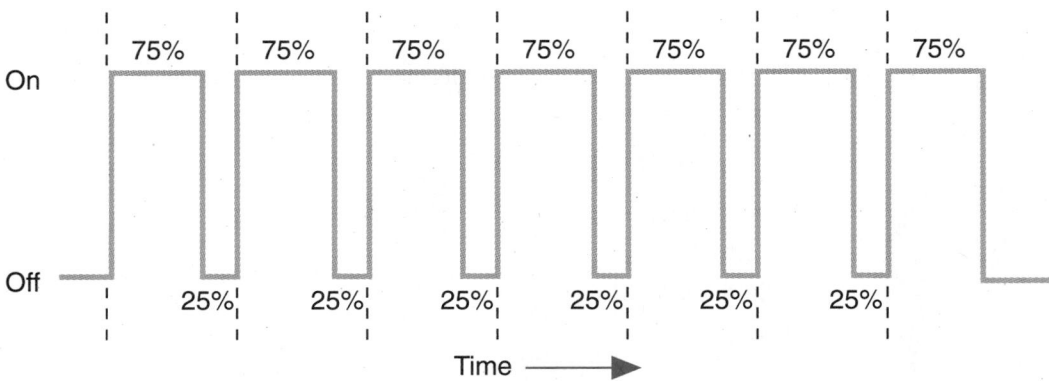

FIGURE 18–28   Pulse width modulation of charging system with 75 percent on-time.

The module computer is used to control current to the field windings in the rotor.

This type of system does not control rotor field current by acting like a variable transistor. Instead, the computer switches or pulses field current on and off at a fixed frequency of about 400 cycles per second. By varying on-off times, a correct average field current is produced to provide correct alternator output. At high engine speeds with little electrical system load, field circuit on time may be as low as 10 percent. At low engine speeds with high loads, the computer may energize the field circuit 75 percent or more of the time to generate the higher average field current needed to meet output demands (Figure 18–28).

A significant feature of this system is its ability to vary the amount of voltage according to vehicle requirements and ambient temperatures. This precise control allows the use of smaller, lighter, storage batteries. It also reduces the magnetic drag of the alternator, increasing engine output by several horsepower. Precise management of the charging rate can result in increased gas mileage and eliminate poten-

tial rough idle problems caused by parasitic voltage loss at low idling speeds. Most importantly, it allows the computer's diagnostic capabilities to be used in troubleshooting charging system problems, such as low- or high-voltage outputs.

Older Voltage Regulator Designs

Older vehicles may be equipped with electromagnetic or partially transistorized voltage regulators. Electromagnetic regulators use two electromagnetically operated contact point relays to control the charging circuit (Figure 18–29).

A **field relay** closes when the alternator begins to produce voltage. It allows a portion of the output current to energize the field coils. A second relay, known as the voltage limiter, has two sets of contact points. When the lower set of contact points open, field current passes through a resistor, and generated voltage decreases. When the possibility of excessive voltage exists during high speed operation, the upper contact closes shutting off all current flow to the field windings.

FIGURE 18–29   Older electromagnetically controlled alternator that uses solenoid-controlled field and voltage relays.

Transistors can be used in place of the electromagnetic relays. Older transistorized voltage regulators often used an electromagnetic field relay and a transistorized voltage relay. As explained in previous sections, modern solid-state regulators are completely transistorized.

Indicators

It is very important to monitor charging system performance during the course of vehicle operation. Vehicles are equipped with an ammeter, voltmeter, and indicator light. These allow the driver to monitor the charging system.

Indicator Light This is the simplest and most common method of monitoring alternator performance. When the charging system fails to supply sufficient current, the light turns on. However, when the ignition switch is first activated, the light also comes on. This is due to the fact that the alternator is not providing power to the battery and other electrical circuits. Thus, the only current path is through the ignition switch, indicator light, voltage regulator, part of the alternator, and ground, then back through the battery (Figure 18–30). Once enough power is provided, the contact in the regulator changes. Only the battery, regulator, and alternator are in the circuit. With no current flowing through the indicator light, it goes out.

With the engine running, the indicator light comes on again if the electrical load is more than the alternator can supply. This occasionally happens when the engine is idling. If there are no problems, the light should go out as the engine speed is increased. If it

does not, either the alternator or regulator is not working properly.

SHOP TALK

On late-model cars, the indicator light can be combined with the oil pressure warning light; it usually is labeled "engine." If this light turns on while the engine is running, either the alternator is not charging or the oil pressure is low—or both. ∎

Voltmeter Voltmeters indicate the amount of voltage across an electrical circuit. The voltmeter shown in Figure 18–31 measures battery voltage when the ignition switch is in the run position. A fully charged battery indicates just over 12 volts. As energy is taken from it, the battery's voltmeter reading drops. At the same time, the voltage regulator senses this and raises the charging voltage output to 14 volts or more. When the battery has been recharged, the alternator cuts back. The voltmeter now shows the fully charged battery voltage of just over 12 volts again. This on again, off again action of the alternator is constantly monitored by the voltmeter.

Ammeter The ammeter is placed in series with the circuit to monitor current flow into or out of the battery (Figure 18–32). When the alternator is delivering current to the battery, the ammeter shows a positive (+) indication. When not enough current (or none at all) is being supplied, the result is a negative (–) indi-

FIGURE 18–30 Electronic regulator with an indicator light "on" due to no alternator output.

FIGURE 18–31   Voltmeter connected to the charging circuit to monitor its operation.

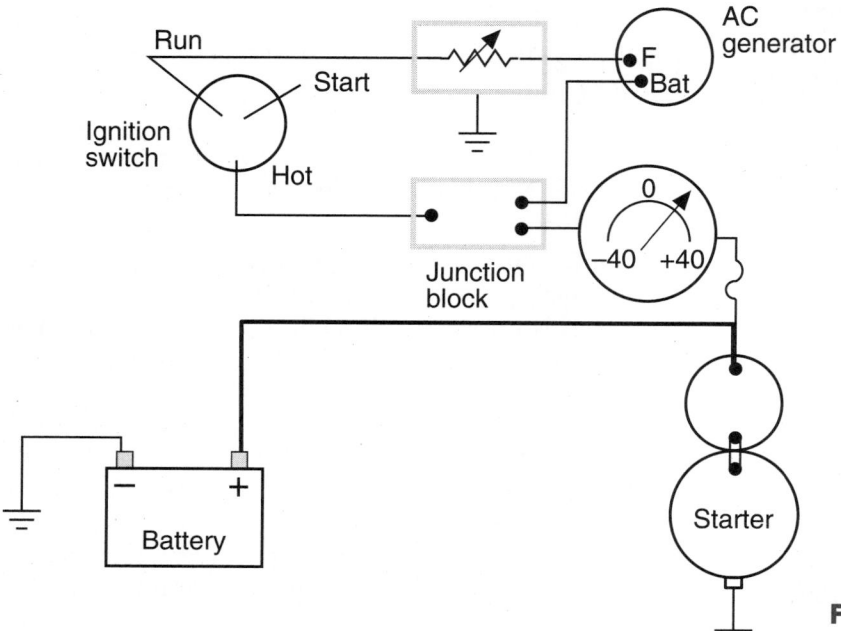

FIGURE 18–32   Ammeter connected in series with the charging system to monitor its operation.

cation. This is because the current flow is in the opposite direction, from the battery to the electrical system.

PRELIMINARY CHECKS

The key in solving charging system problems is getting to the root of the trouble the first time. Once a customer drives away with the assurance that the problem is solved, another case of a dead battery is very costly—both in terms of a free service call and a damaged reputation. Add to this the many possible hours of labor trying to figure out why the initial repair failed, and the importance of a correct initial diagnosis becomes all too clear.

When it comes to choosing equipment, the best tool to use for diagnosing the full spectrum of charging system problems is a charging-starting battery (CSB) analyzer. While a voltmeter helps in making intelligent decisions, the analyzer pinpoints the exact source of the trouble. Choose an analyzer that combines the functions of the carbon pile and separate meters to test the battery, alternator, regulator, and wiring.

Safety Precautions

◆ Disconnect the battery ground cable before removing any leads from the system. Do not reconnect the battery ground cable until all wiring connections have been made.

◆ Avoid contact with the alternator output terminal. This terminal is hot (has voltage present) at all times when the battery cables are connected.

◆ Always make sure the ignition switch is off, except during actual test procedures.

◆ The alternator is not made to withstand a lot of force. Only the front housing is relatively strong. When adjusting belt tension, apply pressure to the front housing only to avoid damaging the stator and rectifier.

♦ Never operate the alternator without first connecting an external load to it. Failure to do so can cause extremely high voltage and possibly burn out the alternator.

♦ When installing a battery, be careful to observe the correct polarity. Reversing the cables destroys the diodes. Proper polarity must also be observed when connecting a booster battery, positive to positive and negative to ground.

♦ Always disconnect the battery ground cable before charging the battery. This greatly lessens the chance of flying sparks that could cause the battery to explode.

♦ Keep the tester's carbon pile off at all times, except during actual test procedures.

♦ Make sure all hair, clothing, and jewelry are kept away from moving parts.

Inspection

In addition to observing the ammeter, voltmeter, or indicator light, there are some common warning signs of charging system trouble. For example, a low state of battery charge often signals a charging problem, as does a noisy alternator. A detailed troubleshooting chart for charging systems is given in the *Tech Manual* that accompanies this textbook.

Many charging system complaints stem from easily repairable problems that reveal themselves during a visual inspection of the system. Remember to always look for the simple solution before performing more involved diagnostic procedures. Use the following inspection procedure when a problem is suspected.

 PROCEDURES
Inspections

1. Before adjusting belt tension, check for proper pulley alignment. This is especially critical with serpentine belts.
2. Inspect the alternator drive belt. Loose drive belts are a major source of charging problems. If a belt does not have the proper tension, it might produce a loud squealing sound. Use a belt tension gauge to check the tension as shown in Figure 18–33. Keep in mind that different belts (V, cogged V, and multi-ribbed V) require different tensions. Always consult the manufacturer's specifications. In addition, check the belt for signs of fraying, cracking, or glazing; replace if needed (Figure 18–34).
3. Inspect the battery. It might be necessary to charge the battery to restore it to a fully charged state. If the battery cannot be charged, it must be replaced. Also, make sure the posts and cable clamps are clean and tight, since a bad connection can cause reduced current flow.
4. Inspect all system wiring and connections. Many automotive electrical systems contain fusible links to protect against overloads. These

FIGURE 18–33 Using a tension gauge to check the tightness of an alternator's drive belt.

FIGURE 18–34 The alternator's drive belt must be replaced if any of these conditions exist.

are wires that melt at a lower temperature than the current-carrying wires they protect. Fusible links can blow like a fuse without being noticed. Also, look for a short circuit, an open ground, or high resistance in any of the circuits that could cause a problem that would appear to be in the charging system.

5. Inspect the alternator and regulator mountings for loose or missing bolts. Replace or tighten as needed. Remember that the circuit completes itself through the ground of the alternator and regulator. Most alternators and regulators complete their ground through their mounting. If the mountings are not clean and tight, a high resistant ground will result.

SHOP TALK

Some late-model Chrysler engines require a torque reading to be taken when tension is applied to the alternator drive belt. This is especially important on the longer, multiribbed V-belts. ■

If the vehicle passes all preliminary visual checks, listen for noisy belts, bad bearings, or the whirring sound of a bad diode. If no unusual sounds are heard, it is time to test the charging system.

General Test Procedure

Troubleshooting charts help a technician diagnose the charging system (Figure 18–35). They give sever-al possible causes for the customer's complaint. They also help the technician decide what tests to conduct next or what service is required.

On-car charging system tests for all cars are basically the same, except for wire color and location and specifications. Not all vehicle manufacturers require all of these tests to be performed, while others suggest even more. During all of these tests, it is very important to refer to the manufacturer's specifications. Even the most accurate test results are no good if they are not matched against the correct specs. If a CSB is not available, separate voltmeters and ammeters can be used.

WARNING!

All of the meter readings that follow apply to 12-volt systems. While it is possible to test 6-, 24-, and 32-volt systems, do not attempt to do so without first checking the specifications provided by the manufacturer of the vehicle or the charging system. ■

Voltage Output Test To check charging system output, begin by recording battery open circuit voltage. To do this, connect the negative lead of the voltmeter to the negative battery cable clamp and the positive lead to the positive battery cable clamp. Note the voltage reading.

Next, start the engine and run it at the manufacturer's suggested rpm for this test. This is usually around 1,500 rpm. With no electrical load, the charging voltage should be approximately 2 volts higher than the open circuit voltage. The exact acceptable

Basic Types of Trouble	Probable Causes	Service Procedures
Alternator noise Note: Water pump noise is sometimes confused with alternator noise. A sound detecting device, such as a stethoscope, will eliminate indecision in this respect.	Alternator drive belt (squealing noise)	Adjust or replace belt, as required. (An application of belt dressing may eliminate noise caused by minor surface irregularities.)
	Alternator bearing (squealing noise)	Replace bearing if found to be out-of-round, worn, or causing shaft scoring.
	Alternator diode (whining noise)	Test alternator output. (A shorted diode causes a magnetic whine and a reduction in output.) Test diodes and replace, as required. Replacing rectifier assembly may be most feasible fix.
Indicator gauge fluctuates —or— Indicator light flickers.	Charging system wiring	Tighten loose connections. Repair or replace wiring, as required.
	Regulator contacts	Oxidized or dirty regulator contacts. Replace regulator, if necessary.
	Brushes	Check for tightness and wear. Replace, if necessary.

FIGURE 18–35   Charging system troubleshooting chart. *Courtesy of Ford Motor Company*

Basic Types of Trouble	Probable Causes	Service Procedures
Indicator light stays on.	Broken, loose, or slipping drive belt	Adjust or replace, as required.
	Battery cables, charging system wiring	Clean battery cables and terminals. Tighten loose connections. Repair or replace as required.
Ammeter registers constant discharge.	Battery specific gravity	If unsatisfactory, replace battery.
Battery will not hold charge.	Alternator output low, or no alternator output	Perform the voltage output test to Determine if trouble is in the regulator, wiring harness or the alternator itself.
	Alternator drive belt	Adjust or replace belt, as required.
	Battery cables, charging system wiring	Clean battery cables and terminals. Tighten loose connection. Repair or replace, as required.
Battery low in charge	Electrolyte (specific gravity)	Test each cell and evaluate condition:
Headlights dim at idle.		All readings even at 1.225 or above—Battery OK.
Note: A history of recurring discharge of the battery, which cannot be explained, suggests the need for checking and testing the complete charging system.		All readings even , but less than 1.225—Recharge and retest. High-low variation between cells less than 50 gravity points—Recharge and retest.
	Battery (capacity)	Test capacity and evaluate condition:
		Minimum voltage 9.6 for 12 volt battery or 4.8 for 6 volt battery. (Both values under specified test load conditions.)
		If capacity is under minimum specifications, perform 3 minute charge test. If below maximum (15.5 volts for 12 volt battery or 7.75 volts for 6 volt battery at 40 and 75 amps, charge rate, respectively) battery is OK—recharge. If above maximum, battery is sulfated. Slow charge at 1 amp/positive plate. Replace battery if it doesn't respond to slow charge.
Lights and fuses fail prematurely.	Charging system wiring, including regulator ground wire voltage limiter setting	Tighten loose connections. Repair or replace wiring, as required.
Short battery life.		
Battery uses excssive water.		Perform the voltage output tests to verify The condition of the regulator.
Burning of distributor points		
Burning of resistor wire.		
Coil damage.		
High charging rate.		

FIGURE 18–35 *Continued*

range varies from model to model, but generally this reading will be between 13.5 to 15.0 volts.

A reading of less than 13.0 volts immediately after starting indicates a charging problem. No change in voltage between battery open circuit and charging voltage means the system is not producing voltage. A reading of 16 or more volts indicates overcharging. A faulty voltage regulator and control voltage circuit are the most likely causes of overcharging.

If the unloaded charging system voltage is within specifications, test the output under a load. To do this, increase engine rpm to about 2,000 rpm and turn on the headlights and other high-current accessories. The charging system output while under

FIGURE 18–36 Ammeter, voltmeter, and carbon pile hook-up for a current output test on an alternator with an internal voltage regulator. *Courtesy of Chrysler Corporaton*

heavy load should still be around 0.5 volt above battery open circuit voltage.

Current Output Test The condition of the charging system can also be checked by testing alternator current output. The exact test procedures vary according to the vehicle and alternator model. Some test procedures call for connecting an ammeter in series between the alternator output terminal and the positive battery terminal. A carbon pile regulator is then connected across the battery terminals. The engine is then operated at moderate speeds and the carbon pile adjusted to obtain maximum current output. This reading is compared against the rated output. Normally, readings more than 10 amperes out of specifications indicate a problem.

When performing a current output test, the use of an inductive ammeter is highly recommended. An inductive ammeter eliminates the need to break battery connections. If you must break connections to hook up an ammeter, make sure you do not create an open circuit any time the alternator is generating current.

Other current output tests can be done by hooking up a voltmeter, ammeter, and carbon pile (Figure 18–36). With the engine running at a set speed, the carbon pile is adjusted to obtain the specified voltage reading. The ammeter will then read the system's current output. Always follow the appropriate instructions when conducting a current output test. Photo Sequence 10 shows a typical procedure to test a charging system.

Regulator By-Pass Test If no or low voltage or current output is indicated, bypassing the voltage regulator by **full-fielding** the alternator will tell you if the alternator is bad. The exact procedure for full-fielding an alternator, which makes it produce maximum output current, varies according to the application. On alternators where the terminals are not very accessible, jumper wires may be needed to make the connections. Some new model alternators cannot be full fielded at all.

On many internal regulator alternators, full-fielding can be done by inserting a screwdriver through a special hole on the back of the unit (Figure 18–37). The normal procedure for full-fielding an A-circuit alternator is to ground the field terminal. If the A-circuit alternator has two field terminals, ground one and feed battery positive voltage to the other to full-field the alternator. With B-circuit alternators, the alternator is full-fielded by connecting the field terminal to battery positive.

An A-circuit alternator has one carbon brush connected to positive battery voltage and the voltage regulator switches between field and negative to control output. With B-circuit systems, one brush is connected to the negative of the battery and the regula-

USING A VOLT AND AMP TESTER TO TEST THE CHARGING SYSTEM

P10–1 Testing the charging system begins with a visual inspection of the battery and its cables. Make sure they are clean and free of corrosion. The alternator drive belt should also be inspected and its tension checked.

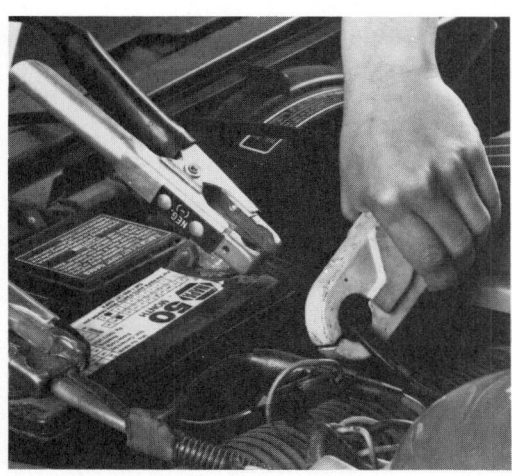

P10-2 To test the charging system, the tester's ampere pick-up probe must be positioned around the battery's negative cable and its cables connected to the battery.

P10-3 To observe the tester's meters during this test, the tester should be placed where it can be easily seen from the driver's seat.

P10-4 It is recommended that engine speed be monitored. Therefore, connect a tachometer to the engine. Some testers, such as the one shown, are equipped with a tachometer that monitors ignition pulses at the battery.

P10-5 At about 2,000 rpm, the charging system will deliver a maximum amount of charge to the battery. This charging system is providing 14.6 volts at 52.5 amperes. Readings should be compared to specifications. Engine rpm doesn't show in the photo because the photo was taken after the test, not during it.

P10-6 If the readings are low, this may indicate that there is a fault in the charging system or that the battery is fully charged and not allowing the alternator to work at its peak. To determine the cause, the voltage regulator should be bypassed according to the procedures outlined in the service manual.

P10-7 With the regulator bypassed, this alternator increased its voltage output. This indicates that the regulator had been regulating voltage output. The amperage reading is also well within specifications. Therefore, the charging system is functioning properly

FIGURE 18–37 Grounding the field terminal with a screwdriver inserted into a special test hole on the back of the alternator.

tor switches between field and positive to control output. If an A-circuit regulator loses positive voltage, the alternator will overcharge if the field coils still have power. If the A-circuit regulator loses its ground, the system will go dead.

In B-circuit alternators, the opposite is true. If a B-circuit system loses ground, it will overcharge. If it loses positive voltage, it will go dead.

If full-fielding an alternator suddenly brings charging system voltage or current output up to specifications, the voltage regulator, not the alternator is at fault. If charging output is still low or nonexistent when full-fielding, the alternator is bad.

Oscilloscope Checks Alternator output can also be checked using an oscilloscope. Figure 18–38 illustrates common alternator voltage patterns for good and faulty alternators. The correct pattern looks like the rounded top of a picket fence. A regular dip in the pattern indicates that one or more of the coil windings is grounded or open, or that a diode in the rectifier circuit of a diode trio circuit has failed. Most battery/charging system testers also have a test function that detects faulty diodes.

Circuit and Ground Resistance These tests measure voltage drop within the system wiring. They help pinpoint corroded connections or loose or damaged wiring.

Circuit resistance is checked by connecting a voltmeter to the positive battery terminal and the output, or battery terminal of the alternator. The positive lead of the meter should be connected to the alternator output terminal and the negative lead to the positive battery terminal. To check the voltage drops across the ground circuit, connect the positive lead to the alternator housing and the negative meter lead to the battery negative terminal. When measuring the voltage drop in these circuits, a sufficient

FIGURE 18–38 Alternator oscilloscope patterns: (A) good alternator under full load, (B) good alternator under no load, (C) shorted diode and/or stator winding under full load, and (D) open diode in diode trio.

amount of current must be flowing through the circuit. Therefore, turn on the headlights and other accessories to ensure that the alternator is putting out at least 20 amps. If a voltage drop of more than 0.5 volt is measured in either circuit, there is a high resistance problem in that circuit.

ALTERNATOR SERVICE

A faulty alternator can be the result of many different types of internal problems. Diodes (Figure 18–39), stator windings (Figure 18–40), and field circuits (Figure 18–41) may be open, shorted (Figure 18–42 and Figure 18–43), or improperly grounded. The brushes or slip rings can become worn. The rotor shaft can become bent and the pulley can work loose or bend out of proper alignment.

After diagnosing a faulty alternator, many shops simply replace it with a new or rebuilt unit. Follow service manual procedures when removing and installing the alternator. Remember, improper connections to the alternator can destroy it.

Most alternator repair or rebuilding work is performed in specialty shops. Internal problems that cause alternator failure include open, shorted, or improperly grounded diodes, stator windings, or field circuits. Brushes and slip rings can also become worn. Rotor shafts and pulleys can become loose or bent out of alignment.

Follow service manual procedures for disassembling, inspecting, testing, and rebuilding alternators. Basic procedures for testing diodes and internal circuits are given in the *Tech Manual* that accompanies this textbook.

FIGURE 18–41   Testing a rotor for opens.

FIGURE 18–39   Using an ohmmeter to test a diode trio.

FIGURE 18–42   Testing a stator for a short to ground.

FIGURE 18–40   Testing a stator for opens.

FIGURE 18–43   Testing a rotor for a short to ground.

CASE STUDY

A customer brought his pick-up truck into the dealership with a complaint that the truck must be jumped to get it started and once it is started, it runs for about 10 minutes then dies.

The technician verified the complaint then did a visual inspection of the charging system. Based on the complaint, he knew that the battery was not being kept in charge by the alternator or that the battery was unable to hold a charge. He found the alternator drive belt extremely frayed and glazed. Knowing this could cause the problem, he replaced the belt. However, before releasing the truck back to the customer he tested the battery to make sure it was able to hold a charge if the alternator was capable of charging it. The battery checked out fine. He then checked the alternator output and found it to be within specifications. This was a good technician, he knew that he shouldn't assume that the obvious problem was the only problem. As a result, the customer was happy and should be for quite some time.

KEY TERMS

Alternator
DC generator
Delta
Fail-safe circuit
Field coils
Field relay
Fingers

Full-fielding
Full-wave rectification
Half-wave rectification
Integrated circuit voltage
    regulator
Magnitude
Pole piece

Rotor
Sine wave
Slip rings
Stator

Three-phase voltage
Voltage regulator
Wye

SUMMARY

◆ Inducing a voltage requires a magnetic field producing lines of force, conductors that can be moved, and movement between the conductors and the magnetic field so the lines of force are cut.

◆ Modern vehicles use an alternator to produce electrical current in the charging system. Diodes in the alternator change or rectify the alternating current to direct current.

◆ A voltage regulator keeps charging system voltage above battery voltage. Keeping the alternator charging voltage above the 12.6 volts of the battery ensures current flows into, not out of, the battery.

◆ Modern voltage regulators are completely solid-state devices that can be an integral part of the alternator or mounted to the back of the alternator housing. In some vehicles, voltage regulation is the job of the computer control module.

◆ Voltage regulators work by controlling current flow to the alternator field circuit. This varies the strength of the magnetic field, which in turn varies current output.

◆ The driver can monitor charging system operation with indicator lights.

◆ Problems in the charging system can be as simple as worn or loose belts, faulty connections, or battery problems.

◆ Circuit resistance, current-output, voltage-output, field-current draw, and voltage regulator tests are all used to troubleshoot AC charging systems.

TECH MANUAL

The following procedures are included in Chapter 18 of the *Tech Manual* that accompanies this book:

1. *Visually inspect the charging system.*
2. *Adjust drive belt.*
3. *Remove and replace an alternator.*
4. *Test the charging system.*
5. *Disassemble and assemble the alternator.*
6. *Test components of an alternator.*

REVIEW QUESTIONS

1. Which of the following is *not* a way to increase the amount of voltage induced in an alternator?
   a. Increase the number of conductors.
   b. Move the conductors through the magnetic field slowly.
   c. Move the conductors at a right angle to the magnetic field.
   d. Increase the current going through the electromagnet.

2. Which of the following is *not* a component of an alternator?
   a. rotor
   c. armature
   b. stator
   d. pole shoe

3. To protect electronic circuits, some voltage regulators have a ____ ____ circuit built into them.

4. What is the purpose of a diode trio?

5. How does a voltage regulator regulate the voltage output of an alternator?

6. Technician A says the waveform produced by an alternator is called a sine wave. Technician B says the waveform produced by the alternator after the output moves through the diodes is a straight line because it is a constant DC voltage. Who is correct?
   a. Technician A
   c. Both A and B
   b. Technician B
   d. Neither A nor B

7. What would happen to the output of an alternator if one of the stator windings has an open?

8. Which of the following precautions should be followed whenever working on or testing a charging system?
   a. Make sure a load is on the system before energizing the alternator.
   b. Ground out the alternator's output terminals before testing the resistance of the output wire.
   c. Disconnect the positive side of the battery before disconnecting any wires to and from the alternator or battery.
   d. All of the above.

9. A rotating magnetic field inside a set of conducting wires is a simple description of ____.
   a. a DC generator
   c. a voltage regulator
   b. an AC alternator
   d. none of the above

10. What part of the alternator produces the rotating magnetic field?
    a. stator
    c. brushes
    b. rotor
    d. poles

11. Which type of stator winding produces higher alternator output?
    a. wye
    c. trio
    b. delta
    d. series

12. Slip rings and brushes ____.
    a. mount on the rotor shaft
    b. conduct current to the rotor field coils
    c. are insulated from each other and the rotor shaft
    d. all of the above

13. The alternating current produced by the alternator is rectified into DC, or direct current, through the use of ____.

    a. transistors
    c. diodes
    b. electromagnetic relays
    d. capacitors

14. Integrated voltage regulators ____.
    a. contain all needed circuitry on a single silicone clip sealed in a plastic module
    b. mount to the back of or inside the alternator housing
    c. are unserviceable and must be replaced if defective
    d. all of the above

15. Voltage regulation or voltage regulator circuitry in the computer control module control alternator output by ____.
    a. using a variable resistor to vary current flow to the rotor field windings
    b. pulsing current flow to the rotor field windings on and off to create a correct average field current supply
    c. either a or b, depending on the system
    d. neither a nor b

16. Technician A uses a current output test to check alternator output. Technician B uses a voltage output test to check output. Who is correct?
    a. Technician A
    c. Both A and B
    b. Technician B
    d. Neither A nor B

17. Technician A says if alternator output rises to specifications when the alternator is full-fielded, the voltage regulator is faulty. Technician B says this indicates an intermittent alternator problem. Who is correct?
    a. Technician A
    c. Both A and B
    b. Technician B
    d. Neither A nor B

18. Before adjusting alternator drive-belt tension, Technician A checks for proper pulley alignment. Technician B looks up the specified belt tension in the vehicle's service material. Who is correct?
    a. Technician A
    c. Both A and B
    b. Technician B
    d. Neither A nor B

19. When checking alternator output using an oscilloscope. Technician A says the correct pattern resembles the rounded tops of a picket fence. Technician B says the correct pattern is a square sine-wave pattern. Who is correct?
    a. Technician A
    c. Both A and B
    b. Technician B
    d. Neither A nor B

20. A voltage drop over ____ indicates high resistance in either the circuit or ground wiring of the charging system.
    a. 0.1
    c. 0.5
    b. 0.2
    d. 1.0

LIGHTING SYSTEMS

19

OBJECTIVES

◆ *Explain the operating principle of the various lighting systems.* ◆ *Describe the different types of headlights and how they are controlled.* ◆ *Understand the functions of turn, stop, and hazard warning lights.* ◆ *Know how backup lights operate.* ◆ *Replace headlights and other burned out bulbs.* ◆ *Explain how to aim headlights.* ◆ *Explain the purpose of auxiliary automotive lighting.* ◆ *Describe the operation and construction of the various automotive lamps.* ◆ *Diagnose lighting problems.*

The lighting system provides power to both exterior and interior lights. It consists of the headlights, parking lights, marker lights, taillights, courtesy lights, dome/map lights, instrument illumination or dash lights, coach lights (if so equipped), headlight switch, and various other control switches (Figure 19–1). Other lights, such as vanity mirror lights, the underhood light, the glove box light, and the trunk compartment light, are used on some vehicles and are also part of the lighting system.

Other lights that are not usually in the main lighting system are turn signal, hazard warning, back-up, and stop lights. These lights, as well as the retractable headlight covers found on some vehicles, are operated by separate control circuits and are covered later in this chapter.

🔧 SHOP TALK

Lighting systems are largely regulated by federal laws, so the systems are similar between the various manufacturers. However, there are many variations. Before attempting to do any repairs on an unfamiliar system, you should always refer to the manufacturer's service manual. ■

Figure 19–1   Basic automotive lighting system. *Courtesy of Ford Motor Company*

Figure 19–2 Single-filament bulb.

Figure 19–3 Double-filament bulb.

LAMPS

A **lamp** generates light as current flows through the filament. This causes it to get very hot. The changing of electrical energy to heat energy in the resistive wire filament is so intense that the filament starts to glow and emits light. The lamp must have a vacuum surrounding the filament to prevent it from burning so hot that the filament burns in half. The glass envelope that encloses the filament maintains the presence of the vacuum. If air is allowed to enter the lamp, the oxygen would cause the filament to oxidize and burn up.

It is important that any burned-out lamp be replaced with the correct lamp. You can determine what lamp to use by checking the lamp's standard trade number, normally present on the lamp's hous-

ing. Lamps are normally one of two types: a single filament (Figure 19–2) or a double filament (Figure 19–3). Double-filament bulbs are designed to serve more than one function. They can be used as the lone bulb in the stop light circuit, taillight circuit, and the turn signal circuit.

HEADLIGHTS

Figure 19–4 is a typical service manual electrical schematic of a standard headlight system. Note that power on this main switch is supplied by the battery directly to the headlight portion of the switch and through a fuse in the fuse panel to the remainder of the switch. Although one of the functions of the headlight switch is to control the headlights, the

Figure 19–4 Headlight circuit components. *Courtesy of Ford Motor Company*

switch has many other functions. For example, it may control operation of all exterior lights except turn signals, hazard warning, and stop lights.

🔧 SHOP TALK

Canadian law requires that vehicles be equipped with daylight running lights (**DRL**) for added safety. The system uses the vehicle's high-beam lights. The control circuit is connected directly to the vehicle's ignition switch so the lights are on whenever the vehicle is running. The circuit is equipped with a module that reduces 12-volt battery voltage to approximately 6 volts. This voltage reduction allows the high beams to burn with less intensity and prolong light life. When the headlight switch is activated for night or poor weather driving, the module is deactivated and the lights burn with their regular intensity and brightness. Applying the parking brake will also disable the DRL systems. Some cars made for sale in the United States have this feature and soon all will. ■

Although the primary function of the headlight switch is the same from one car model to another, the operation, type, and design vary according to the particular lighting used on the vehicle. There are three basic types of headlight switches. The **pull-out** switch design has three positions: off, park, and head. Pulling a typical switch knob out to the park or first detent (knob catches at stop) illuminates all exterior lights except the headlights. Instrument panel lights are also illuminated in this position. Pulling the head switch knob out to the head or second detent illuminates the headlights plus all of those lights illuminated in park position. In the switch

Figure 19–5 The rotary pull-out headlight switch mounts in the dash. A button is usually provided on the switch. When pressed, it releases the knob, after which the retainer and switch can also be removed. *Courtesy of Ford Motor Company*

Figure 19–6 Typical push button headlight switch. *Courtesy of Toyota Motor Corporation*

shown in Figure 19–5, a dimmer rheostat controls the brightness of dash or instrument illumination lights. When the switch knob is rotated completely counterclockwise, the instrument panel illumination is at maximum brightness level. This position may also turn on the courtesy and dome/map lights. The second type of headlight switch is the push-button design. The vehicle shown in Figure 19–6 has three lighting push-button controls: off, park, and head. When the park button is pressed in, power is applied to all circuits except the headlights. When the headlight button is depressed, all of those lights illuminated in the park position are on. Some models have a three-position toggle switch, and not separate switches. Some vehicles have the headlight switch located on the steering column (Figure 19–7). The rheostat for the dash lights may be a separate switch or mounted on the dash near the instrument panel.

📖 USING SERVICE MANUALS

One problem a technician often has is tracing a circuit through its various operational phases. Figure 19–8 shows a headlight switch as it appears in a typical schematic. To understand how the switch operates, you must understand what is happening in the various switch positions. ■

Let us follow the current through the switch and see how it works. With the switch off, B+ flows through a common point and is made available to the ignition switch and emergency light circuits. The common point in the circuit is the battery feed from the starter relay hot terminal. Notice the circuit from this common point is open through the switch's internal circuit breaker and the switch wiper, when the

Figure 19–7 Headlight switch mounted on the steering column with a separate control on the dash to control the brightness of the instrument panel lights.

Figure 19–8 Schematic of a headlight switch (A) in the off position; (B) in the parking light position; and (C) in the on position. *Courtesy of Ford Motor Company*

switch is in the off (#1) position (Figure 19–8A). As the switch is moved to the #2 position, current flows through the right circuit breaker and the wiper to the parking lights (Figure 19–8B). Notice that the left wiper is now connected to a vacant contact on the switch. The only light circuits powered are the park lights and the dashboard lights. As the switch is moved to the full on (#3) position, notice that current is available to the headlights and still flowing to the instrument panel and park lights (Figure 19–8C).

HEADLIGHT DIMMER SWITCH Headlights have both a high and low beam. Switching from high beam to low beam is controlled by a **dimmer switch**. Older vehicles used a floor-mounted, foot-operated dimmer switch (Figure 19–9A). Current models use a multifunction steering column switch that may control the horn, turn signals, and the high- and low-

Figure 19–9 (A) Floor-mounted and (B) steering column headlight dimmer switches. *Courtesy of Ford Motor Company*

beam headlight circuit (Figure 19–9B). Electrically, the dimmer switch is a simple two-position switch that controls the output of the headlight switch.

AUTOMATIC HEADLIGHT DIMMER The automatic headlight dimmer is a driver-controlled electronic device. It automatically switches the headlights from high to low beam in response to light from an approaching vehicle or light from the taillights of a vehicle being overtaken. Major components of the system are a hi-lo beam photocell, an amplifier, a hi-lo beam relay, a dimmer switch, and a hi-lo beam range control.

When the switch is turned on, voltage is applied to both the hi-lo beam relay and the dimmer switch portion of the multifunction switch. If the dimmer switch is in the low position, this voltage passes through the dimmer switch to the coil of the hi-lo beam relay. With battery voltage on one side and ground on the other side of the coil, the relay energizes. The headlight voltage then passes through the low-side relay contacts and only the low-beam headlights are illuminated. If the dimmer switch is moved to the high (or automatic) position, control of the hi-lo beam relay is switched to the hi-lo beam photocell amplifier. Power for the operation of the amplifiers is from the switch with additional circuit protection from a fuse. This same voltage is also applied to one side of the potentiometer in the hi-lo beam range control unit. The other side of the potentiometer is grounded. The voltage applied to the amplifier depends on the setting of the potentiometer. This voltage determines the sensitivity of the amplifier.

If the automatic dimmer system is not working, check to see if the high and low beams can be switched back and forth by using the dimmer switch. Make sure the hi-lo beam range control is in the off position. If the beams can be switched back and forth, the problem is definitely in the automatic dimmer system. If the beams cannot be switched, the problem may be in the multifunction switch or in the wiring.

If the problem is in the automatic dimmer circuit, make sure the hi-lo beam photocell amplifier lens is clean and the unit is properly adjusted. Refer to the appropriate service manual for adjustment procedures.

FLASH-TO-PASS SYSTEM The multifunction switch (Figure 19–10) on some vehicles also contains a **flash-to-pass** switch that allows the driver to flash the high-beam headlights rapidly without using the main light switch.

When the multifunction switch lever is pulled towards the driver, the flash-to-pass switch contacts close. Current flows through the main light switch circuit breaker, the flash-to-pass switch contacts, and

Figure 19–10 Typical multifunction switch.

the high-beam headlights to ground. The high-beam headlights illuminate until the lever is released (Figure 19–11).

AUTOMATIC LIGHT SYSTEMS These systems provide light-sensitive, automatic on-off control of the light normally controlled by the regular headlight switch. It consists of a light-sensitive **photocell sensor/amplifier** assembly and a headlight control relay. Turning the regular headlight switch on overrides the automatic system. In other words, automatic operation is not possible until the regular headlight switch is turned off.

In normal operation, the photocell sensor/amplifier, which is usually mounted under a group of perforated holes in the upper instrument panel pad or slotted holes in the defroster grille panel, is exposed to ambient light. As the light level decreases, the light sensor's resistance increases. When resistance increases to a preset amount, the amplifier applies power to the headlight coil relay. The headlights, exterior lights, and instrument illumination lights turn on. The lights remain on until the system is turned off or the ambient light level increases.

CUSTOMER CARE

If the customer's car is equipped with an automatic light control system, point out the location of the perforated holes or slots. Warn the customer not to place any items that may block light from the sensor/amplifier assembly. This causes erratic operation of the system. The photocell must always be exposed to an outside light to function properly. ■

Figure 19–11 Flash-to-pass feature added to the headlight circuit. *Courtesy of Chrysler Corporation*

Figure 19–12 Automatic headlight dimmer circuit with a delayed-exit system. *Courtesy of Ford Motor Company*

Figure 19–13 Concealed headlights enhance the vehicle's styling and aerodynamics.

DELAYED-EXIT SYSTEM An automatic **delayed-exit** system is usually part of the automatic light operation (Figure 19–12). That is, the delayed-exit system keeps the lights operated by the automatic light system on for a preselected period of time after the ignition switch is turned off. It is turned on by the same switch that controls the automatic light switch system.

When the ignition switch is turned off, the delay system continues to energize the headlight relay. The exterior lights and instrument panel bulbs stay on for a few seconds or up to 5 minutes, depending on the setting selected by the driver. The driver typically selects the delayed-exit time period by rotating the autolight dial located behind the main light switch knob. Turning the dial clockwise increases the period of time the lights stay on.

RETRACTABLE HEADLIGHT COVERS Some automobiles have retractable headlight covers or doors (Figure 19–13), which must be elevated before the headlights can serve their purpose.

These covers are powered by vacuum or electricity. Electrically operated covers stay elevated when power is lost to the headlight cover motor because the motor needs electricity to turn in the opposite direction and close the doors. The motors are equipped with a manual control, which allows the covers to be elevated in the event of an electrical problem (Figure 19–14). Vacuum-operated covers are raised or lowered by the vacuum system in a car. In such a system, the intake manifold vacuum is stored in a reservoir that allows a vacuum motor to close the doors against spring pressure when the light switch is turned off. Should the engine fail while the lights are on, spring pressure keeps the doors from closing.

Figure 19–14 Manual control knob can be used to open headlight doors when the doors won't open automatically. *Courtesy of General Motors Corporation*

Figure 19–15 Sealed-beam headlight construction.

Headlight Bulbs

Most headlight systems consist of two or four **sealed-beam** tungsten headlight bulbs. On a two-headlight system, each headlight has two filaments, a high beam and a low beam. On the four-headlight system, the two outer headlights are of the two-filament type, and the two inner headlights have only one high-beam filament (Figure 19–15). In the vertical arrangement, the two upper lights are double filament. A few years ago all headlights were round. Styling developments created a need for rectangular light, which is more efficient and allows for more aerodynamic body styles.

WARNING!

Sealed-beam lights are made of a single piece of molded glass and tungsten filaments that operate in an atmosphere of inert gas. The filaments quickly burn out if exposed to air. ■

Some late-model cars use headlights that have a separate small light bulb enclosed in a reflector, with a separate lens in front. This type offers better light control and brightness when compared to sealed-beam types.

Halogen lights are commonly used as headlights. A halogen light contains a small quartz-glass bulb. Inside the bulb is a fuel filament surrounded by halogen gas. The small, gas-filled bulb fits within a larger metal reflector and lens element. A glass balloon sealed to the metal reflector allows the halogen bulb to be removed without danger of water or dirt damaging the optics within the light (Figure 19–16). The replaceable bulbs are removed by unplugging the electrical connector, twisting the retaining ring about 1/8 turn counterclockwise, and then removing the bulb from its socket. The new bulb is installed by reversing this procedure (Figure 19–17). Sealed beam halogen lights are also available.

A CONNECTOR, ELECTRICAL	11 BULB ASSEMBLY, HEADLAMP
B CONNECTOR, ELECTRICAL	12 BRACKET, HEADLAMP
C PIVOT, SLIDE	14 BOLT/SCREW, HEADLAMP BRACKET
4 BULB, FRONT PARKING AND TURN SIGNAL LAMP	15 NUT, HEADLAMP BRACKET
6 BOLT/SCREW, HEADLAMP BRACKET	16 NUT, HEADLAMP BRACKET
7 BOLT/SCREW, HEADLAMP CAPSULE	17 CAPSULE ASSEMBLY, HEADLAMP
8 SUPPORT ASSEMBLY, RADIATOR	67 SHIM, HEADLAMP
9 RETAINER, HEADLAMP BULB	

Figure 19–16 Replaceable-bulb halogen headlights are found on many import vehicles. While the conventional sealed-beam halogen is still most popular in the American market, the use of the European-style halogen headlight is on the increase.

HALOGEN
HEADLIGHT BULB

DO NOT TOUCH BULB WITH FINGERS.
HANDLE BULB BY BASE ONLY.

Figure 19–17   Installing a halogen bulb in its sealed enclosure. *Courtesy of Ford Motor Company*

Halogen-sealed beams provide substantially more light on high beam to extend the driver's range of visibility for safer night driving. A halogen headlight puts out approximately twice the candlepower on high beam as a conventional incandescent-sealed beam (150,000 vs. 75,000). On low beam, there is no difference in range between halogen and conventional incandescent-sealed beams. Both are limited by federal regulations (FSVSS 108) to a maximum of 20,000 candlepower output. Halogen bulbs do, however, produce a whiter light that helps improve visibility, last longer, and stay brighter. They also use less wattage for the same amount of light produced, which helps lessen the parasitic horsepower drain on the engine that is needed to drive the alternator.

CUSTOMER CARE

Both conventional sealed-beam halogen and replaceable type are more expensive than incandescent-sealed beams. When helping a customer decide which type of replacement headlight should be used, point out the numerous advantages of either type of halogen and suggest upgrading to halogen if the vehicle currently has conventional incandescent-sealed beams. Discourage your customer from downgrading to cheaper replacement headlights if the vehicle currently has halogen.   ■

There are various methods used to identify headlights, such as #1, #2, and the halogen marking molded into the front lens. Type #1 is high beam with two connections on the back. Type #2 is both hi/lo beam with three connections. A technician should be aware of their possible locations. Halogen headlights can be substituted for regular sealed beams, but it is suggested that this only be done in pairs. Some halogen headlight assemblies have replaceable bulbs and are not

sealed beams. H1 and H2 quartz halogen are generally used in passenger vehicles.

CAUTION:

The halogen light bulb contains gas under pressure. The bulb may shatter if the glass envelope is cracked. Handle it carefully. Grasp the bulb only by its plastic base. Avoid touching the glass envelope. Skin oil can cause the bulb to shatter when turned on.   ■

Headlight Replacement

There can be slight variations in procedure from one model to another when replacing headlights. For instance, on some models the turn signal light assembly must be removed before the headlight can be replaced. Overall, however, the procedure does not differ much from the following typical instructions.

PROCEDURES
Replacing Headlights

1. Remove the headlight bezel retaining screws (Figure 19–18). Remove the bezel. If necessary, disconnect the turn signal wires.
2. Remove the retaining ring screws from one or both lights.
3. Remove the retaining rings.
4. Remove the light from the housing. Disconnect the wiring connector from the back of the light.
5. Push the wiring connector onto the prongs at the rear of the new light.
6. Place the new light in the headlight housing. Position it so the embossed number in the light lens is on the top.
7. Place the retaining ring over the light and install the retaining ring screws. Tighten them slightly.
8. Check the aim of the headlight and adjust it, if necessary.
9. Install the headlight bezel. Secure it with the retaining screws. Connect the turn signal wiring (if it was disconnected).

SHOP TALK

Some manufacturers recommend coating the prongs and base of a new sealed beam with

Figure 19–18 Headlight removal. *Courtesy Ford Motor Company*

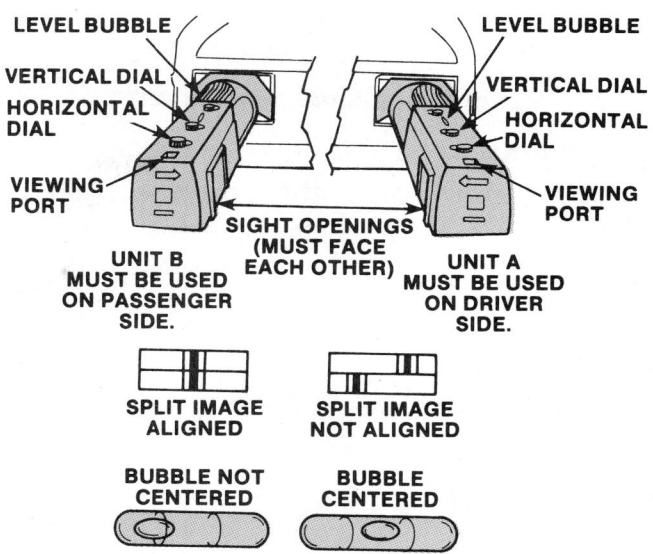

Figure 19–19 These popular mechanical headlight aiming units are mounted on the lights with suction cups. Horizontal adjustment is achieved by aligning split images in the viewer on each unit. Vertical adjustment is achieved by centering the level bubble on each unit. *Courtesy of Chrysler Corporation*

dielectric grease for corrosion protection. Use an electrical lubricant approved by the manufacturer. ∎

Headlight Adjustments

Headlights must be kept in adjustment to obtain maximum illumination. Sealed beams that are properly adjusted cover the correct range and afford the driver the proper nighttime view. Headlights that are out of adjustment can cause other drivers discomfort and sometimes create hazardous conditions.

Before adjusting or aiming a vehicle's headlights, however, make the following inspections to ensure that the vehicle is level. Any one of the adverse conditions listed here can result in an incorrect setting.

♦ If the vehicle is heavily coated with snow, ice, or mud, clean the underside with a high-pressure stream of water. The additional weight can alter the riding height.
♦ Ensure that the gas tank is half full. Half a tank of gas is the only load that should be present on the vehicle.
♦ Check the condition of the springs or shock absorbers. Worn or broken suspension components affect the setting.
♦ Inflate all tires to the recommended air pressure levels. Take into consideration cold or hot tire conditions.
♦ Make sure the wheel alignment and rear axle tracking path are correct before adjusting the headlights.
♦ After placing the vehicle in position for the headlight test, bounce the vehicle to settle the suspension. Stand on the bumper or push down on the front fender.

To properly adjust the headlights, headlight aim must be checked first. Various types of mechanical headlight aiming equipment are available commercially (Figure 19–19). These aimers use mirrors with split images, like split-image finders on some cameras, and spirit levels to determine exact adjustment. When using any mechanical aiming equipment, follow the instructions provided by the equipment manufacturer. Where headlight aiming equipment is not available, headlight alignment can be checked by projecting the upper beam of each light upon a screen or chart at a distance of about 25 feet ahead of the headlight (Figure 19–20). The vehicle must be exactly perpendicular to the chart.

The chart should be marked in the following manner (Figure 19–21). First, measure the distance between the centers of the matching headlights. Use this measurement to draw two vertical lines on the screen with each line corresponding to the center of a headlight. Then, draw a vertical centerline halfway between the two vertical lines. Next, measure the distance from the floor to the centers of the headlights. Subtract 2 inches from this height and then draw a horizontal line on the screen at this new height.

With headlights on high beam, the hot spot of each projected beam pattern should be centered on the point of intersection of the vertical and horizontal lines on the chart. If necessary, adjust headlights vertically and laterally to obtain proper aim.

Headlight adjusting screws are provided to move the headlight within its shell assembly to obtain correct headlight aim. Lateral or side-to-side adjustment is accomplished by turning the adjusting screw at the side of the headlight (Figure 19–22). Vertical or up-and-down adjustment is accomplished by turning the

Figure 19–20   Checking headlight alignment without the luxury of aiming equipment.

Figure 19–21   (A) Correct upper headlight beam alignment; and (B) correct lower headlight beam alignment.

screw at the top of the headlight. Adjustments can be made without removing headlight bezels.

A properly aimed headlight normally does not need to be re-aimed after installation of a bulb. A burned out bulb should not be removed from the headlight reflector until just before a replacement bulb is to be installed. Removal of a bulb for an extended period of time may allow contaminants (dust, moisture, smoke) to enter the headlight body and affect the performance of the headlight. When servicing the headlight bulb, energize the bulb only while it is contained within the headlight body.

INTERIOR LIGHT ASSEMBLIES

The types and numbers of interior light assemblies used vary significantly from one vehicle to another. Following are the more common ones.

ENGINE COMPARTMENT LIGHT Operating the hood causes the engine compartment light mercury switch to close and light the underhood area.

Figure 19–22   Headlight adjusting screws.

GLOVE BOX LIGHT Operating the glove box door closes the glove box light switch contacts and the light comes on.

LUGGAGE COMPARTMENT LIGHT The light is mounted in the underside of the trunk deck lid in the luggage compartment.

TRUNK LID LIGHT Lifting the trunk lid causes the light mercury switch to close and the light comes on.

VANITY LIGHT Piloting the sun visor and opening the vanity mirror cover causes the vanity light switch contacts to close and the light to come on.

COURTESY LIGHTS There are several types of courtesy lights. Some vehicles have courtesy lights

that are in the door trim panels, under each side of the instrument panel, and in the center of the headlining. These are illuminated when the doors are opened or by rotating the headlight switch to the full counterclockwise position (Figure 19–23).

Front compartment foot well courtesy lights are mounted on the lower closeout panels at both ends of the instrument panel. The bulbs are accessible from under the instrument panel for replacement without removing other parts.

Some courtesy lights are a combination of map lights located on each side of the dome light housing. The map lights are operated independently of the dome light by two switches located at each map light housing. The dome light is actuated by turning

Figure 19–23 Typical courtesy light circuit.

Figure 19–24 Illuminated entry actuator circuit.

the headlight switch control knob fully counterclockwise.

Power is supplied from the fuse block to the courtesy or dome/map light. The ground for the light is controlled by the position of the door switch. That is, these door switches are held in open position and do not provide for a ground circuit. When the door is opened, a spring pushes the switch closed to ground the circuit, and the dome/map or courtesy lights come on.

ILLUMINATED ENTRY SYSTEM This system assists vehicle entry during the hours of darkness by illuminating the door lock cylinder so it may be easily located for key insertion. The vehicle interior is also illuminated by the courtesy lights.

As illustrated in Figure 19–24, the system consists of four main components: electronic module, illuminated door lock cylinder, door latch switch, and wiring harness.

Activation of the system is accomplished by raising the outside door handle or by pressing a code button on the keyless entry system. This action momentarily closes a switch mounted on the door latch mechanism, which completes the ground circuit of the electronic actuator module and switches the system on. The vehicle interior lights turn on, and both front door lock cylinders are illuminated by a ring of light around the area where the key enters. This illumination remains on for approximately 25 seconds, then automatically turns off. During this 25-second period, the system can be manually deactivated by turning the ignition switch to either run position.

The system is activated every time the outside front door handles are operated, whether the vehicle is locked or not. Opening the doors from the inside of the vehicle does not activate the system. If the outside door handle is held up indefinitely so the latch

switch is continuously closed, the system operates as normal and turns off after 25 seconds. At the completion of this cycle, if the door handle is still in the raised position, the system remains off. It is impossible to activate the system from the other front door handle until the raised handle is returned to its normal position. This function is built into the logic circuitry of the system to prevent battery discharge should the outside door handle be intentionally propped up or become jammed in any way.

Interior lights all basically operate the same. Whether the courtesy lights are on the door, under the seats, under the instrument panel, or on the rear interior quarter panels does not change how they are controlled. Also, whether the illumination lights are just behind the instrument panel or are also used in center consoles or door arm rests does not affect their operation. The only difference is the number of lights and variances in electrical wiring.

Interior and courtesy lights rarely give any trouble. However, if they do not operate, check the fuse, bulb, switch, and wiring.

REAR EXTERIOR LIGHT ASSEMBLIES

The rear light assembly includes the taillights, turn signal/stop/hazard lights/high-mounted stop lights, rear side marker lights, back-up lights, and license plate lights (Figure 19–25). Taillights operate when the parking lights or headlights are turned on.

TURN, STOP, AND HAZARD WARNING LIGHT SYSTEMS Power for the turn (directional signal), stop, and hazard warning light systems is provided by the fuse panel (Figure 19–26). Each system has a switch that must close to turn on the lights in the circuit. Hazard lights are commonly referred to as 4-way flashers because the lights at all four corners of the vehicle will flash when the circuit is turned on.

Figure 19–25 Typical rear light assembly.

Figure 19–26 Turn signal circuit for a two-bulb system. *Courtesy of Chrysler Corporation*

The turn signal and hazard light switches on many current vehicles are part of a **multifunctional switch**. This switch also may include the horn and dimmer switches. On earlier models and some current light-duty truck models, these are separate switches. The directional and hazards controls are normally on the steering column. When the turn or directional signal switch is activated, only one set of the switch contacts is closed—left or right (Figure 19–27). However, when the hazard switch is activated, all contacts are closed and all turn signal lights and indicators flash together and at the same time.

Figure 19–27   Turn signal circuit with the switch in the left turn position. *Courtesy of Chrysler Corporation*

The power for the turn signals is provided through the fuse panel but only when the ignition switch is on. The hazard lights are also provided their power through the fuse panel; however, they have power at all times regardless of ignition switch position.

Some cars are equipped with cornering side lights, which are generally fed from the multifunction main switch. When the turn signal switch is activated, the cornering light on the appropriate side burns with a steady glow.

Side markers are connected in parallel with the feed circuit (from the headlight switch) that feeds the minor filaments of the front parking lights and rear taillights (Figure 19–28).

Figure 19–28 Typical side marker lighting system. *Courtesy of Ford Motor Company*

FLASHER SCHEMATIC

Figure 19–29 (A) Common location for flashers in the fuse panel. (B) Flashers contain a bimetallic strip, contact points, and a heating element. *Courtesy of Ford Motor Company*

FLASHERS Flashers are components of both turn and hazard systems. They contain a temperature-sensitive bimetallic strip and a heating element (Figure 19–29). The bimetallic strip is connected to one side of a set of contacts. Voltage from the fuse panel is connected to the other side. When the left turn signal switch is activated, current flows through the flasher unit to the turn signal bulbs. This current causes the heating element to emit heat, which in turn causes the bimetallic strip to bend and open the circuit. The absence of current flow allows the strip to cool and again close the circuit. This intermittent on/off interruption of current flow makes all left turn signal lights flash. Operation of the right turn is the same as the operation of the left turn signals.

Turn signal flashers are installed on the fuse panel on current car models and most current truck models. However, on earlier models this is not true. Hazard flashers are also mounted in various locations. Refer to the service manual for locations on the model being serviced.

A testlight can be used to determine which flasher is used for the turn signals and which is used for the hazard warning light. An easier way is to turn on both the directionals and the hazards. This activates both flasher units. By removing one of the flashers, the affected circuit no longer flashes. Therefore, that flash unit controls that particular circuit. If the turn

signals fail to operate and the fuse is good, the flasher has probably failed.

Occasionally, the flasher does not flash as fast as it once did, or it flashes faster. This is also cause for replacement. If it flashes too fast or too slowly, check for a burned-out bulb first. OEM flashers are designed to cause the turn signals to blink faster if a light bulb is burned out. The fast blinking alerts the driver to the bad bulb.

A flasher features two or three prongs that plug into a socket. Just pull the flasher out of the socket and replace it with a new one.

Flashers are designed to operate a specific number of bulbs on a specific **candlepower** (brightness). If the candlepower on the turn signal bulbs are changed, or if additional bulbs are used (if a vehicle is hooked up to a trailer, for instance), a heavy-duty flasher must be used. This usually fits the socket without modifications. Although heavy-duty flashers will operate additional bulbs, they have one big disadvantage and should not be used unless it is necessary. These flashers will not cause the turn signals to flash faster if a

Figure 19–30   Typical brake pedal switch operation.

bulb burns out. When a turn signal bulb fails, the driver has no idea that it did.

STOP LIGHT SWITCH The stop lights are usually controlled by a stop light switch that is normally mounted on the brake pedal arm (Figure 19–30). Some cars are equipped with a brake or stop light switch mounted on the master cylinder, which closes when hydraulic pressure increases as the brake pedal is depressed. In either case, voltage is present at the stop light switch at all times. Depressing the brake pedal causes the stop light switch contacts to close. Current can now flow to the stop light filament of the rear light assembly. These stay illuminated until the brake pedal is released.

In addition to the stop lights at the rear of the vehicle, all late-model cars have a high-mounted center stop light that provides an additional clear warning signal that the car is braking. Federal studies have shown the additional stop lights to be effective in reducing the number and severity of rear collisions. The high-mounted stop light is activated when current is applied to it from the stop light switch. It stays illuminated until the brake pedal is released. Kits are available to upgrade older cars with this important safety feature. Follow the kit manufacturer's instructions when installing a high-mounted stop light. When the contacts are closed, the stop light switch can also provide current to flow to the speed control amplifier, and antilock brake module, and the electric brake controller connector.

USING SERVICE MANUALS

In addition to the taillight system, the rear of vehicles have many other lighting circuits. Most cars have brake lights, run lights, turn signals, and back-up lights. In addition, all vehicles produced since 1986 have collision-avoidance lights. Let us look at these circuits (Figure 19–31) and see that their diagnosis is very simple once you are aware of how they appear in the service manual. Start with the brake lights. The easiest circuit to look at first is the three-bulb circuit found on many vehicles. The drawing shows a typical taillight circuit, which contains three separate filaments for each side of the rear of the vehicle. There is a separate filament for each function: brake, turn, and run. A constant source of fused B+ is made available to the brake switch. The brake switch is usually located on the brake pedal and is closed by pushing down on the brake pedal. B+ is now available to the bulbs, wired in parallel, at the rear of the vehicle. Releasing the brake pedal allows the spring-loaded normally-open (NO) switch to open and turn the brake lights off. This is a simple circuit that requires only a 12-volt testlight or a voltmeter for diagnosis. The most common cause of failure is bulbs that burn out. Testing for B+ and ground at the bulb socket should verify the circuit. If B+ is

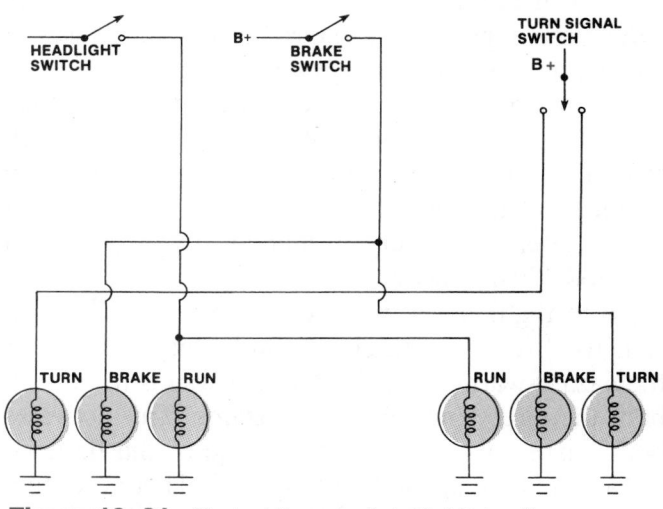

Figure 19–31   Typical three-bulb taillight circuit.

not available at the socket, test for power at each connector, moving back toward the switch until it is found. Repair the open. Do not forget that the circuit is only hot if the brake pedal is depressed. ■

BACK-UP LIGHTS When the vehicle is placed in reverse gear, back-up lights are turned on to illuminate the area behind the vehicle. The major components in the system are the back-up light switch and the lights.

Power for the back-up light system is provided by the fuse panel. When the transmission is shifted to reverse, the back-up light switch closes and power is provided to the back-up lights. That is, anytime the transmission is in reverse, current flows from the fuse panel through the back-up light switch to the back-up lights. On many vehicles, the fuse that protects the back-up light system also protects the turn signal system.

Various types of back-up light switches are used depending on the type of transmission used on the vehicle. In general, vehicles with a manual transmission have a separate switch. Those with an automatic transmission use a combination neutral start/back-up light switch. The combination neutral start/back-up light switch used with automatic transmission is actually two switches combined in one housing. In park or neutral, current from the ignition switch is applied through the neutral start switch to the starting system. In reverse, current from the fuse panel is applied through the back-up light switch to the back-up lights.

The back-up light system is relatively easy to troubleshoot. On vehicles that use one fuse to protect both the turn signals and the back-up lights, the fuse can be checked. If the back-up lights are not working, check turn signal operation. If they work, the fuse is good. Check the power at the back-up light switch input and the power at the switch outlet with the transmission in reverse. (Make sure the parking brake is set.)

If the switch is okay, or there is no power to the switch, check the wiring—especially the connectors. If the back-up lights stay on when the transmission is not in reverse, suspect a short in the back-up light switch.

LIGHT BULBS

Besides headlight bulbs, there are several different types of light bulbs used in modern vehicles.

Other Bulbs

Bulbs used in most other lighting fixtures fit into sockets and are held in place by spring tension or mechanical force (Figure 19–32). Bulbs are coded with numbers for replacement purposes. Bulbs with

A,B MINIATURE BAYONET FOR INDICATOR AND INSTRU-
MENT LIGHTS
C—SINGLE CONTACT BAYONET FOR LICENSE AND
COURTESY LIGHTS
D—DOUBLE CONTACT BAYONET FOR TRUNK AND UNDER-
HOOD LIGHTS
E—DOUBLE CONTACT BAYONET WITH STAGGERED
INDEXING LUGS FOR STOP, TURN SIGNALS, AND
BRAKE LIGHTS
F—CARTRIDGE TYPE FOR DOME LIGHTS
G—WEDGE BASE FOR INSTRUMENT LIGHTS

Figure 19–32 Common types of automotive bulbs.

different code numbers might appear physically similar but have different wattage ratings.

Light systems normally use one wire to the light, making use of the car body or frame to provide the ground back to the battery. Since many of the manufacturers have gone to plastic socket and mounting plates (as well as plastic body parts) to reduce weight, many lights must now use two wires to provide the ground connection. Some double-filament lights use two hot wires and a third ground wire. That is, double-filament bulbs have two contacts and two wire connections to them if grounded through the base (Figure 19–33). If not grounded through the base of the bulb, a two-filament bulb has three contacts and three wires connected to it. Single-filament bulbs may be single- or double-contact types. Single-contact types are grounded through the bulb base, while double-contact, single-filament types have two wires— one live and the other a ground.

When replacing a bulb, inspect the bulb socket. If the socket is rusty or corroded, the socket or light assembly base should be replaced. Also, inspect the lens and gasket for damage while the lens is removed and replace any damaged part.

SINGLE-FILAMENT BULB   DOUBLE-FILAMENT BULB

Figure 19–33 Single-filament bulbs are commonly used for license plate and side marker lights, while double-filament bulbs are ideal for front parking lights and taillights.

Figure 19–34 Methods of securing bulbs: (A) socket with lugs that lock into the light body; (B) prongs that are pushed in and turned; (C) wedge base that simply slides in and out; and (D) double-ends that are snapped in place. *Courtesy of Nissan Motors*

There are two basic construction designs for exterior lights: those in which the lens is removed and then the bulb removed from the front, and those in which the light assembly must first be removed then the socket from the back of the assembly, and finally the bulb from the socket. Removing the lens from the latter type assembly could cause serious damage to the reflector due to dust and other contaminants. Wiping the reflector surface to clean it can also seriously reduce the light's brightness. Therefore, do not remove the lens from light assemblies in which the socket and bulb are removed from the back of the assembly.

The bulbs are held in their sockets in a number of ways (Figure 19–34). Some bulbs are simply pushed into and pulled out of their sockets, and some are screwed in and out. To release a bayonet-style bulb from its socket, the bulb is pressed in and turned counterclockwise. The blade-mount style is removed by pulling the bulb off the mounting tab, then turning the bulb and removing it from the retaining pin.

Auxiliary Lights

While the car's headlights are adequate in normal driving circumstances, some customers desire auxiliary lights for special conditions such as fog or extended night driving. In addition to the standard auxiliary fog, driving, and passing lights, there are off-road lights, worklights, rooflights, decklights, deckbars, and hand-held spot lights.

Auxiliary lights are easy to install when the manufacturer's instructions are carefully followed. The mounting of auxiliary lights, of course, varies according to the type of lights being installed. For example, the ideal position for fog lights differs from that of driving and passing lights. Before beginning, remember that regulations involving auxiliary lights differ from state to state. For this reason, it is crucial that the technician be familiar with the state's regulations and adhere to them. These regulations are listed in the manual that accompanies this text or may be obtained from your state's department of transportation. Always follow all federal, state, and local laws when aiming headlights.

CUSTOMER CARE

If a customer is installing auxiliary lights, advise that the job is easier if a wiring kit is purchased along with the lights. A typical kit includes a switch and switch panel, 14-gauge wire, scotch lock connectors, solderless insulated terminals, sheet metal screws, wiring ties, fuse and fuse carrier, and a fuse box tap clip. ∎

DRIVING AND PASSING LIGHTS Driving lights enhance the output of even the best factory headlights, affording the driver an additional margin of safety. Driving lights typically use an H3 or H4 quartz halogen bulb and a high-quality reflector and lens to project an intense, pencil-thin beam of light way down the road.

Proper aiming of the auxiliary lights is extremely important. Driving lights are used to supplement the high beams for greater distance and width. They should be used only in conjunction with the high beams. That is, driving lights should be wired so they are off when the high beams are off. One way to do this is to supply the controlling switch with current from the high-beam circuit, rather than from a circuit that is live all the time. Passing lights are added to supplement the low beams and provide a more complete and uniform light pattern.

SHOP TALK

When adding auxiliary lights, make sure the alternator and wiring are heavy enough to handle the increased wattage. Installing a higher output may be recommended, especially if other electrical accessories are also being installed. The choice of wire size should be based on the load the wire will be powering. ∎

FOG LIGHTS Light does not penetrate fog well at all. Focus a powerful beam of light at the fog and all the driver gets is a powerful glare back. To deal with that problem, fog lights use the same bulbs but, instead of trying to pierce the darkness, they attempt to sneak a flat, wide beam of light under the blanket of fog. This makes it important to mount them low and to aim them low and parallel to the road. Also, because fog tends to reflect light back at the driver, some fog lights are equipped with yellow or amber lenses to reduce the discomfort caused by the glare.

While some vehicles have OEM fog lights, most are auxiliary lighting add-ons. Their circuits, however, are basically the same as drive lights. They involve a relay switch and the lights themselves. A relay is used because the amount of current that fog lights require, especially halogen ones, can be quite high. It is not unusual that they require as much as 25 amperes.

Fog lights are generally not wired directly from an unswitched battery power source. This would allow them to be left on with the vehicle off. Their high current draw would quickly drain the battery. The dash switch controls the current to one side of the relay's coil. A direct ground is supplied to the other side of the relay coil. With both battery voltage and ground applied, current flows through the coil and a magnetic field develops. The field closes the contacts in the relay. Notice that one side of the contacts is connected to a fused source of battery voltage. The other side is connected to the fog lights, which are wired in parallel. Each filament has its own remote ground connection.

When adding fog lights, or any accessory, place the fuse as close to the source as possible. Picking up the power source under the hood is easy. There are many choices available. Solenoids, horn relays, and alternators are some of the common choices. An in-line fuse should be replaced as close as is practical to this source. An overload or a short circuit would safely open the circuit protector and eliminate B+ for the entire circuit.

WARNING!

Fuse the circuit for the size of the wire. Overfusing and underwiring are two common problems that must be avoided. Also, keep in mind that amperage rating must be equal to or greater than the maximum electrical load the circuit is expected to carry. You can safely use a switch with more ampere capacity than the auxiliary lighting circuit requires, but never one with an underrated capacity. ∎

Driving and fog lights have tremendous output and have correspondingly high electrical requirements. This means the car should have an efficient charging system and a heavy-duty battery.

SHOP TALK

When replacing fog light bulbs, avoid touching the glass port of the new bulb assembly. Skin oil, present on even recently washed hands, remains on the glass. This oil prevents the bulb from dissipating heat. The increased heat inside the bulb causes the filament to burn out prematurely. ∎

LIGHTING MAINTENANCE

In addition to replacing all burnt out lights and bulbs, when a vehicle comes in for servicing, periodically check to see that all wiring connections are clean and tight, that light units are tightly mounted to provide a good ground, and that headlights are properly adjusted. Loose or corroded connections can cause a discharged battery, difficult starting, dim lights, and possible damage to the alternator and regulator. Often moisture gets into a bulb socket and causes corrosion of the electrical contacts and the bulb. Corrosive conditions can be repaired by using sandpaper on the affected areas. For severe cases, replace the socket and bulb. After any repair, always attempt to waterproof the assembly to prevent future problems. Cracked or broken assemblies are easily replaced. They are secured by attaching hardware that is normally readily accessible to the technician.

Another common electrical lighting problem is flickering lights (going on or off). The cause of this is usually a loose electrical connection or a circuit breaker that is kicking out because of a short. If all or several of the lights flicker, the problem is in a section of the circuit common to those lights. Check to see if the lights flicker only with the light switch in one position. For example, if the lights flicker only when the headlights are on high beam, check the components and wiring in the high-beam section of the circuit. If only one light flickers, the problem is in that section of the circuit. Check the bulb socket for corrosion. Also, make sure the bulb terminals are not worn. This could upset the electrical connection. If needed, replace the bulb socket and bulb.

Look at the turn signal in Figure 19–35A. The diagram shows the inside of a turn signal switch for a two-bulb system. The turn signal switch determines whether one of the bulbs is used for turning or brake lighting. The rectangular bars on the diagram are stationary contacts that the circuit wires connect to. Each contact has one wire connected to it. The top connection is from the brake switch and is B+ if the brakes are applied. The middle row connections are for rear combination lights (combination brake/turn signal). The bottom row of connections is for the front lights, including the dash indicators, and the B+ coming from the flasher. The triangles drawn over the bars are a set of three movable conductive pads that connect the different bars together depending on the position of the switch. They are drawn in the no turn or neutral position. This allows B+ from the brake switch to activate both rear lights at the same time. Figure 19–35B shows the same switch in a left turn. Notice that the conductive pads or triangles have moved to the right. This allows the brake switch to power only the right taillight, while the flasher connection is now in contact with the left rear taillight and the left front/indicator lights. The right taillight is being operated as a brake light, while the left one is in a turn signal operation. Figure 19–35C shows the same switch in a right turn mode. Notice that the conductive pads have moved to the left and have connected the brake switch to the left taillight, while the right is now powered off the turn signal flasher. This style of switch is very popular and normally is very durable. The most common problem encountered with the switch is usually mechanical rather than electrical. As the vehicle is driven around the corner, the canceling mechanism must put the switch back into a neutral position so that both taillights can be used for brake warning. When this canceling does not take place, the turn signal switch is normally replaced to correct the problem.

A

B

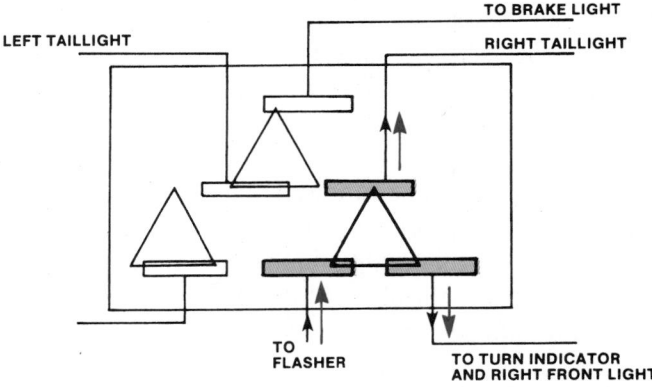

C

Figure 19–35 Turn signal switch (A) not in use, (B) with a left turn indicated, and (C) with a right turn indicated. *Courtesy of Ford Motor Company*

CASE STUDY

The customer complains that the turn signals on his vehicle do not operate as they are supposed to, and they seldom cancel out properly.

Turn signal circuits are frequent sources of difficulties. Their diagnosis, however, is not difficult and can usually be accomplished with just a 12-volt light or a voltmeter. Look at the common circuits, starting first with the flasher. The flasher is actually a type of circuit breaker, which is an overload protection device designed to open the circuit because of heat developed from excessive current. Flashers are usually mounted in the fuse box and made up of a fixed contact and a movable bimetallic contact.

KEY TERMS

Candlepower	Halogen
Delayed exit	Lamp
Dimmer switch	Multifunctional switch
DRL	Photocell sensor/amplifier
Flash-to-pass	Pull-out switch
Flasher	Sealed-beam

SUMMARY

◆ The headlight switch controls the headlights and all other light systems, with the exception of the turn signals, hazard warning, and stop lights.

◆ Dimmer switches, located on either the steering wheel or the floor, permit the headlights to change from high to low beam and vice versa.

◆ An automatic headlight dimmer circuit switches the headlights from high to low beam, in response to either light from an approaching vehicle or light from the taillights of a vehicle being overtaken.

◆ Depending on the make or model of the vehicle, courtesy lights can be found on the door, under the seats, under the instrument panel, on the rear interior quarter panels, or on the ceiling.

◆ The rear light assembly includes the taillights, turn signal/stop/hazard lights, high-mounted stop light, rear side marker lights, back-up lights, and license plate lights. Taillights operate when the parking lights or headlights are on.

◆ Headlights must be kept in adjustment to obtain maximum illumination and vehicle occupant safety.

◆ Flashers are used in turn signal, hazard warning, and side marker light circuits.

◆ The back-up light system illuminates the area behind the vehicle when it is put in reverse gear.

◆ Headlight systems consist of two or four sealed-beam tungsten or halogen headlight bulbs.

REVIEW QUESTIONS

1. Name the three types of headlight switches.
2. When is the taillight assembly activated?
3. Why are halogen bulbs used on today's vehicles?
4. What lights are used to supplement the high beams?
5. What lights are used to supplement the low beams?
6. Which of the following is usually *not* included in the main lighting system?
   a. glove box light c. dome/map lights
   b. turn signals d. headlight switch
7. Which of the following is often controlled by a mercury switch?
   a. trunk light c. both A and B
   b. underhood light d. neither A nor B
8. The rear light assembly includes the ____.
   a. rear side marker lights
   b. taillights
   c. license plate light
   d. all of the above
9. Circuits that can energize both the high and low beams even if the headlight switch is off are known as ____ circuits.
   a. flash-to-pass c. dimmer
   b. mercury d. retractable
10. Technician A says the condition of the vehicle's springs and shocks should be checked before aligning the headlamps. Technician B says the vehicle should have a full tank of fuel when its headlamps are being adjusted. Who is correct?
    a. Technician A c. Both A and B
    b. Technician B d. Neither A nor B
11. Technician A handles halogen headlight bulbs by grasping the glass envelope. Technician B handles halogen headlight bulbs by grasping the plastic base. Who is correct?
    a. Technician A c. Both A and B
    b. Technician B d. Neither A nor B

12. Technician A adjusts a headlight side-to-side by turning the adjusting screw at the top of the headlight. Technician B makes the same adjustment by turning the adjusting screw at the side of the headlight. Who is correct?
    a. Technician A
    b. Technician B
    c. Both A and B
    d. Neither A nor B

13. Which of the following statements is incorrect?
    a. OEM flashers will cause the lamps to blink faster if one bulb in the circuit is burned out.
    b. Heavy-duty replacement flashers will cause the lamps to blink faster if one bulb in the circuit is burned out.
    c. OEM flashers should not be used if lights have been added to the turn signal circuit.
    d. Heavy-duty flashers should be used if lights have been added to the turn signal circuit.

14. The stop light switch is normally mounted on the ____.
    a. instrument panel
    b. transmission
    c. brake pedal arm
    d. none of the above

15. Technician A says the fuse that protects the back-up light system is sometimes the same fuse that protects the turn signal system. Technician B says these two fuses are always separate. Who is correct?

    a. Technician A
    b. Technician B
    c. Both A and B
    d. Neither A nor B

16. The ideal position for fog lights ____.
    a. differs from state to state
    b. differs from that of driving and passing lights
    c. both A and B
    d. neither A nor B

17. Technician A uses a relay switch when installing auxiliary fog lights, but Technician B does not. Who is correct?
    a. Technician A
    b. Technician B
    c. Both A and B
    d. Neither A nor B

18. Technician A says flickering vehicle lights can be caused by a circuit breaker that is kicking out due to a short. Technician B says flickering vehicle lights can be caused by a loose electrical connection. Who is correct?
    a. Technician A
    b. Technician B
    c. Both A and B
    d. Neither A nor B

19. Headlamps either have a replaceable light bulb or are ____ ____, which must be replaced as a unit.

20. Some manufacturers recommend coating the prongs and base of headlamps with ____ ____ for corrosion protection.

ELECTRICAL INSTRUMENTS AND ACCESSORIES

20

OBJECTIVES

◆ *Know the purpose of the various designs of gauges and how they function.* ◆ *Describe the operation of the various gauges used in an instrument cluster.* ◆ *Describe the two types of instrument panel displays.* ◆ *Know the basic operation of electric windshield wiper and washer systems.* ◆ *Explain the operation of power door locks, power windows, and power seats.* ◆ *Determine how well the defroster system performs.* ◆ *Understand how cruise or speed control operates and the differences of various systems.* ◆ *Consider the use and value of engine cooling fans.*

Every automobile is equipped with a number of electrical instruments and accessories. The numbers and types of these systems and components vary significantly from vehicle model to model and year to year. Instrument gauges, lights, and warning indicators provide valuable information to the driver concerning various systems in the automobile. These range from engine coolant temperature indicators to fasten seat belt reminders. On the other hand, electrical accessories provide the driver with safety and warning devices, such as windshield wipers, horns, and speed controls, and make driving more pleasant by offering such items as power seats, power windows, clocks, and radios.

INSTRUMENT PANELS

In horse-and-wagon days, the dashboard really was a vertical board placed in front of the driver to protect from the mud slung up from horse hoofs just ahead. Today's dashboard is more properly called the **instrument panel**. It mounts an array of electrical gauges, switches, and controls all connected to mazes of wiring, printed circuitry, and air hoses beneath stylishly finished sheets of plastic or metal.

There are various instrument panel designs and layouts. The two basic types of instrument panel displays are analog and digital. In a traditional analog display (Figure 20–1), an indicator moves in front of a fixed scale to give variable readout. The indicator is often a needle, but it can also be liquid crystal or graphic display. A digital (or electronic) display uses numbers instead of a needle or graphic symbol. The advantage of analog displays is that they show relative change better than digital displays (Figure 20–2). Analog displays are useful when the driver must see something quickly and the exact reading is not important. For example, an analog tachometer shows the rise and fall of the engine speed better for shifting than a digital display. The driver does not need to know exactly how many rpm the engine is running. The most important thing is how fast the engine is reaching the red line on the gauge. A digital display is better for showing exact data such as miles or operating hours. Many speedometer-odometer combinations are examples of both analog (speed) and digital (distance).

A digital signal has only two states. It is either on or off. If a switch is turned on and off many times, the number of pulses can be counted. For example, a speed sensor can be made to turn on and off each time a wheel moves a certain distance. The number of pulses that are counted in a given period of time allows the computer to display the speed. The pulses can also be used by the computer to change the odometer reading.

There are three types of digital electronic displays used today. A description of each follows.

LIGHT-EMITTING DIODE (LED) These are used as either single indicator lights, or they can be grouped to show a set of letters or numbers. LED displays are commonly red, yellow, or green, and use more power than other displays. They can also be hard to see in bright light.

Indicator/Warning Light Key

1. Turn signals
2. Charging system (AMP)
3. Door ajar
4. Malfunction of anti-lock brake system
5. High beam
6. Brake
7. Engine temp. gauge
8. Fuel gauge
9. Seat belt
10. Check engine
11. Speedometer
12. Tachometer
13. Boost gauge
14. Low Fuel *
15. Low oil pressure*
16. Trac-control active

* Low oil pressure/hi coolant temp/low fuel (below 1/8) redundant with gauges

FIGURE 20–1 Analog instrument panel. *Courtesy of Chrysler Corporation*

LIQUID CRYSTAL DISPLAY (LCD) These have become very popular for many uses, including watches, calculators, and dash gauges. They are made of sandwiches of special glass and liquid. A separate light source is required to make the display work. When there is no voltage, light cannot pass through the fluid. When voltage is applied, the light passes through the segment. LCDs do not like cold temperatures, and the action of the display slows down in cold weather. These displays are also very delicate and must be handled with care. Any rough handling of the display can damage it.

VACUUM FLUORESCENT These displays use glass tubes filled with argon or neon gas. The segments of the display are little fluorescent lights, like the ones in a fluorescent fixture. When current is passed through the tubes, they glow very brightly. These displays are both durable and bright.

The choice of either an analog or a digital display is a matter of designer or buyer preferences.

SHOP TALK

Most warning or instrument controls use International Standards Organization (**ISO**) symbols. These ISO automotive symbols were developed by this organization to provide easily recognizable symbols throughout the world. ISO symbols are illustrated in Figure 20-3. ∎

FIGURE 20–2 Digital instrument panel. *Curtesy of Ford Motor Company*

FIGURE 20–3 A few ISO symbols used to identify gauges. *Courtesy of Chrysler Corporation*

INSTRUMENT GAUGES

Gauges provide the driver with a scaled indication of the condition of a system. For example, the fuel tank is half full. Gauges that indicate a relative scale of values are known as analog instruments. Those that indicate an exact number for a measured quantity are known as digital instruments.

Two additional components are required besides the electrical gauge itself. These are instrument voltage regulators and sender units. Instrument voltage regulators (**IVR**) are used to stabilize and limit voltage for accurate instrument operation (Figure 20-4). Sender or sensor units change electrical resistance in response to changes or movements made by an external component. Movement may be caused by pressure against a diaphragm, heat, or motion of a float as liquid fills a fuel tank.

All gauges (analog or digital) require an input from either a sender or a sensor. However, with modern computer-controlled displays, the sensor's output is used in two ways. The engine control computer needs the same information as the electronic display, so the information passes through the computer first. It then goes on to the gauge.

Two types of electrical analog gauges are commonly used with sensor or sending units—magnetic and thermal.

Magnetic Gauges

There are several types of magnetic gauges. The simplest form is the ammeter type (Figure 20–5A). In this gauge, a permanent magnet attracts a ferrous indicator needle connected to a pivot point and holds it centered. An armature, or coil of wire, is wrapped around the base of the needle, near the pivot point. Current can flow through a conductor beneath the armature. When current flows, a magnetic field around the conductor induces magnetism in the armature. This magnetism opposes that of the permanent magnet. Attractive or repulsive magnetic forces

FIGURE 20–4 IVR.

FIGURE 20-6   Balancing coil gauge. *Courtesy of Ford Motor Company*

FIGURE 20-5   (A) Simple ammeter; (B) magnetic bobbin gauge. *Courtesy of Ford Motor Company*

cause the needle to swing left or right. The direction the needle swings depends on the direction of current flow in the conductor.

Figure 20-5B shows the magnetic **bobbin gauge** often used as an analog fuel indicator. In this type of gauge, the bobbin assembly creates a magnetic field. The pointer is attached to a magnet that reacts to the strength of that field. Changing current is again used to drive the gauge. The higher the level, temperature, or pressure, the more current flows in the gauge circuit. The current creates a magnetic field that moves the pointer.

In a typical example of the magnetic type of gauge, consider that a voltage of approximately 5 volts is applied by the IVR to each gauge circuit. By varying the resistance in the sender, the current level reading on the gauge can be changed. The higher the resistance in the sender, the lower the current in the circuit, which is indicated by a smaller indicator

movement on the gauge. As stated in Ohm's law: voltage (E) is equal to current (I) times resistance (R) or $E = IR$.

A **balancing coil** gauge also operates on principles of magnetic attraction and repulsion. However, a permanent magnet is not used. The base of the indicating arm is pivoted and includes an armature. Two coils are used to create magnetic fields (Figure 20-6).

A sending unit has a variable resistance. The two coils are connected so that electricity can flow through either one. When the resistance of a sending unit is low, the right-hand coil receives more current than the left-hand coil, attracting the armature. Thus, a gauge needle moves to the right.

When resistance of a sending unit is high, the left-hand coil receives more current. More magnetic force is created in the left-hand coil. A gauge needle swings to the left.

Thermal or Bimetallic Gauge

A bimetallic or **thermal gauge** operates through heat created by current flow (Figure 20-7). A variable-resistance sending unit causes different amounts of current to flow through a heating coil within a gauge. The heat acts on a bimetallic spring attached to a gauge needle. When more heat is created, the needle swings farther up the scale. When less heat is created, the needle moves down the scale.

BASIC INFORMATION GAUGES

The following gauges are found on almost every instrument panel, whether analog or digital. The detailed operation of some gauges is described in other chapters.

Speedometer

Until recently, the speedometer was always considered a nonelectrical or mechanical gauge. The typical

FIGURE 20–7 Typical bimetallic fuel gauge circuit. *Courtesy of Chrysler Corporation*

FIGURE 20–8 Typical conventional speedometer.

mechanical speedometer had a drive cable attached to a gear in the transmission that turns a magnet inside a cup-shaped metal piece (Figure 20–8). The cup is attached to a speedometer needle and held at zero by a hairspring (a fine wire spring). As the cable rotates faster with increasing speed, magnetic forces act on the cup and force it to rotate. The speedometer needle, attached to the cup, moves up the speed scale.

Electric speedometers are used in more and more cars. While there are several systems in use, one of the most common types receives its speed information from the transmission-mounted vehicle speed sensor (Figure 20–9). This speed signal is also used by other modules in the vehicle, including speed control, ride control module, the engine control module, and others. In the event of a short or open in the system, check the connections for these other components.

For each 40,000 pulses from the vehicle speed sensor (VSS), the speedometer electronics increment the trip and total odometers in miles. Speed is determined by taking the input pulse frequency (in Hertz) and dividing by 2.2 Hertz/mph. The circuit electronics are calibrated to drive the pointer to a location in proportion to the speed input frequency. That is, as the pulse rate increases, the speedometer records it on an analog display. This display may be limited to a maximum of 85 mph or 199 km/h.

Most digital speedometers display vehicle speeds from 0 to 85 mph (199 km/h). If vehicle speed exceeds these values, the speedometer continues to display 85 mph (199 km/h). Vehicle speed is displayed whether the vehicle is moving forward or backward.

A variation of the electric speedometer employs a permanent magnet generator. An electric signal is sent from the generator sensor to a speed buffer and then to the speedometer.

Odometer

The **odometer** is a digital gauge that is usually driven by a spiral gear cut on the speedometer's magnet shaft. The odometer's numbered drums are geared so that any one drum finishes a complete revolution. The next drum to the left is turned one-tenth of a revolution (Figure 20–10).

Like the mechanical speedometer, the conventional odometer is giving way to the electrical type. Generally, the electric odometer receives its information from the VSS. Electrical odometers display seven digits, with the last digit in tenths of a unit. The odometer range is limited by the cluster memory space. The English units range from 000000.5 to 925,691.9 miles. The display freezes at this value. In metric units, the range is from 000000.8 to 858,993.4 km where the value rolls over to 000000.0 and continues accumulating up to 622,113.6 km. (The total distance is then the equivalent of 925,691.9 total miles.) The accumulated mileage value of the digital display odometer is stored in a nonvolatile memory (ROM) that retains the mileage value even if the battery is disconnected.

Since the odometer records the number of miles a vehicle has traveled, federal law requires that the odometer, in any replacement speedometer, must register the same mileage as that registered on the removed speedometer. Therefore, if a speedometer has been replaced, set the odometer of the new one to match the old. The trip odometer may be reset whenever desired.

Other Gauges

Some other electrical gauges that are commonly used on vehicles follow.

OIL PRESSURE GAUGE This gauge indicates engine oil pressure. The oil pressure typically should

Instrument
panel cluster
(IPC)
Solid State
Do not measure
resistance

888 km/h MPH

Cruise   Lights on

Data line

See BCM/ECM data line cell 50

800

Body computer module (BCM) solid state do not measure resistance

Ignition

Data line

Vehicle speed input 8060

Rotor driven by gear in transaxle

Vehicle speed sensor (VSS) 40,000 pulses per mile

See BCM/ECM data line cell 50

800

0.8 BN   437   2B3

L6   C216

0.8 BN   437

2B11

B   A

P103

0.8 PL   401   0.8 YL   400

2B9   2B10

Data line

4000 Pulses per mile

Vehicle speed output

Ground

Vehicle speed sensor input ED12

Engine control module (ECM) SolidState Do not measure resistance

FIGURE 20–9   The signals from the VSS are shared by the instrument panel and the ECM. *Courtesy of General Motors Corporation*

be between 45 and 70 psi when the engine is running at a specified engine speed, with SAE 10W-30 oil, and at operating temperature. A lower pressure is normal at low idle speed.

SPEEDOMETER SPIRAL GEAR

GEAR TRAIN

ODOMETER

FIGURE 20–10   Odometer.

The oil pressure switch determines whether or not current flows through the oil pressure gauge winding (Figure 20–11). With low oil pressure (or with the engine shut off), the oil pressure switch is open and no current flows through the gauge winding. The needle points to L. With oil pressure above a specific limit, the switch closes and current flows through the gauge winding to ground. A resistor limits current flow through the winding and ensures that the needle points to about mid-scale with normal oil pressure.

A piezoresistive sensor (Figure 20-12) is threaded into the oil delivery passage of the engine. The pressure exerted by the oil causes the flexible diaphragm to move. This movement is transferred to a contact arm that slides down the resistor. The position of the sliding contact on the arm in relation to the resistance coil determines the resistance value and the amount of current flow through the gauge to ground.

MAGNETIC OIL
PRESSURE
INDICATOR

OIL PRESSURE
SWITCH

NORMALLY OPEN, CLOSES AT
4.5 TO 7.5 PSI. GAUGE READS
MID SCALE OR SLIGHTLY
ABOVE WHEN SWITCH CLOSES.

RESISTOR IS USUALLY LOCATED ON
INSTRUMENT CLUSTER BACK PLATE
FLEXIBLE CIRCUIT.

A

COOLANT
TEMPERATURE
SENDER

B

LOW-FUEL
WARNING
INDICATOR
(IF EQUIPPED)

FUEL TANK

FUEL
SENDER

ANTI-SLOSH
LFW MODULE

C

FIGURE 20–11 (A) Typical pressure indicator; (B) coolant temperature gauge; and (C) fuel indicating gauge.

COOLANT TEMPERATURE GAUGE This gauge indicates engine coolant temperature. It should normally indicate between 170° and 195°F. Somewhat higher temperatures might occur under certain conditions. Typically, the maximum allowable temperature is 210°F.

Terminal

Contact arm

Variable resistor

Diaphragm

Oil pressure is
applied to this area

FIGURE 20–12 Piezoresistive sensor used for measuring engine oil pressure.

The sender or sensor is a variable resistance, such as a thermistor (Figure 20-13). It determines current flow through the temperature gauge winding. With low coolant temperature, sender resistance is high and current flow is low. The needle points to C. As coolant temperature increases, sender resistance decreases and current flow increases. The needle moves toward H.

The temperature gauge on a digital panel is of the bar type with a set number of segments. The number of illuminated bars varies according to the voltage across the gauge sender. With low coolant temperature, sender resistance is high and few segments are turned on. As coolant temperature increases, sender resistance decreases and the number of illuminated segments increases.

FUEL LEVEL GAUGE This gauge indicates the fuel level in the fuel tank. It is a magnetic indicating system that can be found on either an analog (meter) or digital (bars) instrument panel.

The fuel sender unit is combined with the fuel pump assembly and consists of a variable resistor controlled by the level of an attached float in the fuel tank (Figure 20–14). When the fuel level is low, resistance in the sender is low and movement of the

Terminal

Insulation

Spring

Resistor
disk

FIGURE 20–13 Thermistor used to sense engine temperature.

FIGURE 20–14   Typical fuel gauge circuit.

gauge indicator dial or number of lit bars is minimal (from empty position). When the fuel level is high, the resistance in the sender is high and movement of the gauge indicator (from the empty position) or number of lit bars is greater.

In some fuel gauge systems, an antislosh/low fuel warning (**LFW**) module is used to reduce fuel gauge needle fluctuation caused by fuel motion in the tank and provide a low fuel warning when fuel reaches 1/8 to 1/16 full.

TACHOMETER   The **tachometer** indicates engine rpm (engine speed). Figure 20–15 illustrates how the tachometer is connected. Electrical impulses from the coil are passed to the tachometer. The tachometer, using a balanced coil gauge, converts these impulses to rpm that can be read. The faster the engine rotates, the greater the number of impulses from the coil. Consequently, the greater the indicated rpm.

In vehicles with digital instrumentation, the bar system is used with numbered segments. The numbers represent the engine's rpm times 1,000.

SHOP TALK

The bar gauge found in some digital displays can also be used to indicate trouble in the system. For example, with one such system, diagnostic bars are displayed on a gauge when only the top and bottom two bar sections appear on the gauge. This can be an indication of a troubled signal or sender. Refer to diagnostic trouble bars given in the service manual.   ■

CHARGING GAUGE   This allows the driver to monitor the charging system. While a few cars use a voltmeter, most charging systems employ either an ammeter gauge or an indicator light. The ammeter gauge is placed in series with the battery and alternator. When the alternator is delivering current to the battery, the gauge displays a positive (+) indication. When the battery is not receiving enough current (or none at all) from the alternator, a negative (–) display is obtained.

INDICATORS AND WARNING DEVICES

Indicator lights and warning devices are generally activated by the closing of a switch. With power from the fuse panel on the other side, the indicator light comes on to warn the driver that something in the system is not functioning properly or that a situation exists that must be corrected. Figure 20–16 shows the warning lights on a typical instrument panel. The functions of some of the more common warning lights are given here.

AIR BAG READINESS LIGHT   On vehicles equipped with air bags, the air bag readiness light lets the driver know the air bag system is working and ready to do its job. It lights briefly when the ignition is turned on. A malfunction in the air bag system causes the light to stay on continuously or to flash, or the light may not come on at all.

FIGURE 20–15   Electrical tachometer connected into the ignition circuit.

FIGURE 20–16 Typical warning indicators. *Courtesy of Ford Motor Company*

AIR SUSPENSION LIGHT Voltage is present at the air suspension indicator at all times. If an air suspension fault is present, the indicator illuminates.

FASTEN BELTS INDICATOR When the ignition is turned to run or start, the warning chime module applies voltage to illuminate the fasten belts indicator for six seconds, whether or not the driver's belt is buckled.

HIGH-BEAM LIGHT With the headlights turned on and the main light switch dimmer switch in the high-beam position, the indicator illuminates.

LEFT AND RIGHT TURN INDICATORS With the multifunction switch in the left or right turn position, voltage is applied to circuit to illuminate the left or right turn indicator. The turn indicator flashes in unison with the exterior turn signal bulbs.

ANTILOCK LIGHT If an antilock brake system fault is present, the antilock brake module grounds the indicator circuit and the antilock light goes on.

RETRACTABLE HEADLIGHT This indicator light turns on only when the headlight raise/down motor is in operation. It comes on and lights for about one second when the headlights move up or down.

OIL TEMPERATURE WARNING LIGHT The warning light is provided for the purpose of preventing the overheating of torque converter fluid in case of repeated start-off operations in sand or on a snowy road, or when the car is operated at very low speed (near the stall speed) continuously under heavily loaded conditions.

If the temperature of the fluid at the torque converter outlet exceeds a specified temperature, the warning light at oil temperature illuminates and warns the driver of high oil temperature.

In such a case, the driver need not stop the car but should avoid undue operation. The warning light goes out as the fluid temperature drops.

CHARGE INDICATOR LIGHT The light indicates the condition of the alternator and charging system. If there is something wrong with the alternator and charging system, the light comes on while the engine is running.

OIL PRESSURE INDICATOR LIGHT The light indicates whether or not the oil pump is feeding oil under normal pressure to various parts of the engine. The indicator light is operated by an oil pressure switch located in the engine's lubricating system.

STOP LIGHT WARNING LIGHT The light is controlled by the stop light checker. This checker consists of a **reed switch** and magnet coils. Under normal conditions, magnetic fields are generated in the magnet coils by the current flowing through each light while the stop light switch is on. These magnetic fields cancel each other because the coils turn in directions opposite each other. As a result, the reed switch remains off, and the warning light is off. If either the left or right side stop light fails, current flows through only one magnet coil, and the resultant magnetic field causes the reed switch to turn on. Therefore, the warning light remains lighted as long as the brake pedal is depressed.

LAMP-OUT WARNING LIGHT The lamp-out warning module is a solid-state unit that is designed to measure small changes in voltage levels. An electronic switch in the module closes to complete a ground path for the indicator lights in the event of a bulb going out. The key to this system being able to detect one bulb out on a multibulb system is the use of the special resistance wires. With bulbs operating, the resistance wires provide 0.5-volt input to the light-out warning module. If one bulb in a particular system goes out, the input off the resistance wire drops to approximately 0.25 volt. The light-out warning module detects this difference and completes a ground path to the indicator light for the affected circuit.

BRAKE WARNING LIGHT When this light is lit, it is an indication that the parking brake is engaged. Some brake warning lamps will light if there is a leak or change in pressure in the brake system. Figure 20-17 shows how this type lamp is activated.

BRAKE FLUID LEVEL WARNING LIGHT The light is connected to the brake fluid level sensor that is incorporated in the brake fluid reserve tank. If brake fluid decreases to less than the specified volume in the reservoir, the sensor is actuated and the light comes on while the engine is running.

LOW FUEL WARNING LIGHT This particular component monitors the fuel level. When it drops below a quarter full, an electronic switch in the module closes and power is applied to illuminate the low fuel indicator light.

CHECK ENGINE WARNING LIGHT This warning is provided for the purpose of indicating the condition of the vehicle's engine and its systems. If there is a fault in the system, the warning light comes on while the engine is running. Check engine lights may be triggered by oil pressure, coolant temperature, or by the engine control computer that monitors several engine systems and illuminates the warning light whenever it senses a fault.

DOOR LOCK INDICATOR LIGHT This indicator tells the driver if the door locks are engaged or not.

DOOR AJAR WARNING LIGHT When the ignition is turned on and if the doors are left open or are ajar, this light comes on.

REAR (OR FRONT) DEFROST INDICATOR LIGHT When this light is lit, the defroster or deicer is operating.

DRIVE INDICATOR LIGHT Some front-wheel/ four-wheel-drive vehicles have a light, which when lit, indicates that the vehicle is in four-wheel-drive mode of operation.

Sound Warning Devices

Various types of tone generators, including buzzers, chimes, and voice synthesizers, are used to remind drivers of a number of vehicle conditions. These warnings can include fasten seat belts, air bag operational, key left in ignition, door ajar, and lights left on. Figure 20-18 is a tone generator system schematic.

FIGURE 20-17   Brake warning light switch as part of the combination valve.

FIGURE 20–18 Tone generator warning system. *Courtesy of Ford Motor Company*

DIAGNOSIS AND TESTING Items to be checked in a malfunctioning gauge or indicator system include the following.

- Fuses
- Indicator bulbs
- Detector switches (indicator systems)
- Sender units (gauge systems)
- IVR (gauge systems)
- Gauges (gauge systems)

Service manuals contain detailed information on the diagnosis and testing of the affected system for a particular vehicle. Always refer to it before beginning to diagnose a circuit.

Driver Information Centers

The various gauges, warning devices, and comfort controls may be grouped together into a **driver information center** or instrument cluster. This information center may be simple or it may be an all-encompassing cluster of information (Figure 20–19). The purpose of this message center is to keep the driver alert to the information provided by the system. The types and extent of information varies from one system to another.

In addition to standard warning signals, the information center may provide such vital data as fuel range, average or instantaneous fuel economy, fuel used since reset, time, date, estimated time of arrival (**ETA**), distance to destination, elapsed time since rest, average car speed, percent of oil life remaining, and various engine-operating parameters. Some vehicles have separate data centers. For instance, the fuel data display (Figure 20–20) gives the driver such information as fuel economy, fuel used since last fill up, and the expected number of miles before more fuel is needed. The separate trip computer reports such information to the driver as the time, distance traveled, average speed, stopwatch time, fuel range, average fuel economy, and instantaneous fuel economy.

Other electronic displays and controls can be found on today's vehicles.

STEERING WHEEL TOUCH CONTROLS Steering wheel touch controls are standard on many vehicles. Four or six large buttons are located convenient-

FIGURE 20–19 Monitored systems in a typical driver information center. *Courtesy of Chrysler Corporation*

FIGURE 20–20   Fuel data center. *Courtesy of General Motors Corporation*

ly in the steering wheel providing control over the more frequently used radio and heating/air-conditioning functions. This provides the driver with fingertip controls where they are easy to use.

HEAD-UP DISPLAY (HUD) This system features visual images that are projected on the windshield by a vacuum fluorescent light source to complement existing traditional in-dash (Figure 20–21). By projecting these images in the driver's peripheral field of view, it is not necessary for the driver to refocus attention or remove one's eyes from the road to obtain certain pertinent information. Among the images a **HUD** system may relate to the driver are vehicle speed, turn-signal indicators, low-fuel warning graphic, and a high-beam indicator.

ELECTRICAL ACCESSORIES

Electrical accessories that make driving safer, easier, and more pleasant include windshield wipers/washers, power door locks, power trunk releases, illuminated entry systems, keyless door entry locks, power windows, power seats, power mirrors, rear-window defrosters and heated mirrors, moon or sun roof systems, radios, horns, clocks, cigarette lighters, cruise controls, and engine cooling fans. Other automotive electric and electronic equipment such as radios and stereos, passive seat belts and air bags, and various auto security systems including keyless locks are described later in this book.

FIGURE 20–21 The heads-up display (HUD) can project the vehicle's speed onto the windshield, freeing the driver from looking down at the speedometer. *Courtesy of General Motors Corporation*

Windshield Wiper/Washer Systems

There are several types of windshield wiper systems. Both rear and front systems are commonly used. The wiper systems function to keep the windshield or back glass clear of rain, snow, and dirt. Headlight wipers are available that work in unison with conventional windshield wipers. There are two basic conventional systems commonly available. In the first system, the wiper motor has two speeds—low and high (Figure 20-22). In the other system a governor is added to the system to allow adjustment of the wiper interval period in addition to the low and high speeds. Both of these systems are with either a depressed or nondepressed park. In the depressed park system the blades drop down below the lower windshield molding. In nondepressed park the blades park at the lower moldings. The major components of a wiper system are the control switch, wiper motor and switch, and washer fluid pump. On systems with intermittent or **interval wipers**, an interval governor is added to the circuit (Figure 20–23). The wiper motor produces a rotational motion, and an assembly of levers connected to an offset motor drive changes the rotational motion of the motor to an oscillation motion, which is needed for the wiper blades. A typical wiper motor oscillator assembly is shown in Figure 20–24. As the center motor rotates, the output is an oscillation motion.

When the wiper switch is moved to the low or high speed position, voltage from the fuse panel is applied through the wiper switch directly to the wiper motor on systems without interval wipers. Shutting off the switch cuts power to the wiper motor. However, the wiper motor park switch maintains power to the motor until it is in the park position (Figure 20-25).

On vehicles with interval wipers the low and high speed signals pass through the interval governor to the wiper motor. When the wiper switch is placed in the int position (interval), the signal is applied to an interval timer circuit in the governor. The time period

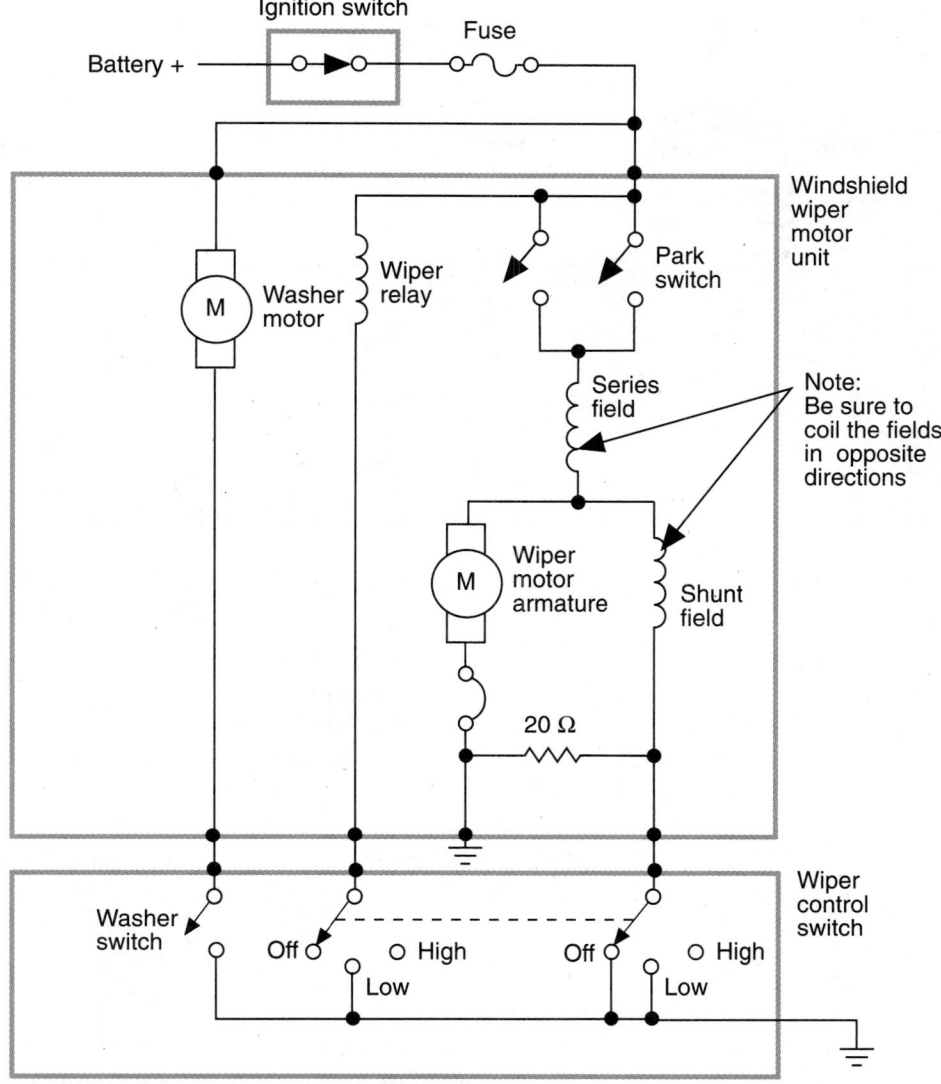

FIGURE 20–22 Schematic of a two-speed wiper circuit.

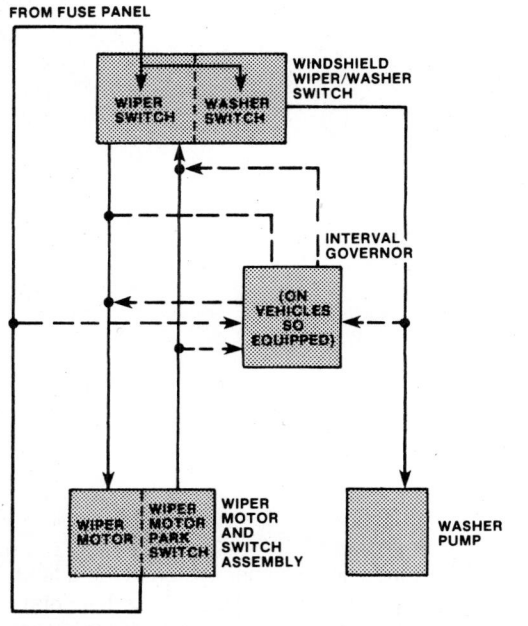

FIGURE 20–23 Windshield wiper/washer system.
Courtesy of Ford Motor Company

of the interval is adjusted by a potentiometer in the wiper switch. The potentiometer is a variable resistor.

Speed-sensitive windshield wipers now are available and adjust wiper speed automatically to vehicle speed. Complete details on the operation and servicing of speed-sensitive wipers can be found in the service manual.

WASHER SYSTEM The washer pump (Figure 20–26) is operated by holding the washer switch in the activate position. On models with interval wipers this signal is also applied to the governor. If the wiper switch is in off or int, an interval override circuit in the governor causes the wipers to operate at low speed until the washer switch is released. Then the wipers operate for several more cycles and park or return to interval operation.

Some vehicles have washers that help keep the integral headlight/foglight clean for maximum visibility (Figure 20–27). Headlight washer systems may

FIGURE 20–24 The rotational motion of the wiper motor is changed to an oscillating motion by the wiper linkage. *Courtesy of Ford Motor Company*

FIGURE 20–25 Exploded view of a wiper motor with a park mode.

FIGURE 20–26 The windshield washer system uses a fluid container, a small washer pump, and hoses and nozzles (jets) to deliver the wash to the windshield. *Courtesy of Volkswagen of America, Inc.*

FIGURE 20–27 Headlight washer system. *Courtesy of General Motors Corporation*

FIGURE 20–28 The oscillation motion from the wiper motor is transferred by a linkage system to the pivot points for the wipers. *Courtesy of Ford Motor Company*

operate from their own switch and pump or work from conventional windshield wiper systems.

A fluid washer nozzle is used on some cars for the front windshield washer system. The system consists of a fluid container, pump, fluid hoses and pipes, and nozzles or jets. When the operator turns on the washer, the small pump forces fluid through the hoses and pipes to the nozzle or jet by the windshield. The pump can be located either at the fluid container or wiper motor.

CUSTOMER CARE

It is good customer relations to advise the customer to check windshield washer fluid level periodically. If it is low, fill the washer reservoir with windshield washer fluid. It works better than plain water. Basically, the fluid is nothing more than a weak ammonia and water solution. Take a few minutes to show the customer where the reservoir is located and how the fluid should be added. ■

Some vehicles are equipped with a low fluid indicator. The washer fluid level switch closes when the fluid level in the reservoir drops below one quarter full. Closing of the switch allows power from the fuse panel to be applied to the indicator.

WINDSHIELD WIPER LINKAGE AND BLADES
Several arms and pivot shafts make up the linkage used to transmit the oscillation motion at the motor to the windshield wipers. Figure 20–28 shows an example of the linkage. As the wiper motor oscillates, arm A moves from left to right. This moves arm B as well. As arm B moves, it causes the two pivot points to oscillate. The windshield wipers are connected to the two pivot points.

The wiper arms and blades are attached directly to the two pivot points operated by the linkage and motor. The condition of wiper blades is critical to safe driving. If they are in poor condition, replace them. Figure 20–29 shows the various ways that wiper blades are attached to the wiper arms.

FIGURE 20–29 Various wiper blade attachment designs. *Courtesy of Chrysler Corporation*

CUSTOMER CARE

After installing new wiper blades, be sure to warn the customer not to operate them on dry windows. The abrasive action caused by dirt and other deposits wear down the blades and reduce their effectiveness. For optimum performance in winter, blades specially designed for snow and ice can be purchased. ■

LIFTGATE WIPER/WASHER SYSTEM This system has an on/off switch to control power to the single-speed wiper motor. The parking function is completed within the liftgate wiper motor and switch. Check the fuse or circuit breaker if any wiper/washer system is not working. If the wiper still does not work, trace the power flow through the system following the electrical schematic in the service manual.

Power Door Lock Systems

Although systems for automatically locking doors vary from one vehicle to another, the overall purpose is the same—to lock all outside doors. There are, however, several variations of door arrangements used that require slight differences in components from one system to another. As a safety precaution against being locked in a car due to an electrical failure, power locks can be manually operated.

When either the driver's or passenger's control switch is activated (either locked or unlocked), power from the fuse panel is applied through the switch to the door lock actuator motor. A rod that is part of the actuator moves up or down in the door latch assembly as required to lock or unlock the door. On some models the signal from the switch is applied to a relay that, when energized, applies an activating voltage to the door lock actuator. The door lock actuator consists of a motor and a built-in circuit breaker. On station wagon models with power door locks, the tailgate lock actuator is also controlled by the door lock switches. Station wagon models without power door locks can be equipped with a separate tailgate power lock system.

Most models use a control switch mounted in the door arm rest or in the door trim panel. However, some models use switches controlled by the front door push-button locks (Figure 20–30).

While most power locks operate off the vehicle's electrical system, a few arrangements use the vacuum from the engine's intake manifold. This vacuum operates a small vacuum motor containing a spring-loaded diaphragm. A rod is connected between the diaphragm at one end and the locking mechanism at the other. When the driver's door is locked, vacuum is transferred to all locks causing rods to pull the latches closed. Opening the driver's lock releases the vacuum, and the springs force the diaphragms back and the locks open.

Power Trunk Release

The power trunk release system is a relatively simple electrical circuit that consists of a switch and a solenoid. Power to the switch is present any time the ignition switch is in run or accessory (accy). When the trunk release switch is pressed, voltage is applied through the switch to the solenoid. With battery voltage on one side and ground on the other, the trunk release solenoid energizes and the trunk latch releases to open the trunk lid.

Power door lock or trunk release systems rarely give trouble. Should a problem occur, check the following.

- If none of the locks work, check the circuit protection devices. If they are okay, check the wiring.
- If power locks operate to lock or unlock but not both, check the relays on vehicles so equipped. On vehicles without relays, check the wiring to and from the control switch on the side that is not working.
- If only one door lock does not operate, check the actuator for that door.
- If only one door lock switch does not work, perform a switch test as described in the service manual.

FIGURE 20–30   Typical door lock control switches. *Courtesy of Ford Motor Company*

FIGURE 20–31 Electric window motor and regulator. *Courtesy of Chrysler Corporation*

FIGURE 20–32 Typical power window master control switch. *Courtesy of Ford Motor Company*

◆ If the trunk release does not work, check the fuse first. Then check for voltage through the switch with the ignition switch in run and the trunk release switch depressed. If the switch is okay, check for continuity through the trunk release solenoid to ground. If the solenoid is okay, check the wiring.

Power Windows

Obviously, the primary function of any power window system is to raise and lower windows. The systems do not vary significantly from one model to another. The major components of a typical system are the master control switch, individual window control switches, and the window drive motors (Figure 20-31). In addition, on four-door models, a window safety relay and in-line circuit breaker are also included.

The master control switch (Figure 20–32) provides overall system control. Power for the system comes directly from the fuse panel on two-door models and from an in-line circuit breaker on four-door models. The window safety relay used on four-door models prevents operation of the system if the ignition switch is not in run or accy. Power for the individual window control switches comes through the master control switch.

Four-door model master control switches usually have four segments while two-door models have two segments (Figure 20–33). Each segment controls power to a separate window motor. Each segment actually operates as a separate independent switch. A

FIGURE 20–33 Power window master control switch electrical schematic. *Courtesy of Ford Motor Company*

window lock switch is included on four-door model master control switches. When open, this switch limits opening and closing of all windows to the master control switch. It is included as a safety device to prevent children from opening door windows without the driver knowing.

The first step in checking out a power window system is to determine whether the whole system is out or just one or two portions. If the whole system is out, the problem can be isolated to fuses, circuit breakers, or the master control switch. If only a portion of the system does not work, check the components used in the portion that is not working.

USING SERVICE MANUALS

Diagnosis and service is a very important part of the electrical accessory system. Use a standard troubleshooting procedure to find an electrical problem. For example, always verify the problem, read the schematic, look for possible causes, test for correct voltages, narrow the problem down to one circuit, find the cause, and correct the problem. Let us examine each power window component as it appears in a typical service manual schematic (Figure 20–34). Circuit breakers are generally used on power windows because they open if an overload occurs. Winter weather might freeze the window closed. Without a circuit breaker to open, the motor might be damaged trying to move the window against the ice. As the ice is removed, the breaker cools, closes, and allows

future window operation. The motor is usually an insulated directional style that runs up or down, depending on the direction of the applied B+ and ground. The master switch has its own B+ source and is the ground for the entire system. Notice that the style of switch used at the window and the master control is basically the same. The switch allows B+ to be directed through the motor from the center terminal and then flow back through the other side of the switch. The window switch and master switch are actually wired in series. A problem with either switch affects motor operation. A deal motor can be diagnosed with a 12-volt light or voltmeter by first ensuring that B+ is available to both switches. Moving the switches should switch the B+ from one side to the other. By connecting a testlight across the switch, the presence of voltage and the switch itself can be checked. The motor is checked easily by jumping the terminals to B+ and ground. Reversing the connections should reverse the direction of the motor, raising and lowering the window. Corroded switch contacts generally indicate the presence of series resistance. ∎

WARNING!

When installing electrical components, make certain they are properly fused. Wires must be insulated, kept from hot areas, and must be secured to prevent chafing. When passing through metal parts, install rubber grommets to protect the wires. Terminals should be clean and tight. ∎

Power Seats

Power seats allow the driver or passenger to adjust the seat to the most comfortable position. The major components of the system are the seat control and the motors.

Power seats generally come in two configurations: four-way and six-way. In the four-way system the whole seat moves up or down, or forward and rearward. In the six-way system (Figure 20-35), the same movements are included plus the ability to adjust the height of the seat front or the seat rear. Generally, a four-way system is used on bench seats and a six-way system is used on split-bench seats. In addition, two different drives are used on the six-way system—rack and pinion and screw-drive. Electrically, the difference between the rack and pinion drive and the screw-drive is minimal.

Two motors are usually employed to make the adjustments on the four-way systems, while three are

FIGURE 20–34 Typical power window service manual schematic. *Courtesy of Ford Motor Company*

Right seat control switch

Right seat assembly

FIGURE 20–35 Six-way power seat circuit.

used on a six-way system. The names of the motors easily identify their function. To raise or lower the entire seat on a six-way system, both the front height and the rear height motors are operated together. The control motors themselves are generally two-directional motor assemblies that include a circuit breaker to protect against circuit overload if the control switch is held in the actuate position for long periods. A typical six-way motor, called a trimotor, rack and pinion system is shown in Figure 20–36. The four-way system and six-way screw-drive motor arrangements are similar.

Cars with on-board computers can store information about seat position. A seat can be returned to a preset position by depressing the memory switch. In addition, some power seats are heated to varying degrees depending on the driver's desires.

Power Mirror System

The power mirror system allows the driver to control both the lefthand and righthand outside rear view mirrors from one switch. The major components in the system are the joystick control switch and a dual motor drive assembly located in each mirror assembly.

Rotating the power mirror switch to the left or right position selects one of the mirrors for adjustment. Now moving the joystick control up and down, or right and left moves the mirror to the desired position. The mirrors are moved by a dual motor drive

FIGURE 20–36   Trimotor power seat installation. *Courtesy of Ford Motor Company*

assembly located behind the mirror glass (Figure 20–37).

Many new vehicles are being equipped with **electrochromic** inside rear-view and side-view mirrors. Requiring no electrical connections, these mirrors operate on the intensity of the glare in much the same manner as a pair of eyeglasses with photochromatic lens. When glare is heavy, the mirror darkens fully (down to 6 percent reflectivity) much the same as

standard mirrors. But, when glare is mild, the electrochromic mirror provides a comfort zone. At this stage, the mirror gives 20 percent to 30 percent reflectivity. Glare is gone without impairing rear visibility. When glare subsides, the electrochromics change to the clear daytime state (Figure 20–38).

Rear- and Front-Window Defrosters and Heated Mirror System

The rear- and front-window defroster (also called a **defogger** or **deicer**) heats the rear-window surface to remove moisture and ice from the window. On some vehicles, the same control heats the outside mirrors.

The major components of a rear-window defroster are the device switch relay assembly and the heating elements on the glass surfaces (Figure 20–39).

Pressing the rear-window defroster switch momentarily to the on position closes the on switch in the defroster switch relay assembly. The time delay circuit applies ground to one side of the relay coil and with battery voltage to the other side, the relay is energized. Battery voltage through the fuse link now flows through closed contacts of the relay to the rear-window defroster grid. On models with a heated mir-

FIGURE 20–37   Power mirror motor switch.

A

B

C

FIGURE 20–38 Operation of an electrochromic side-view mirror: (A) daytime up to 85 percent reflectivity; (B) mild glare from 20 to 30 percent reflectivity; and (C) high glare as low as 6 percent reflectivity. *Courtesy of Gentex Corporation*

FIGURE 20–40 The power and ground circuits are connected to the silver and zinc coating through busbars. *Courtesy of Ford Motor Company*

Heater, or self-defrosting, front windshield systems are offered as an option on a growing number of vehicles. These systems work like rear-window defrosters, heating the glass directly. Ice and frost are melted faster than with standard forced air systems. Rather than a wire grid that could hinder overall driver's vision, advanced glass making technology allows for a micro-thin metallic coating inside the windshield, where it is nearly undetectable (Figure 20-40).

The typical windshield defroster system is turned on by pressing a switch on the instrument panel. Once pushed on, the alternator output is redirected from the normal electrical system to the windshield circuit. All other electrical circuits operate on power from the battery. When the alternator output is no longer going directly through the battery, the voltage regulator senses a drop in battery voltage and fully charges the alternator to between 30 and 90 volts (Figure 20-41). If the battery voltage drops below 11 volts, alternator output is directed to the battery, and the system is turned off. Some systems use a specially designed generator to provide the necessary power to operate the system without draining the battery. Check the defroster service manual for specific voltage details.

ror, the voltage through the relay contacts also flows through a separate fuse to the mirror heated grid.

After about 10 minutes, the time delay circuit opens the ground path to the coil and the coil de-energizes. This removes power from the system, and the grids cease to heat the glass surface. The time delay circuit prevents the system from remaining on during periods of extended driving. The system can also be shut off by momentarily moving the defroster switch to the off position.

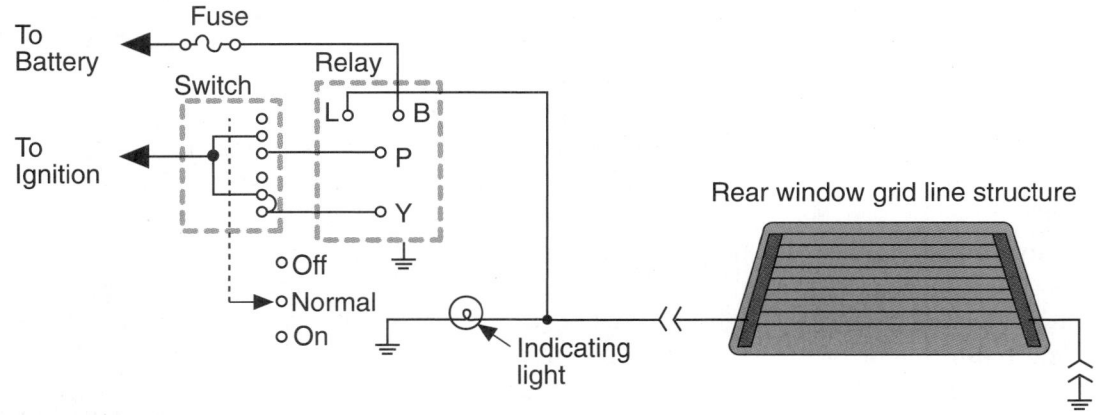

FIGURE 20–39 Rear defogger circuit schematic.

FIGURE 20–41 Schematic of an alternator used on vehicles equipped with a heated windshield. The three terminals provide AC to the power module.

The defrost cycle generally lasts for about 4 minutes. After that, the alternator is switched to the normal charging operation controlled by the voltage regulator. If the windshield is not clear, the system can be selected again.

WARNING!

The operating voltage of windshield defroster systems is high—between 30 and 90 volts. Be very careful when servicing or testing any parts or wiring. Do not pierce the insulation when checking the wire. ∎

Moon (Sun) Roof System

The power **moon roof** or **sun roof** panel that is an option on some car models slides open or tilts up in the back to give the passenger compartment just the right amount of fresh air and natural light. With the roof tilted up, some moon roofs have a sliding louvered shade panel to block out bright rays and provide additional ventilation.

The major components of any roof panel system are a relay, control switch, sliding roof vent, and motor.

Power to the control switch is applied through a relay. The relay coil is energized only when the ignition switch is in accy or run. When the relay is energized, battery voltage can pass through the closed relay contacts to the control switch (Figure 20–42). This circuit is normally protected by the in-line circuit breaker.

When the two-position control switch is moved to the open position, battery voltage passes through the switch contacts into the motor terminals. The sun or moon roof begins to move back into a storage area between the headliner and the roof. The panel stops moving anytime the switch is released. Moving the switch to the close position reverses the power flow through the motor.

If the system is not operating, check the fuse and circuit breaker. If these are okay, check for power to the switch with the ignition switch in accy or run. If the voltage is present, the relay is okay. Check for power to the motor with the switch held in the open position. Refer to the service manual for additional diagnosis and testing information.

FIGURE 20–42 Typical moon roof system. *Courtesy of Ford Motor Company*

Horns/Clocks/Cigarette (Cigar) Lighter System

The function and operation of these systems are obvious. Circuits may vary from one model to another and from one year to another (Figure 20–43). However, the overall operation remains the same.

HORN Most horn systems are controlled by relays. When the horn button, ring, or padded unit is depressed, electricity flows from the battery through a horn lead, into an electromagnetic coil in the horn relay to the ground. A small flow of electric current through the coil energizes the electromagnet, pulling a movable arm. Electrical contacts on the arm touch, closing the primary circuit and causing the horn to sound.

Most light truck models and some import cars have the horn switch mounted in the steering wheel hub assembly. Many current car horn switches are

FIGURE 20–43 Typical horn/clock/cigar lighter circuit. *Courtesy of Ford Motor Company*

FIGURE 20–44 Typical dual horn assembly. *Courtesy of Chrysler Corporation*

now part of the multifunction or combination switch. This difference does not change the electrical operation of the horn system. Some vehicles are equipped with two horns. Each one is designed to emit a different tone. The purpose of a dual horn system is simply to provide fuller sound. Figure 20–44 shows a typical dual horn assembly.

CLOCK The clock operates as a result of power from the fuse panel. Some clocks have additional functions. These are adequately discussed in the service manual and owner's guide for the particular vehicle being serviced.

CIGARETTE LIGHTER The cigarette (cigar) lighter is a heating element that automatically releases itself from the pushed in position when the appropriate heat level is reached.

For an inoperative system, first check the fuse(s). If the fuse is good, make certain that power is pre-

sent at the lighter receptacle. If power is present, the lighter unit is probably bad. Refer to the service manual for added troubleshooting information.

Cruise (Speed) Control System

Cruise or speed control systems are designed to allow the driver to maintain a constant speed (usually about 30 mph) without having to apply continual foot pressure on the accelerator pedal. Selected cruise speeds are easily maintained and speed can be easily changed. Several override systems also allow the vehicle to be accelerated, slowed, or stopped. Because of the constant changes and improvements in technology, each cruise control system may be considerably different. There are several types that are used, including the nonresume type, the resume type, and the electronic type.

When engaged, the cruise control components set the throttle position to the desired speed. The speed is maintained unless heavy loads and steep hills interfere. The cruise control is disengaged whenever the brake pedal is depressed. The common speed or cruise control system components function in the following manner.

◆ The cruise control switch is located on the end of the turn signal or near the center or sides of the steering wheel (Figure 20–45). There are usually several functions on the switch, including off-on, resume, and engage buttons. The switch is different for resume and nonresume systems.

◆ The transducer is a device that controls the speed of the vehicle. When the transducer is engaged, it senses vehicle speed and controls a vacuum source (usually the manifold). The vacuum source is used to maintain a certain position on a servo. The speed control is sensed from the lower cable and casing assembly attached to the transmission.

Turn signal lever

Mode control, steering wheel and on-off rocker switch

FIGURE 20–45 The cruise control switch can be mounted on the turn signal stock or into the steering wheel assembly. *Courtesy of General Motors Corporation*

◆ The servo unit is connected to the throttle by a rod or linkage, a head chain, or a bowden cable. The servo unit maintains the desired car speed by receiving a controlled amount of vacuum from the transducer. The variation in vacuum changes the position of the throttle. When a vacuum is applied, the servo spring is compressed and the throttle is positioned correctly. When the vacuum is released, the servo spring is relaxed and the system is not operating.

◆ There are two brake-activated switches. They are operated by the position of the brake. When the brake pedal is depressed, the brake release switch disengages the system. A vacuum release valve is also used to disengage the system when the brake pedal is depressed.

ELECTRICAL AND VACUUM CIRCUITS Figure 20–46 shows an electrical and vacuum circuit dia-

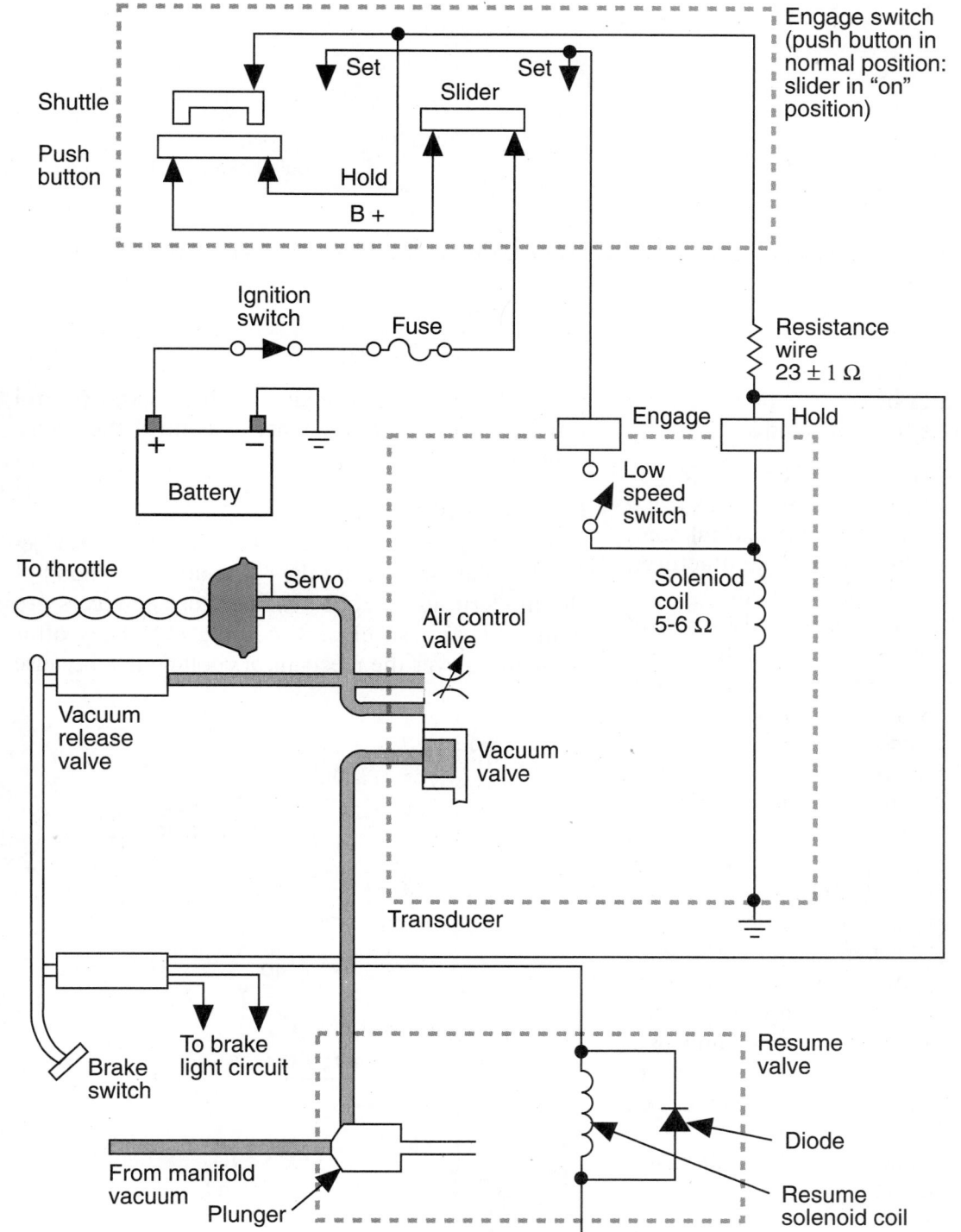

FIGURE 20–46

Cruise control circuit with vacuum and electrical systems. *Courtesy of General Motors Corporation*

FIGURE 20–47 Electronic cruise control uses an electronic control module (controller) to operate a servo that controls the position of the throttle. *Courtesy of General Motors Corporation*

gram. The system operates by controlling vacuum to the servo through various solenoids and switches.

ELECTRONIC CRUISE CONTROL COMPONENTS Cruise control can also be obtained by using electronic components rather than mechanical components. Depending on the vehicle manufacturer, several additional components may be used.

The electronic control module is used to control the servo unit. The servo unit is again used to control the vacuum, which in turn controls the throttle. The vehicle speed sensor (VSS) buffer amplifier is used to monitor or sense vehicle speed. The signal created is sent to the electronic control module. A generator speed sensor may also be used in conjunction with the VSS. The clutch switch is used on vehicles with manual transmissions to disengage the cruise control when the clutch is depressed. The accumulator is used as a vacuum storage tank on vehicles that have low vacuum during heavy load and high road speed.

Figure 20–47 shows how electronic cruise control components work together. The throttle position is controlled by the **servo unit**. The servo unit uses vacuum working against a spring pressure to operate an internal diaphragm. The servo unit vacuum circuit is controlled electronically by the controller.

The **controller** has several inputs that help determine how it will affect the servo. These inputs include a brake release switch (clutch release switch), a speedometer, buffer amplifier, or generator speed sen-

sor, and a turn signal mode switch or speed control on the steering wheel (signal to control the cruise control).

Engine Cooling Fan

With the advent of transverse-mounted engines, electrical cooling fans found their way under the hood of the modern automobile. Today, most new cars are equipped with an electric cooling fan. They offer advantages over the mechanical cooling fans because

FIGURE 20–48 Cooling fan circuit, non-A/C equipped.

FIGURE 20–49 System in which the compressor and fan are cycled at the same time.

FIGURE 20–50 Cooling fan circuit with pressure switching.

of their ability to move large amounts of air independent of engine speed. Their circuitry is very simple, especially on a vehicle that is not air-conditioned. Figure 20–48 shows an electric cooling fan circuit.

Air-conditioned vehicles, especially those with small engines, usually have additional circuitry to ensure that the cooling fan comes on when the compressor cycles on. Airflow through the condenser must be present for A/C to function correctly. With the condenser mounted in front of the radiator, the logical method of ensuring airflow is to turn the cooling fan on as the A/C compressor cycles on. Most of the manufacturers follow one of two methods. Either they cycle the compressor and the fan at the same time as Figure 20–49 shows, or they cycle the fan on when A/C high side pressure reaches a predetermined level (Figure 20–50). In either case, this ensures that airflow through the condenser keeps both the A/C and the engine cool.

⚠️ WARNING!

Never replace a fuse with a higher capacity rating or bypass it with a wire. The fuse of correct capacity must be in the circuit. ∎

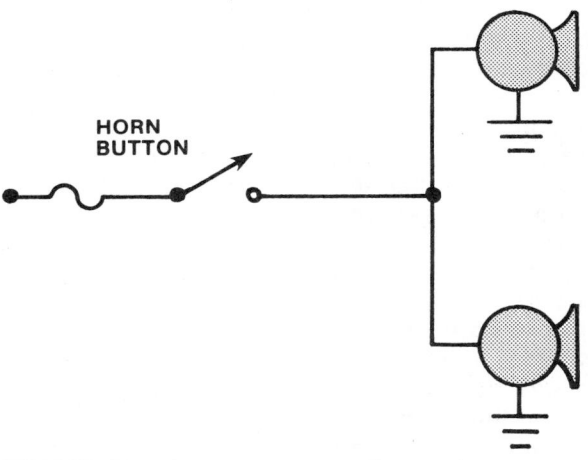

FIGURE 20–51 Two-horn circuit without relay.

FIGURE 20–52 Horn circuit utilizing a relay.

CASE STUDY

A *customer complains that the horn does not operate.*

To correct this situation, the technician must determine whether the horn system has a relay or not. Figure 20–51 shows a two-horn circuit without a relay. A fused B+ goes up the steering column to the horn button, which is normally open (NO). Closing the switch closes the circuit, bringing B+ down the column through the bulkhead connector to a common point where the two horns are connected in parallel. On the other side of the horn is a ground and the circuit is complete, a good example of a simple series-parallel circuit with one control. The circuit is easily diagnosed with a 12-volt testlight, following the usual procedure of looking for B+ with the horn button pushed in. Correct diagnosis is important, especially because many horn switches are part of a multiple function switch, which is very costly. The same stalk on the steering column might be used for the horn, turn signals, windshield wipers, and cruise control. Make sure your diagnosis is correctly arrived at before you spend your customer's money. Power in at the switch and no power out with the button depressed would be the only reason to replace the switch unit.

Figure 20–52 shows an adaptation of the simple horn circuit. Notice that a fused B+ is run to the horn relay rather than to the switch. A NO relay is used. Notice that internally the relay coil receives B+ from the same fused source as the contacts do. The other end of the relay coil runs through the bulkhead connector and up into the steering column where a NO switch is located. Closing the switch grounds the relay coil, which develops a magnetic field, closing the contacts. The closed contacts bring B+ over to the common point for the two horns, which are grounded. You can see that the circuit is slightly more complicated but an excellent example of the use of a relay and ground side switching, which we have discussed before. Remember, any relay circuit must be diagnosed as two separate circuits wired in parallel. The relay coil is a separate circuit that needs a path for it to develop the magnetic field necessary to close the contacts. Closing the contacts allows current flow through the other circuit with the horns as the load. There are actually three loads in the previous example, two horns and the relay coil. Diagnose them separately, as you would any relay circuit, and you are less likely to make mistakes. Use a 12-volt testlight with a wiring diagram to trace the power through the circuit.

KEY TERMS

Balancing coil	Interval wipers
Bobbin gauge	ISO
Controller	IVR
Defogger	LFW
Deicer	Moon roof
Driver information center	Odometer
	Reed switch
Electrochromic	Servo unit
ETA	Sun roof
HUD	Tachometer
Instrument panel	Thermal gauge

SUMMARY

◆ Analog instrument gauges must have voltage regulators and senders or sensors in their circuit to function properly.

◆ Two types of electrical gauges are magnetic and thermal.

◆ The speedometer and odometer can operate on either an electrical or nonelectrical principle.

◆ Indicators and warning devices generally operate as the result of a switch closing. They provide valuable information to the driver concerning the various systems in the automobile.

◆ Lamps (lights), sound devices (chimes and buzzers), and graphic displays are popular warning systems.

◆ Instrument panels have two types of displays: analog and digital.

◆ There are three types of digital electronic displays: light- emitting diode (LED), liquid-crystal diode (LCD), and vacuum fluorescent.

◆ A printed circuit is composed of a film of plastic with small strips of copper. The electric current for various sections of the instrument panel run through these strips of copper. Lights, gauges, and indicators are plugged directly into the printed circuit board.

◆ The windshield wiper system uses several components. The windshield wiper motor is a permanent magnetic motor used to operate the windshield wipers. There is also a mechanism used to change the rotational motion of the motor to oscillation motion for the wipers. Each vehicle also uses mechanical linkage to connect the oscillation motion of the motor output to the wiper blades.

◆ A fluid washer nozzle and pump are used to pump cleaning fluid to the windshield.

◆ The power seats operate by using several motors on the bottom of the seats. The motors can operate in either direction. The switches, which are controlled by the operator, tell the motors in which direction to turn.

◆ The deicer or defogger operates by using a switch, a timer to hold accessory on for a certain period of time, and a fuse panel.

◆ The horn circuit uses electricity from the battery, through the horn button, to the horn solenoid. A solenoid is also used to energize the horn.

◆ Cruise control is used to mechanically or electronically control the position of the throttle during highway operation. These systems help the operator to maintain a constant speed without having to apply foot pressure to the accelerator pedal. A cruise control switch is used to engage or disengage the system.

◆ There are several common parts used on cruise control systems. The servo is connected to the throttle linkage to control its position. It uses vacuum to move a wire or chain connected to the throttle mechanism. The transducer is used to control the vacuum sent to the servo. A brake-activated switch is used to disengage the system when the brakes are applied. The electrical circuit is used to control valves, which in turn control the vacuum to the transducer.

◆ Electronic cruise control systems use several additional parts. These include the electronic control module, a vehicle speed sensor (VSS), a clutch switch, and an accumulator used to store vacuum.

TECH MANUAL

The following procedures are included in Chapter 20 of the *Tech Manual* that accompanies this book:

1. Remove and replace a temperature sensor.

2. Test and repair a rear window defogger grid.

3. Speed or cruise control simulated road test.

REVIEW QUESTIONS

1. What is the simplest type of magnetic gauge?

2. What gauge indicates engine speed?

3. Name the three types of digital electronic displays used today.

4. What component in an electronic cruise control system is used to monitor or sense vehicle speed?

5. What component in a wiper system makes it possible to adjust the wiper interval period?

6. Technician A says a common check for inoperative taillights is the headlight switch. Technician B says a common check for inoperative taillights is the ground at the rear of the vehicle. Who is correct?
   a. Technician A   c. Both A and B
   b. Technician B   d. Neither A nor B

7. Which device on a cruise control system is used to adjust and control the position of the throttle?
   a. servo
   b. solenoid
   c. brake-activated switch
   d. transducer
   e. magnetic switch

8. Which of the following is *not* a type of gauge design?
   a. thermal   d. magnetic bobbin
   b. balancing coil   e. none of the above
   c. variable resistance

9. Technician A states horn buttons in circuits with relays are B+ switches. Technician B states horn buttons in circuits without relays are actually switches to ground. Who is correct?
   a. Technician A   c. Both A and B
   b. Technician B   d. Neither A nor B

10. Depressed park windshield wiper systems park the blades by generally ____.
    a. turning off B+ to the motor
    b. applying B+ to the motor
    c. ungrounding the switch
    d. reversing the motor direction

11. Rear defrosters generally have a relay with a timer. This allows ____.
    a. the defogger to operate for only a specific amount of time
    b. the defogger to function just until the rear window is clear
    c. the defogger to be independent of the ignition switch
    d. none of the above

12. The right front window does not function on a power window vehicle. Technician A states that the window motor might be insulated from ground causing the problem. Technician B states that either the master or right door switch could be the problem. Who is correct?

    a. Technician A
    b. Technician B
    c. Both A and B
    d. Neither A nor B

13. On an air-conditioned vehicle the cooling fan does not turn off. A possible cause could be ____.

    a. a grounded coolant temperature switch
    b. an open relay
    c. a grounded cooling fan motor
    d. a burned-out fuse link

14. Information that the trip computer can supply includes ____.

    a. miles per gallon of fuel
    b. miles to predetermined destination
    c. estimated arrival time
    d. all of the above

15. Technician A says the odometer reports the total miles or kilometers the car has traveled. Technician B says the speedometer reports the miles or kilometers per hour the car is traveling. Who is correct?

    a. Technician A
    b. Technician B
    c. Both A and B
    d. Neither A nor B

16. The indicator needle on a speedometer is held to the zero position by ____.

    a. magnetic force
    b. the weight of the needle
    c. the speedometer cable
    d. a coiled spring

17. Power window systems use ____.

    a. electric motors
    b. permanent magnet motors
    c. reversible motors
    d. all of the above

18. The horn has ____.

    a. vibrating contact points
    b. a vibrating diaphragm
    c. an electromagnet
    d. all of the above

19. The oil pressure light stays on whenever the engine is running. The oil pressure has been checked and it meets specifications. Technician A says a ground in the circuit between the indicator light and the pressure switch could be the cause. Technician B says an open in the pressure switch could be the cause. Who is correct?

    a. Technician A
    b. Technician B
    c. Both A and B
    d. Neither A nor B

20. Which device on a cruise control system is used to control the amount of vacuum in the system?

    a. servo
    b. solenoid coil
    c. brake-activated switch
    d. transducer
    e. none of the above

SECTION 4

ENGINE PERFORMANCE

To have an efficient running engine, there must be the correct amount of fuel mixed with the correct amount of air. These must be present in a sealed container and shocked by the right amount of heat, at the correct time. With total efficiency, the engine would burn all the fuel it receives and would release extremely low amounts of pollutants in its exhaust. Although total efficiency is not possible at this time, late-model engines emit very low amounts of pollutants, thanks to emission control devices.

To have highly efficient engines, the basic engine needs highly efficient ignition, fuel, and emission control systems. Although there are many different designs of these systems, the designs are similar in operation. Engine performance systems are some of the most technologically advanced systems found on modern vehicles. They all rely on a network of input sensors and output devices and tie directly into the electronic engine control system. Mastery of these systems is necessary for an automotive technician.

The material in Section 4 matches the content areas of the ASE certification test on engine performance and sections of the certification test on engine repair.

WE ENCOURAGE
PROFESSIONALISM

THROUGH TECHNICIAN
CERTIFICATION

IGNITION SYSTEMS

21

OBJECTIVES

◆ Describe the three major functions of an ignition system. ◆ Name the operating conditions of an engine that affect ignition timing. ◆ Name the two major electrical circuits used in ignition systems and their common components. ◆ Describe the operation of ignition coils, spark plugs, and ignition cables. ◆ Describe the various types of spark timing systems, including electronic switching systems and their related engine position sensors. ◆ Describe the operation of distributor-based ignition systems. ◆ Describe the operation of distributorless ignition systems.

One of the requirements for an efficient engine is the correct amount of heat shock, delivered at the right time. This requirement is the responsibility of the ignition system. The ignition system supplies properly timed, high-voltage surges to the spark plugs. These voltage surges cause combustion inside the cylinder. For each cylinder in an engine, the ignition system has three main jobs. First, it must generate an electrical spark that has enough heat to ignite the air/fuel mixture in the combustion chamber. Secondly, it must maintain that spark long enough to allow for the combustion of all the air and fuel in the cylinders. Lastly, it must deliver the spark to each cylinder so combustion can begin at the right time during the compression stroke of each cylinder.

When the combustion process is completed, a very high pressure is exerted against the top of the piston. This pressure pushes the piston down on its power stroke. This pressure is the force that gives the engine power. For an engine to produce the maximum amount of power it can, the maximum pressure from combustion should be present when the piston is at 10 to 23 degrees after top dead center (ATDC). Because combustion of the air/fuel mixture within a cylinder takes a short period of time, usually measured in thousandths of a second (milliseconds), the combustion process must begin before the piston is on its power stroke. Therefore, the delivery of the spark must be timed to arrive at some point before the piston reaches top dead center.

Determining how much before TDC the spark should begin gets complicated by the fact that as the speed of the piston as it moves from its compression stroke to its power stroke increases, the time needed for combustion stays about the same. This means the spark should be delivered earlier as the engine's speed increases (Figure 21–1). However, as the engine has to provide more power to do more work, the load on the crankshaft tends to slow down the acceleration of the piston and the spark should be somewhat delayed.

Figuring out when the spark should begin gets more complicated with the fact that the rate of combustion varies according to certain factors. Higher compression pressures tend to speed up combustion. Higher octane gasolines ignite less easily and require more burning time. Increased vaporization and turbulence tend to decrease combustion times. Other factors, including intake air temperature, humidity, and barometric pressure, also affect combustion. Because of all of these complications, delivering the spark at the right time is a difficult task.

IGNITION TIMING

Ignition timing refers to the precise time spark occurs. Ignition timing is specified by referring to the position of the #1 piston relation to crankshaft rotation. Ignition timing reference timing marks can be located on engine parts and on a pulley or flywheel to indicate the position of the #1 piston (Figure 21–2). Vehicle manufacturers specify initial or **basic ignition timing**.

When the marks are aligned at TDC, or 0, the piston in cylinder #1 is at TDC of its compression

SPARK OCCURS
18° BTDC

COMBUSTION
ENDS 23° ATDC

41°
TRAVEL

SPARK MUST BE
TIMED EARLIER
AS ENGINE
SPEED INCREASES

1200 RPM

SPARK OCCURS
40° BTDC

COMBUSTION
ENDS 23° ATDC

63° TRAVEL

3600 RPM

FIGURE 21–1 Ignition must begin earlier as engine speed increases. *Courtesy of Ford Motor Company*

NOTCH

TIMING
MARK SCALE

CRANKSHAFT
PULLEY

FIGURE 21–2 Reading ignition timing marks using a timing light.

If optimum engine performance is to be maintained, the ignition timing of the engine must change as the operating conditions of the engine change. Ignition systems allow for these necessary changes in many ways; these are covered in greater detail later in this chapter. All the different operating conditions affect the speed of the engine and the load on the engine. All ignition timing changes are made in response to these primary factors.

Engine RPM

At higher rpms, the crankshaft turns through more degrees in a given period of time. If combustion is to be completed by 10 degrees ATDC, ignition timing must occur sooner or be advanced.

However, air/fuel mixture turbulence (**swirling**) increases with rpm. This causes the mixture inside the cylinder to turn faster. Increased turbulence requires that ignition must occur slightly later or be slightly retarded.

These two factors must be balanced for best engine performance. Therefore, while the ignition timing must be advanced as engine speed increases, the amount of advance must be decreased some to compensate for the increased turbulence.

Engine Load

The load on an engine is related to the work it must do. Driving up hills or pulling extra weight increases engine load. Under load, the pistons move slower and the engine runs less efficiently. A good indication of engine load is the amount of vacuum formed during the intake stroke.

Under light loads and with the throttle plate(s) partially opened, a high vacuum exists in the intake manifold. The amount of air/fuel mixture drawn into

stroke. Additional numbers on a scale indicate the number of degrees of crankshaft rotation before TDC (**BTDC**) or after TDC (**ATDC**). In a majority of engines, the initial timing is specified at a point between TDC and 20 degrees BTDC. A few manufacturers specified initial timing from 1 to 5 degrees ATDC for vehicles built during the 1970s.

the manifold and cylinders is small. On compression, this thin mixture produces less combustion pressure and combustion time is slow. To complete combustion by 10 degrees ATDC, ignition timing must be advanced.

Under heavy loads, when the throttle is opened fully, a larger mass of air/fuel mixture can be drawn in, and the vacuum in the manifold is low. High combustion pressure and rapid burning results. In such a case, the ignition timing must be retarded to prevent complete burning from occurring before 10 degrees ATDC.

Firing Order

Up to this point, the primary focus of discussion has been ignition timing as it relates to any one cylinder. However, the function of the ignition system extends beyond timing the arrival of a spark to a single cylinder. It must perform this task for each cylinder of the engine in a specific sequence.

Each cylinder of an engine must produce power once in every 720 degrees of crankshaft rotation. Each cylinder must have a power stroke at its own appropriate time during the rotation. To make this possible, the pistons and rods are arranged in a precise fashion. This is called the engine's **firing order**. The firing order is arranged to reduce rocking and imbalance problems. Because the potential for this rocking is determined by the design and construction of the engine, the firing order varies from engine to engine. Vehicle manufacturers simplify cylinder identification by numbering each cylinder (Figure 21–3). Regardless of the particular firing order used, the number 1 cylinder always starts the firing order, with the rest of the cylinders following in a fixed sequence.

FIRING ORDER:
1-3-4-2

FIRING ORDER:
1-8-4-3-6-5-7-2

FIRING ORDER:
1-4-3-6-5-2

FIGURE 21–3 Examples of typical firing orders.

The ignition system must be able to monitor the rotation of the crankshaft and the relative position of each piston to determine which piston is on its compression stroke. It must also be able to deliver a high-voltage surge to each cylinder at the proper time during its compression stroke. How the ignition system does these things depends on the design of the system.

BASIC CIRCUITRY

All ignition systems consist of two interconnected electrical circuits: a **primary** (low voltage) **circuit** and a **secondary** (high voltage) **circuit** (Figure 21–4).

Depending on the exact type of ignition system, components in the primary circuit include the following.

- Battery
- Ignition switch
- Ballast resistor or resistance wire (some systems)
- Starting by-pass (some systems)
- Ignition coil primary winding
- Triggering device
- Switching device or control module

The secondary circuit includes these components.

- Ignition coil secondary winding
- Distributor cap and rotor (some systems)
- Ignition cables
- Spark plugs

Primary Circuit Operation

When the ignition switch is on, current from the battery flows through the ignition switch and primary circuit resistor to the primary winding of the ignition coil. From here it passes through some type of switching device and back to ground. The switching device can be electronically or mechanically controlled by the triggering device. The current flow in the ignition coil's primary winding creates a magnetic field. The switching device or control module interrupts this current flow at predetermined times. When it does, the magnetic field in the primary winding collapses. This collapse generates a high-voltage surge in the secondary winding of the ignition coil. The secondary circuit of the system begins at this point.

Secondary Circuit Operation

The secondary circuit in the ignition system carries high voltage to the spark plugs. The exact manner in which the secondary circuit delivers these high-voltage surges depends on the system design. Until 1984 all ignition systems used some type of **distributor** to accomplish this job. However, in an effort to reduce emissions, improve fuel economy, and boost compo-

FIGURE 21–4 Ignition systems have a primary and secondary (high voltage) circuit.

nent reliability, many auto manufacturers are using distributorless systems.

In a system using a distributor, such as that shown in Figure 21–4, high voltage from the secondary winding passes through an ignition cable running from the coil to the distributor. The distributor then distributes the high voltage to the individual spark plugs through a set of ignition cables. The cables are arranged in the distributor cap according to the firing order of the engine. A **rotor**, which is driven by the distributor shaft, rotates and completes the electrical path from the secondary winding of the coil to the individual spark plugs. The distributor delivers the spark to match the compression stroke of the piston. The distributor assembly may also have the capability of advancing or retarding ignition timing.

Distributorless or **direct ignitions** have no distributor, rather spark distribution is controlled by the vehicle's computer. Instead of a single ignition coil for all cylinders, each cylinder may have its own ignition coil, or two cylinders may share one coil. The coils are wired directly to the spark plug they control. An ignition control module, tied into the vehicle's computer control system, controls the firing order and the spark timing and advance. This module is typically located under the coil assembly. It may also be integrated into a special housing that contains most of the system's ignition parts.

IGNITION COMPONENTS

All ignition systems share a number of common components. Some, such as the battery and ignition switch, perform simple functions. The battery supplies low-voltage current to the ignition primary circuit. The current flows when the ignition switch is in the start or run position. Full-battery voltage is always present at the ignition switch, as if it were directly connected to the battery.

Ignition Coils

To generate a spark to begin combustion, the ignition system must deliver high voltage to the spark plugs. Vehicles manufactured in recent years may require a voltage level between 30,000 and 60,000 volts to force a spark across the air gap of a spark plug. Since the battery typically delivers only 10 to 12 volts, a method of stepping up the voltage must be used. Multiplying battery voltage is the job of a coil.

The ignition coil is a **pulse transformer**. It transforms battery voltage into short bursts of high voltage. As explained previously, when a wire is moved through a magnetic field, voltage is induced in the wire. The inverse of this principle is also true—when a magnetic field moves across a wire, voltage is induced in the wire.

If a wire is bent into loops forming a coil and a magnetic field is passed through the coil, an equal amount of voltage is generated in each loop of wire. The more loops of wire in the coil, the greater the total voltage induced.

Also, the faster the magnetic field moves through the coil, the higher the voltage induced in the coil. If the speed of the magnetic field is doubled, the voltage output doubles.

An ignition coil uses these principles and has two coils of wire wrapped around an iron core. An iron or steel core is used because it has low **inductive reluctance**. In other words, iron freely expands or strengthens the magnetic field around the windings. The first, or primary, coil is normally composed of 100 to 200 turns of 20-gauge wire. This coil of wire conducts battery current. When a current is passing through the primary coil, it magnetizes the iron core. The strength of the magnet depends directly on the number of wire loops and the amount of current flowing through those loops. The secondary coil of wires may consist of 15,000 to 25,000, or more, turns of very fine copper wire.

Because of the effects of counter EMF on the current flowing through the primary winding, it takes some time for the coil to become fully magnetized or saturated. The CEMF that opposes current flow in the winding is called **inductive reactance**. Therefore, primary current flow is present for some time between firings of the spark plugs. When the primary coil circuit is suddenly opened, the magnetic field instantly collapses. The sudden collapsing of the magnetic field produces a very high voltage in the secondary windings. This high voltage is used to push current across the gap of the spark plug. Figure 21–5 simplistically shows the coil's primary and secondary circuits.

The number of ignition coils used in an ignition system varies depending on the type of ignition system found on a vehicle. In most ignition systems with a distributor, only one ignition coil is used. Figure 21–6 shows a cutaway view of the type of ignition coil used in these systems. The high voltage of the secondary winding is directed, by the distributor, to the various spark plugs in the system. Therefore, there is one secondary circuit with a continually changing path.

While distributor systems have a single secondary circuit with a continually changing path, distributorless (**DIS**) systems have several secondary circuits, each with an unchanging path.

Spark Plugs

Every type of ignition system uses spark plugs. The spark plugs provide the crucial air gap across which the high voltage from the coil flows in the form of an arc. The three main parts of a spark plug are the steel core, the ceramic core, or insulator, which acts as a heat conductor; and a pair of electrodes, one insulated in the core and the other grounded on the shell. The shell holds the ceramic core and electrodes in a gas-tight assembly and has the threads needed for plug installation in the engine (Figure 21–7). An igni-

FIGURE 21–5   Current passing through the coil's primary winding creates magnetic lines of force that cut across and induce voltage in the secondary windings.

tion cable connects the secondary to the top of the plug. Current flows through the center of the plug and arcs from the tip of the center (or side) electrode to the ground electrode. The resulting spark ignites the air/fuel mixture in the combustion chamber. Most automotive spark plugs also have a resistor between the top terminal and the center electrode. This resistor reduces the amount of current and, therefore, reduces the amount of radio interference caused by the spark plug. The resistor, like all other

FIGURE 21–6   Ignition coil design. *Courtesy of Chrysler Corporation*

FIGURE 21–7 Components of a typical spark plug.

TAPERED SEAT **FLAT SEAT**
FIGURE 21–8 Spark plug seats: tapered versus flat.

resistances in the secondary, increases the voltage needed to jump the gap of the spark plug.

Spark plugs come in many different sizes and designs to accommodate different engines. To fit properly, spark plugs must be of the proper size and reach. Another design factor that determines the usefulness of a spark plug for a specific application is its **heat range**. The desired heat range depends on the design of the engine and on the type of driving conditions the vehicle is subject to. Once a technician selects a spark plug with the correct size, reach, and heat range for a particular application, there is one more spark plug characteristic that must be checked and adjusted—the spark plug **air gap**. Although the size, reach, and heat range of a spark plug are already determined by the manufacturer, the technician has the responsibility to properly gap the plug.

Size Automotive spark plugs are available in either 14- or 18-millimeter diameters. All 18-millimeter plugs feature tapered seats that match similar seats in the cylinder head and need no gaskets. The 14-millimeter variety can have either a flat seat that requires a gasket or a tapered seat that does not (Figure 21–8). The latter is the most commonly used. All spark plugs have a hex-shaped shell that accommodates a socket wrench for installation and removal. The 14-millimeter, tapered seat plugs have shells with a 5/8-inch hex; 14-millimeter gasketed and 18-millimeter tapered seat plugs have shells with a 13/16-inch hex.

Reach One of the most important design characteristics of spark plugs is the **reach** (Figure 21–9). This refers to the length of the shell from the contact surface at the seat to the bottom of the shell, including both threaded and nonthreaded sections. Reach is crucial. The plug's air gap must be properly placed in the combustion chamber so it can produce the correct amount of heat. Installing plugs with too short a reach means the electrodes are in a pocket and the arc is not able to adequately ignite the air/fuel mixture. In addition, the exposed threads in the cylinder head will accumulate carbon deposits. If the reach is too long, the exposed plug threads can get so hot they will ignite the air/fuel mixture at the wrong time, causing **preignition**. Preignition is a term used to describe abnormal combustion, which is caused by something other than the heat of the spark.

Heat Range Spark plugs are available in different heat ranges. A heat range indicates how well a spark plug can conduct heat away from its tip. A cooler plug transfers heat rapidly, resulting in lower tip temperatures. A hotter plug transfers heat slowly, resulting in higher tip temperatures (Figure 21–10). The shape of the porcelain insulator and its point of contact with the outer metal shell determines spark plug heat range. A spark plug's heat is transferred from the core to the shell to the cylinder head to the engine's coolant, which moves the heat away from the head.

FORMED POCKET **EXPOSED THREADS**
SHORT REACH **LONG REACH**
FIGURE 21–9 Spark plug reach: long versus short.

HOT PLUG   **COLD PLUG**

FIGURE 21–10   Spark plug heat range: hot versus cold.

Installing a plug with the correct heat range is important because the plug must remain hot enough to burn away fouling deposits while the engine is idling, yet cool enough at higher speed to prevent preignition and electrode wear. The heat range is indicated by a code imprinted on the side of the plug, usually on the porcelain insulator.

🔧 SHOP TALK

When spark plugs must be replaced, follow the recommendations for plug type as specified by the engine and plug manufacturers. These are recommendations only. For example, continuous heavy driving demands a much cooler plug than if the vehicle does a lot of stop-and-go driving. However, until you know more about the engine and its operating conditions than the manufacturers, follow their recommendations. ■

Spark Plug Air Gap The correct spark plug air gap is essential to achieve optimum engine performance and long plug life. A gap that is too wide (Figure 21–11) requires higher voltage to jump the gap. If the required voltage is greater than what is available, the result is **misfiring**. Misfiring results from the inability of the ignition to jump the gap or the inability to maintain the spark. On the other hand, a gap

Glass and cotton braid

Core

Jacket

Insulation

• Hypalon — normal
• Silicon — high temperature

FIGURE 21–12   Spark plug cable construction. *Courtesy of Chrysler Corporation*

that is too narrow requires lower voltages, which leads to rough idle and prematurely burned electrodes, due to higher current flow. Always set the gap according to the manufacturer's specifications. New electronic ignition systems call for wider air gaps than older systems due to higher available voltages and leaner air/fuel mixtures.

Ignition Cables

Spark plug, or ignition cables make up the secondary wiring. These cables carry the high voltage from the distributor or the multiple coils (DIS systems) to the spark plugs. The cables are not solid wire, rather they contain fiber cores that act as resistors in the secondary circuit (Figure 21–12). They cut down on radio and television interference, increase firing voltages, and reduce spark plug wear by decreasing current. Insulated boots on the ends of the cables strengthen the connections as well as prevent dust and water infiltration and voltage loss.

SPARK TIMING SYSTEMS

To better understand the operation of current ignition systems, it is helpful to first review how older, fully mechanical distributor systems worked.

Breaker Point Ignition

Breaker point ignition systems were used on vehicles for more than 60 years but were abandoned many years ago as engineers looked for ways to decrease emissions and increase fuel efficiency. The breaker point system had three major functions.

SWITCHING DEVICE The distributor assembly acted as a mechanical switch to turn the primary circuit on and off. The distributor's shaft, cam, breaker points, and condenser performed this function.

As shown in Figure 21–13, mechanical breaker, or **contact**, **points**, are used as the primary circuit triggering and switching device. The breaker point assembly, which was mounted on the **breaker plate** inside the distributor, consisted of a fixed contact, movable contact, movable arm, rubbing block, pivot, and spring. The fixed contact was grounded through the distribu-

FIGURE 21–11   It is difficult for current to jump a gap this wide.

FIGURE 21–13 Older ignition systems used breaker points as the switching device in the primary circuit.

FIGURE 21–15 Ignition resistor by-pass circuit controlled by the ignition switch.

tor housing, and the movable contact was connected to the negative terminal of the coil's primary winding. As the cam was turned by the camshaft, the movable arm opened and closed, which opened and closed the primary circuit in the coil. When the points were closed, primary current flow attempted to saturate the coil. When the points opened, primary current stopped and the magnetic field collapsed causing high voltage to be induced in the secondary. The firing of the plug was the result of opening the points.

Because voltage was still present at the movable arm when the breaker arms opened, current could continue to arc across the open point gap, which could damage the points. To prevent this, a condenser (Figure 21–14) was attached to the movable arm. In this way, the voltage at the movable arm was retained by the condenser instead of arcing across the gap.

A primary or **ballast resistor** was located in series between the battery and the primary coil winding and was responsible for keeping the primary voltage at the

desired level (about 9 or 10 volts). This prevented the contact points from burning due to high voltage. The ballast resistor could be either a separate unit or a specially made wire. During starting, the ballast resistor was bypassed to provide maximum current flow to the primary circuit (Figure 21–15).

TIMING ADJUSTER The distributor also mechanically adjusted the time the spark arrived at the cylinder through the use of two mechanisms: the centrifugal advance and the vacuum advance units. This improved engine performance, fuel efficiency, and emission levels.

SPARK DISTRIBUTION As its name implies, the distributor mechanically distributed the spark so it arrived at the right time during the compression stroke of each cylinder. The distributor's shaft, rotor, and cap performed this function.

Electronic or Solid State Ignition

From the fully mechanical breaker point system, ignition technology progressed to basic electronic or solid state ignitions (Figure 21-16). Breaker points were replaced with electronic triggering and switching devices. The electronic switching components are normally inside a separate housing known as a **control module** or control unit. The original (solid state) electronic ignitions still relied on mechanical and vacuum advance mechanisms in the distributor.

As technology advanced, many manufacturers expanded the ability of the ignition control modules. For example, by tying a manifold vacuum sensor into the ignition module circuitry, the module could now detect when the engine was under heavy load and retard the timing automatically. Similar add-on sen-

FIGURE 21–14 A condenser prevents current from jumping across the open point gap.

FIGURE 21–16 Typical solid-state ignition system. *Courtesy of Chrysler Corporation*

sors and circuits were designed to control spark knock, start-up emissions, and altitude compensation.

Computer-Controlled Electronic Ignition

Computer-controlled ignition systems offer continuous spark timing control through a network of engine sensors and a central microprocessor. Based on the inputs it receives, the central microprocessor or computer makes decisions regarding spark timing and sends signals to the ignition module to fire the spark plugs according to those inputs and the programs in its memory.

Computer-controlled ignition systems may or may not use a distributor to distribute secondary voltage to the spark plugs. As mentioned earlier, distributorless systems use multiple coils and modules to provide and distribute high secondary voltages directly from the coil to the plug.

ADVANTAGES OF ELECTRONIC IGNITION

Electronic ignition systems have many advantages over breaker point ignition systems.

High Secondary Voltages

Electronic ignition systems can carry the increased primary current needed to produce the higher secondary system voltages needed to ignite leaner air/fuel mixtures.

The primary circuit in most breaker point systems carried 3.5 to 4.0 amperes. When the breaker points opened, this current tried to arc across the points. Point arcing caused electrolysis and corrosion on the metal surface of the contacts. When primary current increases above 4 amperes, point life begins to decrease at an increased rate, resulting in very limited point life. Faster wearing points require extra maintenance and result in an ever-decreasing **dwell** period, which in turn decreases the potential voltage induced in the secondary system. Dwell is the period of time that current flows through the primary circuit.

Better High-Speed Performance

Another handicap of the old breaker point system was that as engine speed increased, the dwell time decreased. This, in turn, decreases the output of the coil. For the ignition coil to generate maximum secondary voltage, maximum primary current flow must be flowing through the primary winding before the field is collapsed. In a breaker point system, the length of time the primary circuit is closed is controlled by the speed of the breaker cam. This period of time is called a dwell angle and is expressed in a number of degrees of distributor shaft rotation. For example, many V-8 engines have a dwell angle of 30 degrees during which time the points are closed and current builds in the primary winding. This dwell angle remains constant regardless of engine speed; but as engine rpm increases, the actual time, in seconds, the

FIGURE 21–17 Current levels of General Motors' high-energy ignition system remain higher over a longer range of engine speeds when compared to breaker point systems.

points are closed decreases. Any increase in engine speed above a specific rpm reduces the saturation time of the ignition coil, causing the available voltage to decrease.

This phenomenon is due to the fact that the current in the coil does not instantaneously reach its maximum value when the contact points close. Current in the coil must build for several milliseconds for this value to be reached. At 1,000 rpm, the distributor shaft rotates once every 0.12 second. Of this time, the points are closed for 0.10 second, or 10 milliseconds, for every cylinder of an 8-cylinder engine. This is sufficient time for saturation of the primary winding. This time versus current relationship is shown in Figure 21–17.

When the engine speed increases to 2,000 rpm, the time that the points are closed for each plug firing is reduced to 5 milliseconds. A dwell period of 5 milliseconds allows the primary current to build to 3.8 amperes. At 3,000 rpm, the dwell period drops to 3.3 milliseconds and the current drops to 3.2 amperes. The reduced saturation time lowers the available secondary voltage. This can result in a misfire as there may be less voltage available than is needed to fire the plug. This increases exhaust emissions and decreases fuel economy and engine performance.

An electronic ignition system, however, is not limited by a fixed dwell angle. The system's control unit can vary the on-time of the primary circuit based on engine speed, load, and temperature. As the chart in Figure 21–17 shows, GM's high-energy ignition (HEI) system maintains a constant voltage level until the engine reaches 3,000 rpm. Because coil primary current levels are not limited by breaker points, low-resistance coils are used in the electronic ignition system. By decreasing the resistance in the primary circuit, the required saturation time of the coil is greatly reduced. It takes 10 milliseconds for the current to reach maximum saturation in a coil with a resistance of 2.6 ohms. In a coil used in electronic ignition systems, the primary winding can have a resistance as low as 0.5 ohm. This allows full current to be reached in about 3.4 milliseconds. Because it takes less time to reach full current, coil saturation can be obtained at much higher engine speeds. For example, the HEI system developed by General Motors in 1974 is able to generate 35,000 volts at engine speeds above 3,000 rpm. A typical breaker point system, on the other hand, developed a maximum of 20,000 volts at 1,000 rpm. Above this speed, the voltage dropped off.

ELECTRONIC SWITCHING SYSTEMS

Electronic ignition systems control the primary circuit, using an NPN transistor instead of breaker contact points. The transistor's emitter is connected to ground and takes the place of the fixed contact point.

FIGURE 21–18 When the triggering device supplies a small amount of current to the transistor's base, the primary coil circuit is closed and current flows.

The collector is connected to the negative (–) terminal of the coil, taking the place of the movable contact point. When the triggering device supplies a small amount of current to the base of the switching transistor, the collector and emitter act as if they are closed contact points (a conductor), allowing current to build up in the coil primary circuit. When the current to the base is interrupted by the switching device, the collector and emitter act as an open contact (an insulator), interrupting the coil primary current. An example of how this works is shown in Figure 21–18, which is a simplified diagram of an electronic ignition system.

Engine Position Sensors

The time when the primary circuit must be opened and closed is related to the position of the pistons and the crankshaft. Therefore, the position of the crankshaft is used to control the flow of current to the base of the switching transistor.

A number of different types of sensors are used to monitor the position of the crankshaft and control the flow of current to the base of the transistor.

These engine position sensors and generators serve as triggering devices and include magnetic pulse generators, metal detection sensors, Hall-effect sensors, and photoelectric sensors.

The mounting location of these sensors depends on the design of the ignition system. All four types of sensors can be mounted in the distributor, which is turned by the camshaft.

Magnetic pulse generators and Hall-effect sensors can also be located on the crankshaft (Figures 21-19 and Figure 21–20). These sensors are also commonly used on DIS ignition systems. Both Hall-effect sensors and magnetic pulse generators can also be used as camshaft reference sensors to identify which cylinder is the next one to fire.

Magnetic Pulse Generator

Basically, a magnetic pulse generator consists of two parts: a timing disc and a pick-up coil. The timing disc may also be called a reluctor, trigger wheel, pulse ring, armature, or timing core. The pick-up coil, which consists of a length of wire wound around a weak permanent magnet, may also be called a stator,

CRANKSHAFT POSITION SENSOR

SCREW AND CLAMP ASSEMBLY

PULSE RING

FIGURE 21–19
Crankshaft position sensor.
Courtesy of Ford Motor Company

FIGURE 21–20 DIS system with Hall-effect switches for camshaft (CID) and crankshaft (PIP) rotation. *Courtesy of Ford Motor Company*

sensor, or pole piece. Depending on the type of ignition system used, the timing disc may be mounted on the distributor shaft (Figure 21–21), at the rear of the crankshaft (Figure 21–22), or on the crankshaft vibration damper (Figure 21–23).

The magnetic pulse or PM generator operates on basic electromagnetic principles. Remember that a voltage can only be induced when a conductor moves through a magnetic field. The magnetic field is provided by the pick-up unit and the rotating timing disc provides the movement through the magnetic field needed to induce voltage.

As the disc teeth approach the pick-up coil, they repel the magnetic field, forcing it to concentrate around the pick-up coil (Figure 21–24A). Once the

tooth passes by the pick-up coil, the magnetic field is free to expand or unconcentrate (Figure 21–24B), until the next tooth on the disc approaches. Approaching teeth concentrate the magnetic lines of force, while passing teeth allow them to expand. This pulsation of the magnetic field causes the lines of magnetic force to cut across the winding in the pick-up coil, inducing a small amount of AC voltage that is sent to the switching device in the primary circuit.

When a disc tooth is directly in line with the pick-up coil, the magnetic field is not expanding or contracting. Since there is no movement or change in the field, voltage at this precise moment drops to zero. At this point, the switching device inside the ignition module reacts to the zero voltage signal by turning the ignition's primary circuit current off. As explained earlier, this forces the magnetic field in the primary coil to collapse, discharging a secondary voltage to the distributor or directly to the spark plug.

As soon as the tooth rotates past the pick-up coil, the magnetic field expands again and another voltage signal is induced. The only difference is that the polarity of the charge is reversed. Negative becomes positive or positive becomes negative. Upon sensing this change in voltage, the switching device turns the primary circuit back on and the process begins all over.

The slotted disc is mounted on the crankshaft, vibration damper, or distributor shaft in a very precise manner. When the disc teeth align with the pick-up coil, this corresponds to the exact time certain pis-

Pick-up coil assembly

Reluctor

Cap clip

Pick-up coil leads

FIGURE 21–21 Magnetic pulse generator located inside a distributor. *Courtesy of Chrysler Corporation*

FIGURE 21–22 Magnetic pulse generator positioned to sense flywheel rotation. *Courtesy of Chrysler Corporation*

FIGURE 21–24 (A) Wide gap produces a weak magnetic signal. (B) Narrow gap produces a strong magnetic field. *Courtesy of Chrysler Corporation*

FIGURE 21–23 Pulse ring location on the vibration damper.

FIGURE 21–25 Magnetic pulse generator (pick-up coil) used on early Chrysler electronic ignition systems.

tons are nearing TDC. This means the zero voltage signal needed to trigger the secondary circuit occurs at precisely the correct time.

The pick-up coil might have only one pole as

shown as Figure 21–25. Other magnetic pulse generators have pick-up coils with two or more poles. The one shown in Figure 21–26 has as many poles as it has trigger teeth.

FIGURE 21–26 Magnetic pulse generator used in early Datsun electronic ignition systems. *Courtesy of Nissan Motors*

Metal Detection Sensors

Metal detection sensors are found on many early electronic ignition systems. They work much like a magnetic pulse generator with one major difference.

A trigger wheel is pressed over the distributor shaft and a pick-up coil detects the passing of the trigger teeth as the distributor shaft rotates. However, unlike a magnetic pulse generator, the pick-up coil of a metal detection sensor does not have a permanent magnet. Instead, the pick-up coil is an electromagnet. A low level of current is supplied to the coil by an electronic control unit, inducing a weak magnetic field around the coil. As the reluctor on the distributor shaft rotates, the trigger teeth pass very close to the coil (Figure 21–27). As the teeth pass in and out of the coil's magnetic field, the magnetic field

FIGURE 21–27 In a metal detecting sensor, the revolving trigger wheel teeth alter the magnetic field produced by the electromagnet in the pick-up coil.

builds and collapses, producing a corresponding change in the coil's voltage. The voltage changes are monitored by the control unit to determine crankshaft position.

Hall-Effect Sensor

Introduced in early 1982, the Hall-effect sensor or switch is now the most commonly used engine position sensor. There are several good reasons for this. Unlike a magnetic pulse generator, the Hall-effect sensor produces an accurate voltage signal throughout the entire rpm range of the engine. Furthermore, a Hall-effect switch produces a square wave signal that is more compatible with the digital signals required by on-board computers.

Functionally, a Hall switch performs the same tasks as a magnetic pulse generator. But the Hall switch's method of generating voltage is quite unique. It is based on the Hall-effect principle, which states: If a current is allowed to flow through a thin conducting material, and that material is exposed to a magnetic field, voltage is produced.

The heart of the Hall generator is a thin semiconductor layer (Hall layer) derived from a gallium arsenate crystal. Attached to it are two terminals—one positive and the other negative—that are used to provide the source current for the Hall transformation.

Directly across from this semiconductor element is a permanent magnet. It's positioned so its lines of flux bisect the Hall layer at right angles to the direc-

U$_H$ = HALL VOLTAGE
B = MAGNETIC FIELD (FLUX DENSITY)
I$_v$ = CONSTANT SUPPLY CURRENT
A$_1$, A$_2$ = HALL LAYER

FIGURE 21–28   In a Hall-effect sensor, the electrons move perpendicular to the lines of magnetic flux and electrical current.

FIGURE 21–29   Hall-effect switch mounted inside a distributor. *Courtesy of Chrysler Corporation*

tion of current flow. Two additional terminals, located on either side of the Hall layer, form the signal output circuit.

When current is passed through the Hall layer, a voltage is produced perpendicular to the direction of current flow and magnetic flux. The signal voltage produced is the direct result of the magnetic field's effect on electron flow. As the magnetic lines of force collide with the electrons in the supply current, current flow in the crystals is distorted and, as a result, electrons are deflected toward what becomes the negative Hall voltage terminals (Figure 21–28). It is this creation of an electron surplus at the Hall voltage terminal that results in the production of a weak voltage potential.

The Hall switch is described as being on any time the Hall layer is exposed to a magnetic field and a Hall voltage is being produced. However, before this signal voltage can be of any use, it has to be modified. After leaving the Hall layer, the signal is routed to an amplifier where it is strengthened and inverted so the signal reads high when it is actually coming in low and vice versa. Once it has been inverted, the signal goes through a pulse-shaping device called the Schmitt trigger where it is turned into a clean square wave signal. After conditioning, the signal is sent to the base of a switching transistor that is designed to turn on and off in response to the signals generated by the Hall switch assembly.

The shutter wheel is the last major component of the Hall switch. The shutter wheel consists of a series of alternating windows and vanes that pass between the Hall layer and magnet. The shutter wheel may be part of the distributor rotor (Figure 21–29) or be separate from the rotor.

The shutter wheel performs the same function as the timing disc on magnetic pulse generators. The only difference is with a Hall switch there is no electromagnetic induction. Instead, the shutter wheel creates a magnetic shunt that changes the field strength through the Hall element. When a vane of the shutter wheel is positioned between the magnet and Hall element, the metallic vane blocks the magnetic field and keeps it from permeating the Hall layer. As a result, only a few residual electrons are deflected in the layer and Hall output voltage is low (Figure 21–30). Conversely, when a window rotates into the air gap, the magnetic field is able to penetrate the Hall layer, which in turn pushes the Hall voltage to its maximum range.

The points where the shutter vane begins to enter and begins to leave the air gap are directly related to primary circuit control. As the leading edge of a vane enters the air gap, the magnetic field is deflected away from the Hall layer; Hall voltage decreases. When that happens, the modified Hall output signal increases abruptly and turns on the switching transistor. Once the transistor is turned on, the primary circuit closes and the coil's energy storage cycle begins.

Primary current continues to flow as long as the vane is in the air gap. As the vane starts to leave the gap, however, the reforming Hall voltage signal prompts a parallel decline in the modified output signal. When the output signal goes low, the bias of the transistor changes. Primary current flow stops.

In summary, the ignition module supplies current to the coil's primary winding as long as the shutter wheel's vane is in the air gap. As soon as the shutter wheel moves away and the Hall voltage is produced,

FIGURE 21-30 Blade and magnetic field action in a Hall-effect switch.

FIGURE 21-31 Distributor with optical-type pick-ups. *Courtesy of Chrysler Corporation*

the control unit stops primary circuit current, high secondary voltage is induced, and ignition occurs.

In addition to ignition control, a Hall switch can also be used to generate precise rpm signals (by determining the frequency at which the voltage rises and falls) and provide the sync pulse for sequential fuel ignition operation.

Photoelectric Sensor

A fifth type of crankshaft position sensor is the **photoelectric sensor**. The parts of this sensor include a light-emitting diode (LED), a light-sensitive phototransistor (photo cell), and a slotted disc called a light beam interrupter (Figure 21-31).

The slotted disc is attached to the distributor shaft. The LED and the photo cell are situated over and under the disc opposite each other. As the slotted disc rotates between the LED and photo cell, light from the LED shines through the slots. The intermittent flashes of light are translated into voltage pulses

by the photo cell. When the voltage signal occurs, the control unit turns on the primary system. When the disc interrupts the light and the voltage signal ceases, the control unit turns the primary system off, causing the magnetic field in the coil to collapse and sending a surge of voltage to a spark plug.

The photoelectric sensor sends a very reliable signal to the control unit, especially at low engine speeds. These units have been primarily used on Chrysler and Mitsubishi engines. Some Nissan and General Motors products have used them as well.

ELECTRONIC IGNITION SYSTEM OPERATION

The primary circuit of an electronic ignition system is controlled electronically by one of the sensors just described and an electronic control unit (module) that contains some type of switching device.

Primary Circuit Control

Figure 21-32 shows a basic electronic ignition system. The system consists of a distributor with a magnetic pulse pick-up unit and reluctor, an electronic control module, and a ballast resistor. As described earlier, when the tooth of the reluctor passes the pick-up, an electrical impulse is sent to the electronic module, which contains the switching transistor. The pulse signals the transistor to open the primary circuit, firing the plug. Once the plug stops firing, the transistor closes the primary coil circuit. The length of time the transistor allows current flow in the primary ignition circuit is determined by the electronic circuitry in the control module. Some systems used a dual ballast resistor. The ceramic ballast resistor assembly is mounted on the fire wall and has a ballast resistor for primary current flow and an auxiliary resistor for the control module.

FIGURE 21–32 Dura Spark II electronic ignition system. *Courtesy of Ford Motor Company*

The ballast resistor has a 0.5-ohm resistance that maintains a constant primary current. The auxiliary ballast resistor uses a 5-ohm resistance to limit voltage to the electronic control unit.

There are some electronic ignition systems that do not require a ballast resistor. For instance, some control units directly regulate the current flow through the primary of the coil. Hall-effect systems do not require ballast resistors either. The signal voltage is not changed by the speed of the distributor as it is in an inductive magnetic signal generating system.

Some systems can be enhanced with additional sensors that increase the capabilities of the control module. The module shown in Figure 21–32 can be equipped with either a barometric pressure switch or vacuum switch. The **barometric pressure switch** enables the module to retard the ignition timing 3 to 6 degrees when the vehicle is operating at low elevations. The vacuum switch does the same, when the engine is under hard acceleration or heavy load. Other modules have the ability to retard ignition timing during start-up or when engine knock is detected.

Timing Advance

As stated, early electronic ignition systems changed the timing mechanically just like breaker point systems.

CENTRIFUGAL ADVANCE At idle, the firing of the spark plug usually occurs just before the piston reaches top dead center. At higher engine rpms, however, the spark must be delivered to the cylinder much earlier in the cycle to achieve maximum power from the air/fuel mixture since the engine is moving through the cycle more quickly. To change the timing of the spark in relation to rpm, the **centrifugal advance** mechanism is used (Figure 21–33).

This mechanism consists of a set of weights and springs connected to the distributor shaft and a distributor armature assembly. During idle speeds, the springs keep the weights in place and the armature and distributor shaft rotate as one assembly. When speed increases, centrifugal force causes the weights to slowly move out against the tension of the springs. This allows the armature assembly to move ahead in relation to the distributor shaft rotation. The ignition's triggering device is mounted to the armature assembly. Therefore, as the assembly moves ahead, ignition timing becomes more advanced.

VACUUM ADVANCE During part-throttle engine operation, high vacuum is present in the intake manifold. To get the most power and the best fuel economy from the engine, the plugs must fire even earlier

FIGURE 21–33 Typical centrifugal advance mechanism.

during the compression stroke than is provided by a centrifugal advance mechanism.

The heart of the vacuum advance mechanism (Figure 21–34) is the spring-loaded diaphragm, which fits inside a metal housing and connects to a movable plate on which the pick-up coil is mounted. Vacuum is applied to one side of the diaphragm in the housing chamber while the other side of the diaphragm is open to the atmosphere. Any increase in vacuum allows atmospheric pressure to push the diaphragm. In turn, this causes the movable plate to rotate. The more vacuum present on one side of the diaphragm, the more atmospheric pressure is able to cause a

FIGURE 21–34 Typical vacuum advance unit operation.
Courtesy of Chrysler Corporation

FIGURE 21–35 Cutaway view of a distributor cap.

change in timing. The rotation of the movable plate moves the pick-up coil so the armature develops a signal earlier. These units are also equipped with a spring that retards the timing as vacuum decreases.

Spark Distribution

The distributor cap and rotor receive the high voltage from the secondary winding via a high-tension wire. The voltage enters the distributor cap through the coil tower, or center terminal. The rotor then sends the voltage from the coil tower to the spark plug electrodes inside the distributor cap. The rotor mounts on the upper portion of the distributor shaft and rotates with it.

The distributor cap (Figure 21–35) is made from silicone plastic or similar material that offers protection from chemical attack. It is attached to the distributor housing with screws or spring-loaded clips. The coil tower contains a carbon insert that carries the voltage from the high-tension coil lead to the raised portion of the electrode on the rotor. Spaced evenly around the coil tower are the spark plug electrodes and towers for each spark plug.

An air gap of a few thousandths of an inch exists between the tip of the rotor electrode and the spark plug electrode inside the cap. This gap is necessary to prevent the two electrodes from making contact. If they did make contact, both would wear out rapidly. This gap cannot be measured when the distributor is assembled; therefore, the gap is usually described in terms of the voltage needed to create an arc between the electrodes.

COMPUTER-CONTROLLED IGNITION SYSTEM OPERATION

Computer-controlled ignition systems (Figure 21–36) control the primary circuit and distribute the firing voltages in the same manner as other types of electronic ignition systems. The main difference between

FIGURE 21–36 TFI-IV computer-controlled ignition system. *Courtesy of Ford Motor Company*

the systems is the elimination of any mechanical or vacuum advance devices from the distributor in the computer-controlled systems. In these systems, the distributor's sole purpose is to generate the primary circuit's switching signal and distribute the secondary voltage to the spark plugs. Timing advance is controlled by a microprocessor, or computer. In fact, some of these systems have even removed the primary switching function from the distributor by using a crankshaft position sensor. The distributor's only job is to distribute secondary voltage to the spark plugs.

Spark timing on these systems is controlled by a computer that continuously varies ignition timing to obtain optimum air/fuel combustion. The computer monitors the engine operating parameters with sensors. Based on this input, the computer signals an

ignition module to collapse the primary circuit, allowing the secondary circuit to fire the spark plugs (Figure 21–37).

Timing control is selected by the computer's program. During engine starting, computer control is bypassed and the mechanical setting of the distributor controls spark timing. Once the engine is started and running, spark timing is controlled by the computer. This scheme or **strategy** allows the engine to start regardless of whether the electronic control system is functioning properly or not.

The goal of computerized spark timing is to produce maximum engine power, top fuel efficiency, and minimum emission levels during all types of operating conditions. The computer does this by continuously adjusting ignition timing. The computer deter-

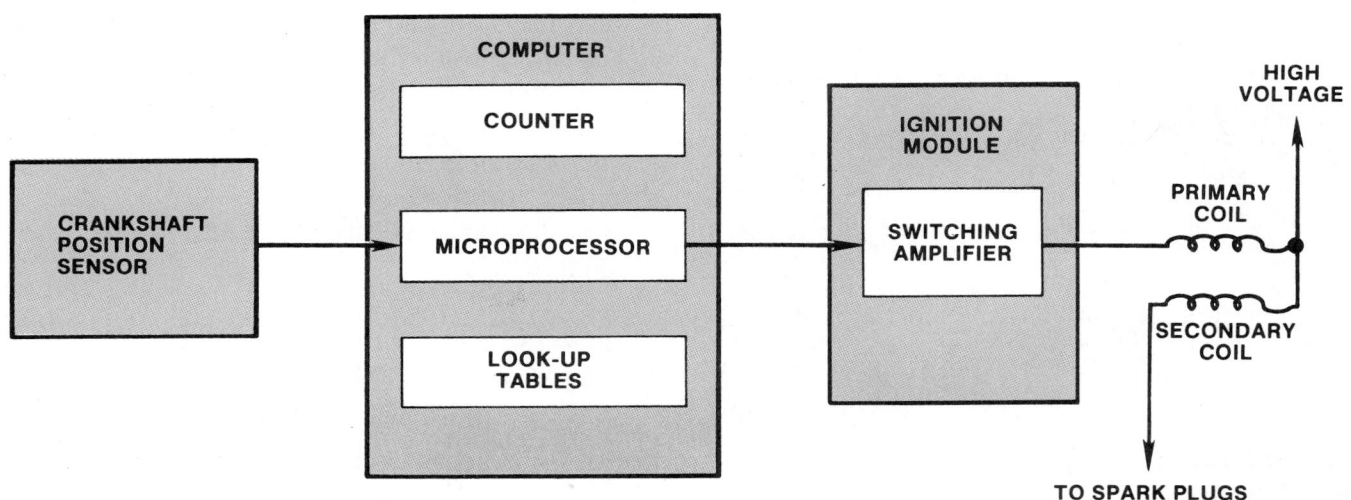

FIGURE 21–37 Typical engine timing control.

mines the best spark timing based on certain engine operating conditions such as crankshaft position, engine speed, throttle position, engine coolant temperature, and initial and operating manifold or barometric pressure. Once the computer receives input from these and other sensors, it compares the existing operating conditions to information permanently stored or programmed into its memory. The computer matches the existing conditions to a set of conditions stored in its memory, determines proper timing setting, and sends a signal to the ignition module to fire the plugs.

The computer continuously monitors existing conditions, adjusting timing to match what its memory tells it is the ideal setting for those conditions. It can do this very quickly, making thousands of decisions in a single second. The control computer typically has the following types of information permanently programmed into it.

- Speed-related spark advance. As engine speed increases to a particular point, there is a need for more advanced timing. As the engine slows, the timing should be retarded or have less advance. The computer bases speed related spark advance decisions on engine speed and signals from the TPS.
- Load-related spark advance. This is used to improve power and fuel economy during acceleration and heavy load conditions. The computer defines the load and the ideal spark advance by processing information from the TPS, MAP, and engine speed sensors. Typically, the more load on an engine, the less spark advance is needed.
- Warm-up spark advance. This is used when the engine is cold, since a greater amount of advance is required while the engine warms up.
- Special spark advance. This is used to improve fuel economy during steady driving conditions. During constant speed and load conditions, the engine will be more efficient with much advance timing.
- Spark advance due to barometric pressure. This is used when barometric pressure exceeds a preset calibrated value.

All this information is looked at by the computer to determine the ideal spark timing for all conditions. The calibrated or programmed information in the computer is contained in what is called software **look-up tables**.

Ignition timing can also work in conjunction with the electronic fuel control system to provide emission control, optimum fuel economy, and improved driveability. They are all dependent on spark advance.

Many computer-controlled ignition systems have a self-diagnostic capability that aids in troubleshooting.

DISTRIBUTORLESS IGNITION SYSTEM OPERATION

Distributorless ignition systems (Figure 21–38) electronically perform the functions of a distributor. They control spark timing and advance in the same manner as the computer-controlled ignition systems. Yet the DIS is a step beyond the computer-controlled system because it also distributes spark electronically instead of mechanically. The distributor is completely eliminated from these systems.

The computer, ignition module, and position sensors combine to control spark timing and advance. The computer collects and processes information to determine the ideal amount of spark advance for the operating conditions. The ignition module uses crank/cam sensor data to control the timing of the primary circuit in the coils. Remember that there is more than one coil in a distributorless ignition system. The ignition module synchronizes the coils' firing sequence in relation to crankshaft position and firing order of the engine. Therefore, the ignition module takes the place of the distributor.

The ignition module also adjusts spark timing below 400 rpm (for starting) and when the vehicle's control computer by-pass circuit becomes open or grounded. Depending on the exact DIS system, the ignition coils can be serviced as a complete unit or separately. The coil assembly is typically called a **coil pack** and is comprised of two or more individual coils.

On those DIS systems that use one coil per spark plug, the electronic ignition module determines when each spark plug should fire and controls the on/off time of each plug's coil.

The systems with a coil for every two spark plugs also use an electronic ignition module, but they use the **waste spark** method of spark distribution. Each end of the coil's secondary winding is attached to a spark plug. Each coil is connected to a pair of spark plugs in cylinders whose pistons rise and fall together. When the field collapses in the coil, voltage is sent to both spark plugs that are attached to the coil. In all V-6s, the paired cylinders are 1 and 4, 2 and 5, and 3 and 6 (or 4 and 1 and 3 and 2 on 4-cylinder engines). With this arrangement, one cylinder of each pair is on its compression stroke while the other is on the exhaust stroke. Both cylinders get spark simultaneously, but only one spark generates power while the other is wasted out the exhaust. During the next revolution, the roles are reversed.

Due to the way the secondary coils are wired, when the induced voltage cuts across the primary and secondary windings of the coil, one plug fires in the normal direction—positive center electrode to

FIGURE 21–38 Distributorless ignition system with two crankshaft position sensors and one camshaft position sensor. *Courtesy of Cadillac Motor Car Division, General Motors Corporation*

negative side electrode—and the other plug fires just the reverse side to center electrode (Figure 21–39). As shown in Figure 21–40, both plugs fire simultaneously, completing the series circuit. Each plug always fires the same way on both the exhaust and compression strokes.

The coil is able to overcome the increased voltage requirements caused by reversed polarity and still fire two plugs simultaneously because each coil is capable of producing up to 100,000 volts. There is very little resistance across the plug gap on exhaust, so the plug requires very little voltage to fire, thereby providing its mate (the plug that is on compression) with plenty of available voltage.

Figure 21–41 shows a waste spark system in which the coils are mounted directly over the spark plugs so no wiring between the coils and plugs is nec-

FIGURE 21–39 Polarity of spark plugs in a DIS system. *Courtesy of Ford Motor Company*

FIGURE 21–40 The manner in which two spark plugs are fired by a single-ignition coil in DIS ignition system circuits.

FIGURE 21–41 Cableless DIS system. *Courtesy of Oldsmobile Division, General Motors Corporation*

FIGURE 21–42 Coil pack for a V-6 engine. Each coil fires two spark plugs.

essary. On other systems, the coil packs are mounted remote from the spark plugs. High-tension secondary wires carry high-voltage current from the coils to the plugs (Figures 21–42 and 21–43).

A few DIS systems have one coil per cylinder with two spark plugs per cylinder. During starting only one plug is fired. Once the engine is running the other plug also fires. One spark plug is located on the intake side of the combustion chamber while the other is located on the exhaust side. Two coil packs are used, one for the plugs on the intake side and the other for the plugs on the exhaust side. These systems are called **dual plug** systems (Figure 21–44). During dual plug operation, the two coil packs are synchronized so each cylinder's two plugs fire at the same time. The coils fire two spark plugs at the same

FIGURE 21–43 6-cylinder distributorless ignition system. *Courtesy of Ford Motor Company*

DUAL PLUG MODE WITH ENGINE RUNNING

FIGURE 21–44 Dual plug system for a 4-cylinder engine. *Courtesy of Ford Motor Company*

time. Therefore, on a four-cylinder engine, four spark plugs are fired at a time: two during the compression stroke of the cylinder and two during the exhaust stroke of another cylinder.

Timing References

From a general operating standpoint, most distributorless ignition systems are similar. However, there are variations in the way different distributorless systems obtain a timing reference in regard to crankshaft and camshaft position.

Some engines use separate Hall-effect sensors to monitor crankshaft (Figure 21–45) and camshaft

(Figure 21–46) position for the control of ignition and fuel injection firing orders. The camshaft sensor helps the computer determine when the number one piston is at TDC on the compression stroke.

Other systems use a dual Hall-effect sensor. One sensor generates three signals per crankshaft rotation, at 120 degree intervals. The other sensor generates one signal per revolution, which tells the computer when the number one cylinder is on TDC. From these signals, the computer can calculate the position of the camshaft, as well as know the position of the crankshaft.

Many different designs of DIS are possible. The **Fast-Start** electronic ignition system used in GM's Northstar system uses two crankshaft positions. A reluctor ring with twenty-four evenly spaced notches and eight unevenly spaced notches is cast onto the center of the crankshaft (Figure 21–47).

When the reluctor ring rotates past the magnetic-type sensors, each sensor produces thirty-two high

FIGURE 21–45 DIS system with a camshaft and crankshaft sensor. *Courtesy of Buick Motor Division, General Motors Corporation*

FIGURE 21–46 Notched ring on camshaft gears. *Courtesy of Chrysler Corporation*

FIGURE 21–47 Crankshaft reluctor ring in a Northstar engine. *Courtesy of Cadillac Motor Car Division, General Motors Corporation*

and low voltage signals per crankshaft revolution. The "A" sensor is positioned in the upper crankcase, and the "B" sensor is positioned in the lower crankcase. Since the A sensor is above the B sensor, the signal from the A sensor occurs 27 degrees before the B sensor signal (Figure 21–48).

The signals from the two sensors are sent to the ignition control module. This module counts the number of B sensor signals between the A sensor signals to sequence the ignition coils properly. There can be zero, one, or two B sensor signals between the A signals. When starting the engine, the module begins counting B sensor signals between the A signals as soon as the module senses zero B signals between sensor signals. After the module senses four B sig-

nals, the module sequences the coils properly. This allows the ignition system to begin firing the spark plugs within 180 degrees of crankshaft rotation while starting the engine. This system allows for much quicker starting than other DIS systems, which required the crankshaft to rotate one or two times before the coils were sequenced.

Finally, some engines use a magnetic pulse generator. The timing wheel is cast on the crankshaft and has machined slots on it. If the engine is a six-cylinder, there will be seven slots, six of which are spaced exactly 60 degrees apart and the seventh—located 10 degrees from the number six notch—is used to synchronize the coil firing sequence in relation to crankshaft position (Figure 21–49). The same triggering wheel can be and is used on four-cylinder engines. The computer needs only to be programmed to interpret the signals differently than on a six-cylinder.

The magnetic sensor, which protrudes into the side of the block to within 0.050 in. (±0.020 in.) of the crankshaft reluctor, generates a small AC voltage each time one of the machined slots passes by.

By counting the time between pulses, the ignition module picks out the unevenly spaced seventh slot, which starts the calculation of the ignition coil sequencing. Once its counting is synchronized with the crankshaft, the module is programmed to accept the AC voltage signals of the select notches for firing purposes.

When the system is working properly, there is no base timing to adjust and there are no moving parts to wear.

The development and spreading popularity of DIS is the result of reduced emissions, improved fuel economy, and increased component reliability brought about by these systems.

FIGURE 21–48 A and B crankshaft sensors in a Northstar engine. *Courtesy of Cadillac Motor Car Division, General Motors Corporation*

FIGURE 21–49 In a typical system, the AC voltage signal produced each time the magnetic pulse sensor passes notches 2, 4, and 6 triggers firing. The seventh notch references the coil firing sequence to the crankshaft position.

DIS offers advantages in production costs and maintenance considerations. By removing the distributor, the manufacturers realize a substantial savings in ignition parts and related machining costs. Also, by eliminating the distributor, they also do away with cracked caps, eroded carbon buttons, burned-through rotors, moisture misfiring, base timing adjustments, and the like.

CASE STUDY

A vehicle equipped with an early electronic ignition system is experiencing spark detonation (knocking) and erratic spark advance problems. The vehicle has 82,000 miles on it.

The technician checks the engine's base timing and finds it to be 5 degrees out of adjustment. The technician makes the adjustment, but it does not seem to hold steady. In fact, the problem still occurs on the test drive made immediately after the timing adjustment is made.

The technician then removes the distributor for closer inspection. The centrifugal advance mechanism appears to be in good order, but the technician notices shiny worn areas on the tangs of the distributor shaft's drive coupling. Wear on the tangs could mean the distributor shaft is not in proper mesh with the camshaft. The technician replaces the worn drive coupling and reinstalls the distributor. After resetting initial timing, the problem of erratic advance disappears.

KEY TERMS

Air gap	Fast-Start
ATDC	Firing order
Ballast resistor	Heat range
Barometric pressure switch	Ignition timing
	Inductive reactance
Basic ignition timing	Inductive reluctance
Breaker plate	Look-up tables
Breaker point	Misfire
BTDC	Photoelectric sensor
Centrifugal advance	Preignition
Coil pack	Primary circuit
Contact points	Pulse transformer
Control module	Reach
Direct ignition	Rotor
DIS	Secondary circuit
Distributor	Strategy
Dual plug	Swirling
Dwell	Waste spark

SUMMARY

◆ The ignition system supplies high voltage to the spark plugs to ignite the air/fuel mixture in the combustion chambers.

◆ The arrival of the spark is timed to coincide with the compression stroke of the piston. This basic timing can be advanced or retarded under certain conditions, such as high engine rpm or extremely light or heavy engine loads.

◆ The ignition system has two interconnected electrical circuits: a primary circuit and a secondary circuit.

◆ The primary circuit supplies low voltage to the primary winding of the ignition coil. This creates a magnetic field in the coil.

◆ A switching device interrupts primary current flow, collapsing the magnetic field and creating a high-voltage surge in the ignition coil secondary winding.

◆ The switching device used in electronic systems is an NPN transistor. Old ignitions use mechanical breaker point switching.

◆ The secondary circuit carries high voltage surges to the spark plugs. On some systems, the circuit runs from the ignition coil, through a distributor, to the spark plugs.

◆ The distributor may house the switching device plus centrifugal or vacuum timing advance mechanisms. Some systems locate the switching device outside the distributor housing.

◆ Ignition timing is directly related to the position of the crankshaft. Magnetic pulse generators and Hall-effect sensors are the most widely used engine position sensors. They generate an electrical signal at certain times during crankshaft rotation. This signal triggers the electronic switching device to control ignition timing.

◆ Direct ignition systems eliminate the distributor. Each spark plug, or in some cases, pair of spark plugs, has its (their) own ignition coil. Primary circuit switching and timing control is done using a special ignition module tied into the vehicle control computer.

◆ Computer-controlled ignition eliminates centrifugal and vacuum timing mechanisms. The computer receives input from numerous sensors. Based on this data, the computer determines the optimum firing time and signals an ignition module to activate the secondary circuit at the precise time needed.

TECH MANUAL

The following procedures are included in Chapter 21 of the Tech Manual that accompanies this book:

1. Set ignition timing dynamically.

2. Check the resistance of primary circuit components.

3. Test spark plug firing voltages.

4. Test secondary circuit insulation.

REVIEW QUESTIONS

1. Under what condition is the ballast resistor in an ignition system's primary circuit bypassed?

2. Under light loads, what must be done to complete air/fuel combustion in the combustion chamber by the time the piston reaches 10 degrees ATDC?

3. At high engine rpm, what must be done to complete air/fuel combustion in the combustion chamber by the time the piston reaches 10 degrees ATDC?

4. How do DIS ignition systems differ from conventional electronic ignition systems?

5. Explain the components and operation of a magnetic pulse generator.

6. What happens when the low-voltage current flow in the coil primary winding is interrupted by the switching device?

   a. The magnetic filed collapses.
   b. A high-voltage surge is induced in the coil secondary winding.
   c. Both a and b.
   d. Neither a nor b.

7. Which of the following is a function of all ignition systems?

   a. to generate sufficient voltage to force a spark across the spark plug gap
   b. to time the arrival of the spark to coincide with the movement of the engine's pistons
   c. to vary the spark arrival time based on varying operating conditions
   d. all of the above

8. Reach, heat range, and air gap are all characteristics that affect the performance of which ignition system component?

   a. ignition coils   c. spark plugs
   b. ignition cables   d. breaker points

9. Technician A says DIS systems typically use one coil for two spark plugs. Technician B says some DIS systems rely on a waste spark system to fire the spark plug. Who is correct?

   a. Technician A
   b. Technician B
   c. Both A and B
   d. Neither A nor B

10. Technician A says the switching transistor in a DIS ignition system turns off current flow to the ignition coil primary winding whenever the pick-up coil is generating a voltage signal. Technician B says the transistor turns off current flow when the pick-up coil is not generating a voltage signal. Who is correct?

    a. Technician A
    b. Technician B
    c. Both A and B
    d. Neither A nor B

11. Which of the following components is *not* found in most electronic ignition systems?

    a. distributor cap
    b. condenser
    c. rotor
    d. spark plug

12. In an electronic ignition system, which of the following actually controls the primary coil current?

    a. breaker points
    b. pick-up coil
    c. reluctor
    d. transistor

13. Which of the following electronic switching devices is not equipped with a permanent magnet?

    a. magnetic pulse generator
    b. metal detection sensor
    c. Hall-effect sensor
    d. none of the above

14. Technician A says ignition systems equipped with Hall-effect sensors do not require a ballast resistor or resistance wire to regulate primary circuit current. Technician B says these systems do require resistance control in their primary circuit. Who is correct?

    a. Technician A
    b. Technician B
    c. Both A and B
    d. Neither A nor B

15. Modern ignition cables contain fiber cores that act as a ____ in the secondary circuit to cut down on radio and television interference and reduce spark plug wear.

    a. conductor
    b. resistor
    c. semiconductor
    d. heat shield

16. In DIS systems using one ignition coil for every two cylinders, Technician A says two plugs fire at the same time, with one wasting the spark on the exhaust stroke. Technician B says one plug fires in the normal direction (center to side electrode) and the other in reversed polarity (side-to-center electrode). Who is correct?

    a. Technician A
    b. Technician B
    c. Both A and B
    d. Neither A nor B

17. The magnetic field surrounding the pick-up coil in a magnetic pulse generator moves when the ____.

    a. reluctor tooth approaches the coil
    b. reluctor tooth begins to move away from the pick-up coil pole
    c. reluctor is aligned with the pick-up coil pole
    d. both a and b

18. The pick-up coil in a magnetic pulse generator does not produce a voltage signal when

    a. a reluctor tooth approaches the coil.
    b. a reluctor tooth is aligned with the coil.
    c. a reluctor tooth begins to move away from the coil.
    d. the coil is midway between two reluctor teeth.

19. Which type of engine position sensor requires its voltage signal be amplified, inverted, and shaped into a clean square wave signal?

    a. magnetic pulse generator
    b. metal detection sensor
    c. Hall-effect sensor
    d. photoelectric sensor

20. Which of the following electronic switching devices has a reluctor with wide shutters rather than teeth?

    a. magnetic pulse generator
    b. metal detection sensor
    c. Hall-effect sensor
    d. all of the above

IGNITION SYSTEM SERVICE

22

OBJECTIVES

◆ *Perform a visual inspection of ignition system components, primary wiring, and secondary wiring to locate obvious trouble areas.* ◆ *Test the components of the primary and secondary ignition circuits.* ◆ *Describe what an oscilloscope is, its scales and operating modes, and how it is used in ignition system troubleshooting.* ◆ *Identify and describe the major sections of primary circuit and secondary circuit trace patterns, including the firing line, spark line, intermediate area, and dwell zone.* ◆ *Describe the difference between fixed and variable dwell ignition systems.* ◆ *Perform cranking output, spark duration, coil polarity, spark plug firing voltage, rotor, secondary resistance, and spark plug load tests using the oscilloscope.* ◆ *Test individual ignition components using test equipment, such as a voltmeter, ohmmeter, and testlight.* ◆ *Service and install spark plugs.* ◆ *Test and set (when possible) ignition timing.*

This chapter concentrates on testing ignition systems and their individual components. It must be stressed, however, that there are many variations in the ignition systems used by auto manufacturers. The tests covered in this chapter are those generally used as basic troubleshooting procedures. Exact test procedures and the ideal troubleshooting sequence will vary between vehicle makers and individual models. Always consult the vehicle's service manual when performing ignition system service.

Two important precautions should be taken during all ignition system tests.

1. Turn the ignition switch off before disconnecting any system wiring.
2. Do not touch any exposed connections while the engine is cranking or running.

VISUAL INSPECTION

All ignition system diagnosis should begin with a visual inspection. The system should be checked for obvious problems.

◆ Disconnected, loose, or damaged secondary cables
◆ Disconnected, loose, or dirty primary wiring
◆ Loose or damaged distributor cap
◆ Damaged distributor cap or rotor

◆ Worn or damaged primary system switching mechanism
◆ Improperly mounted electronic control unit

Secondary and Primary Wiring Connections

Spark plug (ignition) and coil cables should be pushed tightly into the distributor cap and coil and onto spark plugs. Inspect all secondary cables for cracks and worn insulation which cause high voltage leaks. Inspect all of the boots on the ends of the secondary wires for cracks and hard, brittle conditions. Replace the wires and boots if they show evidence of these conditions. Some vehicle manufacturers recommend spark plug wire replacement only in complete sets.

The secondary coil cable should also be inspected. When checking this cable, check the ignition coil. The coil should be inspected for cracks or any evidence of leakage in the coil tower. The coil container should be inspected for oil leaks. If oil is leaking from the coil, air space is present in the coil which allows condensation to form internally. Condensation in an ignition coil causes high voltage leaks and engine misfiring.

Secondary cables must be connected according to the firing order. Refer to the manufacturer's service manual to determine the correct firing order and cylinder numbering (Figure 22–1).

White or grayish powdery deposits on secondary cables at the point where they cross or are near

FIGURE 22–1 Spark plug wire routing. *Courtesy of Chrysler Corporation*

metal parts indicate that the cable's insulation is faulty. The deposits occur because the high voltage in the cable has burned the dust collected on the cable. Such faulty insulation may produce a spark that sometimes can be heard and seen in the dark. An occasional glow around the spark plug cables, known as a **corona effect**, is not harmful but indicates the cable should be replaced.

Spark plug cables from consecutively firing cylinders should cross rather than run parallel to one another (Figure 22–2). Spark plug cables running parallel to one another can induce firing voltages in one another and cause the spark plugs to fire at the wrong time.

Primary ignition system wiring should be checked for tight connections, especially on vehicles with electronic- or computer-controlled ignitions. Electronic circuits operate on very low voltage. Voltage drops caused by corrosion or dirt can cause running problems. Missing tab locks on wire connectors are often the cause of intermittent ignition problems due to vibration or thermal related failure.

FIGURE 22–2 Routing spark plug cables to avoid inducing voltages. *Courtesy of Chrysler Corporation*

Test the integrity of a suspect connection by tapping, tugging, and wiggling the wires while the engine is running. Be gentle. The object is to recreate an ignition interruption, not to cause permanent circuit damage. With the engine off, separate the suspect connectors and check them for dirt and corrosion. Clean the connectors according to the manufacturer's recommendations.

Many late-model vehicles require the use of a special dielectric grease on connector terminals. This grease seals the connections from outside elements.

Do not overlook the ignition switch as a source of intermittent ignition problems. A loose mounting rivet or poor connection can result in erratic spark output. To check the switch, gently wiggle the ignition key and connecting wires with the engine running. If the ignition cuts out or dies, the problem is located.

Check the battery connection to the starter solenoid. Remember, some vehicles use this connection as a voltage source for the coil. A bad connection can result in ignition interruption.

SHOP TALK

Any time you are faced with an intermittent or no-start problem on a General Motors HEI system, make sure you check the battery positive connection at the coil for a proper fit. Even if the connection looks good and feels tight, pull it apart and clean the terminals. After cleaning, lightly crimp the make end of the terminal to ensure a good connection; then reconnect it. ■

Ground Circuits Keep in mind that to simplify a vehicle's electrical system, auto makers use body panels, frame members, and the engine block as current return paths to the battery.

Unfortunately, ground straps are often neglected, or worse, left disconnected after routine service. With the increased use of plastics in today's vehicles, ground straps may mistakenly be reconnected to a nonmetallic surface. The result of any of these problems is the current that was to flow through the disconnected or improperly grounded strap is forced to find an alternate path to ground. Sometimes the current attempts to back up through another circuit. This may cause the circuit to operate erratically or fail altogether. The current may also be forced through other components, such as wheel bearings or shift and clutch cables that are not meant to handle current flow causing them to wear prematurely or become seized in their housing.

SPARK PLUG CABLES

FIGURE 22–3 Distributor cap holddown devices. *Courtesy of Chrysler Corporation*

Examples of bad ground circuit induced ignition failures include burnt ignition modules resulting from missing or loose coil ground straps, erratic performance caused by a poor distributor-to-engine block ground and intermittent ignition operation resulting from a poor ground at the control module.

Electromagnetic Interference Electromagnetic interference (**EMI**) can cause problems with the vehicle's on-board computer. EMI is produced when electromagnetic radio waves of sufficient amplitude escape from a wire or conductor. Unfortunately, an automobile's spark plug wires, ignition coil, and

alternator coils all possess the ability to generate these radio waves. Under the right conditions, EMI can trigger sensors or actuators. The result may be an intermittent driveability problem that appears to be ignition system related.

To minimize the effects of EMI, check to make sure sensor wires running to the computer are routed away from potential EMI sources. Rerouting a wire by no more than an inch or two may keep EMI from falsely triggering or interfering with computer operation.

Distributor Cap

The distributor cap should be properly seated on its base. All clips or screws should be tightened securely (Figure 22–3).

The distributor cap and rotor also should be removed for visual inspection. Physical or electrical damage is easily recognizable.

Electrical damage from high voltage can include corroded or burned metal terminals and **carbon tracking** inside distributor caps. Carbon tracking is the formation of a line of carbonized dust between distributor cap terminals or between a terminal and the distributor housing. Carbon tracking indicates that high-voltage electricity has found a low-resistance conductive path over or through the plastic. The result is a cylinder that fires at the wrong time or a misfire. Check the outer cap towers and metal terminals for defects. Cracked plastic requires replacement of the unit. Damaged or carbon-tracked distributor caps or rotors should be replaced (Figure 22–4).

The rotor should be inspected carefully for discoloration and other damage (Figure 22–5). Inspect the top and bottom of the rotor carefully for grayish, whitish, or rainbow-hued spots. Such discoloration indicates the rotor has lost its insulating qualities. High voltage is being conducted to ground through the plastic.

FIGURE 22–4 Types of distributor cap and rotor damage.

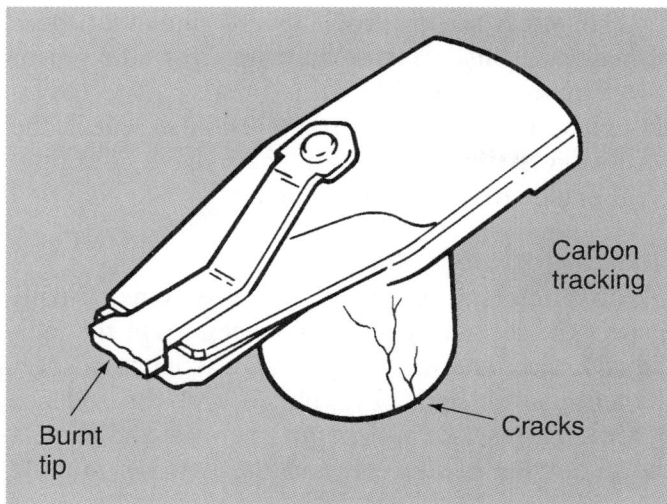

FIGURE 22–5 Inspect rotor for damage and signs of high-voltage leaks. *Courtesy of Chrysler Corporation*

If the distributor cap or rotor has a mild buildup of dirt or corrosion, it should be cleaned. If it cannot be cleaned up, it should be replaced. Small, round brushes are available to clean cap terminals. Wipe the cap and rotor with a clean shop towel, but avoid cleaning these components in solvent or blowing them off with compressed air, which may contain moisture. Cleaning these components with solvent or compressed air may result in high voltage leaks.

Timing Advance Mechanisms

The hoses to the vacuum advance unit should be attached securely to the unit. Disconnected hoses can cause poor fuel economy and performance, poor idle, and stalling.

Centrifugal advance mechanisms can be checked for free motion. Move the rotor on the distributor shaft clockwise and counterclockwise. The rotor should rotate in one direction approximately 1/4 inch, then spring back. If not, the centrifugal advance mechanism might be binding or rusty. A lubricant might be necessary on advance mechanism pivots and rubbing surfaces after the mechanism is cleaned.

Electronically controlled advance mechanisms eliminate centrifugal and vacuum advance/retard mechanisms within the distributor. However, all wiring connections to and from the distributor and ignition module should be thoroughly inspected for damage.

Primary Circuit Switches and Sensors

Several different types of switching systems are used to control current flow in the ignition's primary circuit.

Breaker Points Older vehicles may be equipped with breaker point switching mechanisms. To inspect the mechanism, remove the distributor cap and rotor.

Check the points and condenser to make sure they are securely fastened. Push the breaker points open with a screwdriver and check the condition of the contact surfaces (Figure 22–6). Badly oxidized (blackened) or pitted points should be replaced.

Control Modules Electronic- and computer-controlled ignitions use transistors as switches. These transistors are contained inside a control module housing that can be mounted to or in the distributor or remotely mounted on the vehicle's fire wall or another engine compartment surface. Control modules should be tightly mounted to clean surfaces. A loose mounting can cause a heat buildup that can damage and destroy transistors and other electronic components contained in the module. Some manufacturers recommend the use of a special heat-conductive silicone grease between the control unit and its mounting (Figure 22–7). This helps conduct heat away from the module, reducing the chance of heat-related failure. During the visual inspection, check all electrical connections to the module. They must be clean and tight.

FIGURE 22–6 Breaker point inspection points.

FIGURE 22–7 When replacing control modules, some manufacturers specify applying silicone lubricant to the mounting surface. *Courtesy of Oldsmobile Division, General Motors Corporation*

Sensors The transistor in the control module is activated by a voltage pulse from a crankshaft position sensor. In most ignition systems, this sensor is either a magnetic pulse generator or Hall-effect sensor. These sensors are mounted either on the distributor shaft or the crankshaft.

Magnetic pulse generators are relatively trouble free. The reluctor or pole piece is replaced only if it is broken or cracked. The pick-up coil wire leads can become grounded if their insulation wears off as the breaker plate moves with the vacuum advance unit. Inspect these leads carefully (Figure 22–8). Position these wires so they do not rub the breaker plate as it moves.

Under unusual circumstances, the nonmagnetic reluctor can become magnetized and upset the pick-up coil's voltage signal to the control module. Use a steel feeler gauge to check for signs of magnetic attraction and replace the reluctor if the test is positive. On some systems, the gap between the pick-up and the reluctor must be checked and adjusted to manufacturer's specifications. To do this, use a properly sized nonmagnetic feeler gauge to check the air gap between the coil and reluctor. Adjust the gap if it is out of specification.

FIGURE 22–8 Inspect pick-up coil wiring for damage.

Hall-effect sensor problems are similar to those of magnetic pulse generators. Wires from the sensor that may move and rub as the breaker plate moves should be inspected (Figure 22–9). Also, check the condition of the distributor shaft drive coupling. Wear could effect the engine timing.

Distributorless Systems

On distributorless or direct ignition systems, visually inspect the secondary wiring connections at the individual coil modules. If a plug wire is loose, inspect the terminal for signs of burning. Check for evidence of terminal resistance. Separate the coils and inspect the underside of the coil and the ignition module wires (Figure 22–10). A loose or damaged wire or bad plug can lead to carbon tracking of the coil. If this condition exists, the coil must be replaced.

If the visual inspection does not reveal obvious problems, test those individual components and circuits that could cause the problem.

FIGURE 22–9 Hall-effect sensor and distributor system. *Courtesy of Chrysler Corporation*

FIGURE 22–10 On distributorless systems, check the wiring linking the coils to the ignition module.

ELECTRICAL TEST PROCEDURES

It is impossible to accurately troubleshoot any ignition system without performing various electrical tests. Two pieces of test equipment, an oscilloscope and a digital volt-ohmmeter (multimeter), are absolutely essential for diagnosing ignition problems.

Oscilloscope Testing

No discussion on ignition troubleshooting would be complete without a comprehensive discussion of oscilloscope use. The job of the oscilloscope is to convert the electrical signals of the ignition system into a visual image showing voltage changes over a given period of time. This information is displayed on a CRT screen in the form of a continuous voltage line called a pattern or trace. By studying the pattern, a technician can determine what is happening inside the ignition system.

The information on the design and use of oscilloscopes given in this text is general in nature. Always follow the oscilloscope manufacturer's specific instructions when connecting test leads or conducting test procedures.

Scales On the face of the CRT screen is a voltage versus time graph (Figure 22–11). The waveform patterns are displayed on the graph. The graph charts the changes in voltage and the time span in which the changes occur. The voltage versus time graph has four scales: two vertical scales (one on the left and one on the right), a horizontal percent of dwell scale, and a horizontal millisecond scale. The technician must select the proper scale for the test being conducted.

The left and right vertical scales measure voltage. The vertical scale on the left side of the graph is divided into increments of 1 kilovolt (1,000 volts) and ranges from 0 to 25 kilovolts (**kV**). This scale is use-

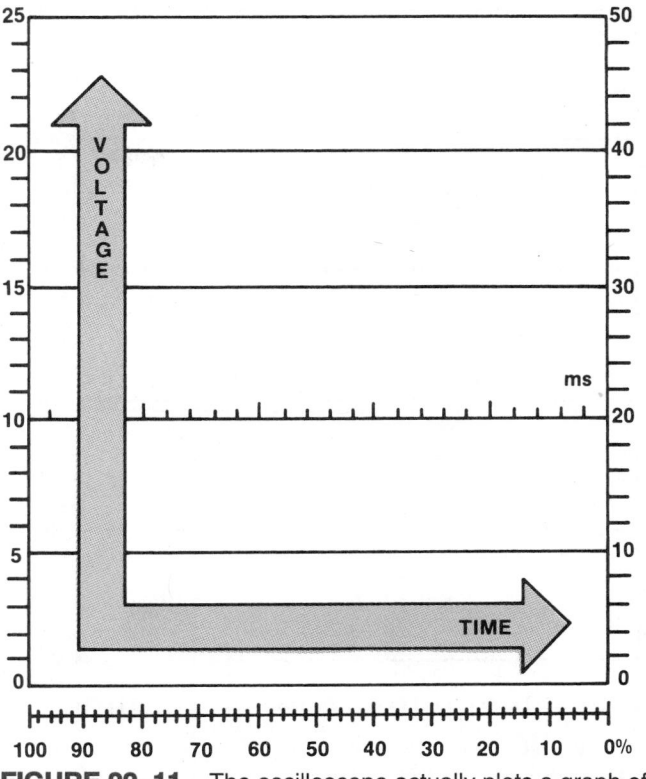

FIGURE 22–11 The oscilloscope actually plots a graph of voltage levels versus time.

ful for testing secondary voltage. It can also be used to measure primary voltage by interpreting the scale in volts rather than kilovolts.

The vertical scale on the right side of the graph is divided into increments of 2 kilovolts and has a range of 0 to 50 kV. This scale is also used for testing secondary voltage and to measure primary voltage in the 0 to 500 volt range.

The horizontal percent of dwell scale is located at the bottom of the scope screen. This scale is used for checking the dwell angle in both the primary and secondary circuits. The dwell scale is divided into increments of 2 percentage points and ranges from 0 to 100 percent.

The fourth scale—the millisecond scale—is a horizontal line that runs along the center of the voltage versus time graph. Depending on the test mode selected by the technician, the millisecond scale shows a range of 0 to 5 milliseconds (ms) or 0 to 25 milliseconds. The 5-ms scale is often used to measure the duration of the spark (Figure 22–12). In the 25-millisecond mode, the complete firing pattern can normally be displayed.

An oscilloscope or scope displays voltage changes from left to right, similar to reading a book. So voltage lines or traces that appear on the left of the CRT screen occurred before those on the right. Oscilloscopes normally have four leads (Figure 22–13): a primary pick-up that connects to the primary circuit,

FIGURE 22–12 5-millisecond pattern showing spark duration.

from specific testing in each one of these areas can be used to piece together a complete ignition picture.

Depending on the oscilloscope function selected by the technician, the scope can display the voltage versus time pattern for either the secondary or primary circuit. A typical secondary pattern is shown in Figure 22–14. A secondary pattern displays the following types of information.

- Firing voltage
- Spark duration
- Coil and condenser oscillations
- Transistor on/off switching or breaker point close and open
- Dwell and cylinder timing accuracy
- Secondary circuit accuracy

A typical primary circuit pattern is shown in Figure 22–15. The primary scope pattern is used when secondary circuit connections are not possible. It is also useful for observing breaker point condition and action by nonelectronic systems and for providing a means to observe dwell and cylinder timing problems.

Pattern Display Modes The oscilloscope has several ways to display the voltage patterns of the primary and secondary circuits. When the **display pattern** is

FIGURE 22–14 Typical secondary pattern.

or negative terminal of the ignition coil; a ground lead that connects to a good engine ground; a secondary pick-up, which clamps around the coil's high tension wire; and a trigger pick-up, which clamps around the spark plug wire of the number 1 cylinder. The information received from these leads is translated into the scope pattern on the CRT screen.

Pattern Types and Phases To monitor various phases of ignition system performance, a typical scope pattern is divided into three main sections: firing, intermediate, and dwell. Information received

FIGURE 22–13 Typical oscilloscope pick-up connections to an ignition system.

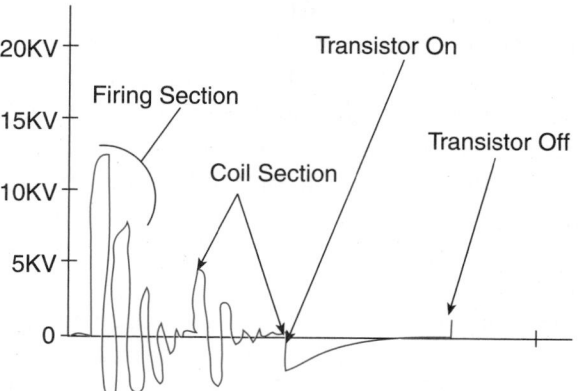

FIGURE 22–15 Typical primary pattern.

FIGURE 22–16 Primary display pattern.

FIGURE 22–17 Secondary raster pattern.

selected, the oscilloscope displays the patterns of all the cylinders in a row from left to right as shown in Figure 22–16. Each cylinder's ignition cycle is displayed in the engine's firing order. In the example of a primary display pattern shown in Figure 22–16, the firing order is 1, 8, 4, 3, 6, 5, 7, 2. The pattern begins with the spark line of the number 1 cylinder and ends with the firing line for the number 1 cylinder. This display pattern allows the technician to compare the voltage peaks for each cylinder.

A second choice of patterns is the **raster pattern** (Figure 22–17). A raster pattern stacks the voltage patterns of the cylinders one above the other. The number 1 pattern is displayed at the bottom of the screen and the rest of the cylinder's firing patterns are arranged above it in the engine's firing order.

In a raster pattern, the patterns for each cylinder are displayed across the width of the graph, also beginning with the spark line and ending with the firing line. This allows for a much closer inspection of the voltage and time trends than is possible with the display pattern.

All of the patterns for the cylinders can also be displayed in a **superimposed pattern**. A superimposed pattern displays all the patterns, one on top of the other. Like the raster pattern, the superimposed voltage patterns are displayed the full width of the screen, beginning with the spark line and ending with the firing line.

A superimposed pattern allows a technician to detect variations of one cylinder's pattern from the others. A superimposed pattern for the primary circuits is shown in Figure 22–18.

FIGURE 22–18 Primary superimposed pattern.

LOOK FOR: FIRING LINE THAT IS 5 TO 10 kV, NO MORE THAN 3 kV VARIATION BETWEEN CYLINDERS.

LOOK FOR: SPARK LINE THAT IS STRAIGHT AND LEVEL. SPARK LINE IS SHORTER IF FIRING LINE IS TOO HIGH.

LOOK FOR: SHARP OSCILLATIONS THAT GRADUALLY DIMINISH IN SIZE.

LOOK FOR: PRIMARY CURRENT "ON" SHORT DOWN-WARD LINE FOLLOWED BY SMALL OSCILLATIONS.

LOOK FOR: PRIMARY CURRENT "OFF" ABRUPT 90° ANGLE THAT BEGINS FIRING LINE OF NEXT CYLINDER.

ZERO LINE

SPARK PLUG FIRING SECTION

COIL INTERMEDIATE SECTION

DWELL SECTION

TESTS: PLUG AND ROTOR GAP, BROKEN WIRES, FUEL MIXTURE, AND CONDITION OF COMBUSTION CHAMBER.

TESTS: PLUGS, WIRES, CAP, ROTOR, OR ENGINE CONDITION AFFECTING PLUG FIRING.

TESTS: DEFECT IN COIL OR PRIMARY CIRCUIT. (AFFECTED BY VOLTAGE USED IN FIRING SECTION.)

TESTS: TRIGGERING DEVICE PROBLEMS. POOR CONTACT FROM DIRTY, BURNED, OR MIS-ALIGNED POINTS AND WEAK POINT TENSION.

TESTS: SWITCHING DEVICE PROBLEMS. PITTED POINTS OR ARCING FROM POOR CONDENSER ACTION.

FIGURE 22–19 Breakdown of a single cylinder secondary circuit pattern. *Courtesy of Sun Electric Corporation*

Understanding Single Cylinder Patterns The following section takes a closer look at the secondary circuit pattern (Figure 22–19). As shown, the firing line of the pattern appears at the left side of the CRT screen. An upward line signifies voltage. The firing line indicates the voltage needed to start the spark. The ignition coil's voltage pressure rises up to the point where it overcomes all electrical resistance in the secondary circuit. Typically, it requires around 10,000 volts to overcome this resistance and initiate a spark.

Keep in mind that cylinder conditions have an effect on this resistance. Leaner air/fuel mixtures increase the resistance and increase the required **firing voltage**.

Once secondary resistance is overcome, the spark jumps the plug gap, establishing current flow, and igniting the air/fuel mixture in the cylinder. The length of time the spark actually lasts is represented by the **spark line** portion of the pattern. The spark line begins at the firing line and continues tracing to the right until the coil's voltage drops below the level needed to keep current flowing across the gap.

In other words, the spark is draining the voltage built up in the coil's secondary windings. As long as the coil has sufficient voltage, the spark continues.

Once coil voltage drops below the level needed to sustain the spark, the next major section of the scope trace pattern begins. This section is called the **intermediate section** or coil-condenser zone. It shows the remaining coil voltage as it dissipates or drops to zero. Remember, once the spark has ended, there is quite a bit of voltage stored in the ignition coil. The voltage remaining in the coil oscillates or alternates back and forth within the primary circuit until it drops to zero. Notice that the lines representing the coil-condenser section steadily drop in height until the coil's voltage is zero.

The next section of the trace pattern begins with the primary circuit current on signal. It appears as a slight downward turn followed by several small oscillations. The slight downward curve occurs just as current begins to flow through the coil's primary winding. The oscillations that follow indicate the beginning of the magnetic field buildup in the coil. This curve marks the beginning of a period known as the dwell section of zone. The end of the dwell zone occurs when the primary current is turned off by the switching device (transistor or breaker points). The trace turns sharply upward at the end of the dwell zone. Turning the primary current off collapses the magnetic field in the coil and generates another high voltage spark for the next cylinder in the firing order. Remember, the primary current off signal is the same as the firing line for the next cylinder. The length of the dwell section represents the amount of time that current is flowing through the primary.

In general, most scope patterns look more or less like the one just described. The patterns produced by some systems have fewer oscillations in the intermediate section. Patterns may also vary slightly in the dwell section. The length of this section depends on when the control module turns the transistor on and off. Several variables may affect this timing. These variables can be categorized as follows.

- Fixed short dwell
- Fixed long dwell
- Variable dwell
- Current limiting

FIXED DWELL Older breaker point systems and some electronic ignition systems use a fixed dwell period. In a fixed dwell system, the number of dwell degrees remain the same during all engine speeds (Figure 22–20). So, if the engine has 30 degrees of dwell at idle, it should have 30 degrees of dwell at 2,000 rpm. This is not saying the actual amount of dwell time has remained the same. A fixed dwell of 30 degrees at 2,000 rpm gives the ignition coil only 1/4 the saturation time it has a 500 rpm. The oscilloscope should show that the number of degrees or the percent of dwell remains the same as engine speed changes.

One exception to this rule is early Chrysler electronic ignition systems. These systems are characterized by a very long, distinctive dwell zone trace. The dwell zone begins just as the spark line ends. At higher engine speeds, the spark line increases slightly, forcing dwell to begin later (Figure 22–21). The change in dwell time is also slight, usually less than 5 degrees. This change in dwell has no effect on ignition timing because timing is controlled by switching off primary current. In these systems, the change takes place by

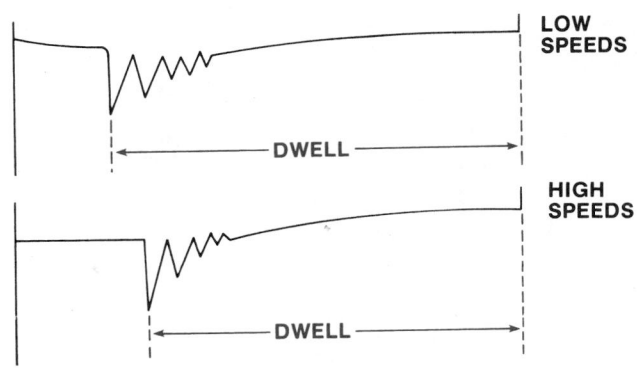

FIGURE 22–21 Speed reduces dwell slightly in this long dwell ignition system.

increasing the spark duration and delaying the primary circuit on signal. Because this dwell change is so slight and has no effect on timing. This Chrysler system is commonly called a long fixed dwell system.

VARIABLE DWELL Most electronic ignition systems have a variable dwell function built into their control modules. In these systems, dwell changes significantly with engine speed. At idle and low rpm speeds, a short dwell provides enough time for complete ignition coil saturation (Figure 22–22A). The current on and current off signals appear very close to each other, usually less than 20 degrees.

As engine speed increases, the control module lengthens the dwell time (Figure 22–22B). This, of course, increases the available time for coil saturation.

Although not common, it is possible for the variable dwell function of the control module to fail and still allow the vehicle to run. If testing indicates a lack of variable dwell on a system equipped with it, the control module must be replaced.

CURRENT LIMITING Many modern electronic ignitions feature **current limiting**. These systems saturate the ignition coil quickly by passing very high current through the primary winding for a fraction of one second. Once the coil is saturated, the need for high current is eliminated, and a small amount of

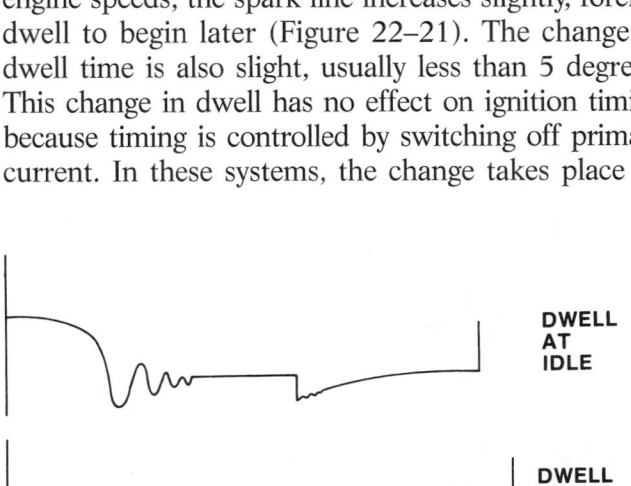

FIGURE 22–20 Pattern of a fixed dwell system at low and high engine speeds.

FIGURE 22–22 Example of variable dwell ignition system.

current is used to keep the coil saturated. This type of system extends coil life.

The point at which the control module cuts back from high to low current appears as a small blip or oscillation during the dwell section of the pattern (Figure 22–23). At very high engine speeds, this telltale blip may be missing; the module keeps high current flow going to keep the coil continually saturated for fast firing.

At the opposite extreme, if the primary winding of the coil has developed excessive resistance or the coil is otherwise faulty, the cutback blip may never occur. This is because the primary winding never becomes fully saturated. Further testing of the coil would be needed to pinpoint the cause of the missing blip.

As with variable dwell, it is possible for the vehicle to run with the current limit function of the control module burned out or faulty. Again, the blip would be missing from the trace.

CAUTION:

Never touch the secondary wiring, cap, or coil if the current limiting blip is missing from the pattern of an ignition system that should have it. The secondary voltage available could easily exceed 100,000 volts. ■

Open Circuit Precautions

Precautions must be taken to prevent open circuits in an electronic ignition system during electrical test procedures.

This point is brought up because a common test performed on breaker point ignition systems involved seeing how much available voltage the ignition coil could produce. The coil wire was removed and the engine cranked or a plug wire was pulled with the engine running. Both procedures forced the ignition coil to produce its maximum output to try to overcome this massive resistance created in the circuit. Typically, the output would exceed 20,000 volts and the technician would have a good idea of what the coil was capable of producing under adverse conditions.

Open circuiting a modern ignition system, however, can damage the system. Features such as variable

dwell and current limiting circuitry pull out all primary resistance if a spark does not occur. This causes tremendous amounts of current to flow through the primary circuit, producing an extremely high-voltage spark that must search out a path to ground. A frequent path to ground chosen by the spark is through the side of coil. This results in an insulation breakdown at the coil and a site where arcing to ground is likely to occur in the future.

To prevent these tremendous voltages from occurring during coil output testing, a special test plug is used when checking the coil voltage output (Figure 22–24). The test plug is connected to the coil wiring running to the distributor or to an ignition cable. A special grounding clip on the test plug is then connected to a good ground source.

The test plug looks like a spark plug, but it has a very large electrode gap. When the engine is cranked to check for voltage output, the ignition coil is forced to produce a higher voltage to overcome the added resistance created by the wide gap. Typically, about 35,000 volts are needed to fire the test plug. This is enough to stress the system without damaging it.

Coil Output Test

To safely perform a coil output test, proceed as follows.

1. Install the test plug in the coil wire or a plug wire if there is not a coil wire.
2. Set the oscilloscope on display and set a voltage range of 50 kV.
3. Crank the engine over and note the height of the firing line.

The firing line should exceed 35 kV and be consistent. Lower-than-specified firing line voltages may indicate the test plug did not fire. This could be the result of lower-than-normal available voltage in the primary circuit. The control module may have devel-

SPARK
TESTER

ENGINE
GROUND

FIGURE 22–23 Pattern showing an ignition system limiting current during dwell.

CURRENT
LIMIT BLIP

FIGURE 22–24 A test plug should be used to limit coil voltage output during testing.

FIGURE 22–25 5-millisecond pattern showing a spark duration of 1.3 milliseconds during a cranking test.

oped high internal resistance. The coil or coil cable may also be faulty. Further testing is needed to help pinpoint the problem.

Spark Duration Testing

Spark duration is measured in milliseconds, using the millisecond sweep of the oscilloscope. Most vehicles have a spark duration of approximately 1.5 milliseconds (Figure 22–25). A spark duration of approximately 0.8 millisecond is too short to provide complete combustion. A short spark also increases pollution and power loss. If the spark duration is too long (over approximately 2.0 milliseconds) the spark plug electrodes might wear prematurely. When the oscilloscope shows a long spark duration, it normally follows a short firing line, which may indicate a fouled spark plug, low compression, or a spark plug with a narrow gap.

Spark duration is normally measured two times—during engine cranking and engine running.

Cranking Test When a vehicle is experiencing a no-start, or a hard start condition, perform a spark duration cranking test. This test also helps identify potential future problems by indicating a borderline condition. To perform the crank test, do the following.

1. Disable the ignition system so the engine does not start. Different oscilloscope manufacturers recom-

mend different methods of preventing engine start-up during a cranking test. Always consult the scope manufacturer's instructions.
2. Set the pattern selector to the 5 millisecond position, the function selector to secondary, and pattern height control to the 0 to 25 kV scale.
3. Crank the engine and quickly note the spark duration.

Compare the recorded duration times to manufacturer's specifications. If spark duration is too short, look for causes of low coil output voltage. Start with a thorough examination of the primary system after checking for proper operation of the battery, starting, and charging systems. If these items appear to be working properly, search for sources of high primary circuit resistance.

Set the oscilloscope in the primary circuit position and check the height of the initial firing line oscillation. If a lower-than-normal height is observed, the most likely causes are a bad ballast resistor (where used), a poor control module ground, or loose, dirty, or corroded connectors in the primary circuit. Remember that a 1-volt loss in the primary circuit can result in a 1,000-volt loss in the secondary circuit.

Running Test The running test measures spark duration while the engine is running at a specific rpm. To perform a running test on the oscilloscope, do the following.

1. Set the pattern selector to the 5-millisecond position, the function selector to secondary, and pattern height control to the 0 to 25 kV scale.
2. Start the engine and adjust the speed to 1,000 rpm.
3. Note the spark duration.

Some oscilloscopes do not have a millisecond sweep. Instead, they are equipped with a percent of dwell scale. In that case, the percent of dwell must be converted to milliseconds. A conversion chart is given in Table 22–1. The table lists percent of dwell at various rpm and the corresponding spark duration in milliseconds. On oscilloscopes without a millisecond sweep, the pattern selector should be set to superimpose or raster when performing the spark duration cranking and running tests.

The raster pattern in Figure 22–26 is a secondary pattern of a 4-cylinder engine at 600 rpm. The spark duration is 3 percent of dwell, or 1.5 millisecond.

Coil Polarity Less voltage is required to fire the spark plugs with proper coil polarity. If the coil polar-

TABLE 22–1 CONVERTING PERCENT OF DWELL TO MILLISECONDS					
	ms	600 rpm	1,200 rpm	2,400 rpm	Spark Duration
8 cylinder	0.5	2%	4%	8%	too short
	1.0	4%	8%	17%	minimum
	1.5	6%	13%	25%	average
	2.0	8%	17%	33%	too long
6 cylinder	0.5	1.5%	3%	6%	too short
	1.0	3%	6%	12%	minimum
	1.5	4.5%	9%	18%	average
	2.0	6%	12%	24%	too long
4 cylinder	0.5	1%	2%	4%	too short
	1.0	2%	4%	8%	minimum
	1.5	3%	6%	13%	average
	2.0	4%	8%	17%	too long

ity is reversed, 20 to 40 percent more voltage is needed to fire the spark plugs.

If the coil polarity is correct, the firing lines of the display pattern extend upward. If the polarity is reversed, the firing lines extend downward. If reverse polarity is indicated, check the coil primary connections. They are probably reversed.

FIGURE 22–26 A secondary raster pattern showing firing duration as 3 percent of dwell.

Spark Plug Firing Voltage

The coil must generate sufficient voltage in the secondary system to overcome the total resistance in the secondary circuit and to establish a spark across the spark plug electrodes. On the oscilloscope, this spark plug firing voltage is seen as the highest line in the pattern. The firing voltage might be affected by the condition of the spark plugs or the secondary circuit, engine temperature, fuel mixture, and compression pressures. To test the spark plug firing voltage on an oscilloscope, observe the firing line of all cylinders for height and uniformity. The normal height of the firing voltages should be between 7 and 13 kV with no more than a 3-kV variation between cylinders.

If during the test, one or more of the firing voltages are uneven, low, or high, consult Table 22–2 for possible causes and corrections.

Rotor Air Gap Voltage Drop

When high firing voltages are present in one or more of the cylinders, perform a rotor air gap voltage drop test. The purpose of this test is to determine the amount of secondary voltage that is required to bridge the rotor gap.

SHOP TALK

Excessive rotor air gap can be caused by a bent distributor shaft or worn shaft bearings. Check shaft movement prior to testing the rotor air gap on the scope.

TABLE 22–2 FIRING LINE DIAGNOSIS

Condition	Probable Cause	Remedy
Firing voltage lines the same, but abnormally high	1. Retarded ignition timing 2. Fuel mixture too lean 3. High resistance in coil wire 4. Corrosion in coil tower terminal 5. Corrosion in distributor coil terminal	1. Rest ignition timing. 2. Readjust carburetor or check for vacuum leak. 3. Replace coil wire. 4. Clean or replace coil. 5. Clean or replace distributor cap.
Firing voltage lines the same, but abnormally low	1. Fuel mixture too rich 2. Breaks in coil wire causing arcing 3. Cracked coil tower causing arcing 4. Low coil output 5. Low engine compression	1. Readjust carburetor or check for plugged air filter. 2. Replace coil wire. 3. Replace coil. 4. Replace coil. 5. Determine cause and repair.
One or more, but not all firing voltage lines higher than the others	1. Idle mixture not balanced 2. EGR valve stuck open 3. High resistance in spark plug wire 4. Cracked or broken spark plug insulator 5. Intake vacuum leak 6. Defective spark plugs 7. Corroded spark plug terminals	1. Readjust idle mixture. 2. Inspect or replace EGR valve. 3. Replace spark plug wires. 4. Replace spark plugs. 5. Repair leak. 6. Replace spark plugs. 7. Replace spark plugs.
One or more, but not all firing voltage lines lower	1. Curb idle mixture not balanced 2. Breaks in plug wires causing arcing 3. Cracked coil tower causing arcing 4. Low compression 5. Defective or fouled spark plugs	1. Readjust idle mixture. 2. Replace spark plug wires. 3. Replace coil. 4. Determine cause and repair. 5. Replace spark plugs.
Cylinders not firing	1. Cracked distributor cap terminals 2. Shorted spark plug wire 3. Mechanical problem in engine 4. Defective spark plugs 5. Spark plugs fouled	1. Replace distributor cap. 2. Determine cause of short and replace wire. 3. Determine problem and correct. 4. Replace spark plugs. 5. Replace spark plugs.

PROCEDURES
Performing a Rotor Air Gap Voltage Drop Test

1. Set the pattern selector to the display position, the function selector to secondary, and the pattern height control to the 0 to 25 kV scale.
2. Start the engine and adjust the speed to 1,000 rpm.
3. Observe the height of the firing lines. Record the height and firing order number of any abnormal cylinder.
4. Shut the engine off.
5. Remove the spark plug wire of the abnormal cylinder from the distributor cap. Connect one end of the jumper lead to ground the other end to the large portion of a grounding probe. Place the other end of the grounding probe in the distributor cap tower terminal.
6. Start the engine and adjust the speed to 1,000 rpm.
7. Observe the firing line of the abnormal cylinder previously recorded. There should be a slight drop in the firing voltage when using the grounding probe.

SHOP TALK

Do not remove the spark plug wire from the distributor cap tower terminal while the engine is running. This causes an open circuit and might damage the ignition system components. ■

The observed voltage represents voltage needed to overcome the resistance in the coil wire and of the rotor air gap. The rotor air gap measurements should not exceed manufacturer's specifications. If during the test, the firing line remains high or drops to a level that does not meet manufacturer's specifications, the rotor or distributor cap might be defective. Visually inspect both and replace as necessary. A bent distributor shaft or worn shaft bushings will cause excessive rotor air gaps on about half the cylinders.

Rotor Register

The procedure for performing a rotor register test is very similar to that for performing a rotor air gap voltage drop test, except, in this test, vacuum is applied to the distributor vacuum advance unit with an external vacuum source.

SHOP TALK

If the vehicle is equipped with computer-controlled spark advance, consult the manufacturer's service manual for proper test procedures. ■

Secondary Circuit Resistance

Analysis of the spark line of a secondary pattern reveals the condition of the secondary circuit. The amount of resistance in the secondary circuit is indicated by the slope of the spark line. Excessive resistance in the secondary circuit causes the spark line to have a steep slope with a shorter firing duration. The excessive resistance restricts the current flow necessary to generate a good spark.

A good spark line should be relatively even and measure 2 to 4 kV in height. High resistance in the secondary circuit produces a firing line and spark line that are higher in voltage with shorter firing durations. If high resistance is shown during testing, see Table 22–3.

To pinpoint the cause of high resistance, use a grounding probe and jumper wire to bypass each component of the secondary circuit on all abnormal cylinders. Connect one end of the jumper lead to ground and the other end to the large portion of a grounding probe. Start the engine and adjust the

PROCEDURES

Performing a Rotor Register Test

1. Set the pattern selector to the display position, the function selector to secondary, and the pattern height control to the 0 to 25 kV scale.
2. With the engine off, remove any spark plug wire from the distributor cap, except for the one connected to the trigger pick-up. Connect one end of the jumper lead to ground and the other end to the large portion of a grounding probe. Place the other end of the grounding probe in the distributor cap tower terminal.
3. Start the engine and adjust the speed to 1,000 rpm.
4. Note the height of the firing line of the circuit connected to the grounding probe.
5. Using the external vacuum source, apply 16 to 22 inches of mercury to the distributor vacuum advance unit. Readjust the engine speed to maintain 1,000 rpm.
6. Again, note the height of the firing lines of the circuit connected to the grounding probe. There should be no more than a 3-kV difference between the firing voltages observed in steps 4 and 6. If at any time during the test, the difference between the firing voltages is over 2 kV, see Table 22–3.

speed to 1,000 rpm. Touch each secondary connector with the point of the grounding probe and observe the spark lines.

If, after grounding, the abnormal spark lines appear normal, the part just bypassed is the cause of the problem. For further diagnosis, see Table 22–3.

While scanning the secondary circuit with the grounding probe, watch the firing lines on the scope. If there is an insulation break in the circuit, the firing lines decrease in height when the high secondary voltage arcs across to the probe.

SHOP TALK

When the voltage arcs across to the grounding probe, an electrical cracking sound might be heard or the spark might be visible. ■

Any insulated part of the secondary circuit can break down and leak. This includes the coil, coil wire and boots, distributor cap and terminals, and spark plug wires and boots.

TABLE 22–3 TROUBLESHOOTING SPARK PLUGS

Symptom	Probable Cause	Remedy
ROTOR REGISTER TEST		
Difference between firing voltages is over 3 kV	1. Defective rotor 2. Defective distributor cap 3. Wrong vacuum advance unit used	1. Replace rotor. 2. Replace distributor cap. 3. Check manufacturer's part number, or use distributor tester to verify advance curve.
SECONDARY CIRCUIT RESISTANCE TEST		
High resistance in spark lines	1. Rotor tip burned 2. High resistance in the spark plug wire 3. Distributor cap segments burned 4. Faulty spark plug	1. Visually inspect. 2. Perform ohmmeter test. 3. Visually inspect. 4. Perform secondary resistance test using the grounding probe.
After grounding spark plug, abnormal spark lines appear normal	1. Faulty spark plug	1. Substitute spark plug.
After grounding spark plug, abnormal spark lines still show high resistance	1. Corroded distributor cap towers 2. Distributor cap segments burned 3. High resistance in the spark plug wires	1. Visually inspect. 2. Visually inspect. 3. Perform ohmmeter test.
All the spark lines show high resistance	1. Defective coil wire 2. Rotor tip burned	1. Perform ohmmeter test. 2. Visually inspect.
SPARK PLUGS UNDER LOAD TEST		
One or more of cylinders show a voltage rise over 4 kV	1. Spark plug gap too wide 2. Worn spark plug electrodes 3. Open or high resistance spark plug wire 4. Improper fuel mixture 5. Open spark plug resistor 6. Leakage in vacuum system	1. Check gap, then regap plug. 2. Replace the spark plug. 3. Perform ohmmeter test. 4. Adjust mixture. 5. Substitute spark plug. 6. Check for leaky vacuum hoses and diaphragms, or gaskets.
One or more cylinders show a voltage rise less than 3 kV or no voltage rise at all	1. Shorted spark plug wire 2. Broken spark plug insulator 3. Fouled spark plug 4. Low compression	1. Perform secondary insulation test. 2. Replace spark plug. 3. Clean or replace spark plug. 4. Perform compression test.
CYLINDER TIMING ACCURACY TEST		
Transistor turn off signals exceed specifications for engine being tested	1. Bent distributor shaft 2. Worn distributor bushings 3. Worn gear on distributor 4. Worn camshaft gear 5. Worn timing chain	1. Perform distributor test. 2. Perform distributor test. 3. Visually inspect. 4. Visually inspect. 5. Visually inspect.

Spark Plugs Under Load

The voltage required to fire the spark plugs increases when the engine is under load. The voltage increase is moderate and uniform if the spark plugs are in good condition and properly gapped. However, if any unusual characteristics are displayed on the scope patterns when load is applied to the engine, the spark plugs are probably faulty. This condition is most evident in the firing voltages displayed on the scope. To test spark plug operation under load, note the height of the firing lines at idle speed. Then, quickly open and release the throttle (snap accelerate), and note the rise in the firing lines while checking the voltages for uniformity. A normal rise would be between 3 and 4 kV upon snap acceleration.

If during testing, one or more of the cylinders show a voltage rise of over 4 kV, or if one or more cylinders show a voltage rise less than 3 kV or no voltage rise at all, check Table 22–3.

Coil Condition The energy remaining in the coil after the spark plugs fire gradually diminishes in a series of oscillations. These oscillations are observable in the intermediate sections of both the primary and secondary patterns. If the scope pattern shows an absence of normal oscillations in the intermediate section, check for a possible short in the coil by testing the resistance of the primary and secondary windings. The procedure is given later in the chapter.

INDIVIDUAL COMPONENT TESTING

Electronic ignition systems have many characteristics unique to the system's manufacturer. It would be impossible in any one textbook to explain all the variations. However, the basic goal of any electrical troubleshooting procedure is always to identify electrical activity under a given set of circumstances. The manufacturer's service manual provides the technician with both the desired activity (specification) and the set of circumstances (procedures).

Tables 22–4 and 22–5 outline a procedure for quickly isolating an ignition-related problem when an

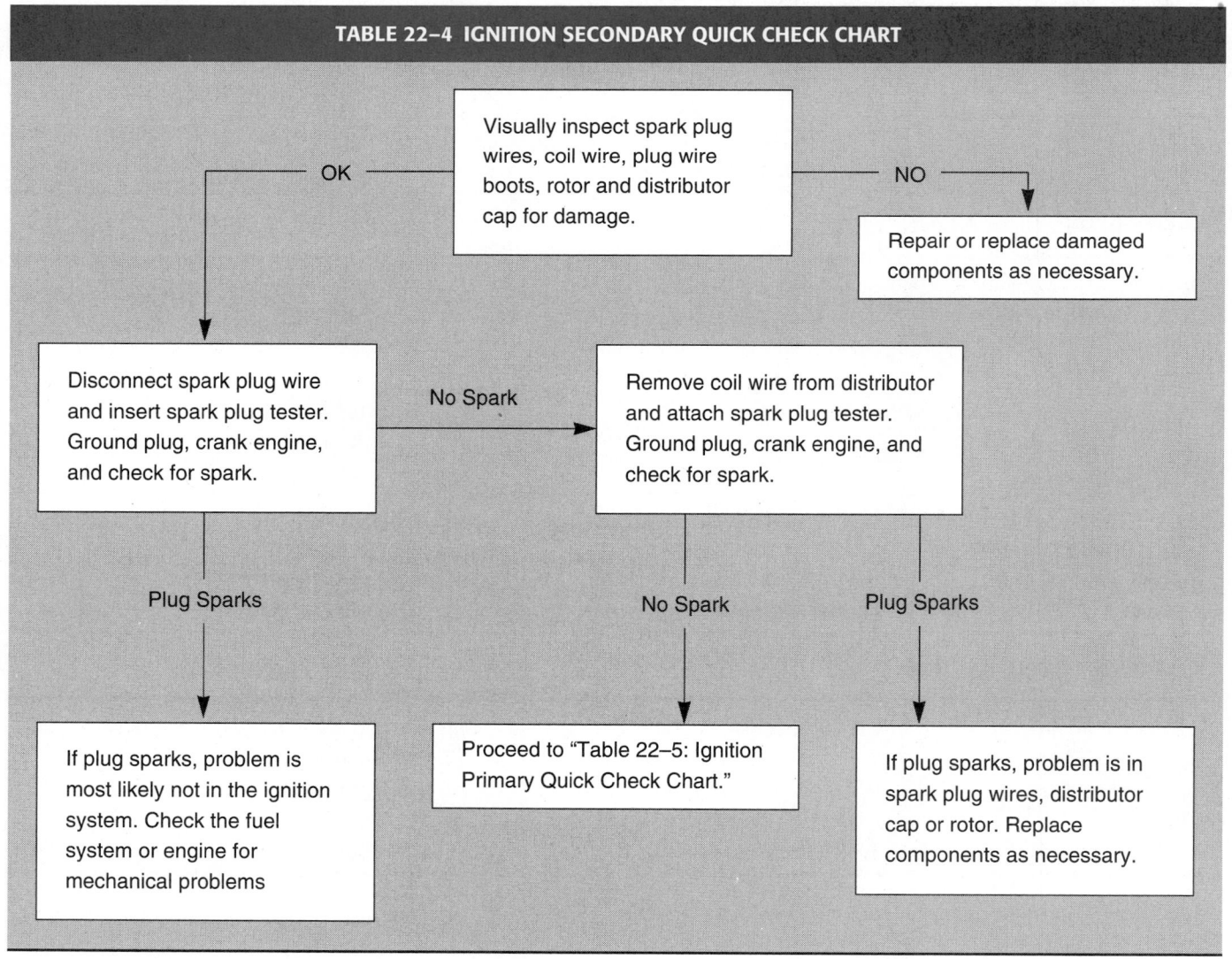

TABLE 22–4 IGNITION SECONDARY QUICK CHECK CHART

Visually inspect spark plug wires, coil wire, plug wire boots, rotor and distributor cap for damage.

OK

NO → Repair or replace damaged components as necessary.

Disconnect spark plug wire and insert spark plug tester. Ground plug, crank engine, and check for spark.

No Spark → Remove coil wire from distributor and attach spark plug tester. Ground plug, crank engine, and check for spark.

Plug Sparks

No Spark

Plug Sparks

If plug sparks, problem is most likely not in the ignition system. Check the fuel system or engine for mechanical problems

Proceed to "Table 22–5: Ignition Primary Quick Check Chart."

If plug sparks, problem is in spark plug wires, distributor cap or rotor. Replace components as necessary.

TABLE 22–5 IGNITION PRIMARY QUICK CHECK CHART

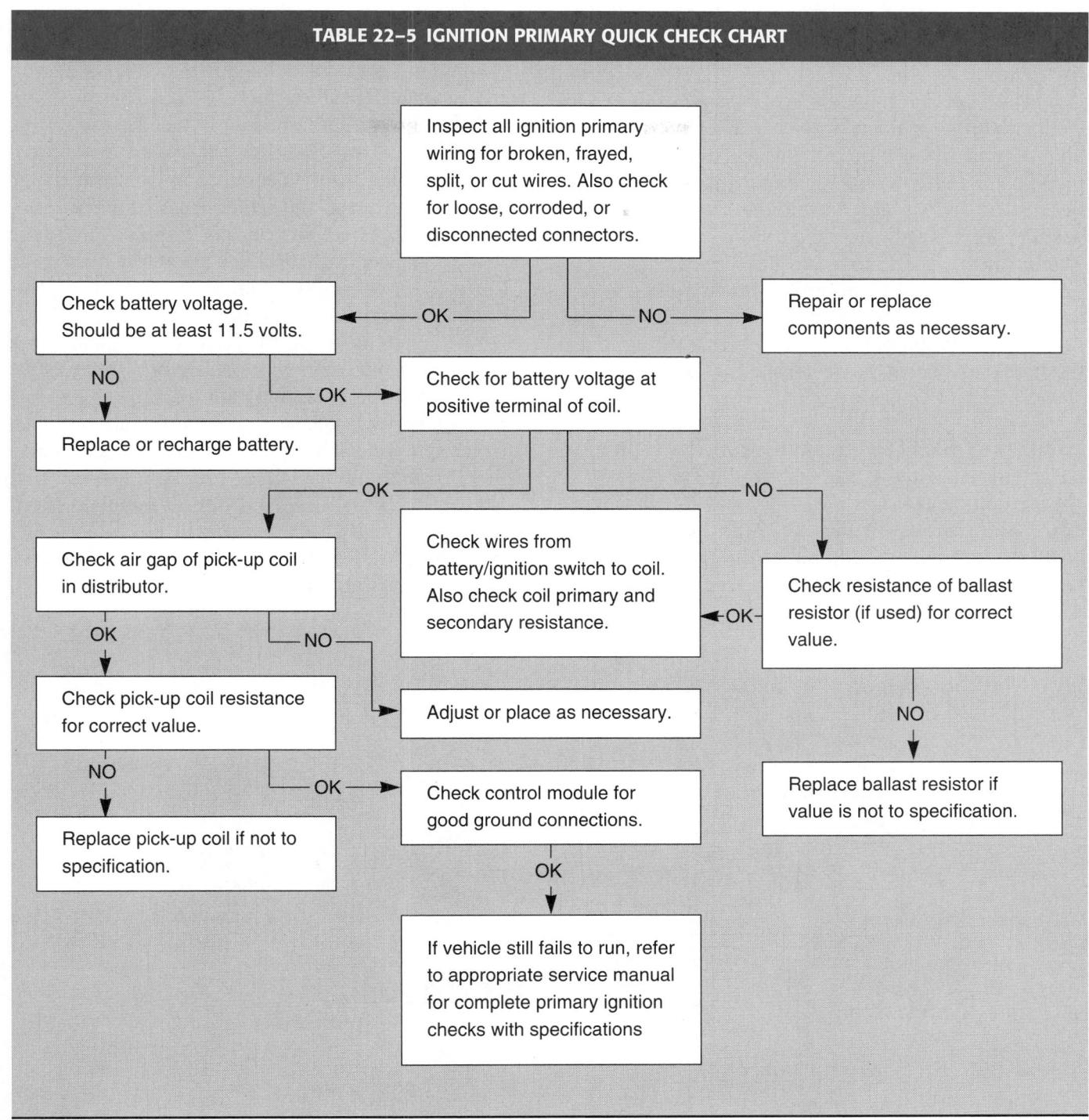

oscilloscope is not available. The first troubleshooting tree determines whether a spark is generated in the secondary system. If no spark is available, the second troubleshooting tree leads step by step through individual component tests until the problem is located.

The secret to component testing is to use good troubleshooting practices. Work systematically through a circuit, testing each wire, connector, and component. Do not jump around back and forth between compo-

nents. The component inadvertently overlooked is probably the one causing the trouble. Checks must be made for available voltage, voltage output, resistance of wires and connectors, and available ground. Always compare the readings with specifications given in the manufacturer's service manual.

The following sections briefly outline common test procedures for individual system components. For accurate testing always refer to service manual wiring diagrams and testing instructions.

USING SERVICE MANUALS

Service manuals are indispensable when troubleshooting ignition problems. They contain such vital information as base and advance timing specifications, color-coded wiring diagrams and terminal connector descriptions, and illustrations showing test connections for voltage, continuity, and resistance checks. The diagnostic charts found in the service manual are particularly helpful in troubleshooting ignition problems. Ignoring the valuable data contained in the ignition service section of these manuals can lead to many frustrating and costly service mistakes. ■

IGNITION SWITCH A faulty ignition switch or bad ignition switch wiring does not supply power to the ignition control module or ignition coil. The ignition system shown in Figure 22–28 has two wires connected to the run terminal of the ignition switch. One is connected to the module. The other is connected to the primary resistor and coil. The start terminal of the switch is also wired to the module.

You can check for voltage using either a 12-volt testlight or a digital voltmeter. To use the testlight method, turn the ignition key off and disconnect the wire connector at the module. Also, disconnect the S terminal of the starter solenoid to prevent the engine from cranking when the ignition is in the run position. Turn the key to the run position and probe the red wire connection to check for voltage (Figure 22–27A). Also check for voltage at the battery (bat) terminal of the ignition coil using the testlight.

Next, turn the key to the start position and check for voltage at the white wire connector at the module and the bat terminal of the ignition coil.

To make the same test using a digital voltmeter, turn the ignition switch to the off position and install a small straight pin into the appropriate module wire as shown in Figure 22–27B. Connect the digital voltmeter's positive lead to the straight pin and ground the negative lead to the distributor base. Turn the ignition to the run or start position as needed and

FIGURE 22–27 Testing for voltage at the ignition module to check ignition switch and wiring (A) testlight method, and (B) digital method. *Courtesy of Ford Motor Company*

FIGURE 22–28 Checking primary (ballast) resistance. *Courtesy of Ford Motor Company*

measure voltage. Do not allow the straight pin to contact the engine or ground. Reading should be within 90 percent of battery voltage.

PRIMARY RESISTOR Measure the resistance of the primary (ballast) resistor using an ohmmeter. Remember, the key must be off when this test is performed or power in the circuit damages the meter. In the ignition system shown in Figure 22–28, ohmmeter leads are connected at the bat terminal of the coil and the wiring harness connector wire that join the red wire in the ignition module connector.

IGNITION COIL RESISTANCE With the key off and the battery lead to the ignition coil disconnected, use the ohmmeter to measure the primary and secondary winding resistance of the ignition coil.

Calibrate the ohmmeter on the X1 scale, and connect the meter leads across the bat (+) and tach (–) terminals of the ignition coil to check the winding for an open, short, or high resistance condition (Figure 22–29). Primary resistance usually ranges from 0.5 to 2 ohms. Check the specifications listed in the service manual.

To measure secondary coil resistance, calibrate the ohmmeter on the X1,000 (X1K) scale and connect it across the bat (+) terminal and the ignition coil's center (high voltage) tower (Figure 22–30). Secondary resistance usually ranges from 8,000 to 20,000 ohms. Again, check service manual specifications.

The ohmmeter tests on the primary and secondary windings indicate the general condition of the coil. However, these tests do not guarantee the coil will work fine. Some defects will only show up on scope tests, such as defective insulation around the coil windings, which causes high voltage leaks.

PICK-UP COIL The pick-up coil of a magnetic pulse generator or metal detection sensor is also checked for proper resistance using an ohmmeter. Connect the ohmmeter to the pick-up coil terminals to test the pick-up coil for an open or a shorted condition. While the ohmmeter leads are connected, pull on the pick-up leads and watch for an erratic reading, indicating an intermittent open in the pick-up leads. Most pick-up coils have 150 to 900 ohms resistance, but always refer to the manufacturer's specifications. If the pick-

FIGURE 22–29 Ohmmeter connected to primary coil terminals. *Courtesy of Chrysler Corporation*

FIGURE 22–30 Ohmmeter connected from one primary terminal to the coil tower to test secondary winding. *Courtesy of Toyota Motor Corporation*

FIGURE 22–31 Ohmmeter-to-pickup coil test connections. *Courtesy of Oldsmobile Division, General Motors Corporation*

FIGURE 22–32 Test Hall-effect sensor operation with a steel feeler gauge.

up coil is open, the ohmmeter will display an infinite reading. When the pick-up coil is shorted, the ohmmeter will display a reading lower than specifications.

Connect the ohmmeter from one of the pick-up leads to ground to test the pick-up for a short to ground. If there is no short to ground, the ohmmeter will give an infinite reading. Refer to Figure 22–31, ohmmeter #1 is testing for a short to ground, while ohmmeter #2 is testing the resistance of the pick-up coil.

The oscilloscope can be used to check pick-up coil operation. The primary scope leads are connected to the pick-up coil leads. The scope is set on its lowest scale. When the distributor shaft is spun, an AC sine wave trace should appear on the CRT screen. The trace is not a true sine wave, but it should have both a positive and negative pulse.

Another method of measuring the pick-up coil's AC signal is with a simple voltmeter set on its low voltage scale. The meter registers AC voltage during cranking. Measure this voltage as close to the control module as possible to account for any resistance in the connecting wire from the pick-up coil to the module.

HALF-EFFECT SENSORS Most Hall-effect sensors can be tested by connecting a 12-volt battery across the plus (+) and minus (–) voltage (supply current) terminals of the Hall layer, and a voltmeter across the minus (–) and signal voltage terminals.

With the voltmeter hooked up, insert a steel feeler gauge or knife blade between the Hall layer and magnet (Figure 22–32). If the sensor is good, the voltmeter should read within 0.5 volt of battery voltage when the feeler gauge or knife blade is inserted and touching the magnet. When the feeler gauge or blade is removed, the voltage should read less than 0.5 volt.

It is often possible to observe the voltage levels of the Hall-effect sensor using an oscilloscope. Set the scope on its low-scale primary pattern position and connect the primary positive lead to the Hall signal lead, using a weather pack jumper wire (Figure 22–33). The negative lead should connect to ground or the ground terminal at the sensor's connector.

With the engine running, the pattern should show a square wave pattern ranging from approximately 0 to 12 volts (Figure 22–34). If the range is out of specifications or distorted, replace the sensor.

TO DISTRIBUTOR WEATHER PACK JUMPER LEADS TO ECM

PRIMARY POSITIVE LEAD TO HALL SIGNAL PIN B OF 4-WAY CONNECTOR

NEGATIVE PRIMARY LEAD TO PIN D OF 4-WAY CONNECTOR

FIGURE 22–33 Connecting oscilloscope leads to late model General Motors' Hall-effect sensor using weather pack jumper leads.

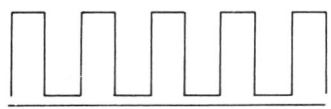

FIGURE 22–34 Square wave trace produced by properly operating Hall-effect sensor.

FIGURE 22–35 Using ohmmeter to check for proper control module grounding. *Courtesy of Ford Motor Company*

CONTROL MODULE Use an ohmmeter to ensure that the control module connection to ground is good. As shown in Figure 22–35, one lead of the meter is connected to the ground terminal at the module. The other is connected to a good engine ground. Zero resistance indicates good continuity in the ground circuit. Any resistance reading during this test is unacceptable.

The most effective method of testing for a defective control module is to use an ignition module tester. This electronic tester evaluates and determines if the module is operating within a given set of design parameters. It does so by simulating normal operating conditions while looking for faults in key components. A typical ignition module tester performs the following tests.

◆ Shorted module test
◆ Cranking current test
◆ Key on/engine off current test
◆ Idle current test
◆ Cruise current test
◆ Cranking primary voltage test
◆ Idle primary voltage test
◆ Cruise primary voltage test

Some ignition module testers are also able to perform an ignition coil-spark test (actually firing the coil) and a distributor pick-up test.

Test selection is made by pushing the appropriate button. The module tester usually responds to these tests with a pass or fail indication.

Unfortunately, many module testers are designed to troubleshoot specific makes and models of ignitions. Many shops find it impractical to have testers for every type of system they service.

Keep in mind that control modules are very reliable. They are also one of the most expensive ignition

system components. So, if a module tester is not available, check out all other system components before condemning the control module.

SPARK PLUG WIRE TESTING The spark plug wires may be left in the distributor cap for testing purposes, so the cap terminal connections are tested with the spark plug wires. Connect the ohmmeter leads from the end of the spark plug wire to the distributor cap terminal inside the cap to which the plug wire is connected (Figure 22–36).

If the resistance reading is more than that specified by the vehicle's manufacturer, remove the wire from the cap and check the wire alone. If the wire has more resistance than specified, replace the wire. If the spark plug wire resistance is satisfactory, check the cap terminal for corrosion. Repeat this test on each spark plug wire and the coil secondary wire.

Stress Testing Components

Often, an intermittent ignition problem only occurs under certain conditions, such as extremes in heat or cold, or during rainy or humid weather. Careful ques-

FIGURE 22–36 Ohmmeter connected to the spark plug wire and distributor cap terminal to test the plug wire. *Courtesy of Toyota Motor Corporation*

tioning of the customer should lead to determining if the problem is stress-condition related. Does the problem occur on cold mornings? Does it occur when the engine is fully warmed up? Is it a rainy day problem? If the answer to any of these questions is positive, you can reproduce the same conditions in the shop during stress testing.

COLD TESTING With the scope on raster, cool major ignition components, such as the control module, pick-up coil, and major connections one at a time using a liquid cool-down agent.

CAUTION:

When using cool-down sprays, wear eye protection and avoid spraying your skin or clothing. Use extreme caution. ■

After cooling a component, watch the pattern for any signs of malfunction, particularly in the dwell zone. If there is no sign of malfunction, cool down the next component after the first has warmed to normal operating temperature. Cool (or heating) more than one component at a time provides inconclusive results.

HEAT TESTING To heat stress components, use a heat gun or hair dryer to direct hot air into the component. Heat guns intended for stripping paint and other household jobs can become extremely hot and melt plastic, wire insulation, and other materials. Use a moderate setting and proceed cautiously. Look for changes in the dwell section of the trace, particularly in the variable dwell or current limiting areas. If connections appear to be the problem, disconnect them, clean the terminals, and coat them with dielectric compound to seal out dirt and moisture.

MOISTURE TESTING A wet stress test is performed by lightly spraying the components, coil and ignition cables, and connections with water. Do not flood the area, a light mist does the job. A scope set on raster or display helps pinpoint problems, but it is often possible to hear and feel the miss or stutter without the use of a scope. As with heat and cold testing, do not spray down more than one area at a time or results could be misleading. If you suspect a poor connection, clean and seat it, then retest it.

CUSTOMER CARE

The term tune-up essentially means replacing spark plugs and other ignition parts and adjusting the air/fuel mixture and setting the timing. Tamper-resistant carburetors, fuel injection systems, and electronic ignition eliminated these once common service procedures over a decade ago. Today, the computer-controlled system normally makes these adjustments. Unfortunately, your customers have probably not kept abreast of these changes. Many shop owners state that over half of the customers coming in for tune-ups still think their vehicles have breaker points.

So when a customer approaches you for a standard tune-up, it's the ideal time to explain in simple terms just how the vehicle operates and what is involved in a modern tune-up. These procedures should include these points.

- An initial test drive with the customer
- Spark plug change
- Compression test or dynamic compression test
- Visual inspection of ignition system
- Base timing check and idle speed check
- Inspection of vacuum lines, air intake ducts, and PCV valve operation
- Check operation of ERG valve and oxygen sensor
- Pull computer trouble codes—if easily accessible
- Replace air and fuel filters if the service interval is reached
- Inspect all belts and hoses
- Check fan operation
- Inspect water pump seal
- Service battery terminals and top all fluids ■

Spark Plug Service

Spark plug service is a vital part of a complete engine tune-up. Vehicle manufacturers' recommendations for service intervals can range anywhere between 20,000 and 100,000 miles, depending on a variety of factors.

- The type of ignition system
- Engine design
- Spark plug design
- Vehicle operating conditions
- The type of fuel used
- Types of emission control devices used

Regardless of what other tools are used, a spark plug socket is essential for plug removal and installation. Spark plug sockets are available in two sizes: 13/16-inch (for 14-millimeter gasketed and 18-millimeter tapered-seat plugs) and 5/8-inch (for 14-millimeter tapered-seat plugs). They can be either 3/8- or 1/2-inch drive, and many feature an external hex so they can be turned using an open end or box wrench.

PROCEDURES

Removing Spark Plugs

1. Remove the cables from each plug, being careful not to pull on the cables. Instead, grasp the boot and twist it off gently.
2. Using a spark plug socket and ratchet, loosen each plug a couple of turns.
3. Use compressed air to blow the dirt away from the base of the plugs.
4. Remove the plugs, making sure to remove the gasket as well (if applicable).

FIGURE 22–38 Cold-fouled spark plug. *Courtesy of Denso Spark Plugs*

SHOP TALK

To save time and avoid confusion later, use masking tape to mark each of the cables with the number of the plug it attaches to. ■

Inspecting Spark Plugs Once the spark plugs have been removed, it is important to "read" them (Figure 22–37). In other words, inspect them closely, noting in particular any deposits on the plugs and the degree of electrode erosion. A plug in good working condition can still have minimal deposits on it. They are usually light tan or gray in color. However, there should be no evidence of electrode burning, and the increase of the air gap should be no more than 0.001 inch for every 10,000 miles of engine operation. A plug that exceeds this wear should be replaced and the cause of excessive wear repaired.

It is possible to diagnose a variety of engine conditions by examining the firing ends of the spark plugs. If an engine is in good shape, they should all look alike. Whenever plugs from different cylinders look different, a problem exists somewhere in the engine or its systems. Following are examples of plug problems and how they should be dealt with.

COLD FOULING This condition is the result of an excessively rich air/fuel mixture. It is characterized by a layer of dry, fluffy black carbon deposits on the top of the plug (Figure 22–38). **Cold fouling** is caused by a rich air/fuel mixture or an ignition fault causing the spark plug not to fire. If only one or two of the plugs show evidence of cold fouling, sticking valves are the likely cause. The plug can be used again, provided its electrodes are filed and the air gap is reset. Correct the cause of the problem before reinstalling or replacing the plugs.

SHOP TALK

If cold fouling is present on a vehicle that operates a great deal at idle and low speeds, plug life can be lengthened by using hotter spark plugs. ■

WET FOULING When the tip of the plug is practically drowned in excess oil, this condition is known as **wet fouling** (Figure 22–39). In an overhead valve engine, the oil may be entering the combustion chamber past worn valve guides or valve guide seals. If the vehicle has an automatic transmission, a likely cause of wet-fouled plugs is a defective vacuum modulator that is allowing transmission fluid into the chamber. On high-mileage engines, check for worn rings or excessive cylinder wear. The best solution is to correct the problem and replace the plugs with the specified type.

FIGURE 22–37 Spark plug in good working order. *Courtesy of Denso Spark Plugs*

FIGURE 22–39 Wet-fouled spark plug. *Courtesy of Denso Spark Plugs*

FIGURE 22–40 Condition of overheating spark plug. *Courtesy of Denso Spark Plugs*

SPLASH FOULING Splash fouling occurs immediately following an overdue tune-up. Deposits in the combustion chamber, accumulated over a period of time due to misfiring, suddenly loosen when the temperature in the chamber returns to normal. During high-speed driving, these deposits can stick to the hot insulator and electrode surfaces of the plug. These deposits can actually bridge across the gap, stopping the plug from sparking. Normally splash-fouled plugs can be cleaned and reused.

GAP BRIDGING A plug with a bridged gap is rarely seen in automobile engines. **Gap bridging** occurs when flying carbon deposits within the combustion chamber accumulate over a long period of stop-and-go driving. When the engine is suddenly placed under a hard load, the deposits melt and bridge the gap, causing misfire. This condition is best corrected by replacing the plug.

GLAZING Under high-speed conditions, the combustion chamber deposits can form a shiny, yellow glaze over the insulator. When it gets hot enough, the glaze acts as an electrical conductor causing the current to follow the deposits and short out the plug. **Glazing** can be prevented by avoiding sudden wide-open throttle acceleration after sustained periods of low-speed or idle operation. Because it is virtually impossible to remove glazed deposits, glazed plugs should be replaced.

OVERHEATING This condition is characterized by white or light gray blistering of the insulator. There may also be considerable electrode gap wear (Figure 22–40). Overheating can result from using too hot a plug, overadvanced ignition timing, detonation, a malfunction in the cooling system, an overly lean air/fuel mixture, using too-low octane fuel, an improperly installed plug, or a heat-riser valve that is stuck closed. Overheated plugs must be replaced.

TURBULENCE BURNING When turbulence burning occurs, the insulator on one side of the plug wears away as the result of normal turbulence in the combustion chamber (Figure 22–41). As long as the plug life is normal, this condition is of little consequence. However, if there is a larger-than-normal air gap, overheating can be the problem. In this case, check for all of the common causes of overheating discussed previously.

Preignition damage is caused by excessive engine temperatures. Preignition damage is characterized by melting of the electrodes, or chipping of the electrode tips (Figure 22-42). When this problem occurs, look for the general causes of engine overheating, including overadvanced ignition timing, a burned head gasket, and using too-low octane fuel. Other possibilities include loose plugs or using plugs of the improper heat range. Do not attempt to reuse plugs with preignition damage.

A sure sign of reverse coil polarity damage is a slight dishing of the ground electrode. The center electrode does not normally wear badly. Misfiring and rough idling may also be present. In addition to

FIGURE 22–41 Condition of spark plug after experiencing turbulence burning. *Courtesy of Denso Spark Plugs*

FIGURE 22–42 This plug shows evidence of preignition damage. *Courtesy of Denso Spark Plugs*

reversal of the coil primary leads, older vehicles can experience reverse coil polarity damage by reversing the battery polarity.

SHOP TALK

It is a good idea to brush used spark plug electrodes with several strokes of a flat distributor point file or spark plug gauge file (Figure 22–43). This helps reduce the required firing voltage of the plug. ■

Regapping Spark Plugs

Both new and used spark plugs have their air gaps set to the engine manufacturer's specifications. Use an approved tool not only to measure the gap but also to bend the side electrode to make the adjustment. The combustion gauge and adjusting tool shown in Figure 22–44 is designed for use on new plugs only. This is because it utilizes flat gauges for the adjustment procedure. The gauges are mounted on the tool like spokes on a wheel. Above the gauges is an anvil,

FIGURE 22–43 It may be helpful to file the electrodes clean.

FIGURE 22–44 Combination spark plug gauge and adjusting tool.

which is used to apply pressure to the electrode. On the opposite end of the tool is a curved seat. This seat performs two functions. It supports the plug shell during the procedure. It also compresses the ground electrode against the gauge, thus setting the air gap.

The tapered regapping tool is simply a piece of tapered steel with leading and trailing edges of different dimensions. Between these two points, the gauge varies in thickness. A scale, located above the gauge, indicates the thickness at any given point. When the gauge is slid between electrodes, it stops when the air gap size reaches the thickness on the gauge. The scale reading is made in thousandths of an inch. Adjusting slots are available to bend the ground electrode as needed to make the air gap adjustment.

In many instances, the electrodes on a used spark plug are no longer flat, thus rendering a flat gauge useless for regapping purposes. Instead, a round wire gauge is required. Combination round and flat feeler gauge sets are available. These multipurpose tools can be used to check air gaps, adjust contact points, bend electrodes, and fire contact points and electrodes.

When regapping a spark plug, always check the air gap of a new spark plug before installing it. Never assume the gap is correct just because the plug is new. Do not try to reduce a plug's air gap by tapping the side electrode on a bench. Never attempt to set a wide gap electronic ignition type plug to a small gap specification. Likewise, never attempt to set a small gap breaker point ignition type plug to the wide gap necessary for electronic ignitions. In either case, damage to the electrodes results. Never try to bend the center electrode to adjust the air gap. This cracks the insulation.

WARNING!

If thread lubricant is used, reduce the torque setting. Keep in mind that many spark plug manufacturers do not recommend the use of thread lubricant. ■

PROCEDURES
Spark Plug Installation

1. Wipe dirt and grease from the plug seats with a clean cloth.
2. Be sure the gaskets on gasketed plugs are in good condition and properly placed on the plugs. If reusing a plug, install a new gasket on it. Be sure there is only one gasket on each plug.
3. Adjust the air gap as needed.
4. Install the plugs and finger-tighten. If the plugs cannot be installed easily by hand, the threads in the cylinder head may require cleaning with a thread-chasing tap. Be especially careful not to cross-thread the plugs when working with aluminum heads.
5. Tighten the plugs with a torque wrench, following the vehicle manufacturer's specifications or the values listed in Table 22–6.

Plug Type	Cast-Iron Head	Aluminum Head
TABLE 22–6 PLUG INSTALLATION TORQUE VALUES (IN FOOT-POUNDS)		
14-mm Gasketed	25 to 30	15 to 22
14-mm Tapered Seat	7 to 15	7 to 15
18-mm Tapered Seat	15 to 20	15 to 20

REPLACING SPARK PLUG WIRES

When spark plug wires are being installed, make sure they are routed properly as indicated in the vehicle's service manual. When removing the spark plug wires from a spark plug, grasp the spark plug boot tightly, and twist while pulling the cable from the end of the plug. When installing a spark plug wire, make sure the boot is firmly seated around the top of the plug; then squeeze the boot to expel any air that is trapped inside.

REPLACING BREAKER POINTS

As already stated, one of the advantages of electronic systems is the elimination of breaker points. Breaker points require regular replacement typically at intervals of 6,000 to 12,000 miles. Replace the condenser with the points.

Most replacement breaker points are sold as pre-assembled sets, with the alignment and spring tension set at the factory. However, replacement points that come as two-piece units require alignment and spring tension and dwell adjustments.

In most cases, the spring tension is adjusted by sliding the spring along its slot. Point alignment is accomplished using a special tool. Be sure to bend only the stationary contact support, never the movable contact arm. Always clean and lubricate the distributor cam and breaker point rubbing block. Special grease is available for this purpose.

To set the gap on a set of points, turn the ignition off and remove the distributor cap and rotor. Then connect a remote starter switch and bump the engine with the starter motor until the rubbing block is exactly on a high point of the cam. Slide a clean feeler gauge of the proper thickness between the points. It should slide between the contacts with a slight drag. Consult the manufacturer's specifications for proper gap dimension, and adjust accordingly. Make the adjustment by loosening the hold-down screw and shifting the position of the point assembly. Finally, tighten the holddown screw and recheck the gap.

As explained earlier, dwell is the amount of time current flows through the primary winding of the ignition coil. It is measured in terms of camshaft rotation using a tach-dwellmeter.

In a breaker point ignition system, dwell indicates the amount of time the points are closed. It is directly related to gap. If the gap is set correctly, the dwell reading matches specifications. Measuring dwell is highly useful when setting and adjusting points. In electronic ignitions, dwell cannot be adjusted. However, a tach-dwellmeter can still be used to check the variable dwell function of the control module.

SETTING IGNITION TIMING

The correct ignition timing procedure varies depending on the make and year of the vehicle and the type of ignition system. Ignition timing specifications and instructions are included on the underhood emission decal, and more detailed instructions are provided in the vehicle's service manual; these must be followed.

Spark plug gap, idle speed, and dwell must be correct before setting ignition timing. Also, the engine must be at operating temperature. The following are some general points common to many systems.

- Base timing is normally checked and adjusted at idle speed or low engine speeds, such as 650 rpm. At this low speed, any mechanical advance mechanism is not activated and does not affect the base reading.

- Many systems require checking timing with the automatic transmission placed in drive. This is often abbreviated as DR on the instruction sticker.
- The vacuum-advance mechanism must also be disabled so it does not affect the base reading. This is done by removing and plugging the vacuum advance line or hose from the manifold.
- In computer-controlled systems, the microprocessor controls ignition timing advance. To set correct base timing, the computer has to be eliminated from the timing control circuit. This is normally done by disconnecting the appropriate connector at the distributor. For example, Ford calls this connector the spout (spark out) connector. GM and other manufacturers have similar methods of disabling computer timing control. Setting base timing is very important in computer-controlled systems. If base timing is incorrect, the computer makes further adjustments based on incorrect data.

Making Base Timing Adjustments

Once you have obtained a base timing reading, compare it to manufacturer's specifications. For example, if the specification reads 10 degrees before top dead center (Figure 22–45A) and the reading found is 3

SPECIAL DISTRIBUTOR WRENCH

DISTRIBUTOR HOLDDOWN CLAMP BOLT

ROTATE SLOWLY

ROTATE IN SLIGHT AMOUNTS

FIGURE 22–46 Turning the distributor to set timing. *Courtesy of Chrysler Corporation*

degrees before top dead center (Figure 22–45B) the timing is retarded or off by 7 degrees.

This means the timing must be advanced by 7 degrees to make it correct. To do this, rotate the distributor until the timing marks align at 10 degrees (Figure 22–46). Then retighten the distributor holddown bolt (Figure 22–47).

Many late-model vehicles have a magnetic timing probe receptacle near the timing indicator (Figure 22–48). Some equipment manufacturers supply a

TIMING MARKS ALIGNED AT 10

A

TIMING MARKS ALIGNED AT 3

B

FIGURE 22–45 (A) Timing marks illuminated by a timing light at 10 degrees BTDC, and (B) timing marks at 3 degrees BTDC.

Holddown screw

FIGURE 22–47 Tighten the distributor holddown screw after the timing is adjusted to specifications. *Courtesy of Chrysler Corporation*

FIGURE 22–48 Magnetic timing probe receptacle near timing indicator. *Courtesy of Chrysler Corporation*

FIGURE 22–50 Timing light with advance control and spark advance meter. *Courtesy of Chrysler Corporation*

magnetic **timing meter** with a pick-up that fits into the probe hole. The meter pick-up must be connected to the number one spark plug wire and the power supply leads must be connected to the battery terminals (Figure 22–49). Many timing meters have two scales: timing degrees and engine rpm.

A magnetic timing **offset** knob on the meter must be adjusted to the manufacturer's specifications to compensate for the position of the probe receptacle. Once the offset is adjusted, the engine may be started and the timing is indicated on the meter scale. The timing adjustment procedure is the same with the timing meter or timing light.

Checking Mechanical Advance Units

Mechanical or centrifugal units advance ignition timing in response to increases in engine speed. To check the operation of this unit, loosen the distributor hold-

down bolt or clamp. Disable any vacuum-advance system. Raise engine speed to 2,000 rpm or speed specified in the service manual. Then shine the light on the vibration damper timing marks, and turn the timing knob on the advance timing light until the base timing reading of 10 degrees is again registering (Figure 22–50). Observe the reading on the timing meter of the timing light. It tells how many degrees the flash of light has been delayed. This meter reading should match the specified advance at that rpm level.

If the reading does not match up, the mechanical advance mechanism is faulty. The vacuum advance can be checked in the same manner. Use a hand-held vacuum pump to draw on the diaphragm until the vacuum specification is reached, and adjust the advance timing light until correct base timing is again register-

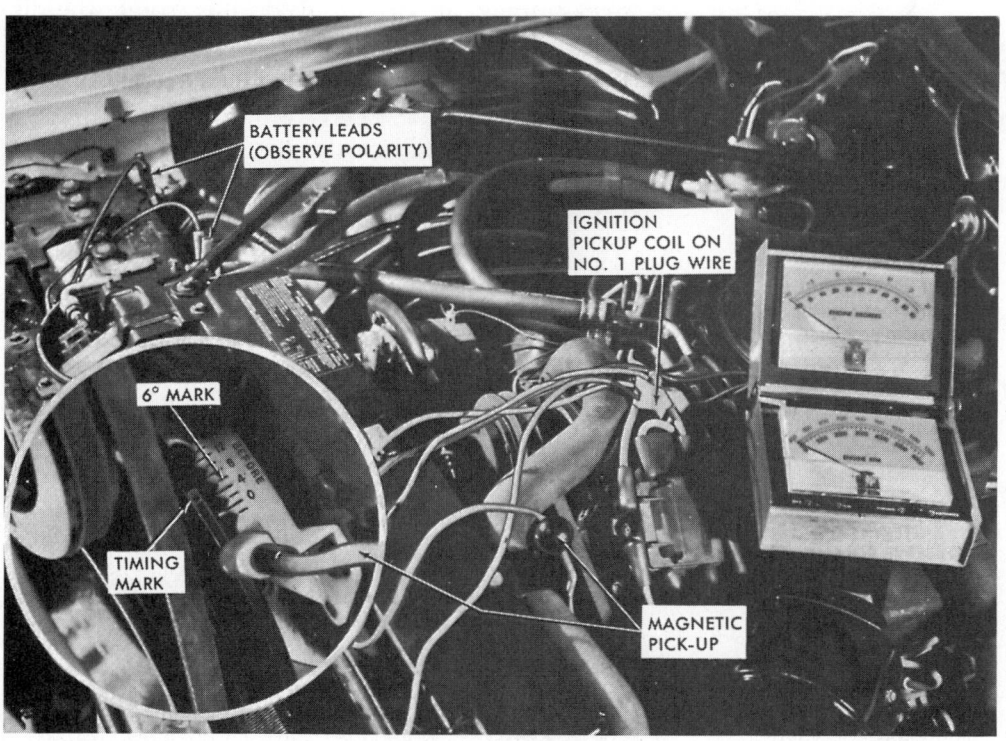

FIGURE 22–49 Magnetic timing meter and related connections. *Courtesy of Cadillac Motor Car Division, General Motors Corporation*

ing. Once again, the amount of flash delay matches the amount of vacuum advance present.

Symptoms of overly advanced timing include pinging or engine knock. Insufficient advance or retarded timing at higher engine rpms could cause hesitation and poor fuel economy.

The normal test procedure is to compare vacuum and mechanical advance to manufacturer specifications at several different engine speeds.

DISTRIBUTOR SERVICE

All service procedures for a distributor depend on the manufacturer and design of the distributor. Always follow the recommended procedures given in the service manual. In most cases, removal of the distributor begins any repairs to the distributor.

Before removing the distributor, check the condition of the distributor's bushing. Do this by grasping the distributor shaft and moving it toward the outside of the distributor. If any movement is detected, remove the distributor and check the bushing on the bench.

Lightly clamp the distributor housing in a soft-jaw vise. Clamp a dial indicator on the top of the distributor housing. Position the plunger of the indicator so it rests on the distributor shaft. When the shaft is pushed horizontally, observe the movement of the shaft on the indicator. Compare this movement to the specifications given in the service manual. If the movement exceeds the allowed amount, the distributor bushings and/or shaft are worn. Many manufacturers recommend complete distributor replacement rather than bushing or shaft replacement.

To remove a typical distributor, begin by disconnecting the distributor wiring connector and vacuum advance hoses. Then, remove the distributor cap and note the position of the rotor. Remove the distributor hold-down bolt and clamp. Note the position of the vacuum advance unit in relation to the engine. Then pull the distributor from the engine. After the distributor has been removed, install a shop towel in the distributor opening to keep foreign material out of the engine. Photo Sequence 11 shows the correct way to re-install a distributor on a typical engine.

COMPUTER-CONTROLLED IGNITION SYSTEM SERVICE

To check the base timing, the manufacturers give specific instructions for readying the engine. Some require disconnecting certain components or connectors. An example of this is many Ford and GM systems, which require that a connector located in the engine compartment be disconnected. The emission's decal may provide information about the location of this connector. It is important that these instructions be followed so as to disable the computer's control over ignition timing. After these preparation steps are followed, the engine may be timed in the normal manner.

Distributor pick-ups can be tested in the way discussed earlier. It is important that all wires and connectors between the distributor and module and the module to the engine control computer be visually checked as well as checked for excessive resistance with an ohmmeter.

If the resistance checks are within specifications, the circuit should be checked with a digital voltmeter. Turn the ignition on and connect the voltmeter across the voltage input wire and ground. Compare the reading to specifications. The voltmeter should also be used to check the resistance across the ground circuit of the distributor. Do this by measuring the voltage drop across the circuit, a drop of more than 0.1 volt is excessive.

Connect the voltmeter from the pick-up signal wire to ground. If the voltmeter does not fluctuate while cranking the engine, the pick-up is defective. A good pick-up will have readings from nearly 0 volts to 12 volts.

On Chrysler optical distributors, the pick-up voltage supply and ground wires may be tested at the four-wire connector near the distributor. With the ignition switch on, connect the voltmeter from the orange voltage supply wire to ground. The reading should be 9.2 to 9.4 volts (Figure 22–51). Because the expected reading may vary with the model year, always refer to the manufacturer's service manual before conducting the test.

Optical distributor
4-way connector

Or–9.2–9.4 volt power supply
Bk/Lb–ground
Gy/Bk–0 or 5 volts (reference pickup)
Tn/Yl–0 or 5 volts (sync pickup)

Optical distributor

FIGURE 22–51 Chrysler optical distributor four-wire connector. *Courtesy of Chrysler Corporation*

INSTALLING A DISTRIBUTOR AND SETTING THE TIMING OF AN ENGINE

P11–1 Remove the number one spark plug.

P11–2 Place your thumb over the number one spark plug opening and crank the engine until compression is felt.

P11–3 Crank the engine a very small length of time until the timing marks indicate the number one piston is at TDC on the compression stroke.

P11–4 Determine the number one spark plug wire position on the distributor cap.

P11–5 Install the distributor with the rotor under the number one spark plug wire terminal in the distributor cap and one of the reluctor high points aligned with the pick-up coil.

P11–6 After the distributor is installed in the block, turn the distributor housing slightly so the pick-up coil is aligned with the reluctor.

P11–7 Install the distributor clamp bolt, but leave it slightly loose.

P11–8 Connect the pick-up leads to the wiring harness.

P11–9 Install the spark plug wires in the cylinder firing order and in the direction of distributor shaft rotation.

When the voltmeter is connected between the black/light blue ground wire and an engine ground, the reading should be less than 0.2 volt. When the voltmeter is connected from the grey/black reference pick-up wire or the tan/yellow SYNC pick-up wire to an engine ground, the voltmeter should cycle from nearly 0 volts to 5 volts while the engine is cranking. If the pick-up signal is not within specifications, the pick-up is defective. A defective SYNC pick-up in this distributor should not cause a no-start problem but will affect engine performance.

DISTRIBUTORLESS SYSTEM SERVICE

Standard test procedures using an oscilloscope, ohmmeter, and timing light can be used to diagnose problems in distributorless ignition systems. Keep in mind, however, that problems involving one cylinder may also occur in its companion cylinder that fires off the same coil. Some oscilloscopes require the pick-ups placed on each pair of cylinders to view all patterns. Special adapters are available to make these hookups less troublesome. Many newer engine analyzers with an oscilloscope use a single adapter that allows viewing of all cylinder patterns at one time.

SHOP TALK

According to the SAE J1930 standards that were recently mandated to the automotive industry, the term distributor ignition (**DI**) replaces all previous terms for distributor-type ignition systems that are electronically controlled. Also according to this mandate, the term electronic ignition (**EI**) replaces all previous terms for distributorless ignition systems. ∎

Follow the testing procedures outlined in the vehicle service manual for DIS systems and other computer-controlled ignition systems. Specific computer-generated trouble codes are designed to help troubleshoot ignition problems on computer-controlled systems. The diagnostic procedure for EI systems varies depending on the vehicle make and model year. Always follow the procedure recommended in the vehicle's service manual.

CAM AND CRANK SENSORS

The following procedure is based on Chrysler EI systems. The crankshaft timing sensor and camshaft reference sensor in these systems are modified Hall-effect switches.

FIGURE 22–52 Crankshaft timing and camshaft reference sensor terminals. *Courtesy of Chrysler Corporation*

If a crank or cam sensor fails, the engine will not start. Both of these sensor circuits (Figure 22–52) can be checked with a voltmeter. If the sensors are receiving the correct amount of voltage and have good low-resistance ground circuits, their output should be a digital signal or a pulsing voltmeter meter reading while the engine is cranking. If any of these conditions do not exist, the circuit needs to be repaired or the sensor needs to be replaced.

If a crankshaft or camshaft sensor needs to be replaced, always clean the sensor tip and install a new spacer (if so equipped) on the sensor tip. New sensors typically have a new spacer already installed on the sensor (Figure 22–53). Install the sensor until the spacer lightly touches the sensor ring and tighten the sensor mounting bolt.

The base timing cannot be adjusted on an EI system, however, if the gap between the blades and the crankshaft sensor (on 3.0L, 3300, 3.8L, and 3800 GM engines) is not correct, the engine may fail to start, stall, misfire, or hesitate on acceleration. To install a sensor with the correct gap, follow these steps.

FIGURE 22–53 Spacer on crankshaft timing sensor and camshaft reference sensor tips. *Courtesy of Chrysler Corporation*

FIGURE 22–54 Crankshaft sensor adjustment for GM 3.0L, 3300, 3.8L, and 3800 engines. *Courtesy of Oldsmobile Division, General Motors Corporation*

1. Install the sensor loosely on its pedestal.
2. Position the sensor and the pedestal on the specified adjusting tool.
3. Position the adjusting tool on the crankshaft surface (Figure 22–54).
4. Tighten the pedestal-to-block mounting bolts to the correct torque.
5. Tighten the pinch bolt to the proper torque.

The interrupter rings on the back of the crankshaft pulley should be checked for a bent condition, and the same crankshaft sensor adjusting tool can be used to check these rings. Place the tool on the pulley extension surface and rotate the tool around the pulley (Figure 22–55). If any blade touches the tool, replace the pulley.

IGNITION COILS

The coils in a DIS system can be checked in the same way as conventional coils; however, they all must be checked and inspected. When checking the resistance across the windings, play particular attention to the meter reading. If the reading is out of specifications, even if it is only slightly out, the coil or coil assembly should be replaced. Steps for the removal and inspection of coil packs and the ignition module are illustrated in Photo Sequence 12.

The specifications for DIS coils varies with manufacturer and design. For GM coils, the resistance in

FIGURE 22–55 Interrupter ring checking procedure.
Courtesy of Oldsmobile Division, General Motors Corporation

the primary of the coil should be between 0.35 to 1.50 ohms. A reading below this indicates a shorted winding and an infinite reading indicates an open. The resistance of the secondary windings varies with system design. The winding in type 1 systems should have 10,000 to 14,000 ohms resistance, whereas the windings in type 2 systems should have 5,000 to 7,000 ohms resistance.

KNOCK SENSORS

Most computer-controlled systems use knock sensors to retard timing when the engine is experiencing ping or knocking. Obviously a faulty knock sensor produces problems that appear ignition-system related. A quick check of a knock sensor is to watch the ignition's timing while the engine is running and the engine block is tapped with a hammer. The noise should cause a change in timing.

CASE STUDY

A customer complains that his vehicle runs poorly, misfiring, and losing power. He is embarrassed because he just performed his first ever preventive maintenance job on the vehicle—replacing spark plugs and ignition cables. He insists he did the job correctly. The problem must be somewhere else in the system.

Since the problem did not occur until after the customer worked on the vehicle, the technician begins troubleshooting by inspecting the plugs and cables. The job appears to be carefully and neatly done. The technician pulls a plug and inspects it. It is properly gapped, cleaned, and has been installed snugly, but not too tightly. The cables are not top quality but have been carefully and neatly installed and routed. Too neatly the technician suspects. At one point, three ignition cables have been wrapped together with several turns of electrical tape. It makes for a neat, tight appearance but may be causing an inductive crossfire situation. The high secondary voltage in a firing plug's ignition cable may be inducing a voltage in the wire running parallel to it, causing it to fire a plug out of turn. The technician removed the tape and routes the wire according to service manual instructions. A test drive confirms this was the problem. Remember, neatly wrapped and routed plug wire may look nice, but engine performance problems could result.

REMOVING AND REPLACING VARIOUS DIS COMPONENTS

P12–1 Late-model engines are equipped with different components than older models and are not equipped with some that were used for many years.

P12–4 The coil pack is removed by first disconnecting the spark plug wires from the coils. Prior to doing this, make sure their exact location is marked.

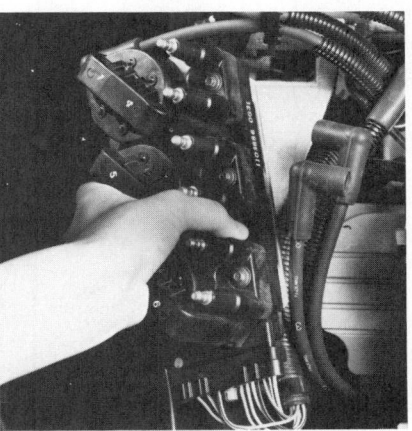

P12–5 Unbolt the assembly from the engine block.

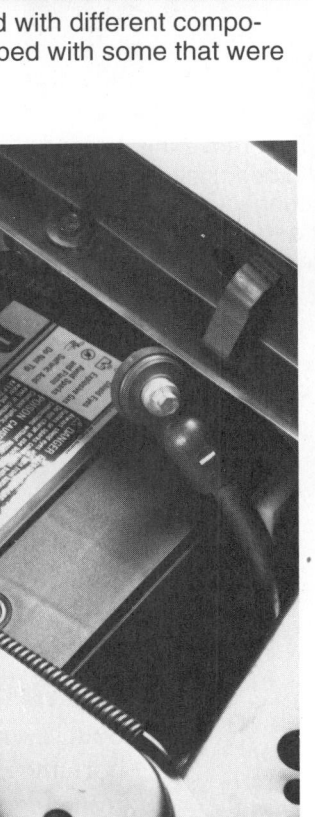

P12–3 Prior to removing or installing any electronic components, it is wise to disconnect the negative battery cable from the battery.

P12–2 This coil pack replaces the ignition coil and distributor assembly.

(continued)

P12–6 The individual coils are bolted to the mounting plate that also houses the ignition module. If a coil or the module is to be replaced, unbolt it from the assembly.

P12–8 Another integral part of the DIS system is the throttle position sensor (TPS).

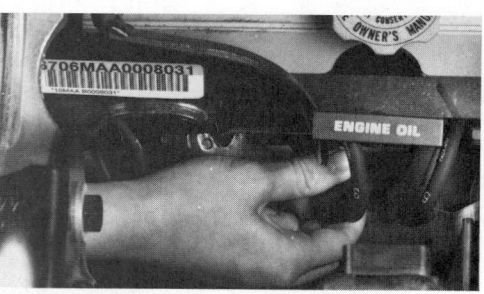

P12–10 Spark plug location has not changed on the DIS engine. To disconnect the spark plug wires from the plugs, grasp the boot and twist while pulling off the wire.

P12–7 Often, service of the assembly is done with the unit totally disconnected from the engine. To do this, loosen the remaining bolt on the electrical connector and pull the connector off the assembly. It is now free from the engine.

P12–9 To remove this sensor and many other similar components, disconnect the electrical connector and loosen the assembly retaining bolts.

P12–11 Spark plugs are removed in the normal manner with a spark plug socket and ratchet.

KEY TERMS

Carbon tracking	Intermediate section
Cold fouling	kV
Corona effect	Offset
Current limiting	Raster pattern
DI	Spark duration
Display pattern	Spark line
EI	Splash fouling
EMI	Superimposed pattern
Firing voltage	Timing meter
Gap bridging	Wet fouling
Glazing	

SUMMARY

- Sound wiring and connections are extremely important in modern electronic- and computer-controlled ignition systems. Loose connections, corrosion, and dirt can adversely affect performance.
- Many late-model vehicles use dielectric grease on connector terminals to seal out dirt and moisture.
- Wires, connections, and ignition components can be tested for intermittent failure by wiggling them or stress testing by applying heat, cold, or moisture.
- The oscilloscope can look inside the ignition system by giving the technician a visual representation of voltage changes over time.

- The trace patterns of the oscilloscope can be viewed in several different modes and scales. Both secondary and primary circuit patterns can be viewed.
- Trace patterns can be broken down into three main sections or zones: the firing section, intermediate section, and dwell section.
- The firing line and spark line of the firing section indicate firing voltage and spark duration.
- The intermediate section shows coil voltage dissipation.
- The dwell section shows the activation of primary coil current flow and primary coil current switch off. The primary current of signal is also the firing line for the next cylinder in the firing order.
- Dwell can be either fixed or variable. Variable dwell ignition systems gradually increase ignition dwell as engine speed increases.
- Ignition systems with current limiting saturate the ignition coil very quickly with a very high current flow and then cut back or limit current flow to the small flow needed to maintain saturation. This system extends coil life.
- Precautions must always be taken to avoid open circuits during ignition system testing. A special test plug is used to limit coil output during testing.
- Spark ignition should be at least 0.8 millisecond. The minimum acceptable spark duration can be computed in percent of dwell if the engine rpm is known.
- Firing voltages are normally between 7 and 13 kV with no more than 3 kV variation between cylinders.
- High secondary circuit resistance produces a higher-than-normal firing line.
- Individual ignition components are commonly tested for excessive internal resistance using an ohmmeter. A voltmeter or oscilloscope can also be used to monitor their operating voltages.
- Proper spark plug gapping and installation is very important to ignition system operation. Spark plug condition, such as cold fouling, wet fouling, and glazing is often a good indication of performance problems.
- Proper dwell and base timing are very important to ignition system operation. Although dwell is not adjustable on electronic systems, it still should be checked, particularly the operation of variable dwell.
- To properly set base timing, all mechanical, vacuum, or computer-controlled advance mechanisms must be temporarily disabled.
- Standard test procedures using an oscilloscope, ohmmeter, and timing light can be used to diagnose problems in distributorless ignition systems.
- According to the SAE J1930 standards that were recently mandated to the automotive industry, the term distributor ignition (DI) replaces all previous terms for distributor-type ignition systems that are electronically controlled. Also according to this mandate, the term electronic ignition (EI) replaces all previous terms for distributorless ignition systems.
- If a crank or cam sensor fails, the engine will not start. Both of these sensor circuits can be checked with a voltmeter. If the sensors are receiving the correct amount of voltage and have good low-resistance circuits, their output should be a digital signal or a pulsing voltmeter reading while the engine is cranking. If any of these conditions do not exist, the circuit needs to be repaired or the sensor needs to be replaced.
- The coils in a DIS system can be checked in the same way as conventional coils.

TECH MANUAL

The following procedures are included in Chapter 22 of the *Tech Manual* that accompanies this book:

1. Set ignition timing dynamically.

2. Check the resistance of primary circuit components.

3. Test sparkplug firing voltages.

4. Test secondary circuit insulation.

REVIEW QUESTIONS

1. Name the three types of stress testing used to test for intermittent ignition component problems and list the procedures for conducting each type of test.

2. Outline the typical procedure for checking base timing including the steps taken to disable any mechanical, vacuum, or computer-controlled advance systems.

3. Name the three types of trace pattern display modes used on an oscilloscope and give examples of when each mode is most useful.

4. List the common types of spark plug fouling and the typical problems each type of fouling indicates.

5. List at least two methods of checking the operation of Hall-effect sensors.

6. Upon inspection, a spark plug reveals a layer of dry, fluffy black carbon deposits on its tip. Technician A says the plug cannot be used again. Technician B says the plug can be cleaned and serviced, then reused. Who is correct?
   a. Technician A   c. Both A and B
   b. Technician B   d. Neither A nor B

7. On an oscilloscope, which section ends with the primary coil current off signal?
   a. intermediate   c. firing
   b. dwell   d. both a and b

8. The firing line on an oscilloscope pattern extends below the waveform. Technician A says the polarity of the coil is reversed. Technician B says the problem is fouled spark plugs. Who is correct?
   a. Technician A   c. Both A and B
   b. Technician B   d. Neither A nor B

9. The firing lines on an oscilloscope pattern are all abnormally low. Technician A says the problem is probably low coil output. Technician B says the problem could be an overly rich air/fuel mixture. Who is correct?
   a. Technician A   c. Both A and B
   b. Technician B   d. Neither A nor B

10. Technician A says dielectric grease is used to seal dirt and moisture out of electrical terminals. Technician B says it is used to dissipate heat away from sensitive electrical components. Who is correct?
    a. Technician A   c. Both A and B
    b. Technician B   d. Neither A nor B

11. Which of the following ignition components have the ability to generate electromagnetic interference?
    a. spark plug wires   c. ignition coil
    b. alternator coil   d. all of the above

12. Leaner air/fuel mixtures, ____.
    a. decrease the electrical resistance inside the cylinder and decrease the required firing voltage
    b. increase the electrical resistance inside the cylinder and increase the required firing voltage
    c. increase the electrical resistance inside the cylinder and decrease the required firing voltage
    d. have no measurable effect on cylinder resistance

13. The spark line of the trace pattern begins about ____ the way up the firing line.
    a. 1/8 to 1/4
    b. 1/4 to 1/3
    c. 1/2 to 3/4
    d. 3/4 to 7/8

14. Technician A says the vehicle does not run if the variable dwell function of the control module fails. Technician B says the vehicle may still run for a time before failing completely. Who is correct?
    a. Technician A   c. Both A and B
    b. Technician B   d. Neither A nor B

15. If the primary winding of the ignition coil develops excessive resistance, the current limiting blip on the dwell section of the pattern trace may ____.
    a. disappear
    b. become more prominent
    c. shift to the intermediate section of the trace
    d. none of the above

16. During a cranking output test ____.
    a. firing line voltage should exceed 20 kV
    b. firing line voltage should exceed 35 kV
    c. firing line voltage should exceed 50 kV
    d. the use of test plugs are not recommended

17. Most electronic ignition systems have a spark duration of approximately ____.
    a. 0.5 millisecond
    b. 0.8 millisecond
    c. 1.5 milliseconds
    d. 2.5 milliseconds

18. While testing the coils in a DIS system, Technician A says an infinite reading means that the windings have zero resistance and are shorted. Technician B says the primary windings in each coil should be checked for shorts to ground. Who is correct?

    a. Technician A   **c.** Both A and B
    b. Technician B   **d.** Neither A nor B

19. If a crankshaft position sensor is working properly, a digital voltmeter, connected to the output of the sensor, will ____ when the engine is cranking.

    a. fluctuate between low and high readings
    b. show a constant low voltage
    c. show a constant high voltage
    d. none of the above

20. Which of the following would *not* cause a higher-than-normal firing line on a scope?

    a. lean air/fuel mixtures
    b. excessive rotor-to-cap gap
    c. shorted plug wires
    d. corrosion at spark plug cable ends

FUEL SYSTEMS

23

OBJECTIVES

◆ **Describe the four performance characteristics of gasoline.** ◆ **Describe the various types of gasoline and additives** ◆ **Describe the different alternative fuels, including diesel.** ◆ **Define the fuel delivery system components and their functions, including the fuel tank, fuel lines, filters, and pump.** ◆ **Describe the operation of a gas cap and its primary purposes.** ◆ **Conduct a visual inspection on a fuel system.** ◆ **Conduct a pressure and volume output test on a mechanical and electric fuel pump.** ◆ **Describe an electronic fuel system.**

The automobile's fuel system is both simple and complicated. It is simple in the systems that transfer fuel to the engine and complex in the carburetor or fuel injector system that mixes fuel with air in the correct amounts and proportion to meet all needs of the engine.

This chapter focuses on the simple part of the fuel system. It covers the basic parts of the fuel delivery or transport system, including the fuel tank, lines, filters, and pump (Figure 23–1). The fuel transport portion of the system is very important in the operation of a gasoline driven vehicle. To fully understand the automotive fuel system, a knowledge of the performance of petroleum-based fuel used to power the engine is necessary. Although there are several different types of fuels, gasoline is the most commonly used motor fuel and is given primary consideration in this chapter. Diesel fuel and other alternative fuels are briefly discussed.

CAUTION:

Extreme care should be used while working with any of the components of the fuel system. Gasoline is a very volatile and flammable substance. Do not expose it to an open flame, spark, or high heat. Disconnect the negative terminal of the battery before doing any task that releases gasoline from any part of the system. Use containers to catch the gasoline and cloths to wipe up the minor spills. Use a flashlight rather than a trouble light or drop light. Gasoline spilled on a hot bulb could cause the bulb to

explode and ignite the gasoline. Never attempt to weld a fuel tank. Even when a fuel tank is empty, it can still contain enough gas fumes to cause an explosion if the fumes come in contact with a flame or excessive heat. Always keep a class B fire extinguisher nearby. It is specially intended for use on gasoline fires. ■

GASOLINE

Crude oil, as removed from the earth, is a mixture of hydrocarbon compounds ranging from gases to heavy tars and waxes. The crude oil can be refined into products, such as lubricating oils, greases, asphalts, kerosene, diesel fuel, gasoline, and natural gas. Before its widespread use in the internal combustion engine of automobiles, gasoline was an unwanted byproduct of refining for oils and kerosene.

Two important factors affect the power and efficiency of a gasoline engine—compression ratio and **detonation** (abnormal combustion). The higher the compression ratio, the greater the engine's power output and efficiency. The better the efficiency, the less fuel consumed to produce a given power output. To have a high compression ratio requires an engine of greater structural integrity. Due to the use of low-octane unleaded gasoline in post-1975 models, compression ratios now generally range from 8:1 to 10:1. High performance cars may have higher compression ratios.

Normal combustion occurs gradually in each cylinder. The **flame front** (the edge of the burning area)

FIGURE 23–1 Typical fuel delivery system. *Courtesy of Ford Motor Company*

advances smoothly across the combustion chamber until all the air/fuel mixture has been burned (Figure 23–2). Detonation occurs when the flame front fails to reach a pocket of mixture before the temperature in that area reaches the point of self-ignition. Normal burning at the start of the combustion cycle raises the temperature and pressure of everything in the cylinder. The last part of the air/fuel mixture is both heated and pressurized, and the combustion of those two factors can raise it to the self-ignition point. At that moment, the remaining mixture burns almost instantaneously. The two flame fronts create a pressure wave between them that can destroy cylinder head gaskets, break piston rings, and burn pistons and exhaust valves. When detonation occurs, a hammering, pinging, or knocking sound is heard. But, when the engine is operating at high speed, these sounds cannot be heard because of motor and road noise.

FUEL PERFORMANCE

Many of the performance characteristics of gasoline can be controlled in refining and blending to provide proper engine function and vehicle driveability. The major factors affecting fuel performance are antiknock quality, volatility, sulfur content, and deposit control.

Antiknock Quality

An **octane** number or rating was developed by the petroleum industry so the **antiknock** quality of a gasoline could be rated. The octane number is a measure of the fuel's tendency not to produce knock in an engine. The higher the octane number, the less tendency to knock. By itself, the antiknock rating has nothing to do with fuel economy or engine efficiency.

Two commonly used methods for determining the octane number of motor gasoline are the motor octane number (**MON**) method and the research octane number (**RON**) method. Both use a laboratory single-cylinder engine equipped with a variable head and knock meter to indicate knock intensity. The test sample is used as fuel, and the engine compression ratio and air/fuel mixture are adjusted to develop a specified knock intensity. There are two primary standard reference fuels, **isooctane** and **heptane**. Isooctane does not knock in an engine but is not used in gasoline because of its expense. Heptane knocks severely in an engine.

SPARK OCCURS **COMBUSTION BEGINS** **CONTINUES (SPONTANEOUS IGNITION)** **DETONATION (FLAME FRONTS COLLIDE)**

FIGURE 23–2 The stages of combustion that lead to detonation.

Isooctane has an octane number of 100. Heptane has an octane number of zero.

A fuel of unknown octane value is run in the special test engine, and the severity of knock is measured. Various proportions of heptane and isooctane are run in the test engine to duplicate the severity of the knock of the fuel being tested. When the knock caused by the heptane/isooctane mixture is identical to the test fuel, the octane number is established by the percentage of isooctane in the mixture. For example, if 85 percent isooctane and 15 percent heptane produce the same severity of knock as the fuel in question, the fuel is assigned an octane number of 85.

Factors that affect knock follow.

LEAN FUEL MIXTURE A lean mixture burns slower than a rich mixture. The heat of combustion is higher, which promotes the tendency for unburned fuel in front of the spark-ignition flame to detonate.

IGNITION TIMING OVERADVANCED Advancing the ignition timing induces knock. Slowing ignition timing suppresses knock.

COMPRESSION RATIO Compression ratio affects knock because cylinder pressures are increased with the increase in compression ratio.

VALVE TIMING Valve timing that fills the cylinder with more air/fuel mixture promotes higher cylinder pressures, increasing the chances for detonation.

TURBOCHARGING Turbocharging or supercharging forces additional fuel and air into the cylinder. This induces higher cylinder pressures and promotes knock.

COOLANT TEMPERATURE Hotspots in the cylinder or combustion chamber due to inefficient cooling or a damaged cooling system raise combustion chamber temperatures and promote knock.

CYLINDER-TO-CYLINDER DISTRIBUTION If an engine has poor distribution of the air/fuel mixture from cylinder to cylinder, the leaner cylinders could promote knock.

EXCESSIVE CARBON DEPOSITS The accumulation of carbon deposits on the piston, valves, and combustion chamber causes poor heat transfer from the combustion chamber. Carbon accumulation also artificially increases the compression ratio. Both conditions cause knock.

AIR INLET TEMPERATURE The higher the air temperature when it enters the cylinder, the greater the tendency to knock.

COMBUSTION CHAMBER SHAPE The optimum combustion chamber shape for reduced knocking is

FIGURE 23–3 Cross section of a hemispherical combustion chamber.

hemispherical with a spark plug located in the center (Figure 23–3). This hemi-head allows for faster combustion, allowing less time for detonation to occur ahead of the flame front.

OCTANE NUMBER Only when an engine is designed and adjusted to take advantage of the higher octane gasoline can the value of the fuel be obtained. Most modern engines are designed to operate efficiently with regular grade gasoline and do not require a high-octane premium grade.

Volatility

As stated earlier, gasoline is very volatile. It readily evaporates so its vapor adequately mixes with air for combustion. Only vaporized fuel supports combustion. To ensure complete combustion, complete vaporization must occur.

The volatility of gasoline affects the following performance characteristics or driving conditions.

COLD STARTING AND WARMUP A fuel can cause hard starting, hesitation, and stumbling during warmup if it does not vaporize readily. A fuel that vaporizes too easily in hot weather can form vapor bubbles in the fuel line and fuel pump, resulting in vapor lock or loss of performance.

TEMPERATURE Because a highly volatile fuel vaporizes at a lower temperature than a less volatile fuel, winter-grade gasoline is more volatile than summer-grade gasoline.

ALTITUDE Gasoline vaporizes more easily at high altitudes, so volatility is controlled in blending according to the elevation of the place where fuel is sold.

CARBURETOR ICING PROTECTION Carburetor icing is not as common in modern engines as in older engines. It can occur when ambient temperatures reach between 28° and 55°F and the relative humidity rises above 65 percent. The humid air enters the carburetor and mixes with drops of fuel. When the fuel evaporates, it removes heat from the air and surrounding metal parts. When this occurs, the throttle temperature is rapidly lowered to below 32°F (if the ambient temperature is within the range indicated), and condensing water vapor forms ice. The ice causes the engine to stall if it is idling during this phase.

CRANKCASE OIL DILUTION A fuel must vaporize well to prevent diluting the crankcase oil with liquid fuel. If parts of the gasoline do not vaporize, droplets of liquid break down the oil film on the cylinder wall, causing scuffing or scoring. The liquid eventually enters the crankcase oil and results in the formation of sludge, gum, and varnish accumulation as well as decreasing the lubrication properties of the oil.

DRIVEABILITY Poor vaporization can also affect the distribution of fuel from cylinder to cylinder since vaporized fuel travels farther and faster in the manifold.

Sulfur Content

Gasoline can contain some of the sulfur present in the crude oil. Sulfur content is reduced at the refinery to limit the amount of corrosion it can cause in the engine and exhaust system.

When the hydrogen in the hydrocarbon of the fuel is burned with air, one of the products of combustion is water. Water leaves the combustion chamber as steam but can condense back to water when passing through a cool exhaust system. When the engine is shut off and cools, steam condenses back to a liquid and forms water droplets. Steam present in crankcase blowby also condenses to water.

When the sulfur in the fuel is burned, it combines with oxygen to form **sulfur dioxide**. This sulfur dioxide can then combine with water to form highly corrosive sulfuric acid. This type of corrosion is the leading cause of exhaust valve pitting and exhaust system deterioration. With catalysts, the sulfur dioxide can cause the obnoxious odor of rotten eggs during vehicle warmup. To reduce corrosion caused by sulfuric acid, the sulfur content in gasoline is limited to less than 0.01 percent.

Deposit Control

Several additives are put in gasoline to control harmful deposits, including gum or oxidation inhibitors, detergents, metal deactivators, and rust inhibitors.

BASIC FUELS

For many years, lead compounds such as tetraethyl lead (**TEL**) and tetramethyl lead (**TML**) were added to gasoline to improve its octane ratings. However, since the mid-1970s, vehicles have been designed to run on unleaded gasoline only. Leaded fuels are no longer available as automotive fuels. The main reason for the change to unleaded gasoline was to provide a fuel for cars with special antipollution devices—catalytic converters. These systems must have unleaded fuel to work properly.

Because of the deactivating or poisoning effect lead has on the catalyst, gasolines are limited to a lead content of 0.06 gram per gallon. Since TEL or TML is not added to unleaded gasolines, the required octane number is obtained by blending compounds of the required octane quality. Methylcylopentadienyl manganese tricarbonyl (**MMT**) is a catalyst-compatible octane improver. Vehicles with catalytic converters are labeled at both the fuel gauge and fuel filler—unleaded fuel only.

GASOLINE ADDITIVES

At one time, all a gasoline-producing company had to do to produce their product was pump the crude from the ground, run it through the refinery to separate the fractions, dump in a couple of grams of lead per gallon, and deliver the finished product to the service station. Of course, automobiles were much simpler then and what they burned was not very critical. As long as gasoline vaporized easily and did not cause the low compression engines to knock, everything was fine.

Times have changed. Today, refiners are under constant pressure to ensure that their product passes a series of rigorous tests for seasonal volatility, minimum octane, existent gum and oxidation stability, as well as to add the correct deicers and detergents to make the product competitive in a price-sensitive marketplace.

Gasoline additives—primarily used in unleaded gasolines—have different properties and a variety of uses.

Anti-Icing or Deicer

Isopropyl alcohol is added seasonally to gasoline as an anti-icing agent to prevent gas line freeze-up in cold climates.

Metal Deactivators and Rust Inhibitors

These additives are used to inhibit reactions between the fuel and the metals in the fuel system that can form abrasive and filter-plugging substances.

Gum or Oxidation Inhibitors

Some gasolines contain aromatic amines and phenols to prevent formation of gum and varnish. During storage, harmful gum deposits can form due to the reaction of some gasoline components with each other and with oxygen. Oxidation inhibitors are added to promote gasoline stability. They help control gum, deposit formation, and staleness. Stale gasoline becomes cloudy and smells like paint thinner.

Gum content is influenced by the age of the gasoline and its exposure to oxygen and certain metals such as copper. If gasoline is allowed to evaporate, the residue left can form gum and varnish.

Gasoline must have as little gum residue as possible to prevent gum formation in the intake manifold, carburetor or fuel injectors, and on intake valve stems.

Detergents

The use of detergent additives in gasoline has been the subject of some public confusion. Detergent additives are designed to do only what their name implies— clean certain critical components inside the engine. They do not affect octane.

Ethanol

By far the most widely used gasoline additive today is **ethanol**, or grain alcohol. Ethanol's value as an octane enhancer becomes more apparent when considered in the context of the government-mandated phasedown of tetraethyl lead. Blending 10 percent ethanol into gasoline is seen as a comparatively inexpensive octane booster that results in an increase of 2.5 to 3 road octane points.

In addition to octane enhancement, ethanol blending keeps the carburetor or fuel injectors clean due to detergent additive packages found in most of the ethanol marketed. It also inhibits fuel system and injection corrosion due to additive packages and decreases carbon monoxide emissions at the tailpipe due to the higher oxygen content of blended fuel.

Methanol

Methanol is the lightest and simplest of the alcohols and is also known as wood alcohol. It can be distilled from coal, but most of what is used today is derived from natural gas.

In the early 1980s, a few companies begin selling a blend of 5 percent methanol in gasoline in the Northeast and Midwest. This showed that methanol plus anticorrosion co-solvents could compete in the motor fuel market as an octane enhancer. Today, both General Motors and Ford have working prototypes on the road that can burn any combination of fuel from nearly neat methanol (85 percent methanol with 15 percent gasoline) to straight gasoline. They key is a fuel line sensor that detects methanol concentration and adjusts spark timing and air/fuel mixture accordingly. The federal government is pushing for methanol acceptance through industry incentives and fleet-sponsored programs.

For now, however, many auto makers continue to warn motorists about using a fuel that contains more than 10 percent methanol and co-solvents by volume. Methanol is recognized as being far more corrosive to fuel system components than ethanol, and it is this corrosion that has auto makers concerned.

MTBE

Methyl tertiary butyl ether (**MTBE**) has become very popular in the past few years as an octane enhancer and supply extender because of excellent compatibility with gasoline. Current U.S. EPA restrictions on oxygenates limit MTBE in unleaded gasoline to 11 percent of volume. At that level, it increases pump octane (RM/2) by 2.5 points. However, it is usually found in concentrations of 7 to 8 percent of volume.

MTBE has found favor among refiner/suppliers and independent marketers alike because it is not nearly as sensitive to moisture as the other oxygenates, has virtually no effect on fuel volatility, and can be shipped through product pipelines whereas ethanol and methanol blends cannot.

MTBE increases octane while reducing carbon monoxide emissions at the tailpipe and does it at a cost that makes it very attractive to gasoline marketers across the country.

Alcohol-in-Fuel Test

Some gasoline may contain a small quantity of alcohol. The percentage of alcohol mixed with the fuel usually does not exceed 10 percent. An excessive quantity of alcohol in gasoline may result in fuel system corrosion, fuel filter plugging, deterioration of rubber fuel system components, and a lean air/fuel ratio. These fuel system problems may result in driver complaints of a lack of power, acceleration stumbles, engine stalling, and hard or no starts. Some vehicle manufacturers supply test equipment to check the level of alcohol in gasoline. The following alcohol-in-fuel test procedure requires only the use of a calibrated cylinder.

1. Obtain a 100-milliliter (100-ml) cylinder graduated in 1-ml divisions.
2. Fill the cylinder to the 90-ml mark with gasoline.
3. Add 10 ml of water to the cylinder so the cylinder is now filled to the 100-ml mark.
4. Install a stopper in the cylinder and shake it vigorously for 10 to 15 seconds.
5. Carefully loosen the stopper to relieve any pressure.
6. Install the stopper and shake the cylinder vigorously for another 10 to 15 seconds.
7. Carefully loosen the stopper to relieve any pressure.

8. Place the cylinder on a level surface for about 5 minutes to allow the liquids to separate.

9. Any alcohol in the fuel is absorbed by the water and settles to the bottom. If the water content in the bottom of the cylinder exceeds 10 ml, there is alcohol in the fuel. For example, if the water content is now 15 ml, there was 5 percent alcohol in the gasoline.

DIESEL FUEL

Diesel fuel, like gasoline, is made from petroleum. However, at the refinery, the petroleum is separated into three major components: gasoline, middle distillates, and all remaining substances. Diesel fuel comes from the middle distillate group, which has properties and characteristics different from gasoline.

The shape of the fuel spray, turbulence in the combustion chamber, beginning and duration of injection, and the chemical properties of the diesel fuel all affect the power output of the diesel engine. The significant chemical properties of diesel fuel are described briefly in the following paragraphs.

Viscosity

Viscosity is a measure of a fluid's resistance to flow, and like most fluids, diesel fuel viscosity varies with temperature.

The viscosity of diesel fuel directly affects the spray pattern of the fuel into the combustion chamber. Fuel with a high viscosity produces large droplets that are hard to burn. Fuel with a low viscosity sprays in a fine, easily burned mist. If the viscosity is too low, however, it does not adequately lubricate and cool the injection pump and nozzles.

Wax Appearance Point and Pour Point

Temperature affects diesel fuel more than it affects gasoline. This is because diesel fuels contain **paraffin**, a wax substance common among middle distillate fuels. As temperatures drop past a certain point, wax crystals begin to form in the fuel. The point where the wax crystals appear is the wax appearance point (**WAP**) or cloud point. The better the quality of the fuel, the lower the WAP. As temperatures drop, the wax crystals grow larger and restrict the flow of fuel through the filters and lines. Eventually, the fuel, which may still be liquid, stops flowing because the wax crystals plug a filter or line. As the temperature continues to drop, the fuel reaches a point where it solidifies and no longer flows. This is called the **pour point**. In cold climates it is recommended that a low-temperature pour point fuel be used.

Volatility

Gasoline is extremely volatile compared to diesel fuel. The amount of carbon residue left by diesel fuel depends on the quality and the volatility of that fuel. Fuel that has a low volatility is much more prone to leaving carbon residue. The small, high-speed diesels found in automobiles require a high-quality and highly volatile fuel because they cannot tolerate excessive carbon deposits. Large, low-speed industrial diesels are relatively unaffected by carbon deposits and can run on low-quality fuel.

Cetane Number or Rating

Diesel fuel's ignition quality is measured by the **cetane** rating. Much like the octane number, the cetane number is measured in a single-cylinder test engine with a variable compression ratio. The diesel fuel to be tested is compared to cetane, a colorless, liquid hydrocarbon that has excellent ignition qualities. Cetane is rated at 100. The higher the cetane number, the shorter the ignition lag time (delay time) from the point the fuel enters the combustion chamber until it ignites.

In fuels that are readily available, the cetane number ranges from 40 to 55 with values of 40 to 50 being most common. These cetane values are satisfactory for medium-speed engines that have rated speeds from 500 to 1,200 rpm and for high-speed engines rated over 1,200 rpm. Low-speed engines rated below 500 rpm can use fuels in the above 30 cetane number range. The cetane number improves with the addition of certain compounds, such as ethyl nitrate, acetone peroxide, and amyl nitrate. Amyl nitrate is commercially available for this purpose.

Diesel Fuel Grades

Minimum quality standards for diesel fuel grades have been set by the American Society for Testing Materials. Two grades of diesel fuels, number 1 and number 2, are used to fuel cars and trucks.

Number 2 diesel fuel is the most popular and widely distributed. Number 1 diesel fuel is less dense than number 2, with a lower heat content. Number 1 diesel fuel is blended with number 2 to improve starting in cold weather. In the winter, passenger car diesel is likely to be a mixture of number 1 and 2 fuels. In moderately cold climates, the blend may be 90 percent number 2 to 10 percent number 1. In severe climates, the ratio may be as high as 50-50.

Diesel fuel economy can be expected to drop off during the winter months due to the use of number 1 diesel in the fuel blend.

ALTERNATIVE FUELS

Tighter federal, state, and local emissions regulations have led to a search for an alternative fuel. Many things are considered when determining the viability of an alternative fuel, including emissions, cost, fuel availability, fuel consumption, safety, engine life, fueling facilities, weight and space requirements of fuel tanks, and the range of a fully fueled vehicle. Currently, the major competing alternative fuels include ethanol, methanol, propane, and natural gas.

Ethanol and methanol were presented earlier under other gasoline additives. Propane is a petroleum-based pressurized fuel used as a liquid. It is a constituent of natural gas. Natural gas comes in two forms: compressed natural gas (CNG) and liquefied natural gas (LNG).

LP-Gas

LP-gas (LP stands for liquefied petroleum) is a byproduct of crude oil refining, and it is also found in natural gas wells. Fuel grade LP-gas is almost pure propane with a little butane and propylene usually present. Because of its high propane content, many people simply refer to LP-gas as propane.

Propane burns clean in the engine and can be precisely controlled. Because it vaporizes at atmospheric temperatures and pressures, it does not puddle in the intake manifold. This means it emits less hydrocarbons and carbon monoxide. Emissions controls on the engine can be simpler. Cold starting is easy, down to much below zero. At normal cold temperatures, the propane engine fires easily and produces power without surge or stumble.

One of the most noticeable differences between propane and gasoline is that propane is a dry fuel. It enters the engine as vapor. Gasoline, on the other hand, enters the engine as tiny droplets of liquid, whether it flows through a carburetor or is sprayed in through a fuel injector.

The propane fuel system is a completely closed system that contains a supply of pressurized LP-gas. Since the fuel is already under pressure, no fuel pump is needed. From the pressurized fuel tanks, the fuel flows to a vacuum filter fuel lock. This serves as a filter and a control allowing fuel to flow to the engine. Fuel flows to a converter or heat exchanger where it changes from a liquid to a gas. When the propane flows through the converter, it expands as it changes into a gas. The carburetor mixes gaseous propane with the gaseous air. Airflow into the engine is controlled by a butterfly valve in the venturi. Mixture is controlled by a fuel metering valve operated by a diaphragm, which is controlled by intake manifold pressure. The idle system is an air bleed, similar to a gasoline engine. In fact, except for the fact that the propane carburetor does not require a fuel bowl, the two carburetor types are basically the same.

Natural Gas

Vehicles have been designed with gasoline/CNG, diesel/CNG, and dedicated (single-fuel) CNG engine applications. Compressed natural gas (**CNG**) vehicles offer several advantages over gasoline.

- The fuel costs less.
- It is the cleanest alternative fuel, generating up to 99 percent less carbon monoxide than gasoline, no particulates, almost no sulfur dioxide, and 85 percent less reactive hydrocarbons than gasoline.
- Natural gas vehicles are safer. The fuel tanks used for CNG are aluminum or steel cylinders with walls that are 1/2 to 3/4 inch thick. They can withstand severe crash tests, direct gunfire, dynamite explosions, and burning beyond any standard sheet metal gasoline tank. Because it is lighter than air, natural gas dissipates quickly. It also has a higher ignition temperature.
- It generally reduces vehicle maintenance since it burns cleanly. Oil changes may not be needed before 12,000 miles and spark plugs could last as long as 75,000 miles.
- Natural gas is abundant and readily available in the United States.

The chief disadvantage of CNG at present is its nonavailability to most users. Fuel facilities are needed in greater numbers than are currently in existence due to the relatively shorter range of CNG vehicles. The space taken by the CNG cylinders and their weight, about 300 pounds, also would be considered disadvantages in most applications.

FUEL DELIVERY SYSTEM

The components of a typical gasoline delivery system are fuel tanks, fuel lines, fuel filters, and fuel pumps.

Fuel Tanks

Modern fuel tanks include devices that prevent vapors from leaving the tank. For example, to contain vapors and allow for expansion, contraction, and overflow that results from changes in the temperature, the fuel tank has a separate air chamber dome at the top. Another way to contain vapors is to use a separate internal expansion tank within the main tank (Figure 23–4). All fuel tank designs provide some control of fuel height when the tank is filled. Frequently, this is achieved by using vent lines within the filler tube or tank (Figure 23–5). With tank

FIGURE 23–4 An internal expansion tank helps contain vapors in the fuel tank.

FIGURE 23–5 Vent lines within the fuel tank filler tube control the fuel level.

FIGURE 23–6 Cars requiring unleaded fuel have restrictors in the filler tube to allow only the insertion of smaller unleaded fuel pump nozzles.

FIGURE 23–7 (A) One-piece and (B) three-piece filler tubes.

designs such as this, only 90 percent of the tank is ever filled, leaving 10 percent for expansion in hot weather. Some vehicles have an overfill limiting valve to prevent overfilling of the tank. If a tank is filled to capacity, it overflows whenever the temperature of the fuel increases.

Fuel tanks can be constructed of pressed corrosion-resistant steel, aluminum, or molded reinforced polyethylene plastic. Aluminum and molded plastic fuel tanks are becoming more common as manufacturers attempt to reduce the overall weight of the vehicle. Metal tanks are usually ribbed to provide added strength. Seams are welded, and heavier gauge steel is often used on exposed sections for added strength.

Most tanks have slosh baffles or surge plates to prevent the fuel from splashing around inside the unit. In addition to slowing down fuel movement, the plates tend to keep the fuel pick-up or sending assembly immersed in the fuel during hard braking and acceleration. The plates or baffles also have holes or slots in them to permit the fuel to move from one end of the tank to the other. Except for rear engine vehicles, the fuel tank in a passenger car is located in the rear of the vehicle for improved safety.

The fuel tank is provided with an inlet filler tube and cap. The location of the fuel inlet filler tube depends on the tank design and tube placement. It is usually positioned behind the filler cap or a hinged door in the center of the rear panel or in the outer side of either rear fender panel. Vehicles designed for unleaded fuel use have a restrictor in the filler tube that prevents the entry of the larger leaded fuel delivery nozzle at the gas pumps (Figure 23–6). The filler pipe can be a rigid one-piece tube soldered to the tank (Figure 23–7A) or a three-piece unit (Figure 23–7B). The three-piece unit has a lower neck soldered to the tank and an upper neck fastened to the inside of the body sheet metal panel.

Filler tube caps are nonventing and usually have some type of pressure-vacuum relief valve arrangement (Figure 23–8). Under normal operating conditions the valve is closed, but whenever pressure or

FIGURE 23–8   Pressure-vacuum gasoline filler cap.
Courtesy of Chrysler Corporation

vacuum is more than the calibration of the cap, the valve opens. Once the pressure or vacuum has been relieved, the valve closes. Most pressure caps have four antisurge tangs that lock onto the filler neck to prevent the delivery system's pressure from pushing fuel out of the tank. By turning such a cap one-half turn, the pressure in the tank will not be released all at once. Then, with another quarter turn, the cap can be removed.

Starting with the 1976 model year, a Federal Motor Vehicle Safety Standard (FMVSS 301) required a control on gasoline leakage from passenger cars and certain light trucks and buses, after they were subjected to barrier impacts and rolled over. Tests conducted under these severe conditions showed the most common gasoline leak path was the gasoline supply line from the fuel tank to the carburetor.

Most rollover leakage protection devices used on carburetor-equipped engines are variations of a basic one-way check valve. These protective check valves are usually installed in the fuel vapor vent line between the tank and the vapor canister and at the carburetor fuel feed or return line fitting (Figure 23–9). In some systems the check valve is part of the carburetor inlet fuel filter (Figure 23–10).

Under normal operation, the mechanical fuel pump pressure is sufficient to open the check valve and supply fuel to the engine. However, if the vehicle is involved in a rollover accident, fuel spills out of the carburetor, the engine stalls, and the fuel pump ceases to operate. This decreases fuel system pressure to the point where the check valve closes. This prevents fuel from reaching the carburetor where it would leak out.

A check valve might also be fitted in the fuel tank filler cap, and most caps' pressure-vacuum relief valve settings have been increased so fuel pressure cannot open them in a rollover.

Many electric fuel pumps found on vehicles with fuel injection systems have an **inertia switch** that shuts off the pump if the vehicle is involved in a colli-

FIGURE 23–9   Rollover leakage protection devices.

FIGURE 23–10 Fuel filter with built-in check valve.

FIGURE 23–12 Steel fuel tubing with retaining clips and short rubber fuel hose. *Courtesy of Oldsmobile Division, General Motors Corporation*

sion or rolls over. The Ford inertia switch (Figure 23–11) consists of a permanent magnet, a steel ball inside a conical ramp, a target plate, and a set of electrical contacts. The magnet holds the steel ball in the bottom of the conical ramp. In the event of a collision, the inertia of the ball causes it to break away from the magnet, roll up the conical ramp, and strike the target plate. The force of the ball striking the plate causes the electrical contacts in the inertia switch to open, cutting off power to the fuel pump. The switch has a reset button that must be depressed to close the contacts before the pump operates again.

Some fuel line systems contain a fuel return arrangement that aids in keeping the gasoline cool, thus reducing chances of vapor lock. The return sys-

tem (Figure 23–12) consists of a special fuel pump equipped with an extra outlet fitting and necessary fuel line. The fuel return line generally runs next to the conventional fuel line (Figure 23–13), except that flow is in the opposite direction. The fuel return system allows a metered amount of cool fuel to circulate through the tank and fuel pump, thus reducing vapor bubbles caused by overheated fuel.

Some form of liquid vapor separator is incorporated into most modern vehicles to stop liquid fuel or bubbles from reaching the vapor storage canister or the engine crankcase (Figure 23–14). It can be located inside the tank, on the tank (Figure 23–15), in fuel vent lines, or near the fuel pump. Check the service manual for the exact location of the liquid vapor separator and line routing.

Inside the fuel tank there is also a sending unit that includes a pick-up tube and float-operated fuel gauge (Figure 23–16). The fuel tank pick-up tube is connected to the fuel pump by the fuel line. Some electric fuel pumps are combined with the sending

CUTAWAY VIEW

EXTERNAL VIEW

FIGURE 23–11 Inertia switch found on Ford vehicles.

FIGURE 23–13 Location of fuel feed and return lines. *Courtesy of Oldsmobile Division, General Motors Corporation*

FIGURE 23–14 A fuel tank vapor separator allows some of the fuel vapors to condense back into liquid and return to the tank.

FIGURE 23–16 Fuel tank sending unit assembly.

FIGURE 23–15 Vapor separator attached to the fuel tank.

FIGURE 23–17 Combination electric fuel pump and sending unit.

unit (Figure 23–17). The pick-up tube extends nearly, but not completely, all the way to the bottom of the tank. Rust, dirt, sediment, and water cannot be drawn up into the fuel tank filter, which can cause clogging. The ground wire is often attached to the fuel tank unit.

Inspecting the Fuel Tank A fuel tank should be inspected for leaks, road damage, corrosion, and rust on metal tanks, loose, damaged, or defective seams, loose mounting bolts, and damaged mounting straps. Leaks in the fuel tank, lines, or filter may cause gasoline odor in and around the vehicle, especially during low-speed driving and idling. In most cases, the fuel tank must be removed for servicing.

Servicing the Fuel Tank Leaks in the metal fuel tank can be caused by a weak seam, rust, or road damage. The best method of permanently solving this problem is to replace the tank. Another method is to remove the tank and steam clean or boil it in a caustic solution to remove the gasoline residue. After this has been done, the leak can be soldered or brazed by a specialty shop that is equipped to do this.

If the tank is leaking because of a puncture or small hole, it can be plugged by installing a sheet metal screw with a neoprene washer. Holes in a plastic tank can sometimes be repaired by using a special tank repair kit. Be sure to follow manufacturer's instructions when doing the repair.

WARNING!

Extreme care must be taken when using steam cleaning equipment or when washing with a caustic solution. Follow the manufacturer's instructions exactly. If the shop does not have steam cleaning or washing facilities, these services can be done by a radiator specialty shop. Do not use a steam cleaning procedure on a plastic tank. Because of the danger of explosion, leave gas tank welding to experts in repair shops that specialize in tank repair. ■

When a fuel tank is leaking dirty water or has water in it, the tank must be cleaned, repaired, or replaced.

PROCEDURES
Replacing the Fuel Tank

1. Disconnect the negative terminal from the battery. Remove the tank filler cap, and drain the tank of all fuel.
2. Attach a piece of masking tape to the tank lines and hoses to ensure correct reinstallation. Disconnect the vent lines and the wire connected to the sending unit.

CAUTION:

Abide by local laws for the disposal of contaminated fuels. Be sure to wear eye protection when working under the vehicle. ■

3. Unfasten the filler from the tank. If it is a rigid one-piece tube, remove the screws around the outside of the filler neck near the filler cap. If it is a three-piece unit, remove the neoprene hoses after the clamp has been loosened.
4. Loosen the bolts holding the fuel tank straps to the vehicle (Figure 23–18) until they are about two threads from the end.

CAUTION:

Do not heat the bolts on the fuel tank straps to loosen them. The heat could ignite the fumes. ■

Holding the tank securely against the underchassis with one hand, remove the strap bolts and lower the tank to the ground. When lowering

the tank, make sure all wires and tubes are unhooked. Keep in mind that small amounts of fuel might still remain in the tank.

CAUTION:

Use a drain pan to catch any spilled fuel or be sure to clean it up immediately. ■

5. To reinstall the new or repaired fuel tank, reverse the removal procedure. Be sure that all the rubber or felt tank insulators are in place. Then, with the tank straps in place, position the tank. Loosely fit the tank straps around the tank, but do not tighten them. Make sure the hoses, wires, and vent tubes are connected properly. Check the filler neck for alignment and for insertion into the tank. Tighten the strap bolts and secure the tank to the car. Install all of the tank accessories (vent line, sending unit wires, ground wire, and filler tube). Fill the tank with fuel and check it for leaks, especially around the filler neck and the pick-up assembly. Reconnect the battery and check the fuel gauge for proper operation.

REMOVING AND REPLACING THE FUEL GAUGE SENDING UNIT The sending unit is held in the tank by either a retaining ring or screws. The easiest way to remove a sending unit retaining ring is to use a special tool designed for this purpose (Figure 23–19). This tool fits over the metal tabs on the retaining ring, and after about a quarter turn, the ring comes loose and the sender unit can be removed. If the special tool is not available, a drift punch or worn screwdriver and ball peen hammer usually do the job (Figure 23–20).

When removing the sending unit from the tank, be very careful not to damage the float arm, the float, or the fuel gauge sender. Check the unit carefully for any damaged components. Shake the float, and if fuel can be heard inside it, replace it. Make sure the float arm is not bent. It is usually wise to replace the filter and O-ring before replacing the unit. Check the fuel gauge as described in the service manual. When reinstalling the pick-up pipe-sending unit, be very careful not to damage any of the components.

Fuel Lines

Fuel lines can be made of either metal tubing, flexible nylon, or synthetic rubber hose. The latter must be

FIGURE 23–18 Fuel tank mounting components.

FIGURE 23–19 Using a special tool to remove the sending unit retaining ring.

FIGURE 23–20 Using a dull screwdriver and ball peen hammer to remove the sending unit.

able to resist gasoline. It must also be nonpermeable, so gas and gas vapors cannot evaporate through the hose. Ordinary rubber hose, such as that used for vacuum lines, deteriorates when exposed to gasoline. Only hoses made for fuel systems should be used for replacement. Similarly, vapor vent lines must be made of material that resists attack by fuel vapors. Replacement vent hoses are usually marked with the designation **EVAP** to indicate their intended use. The inside diameter of a fuel delivery hose is generally larger (5/16 to 3/8 inch) than that of a fuel return hose (1/4 inch).

Many fuel tanks have vent hoses to allow air in the fuel tank to escape when the tank is being filled with fuel. Vent hoses are usually installed alongside the filler neck.

The fuel lines carry fuel from the fuel tank to the fuel pump, fuel filter, and carburetor or fuel injection assembly. These lines are usually made of rigid metal, although some sections are constructed of rubber hose to allow for car vibrations. This fuel line, unlike

filler neck or vent hoses, must work under pressure or vacuum. Because of this, the flexible synthetic hoses must be stronger. This is especially true for the hoses on fuel injection systems, where pressures reach 50 psi or more. For this reason, flexible fuel line hose must also have special resistance properties. Many auto manufacturers recommend that flexible hose be used only as a delivery hose to the fuel metering unit in a fuel injection system. It should not be used on the pressure side of the injector systems. This application requires a special high-pressure hose.

All fuel lines should occasionally be inspected for holes, cracks, leaks, kinks, or dents. Many fuel system troubles that occur in the lines are blamed on the fuel pump or carburetor. For instance, a small hole in the fuel line admits air but does not necessarily show any drip marks under the car. Air can then enter the fuel line, allowing the fuel to gravitate back into the tank. Then, instead of drawing fuel from the tank,

FIGURE 23–21 Gaps between the frame and tank or fuel pump are joined with flexible hose.

the fuel pump sucks only air through the hole in the fuel line. When this condition exists, the fuel pump is frequently tested, and if there is insufficient fuel, it is considered faulty, when in fact there is nothing wrong with it. If a hole is suspected, remove the coupling at the tank and the pump and pressurize the line with air. The leaking air is easily spotted.

Since the fuel is under pressure, leaks in the line between the pump and carburetor or injectors are relatively easy to recognize. When a damaged fuel line is found, replace it with one of similar construction—steel with steel, and the flexible with nylon or synthetic rubber. When installing flexible tubing, always use new clamps. The old ones lose some of their tension when they are removed and do not provide an effective seal when used on the new line.

⬤ CAUTION:

Do not substitute aluminum or copper tubing for steel tubing. Never use hose within 4 inches of any hot engine or exhaust system component. A metal line must be installed. ■

Fuel supply lines from the tank to the carburetor or injectors are routed to follow the frame along the underchassis of vehicles. Generally, rigid lines are used extending from near the tank to a point near the fuel pump. To absorb engine vibrations, the gaps between the frame and tank or fuel pump are joined by short lengths of flexible hose (Figure 23–21).

Steel tubing should be inspected for leaks, kinks, and deformation (Figure 23–22). This tubing should also be checked for loose connections and proper

clamping to the chassis. If the fuel tubing threaded connections are loose, they must be tightened to the specified torque (Figure 23–23).

Any damaged or leaking fuel line—either a por-

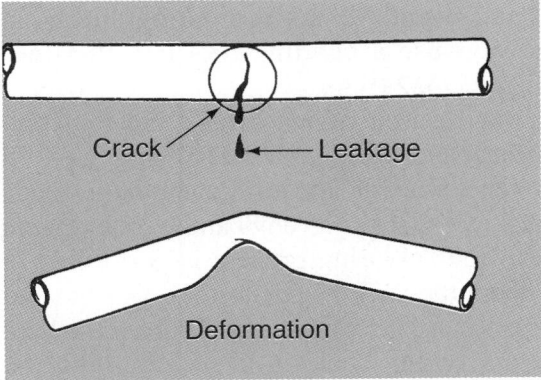

FIGURE 23–22 Steel tubing should be inspected for leaks, kinks, and deformation. *Courtesy of Toyota Motor Corporation*

FIGURE 23–23 Fuel line fittings should be tightened to torque specifications. *Courtesy of Toyota Motor Corporation*

FIGURE 23–24   Two types of steel tubing bending tools.

FIGURE 23–26   The double-flare tubing fitting is made with an anvil and cone.

tion or the entire length—must be replaced. To fabricate a new fuel line, select the correct tube and fitting dimension and start with a length that is slightly longer than the old line. With the old line as a reference, use a tubing bender to form the same bends in the new line as those that exist in the old. Although steel tubing can be bent by hand to obtain a gentle curve (Figure 23–24A), any attempt to bend a tight curve by hand usually kinks the tubing. To avoid kinking, always use a bending tool like the ones shown in Figure 23–24B.

The two most-used tubing fittings are the **compression fittings** and the **double-flare** (Figure 23–25). The double-flare, which is the most common, is made with a special tool that has an anvil and a cone (Figure 23–26). The double-flaring process is performed in two steps. First, the anvil begins to fold over the end of the tubing. Then, the cone is used to finish the flare by folding the tubing back on itself, doubling the thickness, and creating two sealing surfaces.

The angle and size of the flare are determined by the tool. Careful use of the double-flaring helps to produce strong, leakproof connections. Figure 23–27 shows other metal fuel line connections that are used by vehicle manufacturers.

The flare tool can also be used to make sure nylon and synthetic rubber hoses stay in place. That is, to make sure the connection is secure, put a partial double-lip flare on the end of the tubing over which the hose is installed. This can be done quickly, with the proper flaring tool, by starting out as if it was going to be a double-flare but stopping halfway through the procedure (Figure 23–28). This provides an excellent sealing ridge that does not cut into the hose. A clamp should be placed directly behind the ridge on the hose caused by the raised section on the metal line.

SHOP TALK

To ensure a flexible fuel replacement hose is the right length, lay the old line alongside the new one. Then, with a sharp knife, cut the new line to the same length as the old one.   ∎

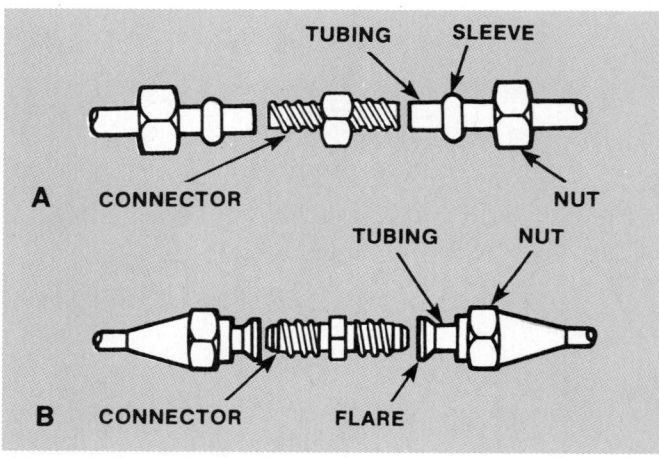

FIGURE 23–25   (A) Compression and (B) double-flare tubing fittings.

There are a variety of clamps used on fuel system lines, including the spring and screw types (Figure

FIGURE 23–27 Common metal fuel line connections.

23–29). The crimp clamps shown in Figure 23–30 are used most for metal tubing, but they require a special tool to install.

To control the rate of vapor flow from the fuel tank to the vapor storage tank, a plastic or metal restrictor may be placed in either the end of the vent pipe or in the vapor-vent hose itself. When the latter hose must be replaced, the restrictor must be removed from the old vent hose and installed in the new one.

Fuel Filters

Automobiles and light trucks usually have an in-tank strainer and a gasoline filter (Figure 23–31). The strainer, located in the gasoline tank, is made of a finely woven fabric. The purpose of this strainer is to prevent large contaminant particles from entering the fuel system where they could cause excessive fuel

FIGURE 23–28 Using a flaring tool to secure hose connections.

FIGURE 23–29 Various clamps used on fuel lines.

pump wear or plug fuel metering devices. It also helps to prevent passage of any water that might be present in the tank. Servicing of the fuel tank strainer is seldom required.

The gasoline filter is usually located in the engine compartment and is the one this section examines because it is replaceable and might require service on a regular basis. The most common types of gasoline filters are in-carburetor filters and in-line filters.

In-Carburetor Filters There are three basic types of in-carburetor gasoline filters. Pleated paper filters use pleated paper as the filtering medium. Paper elements are more efficient than screen-type elements, such as nylon or wire mesh, in removing and trapping small particles, as well as large-size contaminants. Sintered bronze filters are often referred to as a stone or ceramic filter. Screw-in filters are designed to screw into the carburetor fuel inlet. The fuel line attaches to a fitting on the filter. This filter has a

FIGURE 23–30 Crimp clamps require a special tool for installation.

FIGURE 23–31 An in-tank fuel pump assembly with a fuel filter at the pump inlet. *Courtesy of Oldsmobile Division, General Motors Corporation*

magnetic element to remove metallic contamination before it reaches the carburetor (Figure 23–32).

In-Line Filters In-line gasoline filters are installed in the fuel line (Figure 23–33). In carbureted engines, the in-line gasoline filter is usually installed between the fuel pump and the carburetor. In vehicles with a fuel injection system, the location of the fuel filter is determined by the manufacturer. Fitted with a pleated paper element, the in-line filter is sometimes installed as an extra protective measure. The optionally installed in-line filter then works in conjunction with the in-tank and in-carburetor gasoline filters. Because of its large capacity, an in-line filter is often the most economical solution to a fuel system's contamination problems. An arrow on the filter shows the direction of fuel flow.

FIGURE 23–32 Screw-in fuel filter with magnetic element.

FIGURE 23–33 In-line fuel filter. *Courtesy of Oldsmobile Division, General Motors Corporation*

Servicing Filters Fuel filters and elements are serviced by replacement only. Replacing the gasoline filter or element at the intervals recommended by the vehicle or engine manufacturer is the most effective method of minimizing fuel starvation and other carburetor problems. On occasions when the fuel system has been subjected to excessive amounts of contaminants, more frequent filter changes may be required.

Fuel Pumps

The fuel pump is the device that draws the fuel from the fuel tank through the fuel lines to the engine's

PROCEDURES

Replacing an In-Carburetor Filter

1. To remove the filter, remove the fuel line from the carburetor fuel inlet nut by using two wrenches, one to hold the inlet nut, the other to turn the fuel line fitting (Figure 23–34).
2. After disconnecting the fuel line, remove the inlet nut from the carburetor and discard the used filter. The inlet nut has a gasket that is loose or permanently attached. This gasket can usually be reused.

SHOP TALK

Take care not to lose the spring located behind the filter. The spring is required to seal the filter to the inlet nut. ∎

3. Installation of the filter is accomplished by simply reversing the steps used to remove the used filter.

SHOP TALK

Be sure to properly start the inlet nut threads into the carburetor. If the threads are crossed, a fuel leak inevitably results. ∎

4. Check fuel line connections for leaks with the engine running.

SHOP TALK

Most late-model automobiles have steel gasoline lines. Non-OEM in-line gasoline filters can be installed using short rubber tubes and tangential screw hose clamps. There should be no bends in the rubber tubes after installation. After installing an in-line gasoline filter, start the engine and check for leaks. ∎

carburetor or injectors. Basically, there are two types of fuel pumps: mechanical and electrical. The latter is the most commonly used today.

Mechanical Fuel Pump The mechanical fuel pump has a synthetic rubber diaphragm inside the unit that is actuated by an eccentric located on the engine's

FIGURE 23–34 Two wrenches are needed to remove an in-carburetor filter.

FIGURE 23–35 Mechanical fuel pump assembly.

camshaft (Figure 23–35). As the camshaft rotates during engine operation, a shaft or rocker arm in the pump is moved up and down or back and forth, depending on the fuel pump's position on the engine. This causes the diaphragm to move back and forth, drawing fuel from the fuel tank.

The mechanical fuel pump is located on the engine block near the front of the engine (Figure 23–36). Normally, it is a sealed unit that cannot be repaired. If the pump leaks from either the vent hole or from a seam, it must be replaced. If engine performance indicates inadequate fuel, the pump, while

FIGURE 23–36 Fuel lines from mechanical fuel pumps. *Courtesy of Chrysler Corporation*

mounted on the engine, should be tested for pressure and volume.

Incorrect fuel pump pressure and low volume (capacity of flow rate) are the two most likely fuel pump troubles that affect engine performance. Low pressure causes a lean mixture. Excessive pressure causes high fuel consumption and an overly rich mixture with fuel injection or carburetor flooding. And, low volume causes fuel starvation at high speeds.

To determine if the fuel pump is in satisfactory operating condition, tests for both fuel pump pressure and fuel pump capacity (volume) should be performed. These tests are performed with the fuel pump installed on the engine and the engine at normal operating temperature and at idle speed.

🔧 SHOP TALK

Before making any tests, be sure the replaceable fuel filter has been changed within the recommended maintenance mileage interval. When in doubt, install a new filter. ∎

This proper procedure for testing fuel pump pressure is shown in Photo Sequence 13. These photos outline the steps to follow while performing the test on an engine with fuel injection. To conduct this test on specific fuel injection systems, refer to the service manual for instructions. However, most systems have a **Schrader valve** on the fuel rail, which can be used to connect the fuel pressure gauge (Figure 23–37). A Schrader valve is very similar to tire valve, the center of the valve must be depressed before anything can

FIGURE 23–37 Port injection fuel rail with a Schrader valve. *Courtesy of Chrysler Corporation*

enter or leave the valve. If the system does not have a Schrader valve, the fuel rail should be relieved of any pressure before loosening a fitting to install the pressure gauge. When performing this test on carbureted engines, the pressure gauge is installed between the fuel filter and the carburetor fuel inlet. A tee fitting can be used to install the gauge.

🔧 SHOP TALK

Fuel pump pressure specifications are given by the manufacturer in pounds per square inch (psi) at a certain engine speed. ∎

CHECKING THE FUEL PRESSURE ON A PFI SYSTEM

P13–1 Many problems on today's cars can be caused by incorrect fuel pressure. Therefore, checking fuel pressure is an important step in diagnosing driveability problems.

P13–2 Prior to testing the injection system, a careful visual inspection of the injectors and fuel rail is necessary. Any sign of a fuel leak should be noted.

P13–3 The fuel supply line into the fuel rail is a likely point for leakage. Check the area around the fitting to make sure no leaks have occurred.

P13–4 Most fuel rails are equipped with a fitting that can be used to relieve pressure and to test pressure.

P13–5 To test fuel pressure, connect the appropriate pressure gauge to the fuel rail fitting.

P13–6 Connect a hand-held vacuum pump to the pressure regulator.

P13–7 Turn the ignition switch to the run position and observe the fuel pressure gauge. Compare the reading to specifications. A reading lower than normal indicates a faulty fuel pump or fuel delivery system.

P13–8 To test the fuel pressure regulator, create a vacuum at the regulator with the vacuum pump. Fuel pressure should decrease as vacuum increases. If pressure remains the same, the regulator is faulty.

To measure fuel pump capacity or discharge volume, allow fuel to discharge from the pump into a graduated container for the amount of time specified in the service manual. Compare the amount of fuel discharged with the specifications. Always follow the proper safety guidelines for handing and storing gasoline.

🔧 SHOP TALK

Manufacturer's specifications generally are given in terms of 1 pint of fuel delivered in a given number of seconds while the engine is at idle and also at a specified speed. Some manual specifications just state a good volume at cranking speed. This usually means a pint of fuel is delivered in 30 seconds or less at an engine speed of 500 rpm. ∎

Figure 23–38 shows the common problems with a mechanical pump. To replace a mechanical fuel pump, remove the inlet and outlet lines at the pump. Use a plug to stop the flow of fuel from the tank. With the correct size socket wrench, remove mounting bolts. Then, remove the pump from the engine. Clean the old gasket material from the engine block. Apply gasket sealer to the mounting surface on the engine and to the threads of the mounting bolts. Install the new gasket, then position the pump by tilting it either toward or away from the block to correctly place the lever against the cam. If the pump is driven by a pushrod, the rod must be held up to permit the rocker arm to go under it. When the pump is properly positioned, there should be an internal squeaking noise with each movement of the pump. Tighten the mounting bolts firmly. Attach the inlet and outlet lines. Start the engine and check for leaks.

FIGURE 23–38   Common problems associated with a mechanical fuel pump.

Electric Fuel Pumps   Electric fuel pumps offer important advantages over mechanical fuel pumps. Because electric fuel pumps maintain constant fuel pressure, they aid in starting and reduce vapor lock problems.

The electric fuel pump can be located inside (Figure 23–39) or outside the fuel tank. An electric fuel pump may also be combined with the fuel gauge's sending unit (Figure 23–40). There are four basic types of electric fuel pumps: the diaphragm, plunger, bellows, and impeller or rotary. The in-tank electric pump is usually a rotary type. The diaphragm, plunger, and bellows type (Figure 23–41) are usually the demand style. That is, when the ignition is turned on, the pump begins operation. It shuts off automatically when the fuel line is pressurized. When there is

FIGURE 23–39   Electric fuel pump located inside the fuel tank.

FIGURE 23–40 Combination of fuel pump and fuel gauge sending unit. *Courtesy of Cadillac Motor Car Division, General Motors Corporation*

FIGURE 23–41 Bellows fuel pump.

a demand for more fuel, the electric pump provides more. When demand is lower, it pumps less, so proper fuel flow and pressure are constantly maintained. A typical wiring diagram for an electric fuel pump is shown in Figure 23–42.

TROUBLESHOOTING Problems in fuel systems using electric fuel pumps are usually indicated by improper fuel system pressure or a dead or inoperative fuel pump. A high pressure reading usually indi-

cates either a faulty pressure regulator or an obstructed return line. To identify the cause, disconnect the fuel return line at the tank. Use a length of hose to route the returning fuel into an appropriate container. Start the engine and note the pressure reading at the engine. If fuel pressure is now within specifications, check for an obstruction in the in-tank return plumbing. The fuel reservoir check valve or aspirator jet might be clogged.

CAUTION:

The fuel supply lines remain pressurized for long periods of time after the engine is shut down. This pressure must be relieved before servicing of the fuel system begins. A valve is normally provided on the throttle body or fuel rail for this purpose. ■

If the fuel pressure still reads high with the return line disconnected from the tank, note the volume of fuel flowing through the line. Little or no fuel flow can indicate a plugged return line. Shut off the engine and connect a length of hose directly to the fuel pressure regulator return port to bypass the return hose. Restart the engine and again check the pressure read-

FIGURE 23–42 Typical wiring diagram for an electric fuel pump.

ing. If bypassing the return line brings the readings back within specifications, a plugged return line is the culprit. If pressure is still high, apply vacuum to the pressure regulator to see if that makes a difference. It should. If there is still no change, replace the faulty pressure regulator. If applying vacuum directly to the regulator lowers fuel pressure, the vacuum hose that controls the operation of the regulator might be plugged, leaking, or misrouted.

Low pressure, on the other hand, can be due to a clogged fuel filter, restricted fuel line, weak pump, leaky pump check valve, defective fuel pressure regulator, or dirty filter sock in the tank. It is possible to rule out filter and line restrictions as a cause of the problem by making a pressure check at the pump outlet. A higher reading at the pump outlet (at least 5 psi) means there is a restriction in the filter or line. If the reading at the pump outlet is unchanged, then either the pump is weak or is having trouble picking up fuel (clogged filter sock in the tank). Either way it is necessary to get inside the fuel tank. If the filter sock is gummed up with dirt or debris, it is also wise to clean out the tank when the filter sock is cleaned or replaced.

Another possible source of trouble is the pump check valve. Some pumps have one, others have two (positive displacement roller vane pumps). The purpose of the check valve is to prevent fuel movement through the pump when the pump is off so residual pressure remains at the injectors. This can be checked by watching the fuel pressure gauge after the engine is shut off.

Depending on the type of pump used, the check valve can also prevent the reverse flow of fuel and

relieve internal pressure to regulate maximum pump output. Check valves can stick and leak. So, if a pump runs but does not pump fuel, a bad check valve is to blame. Unfortunately, the check valve is usually an integral part of the pump assembly, which is sealed at the factory. Therefore, if the check valve is causing trouble, the entire pump must be replaced.

When an engine fails to start because there is no fuel delivery, the first check is the fuel gauge. A gauge that reads higher than a half tank probably means there is fuel in the tank, but not always. A defective sending unit or miscalibrated gauge might be giving a false indication. Sticking a wire or dowel rod down the fuel tank filler pipe tells whether or not there is really fuel in the tank. If the gauge is faulty, repair or replace it.

Listen for pump noise. When the key is turned on, the pump should buzz for a couple of seconds to build system pressure. The pump is usually energized through an oil pressure switch (the purpose of which is to shut off the flow of fuel in case of an accident that stalls the engine). On most late-model cars with computerized engine controls, the computer energizes a pump relay when it receives a cranking signal from the distributor pick-up or crankshaft sensor. An oil pressure switch might still be included in the circuitry for safety purposes and to serve as a backup in case the relay or computer signal fails. Failure of the pump relay or computer driver signal can cause slow starting because the fuel pump does not come on until the engine cranks long enough to build up sufficient oil pressure to trip the oil pressure switch.

If a buzzing sound is not heard when the key is on or while the engine is being cranked, check for the

PROCEDURES
Replacing an Electric Fuel Pump

1. Disconnect the ground terminal at the battery.
2. Disconnect the electrical connectors on the electric fuel pump. Label the wires to aid in connecting it to the new pump. Reversing polarity on most pumps destroys the unit.
3. Fuel and vapor lines should be removed from the pump. Label the lines to aid in connecting them to the new pump.
4. The inside tank pump can usually be taken out of the tank by removing the fuel sending unit retaining or lock ring (Figure 23–43). However, it may be necessary to remove the fuel tank to get at the retaining ring. Removal of the fuel tank can be accomplished as described earlier in this chapter.
5. On a fuel pump that is outside the tank, remove the bolts holding it in place. On in-tank models, loosen the retaining ring. Pull the pump and sending unit out of the tank (if they are combined in one unit) and discard the tank O-ring seal.
6. To remove the pump, twist off the filter sock, then push the pump up until the bottom is clear of the bracket. Swing the pump out to the side and pull it down to free it from the rubber fuel line coupler. The rubber sound insulator between the bottom of the pump and bracket and the rubber coupler on the fuel line are normally discarded because new ones are included with the replacement pump. Some pumps have a rubber jacket around them to quiet the pump. If this is the case, slip off the jacket and put it on the new pump.
7. Compare the replacement pump with the old one. If necessary, transfer any fuel line fittings from the old pump to the new one. Note the position of the filter sock on the pump so you can install a new one in the same relative position.
8. When inserting the new pump back into the sending unit bracket, be careful not to bend the bracket. Make sure the rubber sound insulator under the bottom of the pump is in place. Install a new filter sock on the pump inlet and reconnect the pump wires. Be absolutely certain you have correct polarity. Replace the O-ring seal on the fuel tank opening, then put the pump and sender assembly back in the tank and tighten the locking ring by rotating it clockwise.

Some pump/sender assembly units are secured by bolts.
9. If the fuel was removed from the vehicle, replace it.

WARNING!
Avoid the temptation to test the new pump before reinstalling the fuel tank, by energizing it with a couple of jumper wires. Running the pump dry can damage it because the pump relies on fuel for lubrication and cooling. ∎

10. Reconnect the electrical connectors.
11. Reconnect the ground terminal at the battery.
12. Start the engine and check all connections for fuel leaks.

presence of voltage at the pump electrical connectors. The pump might be good; but if it does not receive voltage and have a good ground, it does not run. To check the ground connect a testlight across the ground and feed wires at the pump to check for voltage, or use a voltmeter to read actual voltage and an ohmmeter to check ground resistance. The latter is the better test technique because a poor ground connection or low voltage can reduce pump operating speed and output. If the electrical circuit checks out but the pump does not run, the pump is probably bad and should be replaced.

No voltage at the pump terminal when the key is on and the engine is cranking indicates a faulty oil pressure switch, pump relay, relay drive circuit in the computer, or a wiring problem. Check the pump fuse to see if it is blown. Replacing the fuse might restore power to the pump, but until you have found out what caused the fuse to blow, the problem is not solved. The most likely cause of a blown fuse would be a short in the wiring between the relay and pump, or a short inside the oil pressure switch or relay.

A faulty oil pressure switch can be checked by bypassing it with a jumper wire. If this restores power to the pump and the engine starts, replace the switch. If an oil pressure switch or relay sticks in the closed position, the pump can run continuously whether the key is on or off, depending on how the circuit is wired.

To check a pump relay, use a testlight to check across the relays and ground terminals. This tells if the relay is getting battery voltage and ground. Next, turn off the ignition, wait about 10 seconds, then turn it on. The relay should click, and you should see battery voltage at the relay's pump terminal. If noth-

FIGURE 23–43 The fuel tank's lock ring can be loosened and tightened with a brass drift and hammer. *Courtesy of Chrysler Corporation*

ing happens, repeat the test checking for voltage at the relay terminal wired to the computer. The presence of a voltage signal here means the computer is doing its job, but the relay is failing to close and should be replaced. No voltage signal from the computer indicates an opening in that wiring circuit or a fault in the computer itself.

CAUTION:

When testing an electric fuel pump, do not let fuel contact any electrical wiring. The smallest spark (electric arc) could ignite the fuel. ■

When replacing an electric pump, but sure the new or rebuilt replacement unit meets the minimum requirements of pressure and volume for that particular vehicle. This information can be found in the service manual.

CUSTOMER CARE

Never release a car from the shop after servicing a fuel pump without checking for fuel leaks. A leak could cause a very serious fire, but even if it does not, an angry customer has to bring the car back so you can fix the leak. ■

ELECTRONIC FUEL SYSTEM

The basic function of an electronic engine control fuel delivery system is the same as the function of a conventional system just described in this chapter. The main difference is that control of the system is

FIGURE 23—44 Electrical fuel delivery system wiring diagram.

obtained through a power relay and computer. Electrically, the system consists of a fuel pump, an inertia switch, a fuel pump relay, a computer power relay, and a control computer.

When the ignition key is placed in the start or run position in a typical electronic system, the computer's power relay applies energizing voltage to the fuel pump relay. The ground path for the relay power circuit is through the computer. This ground path is present only when the ignition key is in start or run.

The computer controls operation of the fuel pump relay during the run mode by opening and closing the ground path to the relay coil (Figure 23–44). The computer also has a time-out feature that shuts off the fuel pump during a key on/engine off situation. Under a condition of engine flooding, the computer shuts off the injectors if the throttle position sensor (**TPS**) signals the wide-open throttle (**WOT**) valve during the crank mode. This allows the driver to start a flooded engine by using the same technique used on engines with a carburetor. Simply hold the accelerator pedal down while cranking the engine.

Detailed information concerning fuel delivery and control in electronic fuel injection systems is given in the next chapter.

CASE STUDY

A customer comes into the shop complaining about a hesitation problem. After taking a test drive with the customer in the car, the technician checks under the hood. He sees that the hot air duct between the exhaust manifold and the air cleaner is intact. The lines that route vacuum to the thermostatically controlled air cleaner are in place, and the heat riser valve moves freely. He checks and finds the rest of the vacuum lines are properly routed and connected.

The technician removes the air cleaner and peers down the carburetor's throat while he works the throttle. He notes the flow of gas is weak. The technician performs pressure and volume tests. The pressure is within the manufacturer's specifications, but the volume is low and large air bubbles are produced during the test. Because of the air bubbles, the technician checks the flexible fuel hoses between the fuel pump and the fuel tank. He finds that one of the clamps has been tightened too much and a crack has resulted.

KEY TERMS

Antiknock	MMT
Cetane	MON
CNG	MTBE
Compression fitting	Octane
Crude oil	Paraffin
Detonation	Pour point
Double-flare	RON
Ethanol	Schrader valve
EVAP	Sulfur dioxide
Flame front	TEL
Heptane	TML
Inertia switch	TPS
Isooctane	WAP
LP-gas	WOT
Methanol	

SUMMARY

◆ Gasoline is made from crude oil.

◆ The major factors affecting fuel performance are antiknock quality, volatility, sulfur content, and deposit control.

◆ An octane number is a measure of a gasoline's burning quality.

◆ Two basic types of gasoline are used in vehicles: leaded and unleaded. The main reason unleaded gasoline was introduced was to provide a fuel for cars with catalytic converters.

◆ Isopropyl alcohol is seasonally added to gasoline as an anti-icing agent. Oxidation inhibitors help control gum, deposit formation, and staleness. Metal deactivators and rust inhibitors reduce reactions between the fuel and the metals in the fuel system. Detergents clean certain critical components inside the engine. Ethanol and methanol are used as octane enhancers. MTBE is an active enhancer and supply extender.

◆ Diesel fuel is made from the middle distillates of crude oil.

◆ The significant chemical properties of diesel fuel are its wax appearance point, pour point, viscosity volatility, and cetane number.

◆ Other alternate fuels include ethanol, methanol, propane, and natural gas.

◆ Because of its high propane content, LP-gas is often referred to as propane. Propane is a dry fuel, meaning that it enters the engine as a vapor. Gasoline, on the other hand, enters as tiny droplets of liquid.

◆ Natural gas costs less than gasoline. It is the cleanest alternative fuel. Therefore, it generally reduces vehicle maintenance. It is safe and abundant and readily available in the United States. The chief disadvantage at this time is its nonavailability to most users.

◆ Modern fuel tanks include devices that prevent vapors from leaving the tank. They have slash baffles or surge plates to prevent the fuel from splashing around. Each tank has an inlet filler tube and a nonvented cap. Rollover protection devices prevent gasoline from leaking out of the fuel tank in an accident. A liquid vapor separator stops liquid fuel or bubbles from reaching the vapor storage canister or the engine crankcase.

◆ The fuel lines carry fuel from the tank to the fuel pump, fuel filter, and carburetor or fuel injection metering pump. They are made of either metal tubing, flexible nylon, or synthetic rubber hose.

◆ The three basic types of fuel filters are in-carburetor filters, in-line filters, and out-pump filters.

◆ Basically, there are two types of fuel pumps: mechanical and electrical. There are four basic types of electric fuel pumps: the diaphragm, plunger, bellows, and impeller (or rotary). Incorrect fuel pressure and low volume are the two most likely fuel pump troubles that affect engine performance.

◆ The control of an electronic fuel delivery system is obtained through a power relay and computer.

TECH MANUAL

The following procedures are included in Chapter 23 of the *Tech Manual* that accompanies this book:

1. Test fuel pump pressure.

2. Remove and replace a fuel filter.

REVIEW QUESTIONS

1. What rating is used as a measure of a diesel fuel's ignition quality?

2. Name the two forms of natural gas commonly used as an automotive fuel.

3. Name the components of a typical fuel delivery system.

4. Name the basic types of gasoline filters.

5. Name the four basic types of electric fuel pumps.

6. Which of the following statements is false?
   a. An octane number is a measure of a fuel's tendency not to produce engine knock.
   b. Turbocharging deters knock.
   c. Both a and b
   d. Neither a nor b

7. Which of the following is the leading cause of exhaust valve pitting and exhaust system deterioration?
   a. gum   c. sulfuric acid
   b. oxidation   d. none of the above

8. Technician A says the main reason unleaded gasoline was introduced was to provide a fuel for cars with catalytic converters. Technician B says the main reason was to offset the effects of isopropyl alcohol in gasoline. Who is correct?
   a. Technician A   c. Both A and B
   b. Technician B   d. Neither A nor B

9. Which of the following is the most widely used gasoline additive today?
   a. ethanol   c. methanol
   b. MTBE   d. propane

10. Which of the following is known as wood alcohol?
   a. ethanol   c. methanol
   b. MTBE   d. propane

11. Which of the following is a major drawback to MTBE?
   a. It cannot be shipped through product pipelines.
   b. It causes elastomers and plastics to swell.
   c. Both a and b
   d. Neither a nor b

12. Which of the following is a measure of fluid's resistance to flow?
   a. wax appearance point
   b. pour point
   c. specific gravity
   d. none of the above

13. Which of the following statements is incorrect?
    a. Diesel fuel is more volatile than gasoline.
    b. Propane is a constituent of natural gas.
    c. Propane burns clean in an engine.
    d. High-viscosity fuel is relatively hard to burn.

14. What percent of a modern fuel tank can ever be filled with fuel?
    a. 40 percent
    b. 60 percent
    c. 90 percent
    d. 100 percent

15. Technician A replaces any leaking metal fuel tank. Technician B steam cleans a leaking metal fuel tank and then solders or brazes it. Who uses the better method?
    a. Technician A
    b. Technician B
    c. Both A and B
    d. Neither A nor B

16. Technician A replaces a damaged steel fuel line with one made of synthetic rubber. Technician B replaces a damaged steel fuel line with one made of steel. Who is correct?
    a. Technician A
    b. Technician B
    c. Both A and B
    d. Neither A nor B

17. What component, located in the gasoline tank, prevents large, contaminant particles from entering the fuel system?
    a. fuel filter
    b. diesel filter
    c. air filter
    d. strainer

18. A vehicle's engine performance indicates inadequate fuel, and a faulty fuel pump is suspected. Technician A tests the fuel pump for pressure and volume while mounted on the engine. Technician B removes the fuel pump to inspect it. Who is correct?
    a. Technician A
    b. Technician B
    c. Both A and B
    d. Neither A nor B

19. In a gasoline engine, _____ occurs when the flame front fails to reach a pocket of air/fuel mixture before the temperature in that area reaches the point of self-ignition.
    a. volatility
    b. carbon depositing
    c. detonation
    d. flaring

20. After a fuel pump is installed, an internal squeaking noise is heard from each movement of the pump. Technician A considers the noise to be normal. Technician B examines the pump for a defective or loose component. Who is correct?
    a. Technician A
    b. Technician B
    c. Both A and B
    d. Neither A nor B

CARBURETORS

24

OBJECTIVES

◆ *Describe the basic principles of carburetion.* ◆ *Explain the purpose and operation of the different carburetor circuits.* ◆ *Describe the various auxiliary carburetor controls.* ◆ *Describe the different types of carburetors.* ◆ *Recognize carburetor-related performance problems.* ◆ *Explain how various carburetor adjustments are made.*

The carburetor is a device used to mix, or meter, fuel with air in proportions that satisfy the energy demands of the engine in all phases of operation. A carburetor is a very complex mechanism (Figure 24–1).

Some of the larger two- and four-barrel carburetors can have over 200 parts. These parts make up the metering systems and subsystems that are necessary for matching air and fuel delivery with engine perfor-

* Exhaust gas recirculation

FIGURE 24–1 Typical late-model carburetor. *Courtesy of Chevrolet Motor Division, General Motors Corporation*

mance demands. Each of these systems must be functional and properly adjusted if the engine is to operate efficiently.

Although fuel injection systems have replaced carburetion in all passenger cars and light trucks, there are many carbureted engines still on the road. Technicians must understand the principles of carburetion and how carburetors are constructed and operate before they can successfully diagnose and tune carbureted engines. Carburetors have a venturi and work under the principle of pressure differential. The amount of air and fuel delivered to the engine depends on the difference between the low pressure (vacuum) in the engine and the pressure of the outside air (atmospheric pressure).

VENTURI

Air is drawn into the engine by the intake stroke. As vacuum is created, it draws air through the carburetor and venturi into the engine.

A **venturi** is a streamlined restriction that partly closes the carburetor bore (Figure 24–2). Air is forced to speed up as it enters the venturi to pass through the restriction. This restriction causes the formation of a vacuum below the venturi. As engine speed increases during acceleration, more air is drawn into the carburetor. As a result, venturi vacuum increases because the greater the velocity of air passing through the venturi, the greater the vacuum.

Venturi vacuum is used to draw in the correct amount of fuel through a discharge tube (Figure 24–3). As the air flows through the venturi, vacuum draws the fuel from the carburetor bowl into the

FIGURE 24–2 A venturi is a restriction in the path of airflow. A vacuum is produced at the point of greatest restriction.

FIGURE 24–3 The vacuum produced at the venturi is used to draw in the fuel from the carburetor.

stream of air going into the engine. More fuel is drawn in as venturi vacuum increases, and less as the vacuum decreases.

CARBURETION

The three general stages involved in carburetion are metering, atomization, and vaporization.

Metering

Metering is another term for measuring. In the process of carburetion, fuel is metered into the air passing through the barrel of the carburetor. The mixture of air and fuel is called an **emulsion**. The ideal air/fuel ratio at which all the fuel blends with all the oxygen in the air is called the **stoichiometric ratio**. This ratio is about 14.7:1. If there is more fuel in the mixture, it is called a **rich** mix. If there is less fuel, it is called a **lean** mix. The amount of fuel metered into the air is varied in relation to the amount of air passing through the carburetor. Additional factors that influence the amount of fuel metered into the air include engine temperature, load and speed requirements, and the amount of oxygen in the exhaust stream.

Atomization

Atomization is the stage in which the metered fuel is drawn into the airstream in the form of tiny droplets. The droplets of fuel are drawn out of passages called discharge ports.

Vaporization

The surface area of an atomized droplet is in contact with a relatively large amount of surrounding air. In addition, the venturi is a low-pressure area. These factors combine to create a fine mist of fuel below the venturi in the bore. This is called **vaporization**—

FIGURE 24–4 The throttle plate is a circular disc attached to a center rod. As the rod is turned, the throttle plate opens and closes.

FIGURE 24–5 Fuel inlet system.

the last stage of carburetion. It occurs below the venturi, in the intake manifold, and within the cylinder. Swirl, turbulence, and heat within the intake manifold and cylinder also enhance vaporization.

THROTTLE PLATE

The throttle plate controls the amount of air and fuel that flows through the carburetor into the engine. It is a circular disc that is placed directly in the flow of air and fuel, below the venturi. It is connected to the driver's throttle pedal so it opens to a vertical position as the pedal is depressed. When the throttle plate is all the way open, there is very little restriction of air. This is a maximum speed condition. As the driver's foot is removed, a spring closes the throttle plate. This restricts the amount of air going into the engine. This is a low speed condition. Figure 24–4 shows a throttle plate assembly.

BASIC CARBURETOR CIRCUITS

Variations in engine speed and load demand different amounts of air and fuel (often in differing proportions) for best performance and present complex problems for the carburetor. At engine idle speeds, for example, there is insufficient air velocity to cause fuel to be drawn from the discharge nozzle and into the airstream. Also, with a sudden change in engine speed, such as rapid acceleration, the venturi effect (pressure differential) is momentarily lost. Therefore, the carburetor must have special circuits or systems to cope with these situations. There are seven basic circuits used on a typical carburetor.

1. Float
2. Idle
3. Off-idle
4. Main metering
5. Full power (or power enrichment)
6. Accelerator pump
7. Choke

Float Circuit

A **float** circuit or fuel inlet system (Figure 24–5) of a typical carburetor consists of the fuel bowl, fuel inlet fitting, fuel inlet needle valve and seat, and the float. A full screen or filter is usually installed at the fuel inlet to prevent dirty fuel from mixing in the carburetor and causing a problem.

The float system stores fuel and holds it at a precise level as a starting point for uniform fuel flow. Fuel enters the carburetor through the inlet line and passes through an inlet filter to the inlet needle valve and seat. The incoming fuel is captured and stored in the reservoir or fuel bowl. The fuel bowl is normally an integral part of the main casting but can be a separate casting attached to the carburetor body with screws. Carburetors with primary and secondary venturis might have two separate fuel bowls.

The level of the fuel in the bowl is maintained at a specified height by the rising and falling of the float in the fuel bowl. Early floats were made of brass stampings soldered into an airtight lung. Floats (Figure 24–6) made of **nitrile rubber**, a closed cell material made of thousands of tiny hollow spheres, are used most exclusively on domestic cars. Hollow plastic floats can also be found in carburetors.

As fuel enters the bowl, the float, which is connected to a hinged lever, rises and closes the inlet needle valve. With the needle valve closed, fuel is prevented from entering the carburetor. Fuel pressure against the inlet needle valve tends to force it open while the buoyancy of the float in the bowl tends to force it closed. This action establishes the precise fuel level for

FIGURE 24–6 Float system with pivoted float, needle, seat, and inlet. *Courtesy of Chrysler Corporation*

FIGURE 24–7 An idle discharge port draws fuel from the carburetor to allow the engine to run at idle.

the carburetor. To prevent the float from bouncing and vibrating, a bumper spring is usually installed under the float or to a tang connected to the float.

The metering systems of a carburetor are designed to function properly only when the fuel level in the bowl is at a specific level. The specific level is adjusted with the carburetor partially disassembled on most models. However, it can be adjusted externally on a few carburetors by turning a threaded inlet valve assembly.

The fuel bowl is vented internally to the air horn by a vent tube in the carburetor body. Prior to the introduction of emission controls, most primary fuel bowls were also vented to the atmosphere when the engine was at idle or turned off. Since the introduction of evaporative control systems, all fuel bowls are vented by a valve to a charcoal canister, which absorbs and stores fuel vapors. The vapors are returned to the engine when it is restarted.

Idle and Off-Idle Circuits

At idle, the engine requires a richer air/fuel mixture than during normal cruising conditions. This is because residual exhaust gases remain in the combustion chambers during low-engine rpm and dilute the air/fuel charge. The idle circuit supplies the richer air/fuel mixture to operate the engine at idle and low speeds.

During idle conditions, there is not enough air entering the venturi to cause a vacuum to move the fuel. The throttle plate is almost all the way closed as shown in Figure 24–7. During this condition, there is a large vacuum below the throttle valve. This vacuum causes fuel to be drawn from the carburetor float bowl through internal passages to the idle port below the throttle plate. As fuel is drawn from the float ball

to the idle port, air is drawn in through an air-bleed passageway near the top of the carburetor. Only a small amount of air passes by the throttle plate. The end result is the richer air/fuel mixture needed for idle operation.

As the throttle plate is opened during low-speed operation, a transfer slot located above the throttle plate is progressively exposed to vacuum, and the air/fuel emulsion is also discharged from the **transfer slot**. The increased air/fuel mixture flow provides a smooth transition between idle and cruising modes of operation. Some carburetors have a series of holes called off-idle air passages, instead of a transfer slot. Like the transfer slot, the holes permit increased fuel delivery as the throttle opens. This is called an off-idle system.

On older carburetors there is an idle mixture needle valve. This valve is used to control or adjust the amount of air and fuel at idle. More current carburetors, however, have limiting caps on the idle mixture screws, which limit the amount of adjustment available. On newer carburetors, the idle mixture screws are sealed with steel plugs to eliminate all adjustment.

To improve idle quality when meeting emission standards, a variable air bleed idle system is used on some carburetors (Figure 24–8). In this system there are two idle air bleeds. One idle air bleed is installed normally in the air horn. An auxiliary idle air bleed is drilled into the lower skirt of the venturi. The air entering through the auxiliary passage is adjusted by an idle air adjusting screw. The screw is turned clockwise to enrich the idle mixture and counterclockwise to lean out the idle air/fuel mixture.

FIGURE 24–8 The idle discharge port and off-idle transfer slot supply fuel to the carburetor at low speeds.

FIGURE 24–10 Air/fuel mixture routed to the venturi via the main metering circuit and discharge nozzle.

SHOP TALK

On most late-model carburetors, the idle mixture is factory set and the adjustment screw is covered with a plate or plug. This ensures that the CO percentage in the exhaust meets emissions standards and prevents anyone from tampering with the factory setting. Earlier carburetors had an idle limiter cap attached to the idle mixture screw (Figure 24–9). The limiter cap prevents the factory setting from being tampered with but allows the idle mixture to be adjusted within a narrow range (about 3/4 of a turn). ∎

Main Metering Circuit

The main metering circuit (Figure 24–10) comes into operation as engine speed increases. Opening the throttle plate past the idle position increases the air flowing through the venturi and creates enough vacuum to allow atmospheric pressure to force fuel through the main metering system and out the main fuel discharge nozzle, located in the center of the venturi. As engine speed is increased, the vacuum at the discharge nozzle increases.

This vacuum or pressure differential causes fuel to flow out of the fuel bowl, through the main metering jet, and into the main well. On most carburetors, the main well is vented through a precisely sized opening called the main well air bleed. The main well air bleed allows air to enter at the top of the main well. Air entering the calibrated main air bleed prevents a vacuum from developing in the main well. The air also allows for aeration of the fuel as it leaves the main well and travels up the well tube. This allows the fuel to be partially atomized as it travels toward the discharge nozzle.

Air flows through the bleeds because it draws air from the high-pressure area above the venturi. The main metering discharge nozzle is in the low-pressure venturi level.

As the air speed increases through the venturi, more fuel is drawn from the main well. This lowers the fuel level in the main well and exposes more air bleed openings in the main well tube. This causes extra air to enter the well tube, mix with the fuel, and dilute or lean the mixture. This action circumvents the richening effect caused by the increased carburetor airflow. If the fuel were not diluted as such, the air/fuel mixture would richen at high speed as the venturi vacuum increased faster than the engine's need for additional fuel.

FIGURE 24–9 Idle limiter caps restrict the amount of adjustment allowed for idle mixture.

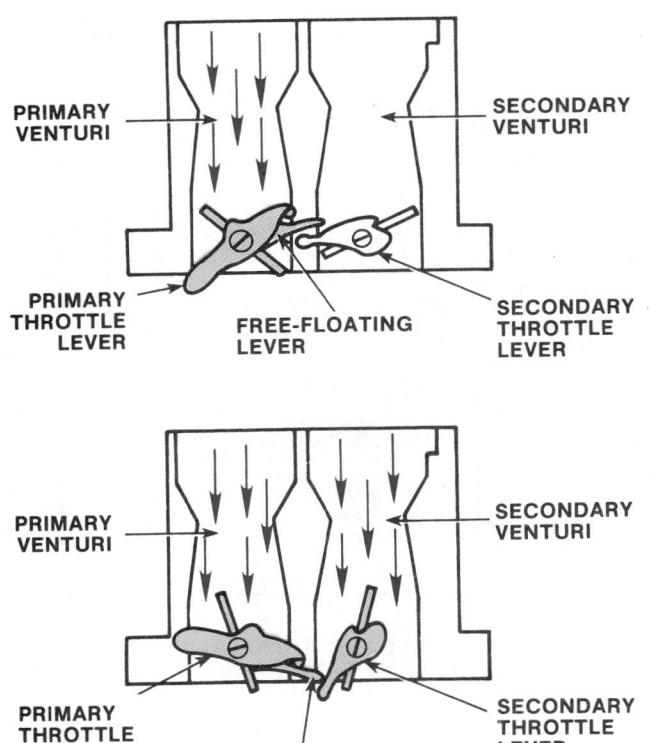

FIGURE 24–11   Mechanically actuated secondary throttle plates.

well as other circuits). When all throttle plates open and close simultaneously, the carburetor is called a **single-stage** carburetor.

Some carburetors have two stages, called **primary** and **secondary stages**. In the primary stage, one or two throttle plates operate normally as in a single-stage carburetor. The secondary stage throttle plates, however, only open after the primary throttle plates have opened a certain amount. Thus, the primary stage controls off-idle and low cruising speeds. The secondary stage opens when high cruising speeds or loads require additional air and fuel. The added flow capacity raises the engine power output.

The secondary throttle plates can be opened mechanically or by a vacuum source. Mechanically actuated secondary throttle plates are opened by a tab on the primary throttle linkage. After the throttle primary plates open a set amount (usually 40 to 45 degrees), the tab engages the secondary throttle linkage, forcing the plates open (Figure 24–11). Vacuum-actuated secondaries have a spring-loaded diaphragm. Vacuum is supplied to the diaphragm from ports in the primary and secondary throttle bores. When the vacuum in the primary bore reaches a specific level, the vacuum supplied to the diaphragm overcomes the spring and opens the secondary throttle plates (Figure 24–12). The vacuum created in the secondary throttle bore increases the vacuum signal to the diaphragm, opening the secondary throttle valves still farther.

Secondary Metering System   Some carburetors have more than one **barrel** or air horn. Each barrel has a throttle plate and main metering system (as

LOW SPEED/LIGHT LOAD

HIGH SPEED/HEAVY LOAD

FIGURE 24–12   Vacuum-controlled secondary system.

FIGURE 24–13   Some power systems consist of metering rods placed in the main jets.

FIGURE 24–14   Power valve system.

Power Enrichment Circuit

At wide open throttle, the engine needs a richer-than-normal air/fuel mixture. This mixture cannot be supplied by the main metering system. So, an additional fuel enrichment or full-power system is provided on most carburetors. The power enrichment system meters additional fuel into the mixture. This can be accomplished in several ways.

Metering Rods   In some carburetors, power enrichment is provided by **metering rods** placed in the main jets (Figure 24–13). The metering rods are actuated mechanically or by vacuum. When the throttle is not wide open (or nearly so), the throttle linkage keeps the rods in the jets, providing normal fuel flow. When the throttle is opened wide, either a mechanical link in the throttle linkage or vacuum-actuated lever lifts the rods out of the jets, enabling more fuel to be forced into the main well. The additional fuel flow richens the air/fuel mixture.

Power Valve   The **power valve** (Figure 24–14) is basically a vacuum-operated metering rod. It consists

of a vacuum diaphragm or piston, a spring-loaded valve, and a metering rod inside an auxiliary fuel jet usually located in the bottom of the fuel bowl. A vacuum passageway machined into the main body casting supplies manifold vacuum to the diaphragm or piston. During idle and low cruising speeds, the vacuum holds the power valve closed. As engine speed and load increases and the vacuum signal drops to a specific level, the spring overcomes the vacuum and forces the power valve out of the jet. This increases the fuel flowing into the main well.

The power valve has been replaced or modified in today's feedback carburetor. In a feedback system, an electrical solenoid controls the metering fuel jets or idle air bleeds to regulate the air/fuel mixture. Feedback carburetors are discussed later in this chapter.

Accelerator Pump Circuit

The off-idle or transfer circuit discussed earlier allows the engine to be accelerated smoothly without hesitation or lags. However, during sudden acceleration, the engine experiences a momentary drop in power unless additional fuel is simultaneously introduced into the air charge.

During sudden acceleration, the air flowing through the carburetor reacts almost immediately to each change in the throttle plate opening. However, since fuel is heavier than air, it has a slower response time. Fuel in the main metering system or idle system takes a fraction of a second to respond to the throttle opening. This lag in time creates a hesitation of fuel flow whenever the accelerator pedal is quickly depressed.

FIGURE 24–15 Diaphragm accelerator pump.

FIGURE 24–16 Plunger accelerator pump.

The accelerator pump system solves this problem by mechanically supplying fuel until the other fuel metering systems are able to supply the proper mixture.

One type of accelerator pump (Figure 24–15) is the diaphragm type located in the bottom of the fuel bowl. Locating the pump in the bottom of the fuel bowl ensures a more solid charge of fuel (fewer bubbles).

When the throttle is opened, the pump linkage, activated by a cam on the throttle lever, forces the pump diaphragm up. As the diaphragm moves up, the pressure forces the pump inlet check ball or valve onto its seat. This prevents the fuel from flowing back into the fuel bowl. At the same time, the pressure of the fuel causes the discharge check ball or valve to rise and fuel is then discharged into the venturi.

As the throttle returns toward the closed position, the linkage returns to its original position and the diaphragm return spring forces the diaphragm down. The pump inlet check valve is moved off its seat and the diaphragm chamber is refilled with fuel from the fuel bowl.

Another common type of accelerator pump is shown in Figure 24–16. This type of pump uses a plunger rather than a diaphragm. As the throttle moves toward the open position, pressure from the plunger forces an inlet ball onto a check valve, sealing the inlet valve. At the same time, a ball is forced off the outlet check valve and fuel is discharged from the shooter nozzle. As the throttle moves back toward the closed position, the plunger retracts, allowing the inlet check valve to open and fuel to refill the pump.

Choke Circuit

A cold engine needs a very rich air/fuel mixture during cranking and startup. Providing the rich mixture is the job of the **choke** circuit (Figure 24–17).

During a cold startup, the choke should be closed. This creates a very high vacuum level in the air horn below the choke plate. As the air pressure outside the carburetor forces its way into the low-pressure areas, it draws with it a rich air/fuel mixture. When the throttle plate is closed, the mixture is forced out through

FIGURE 24–17 Choke system.

the idle port or ports below the throttle valve. If the throttle valve is opened to assist in starting the engine, additional ports are exposed to the low-pressure manifold pressure and additional fuel is forced into the air horn. After the engine starts, a leaner mixture can be used to keep the engine running. Therefore, the choke should be opened some to allow increased airflow. After the engine has warmed to normal operating temperatures, the choke should be opened completely to allow the throttle to control airflow and fuel metering.

Before the introduction of automatic chokes, the opening and closing of the choke plate was manually controlled by the driver. A choke cable was connected to a knob inside the passenger compartment on the dash. To close the choke, the driver simply pulled the knob out. As the engine warmed, the choke knob was gradually pushed in to open the choke.

Modern carbureted vehicles have an automatic choke that operates without any driver assistance. Being more sensitive to engine temperature, an automatic choke is more efficient.

The typical automatic choke has a bimetal coil called a thermostatic spring. When the coil is cold, it forces the choke plate closed. As the bimetal coil warms, it expands and pulls the choke plate open (Figure 24–18).

The bimetal coil can be mounted directly on the carburetor. This type is called an integral choke (Figure 24–19). The bimetal coil may also be mounted on the intake manifold or in a heat well in the exhaust heat passage of the intake manifold. This type is called a divorced or remote choke (Figure 24–20).

The integral choke normally has a heat source to warm the bimetal. The heat source might be hot air (Figure 24–21) or coolant. Many integral chokes also have an electrical heater to assist in warming the coil during warm weather or hot startup. The bimetal coil

FIGURE 24–19 Integral automatic choke.

FIGURE 24–20 Divorced choke thermostatic element mounted in heat well.

FIGURE 24–18 Principle of a bimetallic spring.

FIGURE 24–21 Hot air choke system.

on many feedback carburetors is heated solely by a solid state heating element. Voltage is usually provided to the heating element from the alternator circuit.

ADDITIONAL CARBURETOR CONTROL

To meet complex fuel economy and emission requirements, carburetors require the help of auxiliary controls. The following describes some of the more common assist devices you are likely to encounter when servicing a carburetor.

Choke Qualifier

Once the engine has started, a leaner mixture is needed. If the choke stays shut, the rich mixture floods the engine and causes stalling. Therefore, the automatic choke has a choke-qualifying mechanism to open the choke plate slightly after the engine has started.

Many integral chokes have a vacuum piston in the choke housing that opens the choke slightly when manifold vacuum reaches a certain level (immediately after the engine starts). Some integral chokes and all divorced chokes have a qualifying diaphragm (also called a choke pull-off diaphragm or vacuum break) instead of a vacuum piston (Figure 24–22). The diaphragm is connected to manifold vacuum. When the engine starts, the diaphragm retracts, pulling the choke open. The amount of opening, or the distance between the upper edge of the choke plate and the side of the air horn, is called the qualifying dimension or setting. In some carburetors, the pull-off diaphragm has a modulator spring that varies the qualifying setting based on ambient temperatures.

Dashpot

The **dashpot** (Figure 24–23) is used during rapid deceleration to retard the closing of the throttle. This allows a smooth transition from the main metering system to the idle system and prevents stalling due to

FIGURE 24–23   Typical carburetor dashpot installation.

the overly rich air/fuel mixture. It also controls the level of HC in the exhaust during deceleration.

The dashpot consists of a small chamber with a spring-loaded diaphragm and a plunger. A link from the throttle comes in contact with the dashpot plunger as the throttle closes. As the throttle linkage exerts force on the plunger, air slowly bleeds out of the diaphragm chamber through a small hole. This slows the closing action of the throttle plate.

Hot-Idle Compensator (HIC) Valve

When the engine is overheated, a hot-idle compensator opens an air passage to lean the mixture slightly (Figure 24–24). This increases idle speed to help cool the engine (by increased coolant flow) and to prevent excess fuel vaporization within the carburetor. The **hot-idle compensator** is a bimetal, thermostatically controlled air bleed valve.

Dual Vacuum Break

Some carburetors are equipped with a fuel vacuum break system, which includes a primary diaphragm and a secondary diaphragm. The primary vacuum diaphragm opens the choke valve slightly as soon as the engine starts to keep the engine from overchoking and stalling. The secondary vacuum diaphragm, which is also attached to the choke lever, opens the

FIGURE 24–22   Vacuum break.

FIGURE 24–24   Hot-idle compensator operation: engine hot, valve open.

choke valve slightly wider in warm weather or when a warm engine is being started.

Vacuum to the secondary diaphragm is controlled by a thermal vacuum switch or valve (**TVV**). The TVV releases vacuum to the secondary vacuum break when the engine reaches a certain temperature. This prevents a rich fuel mixture and the high emissions that result form starting a cold engine in warm weather or when a warm engine is started.

Choke Unloader

To be able to start a cold engine that has been flooded with gasoline, a **choke unloader** is required. The choke unloader (Figure 24–25) is throttle linkage actuated and opens the choke whenever the accelerator pedal is floored. At wide-open throttle, the partially opened choke allows additional air to lean out the mixture and reduce fuel flow.

Deceleration Valve

The deceleration valve (Figure 24–26) is designed to prevent backfire during deceleration as the fuel mixture becomes richer. The valve, which operates only during deceleration, is usually located between the intake manifold and the air cleaner. A typical valve has a cam-shaped diaphragm housing on one end. A control manifold-vacuum line is attached to a port under the diaphragm housing. The other end of the valve is connected by hoses to the intake manifold and air cleaner. When deceleration causes an increase in manifold vacuum, the diaphragm opens the **deceleration valve** and allows air to pass from the air

FIGURE 24–26 Vacuum-operated decel valve. *Courtesy of Pontiac Motor Division, General Motors Corporation*

cleaner into the intake manifold, leaning the fuel mixture and preventing exhaust system backfire.

Throttle Position Solenoid

The throttle position solenoid is used to control the position of the throttle plate (Figure 24–27). It can have several functions, depending on its application. When the basic function is to prevent dieseling, the solenoid is called a **throttle stop solenoid** or an **idle stop solenoid**. When the engine is started, the solenoid is energized and the plunger extends, pushing against the throttle linkage. This forces the throttle plates open slightly to the curb idle position. When the ignition switch is turned off, the solenoid is de-energized and the plunger retracts. This allows the throttle plate to close completely, and it shuts off the air/fuel supply to prevent dieseling or run-on.

FIGURE 24–25 The choke unloader opens the choke any time the gas pedal is floored. The lug pushes on the cam counterweight to open the choke.

FIGURE 24–27 An idle stop solenoid is used to control the position of the idle setting when the ignition is turned off and on. *Courtesy of Echlin Manufacturing Company*

The throttle position solenoid is also used to increase the curb idle speed to compensate for extra loads on the engine. When this is its primary function, the solenoid might also be called an idle speed-up solenoid or a **throttle kicker**. This feature is most often used on cars with air conditioners. When the air conditioning is turned on, a relay energizes the solenoid so the plunger extends farther, raising the idle rpm. This keeps the engine running at a higher speed, which is required to maintain a smooth idle speed and to ensure adequate emission control.

The throttle position solenoid is also used to control idle speed when the transmission is engaged. A relay in the park/neutral switch signals the solenoid to extend when the transmission is shifted into gear. This opens the throttle slightly to compensate for the increased load on the engine.

FIGURE 24–28 Carburetors are also classified by stating the number of barrels. This is a two-barrel carburetor with two throttle plates.

TYPES OF CARBURETORS

Many types of carburetors have been built to accommodate different load conditions, engine designs, and air/fuel requirements. Different carburetors feature different drafts, different numbers of barrels, different types of venturi, and different flow rates.

Carburetor Draft

Draft is defined as the act of pulling or drawing air. A carburetor's direction of draft is one way in which carburetors are classified. Most engines have a **down-draft** carburetor that has air flowing vertically down into the engine. In the **sidedraft** carburetor, air flows through the carburetor in a horizontal direction. Many early sports cars used a sidedraft carburetor. An **updraft** carburetor brings the air and fuel into the engine in an upward direction. Not many automobiles use this type, but they are used in forklifts and other industrial engine applications.

Carburetor Barrels

A carburetor barrel is a passageway or bore used to mix the air and fuel. It consists of the throttle plate, venturi, and air horn. A one-barrel carburetor is used on small engines that do not require large quantities of air and fuel.

A two-barrel carburetor has two throttle plates and two venturis. Figure 24–28 shows the throttle plates of a two-barrel carburetor. The area where the air comes into the carburetor is common on both barrels. A two-barrel carburetor may have one barrel that is smaller in diameter than the other one.

Figure 24–29 shows a four-barrel carburetor. It has four barrels to mix the air and fuel. The engine

FIGURE 24–29 A four-barrel carburetor has four barrels and four throttle plates.

FIGURE 24–30
Carburetors have several types of venturis. One, two, and three venturis can be used. These can also be called boost venturis.

operates on two barrels during most driving conditions. When more power is needed, the other two barrels add fuel to increase the amount of horsepower and torque produced by the engine.

Venturi Types

Carburetors are also categorized according to the type of venturi they use (Figure 24–30). Simple carburetors have a single venturi. The double (dual) venturi has an additional secondary or **boost venturi**. The bottom of the center (boost) venturi is located at the greatest restriction area of the next larger venturi. This arrangement multiplies the vacuum developed in the venturi. The result is better vaporization and atomization and more control of fuel entering into the air stream. Thus, increasing the venturi effect increases the efficiency of the carburetor.

Even more control and atomization occur with a triple venturi design. The discharge tube feeds fuel into the smallest venturi for maximum control and atomization. Some carburetors have a variable or changing venturi. As the throttle pedal is depressed, the venturi increases in size. The venturi decreases in size when the throttle pedal is released.

VARIABLE VENTURI CARBURETOR

A fixed venturi does not change shape and size to accommodate changing engine performance demands. Therefore, the speed of the air flowing through the venturi varies according to engine rpm and load. Because the vacuum in the venturi is the result of moving air, the amount of fuel drawn from the discharge nozzle varies as air velocity (and vacuum) in the venturi fluctuates. In some engine operating modes, the air speed, vacuum level, and fuel discharge are matched to the needs of the engine. At other times, the fuel discharge might be too little or too much. To compensate for the inadequacies of a fixed venturi,

idle systems, power systems, and choke systems are needed to supplement the main metering system.

These assist systems are not necessary when a **variable venturi** is used. A variable venturi increases in size as engine demands increase. In this way, airflow speed through the venturi and the resulting pressure differential remains fairly constant. Thus, a variable venturi carburetor is also known as a constant velocity carburetor or a constant depression (vacuum) carburetor.

An example of a variable venturi carburetor is shown in Figure 24–31. The venturi valves are controlled by a vacuum diaphragm that receives vacuum from ports in the throttle bores between the venturi valves and the throttle plates. As the throttle plates open, vacuum in the throttle bore increases and the venturi valves open farther. As the valves open, tapered metering rods attached to the valves retract from metering jets in the sides of the throttle bores. This increases the size of the jet openings, allowing additional fuel to be drawn into the airstream so the air/fuel ratio remains constant. By metering both the fuel and airflow simultaneously, better fuel economy and lower emissions are possible.

FEEDBACK CARBURETOR SYSTEM

The latest type of carburetor system is the electronic feedback design, which provides better combustion by improved control of the air/fuel mixture.

The feedback carburetor was introduced following the development of the three-way catalytic converter. A three-way converter not only oxidizes HC and CO but also chemically reduces oxides of nitrogen (NO_X).

However, for the three-way catalyst to work efficiently, the air/fuel mixture must be maintained very close to a 14.7 to 1 ratio. If the air/fuel mixture is too lean, NO_X is not converted efficiently. If the mixture

METERING ROD FULLY IN JET

NO VACUUM ACTS ON DIAPHRAGM.

AT IDLE, VENTURI IS VERY SMALL AND METERING ROD REDUCES FUEL FLOW TO AIR HORN.

AT FAST-IDLE, AIR HORN IS SLIGHTLY LARGER. MORE FUEL IS DRAWN INTO IT.

AT IMMEDIATE SPEED, STILL MORE FUEL AND AIR ARE DRAWN INTO THROAT.

METERING ROD PULLED OUT OF JET

HIGH VACUUM IN DIAPHRAGM CHAMBER

WITH WIDE-OPEN THROTTLE, VARIABLE VENTURI IS FULLY WITHDRAWN, AS IS METERING ROD.

FIGURE 24–31 Diaphragm controls variable venturis in this carburetor design.

is too rich, HC and CO does not oxidize efficiently. Monitoring the air/fuel ratio is the job of the exhaust gas oxygen sensor (Figure 24–32).

An oxygen sensor senses the amount of oxygen present in the exhaust stream. A lean mixture produces a high level of oxygen in the exhaust. A rich mixture produces little oxygen in the exhaust. The oxygen sensor, placed in the exhaust before the catalytic converter, produces a voltage signal that varies with the amount of oxygen the sensor detects in the exhaust. If the oxygen level is high (a lean mixture),

FIGURE 24–32 Exhaust gas oxygen sensor.

the voltage output is low. If the oxygen level is low (a rich mixture), the voltage output is high.

The electrical output of the oxygen sensor is monitored by an electronic control unit (ECU). This microprocessor is programmed to interpret the input signals from the sensor and in turn generate output signals to a mixture control device that meters more or less fuel into the air charge as it is needed to maintain the 14.7 to 1 ratio.

Whenever these components are working to control the air/fuel ratio, the carburetor is said to be operating in **closed loop**. Closed loop is illustrated in the schematic shown in Figure 24–33. The oxygen sensor is constantly monitoring the oxygen in the exhaust, and the control module is constantly making adjustments to the air/fuel mixture based on the fluctuations in the sensor's voltage output. However, there are certain conditions under which the control module ignores the signals from the oxygen sensor and does not regulate the ratio of fuel to air. During these times, the carburetor is functioning in a conventional manner and is said to be operating in **open loop**. (The control cycle has been broken.)

FIGURE 24–33 Closed loop operation.

FIGURE 24-34 Remote-mounted fuel control solenoid.

FIGURE 24-35 Electronic feedback carburetor.

FIGURE 24-36 Carter thermo-quad with O_2 feedback.

The carburetor operates in open loop until the oxygen sensor reaches a certain temperature (approximately 600°F). The carburetor also goes into open loop when a richer-than-normal air/fuel mixture is required, such as during warm-up and heavy throttle application. Several other sensors are needed to alert the electronic control module to these conditions. A coolant sensor provides input relating to engine temperature. A vacuum sensor and a throttle position sensor indicate wide open throttle.

Early feedback systems used a vacuum switch to control metering devices on the carburetor. Closed loop signals from the electronic control module are sent to a vacuum solenoid regulator (Figure 24–34), which in turn controls vacuum to a piston and diaphragm assembly in the carburetor. The vacuum diaphragm and a spring above the diaphragm work together to lift and lower a tapered fuel metering rod that moves in and out of an auxiliary fuel jet in the bottom of the fuel bowl. The position of the metering rod in the jet controls the amount of fuel allowed to flow into the main fuel well.

The more advanced feedback systems use electrical solenoids on the carburetor to control the metering rods (Figure 24–35). These solenoids are generally referred to as duty-cycle solenoids or **mixture control (M/C) solenoids**. The solenoid is normally wired through the ignition switch and grounded through the electronic control module. The solenoid is energized when the electronic control module completes the ground. The control module is programmed to cycle (turn on and off) the solenoid ten times per second. Each cycle lasts 100 milliseconds. The amount of fuel metered into the main fuel well is determined by how many milliseconds the solenoid is on during each cycle. The solenoid can be on almost 100 percent of the cycle or it can be off nearly 100 percent of the time. The M/C solenoid can control a fuel metering rod, an air bleed, or both.

In the Carter thermo-quad carburetor shown in Figure 24–36, variable air bleeds control the air/fuel

ratio. This carburetor contains two fuel supply subsystems: the high-speed system and the low-speed system. The high-speed system meters fuel with a tapered metering rod positioned in the jet by the throttle. Fuel is metered into the main nozzle well where air from the feedback-controlled variable air bleed is introduced. Since this air is delivered above the fuel level, it reduces the vacuum signal on the fuel, thereby reducing the amount of fuel delivered from the nozzle.

The idle system is needed at times of low airflow through the venturi because there is insufficient vacuum at the nozzle to draw fuel into the airstream. After leaving the main jet, fuel is supplied to the idle system by the low-speed jet. It is then mixed with air from the idle by-pass, then accelerated through the economizer and mixed with additional air from the idle bleed before being discharge from the idle ports below the throttle. Air from the variable air bleed is introduced between the idle air bleed and idle port. This air reduces the vacuum signal on the low-speed jet and, consequently, the amount of fuel delivered to the idle system.

The thermo-quad uses a mixture control or pulse solenoid to control the variable air bleeds. The sole-

FIGURE 24-37 Back suction feedback system.

FIGURE 24-38 Air bleed feedback system.

noid has only two positions of operation: opened when energized to bleed air to both the high speed and low-speed circuits or closed when de-energized, cutting off the air bleeds.

A less common method to control the air/fuel mixture is with a back suction system feedback. Figure 24-37 shows a variable venturi carburetor with an electric stepper motor rather than a duty-cycle solenoid. The back suction system consists of an electric stepper motor, a metering pintle valve, an internal vent restrictor, and a metering orifice. The stepper motor regulates the pintle movement in the metering orifice, thereby varying the area of the opening communicating control vacuum to the fuel bowl. The larger this area, the leaner the air/fuel mixture. Some of the control vacuum is bled off through the internal vent restrictor. The internal vent restrictor also serves to vent the fuel bowl when the back suction control pintle is in the closed position.

The 7200 VV carburetor was also produced with a feedback stepper motor that controls the main air bleed (Figure 24-38). The stepper motor controls the pintle movement in the air metering orifice thereby varying the amount of air being metered into the main system discharge area. The greater the amount of air, the leaner the air/fuel mixture. A hole in the upper body casting of the carburetor allows air from beneath the air cleaner to be channeled into the main system discharge area. The metered air lowers the metering signal at the main fuel metering jets.

Electronic Idle-Speed Control

To maintain federally mandated emission levels, it is necessary to control the idle speed. Most feedback systems operate in open loop when the engine is

idling. To reduce emissions during idle, most feedback carburetors idle faster and leaner than nonfeedback carburetors.

To adjust idle speed, many feedback carburetors have an idle speed control (**ISC**) motor controlled by an electronic control module. The ISC motor is a small, reversible, electric motor. It is part of an assembly that includes the motor, gear drive, and plunger (Figure 24-39). When the motor turns in one direction, the gear drive extends the plunger. When the motor turns in the opposite direction, the gear drive retracts the plunger. The ISC motor is mounted so the plunger can contact the throttle level. The ECU controls the ISC motor and can change the polarity applied to the motor's armature to control the direction in which it turns. When the idle tracking switch is open (throttle closed), the ECU commands the ISC motor to control idle speed. The ISC provides the correct throttle opening for cold or warm engine idle.

The electronic control module receives input from various switches and sensors to determine the best idle speed. Some of the possible inputs follow.

FIGURE 24-39 The idle speed control (ISC) motor stem contacts the throttle linkage. *Courtesy of Ford Motor Company*

- Engine coolant temperature sensor
- Air charge temperature (ACT) sensor
- Manifold absolute pressure (MAP) sensor
- Barometric pressure (BP) sensor
- Park/neutral or neutral gear switch
- Clutch engaged switch
- Power steering pressure switch
- A/C clutch compressor switch
- Idle tracking switch (ITS)

Based on the input signals from the system's sensors, the ECU increases the curb idle speed if the coolant is below a specific temperature, if a load (such as air conditioning, transmission, power steering) is placed on the engine, or when the vehicle is operated above a specific altitude.

During closed choke idle, the fast-idle cam holds the throttle blade open enough to lift the throttle linkage off the ISC plunger. This allows the ISC switch to open so the ECU does not monitor idle speed. As the choke spring allows the fast-idle cam to fall away and the throttle returns to the warm idle position, the ECU notes the still low coolant temperature and commands a slightly higher idle speed.

As the engine warms up, the plunger is retracted by the electronic control module. If the A/C compressor is turned on, the ECU extends the plunger a certain distance to increase engine idle speed to compensate for the added load. When the throttle is opened and the lever leaves contact with the plunger, an idle tracking switch (**ITS**) in the end of the plunger signals the ECU. The electronic control module then fully extends the plunger where, upon contact with the lever (during deceleration), it acts as a dashpot, slowing the return of the throttle lever. When the engine is shut down, the plunger retracts, preventing the engine from dieseling. It then extends for the next engine startup.

In some systems, if the engine starts to overheat, the ECU commands a higher idle speed to increase coolant flow. Also, if system voltage falls below a predetermined value, the ECU commands a higher idle speed to increase alternator speed and output.

Normally, idle speed adjustments are not possible on carburetors with electronic idle speed control. Attempting to adjust idle speed by adjusting the ISC plunger screw results in the ECU moving the plunger to compensate for the adjustment. Idle speed does not change until the ISC motor uses up all of its plunger travel trying to compensate for the adjustment, at which point the system is completely out of calibration. When idle speed driveability problems occur, the ISC system is usually responding to or being affected by the problem, not causing it.

CUSTOMER CARE

Remember that the customer is not a technician. Listen to the customer's description and analysis of a problem, but do not accept the customer's conclusions without performing a test drive and the appropriate diagnostic test yourself. For instance, the average driver cannot detect a miss in one cylinder. While driving down the highway at 50 to 70 mph, the car runs reasonably well; but when the driver pulls up to a stop signal and returns to an idle condition the engine idles roughly. So the driver brings the car to you complaining of a rough idle. Accepting that diagnosis without making your own and attempting to adjust the idle does more harm than good. ∎

CARBURETOR DIAGNOSIS AND ADJUSTMENT

The tuneup procedure of a late-model carbureted engine does not include as many carburetor adjustments as were once required, prior to the introduction of feedback carburetors and electronic engine controls. Idle mixture is factory set to meet precise emission control levels and is no longer an adjustable item. Idle speed is more often than not controlled by a computer and cannot be adjusted. About the only adjustment necessary on a properly operating carburetor is the fast-idle speed.

However, a malfunctioning carburetor can cause a variety of performance problems. Sometimes the problem is easily observed, such as a choke plate stuck open or an accelerating pump that is not pumping. Other problems require further testing.

A troubleshooting chart for carburetors is included in the *Tech Manual*. Use of the chart assumes that the engine is in good mechanical condition and properly tuned. Keep in mind that many ignition and carburetor problems have similar symptoms. An analysis of the engine's performance, using an engine analyzer with oscilloscope and exhaust analysis functions, help pinpoint the actual fault.

Some general test and adjustment procedures are given in the remainder of this chapter. However, for specific instructions and specifications, always refer to the manufacturer's service manual.

Carburetor Adjustments

Often a carburetor problem cannot be corrected without removing the carburetor from the engine and rebuilding it. Carburetor rebuilding goes beyond the scope of engine tuneup. However, there are other tests and adjustments that can be made without removing the carburetor. Some of those procedures are given here.

Idle Speed Adjustment As mentioned earlier, most vehicles with computer-controlled fuel systems have no provision for adjusting the idle speed. This is a function of the electronic control module. An idle speed that is not to specifications is a sign that a malfunction, such as an air leak, is occurring somewhere in one of the engine systems. Idle speed is checked using a tachometer.

If idle speed adjustment is possible on the carburetor, be sure to follow the manufacturer's instructions given on the emissions decal. Typical instructions might include the following.

1. Warm the engine to normal operating temperatures.
2. Make sure the choke plate is open and the throttle linkage is off fast-idle.
3. Set the parking brake and block the wheels.
4. Turn off all accessories (such as the air conditioner) and close the doors.
5. Shift the transmission into park, neutral, or drive.
6. Vehicles with feedback carburetion might also require that certain connectors be disconnected to keep the carburetor in open loop.

Then, while watching the tachometer, turn the idle-speed adjusting screw to adjust the idle rpm (Figure 24–40).

Fast-Idle Adjustment Instructions for setting **fast-idle speed** are also contained on the emissions decal or in the manufacturer's service manual. Most carburetors have a fast-idle screw (Figure 24–41) that can be adjusted to correct the fast-idle speed. After satisfying any pretest conditions (such as A/C off or transmission in gear), place the specified step of the fast-idle cam on the adjusting screw. Turn the screw clockwise to increase rpm and counterclockwise to decrease rpm.

FIGURE 24–41 Adjusting a fast-idle screw.

USING SERVICE MANUALS

Beside providing disassembly instructions, checks, tests, adjustments, and troubleshooting charts, carburetor service manuals offer tuning tips and methods for controlling fuel percolation. ■

Idle Mixture Adjustment As stated earlier, idle mixture adjustments have been eliminated on the newer carburetors. On older carburetors that allow for idle mixture adjustment, a simple procedure is as follows.

1. Adjust the idle speed to the specified rpm.
2. Turn the mixture screws to obtain the smoothest idle.
3. Readjust the idle speed to specifications.
4. Repeat steps 2 and 3 until the engine idles smoothly at the correct engine rpm.
5. Turn the idle mixture adjustment screw in (in the lean direction) as far as possible without a loss of smoothness. Some procedures require leaning the mixture until there is a definite drop in rpm and loss of smoothness and then backing out the idle mixture screws one quarter.

Idle Adjustment Using Propane Enrichment Method By the mid-1970s, the combination of catalytic converters and very lean mixtures made it difficult to properly perform curb idle speed and mixture adjustments. However, these adjustments must be properly made to ensure that emission control devices limit CO, HC, and NO_X to the specified levels. The solution was to use propane gas to assist in achieving correct idle settings.

When a controlled amount of propane is injected into the carburetor at idle, there is a direct correlation between the air/fuel ratio and engine rpm gain. If the rpm gain is less than the specifications found on the emissions control decal, the air/fuel ratio is too rich. If the rpm gain is more than specified, the air/fuel ratio is too lean.

FIGURE 24–40 Adjusting the idle speed.

Setting idle mixture using the artificial enrichment method requires a commercially available bottle of propane, a metering valve, a length of hose, and an adapter to connect the hose to the carburetor or air cleaner.

SHOP TALK

During the enrichment test, the propane tank must be upright to allow an even flow of gas. A practical and common way to do this is to hang the tank from the hood. ∎

Although the propane injection method varies slightly from one manufacturer to another (check the service manual), the following procedure can be considered basic.

PROCEDURES
Adjusting the Idle—the Propane Injection Method

1. Apply the parking brake and block the wheels. Disconnect the automatic brake release, and plug the vacuum connection.
2. Connect a tachometer to the engine.
3. Disconnect the fuel evaporative purge return hose at the engine and plug the connection.
4. Disconnect the fuel evaporative purge hose at the air cleaner and plug the nipple.
5. Disconnect the flexible fresh air tube from the air cleaner duct or adapter. Using a propane enrichment tool, insert the tool's hose approximately 3/4 inch of the way into the duct or fresh air tube. If necessary, secure the hose with tape and hold the bottle upright for an even flow of propane.
6. For vehicles equipped with an air injector system, revise the dump valve vacuum hoses.
   ◆ For dump valves with two vacuum fittings, disconnect and plug the hoses.
   ◆ For dump valves with one fitting, remove the hose at the dump valve and plug it. Connect a slave hose from the dump valve vacuum fitting to an intake manifold vacuum fitting.
7. Verify that the idle mixture limiter is set to the maximum rich position (counterclockwise against the stop). Correct if required.

8. Check the engine curb idle rpm (for A/C-off rpm). If necessary, reset to specification.
9. With the transmission in neutral, run the engine at approximately 2,500 rpm for 15 seconds before each mixture check.
10. With the engine idling at normal operating temperature, place the transmission selector in the position specified for the mixture check. Gradually open the propane tool valve and watch for engine speed gain, if any, on the tachometer. When the engine speed reaches a maximum and then begins to drop off, note the amount of speed gain.
11. Compare the measure speed gain to the specified speed gain on the engine decal or specification sheet. If the idle rpm gain is not to specifications, adjust the mixture according to the reset rpm specification.
    ◆ If the measured speed gain is higher than the speed gain specification, turn the mixture screw/limiter counterclockwise (rich) in equal amounts. Simultaneously repeat steps 8 through 10 until the measured speed rise meets the reset rpm specification.
    ◆ If the measured speed gain is lower than the speed gain specification, turn the mixture screw/limiter clockwise (lean) in equal amounts. Simultaneously repeat steps 8 through 10 until the measured speed rise meets the reset rpm specification.

Choke Adjustments

A malfunctioning choke can cause a variety of performance problems, from no-start to missing and power loss at cruising speeds. These problems can be caused by choke stuck closed, choke stuck open, inoperative choke pull-off, or malfunctioning bimetal choke coil.

A visual inspection might identify the trouble spot quickly. Remove the air cleaner, making sure to label each vacuum hose as it is disconnected. If the engine is cold, the choke should be closed. Watch the choke plate as another technician cranks the engine. When the engine starts, the choke pull-off should open the choke slightly (about 1/4 inch). As the engine warms, make sure the bimetal coil slowly opens the choke to its fully-open position. The absence of one or more of these choke movements indicates the cause of a driveability problem.

Exact choke servicing and adjustment procedures vary with choke type and carburetor model. In fact, on today's electronically controlled vehicles, the electronic choke is sealed to prevent tampering and misadjusting. Operation of the heating element is checked with a digital volt-ohmmeter. Refer to the manufacturer's service manual for procedures and specifications.

Before making any choke adjustments, move its linkage by hand to be certain there is no binding or sticking in the linkage, shaft, or choke plate. Use an approved carburetor cleaner to remove any gum deposits that interfere with its operation.

Adjusting the Choke Index If the choke housing permits adjustment of the choke setting, the choke can be adjusted to enrich or lean the air/fuel mixture. With an integral choke, manufacturers recommend specific alignment of the choke index marks. A mark on the plastic choke cover must be lined up with a mark on the metal choke housing or body. This initial choke setting usually provides adequate choke operation.

Check the thermostat housing index setting (Figure 24–42) against the specification on the engine decal or the vehicle's service manual.

For example, if the choke setting is specified as index, the index mark on the cap should be aligned with the center mark on the cap, which should be aligned with the center (index) notch on the housing. A specification of 1R, 2R, or 3R means the cap index mark should be aligned with the housing marks 1, 2, or 3 notches to the right of the center notch. Specifications reading 1L, 2L, or 3L, require positioning the index mark to the left of the center notch.

To adjust the choke setting, loosen the cap screws and the hot air or coolant tubes (if applicable). Turn the cap to realign the index mark with the specified notch on the housing. Then, retighten the tubes and screws.

CHOKE CAP INDEX MARK

CHOKE HOUSING

CHOKE CAP INDEX MARK

FIGURE 24–42 Choke index adjustment.

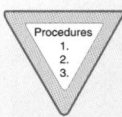 **PROCEDURES**
Divorced Choke Adjustment

1. Disconnect the choke rod from the choke plate and close the plate.
2. Move the rod up or down as directed in the service manual. Check whether or not the rod is above or below the hose in the check plate. The bottom of the rod should align with the top edge of the hole. With choke plates that use a sliding fit, the rod is usually set at the middle of the slot. However, always check the manufacturer's instructions.
3. Bend the choke rod to lengthen or shorten it as required.

 ### WARNING!

Improper bending can cause the choke rod to bind. ■

4. Test for free movement between open and closed choke positions. There must not be any binding or interference.

 ## CAUTION:

Never attempt an adjustment on the thermostatic coil spring. ■

Choke Pulldown Adjustments If the choke plate is not opening when the engine starts, check for a vacuum leak in the choke qualifying mechanism. If a diaphragm vacuum break is used, look for a cracked vacuum hose or loose hose connections. To check the diaphragm, remove the vacuum hose, and install a vacuum pump (Figure 24–43). Apply vacuum to the pump diaphragm. If the diaphragm does not hold vacuum or if the vacuum leaks down faster than the manufacturer specifies it should, the vacuum break should be replaced.

SHOP TALK

Before many types of vacuum breaks can be tested with a vacuum pump, a bleed hole must be plugged. To do so, place your finger or a piece of tape over the bleed hole. Figure 24–44 shows several vacuum break styles with the recommended procedure for blocking the bleed hole prior to testing. ■

FIGURE 24–43 Checking vacuum break diaphragm with a vacuum pump.

PUMP CUP OR VALVE STEM SEAL

TAPE HOLE IN TUBE.

TAPE END OF COVER.

FIGURE 24–44 Methods of plugging air bleed holes prior to testing a vacuum break.

If the carburetor has a secondary vacuum break, test the thermal vacuum valve or choke vacuum thermal switch. Consult the manufacturer's service manual for temperature specifications. Connect a vacuum pump to the lower port and a vacuum gauge to the upper port. Apply the specified vacuum and alternately warm and cool the valve or switch. The valve should permit vacuum passage when the valve is warm, and block vacuum when the valve is cold.

If a vacuum piston is used to open the choke, remove the choke housing cap and inspect the piston and cylinder for carbon deposits. If the piston is sticking and not moving freely, remove the choke housing and clean the pull-off piston and vacuum passageways. Also, check the choke heat tube for carbon deposits. An exhaust leak in the area of the choke stove causes the carbon deposits. Locate and correct the problem.

If the engine runs rough initially after startup, the choke might not be opening the specified amount. To check the qualifying dimension, apply the specified vacuum to the diaphragm, using a vacuum pump. Measure the clearance between the upper edge of the choke plate and the air horn wall, using a drill bit with a diameter equal to the specified dimension. To adjust the dimension, bend the choke linkage with a pair of pliers.

Choke Unloader Adjustment The unloader can be adjusted following this procedure.

1. With the throttle plates wide open, close the choke plate as far as possible without forcing it.
2. Use a drill bit with a diameter equal to the specified unload dimension as a gauge. Place it between the upper edge of the choke valve and the air horn.
3. Bend the unloader tang on the throttle lever to obtain the dimension as listed in the specifications.

Checking the Accelerator Pump

If the accelerator pump is not operating properly, the engine hesitates when the accelerator pedal is depressed.

To check for accelerator pump operation, remove the air cleaner top. Make sure the actuating linkage is not binding. Using a flashlight, look down into the air horn while quickly moving the throttle linkage forward (Figure 24–45). Each time you do so, a stream or squirt of fuel from the discharge tube should be visible. If not, remove the air horn and service the accelerator pump following the specific procedures outlined in the manufacturer's service manual.

Float Adjustments

An improperly operating float system can result in a variety of performance problems: flooding, rich fuel mixture, lean fuel mixture, fuel starvation (no fuel), stalling, low-speed engine miss, and high-speed engine

FIGURE 24–45 Checking accelerator pump operation.

miss. Thus, a faulty float system can affect engine operations at all speeds.

On some carburetors, the fuel level in the fuel bowl can be checked without removing the air horn assembly from the carburetor. A gauge is placed into the fuel bowl through a vent hole. The level of the fuel in the bowl is an indication of the float condition. Most carburetors, however, require the air horn assembly be removed from the carburetor to inspect and adjust the float.

An error in float adjustment as small as 1/32 inch can change the air/fuel ratio sufficiently to make other carburetor adjustments difficult, if not impossible. Adjustments include the float level, **float drop, float toe,** and float adjustment. Since most do not require all four adjustments, check the vehicle's service manual or the rebuilding kit instruction sheet for the adjustment that must be performed.

Some carburetors have a sight glass or plug in the fuel bowl that makes it possible to check the float level while the engine is operating. Float levels on these car-

FIGURE 24–46
Float gauge.

buretors can be adjusted by an external screw or threaded inlet valve. Checking the fuel level on a carburetor with a sight glass not only aids in adjusting the float level but also in locating float problems.

Float Toe Adjustment In addition to the float level and drop adjustments, some carburetors also have a float toe adjustment. To make this adjustment, the air horn is turned over (no gasket installed) and checked to make sure the float toes are flush with the air horn casting (Figure 24–47A). If the float has dimples (Figure 24–47B), measure from the dimples to the top of the gasket. In either case the float arm is bent to where it meets the float.

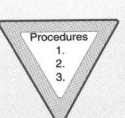

PROCEDURES
Float Level Adjustment

1. Remove the upper body assembly (air horn assembly) and the upper body gasket. Install a new gasket before making the adjustment.
2. From cardboard, fabricate a gauge to the specified dimension following the specifications given in the service manual or rebuilding kit. Figure 24–46 shows a typical float gauge. Carburetor rebuilding kits often have these gauges included. Check the service manual for the exact dimensions.
3. With the upper body inverted, place the fuel level gauge on the cast surface of the upper body or gasket and measure the vertical distance from the surface and the bottom of the float. The service manual notes the desired location of the gauge for this check.
4. To adjust, bend the float operating level away from the fuel inlet needle to decrease the setting and toward the needle to increase the setting.
5. Check and adjust the float drop by turning the upper body over and allowing the float to drop.
6. Place the gauge into position and measure float drop.
7. Correct as needed, by bending the float's stop tab.
8. Reinstall the upper body assembly.

A   FLOAT TOE ADJUSTMENT WITHOUT DIMPLE

B   FLOAT TOE ADJUSTMENT WITH DIMPLE
FIGURE 24–47 Checking float toe.

After making a toe adjustment, be sure to recheck the float level and drop to see if they have changed.

CASE STUDY

A customer mentions he noticed when checking the oil that the level has increased.

In response, the technician checks the oil by smelling it. The odor of gasoline in the oil leads the technician to check the fuel pump for a leak, but the pump is in good working order. The technician checks for an alternative cause. Realizing that a heavily choked engine will cause raw fuel to slip past the rings and into the crankcase area, the technician verifies by a visual inspection that the choke is not adjusted properly. The choke is readjusted according to the manufacturer's specifications. The oil and filter are changed. No further problems are reported.

KEY TERMS

Atomization	Metering rod
Barrel	Mixture control (M/C)
Boost venturi	solenoids
Choke	Nitrile rubber
Choke unloader	Open loop
Closed loop	Power valve
Dashpot	Primary stage
Deceleration valve	Rich
Downdraft	Secondary stage
Draft	Sidedraft
Emulsion	Single stage
Fast-idle speed	Stoichiometric ratio
Float	Throttle kicker
Float drop	Throttle stop solenoid
Float toe	Transfer slot
Hot-idle compensator	TVV
Idle stop solenoid	Updraft
ISC motor	Vaporization
ITS	Variable venturi
Lean	Venturi
Metering	

SUMMARY

- Carburetion means enriching a gas by combining it with a carbon-containing compound. Three general stages of carburetion are metering, atomization, and vaporization.
- A venturi is a streamlined restriction that partly closes the carburetor bore. This restriction causes an increase in vacuum.
- The flow of air and fuel through the carburetor is controlled by the throttle plate.
- There are six basic carburetor circuits: float, idle, main metering, full power, accelerator pump, and choke.
- The float system stores fuel and holds it at a precise level as a starting point for uniform fuel flow.
- The idle circuit supplies a richer air/fuel mixture to operate the engine at idle and low speeds.
- The main metering circuit comes into operation when the engine speed reaches about 1,500 rpm or higher.
- The power system provides the engine with a richer air/fuel mixture at wide open throttle.
- The accelerator pump mechanically supplies extra fuel during sudden acceleration.
- The choke circuit provides a very rich mixture during cranking and startup of a cold engine.
- Additional carburetor controls include the choke qualifier, dashpot, hot-idle compensator, dual vacuum break, choke unloader, deceleration valve, and throttle position solenoid.
- Carburetors are designed with different drafts, different numbers of barrels, different types of venturi, and different flow rates.
- The latest type of carburetor system is the electronic feedback design, which provides better combustion by control of the air/fuel mixture.
- About the only adjustment necessary on a properly operating carburetor is the fast-idle speed.
- A malfunctioning choke can cause a variety of performance problems, from no-start to missing and power loss at cruising speeds. If the accelerator pump is not operating properly, the engine hesitates when the accelerator pedal is depressed. An improperly operating float system can result in a variety of performance problems: flooding, rich fuel mixture, lean fuel mixture, fuel starvation (no fuel), stalling, low-speed engine miss, and high-speed engine miss.

TECH MANUAL

The following procedures are included in Chapter 24 of the *Tech Manual* that accompanies this book:

1. Adjust fast idle.

2. Adjust float levels.

REVIEW QUESTIONS

1. Name the narrow passageway in a carburetor that speeds up the flow of intake air.

2. Name the component that speeds up the idle speed to compensate for the operation of the air conditioner.

3. A vacuum break is part of which carburetor system circuit?

4. Name the three general stages involved in carburetion.

5. What are the electrical solenoids used to control the metering rods on the more advanced feedback carburetor systems called?

6. On cold startup, which of the following is true?
   a. The throttle valve and the choke valve are closed.
   b. The throttle valve and the choke valve are open.
   c. The throttle valve is open and the choke valve is closed.
   d. The throttle valve is closed and the choke valve is open.

7. Which of the following draws air from the high-pressure area in the carburetor barrel above the venturi?
   a. idle air bleed
   b. accelerator pump system
   c. main air bleed
   d. choke

8. Which of the following statements about a vacuum break is true?
   a. The vacuum break is operated by ported vacuum.
   b. The vacuum break opens the choke after the engine has started.
   c. All integral chokes use a diaphragm vacuum break.
   d. All of the above.

9. Which of the following is used to speed up the opening of the choke?
   a. choke air modulator
   b. choke delay valve
   c. electric assist heating element
   d. all of the above

10. Which of the following components controls slow-idle speed?
   a. throttle stop solenoid
   b. idle mixture screw
   c. dashpot
   d. none of the above.

11. On vehicles with catalytic converters, propane gas is injected into the carburetor to fine-tune which of the following adjustments?
   a. choke setting   c. fast-idle speed
   b. idle mixture   d. all of the above.

12. Technician A says an acceleration pump is necessary because the fuel pump cannot supply fuel rapidly enough when the throttle is suddenly operated. Technician B says an acceleration pump is needed because the air/fuel mixture gets leaner when the throttle is suddenly opened. Who is correct?
   a. Technician A   c. Both A and B
   b. Technician B   d. Neither A nor B

13. During a discussion about carburetors with automatic chokes, Technician A says some carburetors are designed to have hot water (radiator coolant) flowing through the choke housing. Technician B says some carburetors are heated electrically. Who is correct?
   a. Technician A   c. Both A and B
   b. Technician B   d. Neither A nor B

14. Technician A says a power valve is a vacuum-operated metering rod. Technician B says the power valve controls the metering jets on a feedback carburetor. Who is correct?
   a. Technician A   c. Both A and B
   b. Technician B   d. Neither A nor B

15. Technician A says a variable venturi carburetor is also known as a constant velocity carburetor. Technician B says variable venturi carburetors are always computer-controlled. Who is correct?
   a. Technician A   c. Both A and B
   b. Technician B   d. Neither A nor B

16. Technician A says a malfunctioning choke can cause power loss at cruising speeds. Technician B says choke index marks are aligned integral chokes. Who is correct?
   a. Technician A   c. Both A and B
   b. Technician B   d. Neither A nor B

17. Technician A says the float cannot be adjusted if there is not a threaded inlet valve assembly. Technician B says all fuel bowls are vented by a valve to a charcoal canister. Who is correct?
   a. Technician A   c. Both A and B
   b. Technician B   d. Neither A nor B

18. Technician A says a richer air/fuel mixture is needed for idle operation. Technician B says some carburetors have a transfer slot instead of an idle port. Who is correct?
   a. Technician A   c. Both A and B
   b. Technician B   d. Neither A nor B

19. Technician A says a very rich air/fuel mixture is needed during cranking and startup. Technician B says a rich mixture is needed at wide open throttle. Who is correct?
   a. Technician A   c. Both A and B
   b. Technician B   d. Neither A nor B

20. Which of the following describes the function of a dashpot?
   a. It opens an air passage to lean the mixture when the engine overheats.
   b. It is designed to prevent backfire during deceleration as the fuel mixture becomes richer.
   c. It is used during rapid deceleration to retard the closing of the throttle.
   d. None of the above.

FUEL INJECTION 25

OBJECTIVES

◆ *Explain the principles of operation of a fuel injection system.* ◆ *List the advantages of fuel injection.*
◆ *Explain the differences in point of injection in throttle body or port injection systems.* ◆ *Explain the design and function of major EFI components.* ◆ *Explain the design and function of CIS-E components.*
◆ *Service and diagnose fuel injection systems.* ◆ *Explain the basics of diesel fuel injection.*

Fuel injection involves spraying or injecting fuel directly into the engine's intake manifold (Figure 25–1). Fuel injection, especially when it is electronically controlled, has several major advantages over carbureted systems. These include improved driveability under all conditions, improved fuel control and economy, decreased exhaust emissions, and an increase in engine efficiency and power.

Although fuel injection technology has been around since the 1920s, it wasn't until the 1980s that manufacturers began to replace carburetors with electronic fuel injection (**EFI**) systems. Many of the early EFI systems were throttle body injection (**TBI**) systems in which the fuel was injected above the throttle plates. Engines equipped with TBI have gradually become equipped with port fuel injection (**PFI**), which has injectors located in the intake ports of the cylinders. Since the 1995 model year, all new cars are equipped with EFI systems.

Diesel engines, for quite some time, have been equipped with fuel injection systems. The two basic differences between gasoline injection and diesel injection are: diesel fuel is injected directly into the cylinders, and diesel fuel injection systems are operated mechanically rather than electronically. Although late-model diesel systems use electronic fuel controls, the fuel injection system is a mechanical system that is controlled mechanically.

GASOLINE FUEL INJECTION

Most electronic fuel injection systems only inject fuel during part of the engine's combustion cycle. The engine fuel needs are measured by intake airflow past a sensor or by intake manifold pressure (vacuum). The airflow or manifold vacuum sensor converts its reading to an electrical signal and sends it to the engine control computer. The computer processes this signal (and others) and calculates the fuel needs of the engine. The computer then sends an electrical signal to the fuel injector or injectors. This signal determines the amount of time the injector opens and sprays fuel. This interval is known as the **injector pulse width**.

Throttle body injection systems have a throttle body assembly mounted on the intake manifold in the position usually occupied by a carburetor. The throttle body assembly usually contains one or two injectors.

FIGURE 25–1 In a port fuel injection system, air and fuel are mixed in the intake manifold runners very close to the intake valve(s) of the combustion chamber.

Fuel pump

Control unit

Injector

Dropping resistor

Detonation (knocking) sensor

Pressure regulator

Power transistor

Throttle chamber

Fuel filter

Air flow meter

Idle control valve

Ignition coil

Air regulator

Exhaust gas sensor

Turbocharger unit

Rotor plate

Water temperature sensor

Distributor

Crank angle sensor

FIGURE 25–2   Main components of a typical EFI system. *Courtesy of Nissan Motors*

On port fuel injection systems, fuel injectors are mounted at the back of each intake valve. Aside from the differences in injector location and number of injectors, operation of throttle body and port systems is quite similar with regard to fuel and air metering, sensors, and computer operation.

Port-type continuous injection systems (**CIS**) have been used on many import vehicles. These systems deliver a steady stream of pressurized fuel into the intake manifold. The injectors do not pulse on and off as in port and throttle body systems. In CIS, the amount of fuel delivered is controlled by the rate of airflow entering the engine. An airflow sensor controls movement of a plunger that alters fuel flow to the injectors. When introduced, CIS was a mechani-

cally controlled system. However, oxygen sensor feedback circuits and other electronic controls have been added to the system. CIS systems that have electronic controls are commonly referred to as **CIS-E** systems.

ELECTRONIC FUEL INJECTION SYSTEM Electronic fuel injection (EFI) has proven to be the most precise, reliable, and cost effective method of delivering fuel to the combustion chambers of today's vehicles. EFI systems must provide the correct air/fuel ratio for all engine loads, speeds, and temperature conditions. To accomplish this, an EFI system uses a fuel delivery system, air induction system, input sensors, control computer, fuel injectors, and some sort of idle speed control (Figure 25–2).

FIGURE 25–3 Components of a typical fuel circuit used in a throttle body fuel injection system.

In a typical EFI fuel delivery system (Figure 25–3), fuel is drawn from the fuel tank by an in-tank or chassis-mounted electric fuel pump. Before it reaches the injectors, the fuel passes through a filter that removes dirt and impurities. A fuel line pressure regulator maintains a constant fuel line pressure that may be as high as 50 psi in some systems. This fuel pressure generates the spraying force needed to inject the fuel. Excess fuel not required by the engine returns to the fuel tank through a fuel return line.

THROTTLE BODY VERSUS PORT INJECTION

Throttle Body Fuel Injection

For some auto manufacturers, TBI served as a stepping stone from carburetors to more advanced port fuel injection systems. TBI units were used on many engines during the 1980s and are still used on some engines. The throttle body unit is similar in size and shape to a carburetor and, like a carburetor, mounts on the intake manifold (Figure 25–4). The injector(s) spray fuel down into a throttle body chamber leading to the intake manifold. The intake manifold feeds the air/fuel mixture to all cylinders.

TBI Operation The basic TBI assembly consists of two major castings: a throttle body with a valve to control airflow and a fuel body to supply the required fuel. A fuel pressure regulator and fuel injector are integral parts of the fuel body (Figure 25–5). Also included as part of the assembly is a device to control idle speed and one to provide throttle valve positioning data.

The throttle body casting has ports that can be located above, below, or at the throttle valve depending on the manufacturer's design. These ports generate vacuum signals for the manifold absolute pres-

FIGURE 25–4 Parts of a throttle body injection unit.

FIGURE 25–5 Fuel and airflow in a TBI injection system. The injector is a bottom fuel feed design. The idle air control allows air to bypass the throttle plate to regulate engine idle in all operating conditions.

FIGURE 25–6 Operation of a diaphragm-operated fuel pressure regulator.

FIGURE 25–7 Solenoid-operated ball valve-type fuel injector used in a TBI system. When electronically energized, the ball valve lifts off the valve seat, allowing fuel to spray into the throttle body housing.

sure sensor and for devices in the emission control system, such as the EGR valve, the canister purge system, and so on.

The **fuel pressure regulator** used on the throttle body assembly is similar to a diaphragm-operated relief valve (Figure 25–6). Fuel pressure is on one side of the diaphragm and atmospheric pressure is on the other side. The regulator is designed to provide a constant pressure on the fuel injector throughout the range of engine loads and speeds. If regulator pressure is too high, a strong fuel odor is emitted and the engine runs too rich. On the other hand, regulator pressure that is too low results in poor engine performance or detonation can take place, due to the lean mixture.

The fuel injector is solenoid operated and pulsed on and off by the vehicle's engine control computer. (NOTE: In this chapter, the terms *control computer* and *electronic control unit* (**ECU**) are used interchangeably.) Surrounding the injector inlet is a fine screen filter where the incoming fuel is directed. When the injector's solenoid is energized, a normally closed ball valve is lifted (Figure 25–7). Fuel under pressure is then injected at the walls of the throttle body bore just above the throttle plate.

TBI Advantages Throttle body systems provide improved fuel metering when compared to carburetors. They are also less expensive and simpler to service. TBI units also have some advantages over port injection. They are less expensive to manufacture, simpler to diagnose and service, and don't have injector balance problems to the extent that port injection systems do when the injectors begin to clog.

However, throttle body units are not as efficient as port systems. The disadvantages are primarily man-

ifold related. Like a carburetor system, fuel is still not distributed equally to all cylinders, and a cold manifold may cause fuel to condense and puddle in the manifold. Like a carburetor, throttle body injection systems must be mounted above the combustion chamber level, which eliminates the possibility of tuning the manifold design for more efficient operation.

Port Fuel Injection

PFI systems use one injector at each cylinder. They are mounted in the intake manifold near the cylinder head where they can inject a fine, atomized fuel mist as close as possible to the intake valve (Figure 25–8). Fuel lines run to each cylinder from a fuel manifold, usually referred to as a **fuel rail**. The fuel rail assembly on a PFI system of V-6 and V-8 engines usually

FIGURE 25–8 Port fuel injection systems use an injector at each cylinder.

FIGURE 25–9 Fuel rail with fuel pressure regulator and fuel injectors for a four-cylinder port fuel injected engine. *Courtesy of Oldsmobile Division, General Motors Corporation*

FIGURE 25–11 Throttle body assembly of a port fuel injection system. *Courtesy of Toyota Motors*

consists of a left- and right-hand rail assembly. The two rails can be connected either by crossover and return fuel tubes or by a mechanical bracket arrangement. A typical fuel rail arrangement is shown in Figure 25–9. Fuel tubes crisscross between the two rails. Since each cylinder has its own injector, fuel distribution is exactly equal. With little or no fuel to wet the manifold walls, there is no need for manifold heat or any early fuel evaporation system. Fuel does not collect in puddles at the base of the manifold. This means the intake manifold passages can be tuned or designed for better low-speed power availability (Figure 25–10). The port-type systems provide a more accurate and efficient delivery of fuel. Some engines are now equipped with variable induction intake manifolds that have separate runners for low and high speeds. This technology is only possible with port injection.

FIGURE 25–10 Typical tuned intake manifold for a port injection engine. *Courtesy of Chrysler Corporation*

The throttle body in a port fuel injection system controls the amount of air that enters the engine as well as the amount of vacuum in the manifold. It also houses and controls the idle air control (**IAC**) motor and the throttle position sensor (TPS). The TPS enables the ECU to know where the throttle is positioned at all times.

The throttle body (Figure 25–11) is a single, cast-aluminum housing with a single throttle blade attached to the throttle shaft. The TPS and the IAC valve/motor are also attached to the housing. The throttle shaft is controlled by the accelerator pedal. The throttle shaft extends the full length of the housing. The throttle bore controls the amount of incoming air that enters the air induction system. A small amount of coolant is also routed through a passage in the throttle body to prevent icing during cold weather.

Port systems require an additional control system that throttle body injection units do not require. While throttle body injectors are mounted above the throttle plates and are not affected by fluctuations in manifold vacuum, port system injectors have their tips located in the manifold where constant changes in vacuum would affect the amount of fuel injected (at a given pulse width). To compensate for these fluctuations, port injection systems are equipped with fuel pressure regulators that sense manifold vacuum and continually adjust the fuel pressure to maintain a constant pressure drop across the injector tips at all times.

Pressure Regulator The pressure regulator in port injection systems is similar to the regulator used in TBI systems. A diaphragm and valve assembly is positioned on the center of the regulator, and a diaphragm spring seats the valve on the fuel outlet (Figure 25–12).

FIGURE 25-12 Fuel pressure regulator for port injection engines. *Courtesy of Chrysler Corporation*

When fuel pressure reaches the setting of the regulator, the diaphragm moves against the spring tension, and the valve opens. This action allows fuel to flow through the return line to the fuel tank. The fuel pressure drops slightly when the pressure regulator valve opens, and the spring closes the regulator valve. In many systems, the regulator maintains fuel pressure at 39 psi (269 kPa).

A vacuum hose is connected from the intake manifold to the vacuum inlet on the pressure regulator. This hose supplies vacuum to the area where the diaphragm spring is located. This vacuum works with the fuel pressure to move the diaphragm and open the valve. When the engine is running at idle speed, high manifold vacuum is supplied to the regulator. Under this condition, the specified fuel pressure opens the regulator valve. When the engine is running under heavy load and/or wide-open throttle, a very low vacuum is supplied to the regulator. During these times, the vacuum does not help open the regulator valve and a higher fuel pressure is required to open the valve.

The change in fuel pressure allows the fuel to be sprayed into the manifold with the same effect, regardless of the pressure present in the manifold. When there is a high vacuum in the manifold, a very low pressure exists and the pressure difference between the fuel spray and the vacuum is the same as when there is a higher pressure in the manifold (low vacuum) and a higher fuel pressure.

Port Firing Control While all port injection systems operate using an injector at each cylinder, they do not fire the injectors in the same manner. This one statement best defines the difference between typical multiport injection systems (**MPI**) and sequential fuel injection systems (**SFI**).

SFI systems control each injector individually so it is opened just before the intake valve opens. This means the mixture is never static in the intake manifold and adjustments to the mixture can be made almost instantaneously between the firing of one injector and the next. Sequential firing is the most accurate and desirable method of regulating port injection.

In MPI systems, the injectors are grouped together in pairs or groups, and these pairs or groups of injectors are turned on at the same time. When the injectors are split into two equal groups, the groups are fired alternately, with one group firing each engine revolution (Figure 25-13).

Since only two injectors can be fired relatively close to the time when the intake valve is about to open, the fuel charge for the remaining cylinders must stand in the intake manifold for varying periods of time. These periods of time are very short; therefore, the standing of fuel in the intake manifold is not that great a disadvantage of MPI systems. At idle speeds, this wait is about 150 milliseconds; at higher speeds, the time is much less. The primary advantage of SFI is the ability to make instantaneous changes to the mixture.

In SFI systems, each injector is connected individually into the computer, and the computer completes the ground for each injector, one at a time. In MPI systems, the injectors are grouped and all injectors within the group share the same common ground wire.

Some injection systems fire all of the injectors at the same time for every engine revolution. This type of system offers easy programming and relatively fast adjustments to the air/fuel mixture. The injectors are connected in parallel so the ECU sends out just one signal for all injectors. They all open and close at the same time. It simplifies the electronics without compromising injection efficiency. The amount of fuel required for each four-stroke cycle is divided in half and delivered in two injections, one for every 360 degrees of crankshaft rotation. The fact that the intake charge must still wait in the manifold for varying periods of time is the system's major drawback.

FIGURE 25-13 Grouped single-fire port injection.

FIGURE 25–14 Typical airflow sensor.

FIGURE 25–15 In a typical airflow sensor, the strength of the voltage signal produced by the potentiometer varies in response to the amount the sensor flap moves.

SYSTEM SENSORS

The ability of the fuel injection system to control the air/fuel ratio depends on its ability to properly time the injector pulses with the compression stroke of each cylinder and its ability to vary the injector "on" time, according to changing engine demands. Both tasks require the use of electronic sensors that monitor the operating conditions of the engine.

Airflow Sensors

To control the proportion of fuel to air in the air/fuel charge, the fuel system must be able to measure the amount of air entering the engine. Several sensors have been developed to do just that.

VOLUME AIRFLOW SENSOR The airflow sensor shown in Figure 25–14 measures airflow, or air volume. The sensor consists of a spring-loaded flap, potentiometer, damping chamber, backfire protection valve, and idle bypass channel. As air is drawn into the engine, the flap is deflected against the spring. A potentiometer, attached to the flap shaft, monitors the flap movement and produces a corresponding voltage signal (Figure 25–15). The strength of the signal increases as the flap opens. The signal voltage is relayed to the electronic control module.

DAMPING CHAMBER The curved shape of the airflow sensor is the damping chamber. The damping flap in this chamber is on the same shaft as the airflow sensing flap and is also about the same area. As a result, the damping flap smooths out any possible pulsations caused by opening and closing of the intake valves. Airflow measurement can be a steady signal, closely related to airflow as controlled by the movement of the flap.

BACKFIRE PROTECTION The airflow sensor flap provides for backfire protection with a spring-loaded

valve. If the intake manifold pressure suddenly rises because of a backfire, this valve releases the pressure and prevents damage to the system.

IDLE BY-PASS The airflow sensor assembly includes an extra air passage for idle, bypassing the airflow sensor plate. This is seen near the top of Figure 25–14. When the throttle is closed at idle, the opening and closing of intake valves can cause pulsations in the intake manifold. Without the idle by-pass, such pulsations could cause the flap to shudder, resulting in an uneven air/fuel mixture. The idle by-pass smooths the flow of the idle intake air, ensuring regular signals to the electronic control.

Another design of airflow sensor, called a Karman Vortex sensor, works on a different operating principle. Air entering the airflow sensor assembly passes through vanes arranged around the inside of a tube. As the air flows through the vanes, it begins to swirl. The outer part of the swirling air exerts high pressure against the outside of the housing. There is a low-pressure area in the center. The low-pressure area moves in a circular motion as the air swirls through the intake tube. Two pressure-sensing tubes near the end of the tube sense the low-pressure area as it moves around. An electronic sensor counts how many times the low-pressure area is sensed.

The faster the airflow, the more times the low-pressure area is sensed. This is translated into a signal that indicates to the combustion control computer how much air is flowing into the intake manifold.

Air Temperature Sensor

Cold air is denser (weighs more) than warm air. Cold, dense air can burn more fuel than the same volume of warm air because it contains more oxygen. This is why airflow sensors that only measure air volume must have their readings adjusted to account for differences in air temperature.

Most systems do this by using an air temperature sensor mounted in the throttle body of the induction system. The air sensor measures air temperature and sends an electronic signal to the control computer. The computer uses this input along with the air volume input in determining the amount of oxygen entering the engine.

In some early EFI systems, the incoming air is heated to a set temperature. In these systems an air temperature sensor is used to ensure that this predetermined operating temperature is maintained.

Mass Airflow Sensors

A **mass airflow sensor** (MAF), (Figure 25–16) does the job of a volume airflow sensor and an air temperature sensor. It measures air mass. The mass of a given amount of air is calculated by multiplying its volume by its density. As explained previously, the denser the air, the more oxygen it contains. Monitoring the oxygen in a given volume of air is important, since oxygen is a prime catalyst in the combustion process. From a measurement of mass, the electronic control unit adjusts the fuel delivery for the oxygen content in a given volume of air. The accuracy of air/fuel ratios is greatly enhanced when matching fuel to air mass instead of fuel to air volume.

The mass airflow sensor converts air flowing past a heated sensing element into an electronic signal. The strength of this signal is determined by the energy needed to keep the element at a constant temperature above the incoming ambient air temperature. As the

volume and density (mass) of airflow across the heated element changes, the temperature of the element is affected and the current flow to the element is adjusted to maintain the desired temperature of the heating element. The varying current flow parallels the particular characteristics of the incoming air (hot, dry, cold, humid, high/low pressure). The electronic control unit monitors the changes in current to determine air mass and to calculate precise fuel requirements.

There are two basic types of mass airflow sensor: hot wire and hot film. In the first type, a very thin wire (about 0.2 mm thick) is used as the heated element. The element temperature is set at 100° to 200°C above incoming air temperature. Each time the ignition switch is turned to the off position, the wire is heated to approximately 1,000°C for 1 second to burn off any accumulated dust and contaminants.

The second type uses a nickel foil sensor, which is kept 75°C above ambient air temperatures. It does not require a burn-off period. Thus, it is potentially longer lasting than the hot wire type.

Manifold Absolute Pressure Sensor

Some EFI systems do not use airflow or air mass to determine the base pulse of the injector(s). Instead, the base pulse is calculated on manifold absolute pressure (MAP).

The MAP sensor measures changes in the intake manifold pressure that result from changes in engine load and speed. The pressure measured by the MAP sensor is the difference between barometric pressure (outside air) and manifold pressure (vacuum). At closed throttle, the engine produces a low MAP value. A wide-open throttle produces a high value. This high value is produced when the pressure inside the manifold is the same as pressure outside the manifold, and 100 percent of the outside air is being measured. This MAP output is the opposite of what is measured on a vacuum gauge. The use of this sensor also allows the control computer to adjust automatically for different altitudes.

The control computer sends a voltage reference signal to the MAP sensor. As the MAP changes, the electrical resistance of the sensor also changes. The control computer can determine the manifold pressure by monitoring the sensor output voltage. A high pressure, low vacuum (high voltage) requires more fuel. A low pressure, high vacuum (low voltage) requires less fuel. Like an airflow sensor, a MAP sensor relies on an air temperature sensor to adjust its base pulse signal to match incoming air density.

In EFI systems with a MAP sensor, the computer program is designed to calculate the amount of air entering the engine from the MAP and engine rpm

HOT WIRE

"COLD WIRE" AMBIENT TEMPERATURE SENSOR

AIRFLOW

FIGURE 25–16 Components of a mass airflow sensor. *Courtesy of Ford Motor Company*

input signals. This type of EFI system is referred to as a **speed density** system because the computer calculates the air intake flow from the engine speed input and the density of the intake manifold vacuum input. Many EFI systems with MAF sensors do not have MAP sensors. However, there are a few engines with both of these sensors. In these cases, the MAP is used mainly as a backup if the MAF fails. When the EFI system has a MAF, the computer calculates the intake air flow from the MAF and rpm inputs.

Other EFI System Sensors

In addition to airflow, air mass, or manifold absolute pressure readings, the control computer relies on input from a number of other system sensors. This input further adjusts the injector pulse width to match engine operating conditions. Operating conditions are communicated to the control computer by the following types of sensors.

COOLANT TEMPERATURE The coolant temperature sensor signals the electronic control unit when the engine needs cold enrichment, as it does during warm-up. This adds to the base pulse, but decreases to zero as the engine warms up.

THROTTLE POSITION The switches on the throttle shaft signal the electronic control unit for idle enrichment when the throttle is closed. These same throttle switches signal the electronic control unit when the throttle is near the wide-open position to provide full load enrichment.

ENGINE SPEED The ignition system sends a tachometer signal reference pulse corresponding to engine speed to the electronic control unit. This signal advises the electronic control unit to adjust the pulse width of the injectors for engine speed. This also times the start of the injection according to the intake stroke cycle.

CRANKING ENRICHMENT The starter circuit sends a signal for fuel enrichment during cranking operations even when the engine is warm. This is independent of any cold-start fuel enrichment demands.

ALTITUDE COMPENSATION As the car operates at higher altitudes, the thinner air needs less fuel. Altitude compensation in a fuel injection system is accomplished by installing a sensor to monitor barometric pressure. Signals from the barometric pressure sensor are sent to the ECU to reduce the injector pulse width (or reduce the amount of fuel injected).

COASTING SHUTOFF Coasting shutoff can be found on a number of control systems. It can improve fuel economy as well as reduce emissions of

hydrocarbons and carbon monoxide. Fuel shutoff is controlled in different ways depending on the type of transmission (manual or automatic). The ECU makes a coasting shutoff decision based on a closed throttle as indicated by the throttle position or idle switch or on engine speed as indicated by the signal from the ignition coil. When the ECU detects that power is not needed to maintain vehicle speed, the injectors are turned off until the need for power exists again.

ADDITIONAL INPUT INFORMATION SENSORS Additional sensors are also used to provide the following information on engine conditions. NOTE: This list does not attempt to cover all of the sensors that are used by all manufacturers. It contains the most common.

- Detonation
- Crankshaft position
- Camshaft position
- Timing of ignition spark
- Air conditioner operation
- Gearshift lever position
- Battery voltage
- Amount of oxygen in exhaust bases
- Emission control device operation

Figure 25–17 shows the typical inputs and outputs of an onboard computer (ECU) responsible for controlling the EFI system.

ELECTRONIC CONTROL COMPUTER

The heart of the fuel injection system is the control computer or electronic control unit (ECU). The ECU is a small computer that is usually mounted within the passenger compartment to keep it away from the heat and vibration of the engine. The ECU includes solid state devices, including integrated circuits and a microprocessor.

The ECU receives signals from all the system sensors, processes them, and transmits programmed electrical pulses to the fuel injectors. Both incoming and outgoing signals are sent through a wiring harness and a multiple-pin connector.

Electronic feedback in the ECU means the unit is self-regulating and is controlling the injectors on the basis of operating performance or parameters rather than on preprogrammed instructions. An ECU with a feedback loop, for example, reads signals from the oxygen sensor, varies the pulse width of the injectors, and again reads the signals from the oxygen sensor. This is repeated until the injectors are pulsed for just the amount of time needed to get the proper amount

1. K4 DG/RD — M.A.P. signal
2. K10 TN/WT — Coolant sensor
3. J11 RD/Wt — Direct battery
4. N5 BK/LB — Sensor return
5. K5 BK/WT — Signal ground
6. K8 VT/WT — 5 Volt supply
7. N6 OR — 9 Volt output
8. Z1 DG/BK — Z1 Voltage sense
9. J2 DB — J2 Supply
10. - - - -
11. K9 LB/RD — Power ground
12. K9 LB/RD — Power ground
13. - - - -
14. - - - -
15. Y12 TN — #2 Injector driver
16. Y11 WT/DB — #1 Injector driver
17. - - - -
18. - - - -
19. J5 BK/GY — Ignition coil #1 driver
20. R3 DG — Alt field driver
21. K13 BK/RD — Throttle body temp sensor (V8)
22. K7 OR/DB — Throttle pos. sensor
23. - - - -
24. N7 GY/BK — Ignition reference
25. DK21 PK — SCI transmit
26. - - - -
27. C20 BR — A/C clutch sense
28. N31 VT — Closed throttle switch
29. D40 WT/PK — Brake switch
30. S4 BR/YL — Park/neutral switch
31. - - - -
32. K3 BK/PK — Check engine lamp
33. X36 TN/RD — S/C vacuum solenoid
34. N13 DB/OR — A/C clutch relay control
35. S6 GY/YL — EGR solenoid
36. N23 BK/OR — Air switching solenoid
37. - - - -
38. - - - -
39. - - - -
40. N2 BR/WT — Automatic idle speed driver
41. N11 BK/DG — Oxygen sensor signal
42. - - - -
43. T21 GY/LB — Tach signal output
44. U4 OR/WT — Overdrive lockout select
45. DK20 LG — SCI receive
46. - - - -
47. G7 WT/OR — Distance sensor signal
48. X31 BR/RD — S/C set switch
49. X32 YL/RD — S/C on-off switch
50. X33 WT/LG — S/C resume switch
51. K19 DB/YL — Auto shutdown relay
52. K1 PK/BK — Purge solenoid
53. X35 LG/RD — S/C vent solenoid
54. U3 OR/BK — PTU solenoid
55. U40 OR/LG — Overdrive solenoid
56. G29 GY/PK — EMR lamp
57. - - - -
58. - - - -
59. - - - -
60. N1 GY/RD — Automatic idle speed driver

FIGURE 25–17 Input sensors from all engine systems supply the control computer (ECU) with the data needed to calculate the correct injector pulse for driving conditions and driver demands. *Courtesy of Chrysler Corporation*

of oxygen into the exhaust stream. While this interaction is occurring, the system is operating in closed loop. When conditions, such as starting or wide-open throttle, demand that the signals from the oxygen sensor be ignored, the system operates in open loop. During open loop, injector pulse length is controlled by set parameters contained in the ECU memory banks.

FUEL INJECTOR

The fuel injector is an electromechanical device that meters and atomizes fuel so it can be sprayed into the intake manifold. Fuel injectors resemble spark plugs in size and shape. As mentioned earlier, they mount into the intake manifold runners (port systems) or throttle body housing (TBI systems). O-rings are used to seal the injector at the intake manifold, throt-

tle body, and fuel rail mounting positions. These O-rings provide thermal insulation to prevent the formation of vapor bubbles and promote good hot start characteristics. They also dampen potentially damaging vibration.

When the injector is electrically energized, a solenoid-operated valve opens, and a fine mist of fuel sprays from the injector tip. Two different valve designs are commonly used.

The first consists of a valve body and a nozzle or needle valve that has a special ground **pintle** (Figure 25–18). A movable armature is attached to the nozzle valve, which is pressed against the nozzle body sealing seat by a helical spring. The solenoid winding is located at the back of the valve body.

When the solenoid winding is energized, it creates a magnetic field that draws the armature back and pulls the nozzle valve from its seat. When the solenoid

FIGURE 25–18 This fuel injector design is equipped with a nozzle or needle valve having a special ground pintle for precise fuel delivery control.

is de-energized, the magnetic field collapses and the helical spring forces the nozzle valve back on its seat.

The second popular valve design uses a ball valve and valve seat. In this case, the magnetic field created by the solenoid coil pulls a plunger upward lifting the ball valve from its seat. Once again, a spring is used to return the valve to its seated or closed position.

Fuel injectors can be either top fuel feeding or bottom fuel feeding (Figure 25–19). Top feed injectors are primarily used in port injection systems that operate using high fuel system pressures. Bottom feed injectors are used in throttle body systems. Bottom feed injectors are able to use fuel pressures as low as 10 psi.

There have been some problems with deposits on injector tips. Since small quantities of gum are present in gasoline, injector deposits usually occur when this gum bakes onto the injector tips after a hot engine is shut off. Most oil companies have added a detergent to their gasoline to help prevent injector tip deposits. Car manufacturers and auto parts stores sell detergents to place in the fuel tank to clean injector tips.

FIGURE 25–19 Examples of bottom and top feed injectors.

TOP FEED **BOTTOM FEED**

WARNING!

Some auto manufacturers do not want you to add any type of injector cleaner to the gasoline. It seems that the chemicals in the cleaner destroy the coating on the coil windings in the injector. ■

Some manufacturers and auto parts suppliers have designed deposit-resistant injectors. These injectors have several different pintle tip and orifice designs to help prevent deposits. On one type of deposit-resistant injector, the pintle seat opens outward away from the injector body and more clearance is provided between the pintle and the body. Another type of deposit-resistant injector has four orifices in a metering plate rather than a single orifice.

SHOP TALK

Some deposit-resistant injectors may be recognized by the color of the injector body. For example, regular injectors supplied by Ford Motor Company are painted black, whereas their deposit-resistant injectors have tan or yellow bodies. ■

COLD START INJECTOR A good number of engines equipped with port injection have an additional injector, the cold start injector. Unlike the individual injectors at the intake ports, the cold start injector is not operated directly by the ECU. Rather, it is operated by a **thermo-time switch**, which senses coolant temperature (Figure 25–20).

When the engine is cranked, voltage is supplied from the starter solenoid to one terminal on the cold start injector. If the coolant temperature is below a certain amount, the thermo-time switch completes the ground for the cold start injector. Doing this energizes the injector while the engine is cranking. The fuel from the cold start injector sprays into the intake manifold and is delivered to the cylinders. Since the injectors at each intake port will also be providing fuel, the fuel from the cold start injector allows for a richer mixture.

A bimetal switch in the thermo-time switch is heated as current flows through the injector coil. The bimetal switch action opens the circuit through the thermo-time switch after the engine has reached a certain temperature.

ELECTRICAL CONNECTOR Each fuel injector is equipped with a two-wire connector. The connector is often equipped with a spring clip that must be

FIGURE 25–20 Cold start injector and thermo-time switch. *Courtesy of Chevrolet Motor Division, General Motors Corporation*

unlocked before the connector can be removed from the injector.

One wire of the connector supplies voltage to the injector. This voltage supply wire may connect directly to the fuse panel. It may connect to the ECU, which, in turn, connects to the fuse panel. In some systems, a resistor at the fuse panel or ECU is used to reduce the 12-volt battery supply voltage to 3 volts or less. Most other injectors are fed battery voltage (12-volts).

The second wire of the connector is a ground wire. This ground wire is routed to the ECU. The ECU energizes the injector by grounding its electrical circuit. The pulse width of the injector equals the length of time the injector circuit is grounded. Typical pulse widths range from 1 millisecond to 10 milliseconds at full load. Port fuel injection systems having four, six, or eight injectors use a special wiring harness to simplify and organize injector wiring.

IDLE SPEED CONTROL

In throttle body and port EFI systems, engine idle speed is controlled by bypassing a certain amount of airflow past the throttle valve in the throttle body housing. Two types of air by-pass systems are used, auxiliary air valves and idle air control (IAC) valves. IAC valve systems are more common.

IAC Valves

The IAC system consists of an electrically controlled stepper motor or actuator that positions the IAC

valve in the air by-pass channel around the throttle valve. The IAC valve is part of the throttle body casting (Figure 25–21). The control computer (ECU) calculates the amount of air needed for smooth idling based on input data such as coolant temperature, engine load, engine speed, and battery voltage. It then signals the actuator to extend or retract the idle air control valve in the air by-pass channel.

If the engine speed is lower than desired, the ECU activates the motor to retract the IAC valve. This opens the channel and diverts more air around the throttle valve. If engine speed is higher than desired, the valve is extended and the by-pass channel is made smaller. Air supply to the engine is reduced and engine speed falls.

During cold starts idle speed can be as high as 2,100 rpm to quickly raise the temperature of the

FIGURE 25–21 Components of an IAC system.

FIGURE 25–22 Operation of an auxiliary air valve. *Courtesy of Robert Bosch Corporation*

catalytic converter for proper control of exhaust emissions. Idle speed that is attained after a cold start is controlled by the ECU. The ECU maintains idle speed for approximately 40 to 50 seconds even if the driver attempts to alter it by kicking the accelerator. After this preprogrammed time interval, depressing the accelerator pedal rotates the throttle position sensor (TPS) and signals the ECU to reduce idle speed.

Auxiliary Air Valve

The major difference between an IAC valve and an auxiliary air valve is that the auxiliary air valve is not controlled by the ECU. But like the IAC system, the auxiliary air valve provides additional air during cold engine starts and warm-up.

The auxiliary air valve consists of an air by-pass channel or hose around the throttle valve, a movable plate or disc, and a heat-sensitive bimetal strip. Figure 25–22 shows how an auxiliary air valve on a port injection system operates. When the plate opens the channel, extra air bypasses the throttle. Opening is controlled by the bimetal strip. As the bimetal heats up, it bends to rotate the movable plate, gradually blocking the opening. When the device is closed, there is no auxiliary airflow.

The bimetal strip is warmed by an electric heating element powered from the run circuit of the ignition switch. This bimetal element is not a switch, but a strip that moves the movable plate directly. The auxiliary air device is independent of the cold start injector. It is not controlled by the ECU but is continuously powered when the ignition key is set to the run position.

When the engine is cold, the passage opens for extra air when the engine starts. When the engine is running and still cold, the passage is open but the heater begins operating to close it gradually. If the engine is warm at start up, the passage is closed and normal air is delivered for idle.

CONTINUOUS INJECTION SYSTEMS

Continuous injection systems (Figure 25–23) are used almost exclusively on import vehicles. The basic technology for CIS was introduced in the early 1970s and has been continuously updated and refined. During the past twenty years, continuous injection systems have gained an excellent reputation for efficiency and reliability.

The major difference between CIS and electronically controlled throttle body and port injection systems is the way in which the amount of fuel injected is controlled. In a CIS-equipped engine, the amount of fuel delivered to the cylinders is not varied by pulsing the injectors on and off. Instead CIS injectors spray fuel continuously. What does vary is the amount of fuel contained in the spray. CIS systems do this by maintaining a constant relative fuel system pressure and metering the amount of fuel to the injectors.

Basic Operation

Metering is done through a **mixture control unit**. This unit consists of an airflow sensor and a special **fuel distributor** with fuel lines running to all injectors. A control plunger in the fuel distributor is mechanically linked to the airflow sensor plate by means of a lever. As the airflow sensor measures the volume of engine intake air, its plate moves. The lever transfers this motion to the control plunger in the fuel distributor. The plunger moves up or down changing the size of the fuel metering openings in the fuel lines. This increases or decreases the volume of fuel flowing to the injectors.

Air Delivery System Air enters the system through the air filter and is measured by the airflow sensor. The amount of airflow is controlled by the throttle. The sensor plate is located in an air venturi or funnel-shaped passage in the mixture control unit. Because of the shape of this venturi or funnel, the airflow sen-

FIGURE 25–23 Components of a continuous injection system (CIS) that meters fuel mechanically. *Courtesy of Robert Bosch Corporation*

sor moves more when more air flows into the engine. Any air that enters the intake without passing the sensor plate interferes with the proper air/fuel mixture, causing the engine to run lean. The same holds true for all other types of injection systems. Proper operation of all systems depends on having no vacuum leaks.

Fuel Delivery System The main components of the CIS fuel delivery system are the fuel tank, electronic fuel pump, prefeed pump (some systems only), fuel accumulator, fuel filter, fuel distributor, and fuel injectors.

As shown in Figure 25–23, fuel is drawn from the tank by an electric fuel pump. It passes through the fuel accumulator and filter before reaching the fuel distributor in the metering control unit. Some models use a **prefeed pump** to supply the main pump. This prefeed pump helps prevent vapor lock in hot driving conditions.

The **fuel accumulator** is needed to prevent a sudden rapid rise in fuel pressure inside the fuel distributor when the vehicle is being started. Besides stabilizing the pressure, the accumulator also maintains a rest pressure within the fuel system when the engine is off. This helps eliminate vapor lock in the fuel lines.

The fuel distributor consists of a fuel control unit, pressure regulating valves for each cylinder, and a system pressure regulator. The fuel control unit

consists of a slotted metering cylinder. This cylinder contains the fuel control plunger. Part of the control plunger protrudes past the fuel distributor and rests on the airflow sensor lever.

Fuel flows through the slots in the fuel metering cylinder. There is one metering slot for each engine cylinder. Control plunger movement within the metering cylinder determines the amount of fuel released to the fuel injectors. Each cylinder has its own pressure regulating valve. These valves maintain a constant pressure differential of approximately 1.5 psi on either side of the fuel metering slot. This pressure differential remains the same, regardless of the size of the slot opening. Without pressure regulating valves, the amount of fuel injected would not remain proportional to the size of the metering slot opening.

The fuel distributor also contains a pressure relief valve that regulates system pressure. Like the fuel pressure regulators used on EFI systems, this regulator maintains a constant system pressure by allowing excess fuel to return to the fuel tank via a return line.

Control Pressure Regulator A control pressure regulator (**warm-up regulator**) is also used to provide correct fuel pressure on top of the fuel control plunger. This helps regulate the engine air/fuel needs. A dampening restriction over the fuel control plunger also eliminates any fluctuations that may occur in the airflow sensor lever.

FIGURE 25–24 Typical CIS injector. *Courtesy of Robert Bosch Corporation*

FUEL INJECTORS CIS fuel injectors (Figure 25–24) open at a set fuel pressure. Once the engine is started, each injector continuously sprays finely atomized fuel into the intake port of the cylinder.

A vibrator pin or needle inside each injector helps break up and atomize the fuel. This vibrating action also helps keep the injectors from clogging. Clogging is much more common on TBI and PFI systems than on CIS-equipped engines.

When the engine is stopped, the pin and spring assembly seal off the injector to retain fuel pressure in the lines. This helps ensure quick starting.

COLD START INJECTORS AND AUXILIARY AIR VALVES CIS systems are normally equipped with a cold start injector and auxiliary air valve system to control cold starting and engine idling. These systems operate similarly to the EFI systems discussed earlier in the chapter.

CUSTOMER CARE

Recommend the periodic inspection and replacement of fuel tubing and hoses to your customers. These items should be replaced at least every three years. Otherwise, particles from deteriorating rubber hoses may plug up injectors, fuel lines, and filters. While replacing a fuel filter is not a major repair, replacing damaged injectors is expensive. ■

Oxygen Control Feedback System

Continuous injection systems can be fitted with an oxygen sensor (sometimes called **lambda sensor**) for feedback control. The sensor is mounted in the exhaust manifold so it heats up rapidly when the engine is started.

Signals from the oxygen sensor are sent to the oxygen control unit. The ECU modifies the fuel flow in the mixture control unit so the engine operates on the proper ratio. The changing exhaust gas affects the oxygen sensor and it sends a signal in a closed loop through the mixture control unit to the engine (Figure 25–25).

The oxygen control valve (sometimes called a timing or **frequency valve**) operates on signals from the oxygen control unit. It opens and closes to allow more or less fuel to return to the tank through the fuel return. This is called dwell time. By reducing the pressure in the lower part of the differential pressure valve,

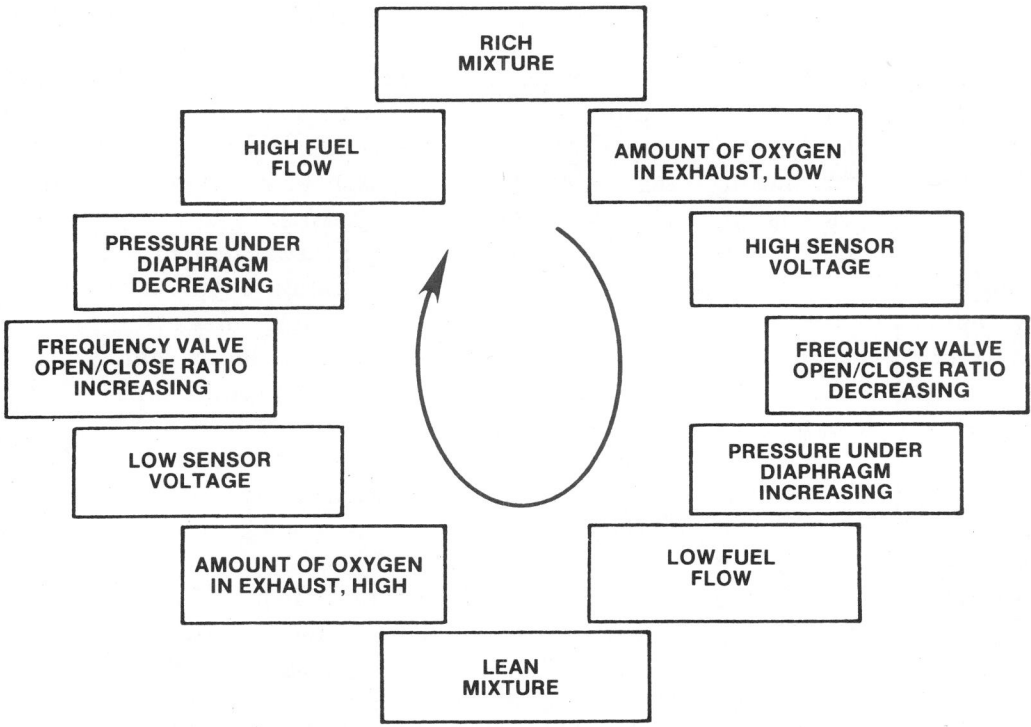

FIGURE 25–25 Closed loop operation refers to the way various components respond to each other to maintain optimum air/fuel proportioning.

fuel flow to the injector can be increased, enriching the mixture. Shortening the time that the oxygen control valve is open increases the pressure beneath the differential pressure valve diaphragm. This lessens the amount of fuel injected, leaning the mixture.

Based on a series of signals from the sensor from oxygen-rich to oxygen-lean, the control valve continually cycles from being open about 40 percent of the time to being open about 60 percent of the time averaging about 50 percent.

The oxygen control unit switches to open loop during conditions when the oxygen sensor is cold or when the engine is cold. This open loop operation holds the oxygen control valve open for a fixed amount of time. When testing the operation of the oxygen control unit and its control valve, it is possible to hear the change in sound caused by the change in open time. A better way to monitor the activity of the unit is to connect a dwellmeter across it and watch the change in cycles.

Adjusting the carbon monoxide (CO) output level is accomplished by turning a mixture screw. If the mixture adjustment is covered with a temperproof plug, this plug must be drilled and removed from the mixture control unit. The oxygen (lambda) sensor wire can be disconnected and the exhaust sample taken at the pipe provided on the exhaust manifold. As an alternate procedure, the mixture is adjusted in closed loop, with oxygen sensor connected, using a dwellmeter. Additional details are provided on the underhood decal.

CIS-E Components

As mentioned earlier, CISs can also be equipped with certain electronic controls. They combine the benefits of a basic mechanically controlled fuel injection system with simple electronic controls for enrichment, cutoff, and closed loop feedback. Economy is improved through the use of minimum enrichment during warm-up and fuel cutoff during coast.

CIS-E uses an electrohydraulic actuator in the fuel distributor, which is controlled by an ECU. The ECU receives signals from the coolant temperature sensor, throttle switch, airflow sensor plate, and the oxygen or lambda sensor.

CIS-E differs from a basic CIS in three ways. First, the airflow sensor mechanism includes a potentiometer, which signals the position and movement of the plate for acceleration enrichment. Secondly, the system pressure regulator maintains a constant pressure. It also relieves electric fuel pump pressure and maintains pressure in the system for easy restarts by controlling return fuel flow from the fuel distributor. Finally, the electrohydraulic actuator is an electro-

magnetic differential pressure regulator on the fuel distributor. It operates a plate valve.

System Operation The system pressure regulator maintains a constant system of primary pressure. Constant system pressure is applied to the control plunger to counter the force of the airflow sensor mechanism. There is no control pressure and no control pressure regulator.

The electrohydraulic actuator provides enrichment reducing the pressure below the diaphragm of each differential pressure valve. This has the effect of increasing the pressure at each metering slit. In turn, this increases the amount of fuel delivered. For fuel cutoff during coasting or for rpm limitation, the electrohydraulic action is reversed. A decrease in the pressure at the metering slits cuts off delivery of fuel.

SERVICING FUEL INJECTION SYSTEMS

Troubleshooting fuel injection systems requires systematic step-by-step test procedures. With so many interrelated components and sensors controlling fuel injection performance, a hit-or-miss approach to diagnosing problems can quickly become frustrating, time-consuming and costly.

Most fuel injection systems are integrated into engine control systems. The self-test modes of these systems are designed to help in engine diagnosis. Unfortunately, when a problem upsets the smooth operation of the engine, many service technicians automatically assume the computer (ECU) is at fault. But in the vast majority of cases, complaints about driveability, performance, fuel mileage, roughness, or hard starting or no-starting are due to something other than the computer itself (although many problems are caused by sensor malfunctions that can be traced using the self-test mode).

Before condemning sensors as bad, remember that weak or poorly operating engine components can often affect sensor readings and result in poor performance. For example, a sloppy timing chain, bad rings, or valves reduce vacuum and cylinder pressure, resulting in a lower exhaust temperature. This can affect the operation of a perfectly good oxygen or lambda sensor, which must heat up to approximately 600°F before functioning in its closed loop mode.

A problem like an intake manifold leak can cause a sensor, the MAP sensor in this case, to adjust engine operation to less than ideal conditions.

One of the basic rules of electronic fuel injection servicing is that EFI cannot be adjusted to match the engine, you have to make the engine match EFI. In other words, make sure the rest of the engine is sound before condemning the fuel injection and engine control components.

Preliminary Checks

The best way to approach a problem on a vehicle with electronic fuel injection is to treat it as though it had no electronic controls at all. As the previous examples illustrate, any engine is susceptible to problems that are unrelated to the fuel system itself. Unless all engine support systems are operating correctly, the control system does not operate as designed.

Before proceeding with specific fuel injection checks and electronic control testing, be certain of the following.

- The battery is in good condition, fully charged, with clean terminals and connections.
- The charging and starting systems are operating properly.
- All fuses and fusible links are intact.
- All wiring harnesses are properly routed with connections free of corrosion and tightly attached.
- All vacuum lines are in sound condition, properly routed, and tightly attached.
- The PCV system is working properly and maintaining a sealed crankcase.
- All emission control systems are in place, hooked up, and operating properly.
- The level and condition of the coolant/antifreeze is good, and the thermostat is opening at the proper temperature.
- The secondary spark delivery components are in good shape with no signs of crossfiring, carbon tracking, corrosion, or wear.
- The base timing and idle speed are set to specifications.
- The engine is in good mechanical condition.
- The gasoline in the tank is of good quality and has not been substantially cut with alcohol or contaminated with water.

EFI SYSTEM COMPONENT CHECKS

In any electronic throttle body or port injection system three things must occur for the system to operate.

1. An adequate air supply must be supplied for the air/fuel mixture.
2. A pressurized fuel supply must be delivered to properly operating injectors.
3. The injectors must receive a trigger signal from the control computer.

If all of these preliminary checks do not reveal a problem, proceed to test the electronic control system and fuel injection components.

Some older control systems require involved test procedures and special test equipment, but most newer designs have a self-test program designed to help diagnose the problem. These self-tests perform a number of checks on components within the system. Input sensors, output devices, wiring harnesses, and even the electronic control computer itself may be among the items tested.

The results of the testing are converted into trouble codes (Figure 25–26) that the technician may read using special test equipment, a testlight, a malfunction indicator lamp (**MIL**), or an analog voltmeter. The meaning of trouble codes vary from manufacturer to manufacturer, year to year, and model to model; so it is important to have the appropriate service manuals.

Always remember that trouble codes only indicate the particular circuit in which a problem has been detected. They do not pinpoint individual components. So if a code indicates a defective lambda or oxygen sensor, the problem could be the sensor itself, the wiring to it, or its connector. Trouble codes are not a signal to replace components. They signal that a more thorough diagnosis is needed in that area.

The following sections outline general troubleshooting procedures for the most popular EFI and CIS designs in use today.

Air System Checks

In an injection system (particularly designs that rely on airflow meters or mass airflow sensors), all the air entering the engine must be accounted for by the air measuring device. If it is not, the air/fuel ratio becomes overly lean. For this reason, cracks or tears in the plumbing between the airflow sensor and throttle body are potential air leak sources that can affect the air/fuel ratio.

During a visual inspection of the air control system, pay close attention to these areas, looking for cracked or deteriorated ductwork. Also make sure all induction hose clamps are tight and properly sealed. Look for possible air leaks in the crankcase, for example, dipstick tube and oil filter cap. Any extra air entering the intake manifold through the PCV system is not measured either and can upset the delicately balanced air/fuel mixture at idle.

Airflow Sensor When looking for the cause of a performance complaint that relates to poor fuel economy, erratic performance/hesitation or hard starting, make the following checks to determine if the airflow

Code	Circuit Affected or Possible Cause	Code	Circuit Affected or Possible Cause
12	No distributor reference pulses to the ECU. This code is not stored in memory and flashes only while the fault is present. Normal code with ignition on, engine not running.	34	Vacuum sensor or manifold absolute pressure (MAP) circuit. The engine must run up to 2 minutes at specified curb idle before this code sets.
13	Oxygen sensor circuit. The engine must run up to 4 minutes at part-throttle under road load before this code sets.	35	Idle speed control (ISC) switch circuit shorted. (Up to 70% TPS for over 5 seconds.)
14	Shorted coolant sensor circuit. The engine must run 2 minutes before this code sets.	41	No distributor reference pulses to the ECU at specified engine vacuum. This code stores in memory.
15	Open coolant sensor circuit. The engine must run 5 minutes before this code sets.	42	Electronic spark timing (EST) bypass circuit or EST circuit grounded or open.
21	Throttle position sensor (TPS) circuit voltage high (open circuit or misadjusted TPS). The engine must run 10 seconds at specified curb idle speed before this code sets.	43	Electronic spark control (ESC) retard signal for too long a time; causes retard in EST signal.
		44	Lean exhaust indication. The engine must run 2 minutes in closed loop and at part-throttle before this code sets.
22	Throttle position sensor (TPS) circuit voltage low (grounded circuit or misadjusted TPS). Engine must run 20 seconds at specified curb idle speed to set code.	45	Rich exhaust indication. The engine must run 2 minutes in closed loop and at part throttle before this code sets.
23	M/C solenoid circuit open or grounded.	51	Faulty or improperly installed calibration unit (PROM). It takes up to 30 seconds before this code will set.
24	Vehicle speed sensor (VSS) circuit. The vehicle must operate up to 2 minutes at road speed before this code sets.	53	Exhaust gas recirculation (EGR) valve vacuum sensor has seen improper EGR vacuum.
32	Barometric pressure sensor (BARO) circuit low.	54	Shorted M/C solenoid circuit or faulty ECU.

FIGURE 25–26 Common ECU trouble codes.

sensor (all types except CIS) is at fault. Start by removing the air intake duct from the airflow sensor to gain access to the sensor flap. Check for binding, sticking, or scraping by rotating the sensor flap (evenly and carefully) through its operating range. It should move freely, make no noise, and feel smooth.

On some systems, the movement of the sensor flap turns on the fuel pump. If the system is so equipped, turn on the ignition. Do not start the engine. Move the flap toward the open position. The electric fuel pump should come on as the flap is opened. If it does not, turn off the ignition, remove the sensor harness, and check for specific resistance values with an ohmmeter at each of the sensor's terminals.

On other models it is possible to check the resistance values of the potentiometer by moving the air flap, but in either case a service manual is needed to identify the various terminals and to look up resistance specifications.

On systems that use a mass airflow meter or manifold pressure sensor to measure airflow, other than checking for good electrical connections, there are usually no actual physical checks. However, a hand-held scan tool can be plugged into the diagnostic connector on some models to check for proper voltage values.

SHOP TALK

To quickly diagnose an intermittent failure of GM's hot film mass airflow meter (MAF), start the engine, let it idle, and lightly tap on the sensor with a plastic mallet or screwdriver handle. If the engine stalls, runs worse, or the idle quality improves while tapping on the sensor, the MAF meter is probably defective and should be replaced. Similarly, if the engine does not start or idles poorly, unplug the MAF. If the engine starts or runs better with the sensor unplugged, the sensor is defective and should be replaced. ∎

Throttle Body Remove the air duct from the throttle assembly and check for carbon buildup inside the throttle bore and on the throttle plate. Soak a cloth with carburetor solvent and wipe the bore and throttle plate to remove light to moderate amounts of carbon residue. Also, clean the backside of the throttle plate. Then, remove the idle air control valve from the throttle body (if so equipped) and clean any carbon deposits from the pintle tip and the IAC air passage.

Fuel System Checks

If the air control system is in working order, move on to the fuel delivery system. It is important to always remember that fuel injection systems operate at high fuel pressure levels. This pressure must be relieved before any fuel line connections can be broken. Spraying gasoline (under a pressure of 35 psi or more) on a hot engine creates a real hazard when dealing with a liquid that has a flash point of –45°F.

Follow the specific procedures given in the service manual when relieving the pressure in the fuel lines. If the procedures are not available, a safe alternative procedure is to apply 20 to 25 inches of vacuum to the externally mounted fuel pressure regulator (with a hand vacuum pump connected to the manifold control line of the regulator), which bleeds fuel pressure back into the tank (Figure 25–27). If the vehicle does not have an externally mounted regulator, or a service valve or injector to energize, use a towel to catch excess fuel, while slowly breaking a fuel line connection. This method should only be used when all other possibilities have been tried.

 CAUTION:

Dispose of the fuel-soaked rag in a fireproof container. ∎

Fuel Delivery When dealing with an alleged fuel complaint that is preventing the vehicle from starting, the first step (after spark, compression, etc., have been verified) is to determine if fuel is reaching the cylinders (assuming there is gasoline in the tank). Checking for fuel delivery is a simple operation on

FIGURE 25–27 With an externally mounted fuel pressure regulator, it's possible to bleed off system pressure into the fuel tank using a hand vacuum pump.

throttle body systems. Remove the air cleaner, crank the engine, and watch the injector for signs of a spray pattern. If a better view of the injector's operation is required, an ordinary strobe light does a great job of highlighting the spray pattern.

It is impossible to visually inspect the spray pattern and volume of port system injectors. However, an accurate indication of their performance can be obtained by performing simple fuel pressure and fuel volume delivery tests. See the service manual for details.

Low fuel pressure can cause a no-start or poor-run problem. It can be caused by a clogged fuel filter, a faulty pressure regulator, or a restricted fuel line anywhere from the fuel tank to the fuel filter connection.

If a fuel volume test shows low fuel volume, it can indicate a bad fuel pump or blocked or restricted fuel line. When performing the test, visually inspect the fuel for signs of dirt or moisture. These indicate the fuel filter needs replacement.

High fuel pressure readings will result in a rich-running engine. A restricted fuel return line to the tank or a bad fuel regulator may be the problem. To isolate the cause of high pressure, relieve system pressure and connect a tap hose to the fuel return line. Direct the hose into a container and energize the fuel pump. If fuel pressure is now within specifications, the fuel return line is blocked. If pressure is still high, the pressure regulator is faulty.

If the first fuel pressure reading is within specs, but the pressure slowly bleeds down, there may be a leak in the fuel pressure regulator, fuel pump check valve, or the injectors themselves. Remember, hard starting is a common symptom of system leaks.

Injector Checks

A fuel injector is nothing more than a solenoid-actuated fuel valve. Its operation is quite basic in that as long as it is held open and the fuel pressure remains steady, it delivers fuel until it is told to stop.

Because all fuel injectors operate in a similar manner, fuel injector problems tend to exhibit the same failure characteristics. The main difference is that in a TBI design, generally all cylinders suffer if the injectors malfunction, whereas in port systems the loss of one injector is not as crucial.

An injector that does not open causes hard starts on port-type systems and an obvious no-start on single-point TBI designs. An injector that is struck partially open causes loss of fuel pressure (most noticeably after the engine is stopped and restarted within a short time period) and flooding due to raw fuel dribbling into the engine. In addition to a rich-running engine, a leaking injector also causes the engine to diesel or run on when the ignition is turned off.

Checking Voltage Signals When an injector is suspected as the cause of a problem, the first step is to determine if the injector is receiving a signal (from the control computer) to fire. Fortunately, determining if the injector is receiving a voltage signal is easy and requires simple test equipment. Unfortunately, the location of the injector's electrical connector can make this simple voltage check somewhat difficult. For example, on some recent Chevrolet 2.8 liter V-6 engines, the cover must be removed from the cast aluminum plenum chamber that is mounted over the top of the engine before the injector can be accessed (Figure 25–28).

Once the injector's electrical connector has been removed, check for voltage at the injector using an ordinary test light or a convenient **noid** light that plugs into the connector (Figure 25–29). After making the test connections, crank the engine. A series of rapidly flickering lights indicates the computer is doing its job and supplying voltage or a ground to open the injector.

When performing this test, keep off the accelerator pedal. On some models, fully depressing the accelerator pedal activates the clear flood mode, in which the voltage signal to the injectors is automatically cut off. Technicians unaware of this waste time tracing a phantom problem.

If sufficient voltage is present after checking each injector, check the electrical integrity of the injectors themselves. Use an ohmmeter to check each injector

FIGURE 25–28 To access the injectors on a Chevy 2.8L V-6, the air plenum must be removed.

winding for shorts, opens, or excessive resistance. Compare resistance readings to the specifications found in the service manual.

Injector Balance Test If the injectors are electrically sound, perform an injector pressure balance test. This test will help isolate a clogged or dirty injector.

FIGURE 25–29 Checking for voltage at the injector using a noid light.

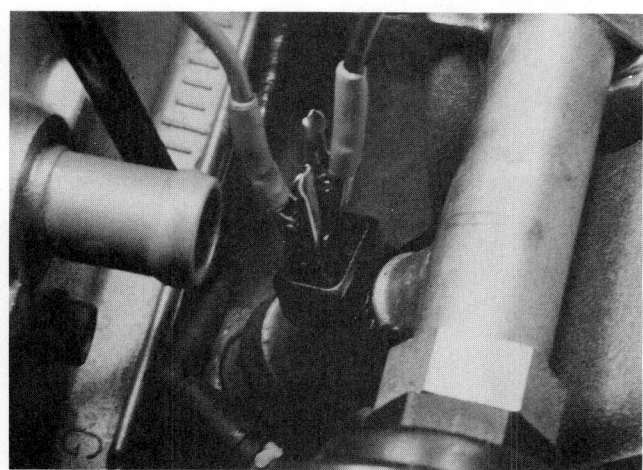

FIGURE 25–30 Performing an injector pressure balance test.

FIGURE 25–31 Injector power balance tester. *Courtesy of Oldsmobile Division, General Motors Corporation*

Photo Sequence 14 shows a typical procedure for testing injector balance. An electronic injector pulse tester is used for this test. Each injector is energized while observing a fuel pressure gauge to monitor the drop in fuel pressure. The tester is designed to safely pulse each injector for a controlled length of time. The tester is connected to one injector at a time (Figure 25–30). To prevent oil dilution, the electrical connectors to the other injectors are removed. The ignition is turned on until a maximum reading is on the pressure gauge. That reading is recorded and the ignition turned off. With the tester, activate the injector and record the pressure reading, after the needle has stopped pulsing. This same test is performed on each injector.

The difference between the maximum and minimum reading is the pressure drop. Ideally, each injector should drop the same amount when opened. A variation of 1.5 to 2 psi (10 kPa) or more is cause for concern. If there is not pressure drop or a low pressure drop, suspect a plugged injector. A higher than average pressure drop indicates a rich condition. If there are inconsistent readings, the nonconforming injectors either have to be cleaned or replaced.

Injector Power Balance Test The injector power balance test is a good method of checking injectors on vehicles with no-start problems (Figure 25–31). When the vehicle runs, several other tests are possible. The injector power balance test is an easy method of determining if an injector is causing a miss.

To perform this test, first hook up a tachometer and fuel pressure gauge to the engine. Once all gauges are in place, start the engine and allow it to reach operating temperature. As soon as the idle stabilizes, unplug each injector one at a time. Note the rpm drop and pressure gauge reading. To ensure accurate test results on many electronic systems, it may be neces-

sary to disconnect some type of idle air control device to prevent the computer from trying to compensate for the unplugged injector.

After recording the rpm and fuel pressure drop, reconnect the injector, wait until the idle stabilizes, and move on to the next one. Note the rpm and pressure drop each time. If an injector does not have much effect on the way the engine runs, chances are it is either clogged or electrically defective. It is a good idea to back up the power balance test with an injector resistance check, pressure balance test, or noid light check.

Alternative Checks

An ohmmeter can be used to test the electrical soundness of an injector. Connect the ohmmeter across the injector terminals (Figure 25–32) after the wires to the injector have been disconnected. If the meter reading is infinite, the injector winding is open. If the meter shows more resistance than the specifications call for, there is high resistance in the winding. A reading that is lower than the specifications indicates that the winding is shorted. If the injector is even a little bit out of specifications, it must be replaced.

FIGURE 25–32 An ohmmeter can be connected across the injector terminals to test the injector's winding. *Courtesy of Toyota Motor Corporation*

TYPICAL PROCEDURE FOR TESTING INJECTOR BALANCE

P14–1 Connect the fuel pressure gauge to the Schrader valve on the fuel rail.

P14–2 Disconnect the number 1 injector, and connect the injector tester lead to the injector terminals.

P14–3 Connect the injector tester power supply leads to the battery terminals with the proper polarity.

P14–4 Cycle the ignition switch several times until the specified pressure appears on the pressure gauge.

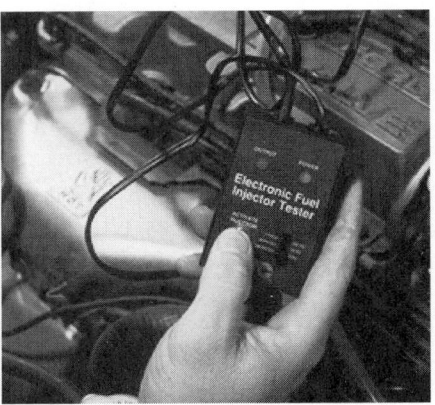

P14–5 Push the injector tester switch and record the pressure on the pressure gauge.

P14–6 Move the injector tester lead to the number 2 injector and cycle the ignition switch several times to restore the fuel pressure.

P14–7 Touch the injector tester switch and observe the fuel pressure.

P14–8 Move the injector tester lead to the number 3 injector and cycle the ignition switch several times to restore the fuel pressure.

P14–9 Touch the injector tester switch and observe the fuel pressure. Follow the same procedure to test number 4 injector. Compare the pressure readings to the vehicle's specifications.

If the injector's electrical leads are difficult to access, an injector power balance test is hard to perform. As an alternative, start the engine and use a technician's stethoscope to listen for correct injector operation. A good injector makes a rhythmic clicking sound as the solenoid is energized and de-energized several times each second. If a clunk-clunk instead of a steady click-click is heard, chances are the problem injector has been found. Cleaning or replacement is in order. If a stethoscope is not handy, use a thin steel rod, wooden dowel, or fingers to feel for a steady on/off pulsing of the injector solenoid.

Another way to isolate an offending cylinder when injector access is limited is to perform the more traditional cylinder power balance test and disable the spark plugs instead of the injectors. (Remember to bypass the idle air control.) Following the same warm-up and idle stabilizing procedures, watch the rpm drop and note any change in idle quality as each plug is shorted. If a lazy or dead cylinder is located, concentrate efforts on the portion of the fuel or ignition system pertaining to that cylinder (assuming, of course, no mechanical problems are present).

⚠️ *WARNING!*

Any time cylinders are shorted during a power balance test, make the readings as quickly as possible. Prolonged operation of a shorted cylinder causes excessive amounts of unburned fuel to accumulate inside the catalytic converter and increase the risk of premature converter failure. ∎

Oscilloscope Checks

An oscilloscope can be used to monitor the injector's pulse width and duty cycle when an injector-related problem is suspected. As covered earlier in the chapter, the pulse width is the time in milliseconds the injector is energized. The duty cycle is the percentage of on-time to total cycle time.

To check the injector's firing voltage on the scope, a typical hookup involves connecting the scope's positive lead to the injector supply wire and the scope's negative lead to an engine ground. Even though these connections are considered typical, it is still a good idea to read the instruction manual provided with the test equipment before making connections.

With the scope set on the low voltage scale and the pattern adjusted to fill the screen, a square-shaped voltage signal should be present with the engine running or cranking (Figure 25–33). If the voltage pattern reads higher than normal, excessive resistance in the injector circuit is indicated. Conversely, a low-

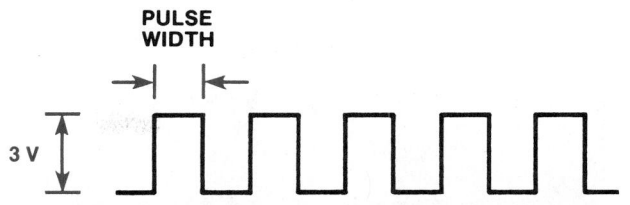

FIGURE 25–33 The trace pattern of the injector voltage pulse should be a square sine wave pattern.

voltage trace indicates low-circuit resistance. If the pattern forms a continuous straight line, it means the injector is not functioning due to an open circuit somewhere in the injector's electrical circuit.

📖 USING SERVICE MANUALS

Consult the service manual for pulse width and duty cycle specifications for the particular vehicle being worked on. The service manual also contains fault code diagnosis for a wide range of fuel injection system tests. ∎

INJECTOR CLEANING

Since a single injector can cost up to several hundred dollars, arbitrarily replacing injectors when they are not functioning properly, especially on multiport systems, can be an expensive proposition. If injectors are electrically defective, replacement is the only alternative. However, if the vehicle is exhibiting rough idle, stalling, slow or uneven acceleration, the injectors may just be dirty and require a good cleaning.

Before covering the typical cleaning systems available and discussing how they are used, several cleaning precautions are in order. First, never soak an injector in cleaning solvent. Not only is this an ineffective way to clean injectors, but it most likely destroys the injector in the process. Also, never use a wire brush, pipe cleaner, toothpick, or other cleaning utensil to unblock a plugged injector. The metering holes in injectors are drilled to precise tolerances. Scraping or reaming the opening results in a clean injector that is no longer an accurate fuel-metering device.

🚹 CUSTOMER CARE

After servicing a clogged injector, remove the fuel filter, open it up with a pipe cutter, slice the element with a razor blade, and examine the interior. If you find excessive rust particles or other contaminants, show the filter to the customer. Then recom-

FIGURE 25–34 Injector cleaner that operates with compressed air. *Courtesy of OTC Division of SPX Corporation*

FIGURE 25–35 State-of-the-art fuel injector cleaning system.

mend that the vehicle fuel tank be removed and cleaned and the fuel line blown out. If the customer declines the recommendation, make a big note on the repair order and customer receipt that his fuel filter replacement should be done more often than specified in the owner's manual. Showing the customer the evidence of contamination also justifies the repairs already made. ∎

Always use an approved on-the-car cleaning system (Figure 25–34) or injector cleaning bench to effectively clean clogged injectors. On-the-car cleaners are by far the most popular and practical method.

The basic premise of all injection cleaning systems is similar in that some type of cleaning chemical is run through the injector in an attempt to dissolve deposits that have formed on the injector's tip. The methods of applying the cleaner can range from single shot, premixed, pressurized spray cans to self-mix, self-pressurized chemical tanks resembling bug sprayers. The pre-mixed, pressurized spray can systems are fairly simple and straightforward to use since the technician does not need to mix, measure, or otherwise handle the cleaning agent.

Other systems require the technician to assume the role of chemist and mix up a desired batch of cleaning solution for each application. The chemical solution then is placed in a holding container and pressurized by hand pump or shop air to a specified operating pressure.

The more advanced units feature electrically operated pumps neatly packaged in roll-around cabinets

that are quite similar in design to an A/C charging station (Figure 25–35).

SHOP TALK

If the fuel delivery system is equipped with a cold start injector, make sure it gets cleaned along with the primary injectors. This step is especially critical if the owner complains of cold starting problems.

To effectively clean the cold start injector, hook up the cleaning system and remove the cold start injector from the engine. Open the control valve on the solvent containers and use an electronic triggering device to manually pulse the injector. Direct the spray into a suitable container. Pulse the injector until the spray pattern looks healthy.

On models where the cold start injector is not readily accessible, check the fuel flow through the injector before and after the cleaning procedure. Pulse as necessary until the maximum flow through the injector is obtained. ∎

INJECTOR REPLACEMENT

Consult the vehicle's service manual for instructions on removing and installing injectors. Before installing the new one, always check to make sure the sealing O-ring is in place (Figure 25–36). Also, prior to installation, lightly lubricate the sealing ring with engine oil or automatic transmission fluid (avoid using silicone grease, which tends to clog the injectors) to prevent seal distortion or damage.

FUEL INJECTOR WIRE CONNECTOR

LOCK RING

O-RINGS

FUEL INJECTOR

FIGURE 25–36 Before replacing an injector, inspect the sealing O-ring.

PROCEDURES
Cleaning Injectors

1. Attach the cleaner's service hose to the fuel rail following the same procedure used when hooking up a fuel pressure gauge.
2. Disable the fuel pump as per the car manufacturer's instructions (for example, pull fuel pump fuse, disconnect lead at pump, etc.). Clamp off the fuel pump return line at the flex connection to prevent the cleaner from seeping into the fuel tank. For an extra margin of safety, clamp off the inlet line also.
3. Before starting the engine, open the cleaner's control valve one-half turn or so to prime the injectors and then start the engine.
4. If available, set and adjust the cleaner's pressure gauge to approximately 5 psi below the operating pressure of the injection system and let the engine run at 1,000 rpm for 10 to 15 minutes or until the cleaning mix has run out. If the engine stalls during cleaning, simply restart it.
5. Run the engine until the recommended amount of fluid is exhausted and the engine stalls. Shut off the ignition, remove the cleaning setup, and reconnect the fuel pump.
6. After removing the clamping devices from around the fuel lines, start the car. Let it idle for 5 minutes or so to remove any leftover cleaner from the fuel lines.
7. On the more severely clogged cases, the idle improvement should be noticeable almost immediately. With more subtle performance improvements, an injector balance test verifies the cleaning results. Once the injectors are clean, recommend the use of an in-tank cleaning additive or a detergent-laced fuel.

Photo Sequence 15 outlines a typical procedure for removing and installing an injector. Always refer to the service manual for the exact procedure for the engine being serviced.

IDLE ADJUSTMENT

In a fuel injection system, idle speed is regulated by controlling the amount of air allowed to bypass the airflow sensor or throttle plates. When presented with a car that tends to stall, especially when coming to a stop, or one that idles too fast, look for obvious problems like binding linkage and vacuum leaks first. If no problems are found, go through the minimum idle checking/setting procedure described on the underhood decal. The instructions listed on the decal spell out the necessary conditions that must be met prior to attempting an idle adjustment. These adjustment procedures can range from a simple twist of a throttle stop screw (Figure 25–37) to more involved procedures requiring circumvention of idle air control devices, removal of casting plugs, or recalibration of the throttle position sensor. Specific idle adjustment procedures can also be found in the service manual.

On engines that have a provision for adjusting idle speed and mixture, the idle speed should be adjusted before adjusting the air/fuel mixture. The mixture is adjusted by turning the mixture adjustment screw clockwise to decrease the by-pass air, which enriches the mixture. This also increases the CO in the exhaust. Backing out the mixture screw increases the by-pass air, leaning the mixture and reducing CO. Because some electronic fuel injection engines run so lean, the CO meter might not react to the mixture

Idle stop screw assembly

Idle stop screw plug

FIGURE 25–37 Adjusting the idle stop screw for minimizing air adjustment. *Courtesy of Chevrolet Motor Division, General Motors Corporation*

REMOVING AND REPLACING A FUEL INJECTOR ON A PFI SYSTEM

P15–1 Often an individual injector needs to be replaced. Random disassembly of components and improper procedures can result in damage to one of various systems located near the injectors.

P15–2 The injectors are normally attached to a fuel rail and inserted into the intake manifold or cylinder head. They must be positively sealed because high pressure fuel leaks can cause a serious safety hazard.

P15–3 Prior to loosening any fitting in the fuel system, the fuel pump fuse should be removed.

P15–4 As an extra precaution, many technicians disconnect the negative cable of the battery.

P15–5 To remove the fuel injector, the fuel rail must be able to move away from the engine. The rail holding brackets should be unbolted and the vacuum line to the pressure regulator disconnected.

P15–7 The injectors are held to the fuel rail by a clip that fits over the top of the injector. An O-ring at the top and at the bottom of the injector seals the injector.

P15–6 Disconnect the wiring harness to the injectors by depressing the center of the attaching wire clip.

P15–8 Pull up on the fuel rail assembly. The bottom of the injectors will pull out of the manifold while the tops are secured to the rail by clips.

P15–9 Remove the clip from the top of the injector and remove the injector unit. Install new O-rings onto the new injector. Be careful not to damage the seals while installing them and make sure they are in their proper locations.

P15–10 Install the injector into the fuel rail and set the rail assembly into place.

P15–11 Tighten the fuel rail hold-down bolts according to the manufacturer's recommendations.

P15–12 Reconnect all parts that were disconnected. Install the fuel pump fuse and reconnect the battery. Turn the ignition switch to the run position and check the entire system for leaks. After a visual inspection has been completed, conduct a fuel pressure test on the system.

adjustment screw unless special enrichment procedures are followed. Instructions are usually given in the service manual for the particular application.

CIS CHECKS AND TESTS

Servicing mechanically controlled continuous injection systems requires the same logical approach and preliminary checks used in troubleshooting throttle body and port EFI systems. CISs are normally very reliable and should not be blamed for a problem until the preliminary ignition and engine system checks given earlier have been completed.

The following diagnostic and service tips apply to most CIS vehicles in use today.

◆ Often difficult cold starting is caused by a faulty cold start valve or thermal time switch.

◆ System pressure, idle mixture or speed, and a faulty air regulator are the common causes for rough-running engines.

◆ Improper pressures or pressure leaks can cause a number of problems, such as rough idling, stalling, surging or missing, or hard start problems.

◆ Surging or missing can also be caused by unequal fuel distribution to the injectors.

◆ An airflow sensor plate that is off-center in its bore can allow air to leak by, causing severe hot start problems.

◆ The two basic adjustments made to the CIS are idle speed and the air/fuel mixture. To set the idle speed on a typical CIS setup, turn the screw next to the throttle plate linkage, which varies the size of a by-pass drilling. Counterclockwise equals faster (Figure 25–38).

◆ Mixture is adjusted by turning a screw, which bears on the air sensor lever. A rubber plug is located between the fuel distributor and the air sensor cone, and must be removed for access to the screw. Use a long, 3-mm Allen wrench to adjust. Clockwise richens the blend.

◆ In a CIS-E engine the control computer uses input signals to decide mixtures for different conditions. It controls idle speed with the idle-speed stabilizer, holding a higher speed for a colder engine and gradually slowing it down as the engine warms. Idle specifications are given in percent of dwell to rpm. Turning the idle screw, as on most domestic cars, does not change the idle speed. The idle stabilizer changes to correct it.

◆ Idle mixture adjustment on CIS-E is done through a hole in the fuel distributor/air flap housing using a long, 3-mm Allen wrench. The key is to set both regulator current and exhaust CO in specifications.

HIGH-PRESSURE DIESEL FUEL INJECTION

All diesel engines use a high-pressure fuel injection system that differs from gasoline fuel injection systems in several key areas.

◆ A diesel engine uses higher fuel injection pressures than a gasoline engine.

◆ Ignition in a diesel engine takes place as the fuel is injected into the cylinder. The heat of the highly compressed air ignites the fuel charge. A diesel engine does not have an electrical ignition system like that found on gasoline engines.

◆ The output power of a diesel engine is directly proportional to the fuel charge injected into the combustion chamber.

◆ In diesel engines, the amount of fuel to be injected is limited by a governor. This device limits the air/fuel ratio for a diesel engine up to a maximum of 10 to 1 by weight. The air/fuel ratio of a typical gasoline engine is approximately 14.7 to 1 by weight.

Combustion Cycle

Combustion in a diesel engine occurs in four sequential stages or periods: the delay period, the uncontrolled-burning period, the controlled-burning period, and the after-burning period (Figure 25–39). When the fuel is first injected into the combustion chamber, there is an initial delay as the fuel changes from a liquid state to a vapor or gas state. This liquid-to-vapor conversion is necessary so the fuel burns. The delay period is followed by a period of uncontrolled burning of the fuel already injected into the chamber. This period is followed by a controlled-burning period as the injector continues to feed fuel into the combustion chamber. If and when the fuel injection stops, all the

FIGURE 25–38 Location of the idle speed and air/fuel mixture screws in a CIS arrangement.

FIGURE 25–39 Four stages of diesel engine combustion.

remaining fuel in the chamber continues to burn until it is consumed. This stage is known as the after-burning period. In the diesel engine, these periods of combustion simultaneously occur in different parts of the combustion chamber during injection.

The combustion of diesel fuel is not identical under all conditions. Combustion is affected by the following.

◆ Injector timing
◆ Length of time (or pulse width) of injection
◆ Position of injector nozzle
◆ Injection pressure
◆ Vaporization of fuel
◆ Distribution of fuel in the combustion chamber

The moment fuel is injected into the cylinder it is ignited. Therefore, the fuel injection pump utilized by the diesel engine system must inject the fuel at the precise instant when the piston is nearing the TDC position of its compression stroke.

DIESEL FUEL SYSTEM COMPONENTS

The diesel fuel injection system contains the following components (Figure 25–40).

◆ Fuel tank and pick-up unit
◆ Fuel lines
◆ Fuel pump system
◆ Fuel filter
◆ Water-in-fuel sensor (some systems)
◆ Water-in-fuel separator (some systems)
◆ Fuel heater (some systems)
◆ Injection nozzles

Pump Assembly

A diesel engine fuel pump assembly or system combines most of the functions of gasoline fuel injection, plus the timing functions of a spark ignition system. The assembly must precisely meter fuel at high pressures. Several different types of pump systems are used.

DISTRIBUTOR PUMPS Some distributor pump designs are a single unit, made up of a supply pump, governor, and injection pump. The supply pump draws the fuel from the fuel tank and delivers it to the distributor pump housing. The injection pump then increases the fuel pressure to the levels needed for the combustion. The **governor** controls the speed of the engine.

Other designs contain a transfer pump, governor, and injection pump within the distributor pump housing. This design also uses an external supply pump to deliver fuel to the transfer pump. The transfer pump increases fuel pressure and passes the fuel on to the injection pump where it is further pressurized for injection into the cylinders.

IN-LINE PUMPS This type of pump uses a separate injection pump for each cylinder.

Injection Pump Timing The injection pump is synchronized or timed to the engine's crankshaft through drive gears. The pump is designed to create or build up high fuel pressure (15,000 psi to as high as 30,000 psi). This allows the diesel fuel to be injected into the cylinder as a fine mist or spray. As a mist, the fuel rapidly evaporates when it is introduced to the high-pressure, high-temperature air charge in the cylinder and allows for ignition of the fuel. In order for the engine to operate smoothly, the following fuel injection conditions must exist.

FIGURE 25–40 Diesel fuel system schematic.

◆ Pressure must be available at the precise instant of fuel injection into the chamber.

◆ Injection rate must be equal for all cylinders so there are equal power pulses from each cylinder.

◆ Pressure must shut off at the precise instant to control the total amount of fuel to be injected.

Distributor Injection Pumps A distributor injection pump is driven by the engine's crankshaft by timing gears. These gears drive the pump's rotor, which is fitted into a close-tolerance bore. There are two types of distributor pumps. One type uses two plungers that operate in a cross-drilled bore in the distributor rotor. The other type uses a single plunger. The two-plunger design allows the plungers to move outward and opposite each other when the pump chamber is filled with fuel. The plungers are forced together by internal cam lobes. This reduces the size of the chamber and forces fuel through the injectors. Typical cam plunger movement in a distributor injection pump is shown in Figure 25–41.

As the rotor turns, the holes in the rotor and the pump's head align with each other and allow fuel to flow between the rotor and the head. When the holes are misaligned, fuel flow stops. The holes in both

components are referred to as ports. Two types of ports are utilized: charging ports and discharging ports. When the charging ports are aligned, the pump chamber fills with fuel. When the discharging ports are aligned, fuel injection takes place.

A vane transfer pump draws and pushes fuel through passages in the pump's head to a fuel metering valve. The size of the opening in the metering valve is controlled by the accelerator pedal acting through a governor. A small opening in the valve is maintained at idle speed. Depressing the accelerator causes the valve opening to increase. When maximum engine speed is attained or an overspeed condition exists, the governor takes over and automatically begins to close the valve.

Fuel from the metering valve is routed to the charging ports on the distributor injection pump. As the fuel enters the pump, it forces the plungers outward or away from each other. At idle speed the metering valve is almost closed. Very little fuel is routed to the pump chamber. This forces the plungers slightly outward, partially charging the chamber. Depressing the accelerator pump causes more fuel to enter the chamber and forces the plungers farther apart. As the rotor turns, the charging ports on the

FIGURE 25–41 Cam plunger movement in a distributor injection pump.

rotor and the hydraulic head misalign, effectively closing the ports. Continued rotation of the rotor then aligns the discharge ports of both components. At this time, the plungers are forced or pushed inward by the rollers contacting the cam lobes. As the plungers move together, the fuel is forced out of the pump chamber into the fuel lines to the injectors. Fuel is prevented from dripping into the combustion chamber after the injection cycle by a delivery valve.

The quality of fuel delivered by the distributor injection pump is directly proportional to the amount of fuel entering the pump chamber through the metering valve. Fuel injection timing is controlled by an internal time-advance mechanism. Timing is altered by rotating an internal cam ring in the rotor and head assembly. A pin in the auto-advance unit is connected to the internal cam and is located between a spring and piston. Fuel pressure from the transfer pump pushes the piston toward the spring and moves the pin. Movement of the pin moves the cam in an advance direction. As the engine speed increases, transfer pump fuel pressure increases, and the timing advances accordingly.

Unused injection fuel from the transfer pump is vented back to the fuel tank through the governor housing. It is also used to lubricate and cool the internal components of the distributor injection pump.

In-Line Injection Pump The multicylinder in-line injection pump (Figure 25–42) has a plunger and barrel assembly for each engine cylinder. The assemblies are grouped together in one housing that resembles cylinders in the block of an in-line engine. A high-pressure fuel line connects each pump assembly to one injector. The pump delivers or pumps an equal amount of fuel on each stroke.

The in-line injection pump used on automotive diesel engines is lubricated with engine oil. The pump does not have a seal around the cam drive end bearing, so the oil returns to the engine through the bearing.

Injection Nozzles

The fuel injection nozzle is designed to vaporize and direct the metered fuel into the combustion chamber. The injection pump forces the required fuel into the injection nozzle at the precise time it is needed. The design of the combustion chamber usually dictates the type of nozzle used, the droplet size, and the spray pattern required for optimum combustion in the given time frame and space. A typical injection nozzle is shown in Figure 25–43.

The typical injection nozzle has small openings, so the pressure can build up under some operating conditions. A spring-loaded needle valve in the injector nozzle keeps the opening of the nozzle closed

FIGURE 25–42   Typical in-line injection pump.

until the pressure reaches the operating level. The fuel pressure opens the nozzle valve and the spring closes it. Fuel from the injection pump enters and pressurizes the fuel lines and the pressure chamber. When the force on the lift area is greater than the set spring force on the spindle, the needle valve lifts off

its seat and rests with its upper shoulder against the face of the holder body. Fuel in a mist or spray-type pattern is then forced out into the combustion chamber. The pattern is determined by the type of tip used on the injector nozzle.

Only the tip of the injection nozzle protrudes into the combustion chamber. Two types of injector tips are used on diesel engines: the hole type and the pintle type. Open combustion chambers use the hole type (Figure 25–44), but it is also used on a few

FIGURE 25–43   Parts of a diesel injection nozzle.

■ **HIGH-PRESSURE FUEL**   ▨ **LOW-PRESSURE FUEL**

FIGURE 25–44   Hole injection nozzle.

NOZZLE   NEEDLE VALVE

ANNULAR GROOVE

STEM

INLET PASSAGE

TRUNK

EXPOSED ANNULAR AREA

NEEDLE VALVE

PRESSURE CHAMBER   PINTLE

FIGURE 25–45 Pintle injection nozzle.

engines with divided combustion chambers. The pintle type tip (Figure 25–45) is used only on engines with a divided combustion chamber.

Governors

Gasoline engines are self-governing because the air entering the engine is controlled by the use of a carburetor throttle valve or by the throttle body in a fuel injected system. The driver can change engine speed by manipulating the throttle pedal.

Because of this method, in most cases, the gasoline engine has no need for a governor. If such an engine is equipped with a governor mechanism, it is for the sole purpose of limiting the maximum road speed of the vehicle and the engine rpm to prevent engine abuse or avoid poor fuel economy.

The diesel engine, on the other hand, operates with an excessive amount of unthrottled air throughout its operating speed range. The fuel injection system is separately controlled from the airflow system. When a diesel engine is started, the air is unthrottled and remains so as the driver opens the fuel control mechanism or throttle linkage to allow the injection system to inject more fuel into the cylinders. Without some form of fuel control, the diesel engine can accelerate very rapidly and self-destruct, especially if the throttle were to be placed in the full-fuel position and left there with no mechanism to regulate the fuel input.

Therefore, a governor is required on diesel engines to regulate the fuel input and prevent engine stalling at the low-speed end and from overspeeding at the high-speed end. The governor controls the speed of the engine.

At minimum speed or idle, the governor controls pump injections, so the engine gets just enough fuel to keep it running. At maximum rpm, the governor controls pump injection to limit fuel flow to keep the engine from overspeeding. At intermediate speeds, the pump responds to movements of the accelerator pedal so the driver can control car speed directly.

During coasting, the governor can cut off fuel delivery for economy. See Figure 25–46 for the operation of a typical governor.

Starting Devices

Since diesel fuel does not vaporize or ignite as readily as gasoline, starting devices are required on diesel engines. These include glow plugs, fuel heaters, and engine block heaters.

Glow plugs (Figure 25–47), located in the combustion chamber, preheat the air and fuel during cranking (or prior to cranking depending on the system design). In colder climates, engine block heaters are used to heat the engine's coolant, which in turn keeps the cylinder block and head at a temperature suitable for starting purposes. A fuel heater preheats the fuel electrically before it reaches the filter. The heater, usually thermostatically controlled, is a resistance type designed to heat the fuel before it enters the filter. This reduces the possibility of wax plugging the filter, which usually occurs when the fuel temperature is 20°F or lower.

A glow plug is a low-voltage heating element that is inserted into the precombustion chamber on the intake manifold. The plug is usually controlled by the ignition switch. However, other design applications might have a separate on-off switch within the passenger compartment. The glow plug is energized only until the air in the combustion chamber is adequately heated and can support ignition at startup. The energized or heating period for a glow plug is directly dependent upon how fast the plug can heat up and what the ambient temperature of the combustion chamber is. Most glow plugs work off the car's 12-volt system.

A control module is the heart of the glow plug system (Figure 25–48). The module senses the engine's coolant temperature and de-energizes the glow plugs when the coolant is sufficiently heated after start-up. Other design variations might use a cycling type of relay to pulse the glow plugs on and off. This type of system usually has a manual on-off switch to control the cycling relay.

Fuel Pick-up

The fuel pick-up is similar to the conventional gasoline pick-up, containing a fuel-level sending unit and a strainer. However, different features are added to accommodate the characteristics of diesel fuel and the diesel fuel system.

One type of pick-up unit uses a fuel pick-up filter (sock) and check valve assembly (Figure 25–49). The sock strains large particles, limits entry of water, and draws fuel from the bottom up to the pick-up tube,

FIGURE 25–46 Governor operation in a diesel fuel injection system: (A) During starting, the metering sleeve is pushed farthest from bottom dead center, resulting in a longer injection period. (B) As engine speed increases, the weights push the governor sleeve to the right, which moves the metering sleeve to the left and shortens the injection period. (C) Depressing the accelerator moves the metering sleeve to the right, which causes more fuel to be injected. (D) Maximum engine speed is governed by limiting fuel delivery as during idle.

acting as a wick. A check valve is added to the sock. It is designed to open when the sock is restricted by wax or ice, allowing the engine to run. This type of pick-up unit is usually equipped with a water-in-fuel sensor since the sock holds back only a certain amount of water before it passes and this system may not have a water-in-fuel separator.

Another type of pick-up unit places the fuel intake in contact with the bottom of the tank supported by several small nibs. Fuel going past the nibs accelerates, creating a pressure drop. This pressure drop attracts water. Water in the diesel fuel is drawn

to the intake, accelerated, and forced through the nylon screen with the fuel. Using this type of pick-up unit necessitates a water-in-fuel separator to filter and eliminate the water. This pick-up unit also has low placement of the return line and a by-pass valve in the event the intake is clogged with wax or ice. With either pick-up unit, the tank must be at least one-quarter full for the by-pass valve to pick up fuel.

Fuel Filters

To protect the fuel injection system of a diesel engine, good filtration is essential. The clearances between

FIGURE 25–47 Cutaway view of a glow plug.

injector parts require close control of solids in the fuel. To avoid erosion and wear, solids must not pass between closely mated injector parts. The primary filter, on the suction side of the transfer pump, protects the system from large solid contaminants. Most of the water in the fuel is also removed by this filter. The secondary filter is located between the transfer pump and the fuel injectors. Since the filter is located on the discharge side of the pump, the pressure drop across the secondary filter can be much higher than on a filter located on the suction side of the pump. This allows the secondary filter to be made in a compact size using a fine filtering media that controls the size of particles allowed to pass into the fuel injectors. It also stops any water that might have passed through the primary filter.

Water Separator

A common diesel fuel problem is water in the fuel. Some vehicles are equipped with a water separator (Figure 25–50) in the fuel system. A fuel water separator works much like a filter, except that the element is replaced by a baffle. When contaminated fuel enters the separator, the heavier water settles at the bottom, while the light fuel rises to the top. A drain plug or

FIGURE 25–48 Electrical schematic of a glow plug system.

FIGURE 25–49 Combination fuel pick-up/fuel level indicator/water sensor.

FIGURE 25–50 Diesel fuel filter/water separator.

petcock in the bottom of the separator allows the accumulated water to be drained periodically.

Fuel Lines

The fuel lines that carry the highly pressurized diesel fuel between the injection pump and fuel injectors are manufactured from special, thick-walled steel tubing. The fuel lines are of equal length to ensure that each cylinder receives an identical or equal fuel charge.

DIESEL FUEL INJECTION ELECTRONIC CONTROL

Like gasoline fuel injection systems, diesel injection systems also use computer controls to monitor and activate various input (sensor) and output devices (Figure 25–51).

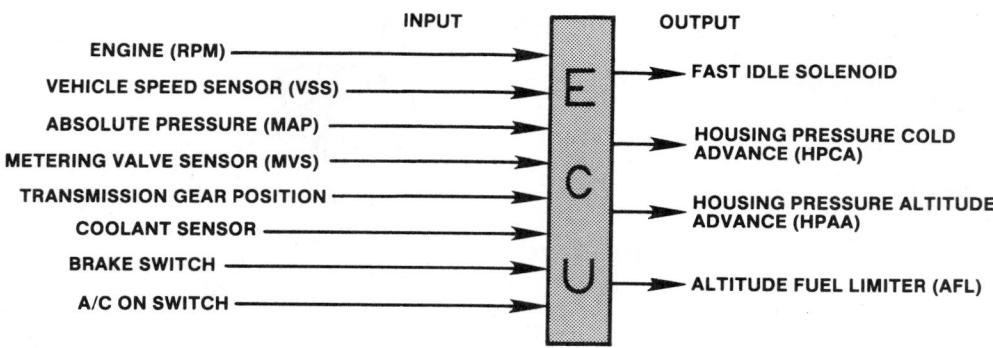

FIGURE 25–51 An electronic control system regulates the diesel fuel injection system.

Input data includes engine rpm, vehicle speed, manifold absolute pressure (MAP), metering valve position, transmission gear position, coolant temperature, and brake and air-conditioning operation.

The electronic control module or unit processes this data and signals various output devices to control engine performance and operation. These output devices include the following.

FAST-IDLE SOLENOID The fast-idle solenoid operates at temperatures below 100° and above 248°F. As the plunger of the solenoid moves, it increases spring pressure on the governor, thereby slightly increasing engine speed.

HOUSING PRESSURE COLD AND ALTITUDE ADVANCE These solenoid-operated mechanisms advance the fuel injection pump on a cold engine and at higher altitudes. This helps reduce engine noise and emissions.

ALTITUDE FUEL LIMITER This solenoid limits the travel of the metering valve at wide open throttle at altitudes above 4,000 feet.

METERING VALVE SENSOR The variable resistor sensor sends a variable voltage signal to the ECU indicating metering valve position.

CASE STUDY

A *customer brings in a late-model GM auto-mobile, with a 2.0L port fuel injected engine, and complains of poor performance and fuel economy. It is also mentioned that the ser-vice-engine-soon light had been on for some time.*

Diagnosis of the problem begins with a visual inspection of the engine, including all hoses and wiring connectors. No problems are found.

Next, a scan tool is connected to the ECU and code 45 is retrieved from the computer's memory. The technician uses a code interpretation list to find a rich exhaust signal is coming from the oxygen sensor.

At first, the technician suspects a faulty oxygen sensor. By referring to the service manual, she finds that this code is set when the oxygen sensor signal to the control computer (ECU) is greater than 0.75 volt for 50 seconds and the system is in closed loop. Keep in mind that a faulty sensor is open, shorted, or has high resistance. An open sensor circuit or sensor would cause the engine to operate in open loop, not in closed loop. A short would cause high amperage, which would do physical damage to the wires and/or ECU. But, the visual inspection did not locate any damage. Excessive resistance in the circuit would cause voltages to be lower. The problem here is higher voltages. Therefore, it is unlikely that the problem is caused by a faulty sensor or sensor wiring harness. To locate the cause of the problem more testing is needed.

Following the appropriate troubleshooting tree, testing continues with the scan tool and reveals that the problem could be caused by an open in the ignition wiring, a saturated charcoal canister, a faulty MAP sensor or fuel pressure regulator, or by the improper use of RTV sealer. Detailed inspection and testing of these reveals the cause of the problem: a ruptured vacuum diaphragm in the fuel injection system's pressure regulator that allowed the excessive fuel pressure and a rich mixture.

The regulator is replaced, and the codes are cleared. The problem is corrected. To verify the repair, the technician runs the engine and observes the scan tool to make sure the engine went into closed loop and that no codes were set by the computer.

KEY TERMS

CIS	Mass airflow sensor
CIS-E	MIL
ECU	Mixture control unit
EFI	MPI
Frequency valve	Noid
Fuel accumulator	PFI
Fuel distributor	Pintle
Fuel pressure regulator	Prefeed pump
Fuel rail	SFI
Glow plug	Speed density
Governor	TBI
IAC	Thermo-time switch
Injector pulse width	Warm-up regulator
Lambda sensor	

SUMMARY

- There are two types of electronic fuel injection systems: throttle body and port injection. In the throttle body injection system, fuel is delivered to a central point. In the port injection system, there is one injector at each cylinder.
- Port injection systems use one of four firing systems: grounded single fire, grouped double fire, simultaneous double fire, or sequential fire.
- The electronic fuel injection system includes a fuel delivery system, system sensors, electronic control unit, and fuel injectors.
- The volume airflow sensor and mass airflow sensor determine the amount of air entering the engine. The MAP sensor measures changes in the intake manifold pressure that results from changes in engine load and speed.
- The heart of the fuel injection system is the electronic control unit. The ECU receives signals from all the system sensors, processes them, and transmits programmed electrical pulses to the fuel injectors.
- Two types of fuel injectors are currently in use: top feed and bottom feed. Top-feed injectors are used in port injection systems. Bottom-feed injectors are used in throttle body injection systems.
- Two methods are used to control idle speed on engines equipped with fuel injection: an auxiliary air valve and an idle speed solenoid.
- While some electronic control elements are being added to the basic system, continuous injection systems (CIS) meter fuel delivery mechanically not electronically.
- CIS injectors spray fuel constantly. They do not pulse on and off. The proper air/fuel mixture is attained by varying the amount of fuel delivered to the injectors.
- Continuous injection systems can be fitted with an oxygen sensor, or lambda sensor, for feedback control. Signals from the oxygen sensor are sent to the oxygen control unit. The oxygen control valve operates on signals from the oxygen control unit.
- Troubleshooting electronic fuel injection systems requires systematic step-by-step test procedures. Using a hit-or-miss approach can be frustrating, time-consuming, and costly.
- If any EFI system three things must occur. First, an adequate air supply must be supplied for the air/fuel mixture. Second, a pressurized fuel supply must be delivered to properly operating injectors. Finally, the injectors must receive a trigger signal from the control computer.
- When checking out the EFI, the air system should be checked first. Then, check the fuel system. The injectors are checked last. Servicing CIS requires the same logical approach and preliminary checks used in troubleshooting EFI systems.
- Diesel fuel injection systems operate under very high fuel and air pressures. The output power of a diesel engine is directly proportional to the fuel charge injected into the combustion chamber. A governor is used to limit the amount of fuel that can be injected. This limits engine speed and power output to levels that do not damage engine components.
- The injection pump is the heart of the diesel fuel injection system. The pump is driven off the engine's crankshaft to control injection timing. The pump is capable of generating the 15,000 to 30,000 psi fuel pressures needed and metering precise amounts of fuel to each injector.

TECH MANUAL

The following procedures are included in Chapter 25 of the *Tech Manual* that accompanies this book:

1. *Perform a fuel injector balance test.*
2. *Clean fuel injectors.*

REVIEW QUESTIONS

1. Explain the major differences between throttle body fuel injection and port fuel injection systems.

2. What is meant by sequential firing of fuel injectors?

3. Describe the purpose of the idle speed solenoid and auxiliary air valve.

4. Describe the purpose of a manifold absolute pressure (MAP) sensor.

5. Describe the basic differences between gasoline fuel injection and diesel fuel injection systems.

6. Which of the following is *not* an advantage that fuel injection offers over carburetion?
   a. leaner air/fuel ratios
   b. better fuel economy
   c. no choke requirements
   d. lower engine torque

7. The length of time that an injector is energized is called ____.
   a. intermittent system
   b. pulsed system
   c. injector pulse width
   d. open loop mode

8. Explain the causes and results of high fuel pressure in a TBI, MFI, or SFI system.

9. While discussing EFI systems, Technician A says the ECU provides the proper air/fuel ratio by controlling the fuel pressure. Technician B says the ECU provides the proper air/fuel ratio by controlling injector pulse width. Who is correct?
   a. Technician A
   b. Technician B
   c. Both A and B
   d. Neither A nor B

10. Technician A performs an injector pressure balance test by activating each injector with an electronic pulse tester. Technician B performs the same test by momentarily applying 12 volts to the injector terminals to activate the injector. Whose method is correct?
   a. Technician A
   b. Technician B
   c. Both A and B
   d. Neither A nor B

11. Bottom-feed injectors are used in ____.
   a. throttle body injection systems
   b. port injection systems
   c. both a and b
   d. neither a nor b

12. While discussing cold start injector systems, Technician A says the cold start injector is operated by a thermo-time switch. Technician B says the cold-start injector is operated by the ECU.

Who is correct?
   a. Technician A
   b. Technician B
   c. Both A and B
   d. Neither A nor B

13. Fuel tubing and hoses should be replaced at least every ____.
   a. year
   b. two years
   c. three years
   d. five years

14. While discussing the causes of higher-than-specified idle speeds, Technician A says an intake manifold vacuum leak may cause a high idle speed. Technician B says if the TPS voltage signal is higher than specified, the idle speed may be higher than normal. Who is correct?
   a. Technician A
   b. Technician B
   c. Both A and B
   d. Neither A nor B

15. An injector balance test produces a pressure drop variation of 2 psi. Technician A says this is acceptable and, therefore, no cause for concern. Technician B says it is a cause for concern. Who is correct?
   a. Technician A
   b. Technician B
   c. Both A and B
   d. Neither A nor B

16. As an alternative to an injector power balance test, Technician A uses a stethoscope to listen for correct operation. Technician B uses a thin steel rod for the same purpose. Who is correct?
   a. Technician A
   b. Technician B
   c. Both A and B
   d. Neither A nor B

17. Which of the following should be done as a preliminary step before attempting an idle adjustment of a fuel injection system?
   a. blocking the drive wheels
   b. connecting a tachometer
   c. checking and adjusting base ignition timing
   d. all of the above

18. An airflow sensor plate that is off-center in its bore can allow air to leak by, causing ____ problems.
   a. idling
   b. cold start
   c. hot start
   d. preignition

19. The governor on a diesel fuel injection system is responsible for ____.
   a. injection timing
   b. injection timing advance
   c. fuel metering
   d. both a and b

20. To relieve fuel pressure on an EFI car, Technician A connects a pressure gauge to the fuel rail. Technician B disables the fuel pump and runs the car until it dies. Who is correct?
   a. Technician A
   b. Technician B
   c. Both A and B
   d. Neither A nor B

EMISSION CONTROL SYSTEMS

26

OBJECTIVES

◆ *Name and describe the three kinds of emissions being controlled in gasoline engines.* ◆ *Name the three major types of emission control systems used on modern vehicles.* ◆ *Describe the inspection and replacement of PCV system parts.* ◆ *Explain the operation of the EGR valve and the function of the various EGR system controls.* ◆ *Describe typical EGR system problems and EGR valve and system testing procedures.* ◆ *Describe the function and operation of the two types of air injection systems.* ◆ *Describe the secondary air system's operation and efficiency test.* ◆ *Name the components of an evaporative emission control system.* ◆ *Describe the testing of the canister and of the canister purge valve.* ◆ *Operate a four-gas exhaust analyzer to check emission levels.* ◆ *Diagnose the cause of high levels of HC, CO, and O_2, as well as low levels of CO_2.*

The three kinds of emissions that are being controlled in gasoline engines today are unburned hydrocarbons, carbon monoxide, and oxides of nitrogen.

Unburned hydrocarbons (**HC**) are particles, usually vapors, of gasoline that have not been burned during combustion. They are present in the exhaust and in crankcase vapors. Of course, any raw gas that evaporates out of the tank or carburetor is classed as HC.

Carbon monoxide (**CO**) is a poisonous chemical compound of carbon and oxygen. It forms in the engine when there is not enough oxygen to combine with the carbon during combustion. When there is enough oxygen in the mixture, carbon dioxide (**CO_2**) is formed. CO_2 is not a pollutant. It is the gas used by plants to manufacture oxygen. CO is found in the exhaust principally but can also be in the crankcase.

Oxides of nitrogen (**NO_x**; pronounced *nox*) are various compounds of nitrogen and oxygen. Both of these gases are present in the air used for combustion. They are formed in the cylinders during combustion and are part of exhaust gas. NO_x is the principle chemical that causes smog.

The federal government has set standards for these pollutants. The exceptions to these standards are a few high-altitude western states and California. Because there is less oxygen at high altitudes to promote combustion, emission standards at high altitudes are slightly less strict. Because of the dense population of the state, California's standards allow less pollution than federal standards. Many states have followed California's mandate and have instituted emission standards of the same levels as California.

Automobile manufacturers have been working toward reduction of automotive air pollutants since the early 1950s, when auto emissions were found to be part of the cause of smog in Los Angeles. Governmental interest in controlling emissions developed around the same time.

In late 1959, California established the first standards for automotive emissions. In 1967, the Federal Clean Air Act was amended to provide for federal standards to apply to motor vehicles.

The first source of emissions to be brought under control was the crankcase. Positive crankcase ventilation systems (PCV) to route these vapors back to the engine intake manifold were developed and incorporated into 1961 cars and light trucks sold in California. These systems were installed on all cars nationwide beginning with the 1963 models.

Control of unburned hydrocarbons and carbon monoxide in the engine exhaust was the next major development. An air injection reactor (**AIR**) system was built into cars and light trucks sold in California in 1966. Other systems, including the controlled combustion system (**CCS**), were developed and used nationwide in 1968. Further improvements in years following improved combustion to reduce hydrocarbon and carbon monoxide emissions.

Fuel vapors from the gasoline tank and the carburetor float bowl were brought under control with the introduction of evaporation control systems. These systems were first installed in 1970 model cars sold in California and in most domestic-made cars beginning with 1971 models.

Most vehicle manufacturers started to provide emission control systems that reduced oxides of nitrogen as early as 1970. The exhaust gas recirculation system used on some 1972 models was used extensively for 1973 models when federal standards for oxides of nitrogen took effect.

Present government goals call for a 98 percent reduction of unburned hydrocarbons, a 97 percent reduction of carbon monoxide, and a 90 percent reduction of oxides of nitrogen compared to precontrolled cars.

In 1994, California specified emission standards for transitional low emission vehicles (**TLEV**). In 1997, this same program specifies a further reduction in emission levels for low emission vehicles (**LEV**), and in the year 2000, emission levels are specified for ultra low emission vehicles (**ULEV**).

In 1998, California emission regulations require 2 percent of the cars sold in the state to be zero emission vehicles (**ZEV**). With present technology, only electric vehicles will meet the ZEV standards. Some other states have adopted, or are considering the adoption of, the California emission standards. The percentage of ZEVs increases in the years 2003 and 2005.

EMISSIONS TESTING

The first Clean Air Act prompted Californians to create the California Air Research Board (**California ARB**). California ARB's purpose was to implement strict air standards. These became the standard for federal mandates. One of the approaches by the ARB to clean the air was to start periodic motor vehicle inspection (**PMVI**). The purpose for the PMVI (or inspection and maintenance or **I/M**) is to inspect a vehicle's emission controls once a year. This inspection included a tailpipe emissions test and an underhood inspection. The tailpipe test certifies that the vehicle's exhaust emissions are within the limits set by law. The underhood and/or vehicle inspection verifies that the pollution control equipment has not been tampered with or disconnected.

The 1970 Clean Air Act made it illegal for professional mechanics to remove, disconnect, or tamper with factory emission controls. The law did not make it illegal for the owner of the vehicle to make the emission control devices inoperable. The Clean Air Act was revised in 1990 and it made it illegal for anyone to remove, disconnect, or tamper with emission controls on any vehicle that would be used on public roads.

Today, California is not the only state that requires annual emissions testing. Many states have incorporated an emissions test with their annual vehicle registration procedures. Most states have or are planning to implement the I/M 240 program, which was first implemented in California. The I/M 240 tests the emissions of a vehicle while it is operating under a variety of load conditions. This is an improvement over exhaust testing during idle and high speed with no load.

The I/M 240 test requires the use of a chassis (road) dynonameter, commonly called a **dyno**. While on the dyno, the vehicle is operated for 240 seconds and under different load conditions. The test drive on the dyno simulates both in-traffic and highway driving and stopping. The emissions tester tracks the exhaust quality through these conditions.

The I/M 240 program also includes a functional test of the evaporative emission control devices and a visual inspection of the total emission control system. If the vehicle fails the test, it must be repaired and certified before it can be registered.

The exhaust analyzer typically used to certify vehicles is an infrared tester. An infrared tester that has been approved to certify exhaust levels must meet specific standards, such as California BAR-80, ETI-80, or BAR-90.

DEVELOPMENT OF EMISSION CONTROL DEVICES

One of the most important developments for lowering emission levels has been the availability and use of unleaded gasolines. Beginning with 1971, cars have been designed to operate on unleaded fuels.

Removing lead from gasoline brings some immediate benefits. It eliminates the emission of lead particles from automobile's exhaust. It increases spark plug life—also important from an emission standpoint. It avoids formation of lead deposits in the combustion chambers that tend to increase hydrocarbon emissions.

The catalytic converter, a later development, provided a means for oxidizing the carbon monoxide and hydrocarbon emissions in the engine exhaust, a process that lowers the amount of these pollutants. Beginning with the 1975 model year, passenger cars and light trucks have been equipped with converters.

Three basic types of emission control systems are used in modern vehicles: precombustion, post-combustion, and evaporating control systems.

Most of the pollution control systems used today prevent emissions from being created in the engine, either during or before the combustion cycle. The common **precombustion control** systems are as follows:

- Positive Crankcase Ventilation (PCV). The PCV system removes pollutants that blow by the pistons into the crankcase and recirculates them into the induction system.
- Engine Modification Systems. These systems improve combustion and reduce HC-CO in the exhaust. They include a heated primary air system, air/fuel control changes, engine breathing refinements, and some spark timing controls.
- Exhaust Gas Recirculating (EGR) Systems. EGR reduces NO_x by diluting the air/fuel mixture with some exhaust gas, which does not burn.

Postcombustion control systems clean up the exhaust gases after the fuel has been burned. Secondary air or air injector systems put fresh air into the exhaust to reduce HC and CO to harmless water vapor and carbon dioxide by chemical (thermal) reaction with oxygen in the air. Catalytic converters help this process. Most catalysts now reduce NO_x as well as HC-CO.

The **evaporative control** system is a sealed system. It traps the fuel vapors (HC) that would normally escape from the fuel tank and carburetor into the air.

PCV SYSTEMS

During the last part of the engine's combustion stroke, some unburned fuel and products of combustion—water vapor, for instance—leak past the engine's piston rings into the crankcase.

This leakage into the engine crankcase is called **blowby**. Blowby must be removed from the engine before it condenses in the crankcase and reacts with the oil to form sludge. Sludge, if allowed to circulate with engine oil, corrodes and accelerates wear of pistons, piston rings, valves, bearings, and other internal working parts of the engine. Blowby gases must also be removed from the crankcase to prevent premature oil leaks. Because these gases enter the crankcase by the pressure formed during combustion, they pressurize the crankcase. The gases exert pressure on the oil pan gasket and crankshaft seals. If the pressure is not relieved, oil is eventually forced out of these seals.

Because the air/fuel mixture in an engine never completely burns, blowby also carries some unburned fuel into the crankcase. If not removed, the unburned fuel dilutes the crankcase oil. When oil is diluted with gasoline, it does not lubricate the engine properly, which causes excessive wear.

Combustion gases that enter the crankcase are removed by a positive crankcase ventilation (PCV) system, which uses engine vacuum to draw fresh air through the crankcase. This fresh air, which dissipates the harmful gases, enters through the air filter or through a separate PCV breather filter located on the inside of the air filter housing. System operation is shown in Figure 26–1. Because the vacuum supply for the PCV system is from the engine's intake manifold, the airflow through this system must be controlled in such a way that it varies in proportion to the regular air/fuel ratio being drawn into the intake manifold. Otherwise, the additional air that is drawn into the system would cause the air/fuel mixture to become too lean for efficient engine operation. Therefore, a PCV valve is placed in the flow just before the intake manifold to regulate the flow according to vacuum.

The positive crankcase ventilation system has two major functions. It prevents the emission of blowby gases from the engine crankcase to the atmosphere. These gases were once vented through a road draft tube. Now they are recirculated to the engine intake and burned during combustion. It also scavenges the crankcase of vapors that could dilute the oil and cause it to deteriorate or that could build undesirable pressure in the crankcase. Fresh air from the air cleaner mixes with these vapors and makes them flow to the intake.

The PCV system benefits the vehicle's driveability by eliminating harmful crankcase gases, reducing air pollution, and promoting fuel economy.

Note that an inoperative PCV system could shorten the life of the engine by allowing harmful blowby gases to remain in the engine, causing corrosion, and accelerating wear.

PCV System Diagnosis and Service Procedures

No adjustments can be made to the PCV system. Service of the system involves a careful inspection, operation, and replacement of faulty parts. When replacing a PCV valve, match the part number on the valve with the vehicle maker's specifications for the proper valve. If the valve cannot be identified, refer to the part number listed in the manufacturer's service manual.

The first step of PCV servicing is a visual inspection. As shown in Figure 26–2, the PCV valve can be located in several places. The most common location is in a rubber grommet in the valve or rocker arm cover (Figure 26–2A). It can be installed in the mid-

2. **FLOWS THROUGH CLOSURE HOSE**
1. **FRESH AIR FROM AIR CLEANER**
7. **PCV VALVE CONTROLS RATE OF FLOW INTO INTAKE MANIFOLD**
3. **THROUGH VALVE COVER**
AIR CLEANER
6. **TO PCV VALVE**
MANIFOLD
ROCKER COVER
5. **FRESH AIR AND BLOWBY GASES FLOW**
NORMAL OPERATION: IDLE, CRUISE, LIGHT ACCELERATION
4. **AND INTO CRANKCASE**
A

5. **FILTER PAD IN AIR CLEANER PREVENTS OIL CONTAMINATION OF INLET**
4. **THESE GASES JOIN INTAKE AIR**
3. **PART OF GASES FLOW THROUGH CLOSURE HOSE TO AIR CLEANER**
2. **PART OF BLOWBY GASES FLOW THROUGH PCV VALVE TO INTAKE**
HEAVY ACCELERATION OR HIGH SPEED
1. **HIGH VOLUME OF BLOWBY GAS CAUSES PRESSURE BUILDUP IN CRANKCASE**
B

FIGURE 26–1   (A) Fresh airflow during normal operation: idle, cruise, and light acceleration; (B) during heavy acceleration or high speed.

dle of the hose connections (Figure 26–2B), as well as installed directly in the intake manifold (Figure 26–2C).

Once the PCV valve is located, inspect the system by using the following procedure.

PROCEDURES
PCV System Inspection

1. Make sure all the PCV system hoses are properly connected and have no breaks or cracks.
2. Remove the air cleaner and inspect the carburetor or fuel injector air filter. Crankcase blowby can clog these with oil. Clean or replace such filters. Oil in the air cleaner assembly indicates that the PCV valve or hoses are plugged. Make sure you check these and replace the valve and clean the hoses and air cleaner assembly.
3. Check the crankcase inlet air filter, which is usually located in the air cleaner (Figure 26–3). As the filter does its job, it gets dirty. If it is oil soaked, it is a good indication that the PCV system is not working the way it should. When the filter becomes so dirty that it restricts the flow of clean air to the crankcase, it can cause the same problems as a clogged PCV valve. So be sure to check this particular filter when checking the PCV system and replace it as necessary.
4. Inspect for dirt deposits that could clog the passages in the manifold or carburetor base. These deposits can prevent the system from functioning properly, even though the PCV valve, valve filter, and hoses might not be clogged.

A

B

C HOSE TO AIR CLEANER

FIGURE 26–2 Various locations of the PCV valve.

4. Turn off the engine and remove the PCV valve. Shake the valve and listen for the rattle of the check needle inside the valve. If the valve does not rattle, replace it.

Proper operation of the PCV system depends on a sealed engine. Remember that the crankcase is sealed by the dipstick, valve cover, gaskets, and sealed filler cap. If oil sludging or dilution is noted and the PCV system is functioning properly, check the engine for oil leaks and correct them to ensure that the PCV system functions as intended. Also, be aware of the fact that a very worn engine may have more blowby than the PCV system can handle. If there are symptoms that indicate the PCV system is plugged (oil in air cleaner, saturated crankcase filter, etc.) but no restrictions are found, check the wear of the engine.

FIGURE 26–3 When inspecting the PCV system, check the PCV inlet filter in the air cleaner. *Courtesy of Ford Motor Company*

Functional Checks of PCV Valve A rough idling engine can signal a number of PCV valve problems, such as a clogged valve or a plugged hose. But before beginning the functional checks, double check the PCV valve part number to make certain the correct valve is installed. If the correct valve is being used, perform these functional checks.

1. Disconnect the PCV valve from the valve cover, intake manifold, or hose.
2. Start the engine and let it run at idle. If the PCV valve is not clogged, a hissing is heard as air passes through the valve.
3. Place a finger over the end of the valve to check for vacuum. If there is little or no vacuum at the valve, check for a plugged or restricted hose. Replace any plugged or deteriorated hoses.

EXHAUST GAS RECIRCULATING (EGR) SYSTEMS

Exhaust gas recirculating (EGR) systems reduce the amount of oxides of nitrogen emitted. The EGR system dilutes the air/fuel mixture with controlled amounts of exhaust gas. Since exhaust gas does not burn, this reduces the peak combustion temperatures. At lower combustion temperatures, very little of the nitrogen in the air combines with oxygen to form NO_x. Most of the nitrogen is simply carried out with the exhaust gases. For driveability/performance, it is desirable to have the EGR valve opening (and the amount of gas flow) proportional to the throttle opening. Driveability is also improved on most applications by shutting off the EGR when the engine is started up cold, at idle,

and at full throttle. Since the NO_x control requirements vary on different engines, there are several different systems, with various controls to provide these functions.

Most of these systems use a vacuum-operated EGR valve to regulate the exhaust gas flow into the intake manifold. Exhaust crossover passages under the intake manifold channel the exhaust gas to the valve. (Some in-line engines route the exhaust gas to the valve through an external tube.) Typical mounting of the EGR valve is either on a plate under the carburetor or directly on the manifold.

Figure 26–4 illustrates the basic valve design. The EGR valve is a vacuum-operated, flow control valve. On most systems, it is attached to a carburetor spacer. The carburetor spacer is sandwiched between the carburetor and intake manifold. Gaskets are used above and below the spacer to seal the EGR system and the carburetor-to-manifold air/fuel flow. A small exhaust crossover passage in the intake manifold admits exhaust gases to the spacer. These gases flow through the spacer to the inlet port of the EGR valve. Opening the EGR valve by control vacuum at the diaphragm allows exhaust gases to flow through the valve and back to another port of the spacer. Here, the exhaust gas mixes with the air/fuel mixture, leaving the carburetor and then entering the intake manifold. The effect is to dilute or lean-out the mixture so it still burns completely but with a reduction in combustion chamber temperatures.

EGR valve control vacuum is from either of two sources (Figure 26–5). In the port vacuum system, a

FIGURE 26–4 Typical vacuum-operated EGR valve.
Courtesy of Chevrolet Motor Division, General Motors Corporation

FIGURE 26–5 Different ways of controlling an EGR valve with vacuum.

FIGURE 26–6 Thermal vacuum switch.

vacuum line connects the EGR valve to a slot port in the carburetor throttle body above the throttle plate. When the throttle plate is closed, no vacuum is transmitted. The port is exposed to increasing manifold vacuum as the throttle plate opens. The exhaust gas flow rate depends on manifold vacuum, throttle position, and exhaust gas back pressure. In a venturi vacuum system, the vacuum that controls the EGR valve is drawn from a port in the carburetor venturi. A **vacuum amplifier** is needed to boost this weak vacuum to operate the EGR valve. While the exhaust gas flow rate depends mainly on engine intake flow, it is also affected by intake vacuum and exhaust.

The EGR system works when the engine reaches operating temperature or when the engine is operating under conditions other than idle or wide-open throttle. EGR systems include various functions that control the operation of the EGR valve. Some applications use cold engine EGR lockout and wide-open throttle EGR lockout. Basically, cold EGR lockout is necessary to keep the EGR valve closed during cold engine operation. Wide-open throttle EGR lockout might be required to keep the EGR valve closed when the engine is operating under maximum load. The following are various controls that relate directly to the EGR system.

THERMAL VACUUM SWITCH (TVS) The **TVS** senses the air temperature in the carburetor air cleaner to control vacuum to the EGR valve (Figure 26–6). When the engine reaches operating temperature, the TVS opens to supply vacuum to the EGR valve. This opens the EGR valve for exhaust gas recirculation.

PORTED VACUUM SWITCH (PVS) The **PVS** senses the coolant temperature to control vacuum to the EGR valve (Figure 26–7). The PVS operates in the same manner as the TVS, except it senses the coolant temperature instead of the air temperature. That is, the PVS function is to cut off vacuum to the EGR valve when the engine is cold and connect the vacuum to the EGR valve when the engine is warm.

VENTURI VACUUM AMPLIFIER (VVA) Some EGR systems use the VVA so the carburetor venturi vacuum can control the EGR valve operation (Figure 26–8). Venturi vacuum is more desirable because it is in proportion to the airflow through the carburetor. Since the venturi vacuum is a relatively weak vacuum signal, the VVA converts it to a strong enough signal to operate the EGR valve. The VVA system uses manifold vacuum for strength and venturi vacuum for the control signal.

EGR DELAY TIMER CONTROL Some vehicles have an EGR delay system, which consists of an electrical timer that connects to an engine-mounted solenoid. Together, the purpose of the delay timer and solenoid is to prevent EGR operation for a predetermined amount of time after warm engine startup. On cold engine startups, the TVS and PVS valves override the delay timer.

FIGURE 26–7 How the two-port PVS switch works.

FIGURE 26–8   Venturi vacuum amplifier circuit.

EARLY FUEL EVAPORATION/THERMAL VACUUM SWITCH (EGR—EFE/TVS)

In most common applications, the EFE uses a valve that increases the exhaust gas flow under the intake manifold during cold engine operation through a crossover passage to heat up the incoming air/fuel charge (Figure 26–9). The EFE is vacuum-operated and controlled by a TVS that applies vacuum to the EFE valve when the coolant temperature is low. Once the engine reaches operating temperature, the TVS blocks off vacuum to the EFE and directs it to the EGR valve for EGR operation.

WIDE-OPEN THROTTLE VALVE (WOT)

Some applications use the WOT valve where it is desirable to cut off EGR flow at wide-open throttle (Figure 26–10).

FIGURE 26–9   Early fuel evaporation/thermal vacuum switch. *Courtesy of Nissan Motors*

FIGURE 26–10   Wide-open throttle valve.

BACK PRESSURE TRANSDUCER

This device can be used to modulate, or change, the amount the EGR valve opens. It controls the amount of air bleed in the EGR vacuum line according to the level of exhaust gas pressure, which is dependent on engine rpm. The EGR valve can be closed or partially opened at different engine speeds. Air bleed is stopped completely when the exhaust back pressure is high. Thus, maximum EGR occurs during acceleration, when back pressure is high. When back pressure decreases, the vacuum line bleed is reopened. This decreases the vacuum at the EGR valve, which then reduces the amount of exhaust gas recirculated. In the past, the back pressure transducer was a separate unit. Now it is incorporated into the design of the EGR valve itself.

These various EGR system controls represent some of the common controls currently used by automobile manufacturers. Control devices used in the various systems might have different labels but actually complete the same function within the EGR system. For further information on EGR system controls, it is advisable to consult the service manual that pertains to each vehicle being tested or serviced.

EGR System Diagnosis and Service

Manufacturers calibrate the amount of EGR gas flow for each engine. If there is too much or too little, it can cause performance problems by changing the engine breathing characteristics. Also, with too little EGR flow, the engine can overheat and detonate. Typical problems that show up in ported EGR systems follow.

◆ Rough idle. Possible causes are an EGR valve stuck open, PVS fails to open, dirt on the valve seat, or loose mounting bolts. Loose mounting causes vacuum leak and a hissing noise.

◆ Surge, stall, or does not start. Probable cause is the valve stuck open.

◆ Detonation (spark knock). Any condition that prevents proper EGR gas flow can cause detonation. This includes a valve stuck closed, leaking valve diaphragm, restrictions in flow passages, EGR disconnected, or a problem in the vacuum source.

◆ Lead poisoning. The use of leaded gas can cause a very restricted exhaust causing detonation and possibly overheating.

◆ Poor fuel economy. This is an EGR condition only if it relates to detonation or other symptoms of restricted or zero EGR flow.

EGR VALVES AND SYSTEMS TESTING

Test the EGR valve by using a vacuum gauge or hand vacuum pump. Follow these procedures for using either piece of test equipment.

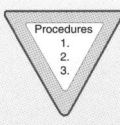

PROCEDURES

Using a Vacuum Gauge to Check Manifold Vacuum

1. Disconnect a vacuum line connected to an intake manifold port.
2. Put a vacuum gauge between the disconnected vacuum line and the intake manifold port.
3. Connect a tachometer.
4. Start the engine and gradually increase speed to 2,000 rpm with the transmission in neutral.
5. The reading from the manifold vacuum gauge (Figure 26–11) should be above 16 inches of vacuum. If not, there could be a vacuum leak or exhaust restriction. Before continuing to test the EGR, correct the problem of low vacuum.

FIGURE 26–11 Reading from the manifold vacuum gauge should be above 16 inches mercury.

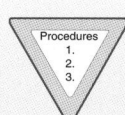

PROCEDURES

Using a Hand Vacuum Pump to Check the Operation of the EGR Valve

1. Check all vacuum lines for correct routing. Ensure they are attached securely. Replace cracked, crimped, or broken lines.
2. With the engine at normal operating temperature, be certain there is no vacuum to the EGR valve at idle.
3. Install a tachometer.
4. On EFI engines (multipoint injection), disconnect the throttle air by-pass valve solenoid.
5. Remove the vacuum supply hose from the EGR valve port and plug the hose.
6. Observe the engine's idle speed. If necessary, adjust idle speed to the emission decal specification.
7. Slowly apply 5 to 10 inches of vacuum to the EGR valve vacuum port, using a hand vacuum pump. The idle speed should drop more than 100 rpm (the engine may stall), and then return to normal (±25 rpm) again when the vacuum is removed.
8. If the idle speed does not respond in this manner, replace the EGR valve.
9. If the EGR valve is operating properly, unplug and reconnect the EGR valve vacuum supply hose.
10. Reconnect the throttle air by-pass valve solenoid, if removed.

Electronic EGR Operation

On vehicles equipped with electronic engine control, the EGR valve within this system resembles and is operated in a manner similar to the conventional EGR valves. This system uses sensors, solenoids, and an electronic control assembly to modulate and control EGR system components as shown in Figure 26–12. A pintle valve is often used in the valve to better control the flow rate of exhaust gases. A sensor mounted on the valve stem sends an electronic signal to the on-board computer, which in turn tells how far the EGR valve is opened. At this time, the EGR control solenoids (EGRV, EGRC) either maintain or alter the EGR flow, depending on engine operating conditions. Source vacuum is manifold vacuum and is applied or vented, depending on the

FIGURE 26–12 Typical EGR system used with an EEC. *Courtesy of Ford Motor Company*

FIGURE 26–13 EGRV/EGRC system is often controlled by two solenoids.

computer commands. A cooler is frequently used to reduce exhaust gas temperatures, which enables the exhaust gas to flow better and in turn reduce the amount of detonation. Early EGR systems used an in-line cooler. Later systems use a cooler sandwiched between the EGR valve and carburetor spacer.

The EGRV/EGRC system is often controlled by two solenoids (Figure 26–13). The solenoids respond to voltage signals from the on-board computer. An EGR vent solenoid, or EGRV, normally an open vent solenoid valve, closes when it is energized (Figure 26–13A). An EGR control solenoid, or EGRC, normally a closed solenoid valve, opens when it is energized (Figure 26–13B).

Voltage signals from the on-board computer can trigger the solenoids to increase EGR flow by applying vacuum to the EGR valve, maintain EGR flow by trapping vacuum in the system, or decrease EGR flow by venting EGR vacuum.

In actual operation, both solenoids constantly shift between the three operating conditions mentioned as engine operating conditions change. If the on-board computer is doing its job, the solenoids click on and off. If not, there may be either a solenoid problem or an electronic control problem.

A schematic diagram of one of the more recent EGR emission control systems, the pressure feedback electronic (PFE) type, is shown in Figure 26–14. The

electronic vacuum regulator (EVR) control applies, traps, or bleeds off vacuum to the EGR valve. That is, the vacuum to the EGR valve is supplied and controlled by the EVR instead of the EGRL and EGRV control solenoids. The EVR operates on a duty cycle output from the computer (Figure 26–15). The computer varies the rate of this cycle according to the signal it receives from a sensor that monitors the control pressure between the metering orifice and the EGR valve pintle. There is also a similar system in which a sensor delivers a voltage signal proportional to the pintle opening instead of the control pressure.

The EGR system is activated only during part-throttle modes of operation and only when the engine is warm and running smoothly. For the EGR system to be enabled, the following conditions must be met.

◆ The engine must be warm. The engine coolant temperature (ECT) sensor must be sending a moderate- to low-voltage signal to the on-board computer.
◆ The throttle plate must be at a part-throttle position as sensed by the throttle plate (TP) sensor.
◆ Manifold absolute pressure (MAP) must be moderate as determined by the sensor and on-board computer.
◆ A calibrated length of time must have elapsed since startup or cranking.

FIGURE 26–14 Functional schematic of a PFE-EVR system. *Courtesy of Ford Motor Company*

FIGURE 26–15 Electronic vacuum regulator (EVR) operation. *Courtesy of Ford Motor Company*

EGR SYSTEM TROUBLESHOOTING

Before attempting to troubleshoot or repair a suspected EGR system on a vehicle, the following conditions should be checked and be within specifications.

◆ Engine is mechanically sound.
◆ Injection system is operating properly.

◆ Mechanical-vacuum advance is properly adjusted (or the electronic advance system is operating properly).

If one or more of these conditions is faulty or operating incorrectly, perform the necessary tests and services to correct the problem before servicing the EGR system.

Most often in the closed loop electronic control EGR systems, the valve (by itself) functions the same as a ported EGR valve. Apart from the electronic control, the system can have all the problems of any EGR system. Some EGR valves are fully electrically controlled and do not use a vacuum signal to open and close them. This type of EGR system can show the same problems as others, with the exception of vacuum leaks and other vacuum-related problems. Sticking valves, obstructions, and loss of vacuum produces the same symptoms as on nonelectronic-controlled systems. If an electronic control component is not functioning, the condition is usually recognized by the computer. Check the service manual for instructions on how to use computer service codes. The EGRV and EGRC solenoids, or the EVR, should normally cycle on and off very frequently when EGR flow is being controlled (warm engine and cruise rpm). If they do not, it indicates a problem in the electronic control system or the solenoids. Generally, an electronic control failure results in low or zero EGR flow and might cause symptoms like overheating, detonation, and power loss.

Check the service manual for a summary of problems that can occur in an electronic EGR system, their possible causes, and suggested remedies. Before attempting any testing of the EGR system, visually inspect the condition of all vacuum hoses for kinks, bends, cracks, and flexibility. Replace defective hoses as required. Check vacuum hose routing. (See the underhood decal or the manufacturer's service manual for correct routing.) Correct any misrouted hoses. If the emissions system is fitted with an EVP sensor, the wires routed to it should also be checked.

USING SERVICE MANUALS

Service manuals have step-by-step instructions for inspecting the various emission control systems. They also provide the technician with troubleshooting flow charts that help the technician logically pinpoint any problems in these systems. A student can learn more about these systems by studying these charts and reasoning through the repair process. ■

AIR TEMPERATURE EMISSION CONTROL

Hydrocarbon and carbon monoxide exhaust emissions are highest when the engine is cold. The introduction of warm combustion air improves the vaporization of the fuel in the carburetor, fuel injector body, or intake manifold. The three systems used on various gasoline engines to heat the inlet air and the air/fuel mixture are heated air inlet, manifold heat control valves, and early fuel evaporation (**EFE**) heaters.

Heated Air Inlet

A heated air inlet control (also called a **thermostatic air cleaner**) is used on gasoline engines with carburetion or central fuel injection. It is not used with turbocharging or ported fuel injection. This system controls the temperature of the air on its way to the carburetor or fuel injection body. By warming the air, it reduces HC and CO emissions by improved fuel vaporization and faster warm-up.

The principle components (Figure 26–16) and functions of a conventional air cleaner system follow.

♦ Heated air inlet duct. Directs air that has been warmed by the heat stove (shroud) on the manifold to the snorkel of the air cleaner.
♦ Air inlet door vacuum motor. Controls a flapper door inside the snorkel to admit manifold heated

FIGURE 26–16 Typical heated air inlet system with conventional air cleaner. *Courtesy of Chrysler Corporation*

air, fresh air, or a mixture of both into the air cleaner.

♦ Air cleaner bimetal sensor. Regulates vacuum to the vacuum motor to determine the position of the air door. It is sensitive to air cleaner temperature.
♦ Cold weather modulator (**CWM**). Traps vacuum to the motor if manifold vacuum drops off due to the throttle opening while the air cleaner is cold.

The air cleaner bimetal sensor (Figure 26–17), which is installed in the air cleaner body or air horn, senses the air cleaner temperature. The sensing element is a bimetal spring, which is linked to a sensing valve. Depending on the calibration, the sensor can be set to operate at 50, 75, 90, or 120°F. It is what controls the operating modes shown in Figure 26–18. The sensor is calibrated to provide a specific output vacuum to the air door motor as it warms to its temperature setting. The calibration is based on 16 inches of source vacuum.

Some vacuum control systems use a retard delay valve instead of a cold weather modulator. The difference is that the retard delay valve traps the vacuum

FIGURE 26–17 Air cleaner bimetal sensor.

1   Vacuum diaphragm motor
2   Diaphragm spring
3   Temperature sensor
4a Air bleed valve–closed
4b Air bleed valve–partially open
4c Air bleed valve–open
5   Vacuum hoses
6   Diaphragm
7   Heat stove
8   Hot air (exhaust manifold)
9   Damper door
10 Outside inlet air
11 Snorkel

A - Hot air delivery mode
B - Regulating mode
C - Outside air delivery mode

FIGURE 26–18 Air cleaner bimetal sensor at (A) cold start-up; (B) modulating partial warm-up; (C) hot engine/hot ambient air. *Courtesy of Chevrolet Motor Division, General Motors Corporation*

for a few seconds when the throttle opens. Its function is to prevent a change in the air door position if vacuum drops off because the throttle opens.

With a remote air cleaner, the functions are the same. As illustrated in Figure 26–19, however, the bimetal sensor is in the air horn assembly and the air inlet vacuum motor and door are in the air cleaner assembly instead of the inlet snorkel.

Troubleshooting the Heated Inlet Control System

In a modern gasoline engine, emission controls that have any effect on the mixture necessarily have an effect on driveability, since all the systems are calibrated to operate as one integral system. Problems with the heated air inlet fall into the following groups.

◆ Obstructions to airflow, causing hard starting, performance problems, and poor fuel economy
◆ Vacuum loss, causing cold driveability problems since the system goes to full fresh air
◆ Air leaks, which bypass the control and usually cause cold driveability problems
◆ Vacuum trap failure (CWM or retard delay valve), which causes stumble on cold acceleration because the engine suddenly gulps in cold air
◆ Failure to switch to fresh air, which can overheat the mixture and cause warm driveability problems and detonation

Manifold Heat Control Valves

The exhaust manifold heat control valve routes exhaust gases to warm the intake manifold when the

Intake air duct

Cover

Rear air
intake duct

Bolt - tighten to
2 N·m (16 in. lb.)

Front air
intake duct

Air filter

Bolt - tighten to
2 N·m (16 in. lb.)

Air cleaner
housing

Nut

FRT

Nut

FIGURE 26–19   Heated air inlet system with a remote air cleaner. *Courtesy of Chevrolet Motor Division, General Motors Corporation*

PROCEDURES
Heated Air Inlet System Inspection and Performance Test

1. Apply the parking brake and block the wheels.
2. Remove the air cleaner cover and element. Inspect the heated air duct for proper installation or damage. Service as required.
3. Remove components as necessary to ensure that the duct door is in the "open to fresh air" position. If the door is in the "closed to fresh air" position, check for binding and sticking. Service or replace as required.
4. Check the vacuum source and integrity of the vacuum hoses to the bimetal sensor, cold weather modulator (CWM), and vacuum motor.
5. Start the engine. If the duct door has moved to the "heat on" position (closed to fresh air), proceed to step 8. If the door stays in the "heat off" position (closed to warm air), place a finger over the bleed of the bimetal sensor. The air duct door must move rapidly to the "heat on" position. If the door does not fully move to this position, stop the engine and test the vacuum motor. Repeat this step with a new vacuum motor. The ambient air must be at least 60°F during this test.
6. With the engine off, allow the bimetal sensor and CWM to cool.
7. Start and run the engine briefly (less than 15 seconds). The duct door should move to the "heat on" position. If the door does not move or moves only partially, replace the sensor. Cool the CWM and bimetal sensor.
8. Shut off the engine and observe the duct door.
   ◆ Vehicles with a retard delay valve: Valve returns slowly to the "heat off" position (10 to 30 seconds).
   ◆ Vehicles with CWM: Valve stays in the "heat on" position for at least 2 minutes. If less than 2 minutes, replace the CWM and repeat this step after cooling the CWM and bimetal sensor.

engine is cold. This heats the air/fuel mixture in the intake manifold and improves ventilation. The result is reduced HC and CO emissions.

The two general types of valves are vacuum-operated and thermostat-operated. Some V-8 engines use a vacuum-operated valve, which is bolted between the left exhaust manifold and exhaust pipe. The vacuum diaphragm connects to the manifold vacuum through a ported vacuum switch (PVS). On electronically controlled engines, the system also includes an electric solenoid-operated vacuum valve.

A thermostat-operated valve is used mostly on six-cylinder engines. It has the same function as the

FIGURE 26–20 Power heat control valve.

PROCEDURES

Testing a Vacuum-Operated Valve

1. Inspect the valve for any abnormal condition (Figure 26–21). Repair or replace it as necessary.
2. Disconnect the hose from the PVS.
3. Apply 15 inches of vacuum to the vacuum motor diaphragm. Trap for 60 seconds. The valve must leak no more than 2 inches of vacuum in 60 seconds.
4. Watch the position of the vacuum motor stem. It must go in the fully closed position with the vacuum on and to the fully open position when the vacuum is released.
5. If necessary, lubricate the shaft with a graphite lubricant.
6. If the valve and motor are all right, check the vacuum system. Look for a leaking or restricted hose. Repair as necessary. Check the hoses for proper routing.
7. If the valve closes with the engine started, let it warm. When the coolant warms, it should open.

vacuum-operated valve. When the engine is cold, the thermostat closes the valve to block exhaust gas flow from the manifold, which forces the gas to flow up through the heat riser and then to the exhaust pipe. On a warm engine, the thermostat opens the valve to a position that seals off the heat riser passage. Exhaust gases flow directly to the exhaust pipe.

Some V-8 engines use a more complicated manifold heat control valve, which is called a power heat control valve (Figure 26–20). It works similarly to the vacuum-controlled valve. It is designed specifically to work with a mini-catalyst and to preheat the air/fuel mixture for improved cold engine driveability. A vacuum actuator keeps the power heat control valve closed during warm-up. All right-side exhaust gas travels up through the intake manifold crossover to the left side of the engine. Then, all exhaust gas from the engine passes through a mini-converter just down from the left manifold. This converter warms up rapidly because it is small and close to the engine. Its rapid warm-up reduces exhaust emissions. As the engine and main converter warm up, a coolant-controlled engine vacuum switch (**CCEVS**) closes. This cuts vacuum to the actuator and allows the valve to open. Exhaust gas flows through both manifolds into the exhaust system and main converter.

FIGURE 26–21 Testing a vacuum-operated valve.

FIGURE 26–22 Inspect the valve and thermostat assembly for damage and lubricate the pivot.

Maintenance of a Vacuum-Operated Heat Control Valve Because of its location, the exhaust heat control valve can stick if the shaft is not serviced regularly with graphite lubricant or heat control solvent. Sticking closed can cause overheating detonation and hot performance problems. Sticking open can cause poor idle or poor performance cold. A vacuum loss usually causes the valve to fail to close, resulting in cold performance conditions.

Thermostat-Operated Heat Control Valve Although a thermostat-operated heat control valve is not as common as the vacuum type, some vehicles have them. Inspect the valve assembly for damage (Figure 26–22). Then turn the valve shaft by hand to see if it is free. It must turn freely and return to closed when cold. Cool or heat the thermostat as required to check for proper opening or closing. After the inspection and repair, lubricate the valve with a graphite lube.

Early Fuel Evaporation (EFE) Heat Control

The early fuel evaporation (EFE) heater contains a resistance grid that heats the mixture from the primary venturi of the carburetor (Figure 26–23). Its purpose is the same as a manifold heat control valve: to improve vaporization in a cold engine. The heater operates for about the first 2 minutes, permitting leaner choke calibrations for improved emissions without cold driveability problems.

The basic EFE system is similar from one engine to the next. In addition to the grid heater, EFE has two other important components.

FIGURE 26–23 EFE heater resistance grid.

FIGURE 26–24 The EFE temperature switch is mounted in the engine.

COOLANT TEMPERATURE SWITCH The EFE temperature switch or solenoid mounts to the engine, usually on the bottom of the intake manifold (Figure 26–24). The switch is closed and provides a ground for the circuit when its temperature is below a specified temperature (generally between 130° to 150°F). The switch opens as the engine coolant temperature goes above the specified temperature. (See the service manual for the exact temperature.)

EFE HEATER RELAY The temperature switch controls the EFE relay or valve. It powers the EFE heater when the temperature switch is cold and closed. After the engine has warmed up and the EFE is no longer needed, the relay de-energizes and the grid heater turns off. The EFE heater relay usually mounts on the body of the vehicle.

EFE HEATER CHECK An open circuit of EFE causes no heating of the mixture on a cold engine resulting in performance problems the first minute or two of cold operation. If the heater is powered continually for some reason, it can cause warm engine driveability problems and possibly overheating and detonation.

To perform a typical EFE electrical system check, use a 12-volt testlight and jumper wires as needed for open-circuit testing. A service manual will provide the circuit checkpoints.

SPARK ADVANCE SYSTEM

Spark advance systems have been in use since the earliest gasoline engines. It was discovered that the proper timing of the ignition spark helped the engine to reduce exhaust emission and develop more power output. Throughout the years, each car manufacturer developed slightly different spark timing controls according to engine requirements and emission standards for each model year, but the systems and devices all operate on the same principles.

AIR INJECTION SYSTEMS

One of the earliest methods used to reduce the amount of hydrocarbons (HC) and carbon monoxide (CO) in the exhaust was by forcing fresh air into the exhaust system after combustion. This additional fresh air causes further oxidation and burning of the unburned hydrocarbons and carbon monoxide. The process is much like blowing on a dwindling fire. Oxygen in the air combines with the HC and CO to continue the burning that reduces the HC and CO concentrations. This allows them to oxidize and produce harmless water vapor and carbon dioxide.

The system can be equipped with or without an external air pump. Formal names of the pump systems include Air Injection Reaction (AIR) by General Motors, Thermactor Emission (**TE**) by Ford, Air Guard by American Motors, and Air Injection Systems by Chrysler. The nonpump systems are often identified on the underhood label by the terms *pulse*, *aspirator*, *suction*, or *reed air injection*.

Pump Type

A typical system with an air pump is shown in Figure 26–25. System components include the following.

AIR PUMP The air pump produces pressurized air that is sent to the exhaust manifold and to the catalytic converter. The air pump is driven by a belt from the crankshaft.

AIR CONTROL VALVE (OR AIR-SWITCHING VALVE) This vacuum-operated valve is used to route the air from the pump either to the exhaust manifold or the catalytic converter. During engine warm-up, the valve directs the air into the exhaust manifold. Once the engine is warm, the extra air in the manifold would affect EGR operation, so the air control valve directs the air to the converter, where it aids the converter in oxidizing emissions.

THERMAL VACUUM SWITCH This switch controls the vacuum to the air control valve. When the coolant is cold, it signals the valve to direct air to the exhaust manifold. Then when the engine warms to normal operating temperature, the thermal vacuum switch signals the air control valve to reroute the air to the converter.

AIR BY-PASS VALVE (OR DIVERTER VALVE) This device is located between the air pump and the air control valve, or sometimes it is combined with the air control valve to make one component. The air by-pass valve diverts, or detours, air during deceleration. Excess air in an exhaust rich with fuel can produce a backfire or explosion in a muffler. A vacuum signal operates the by-pass valve during deceleration. Compressed air is diverted to the atmosphere.

ONE-WAY CHECK VALVES These valves allow air into the exhaust but prevent exhaust from entering the pump in the event the drive belt breaks. Their location in the system is behind the air control valve and before the exhaust manifold and catalytic converter.

HOSES AND NOZZLES These are necessary to distribute and inject the air.

Pulse Type (Nonpump Type)

This system uses the natural exhaust pressure pulses to pull air from the air cleaner into the catalytic converter.

The typical pulsed air system operates in the following manner. An air check valve and silencer

FIGURE 26–25 Engine-driven air pump-type air injection system.

FIGURE 26–26 Typical pulse air system's check valves.

FIGURE 26–27 A reed valve opens and closes the air-check valve.

(Figure 26–26) connects in-line between the air cleaner and the catalytic converter. When pressure in the exhaust system is greater than the pressure in the air cleaner, the reed valve (Figure 26–27) inside the air check valve closes. When the pressure in the exhaust system is less than the pressure in the air cleaner, the reed valve opens and draws air into the catalytic converter. The incoming oxygen reduces the hydrocarbons and carbon monoxide content of the exhaust gases by continuing the combustion of unburned gases in the same manner as the conventional system (with an air pump).

Air injector systems rarely cause problems. If one should cause a difficulty, check the vehicle's service manual.

SECONDARY AIR SYSTEM

The typical electronic secondary air system, like the conventional air injection system, consists of an air pump to a secondary air by-pass (SAB) valve, which directs the air either to the atmosphere or to the catalytic converter (Figure 26–28). The major difference between the two systems is, of course, the on-board computer and diverter valve.

FIGURE 26–28 Typical secondary air system.

The air pump is driven by a belt on the front of the engine and supplies air to the system. Intake air passes through a centrifugal filter fan at the front of the pump where foreign materials are separated from the air by centrifugal force. In many systems, air flows from the pump to a secondary air by-pass (**SAB**) valve, which directs the air either to the atmosphere or to the secondary air diverter (**SAD**) valve. The SAD valve directs the air either to the exhaust manifold or to the catalytic converter. Therefore, secondary airflow can be directed to three points.

1. Vented (or bypassed) to the atmosphere via the air filter.
2. Upstream to the exhaust manifold.
3. Downstream to the catalytic converter.

Both the SAB and SAD valves have solenoids that are controlled by the on-board computer. When either solenoid is energized by the computer, vacuum is applied to the SAB valve. Secondary air is vented to the atmosphere. When no vacuum is applied to the SAD valve, secondary air (if present) is directed to the catalytic converter.

There are two check valves in the secondary air system. Secondary air must flow through a check valve before it reaches either the exhaust manifold or the catalytic converter. These check valves prevent the backflow of exhaust gases into the pump in the event of an exhaust backfire or if the pump drive belt fails.

By-pass Mode

In the by-pass mode, vacuum is not applied to either the SAB or the SAD valve and secondary air is vented to the atmosphere. Secondary air may be vented or bypassed due to a fuel-rich condition, which the on-board computer recognizes as a problem in the system, or during deceleration. Secondary air is also typically bypassed during cold engine cranking and cold idle conditions.

When engine coolant temperature is below 55°F at startup, secondary air is automatically bypassed. The system maintains a by-pass mode of operation until the coolant temperature reaches 170°F. The computer has an internal electronic timer that keeps track of the length of time since the engine was started. Secondary air is also maintained in the by-pass mode until a pre-set length of time has elapsed.

Upstream Mode

Figure 26–29 shows secondary air being routed through the SAB valve and the SAD valve to the exhaust manifold. The upstream mode is actuated when the computer senses a warm crank/startup condition. The secondary airflow remains upstream for 1 to 3 minutes after startup to help control emissions.

The air/fuel mixture at startup is typically very rich. This rich mixture results in unburned HC and CO in the exhaust after combustion. By switching to the upstream mode, the hot HC and CO mix with the incoming secondary air and are burned up.

FIGURE 26–29 Secondary air system upstream mode of operation.

This reburning of HC and CO compounds causes the exhaust gases to get hotter, which in turn heats up the oxygen sensor. Therefore, switching to the upstream mode allows the electronic engine control system to switch to the closed loop operation sooner because the oxygen sensor is ready to function sooner.

The warm (and activated) oxygen sensor sends exhaust gas oxygen information to the computer. When the electronic engine control system is in the closed loop operation, the computer uses this information to adjust the air/fuel mixture.

It should be noted that the upstream mode of operation increases the oxygen level in the exhaust gases. The voltage signal from the oxygen sensor to the computer maintains a continuous low level. The computer interprets this signal as a continuous lean condition. That is, there is too much oxygen in the air/fuel mixture. It can readily be seen, then, that the upstream mode results in inaccurate exhaust gas oxygen measurements.

To solve this dilemma, the computer automatically switches to the open loop fuel control whenever the upstream mode is activated. It ignores the oxygen sensor input.

Downstream Mode

Figure 26–30 illustrates secondary air being routed through the SAB valve and the SAD valve to the cat-alytic converter. The secondary air system operates in the downstream mode during a majority of engine conditions.

The catalytic converter is most efficient at reducing NO_x when the air/fuel mixture is near stoichiometry (a chemically correct air/fuel mixture expressed by the ratio of 14.7:1). As already stated, the oxygen sensor has a big part in producing that optimum air/fuel mixture in the closed loop fuel control mode. When secondary air is diverted downstream, the oxygen sensor can provide accurate information about the level of oxygen in the exhaust gases to the computer. Therefore, the electronic engine control system can operate in the closed loop fuel control mode only when the secondary air system is diverted downstream.

After the engine has warmed up sufficiently, the air/fuel mixture tends to run lean, leaving fewer excess hydrocarbons remaining after combustion. Therefore, it is not necessary to run the secondary air system in the upstream mode of operation. The computer automatically switches the system to the downstream mode to allow the secondary air to mix with the exhaust gases inside the catalytic converter. The fresh secondary air diverted downstream allows the converter to reduce the NO_x emissions NO_x emissions are also reduced by the closed loop mode.

FIGURE 26–30 Secondary air system downstream mode of operation.

SECONDARY AIR SYSTEM TROUBLESHOOTING

Both the SAB valve and the SAD valve are operated by solenoids that are controlled by the computer. If no air (oxygen) enters the exhaust stream at the exhaust manifold or catalytic converter, HC and CO emission levels are too high. Air flowing to the exhaust manifold at all times can increase the temperature of the catalytic converter and cause damage to the catalyst. On the other hand, if air is flowing continuously to the catalytic converter, it can cause the converter to overheat during fuel rich operations. An electrical feature (open circuit) of the SAB valve diverts air to the atmosphere for all engine operations. Secondary air continuously flows to the catalytic converter if an open circuit occurs in the SAD valve. Mechanical failures in either or both of the valves can cause incorrect airflow to the exhaust manifold or the catalytic converter.

System Efficiency Test

Run the engine at idle with the secondary air system on (enabled). Using an exhaust gas analyzer, measure and record the oxygen (O_2) levels. Next, disable the secondary air system and continue to allow the engine to idle. Again, measure and record the oxygen level in the exhaust gases. The secondary air system should be supplying 2 to 5 percent more oxygen when it is operational (enabled).

CATALYTIC CONVERTER

Catalytic converters are the most effective devices for controlling exhaust emissions. Until 1975, car makers had done an effective job of controlling emissions by the use of other systems—auxiliary air injection systems, exhaust gas recirculation systems, and positive crankcase ventilation. Controlling emissions with these systems alone also meant lean mixtures and

exotic ignition timing, which often severely penalized power and fuel economy. When catalytic converters were introduced, much of the emission control could be taken out of the engine and moved into the exhaust system. This change allowed manufacturers to return the engine to better performance and improved fuel economy.

CUSTOMER CARE

You can assure your customer that a rotten egg odor is not necessarily an indication of a bad catalytic converter. On most vehicles, odor is caused by either high sulfur fuel (recommended switching brands of gasoline) or by an excessively rich or lean fuel mixture. ■

Many changes will be necessary in vehicles, engines, and emission systems to meet the emission standards of the 1990s. Since approximately 90 percent of HC emissions occur before the catalytic converter is hot enough to provide for proper HC oxidation, engineers are designing catalytic converters that are heated from the vehicle's electrical system. Since these heaters have high current flow requirements, some charging system modifications may be necessary.

EVAPORATIVE EMISSION CONTROL SYSTEM

The fuel evaporative emission control system reduces the amount of raw fuel vapors (HC) that are emitted into the air from the fuel tank and carburetor (if so equipped). While different manufacturers have slight variations and names for their evaporative emission control systems, they are very similar in operation. Since the first systems were used nationwide in the early 1970s, several refinements have been added (Figure 26–31). Current systems include the following components.

FIGURE 26–31 Typical evaporative emission control system.

PRESSURE RELIEF

PRESSURE RELIEF VALVE OPEN

VACUUM RELIEF

VACUUM RELIEF VALVE OPEN

FIGURE 26–32 Sealed fuel tank cap.

FIGURE 26–34 Charcoal canister. *Courtesy of Cadillac Motor Car Division, General Motors Corporation*

◆ A special filler design to limit the amount of fuel that can be put in the tank.

◆ A pressure/vacuum relief fuel tank cap instead of a plain vented cap (Figure 26–32).

◆ A vapor separator in the top of the fuel tank (Figure 26–33). This device collects droplets of liquid fuel and directs them back into the tank.

◆ A domed fuel tank in which its upper portion is raised. Fuel vapors rise to this upper portion and collect.

◆ Check, or one-way, valves keep vapors confined. When an engine runs, vacuum- or electrically-operated valves open.

◆ Hoses and tubes connect parts of a vapor-recovery system. Special fuel/vapor rubber tubing must be used.

The most obvious part of the evaporative emission control system is the **charcoal (carbon) canis-** ter in the engine compartment. This canister (Figure 26–34) is located in or near the engine compartment. Fuel vapors from the gas tank (and carburetor float bowl) are routed to and absorbed onto the surfaces of the canister's charcoal granules. When the vehicle is restarted, vapors are drawn by the vacuum into the carburetor or intake manifold to be burned in the engine. Canister purging varies widely with make and model. In some instances, a fixed restriction allows constant purging whenever there is manifold vacuum. In others, a staged valve provides purging only at speeds above idle. Generally,

FIGURE 26–33 (A) Normal operation of vapor separator; (B) with liquid in separator.

FIGURE 26–35 Typical purge valve mountings.

the **canister purge** valve is normally closed. It opens the inlet to the purge outlet when vacuum is applied. Some units incorporate a thermal-delay valve so the canister is not purged until the engine reaches operating temperature. Purging at idle or with a cold engine creates other problems, such as rough running and increased emissions because of the additional vapor added to the intake manifold. Typical purge valve mountings are in Figure 26–35.

Canister purging may also be electronically controlled. The on-board computer enables a purge solenoid to initiate the purge cycle. The canister purge solenoid is mounted in-line between the canister and intake manifold. The purge solenoid is a normally closed solenoid. The on-board computer cycles the solenoid while the solenoid itself controls the release of fuel vapors trapped in the charcoal canister. When the solenoid is energized by the computer, the purge valve opens and allows the intake manifold vacuum to draw the trapped fuel vapors from the canister.

In the electronically controlled canister, fuel vapors are purged only under the following conditions.

◆ After a predetermined length of time has elapsed following engine start-up.
◆ The engine coolant temperature sensor must indicate that engine temperature is within a predetermined range.
◆ The engine must be operated at stabilized, part-open throttle condition.
◆ The engine must be operating above a predetermined high rpm limit.

Normal service of the electronic fuel evaporative system consists of replacing the canister or canister filter at the manufacturer's suggested interval and replacing any worn or damaged hoses. Failure of the system to purge on command indicates a failed canister purge solenoid valve.

FIGURE 26–36 The canister should be checked for damage.

Canister Testing

Check the canister to make sure it is not cracked or otherwise damaged (Figure 26–36). Also make certain the canister filter is not completely saturated. Remember that a saturated charcoal filter can cause symptoms that can be mistaken for fuel system problems. Rough idle, flooding, and other conditions can indicate a canister problem. A canister filled with liquid or water causes back pressure in the fuel tank. It can also cause richness and flooding symptoms during purge or start-up. (Some trucks have intentionally pressurized fuel tank systems. Check the calibration and engine decal before diagnosing.)

To test for saturation, unplug the canister momentarily during a diagnosis procedure and observe the engine's operation. If the canister is saturated, either it or the filter must be replaced depending on its design. That is, some models have a replaceable filter, others do not.

🔧 SHOP TALK

Sometimes a partially saturated canister can be evacuated by removing it from its mounting area (leaving the hoses connected), inverting it, and running the engine at high idle for 3 to 5 minutes. Be sure to replace the canister filter if it can be separated from the canister. ■

Testing the Canister Purge Valve A vacuum leak in any of the evaporative emission components or hoses can cause starting and performance problems as can any engine vacuum leak. It can also cause complaints of fuel odor. Incorrect connection of the components can cause rich stumble or lack of purging (resulting in fuel odor). To conduct a vacuum-on, valve-open test, consult the vehicle's service manual. Check the service manual for other common evaporative emission control system problems.

Float Bowl Vent Control

If a carburetor's float bowl does not vent properly, there can be flooding on startup, especially if the vent fails to open with a hot carburetor. Flooding can also occur if vapors back up into the carburetor from the canister due to a failed thermal vent valve (**TVV**). A failed open carburetor bowl vent solenoid or vacuum/thermal bowl vent can cause suction in the fuel bowl during canister purging, resulting in lean driveability problems.

To test the fuel bowl vent or canister purge shutoff, follow the service manual procedure.

EMISSIONS TESTING

Testing the quality of the exhaust is both a procedure for testing emission levels and a diagnostic routine. One of the most valuable diagnostic aids is the exhaust analyzer.

A typical infrared exhaust analyzer has a long sample hose with a probe in the end of the hose. The probe is inserted in the vehicle's tailpipe. When the analyzer is turned on, an internal pump moves an exhaust sample from the tailpipe through the sample hose and the analyzer. A water trap and filter in the hose removes moisture and carbon particles.

The pump forces the exhaust sample through a sample cell in the analyzer. The exhaust sample is then vented to the atmosphere (Figure 26–37). In the sample cell, a beam of infrared light passes through the exhaust sample. The analyzer then determines the quantities of HC and CO, if the analyzer is a 2-gas analyzer, or HC, CO, CO_2, and O_2, if it is a 4-gas analyzer. Some analyzers can also measure NO_x and are called 5-gas analyzers.

HC emissions are caused by incomplete combustion. Some of the fuel that entered the engine's cylinders did not burn and, therefore, is expelled out the tailpipe. An infrared analyzer provides a HC reading in parts per million (**ppm**).

CO emissions are caused by a lack of air or too much fuel in the air/fuel mixture. CO will not occur if combustion does not take place in the cylinders; therefore, the presence of CO means combustion is taking place. An infrared analyzer provides a CO reading as a percentage.

O_2 is not a pollutant; therefore, it's presence in the exhaust does not pose any threat to our environment. However, too much oxygen in the exhaust does indicate that an improper mixture was in the cylinders or poor combustion has occurred in the engine (Figure 26–38). An improper air/fuel mixture will

FIGURE 26–37 Infrared exhaust analyzer internal design. *Courtesy of Chrysler Corporation*

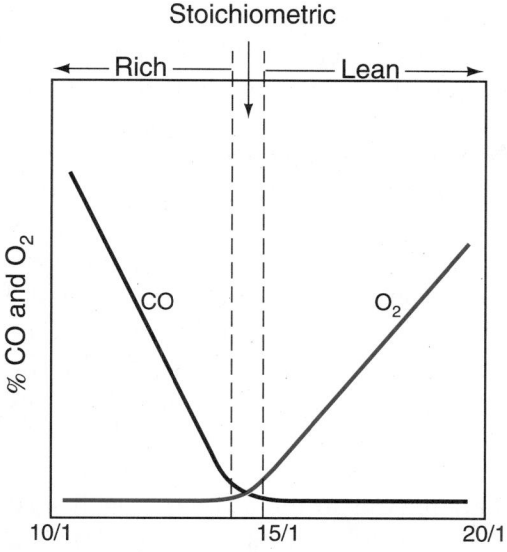

FIGURE 26–38 Oxygen and carbon monoxide levels in relation to air/fuel ratios. *Courtesy of Sun Electric Corporation*

also cause a high reading of oxygen. O_2 is displayed on the exhaust analyzer as a percentage.

CO_2 is also not a pollutant and it's presence in the exhaust does not pose a great threat to our environment. An ideal by-product of combustion is CO_2; therefore, large amounts of this gas are desired. CO_2 is displayed on the exhaust analyzer as a percentage.

Excessive HC emissions may be caused by:

♦ Ignition system misfiring.
♦ Improper ignition timing.
♦ Excessively lean or rich air/fuel ratio.
♦ Low cylinder compression.
♦ Defective valves, guides, or lifters.
♦ Defective rings, pistons, or cylinders.
♦ Vacuum leaks.

Excessive CO emissions may be caused by:

♦ Rich air/fuel mixtures.
♦ Dirty air filter.
♦ Faulty injectors.
♦ Higher-than-normal fuel pressures.
♦ Defective system input sensor.

Excessive HC and CO emissions may be caused by:

♦ Plugged PCV system.
♦ Excessively rich air/fuel ratio.
♦ Stuck open heat riser valve.
♦ AIR pump inoperative or disconnected.
♦ Engine oil diluted with gasoline.

Lower-than-normal O_2 readings may be caused by:

♦ Rich air/fuel mixtures.
♦ Dirty air filter.
♦ Faulty injectors.
♦ Higher-than-normal fuel pressures.
♦ Defective system input sensor.
♦ Restricted PCV system.
♦ Charcoal canister purging at idle and low speeds.

Lower-than-normal CO_2 readings may be caused by:

♦ Leaking exhaust system.
♦ Rich air/fuel mixture.

Higher-than-normal O_2 readings may be caused by:

♦ An engine misfire.
♦ Lean air/fuel mixtures.
♦ Vacuum leaks.
♦ Lower-than-specified fuel pressures.
♦ Defective fuel injectors.
♦ Defective system input sensor.

When using the exhaust analyzer as a diagnostic tool, it is important to realize that the severity of the problem dictates how much higher than normal the readings will be. When attempting to identify the exact cause of the abnormal readings, disable the secondary air system. Then rerun the tests. Without the secondary air, the readings will give an accurate look at the air/fuel mixture. This should help to find the cause of the problem.

CASE STUDIES

Case 1

A customer complains of severe detonation. The technician checks all the EGR vacuum lines and finds them intact and properly routed.

The technician pushes the EGR valve stem against spring pressure. It moves freely and returns fully. With the engine at normal operating temperature, a helper opens the throttle enough to reach 2,500 rpm while the technician watches the EGR valve stem. When the throttle is released, the valve stem does not retract. The technician removes the hose and feels no vacuum when the engine is revved. Next, the technician pulls off the source line from the thermostatic vacuum switch and feels for vacuum. Because there is vacuum there, but none gets to the valve with the engine warm, the technician replaces the thermostatic vacuum switch.

Case 2

A customer complains of a loud rapping or ticking noise (sounding similar to a rod knock) that seems to occur only during acceleration when the engine is cold.

When the technician pulls the vacuum line off the heat riser canister, the noise goes away. The technician replaces the vacuum check valve located between the vacuum switch and the heat riser vacuum motor.

KEY TERMS

AIR	NO$_x$
Blowby	PMVI
Canister purge	Postcombustion control
California ARB	PPM
CCEVS	Precombustion control
CCS	PVS
Charcoal (carbon)	SAB
canister	SAD
CO	TE
CWM	Thermostatic air cleaner
Dyno	TLEV
EFE	TVS
Evaporative control	TVV
HC	ULEV
I/M	Vacuum amplifier
LEV	ZEV

SUMMARY

- Unburned hydrocarbons, carbon monoxide, and oxides of nitrogen are three types of emissions being controlled in gasoline engines.
- Precombustion control systems prevent emissions from being created in the engine, either during or before the combustion cycle. Postcombustion control systems clean up exhaust gases after the fuel has been burned. The evaporative control system traps fuel vapors that would normally escape from the fuel and carburetor into the air.
- The PCV system removes blowby gases from the crankcase and recirculates them to the engine intake. The PCV system benefits the vehicle's driveability by eliminating harmful crankcase gases, reducing air pollution, and promoting fuel economy.

- The EGR system reduces the amount of NO$_x$ emitted by the exhaust system by diluting the air/fuel mixture with controlled amounts of exhaust gas. The EGR valve may be controlled by a port vacuum system or a venturi vacuum system.
- The EGR valve can be tested with a vacuum gauge or a hand vacuum pump.
- In vehicles equipped with electronic engine controls, the EGR valve has a sensor that relays the position of its stem to the on-board computer. The computer signals two control solenoids, EGKV and EGRC, that either maintain or alter the EGR flow, depending on engine operating conditions.
- Air temperature emission control systems reduce HC and CO emissions in the exhaust. The heated air inlet control system, used on all carbureted and central fuel injected engines, controls the inlet air temperature on the way to the carburetor or fuel injector body. The manifold heat control valve routes exhaust gases to warm the intake manifold when the engine is cold. This valve may be vacuum-operated or thermostat-operated. The early fuel evaporation (EFE) heater contains a resistance grid that heats the mixture before it enters the cylinders.
- The air injection system reduces the amount of HC and CO in the exhaust by forcing fresh air into the exhaust system after combustion. The system can be equipped with or without an external air pump.
- The secondary air system is a more complex electronic version of the air injection system. In its bypass mode, secondary air is vented to the atmosphere. In its upstream mode, the air is directed to the exhaust manifold to aid in the burning of the HC and CO compounds. This also warms the oxygen sensor faster. Air is directed to the catalytic converter in the downstream mode.
- The secondary air system's SAB and SAD valves together control where secondary air is directed.
- The catalytic converter is the most effective device for controlling exhaust emissions.
- The fuel evaporative emission system reduces the amount of raw fuel vapors (HC) emitted into the air from the fuel tank and carburetor. Current systems include a special filler design, a pressure/vacuum relief fuel tank cap, a vapor separator, a domed fuel tank, check valves, hoses and tubes, and a charcoal canister.

TECH MANUAL

The following procedures are included in Chapter 26 of the *Tech Manual* that accompanies this book:

1. Use an exhaust analyzer to test the condition of the engine.

2. Test operation of a PCV system.

3. Test operation of an EGR system.

4. Test the operation of a fuel vapor control system.

REVIEW QUESTIONS

1. Name the three types of emissions being controlled in gasoline engines.

2. Name the three basic types of emission control systems used in modern vehicles.

3. List three ways the PCV system benefits the vehicle's driveability.

4. Name three air temperature control systems.

5. Name the three modes of the secondary air system.

6. Which of the following is a postcombustion control system?
   a. exhaust gas recirculating (EGR) system
   b. catalytic converter
   c. both a and b
   d. neither a nor b

7. What is the leakage of unburned fuel and products of combustion into the engine crankcase called?
   a. blowby   c. both a and b
   b. sludge   d. neither a nor b

8. The exhaust gas recirculating system reduces what kind of emissions?
   a. HC   c. NO_x
   b. CO   d. all of the above

9. The vacuum used to control the EGR valve is taken from which of the following?
   a. a port in the carburetor throttle body above the throttle plate
   b. a port at the throat of the carburetor venturi
   c. both a and b
   d. neither a nor b

10. Which of the following causes detonation?
    a. an EGR valve stuck closed
    b. a leaking valve diaphragm
    c. restrictions in flow passages
    d. all of the above

11. Technician A says the EGR vent solenoid is normally open. Technician B says the EGR control solenoid is normally open. Who is correct?
    a. Technician A
    b. Technician B
    c. Both A and B
    d. Neither A nor B

12. Which of the following systems is/are used on gasoline engines to heat the inlet air and the air/fuel mixture?
    a. heated air inlet controls
    b. manifold heat control valves
    c. early fuel evaporation (EFE) heaters
    d. all of the above

13. Which of the following systems supplies fresh air to the exhaust system?
    a. pump air injection system
    b. pulse air injection system
    c. both a and b
    d. neither a nor b

14. A vehicle is experiencing flooding. Technician A says the bowl vent valve has failed in the open position. Technician B says the charcoal filter is saturated. Who is probably correct?
    a. Technician A   c. Both A and B
    b. Technician B   d. Neither A nor B

15. Which of the following is/are functions of the heated air inlet system?
    a. warming the inlet air
    b. improving fuel vaporization
    c. reducing HC and CO emissions
    d. all of the above

16. Technician A says SAB valve directs secondary air either to the exhaust manifold or to the catalytic converter. Technician B says secondary air may be vented during deceleration. Who is correct?
    a. Technician A   c. Both A and B
    b. Technician B   d. Neither A nor B

17. Which of the following components is *not* a part of the early fuel evaporation (EFE) control system?

   a. power heat control valve

   b. resistance grid

   c. coolant temperature switch

   d. EFE relay

18. Which of the following devices delays the introduction of exhaust gases into the intake manifold until after the engine warms up?

   a. thermal vacuum switch

   b. ported vacuum switch

   c. delay timer control

   d. all of the above

19. Technician A says the canister purge valve is normally open. Technician B says the purge solenoid is normally open. Who is correct?

   a. Technician A   **c.** Both A and B

   b. Technician B   **d.** Neither A nor B

20. Technician A says if secondary air flows continuously to the catalytic converter, the catalytic converter overheats during rich fuel operations. Technician B says secondary air flows continuously to the catalytic converter if an open circuit occurs in the SAD valve. Who is correct?

   a. Technician A   **c.** Both A and B

   b. Technician B   **d.** Neither A nor B

COMPUTERIZED ENGINE CONTROLS

27

OBJECTIVES

◆ *Explain the advantage of using computerized engine control systems.* ◆ *Identify and explain computerized control system components.* ◆ *Understand how a typical computerized engine control system operates.* ◆ *Know the various memory systems used in automotive computers.* ◆ *Explain the operation of the various input and output sensors.* ◆ *Explain what is meant by open loop and closed loop.* ◆ *Know how to use computer logic and troubleshooting logic.* ◆ *Understand self-diagnostic systems.* ◆ *Explain the changes brought about by OBD-II.*

Computerized engine control systems present service technicians with a totally new way of troubleshooting performance problems. An on-board diagnostic capability allows the computer to aid the technician in pinpointing the source of many performance problems.

Because all manufacturers continually update, expand, and improve their computerized control systems, there are now hundreds of different domestic and import systems on the road. Methods of reading on-board diagnostic data and troubleshooting systems can vary greatly between manufacturers and between model lines and years of the same manufacturer. That is why it is absolutely essential that the service manual be used during all diagnostic procedures.

Fortunately for technicians, laws have been passed that call for a standardized test procedure for all electronic control systems. As a result of this mandate, known as **OBD-II**, vehicles will use the same terms, acronyms, and definitions to describe their components (commonly referred to as the SAE **J1930** standards). They will also have the same type of diagnostic connector, the same basic test sequences, and will display the same trouble codes. OBD-II is gradually being phased into production. It began in 1994 and will be on all vehicles sold in North America by 1997.

SYSTEM FUNCTIONS

In a computerized engine control system, four factors are carefully balanced to achieve maximum results with minimum waste.

EMISSIONS Factors that result in low emissions follow.

◆ Air/fuel ratio held as closely to 14.7 to 1 as possible, allowing maximum catalytic converter efficiency.
◆ Emission control devices, such as EGR valve, carbon canister, and air pump, operated at high efficiency.
◆ Engine operated as efficiently as possible when cold and warmed up rapidly, reducing unburned hydrocarbon (raw gas) emissions.

MILEAGE Factors that result in increased mileage follow.

◆ Timing advanced as much as possible under all conditions.
◆ Air/fuel ratio kept as close to ideal (14.7 to 1 by weight) as possible.
◆ EGR valve positioned as accurately as possible.
◆ Lockup torque converter applied in manner to give more efficient operation.

PERFORMANCE (POWER AND DRIVEABILITY) Factors that result in improved engine performance follow.

◆ Timing and air/fuel ratio precisely controlled under all operating conditions.
◆ Control loop operation that enables the engine to make rapid changes to match changes in temperature, load, and speed.

◆ Engines that can be designed for higher power output and still meet mileage and emissions standards.

PROTECTION (DURABILITY) Factors that protect the engine follow.

◆ A system able to make changes in timing and air/fuel to compensate for excessive engine temperature or load.
◆ A system able to retard ignition timing to eliminate engine knock (detonation).
◆ An engine that can warm up faster, with less engine wear from raw gas washing oil from the piston rings and getting into the crankcase to form sludge and varnish.

All these factors are especially important with today's smaller, harder working engines.

To control these factors under all modes of operation (startup, warm-up, off-idle, cruising, and wide-open throttle), each manufacturer has developed computerized control systems that monitor engine performance, tailor fuel and spark delivery to match performance demands, and control emission systems to minimize the level of pollutants in the exhaust stream.

SYSTEM COMPONENTS

The three basic components of a computer control system are the sensors, computer (sometimes called a microprocessor, control module, or control unit), and actuators. **Sensors** supply the computer with input on engine conditions. The computer analyzes this data and calculates a response to these conditions. It then signals an output or **actuator**, such as a relay or solenoid, to adjust engine operation (Figure 27–1).

The sensors, actuators, and computer communicate through the use of electronic circuits. For example, when the incoming voltage signal from the coolant sensor tells the computer the engine is getting hot, it generates an output command to turn on the electric cooling fan. The computer does this by

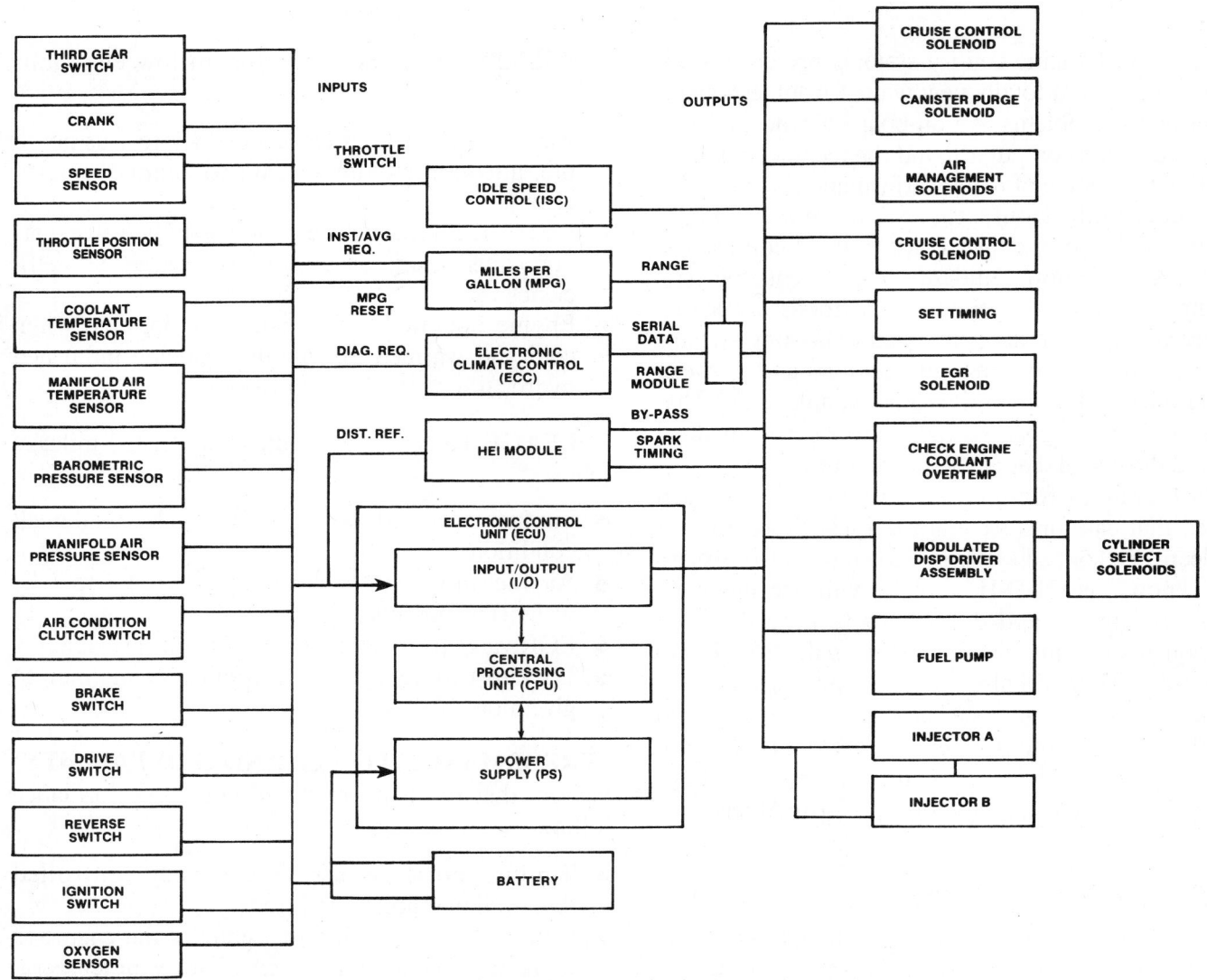

FIGURE 27–1 Typical computerized engine control system inputs and outputs. *Courtesy of* Counterman *magazine*

FIGURE 27–2 Typical engine control microcomputer or computer.

FIGURE 27–3 On General Motors' computers, the PROM is replaceable. If the computer is replaced, the PROM must be removed from the old computer and installed in the replacement. *Courtesy of* Counterman *magazine*

FIGURE 27–4 Use the proper tool when removing the PROM chip. *Courtesy of* Counterman *magazine*

grounding the relay circuit that controls the electric cooling fan. When the relay clicks on, the electric cooling fan starts to spin and cools the engine.

The engine control computer or microcomputer (Figure 27–2) has two basic types of memory. The first is random access memory (RAM). RAM is used to store data collected by the sensors, the results of computer calculations, and other information that is constantly changing during engine operation. Information in volatile RAM is erased when the ignition is turned off or when the power to the computer is disconnected. Nonvolatile RAM does not lose its data if its power source is disconnected.

The computer's permanent memory is stored in read only memory (ROM) or programmable read only memory (PROM). Like nonvolatile RAM, ROM and PROM are not erased when the power source is disconnected. ROM and PROM are used to store computer control system strategy and look-up tables. PROM-integrated circuit chips are used in control computers on General Motors vehicles (Figure 27–3). These rectangular black chips have legs that plug into the computer circuitry. Changing the PROM chip recalibrates the fuel and ignition curves stored in the computer memory. PROM chips enable the same computer to be recalibrated for use in different applications.

When removing or installing a PROM chip, take care not to damage the chip. Always use a PROM removal tool (Figure 27–4) and never touch the legs of the PROM.

Two types of information stored in ROM are the system strategy and look-up tables. System adaptive strategy is a plan, created by engine designers and calibration engineers, for the timing and control of computer-controlled systems. In designing the best strategies, it is necessary to look at all the possible conditions an engine may encounter. It is then determined

how the system should respond to these conditions. In other words, a **strategy** is a blueprint for how the system operates to reach a desired goal. The strategy goal may be increased power, improved mileage, lowered temperature, reduced emissions, or rapid warm-up. To do this, the ROM strategy includes all the equations and decision-making logic, and serves as a guide or plan in controlling engine operation. To be useful, the strategy requires additional data, which are obtained from the look-up tables.

The **look-up tables** (sometimes called maps) contain calibrations and specifications (Figure 27–5). Look-up tables indicate how an engine should perform. For example, a piece of information (a reading of 20 in. Hg) is received from the manifold absolute pressure (MAP) sensor. This information, plus information from the engine speed sensor, is compared to a table for spark advance. This preprogrammed table

FIGURE 27–5 Graphic illustration of spark advance look-up table or map.

tells the computer what the spark advance should be for that throttle position and engine speed (Figure 27–6). The computer then modifies this spark advance value, by consulting other tables, with information concerning engine temperature and atmospheric pressure. To determine how much spark should be advanced, the microprocessor refers to a special look-up table called an **adder**. The adder indicates how much spark advance should be added with EGR gases flowing. Because these tables are stored in ROM, information in the look-up tables is retained when power to the microprocessor is turned off.

When making decisions, the microprocessor is constantly referring to three sources of information: the look-up tables, system strategy, and the input from sensors. By comparing information from these sources, the computer makes informed decisions.

PRIMARY SENSORS

To monitor and adjust engine conditions, as already mentioned, the computer uses a variety of sensors (Figure 27–7). The following represent the principal system sensors. It should be noted that these sensors are shared between the systems. For example, MAP sensor input is used to control fuel, ignition, EGR, emission system airflow, air intake, and idle speed systems. It is also important to remember that not all sensors are used on all vehicles. Some of these sen-

sors perform essentially the same job in slightly different ways. The manufacturer's names for these devices may differ, but the description and operation of the sensors are basically the same. For specific application information, check the service manual.

AIR-CONDITIONING (A/C) DEMAND SENSOR
This is a pressure switch that signals the computer control module that the A/C clutch is cycling. When the pressure switch is closed, a voltage signal is sent to the computer. The computer uses this data to help determine engine load and control engine idle speed. The timing on some engines can also be altered to prevent hesitation.

AIR TEMPERATURE SENSOR Also called air change or manifold air temperature sensor, this sensor is a thermistor. Its resistance decreases as manifold air temperature increases, and increases as manifold air temperature decreases. The control module measures the voltage drop across the air temperature sensor and uses this input to help calculate fuel delivery. The input from this sensor may also be used to control the preheated air and early fuel evaporation systems.

In some vehicles, an ambient air temperature sensor is used to control the vehicle's automatic climate control system for passenger comfort.

BRAKES ON OR OFF This input signals the microprocessor to disengage the torque converter clutch. It can also lower idle speed.

BAROMETRIC PRESSURE (BARO) SENSOR
This sensor alters the air/fuel mixture and timing controls, depending on the altitude in which the car is being operated.

COOLANT TEMPERATURE SENSOR The coolant temperature sensor is very important. Its input is used to regulate many engine functions.

◆ Activating and deactivating the early fuel evaporation system.

◆ Controlling the open- and closed-loop feedback modes of the system. The coolant temperature sensor controls the air/fuel mixture (open loop)

		500	1000	2000	3000
MANIFOLD ABSOLUTE PRESSURE IS 20 HG.	29 HG	10°	10°	17°	20°
	20 HG	20°	15°	15°	25°
	10 HG	30°	30°	32°	34°
	5 HG	30°	30°	32°	34°

LOOK-UP TABLE INDICATES SPARK SHOULD BE ADVANCED 25° BTDC

ENGINE SPEED IS 3000 RPM

FIGURE 27–6 Example of base spark advance look-up table. *Courtesy of Ford Motor Company*

"G" CARLINE   RPO: L67   VIN CODE: 1   3800 V6 SFI

▢ COMPUTER HARNESS

C1 Powertrain Control Module (PCM)
C2 Diagnostic Link Connector (DLC)
C3 MIL ("SERVICE ENGINE SOON")
C4 PCM harness ground
C5 Fuse panel
C6 Fuel pump test connector
C7 Underhood electrical center
  • A/C compressor relay
  • Series/Parallel cooling fan relay
  • High speed cooling fan relay
  • 60 Amp cooling fan maxifuse
C8 8-way ignition jumper harness
  connector
C9 Engine and EI module ground

⬚ NOT PCM CONNECTED

N1 Crankcase Vent Valve
N2 Blower motor relay
N3 Oil pressure sending unit

▢ OUTPUTS (ACTUATORS)

1 Fuel injectors
2 Idle Air Control (IAC)
3 Transaxle connector
4 Electronic Ignition (EI) module/coil
  assembly
5 EVAP solenoid
6 Boost control solenoid
7 Linear exhaust gas recirculation
  valve
8 Cruise control servo
9 Low speed fan relay

◯ INPUTS

A Heated Oxygen Sensor (HO2S)
B Throttle Position (TP) sensor
C Engine Coolant Temperature (ECT) sensor
D Vehicle Speed Sensor (VSS)
E Camshaft position sensor
F Crankshaft position sensor
G Knock Sensor (KS)
H Mass Air Flow (MAF) sensor
J Intake Air Temperature (IAT) sensor
K Transmission range switch
L A/C head pressure switch
M A/C high pressure cutout switch
N A/C pressure cycling switch
P Transaxle Fluid Temperature (TFT) sensor
  (inside transaxle)

⊗ SIR SYSTEM COMPONENTS

Refer to SECTION 9J of the Service
Manual for CAUTIONS and information
on SIR Components.

FIGURE 27–7 Typical location of major engine sensors and actuators.

FIGURE 27–8 Typical engine coolant temperature (ECT) sensor. *Courtesy of Ford Motor Company*

until the engine is warm enough for the oxygen sensor to take over air/fuel mixture control (closed loop).

◆ Startup fuel enrichment on fuel-injected engines.
◆ Spark advance and retard. Spark advance is often limited until the engine reaches normal operating temperature.
◆ EGR flow, which is blocked while the engine is cold to improve driveability.
◆ Canister purge, which does not occur until the engine is warm.
◆ Throttle kicker or idle speed.
◆ Transmission torque converter clutch lockup.

The coolant temperature sensor (Figure 27–8) is usually located on the cylinder head or intake manifold. The sensor screws into the water jacket. On most systems, the coolant sensor is a variable resistance thermistor. On older systems, a switch coolant sensor may be used. This type of sensor may be designed to remain closed within a certain temperature range (55° to 235°F, for example) or to open only when the engine is warm (125 degrees Fahrenheit or hotter).

Because the coolant sensor's major role is triggering so many engine functions, a faulty sensor or sensor circuit can cause a variety of problems. The most common is the failure to switch to the closed-loop mode once the engine is warm. Other problems may include poor cold idling caused by no early fuel evaporation, heated air, or rich fuel mixture; stalling due to a rich mixture, retarded timing, or as low idle speed; cold hesitation or stumble due to no EFE or EGR occurring too soon; or poor fuel mileage due to a rich mixture, open loop operation, or a retarded spark.

Coolant temperature sensor problems are often due to wiring faults or loose or corroded connection rather than failure of the sensor itself. Correct operation of the sensor can also be upset by installing the wrong temperature range thermostat.

ENGINE POSITION SENSORS Engine position sensors tell the computer the speed of the engine and when the piston in each cylinder reaches top dead center (TDC). This input is used to set ignition timing and fuel injection delivery. Several distinct types of engine position sensors are used, but all communicate with the computer by generating a voltage signal. The sensor does this using a Hall-effect switch or electro-magnetic induction. The engine position sensor may be called a distributor pick-up coil, crankshaft or camshaft position sensor, or a profile ignition pick-up sensor (Figure 27–9).

EGR DIAGNOSTIC SWITCH On some vehicles with port fuel injection systems that control EGR operation, an EGR diagnostic switch is used to tell the computer if the EGR is actually being applied when it is commanded to be applied.

EGR VACUUM DIAGNOSTIC CONTROL SWITCH Some cars include a vacuum-operated switch that is tied into the vacuum hose between the EGR valve and the EGR control solenoid. When vacuum is applied to the EGR valve, the switch closes. If the computer detects a closed EGR diagnostic switch during starting, idle, or any other time, it has not commanded the EGR to be applied. It turns on the

FIGURE 27–9 Profile ignition pick-up (PIP) sensor. *Courtesy of Ford Motor Company*

check engine light and sets a fault code in its diagnostic memory. If it sees an open switch during any time it has commanded the EGR to be applied, it turns on the check engine light and sets the same code.

EGR VALVE POSITION SENSOR Car manufacturers use a variety of sensors or switches to determine when the EGR valve is open. This information is used to adjust the air/fuel mixture. The exhaust gases introduced by the EGR valve into the intake manifold reduce the available oxygen and thus less fuel is needed to maintain low HC levels in the exhaust.

ENGINE SPEED SENSOR Similar to the engine position sensor, the information from this sensor may be used by the computer for determining timing (advance based on speed), fuel delivery, emission control, converter clutch operation, and idle speed.

HEATED WINDSHIELD MODULE This input tells the computer the heated windshield system is operating. This helps the computer accurately determine engine load and idle speed.

HIGH GEAR SWITCH This input tells the computer when the car's automatic transmission is in high gear and allows the torque converter clutch to lock up.

KNOCK SENSOR The knock sensor tells the microprocessor that the engine is pinging. In turn, the computer retards the timing (Figure 27–10). The knock sensor is a piezoelectric device that converts engine knock vibrations into a voltage signal. Some of the latest systems retard timing on an individual cylinder basis.

IDLE TRACKING SWITCH (ITS) In the body of the idle speed control motor assembly (used on some carbureted and fuel injected applications) is a normally closed switch. When the throttle is closed, the throttle level presses against a plunger extending from the nose of the assembly. The pressure forces the plunger to move slightly back into the assembly and causes the switch to open. When the throttle is open, the switch closes again. The computer monitors the switch and can determine when the throttle is open or closed. It uses this information to function with the idle speed control (ISC) motor.

FIGURE 27–10
Typical knock sensor.
Courtesy of Ford Motor Company

FIGURE 27–11 Computer-controlled fuel mixture is achieved through several sensors. To make the mixture leaner during deceleration, the microprocessor uses a decrease in MAP and a decrease in throttle position to shorten the open time (pulse width).

MANIFOLD ABSOLUTE PRESSURE (MAP) SENSOR The function of a MAP sensor is to sense air pressure or vacuum in the intake manifold. The computer uses this input as an indication of engine load to adjust the air/fuel mixture and spark timing (Figure 27–11). The MAP sensor reads vacuum and pressure through a hose connected to the intake manifold. A pressure-sensitive ceramic or silicon element and electronic circuit in the sensor generates a voltage signal that changes in direct proportion to pressure.

MAP sensors should not be confused with vacuum sensors or barometric pressure sensors. While a vacuum sensor reads the difference between manifold vacuum and atmospheric pressure, a MAP sensor measures manifold air pressure against a precalibrated absolute pressure. Because it bases its readings on preset absolute pressure, MAP sensor readings are not adversely altered by changes in operating altitudes or barometric pressure.

CUSTOMER CARE

It is a service to your customer to point out the vacuum hoses leading to MAP sensors. They should be checked at every tuneup. During winter months, the inside of the vacuum hoses should be checked for moisture buildup. Hoses can freeze and prevent the MAP from functioning. ■

MASS AIRFLOW (MAF) SENSOR This sensor measures the flow of air entering the engine. This measurement of airflow is a reflection of engine load (throttle opening and air volume). It is similar to the relationship of engine load to MAP or vacuum sensor signal. Since there are several types of MAFs (vane airflow, ultrasonic system and hot-wire), check the service manual for the one used.

NEUTRAL DRIVE/NEUTRAL GEAR SWITCH A neutral drive switch is used with automatic transmission vehicles to adjust idle speed due to the increased loading of an engaged transmission/transaxle. Vehicles with a manual transmission or transaxle use a neutral gear to inform the computer that the vehicle is out of gear.

OXYGEN SENSORS The exhaust gas oxygen sensor, or Lambda sensor as it is referred to on many import vehicles, is the key sensor in the closed-loop mode (Figure 27–12). Its input is used by the computer to maintain a balanced air/fuel mixture.

One type of oxygen sensor, made with a zirconium dioxide element, generates a voltage signal proportional to the amount of oxygen in the exhaust gas. It compares the oxygen content in the exhaust gas with the oxygen content of the outside air. As the amount of unburned oxygen in the exhaust gas increases, the voltage output of the sensor drops. Sensor output ranges from 0.1 volt (lean) to 0.9 volt (rich). A perfectly balanced air/fuel mixture of 14.7 to 1 produces an output of around 0.5 volt. When the sensor reading is lean, the computer enriches the air/fuel mixture to the engine. When the sensor reading is rich, the computer leans the air/fuel mixture.

Because the oxygen sensor must be hot to operate, some sensors are equipped with an internal heating element. This helps the sensor reach operating temperature more quickly and maintains temperature during periods of idling or low engine load.

A second type of oxygen sensor does not generate a voltage signal. Instead it acts like a variable resistor, altering a base voltage supplied by the control module. When the air/fuel mixture is rich, sensor resistance is low. When the mixture is lean, resistance increases. Variable-resistance oxygen sensors do not need an outside air reference. This eliminates the need for internal venting to the outside. They feature very fast warm-up, and they operate at lower exhaust temperatures.

The normal life span of this important sensor is between 30,000 and 50,000 miles. Sensors can fail prematurely if they become clogged with carbon or solvents from the misuse of RTV silicone sealers. Older sensors may operate sluggishly as indicated by loss of power, rough idle, poor fuel mileage, or increased emissions.

The accuracy of the oxygen sensor reading can be affected by air leaks in the intake or exhaust manifold. A misfiring spark plug that allows unburned oxygen to pass into the exhaust also causes the sensor to give a false lean reading.

PRESSURE FEEDBACK EGR (PFE) The **PFE** sensor used in some vehicles is a pressure-sensing voltage divider (functions as a potentiometer) similar to the ones used as MAP and BP sensors. It senses exhaust pressure in a chamber just under the EGR valve pintle (Figure 27–13). This pressure causes the PFE to vary its output voltage signal to the computer. When the EGR valve is closed, the pressure in the sensing chamber is equal to exhaust pressure. When the EGR valve opens, pressure in this chamber drops because of the restricting orifice that lets exhaust into the sensing chamber from the exhaust system. The more the valve opens, the more the pressure drops. The PFE voltage signal tells the computer how far the EGR valve is open. The computer uses this information to fine tune its control of the electronic vacuum regulator (EVR), which controls vacuum to the EGR valve. This information also allows the computer to more accurately control air/fuel ratios and ignition timing.

POWER STEERING (PS) SWITCH This switch causes the computer to raise the idle speed when the power steering is turned to lock. This prevents stalling when the automobile is engaged in tight turns or is being parked.

FIGURE 27–12
Exhaust gas oxygen sensor.

FIGURE 27–13 Circuit using pressure feedback EGR (PFE) sensor. *Courtesy of Ford Motor Company*

FIGURE 27–14 Throttle position sensor.

FIGURE 27–15 Vehicle speed sensor. *Courtesy of General Motors' Product Service Training*

SYSTEM BATTERY VOLTAGE This voltage provides power for the system. Poor grounds can cause all or any part of the computer-controlled system to malfunction.

THROTTLE POSITION SENSOR (TPS) Engines with electronic fuel injection or feedback carburetors use a throttle position sensor to inform the computer about the rate of throttle opening and the relative throttle position (Figure 27–14). A separate idle switch or wide open throttle (WOT) switch may also be used to signal the computer when these throttle positions exist.

The TPS is a variable resistor that changes resistance as the throttle opens. As resistance readings tell the computer that the throttle is opening, it enriches the air/fuel mixture to maintain the proper air/fuel ratio.

The initial setting of the TPS is critical. The voltage signal the computer receives is referenced to this setting. Many service manuals list the initial TPS setting to the nearest one-hundredth volt, a clear indication of the importance of this setting.

The most common symptom of a bad or misadjusted TPS is hesitation or stumble during acceleration. The fuel mixture leans out because the computer does not receive the right signal telling it to add fuel as the throttle opens. Eventually, the oxygen sensor senses the problem and adjusts the mixture, but not before the engine stumbles.

VACUUM SENSOR Vehicles that do not have MAP or BARO sensors may use a vacuum sensor to provide engine load and speed change information. The vacuum sensor measures the difference between atmospheric pressure (outside air) and engine vacuum.

VEHICLE SPEED SENSOR This sensor tells the computer the vehicle's speed in miles per hour

(Figure 27–15). This input controls when the torque converter clutch locks up and also can be used to control EGR flow and canister purge.

🔧 SHOP TALK

The terms *hardware* and *software* are frequently used in descriptions of computers and electronic control systems. Hardware refers to those parts of the system that are literally hard. It includes the parts of the system that can be seen and touched. Hardware includes the actual system components such as the sensors, actuators, computers, the wiring, and the connectors between these components. In general, hardware cannot be changed once it is created. Modern electronic control systems also include software. Software is information, stored computer memory as tiny electrical signals. Software can be changed or modified, thus it is called soft. Software includes the information stored in computer memory, such as engine calibration information. Software also includes the programs that guide the computer through each decision. ■

COMPUTER OUTPUTS AND ACTUATORS

Computer outputs are electronic signals to control devices or actuators. As mentioned earlier, these actuators perform mechanical movements or actions that change the operating conditions of the engine or vehicle. The major actuators in a computer-controlled engine include the following components.

AIR MANAGEMENT SOLENOIDS Air by-pass and diverter solenoids control the flow of air from the air pump to either the exhaust manifold (open loop) or the catalytic converter (closed loop).

CANISTER PURGE SOLENOID This solenoid controls when stored fuel vapors in the canister are drawn into the engine and burned. The computer only activates this solenoid valve when the engine is warm and above idle speed.

EGR FLOW SOLENOIDS EGR flow is controlled by a pair of electronically controlled vacuum solenoids. One supplies manifold vacuum to the EGR valve when EGR is required. The second vents the vacuum when EGR is not required.

MIXTURE CONTROL SOLENOIDS In some carbureted engines, an electrical solenoid is used to operate the metering rods and idle air bleed valve in the carburetor.

FUEL INJECTORS These solenoid valves deliver the fuel spray in fuel-injected systems.

IDLE SPEED CONTROLS These actuators are small electric motors. On carbureted engines, this idle speed motor is mounted on the throttle linkage. On fuel-injected systems a stepper motor is used to control the amount of air bypassing the throttle plate.

OTHER SOLENOIDS Computer-controlled solenoids may also be used in the operation of cruise control systems, torque converter lockup clutches, automatic transmission shift mechanisms, and many other systems where mechanical action is needed.

IGNITION MODULE This is actually an electronic switching device triggered by a signal from the control computer.

MOTORS AND LIGHTS Using electrical relays, the computer is used to trigger the operation of electric motors such as the fuel pump, or various warning light or display circuits.

SYSTEM OPERATION

Control loops are the cycles by which a process can be controlled by information received from input sensors, ROM, computer processing, and output of specific commands to control actuator devices.

The basic purpose of all computerized engine control loops is the same: to create an ideal air/fuel ratio, which allows the catalytic converter to operate at maximum efficiency, while giving the best mileage and performance possible and protecting the engine.

Closed Loop Mode

The closed loop mode is basically the same for any automotive system. Sensor inputs are sent to the computer; the computer processes them and sends commands to the output devices. The output devices adjust timing, air/fuel ratio, and emission control operation. The resulting engine operation affects the sensors, which send new messages to the computer, completing the cycle of operation. The complete cycle is called a closed loop.

Closed control loops are often referred to as feedback systems. This means the sensors provide constant information, or feedback, on what is taking place in the engine. This allows the engine to make constant decisions and changes to output commands.

Open Loop Mode

When the engine is cold, most electronic engine controls go into what is called the open loop mode. In this mode, the control loop is not a complete cycle because the computer does not react to feedback information. Instead, the computer makes decisions based on preprogrammed information that allows it to make basic ignition or air/fuel settings and to disregard sensor inputs. The open loop mode is activated when a signal from the temperature sensor indicates the engine temperature is too low for gasoline to properly vaporize and burn in the cylinders. Systems with oxygen sensors may also go into the open loop mode while idling, or any time the oxygen sensor cools off enough to stop sending a signal, and at wide-open throttle.

Fail Safe or Limp-In Mode

Most computer systems also have what is known as the fail safe or limp-in mode. The limp-in mode is nothing more than the computer's attempt to take control of vehicle operation when input from one of its critical sensors—the MAP, throttle position, coolant temperature and temperature sensor—has been lost. To be more specific, if the computer sees a problem with the input from any one of those devices, it either works with fixed values in place of the failed sensor input, or depending on which input was lost, it can also generate a modified value by combining two or more related sensor inputs.

To illustrate this last point, let us assume the MAP sensor stops working. Instead of an actual MAP measurement, the computer compensates by creating an artificial MAP signal from the combination of throttle position input and engine speed data. While this may not result in the most efficient operation, considering the alternatives, a modified MAP signal is better than no MAP signal at all. This allows the engine to run until the driver can reach a service location.

Some systems have an adaptive learning feature, referred to as FMEM, which makes adjustments to the entire system to compensate for faulty inputs or outputs. In this mode the driver will have little awareness that there is a problem as the engine will run quite well. Depending on the fault identified by the computer, the malfunction indicator lamp (**MIL**) may not even be lit.

Spark Control System

In spark control systems, input to the computer usually consists of engine temperature, engine speed, and manifold vacuum. There may be other sensors for throttle position, incoming air temperature, or engine knocking (detonation).

The computer processes these inputs and advances or retards spark timing as required. This causes changes in engine operation, which sends new messages to the computer, continuing the control loop cycle. The computer can constantly adjust timing for maximum efficiency.

When the engine is cold, the spark control system is in the open loop and runs the engine on preprogrammed settings, disregarding sensors until the engine reaches normal operating temperature. Figure 27–16 shows a typical spark control system control loop. This system is much more efficient than earlier spark control systems, such as those with vacuum and centrifugal advance mechanisms.

The advantage of the electronic spark control system is threefold. It compensates for changes in engine (and sometimes outside air) temperature. It makes changes at a rate many times faster than older systems. Finally, it has a feedback mechanism in which sensor readings allow it to complete its control loop and constantly compensate for changing conditions.

Fuel Control System

In carbureted fuel control systems, input to the computer comes from sensors for manifold vacuum,

FIGURE 27–17 Typical carbureted engine fuel control system control loop.

engine temperature, and exhaust-gas oxygen. The computer processes this information and sends commands to the solenoid on the feedback carburetor, adjusting the air/fuel mixture entering the cylinder.

This electronic control is superior to the earlier carburetor system as it compensates for changes in the engine load, speed, and temperature much more quickly and accurately. It also constantly compensates for changes in air/fuel ratio due to its control loop feature. Figure 27–17 shows a typical fuel control system control loop.

In fuel-injected systems, typical inputs to the computer are manifold vacuum, throttle position, engine speed, position, and engine temperature, inlet air temperature, and oxygen in the exhaust.

The computer processes these inputs and sends commands to the fuel injectors, telling them how long to stay open. This system controls air/fuel ratios much more precisely than any carburetor system. The constant sensor inputs and precise fuel control provide a very accurate air/fuel mixture. This fuel-injected system control loop is shown in Figure 27–18.

Emission Control System

Three main emission-controlled devices are controlled by the computer. These are the EGR valve, the air pump (thermactor), and the evaporative emissions canister. The computer keeps the level of the three major pollutants (CO, HC, and NO_x) at acceptably low levels.

Other emission control devices may be wholly or partly controlled by the computer. These include the thermostatic air cleaner, early fuel evaporation devices, and electric choke. Consult the appropriate service manual for exact applications.

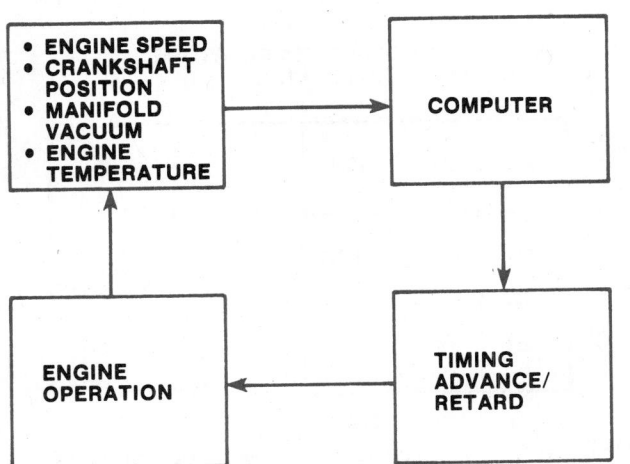

FIGURE 27–16 Typical spark control system control loop.

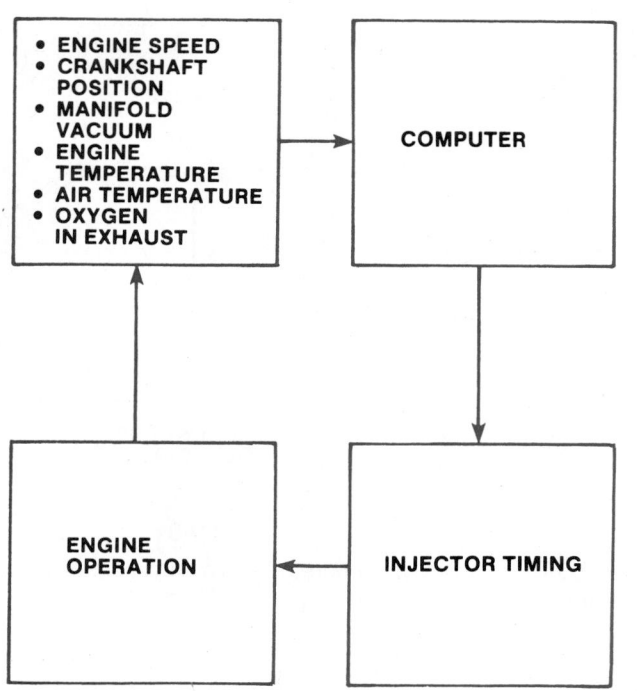

FIGURE 27–18 Typical fuel-injected engine control loop.

Combined Spark/Fuel Emission Control System

Typical inputs to the spark and fuel control computer include the following.

◆ Engine temperature
◆ Engine speed
◆ Throttle position
◆ Manifold vacuum/manifold air pressure
◆ Inlet/charge air temperature
◆ Oxygen in exhaust
◆ Engine detonation (knock)
◆ EGR valve position

The computer processes this information and controls the following areas.

◆ Ignition timing
◆ Air/fuel ratio (carburetor or fuel injection)
◆ Air pump (thermactor) operation
◆ EGR valve operation
◆ Evaporative emissions canister purge

Control of Nonengine Functions

Some devices that are not directly connected to the engine are also controlled by the computer to ensure maximum efficiency.

For example, air-conditioner compressor clutches can be turned on or off, depending on various conditions. One common control procedure turns off the compressor when the throttle is fully depressed. This allows maximum engine acceleration by eliminating the compressor load.

On some vehicles, the torque converter lock-up clutch is applied and released by a signal from the computer. The clutch is applied by transmission hydraulic pressure, which is controlled by electrical solenoids that are in turn controlled by the computer.

LOGICAL TROUBLESHOOTING

The importance of logical troubleshooting cannot be overemphasized. The ability to diagnose a problem (to find its cause and its solution) is what separates the automotive technician from the parts changer.

There are two logics used when servicing electronic engine controls: computer logic and a technician's logical diagnosis.

Computer Logic Flow

To control an engine system, the computer makes a series of decisions. Decisions are made in a step-by-step fashion until a conclusion is reached. Generally, the first decision is to determine the engine mode. For example, to control air/fuel mixture the computer first determines whether the engine is cranking, idling, cruising, or accelerating. Then, the computer can choose the best system strategy for the present engine mode. In a typical example, sensor input indicates the engine is warm, rpm is high, manifold absolute pressure is high, and the throttle plate is wide open. The computer determines the vehicle is under heavy acceleration or wide-open throttle. Next, the computer determines the goal to be reached. For example, with heavy acceleration, the goal is to create a rich air/fuel mixture. When operating in open loop fuel control, the computer uses a look-up table similar to that shown in Figure 27–19. At wide-open throttle, with high manifold absolute pressure and

HIGH MAP. ENGINE COOLANT TEMPERATURE OF 170° F. AIR/FUEL RATIO IS 13:1.

FIGURE 27–19 A typical look-up table for open loop fuel control.

coolant temperature of 170°F, the table indicates the air/fuel ratio should be 13:1. That is, 13 pounds of air for every 1 pound of fuel. An air/fuel ratio of 13:1 creates the rich air/fuel mixture needed for heavy acceleration.

In a final series of decisions, the computer determines how the goal can be achieved. In our example, a rich air/fuel mixture is achieved by increasing fuel injector pulse width. The injector nozzle remains open longer and more fuel is drawn into the cylinder, providing the additional power needed.

Technician's Logical Diagnosis

The best automotive technicians use this same logical process to diagnose engine problems. When faced with an abnormal engine condition, they compare clues (such as meter readings, oscilloscope readings, visible problems) with their knowledge of proper conditions and discover a logical reason for the way the engine is performing. Logical diagnosis means following a simple basic procedure. Start with the most likely cause and work to the most unlikely. In other words, check out the easiest, most obvious solutions first before proceeding to the less likely, and more difficult, solutions. Do not guess at the problem or jump to a conclusion before considering all of the factors.

The logical approach has a special application to troubleshooting electronic engine controls. Always check all traditional nonelectronic engine control possibilities before attempting to diagnose the electronic engine control itself. For example, low battery voltage might result in faulty sensor readings. The distributor could also be sending faulty signals to the computer, resulting in poor ignition timing.

An additional problem that occurs when diagnosing any electronic part is that the part itself cannot be accurately tested. Most electronic parts are completely sealed and, because of complex, interlocking circuitry, cannot be checked at their input and output connections.

This problem can be overcome by using a logical procedure called the process of elimination. In other words, if every related part checks out okay, it must be the electronic part that is bad. This means thoroughly checking every component in a system, without assuming anything, as well as checking for such basic factors as proper current supply and good grounds.

CUSTOMER CARE

When a computer system component is replaced, it is possible that the vehicle runs poorly for a short time while the computer readjusts to the new component. This adjustment period usually lasts for about 5 miles, but if you do not explain this to your customers, they might blame you for the temporary poor performance (surging, high idle, hesitation).

One way to save your reputation and avoid this situation is to erase the memory or road test the vehicle (at least 5 miles) before releasing the vehicle to the customer. The computer's memory can be erased by disconnecting the battery or following the manufacturer's specific instructions, in some systems, for example, pulling the microprocessor fuse out for 10 seconds erases previously learned information without causing a complete power failure. This comes in handy, especially if your customer has an electronically tuned radio with a digital clock and preset channels that must be reprogrammed each time system power is lost.

This is also true of seat position, climate control settings, and other driver programmable options. Again while you must advise that he or she must reprogram these accessories, it would be better to record these settings before beginning the job and reprogram them before delivery. ■

ISOLATING COMPUTERIZED ENGINE CONTROL PROBLEMS

Determining which part or area of a computerized engine control system is defective requires having a thorough knowledge of how the system works and following the logical troubleshooting process previously explained.

There are many variations in the operation of electronic engine controls. Therefore, always consult the specific applications chapters in the factory service manual before beginning any diagnosis and repair. However, here are some guidelines to follow.

Electronic engine control problems are usually caused by defective sensors and, to a lesser extent, output devices. The logical procedure in most cases is, therefore, to check the input sensors and wiring first, then the output devices and their wiring, and, finally the computer.

Most late-model computerized engine controls have self-diagnosis capabilities. A malfunction in any sensor, output device, or in the computer itself is stored in the computer's memory as a trouble code. Stored codes can be retrieved and the indicated problem areas checked further.

Systems without self-diagnostics must be checked out by the process of elimination. All possible causes of the problem that can be are tested. If the fault is not found, the components that cannot be tested may be malfunctioning or faulty.

OHMMETER

FIGURE 27-20 Checking a temperature sensor with an ohmmeter. *Courtesy of Toyota Motors*

Four methods can be used to check individual components.

VISUAL CHECKS This means looking for obvious problems. Any part that is burned, broken, cracked, corroded, or has any other visible problem must be replaced before continuing the diagnosis. Examples of visible problems include disconnected sensor vacuum hoses and broken or disconnected wiring.

OHMMETER CHECKS Most sensors and output devices can be checked with an ohmmeter. For example, Figure 27-20 shows an ohmmeter used to check a temperature sensor. Normally, the ohmmeter reading is low on a cold engine and high or infinity on a hot engine, if the sensor is a PTC. If the sensor is an NTC, the opposite readings would be expected.

Output devices such as coils or motors can also be checked with an ohmmeter.

VOLTMETER CHECKS Many sensors, output devices, and their wiring can be diagnosed by checking the voltage to them, and in some cases, from them. Even some oxygen sensors can be checked in this manner.

In some cases, a final check on the computer can be made only by substitution. Also some vacuum, MAP, and barometric pressure sensors can only be checked by substitution. Substitution is not an allowable diagnostic method under the mandates of OBD-II. Nor is it the most desirable way to diagnose problems. However, to substitute, replace the suspected part with a known good unit and recheck the system. If the system now operates normally, the original part is defective.

SHOP TALK

Substitution can be an expensive way to test for problems since most parts suppliers do not

allow electrical problems to be returned. To use this procedure, it is a good idea to build up a supply of known good parts, such as ignition modules, electronic regulators, and computers to use as substitutes. These parts usually can be located at junkyards or body shops or from other sources. ◼

Self-Diagnostic System

Today's computer-controlled systems are complicated. It would take endless amounts of time to diagnose these systems using precomputer control methods. For this reason, most computerized engine controls have self-diagnostic capabilities. By entering a self-test mode, the computer is able to evaluate the condition of the entire electronic engine control system, including itself. If problems are found, they are identified as either hard faults (on-demand) or intermittent failures. Each type of fault or failure is assigned a numerical trouble code that is stored in computer memory (Figure 27-21).

A **hard fault** means a problem has been found somewhere in the system at the time of the self-test. An intermittent problem, on the other hand, indicates a malfunction occurred (for example, a poor connection causing an intermittent open or short) but is not present at the time of the self-test. As men-

SENSOR TROUBLE CODES			
Sensor	**Trouble Codes**		
	GM	**Ford**	**Chrysler**
Oxygen (EGO)	13,44, 45,55	43,91, 92,93	21,51,52
Throttle Position (TPS)	21,22	23,53, 63,73	24
Engine Vacuum (MAP)	31,33,34	22,72	13,14
Barometric Pressure (BARO)	32	—	37
Coolant (ECT)	14,15	21,51,61	17,22
Knock	42,43	25	17 (some only)
Vehicle Speed (VSS)	24	—	15
Air Temperature (MAT, VAT, ACT)	23,25	24,54,64	23
Airflow (VAF, MAF)	33,34, 44,45	26,56, 66,76	—
EGR Valve (EGR, EVP)	—	31,32,33, 34,83,84	31

FIGURE 27-21 Different systems use different numerical codes to indicate problems. *Courtesy of* Counterman *magazine*

tioned earlier in the chapter, non-volatile RAM allows intermittent faults to be stored for up to a specific number of ignition key on/off cycles. If the trouble does not reappear during that period, it is erased from the computer's memory.

There are various methods of assessing the trouble codes generated by the computer. Most manufacturers have diagnostic equipment designed to monitor and test the electronic components of their vehicles. Aftermarket companies also manufacture scan tools that have the capability to read and record the input and output signals passing to and from the computer. Another method of reading trouble codes is with an analog voltmeter. Some vehicles also flash trouble codes on dash lights or display them on CRT screens.

For each individual make and model, it is important that the technician consult the appropriate service manual to determine how trouble codes should be accessed and how to interpret the codes. The following sections give several examples of retrieving trouble codes, each using a different method.

Before reading self-diagnostic or trouble codes, do a visual check to make sure the problem is not a result of wear, loose connections, or vacuum hoses. Inspect the air cleaner, throttle body, or injection system. Do not forget the PCV system and vacuum hoses. Make sure the vapor canister is not flooded. Look at the wiring harnesses and connectors and the charging and alternator system. Also, check the connectors for signs of corrosion. The low-level electrical signals in today's electronic circuits cannot tolerate the increased resistance caused by corrosion in contacts.

Unlocking Trouble Codes

Although parts in any computerized system are amazingly reliable, they do occasionally fail. Diagnostic charts in service manuals (Figure 27–22) help you through troubleshooting procedures in the proper order. Start at the top and follow the sequence down. There will be branches of the "tree"—yes or no, on or off, ok or not ok—to follow after making the check required in each step.

Tools to use when checking circuits, connections, sensors, and signals include the following.

◆ A digital VOM (volt/ohmmeter) with 10 mega-ohm impedance
◆ Dwell meter
◆ Tachometer
◆ Vacuum gauge and pump
◆ Scan tool analog VOM (used with some computer systems)
◆ Service manuals with trouble code charts and diagnostic procedures

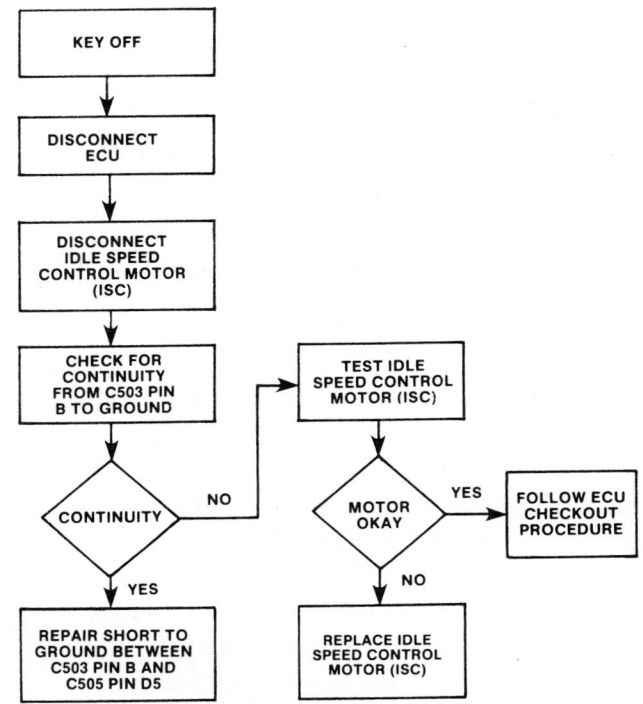

FIGURE 27–22 A diagnostic chart to be followed for a specific trouble code. *Courtesy of Chrysler Corporation*

A spark tester, fuel pressure gauge, a jumper wire with two alligator clips, and a nonpowered testlight can also come in handy.

There are two things that would tell the driver there is a problem with some part of the computer system: the MIL, check engine, power loss, or service engine soon light, or the car simply does not start.

The check engine light (**CEL**) or malfunction indicator lamp (MIL) comes on normally for a few seconds when the key is turned on and during cranking. It should go off when the engine starts. The check engine light should not come back on unless the computer finds a problem. If it does come on, there is probably a trouble code stored in memory.

Self-diagnostic procedures and diagnostic or trouble codes differ with vehicle make and year. Each time the key is turned to the on position, the system does a self-check. The self-check makes sure all the bulbs, fuses, and electronic modules are working. If the self-test finds a problem, it might store a code for later servicing. It may also instruct the computer to turn on the MIL to show service is needed.

General Motors' System The main components of General Motors' CCC onboard diagnostic system include the electronic control module (ECM) or powertrain control module (PCM), a MIL, check engine, or service engine soon warning light, and an assembly line communications link (ALCL). The check engine light serves two purposes (Figure 27–23). First, it is a

FIGURE 27–23 General Motors' CCC system warning light.

signal to the vehicle operator that a detectable CCC failure has occurred. Secondly, it can also be used by a technician to aid in the location of system malfunctions. Newer systems that are in compliance with OBD-II do not have this flashout feature. All codes must be retrieved with the use of a scan tool.

To find the problem, you must perform a diagnostic circuit check to be sure the diagnostic system is working. Turn the ignition key on, but do not start the engine. If the check engine light does not come on, follow the diagnostic chart in the service manual. If the light comes on, ground the diagnostic test terminal. This terminal is located on the DLC or **ALDL** connection (Figure 27–24). Connect pin A (ground) to pin B (test terminal). Watch the check engine light to see if it displays code 12. Code 12 (think of it as 1,2) is one flash, a short pause, and two flashes (Figure 27–25). If the computer's diagnostic program is working properly, it flashes code 12 three times. If code 12 does not appear, follow the diagnostic chart in the manual. The system then displays any fault codes in the same manner.

Codes are identified through the flashing MIL as follows. The number of times the light flashes on before it pauses tells the number to which it refers. In other words, if the MIL flashes like this: "on-off-on-off-on-off, pause," that means number 3 because it was on three times before it paused. If it flashed "on-

DIAGNOSTIC CODE DISPLAY

FIGURE 27–25 The check engine light signals the codes. Code 12 is a signal that the computer's diagnostic program is working properly. *Courtesy of General Motors Corporation*

off-on-off, pause," that means number 2. If it flashes "on-off, pause," that means number 1.

Because each code has two numbers to it, such as 12, 23, or 32, the flashes are read as a set. This means you always see two series of flashes separated by a pause: first number, pause, second number. As an example, a code 32 causes the light to go: "on-off-on-off-on-off" (it is on three times, which means the first number is 3), "pause, on-off-on-off" (it is on two times, which means the second number is 2). Together, they result in the number 32. The sequence repeats itself three times.

FIGURE 27–24 To initiate self-diagnostics, connect ground terminal, and test terminal at the DLC.

If the PCM has stored more than one trouble code, the codes flash starting with the lowest number code first and then work their way to the highest number code. For example, if the codes were 13 and 24, then 13 would flash first, then 24 would flash. Keep in mind you have to watch closely while you do this.

If the PCM is good, the first code flashes when the connector is grounded and the key is turned on. The code should be twelve (12). This is the tachometer code. It is a normal condition when the key is on but the engine is not running. If a code 12 is not received, there is something wrong in the DLC or related circuits.

Once the codes have been identified, consult the service manual (Figure 27–26). Each code directs you to a specific troubleshooting tree. If you have a code, follow the tree exactly. Never try to skip a step, or you'll be certain to miss the problem. This is because, even though the codes may mean the same thing, how you trace the problems is different for different cars. This is one of the main reasons a manual for the car on which you are working is needed.

A hand-held scan tool (Figure 27–27) can be used by itself or in conjunction with MIL. When using a scan tool, follow the manufacturer's directions to the letter.

DIAGNOSTIC CODE IDENTIFICATION

The "Service Engine Soon" light will only be "ON" if the malfunction exists under the conditions listed below. If the malfunction clears, the light will go out and the code will be stored in the ECM/PCM. Any codes stored will be erased if no problem reoccurs within 50 engine starts.

CODE AND CIRCUIT	PROBABLE CAUSE	CODE AND CIRCUIT	PROBABLE CAUSE
Code 13 - Oxygen O₂ Sensor Circuit (Open Circuit)	Indicates that the oxygen sensor circuit or sensor was open for one minute while off idle.	Code 33 - Manifold Absolute Pressure (MAP) Sensor Circuit (Signal Voltage High- Low Vacuum)	MAP sensor output to high for 5 seconds or an open signal circuit.
Code 14 - Coolant Temperature Sensor (CTS) Circuit (High Temperature Indicated)	Sets if the sensor or signal line becomes grounded for 3 seconds.	Code 34 - Manifold Absolute Pressure (MAP) Sensor Circuit (Signal Voltage Low-High Vacuum)	Low or no output from sensor with engine running.
Code 15 - Coolant Temperature Sensor (CTS) Circuit (Low Temperature Indicated)	Sets if the sensor, connections, or wires open for 3 seconds.	Code 35 - Idle Air Control (IAC) System	IAC error
Code 21 - Throttle Position Sensor (TPS) Circuit (Signal Voltage High)	TPS voltage greater than 2.5 volts for 3 seconds with less than 1200 RPM.	Code 42 - Electronic Spark Timing (EST)	ECM/PCM has seen an open or grounded EST or bypass circuit.
Code 22 - Throttle Position Sensor (TPS) Circuit (Signal Voltage Low)	A shorted to ground or open signal circuit will set code in 3 seconds.	Code 43 - Electronic Spark Control (ESC) Circuit	Signal to the ECM/PCM has remained low for too long or the system has failed a functional check.
Code 23 - Intake Air Temperature (IAT) Sensor Circuit (Low Temperature Indicated)	Sets if the sensor, connections, or wires open for 3 seconds.	Code 44 - Oxygen (O₂) Sensor Circuit (Lean Exhaust Indicated)	Sets if oxygen sensor voltage remains below .2 volt for about 20 seconds.
Code 24 - Vehicle Speed Sensor (VSS)	No vehicle speed present during a road load decel.	Code 45 - Oxygen (O₂) Sensor Circuit (Rich Exhaust Indicated)	Sets if oxygen sensor voltage remains above .7 volt for about 1 minute.
Code 25 - Intake Air Temperature (IAT) Sensor Circuit (High Temperature Indicated)	Sets if the sensor or signal line becomes grounded for 3 seconds.	Code 51 - Faulty MEM-CAL or PROM Problem	Faulty MEM-CAL, PROM, or ECM/PCM.
Code 32 - Exhaust Gas Recirculation (EGR) System	Vacuum switch shorted to ground on start up OR Switch not closed after the ECM/PCM has commanded EGR for a specified period of time. OR EGR solenoid circuit open for a specified period of time.	Code 52 - Fuel CALPAK Missing	Fuel CAL-PAK missing or faulty.
		Code 53 - System Over Voltage	System overvoltage. Indicates a basic generator problem.
		Code 54 - Fuel Pump Circuit (Low Voltage)	Sets when the fuel pump voltage is less than 2 volts when reference pulses are being received.
		Code 55 - Faulty ECM/PCM	Faulty ECM/PCM

FIGURE 27–26 These are typical General Motors' trouble codes with their probable causes. Check the service manual for information on a specific model. *Courtesy of Chevrolet Motor Division, General Motors Corporation*

FIGURE 27–27   Use of the hand-held scan tool for diagnostic testing.

FIGURE 27–28   Logic module location.

After correcting all faults or problems, clear the PCM memory of any current codes by pulling the PCM fuse at the fuse panel for 10 seconds. Then, to make sure the codes have cleared, remove the test terminal ground, and set the parking brake. Put the transmission in park, and run the engine for 2 to 5 minutes. Watch the check engine light. If the light comes on again, ground the test lead and note the flashing trouble code. If no light comes on, check the codes recorded earlier, if any.

It is a good idea to give the vehicle a road test. Some parts, such as the vehicle speed sensor, do not show any problems with the engine just idling.

Chrysler's System   As far as basic system operation is concerned, Chrysler's engine control system is typical of most computer-controlled designs. At the heart of Chrysler's computer-controlled system is a digital preprogrammed microprocessor known as the logic module (**LM**). From its location behind the right front kick pad (in the passenger compartment), the LM issues commands affecting fuel delivery, ignition timing, idle speed, and the operation of various emission control devices (Figure 27–28).

To accomplish all these tasks, the logic module operates in conjunction with a subordinate control unit called the power module (PM). The power module, located inside the engine compartment (Figure 27–29), is given the responsibility of controlling the injector and ignition coil ground circuit (based on the LM's commands). It is also in charge of supplying the ground to the automatic shutdown relay (**ASD**). The ASD relay controls the voltage supply to the fuel pump, logic module, injector, and coil drive circuits and is energized through the PM when the ignition switch is turned on.

Current Chrysler products have a single unit that actually consists of the logic and power modules. This unit is called the Single Board Electronic Controller (SBEC). On these systems, the LM and PM function as a single unit. However, each of these still have the same primary purposes as they did when they were in separate units.

Under normal operating conditions, the LM bases its decisions on information from several input devices (Figure 27–30).

From the information it receives, the logic module calculates the injector's pulse width, determines precise spark advance, maintains proper idle speed, governs turbo boost, controls the EGR and purge solenoids, and directs the operation of the electric cooling fan (among other things). When a computer-related failure occurs, the LM switches to a limp-in mode.

Chrysler has a simple method for checking trouble codes. Without starting the engine, turn the ignition key on and off three times within 5 seconds, ending with it on. The check engine or power loss light glows a short time to test the bulb, then starts flashing. Count the first set of flashes as tens. There

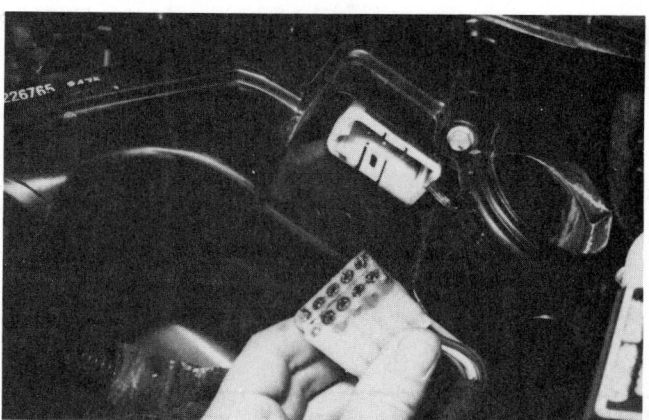

FIGURE 27–29   Power module location.

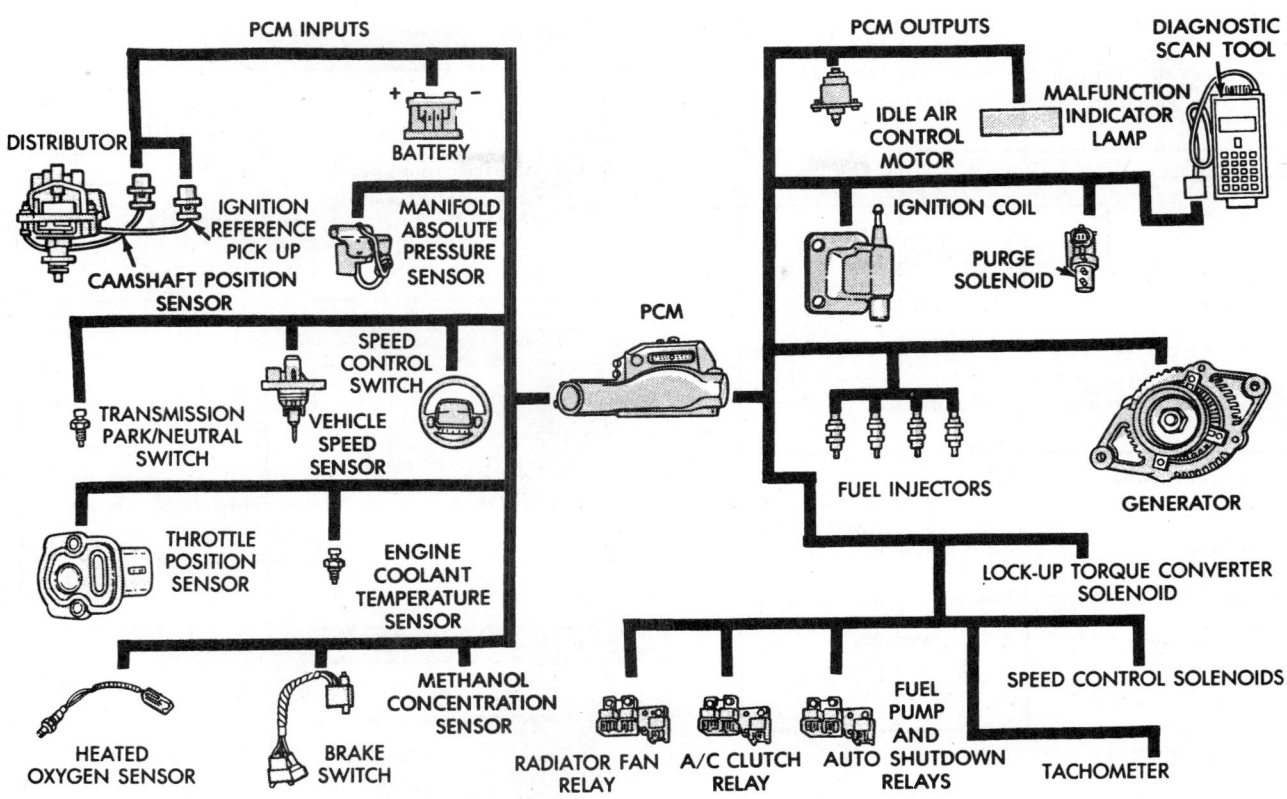

FIGURE 27-30 Chrysler's electronic engine control system with self-diagnosis.

is a half-second pause before the light starts flashing again. This time count by ones. Add the two sets of flashes together to obtain the trouble code. For example, 3 flashes, a half-second pause, followed by 5 flashes would be read as code 35. Watch carefully, because each trouble code is displayed only once. Look the code up in the service manual. This tells you which circuit to check. Once the trouble codes are flashed, the computer signals a code 55. If the light does not flash at all, there are no trouble codes stored. The problem could be a mechanical one, or the computer could be defective. Keep in mind that replacing the computer should be one of the last options. Check everything else first.

The same diagnostic or trouble code tests can be done using a scan tool. Connect the tool to the diagnostic connectors on the left fender apron. Follow the same sequence with the ignition key. The trouble codes are displayed on the scan tool readout. You can also check the circuits, switches, and relays with the scan tool. The service manual contains the troubleshooting trees (Figure 27-31) to continue your diagnosis of the problem.

A code 53 points to a problem with the logic module or SME controller. If a code 53 is received, turn off the ignition and recheck all electrical connections. Repeat the test procedure. If another code 53 is received, the module may be faulty.

Ford's System

USING SERVICE MANUALS

In this book we have described and illustrated service manual logic diagrams called tree charts. These so-called road maps are especially valuable in electronic service. However, the diagnostic procedure chart shown in Figure 27-32 for the Ford ECA is designed to make it easy to move quickly from one check to the next. The information is generally organized by system, trouble code, or test meter reading. ∎

The main brain of the Ford's EEC-IV is a computer unit called an electronic control assembly (ECA) or PCM. Like the other computer-controlled systems discussed, the PCM is endowed with self-diagnostic capabilities. By entering a mode known as self-test (Figure 27-33), the computer is able to evaluate the condition of the entire electronic system, including itself. If problems are found, they show up as either hard faults (on demand) or intermittent failures.

On 1988 and newer model vehicles, the diagnostic or trouble codes are displayed by the MIL on the instrument panel. Since 1994, Ford has equipped

FIGURE 27-31 Typical service manual troubleshooting tree.

FIGURE 27-32 Typical service manual diagnostic procedure chart. *Courtesy of Ford Motor Company*

some models with the EEC-V system, which is an OBD-II compliant system. This system does not display codes on the MIL. The Ford self-test diagnostic procedure can be broken down into four parts.

◆ Key on/engine off: checks system inputs for hard faults (malfunctions that occur during the self-test) and intermittent faults (malfunctions that occurred sometime prior to the self-test and were stored in memory).
◆ Computed ignition timing check: determines the ECA's ability to advance or retard ignition timing. This check is made while the self-test is activated and the engine is running.
◆ Engine running segment: checks system output for hard faults only.
◆ Continuous monitoring test (wiggle test): allows the technician to look for and set intermittent faults while the engine is running.

Within these four tests, there are six types of service codes. There are on-demand codes, **keep-alive**

memory codes, separator codes, dynamic response codes, fast codes, and engine identification codes (I.D.). To understand what you are dealing with when the codes start to display, a brief explanation of each type is necessary.

On-demand codes are used to identify hard faults. As mentioned earlier, a hard fault means that a system failure has been detected and is still present at the time of testing. The term *on-demand* simply means a technician is asking the computer if a prob-

FIGURE 27-33 Self-test connectors are used to connect test equipment to the system's computer.

lem exists right now. That is, the computer locates them while it is running its own self-test.

Keep-alive memory codes mean a malfunction was noted sometime during the last twenty vehicle warm-ups but is not present now. (If it were, it would be recorded as a hard fault.) The continuous memory code comes on after an approximate 10-second delay. Make the on-demand code repairs first. Once you have completed repairs, repeat the key on, engine off test. If all the parts are repaired correctly, a pass code of 11 should be received.

A separator code (10) indicates the on-demand codes are over and the memory codes are about to begin. The separator code occurs as part of the key-on, engine-off segment of the self-test only.

When a code 10 appears during the engine running segment of the self-test, it is referred to as a dynamic response code. The dynamic response code is a signal to the technician to goose the throttle momentarily so the ECA can verify the operation of the throttle position (TP) and manifold absolute pressure (MAP) sensors. On some models, the technican must goose the throttle, step on the brake pedal, and turn the steering wheel 180 degrees. Failure to respond to the dynamic code within 15 seconds after it appears sets a code 77 (operator did not respond).

Fast codes are of no value to the service technician unless he happens to have a scan tool that is capable of reading them. They are designed for factory use and are transmitted about 100 times faster than even a scan or Ford's star tester can read. On the voltmeter, fast codes cause the needle to rapidly pulse between 0 and 3 volts. On the scan tester, the LED light flickers. Although fast codes have no practical use in the service bay, pay attention to when they occur so you know what is coming next. Fast codes appear twice during the entire self-test: once at the very beginning of the key-on, engine-off test (right before the on-demand codes) and again after the dynamic response code (prior to hard fault transmission).

Engine identification codes are used to tell automated assemblyline equipment how many cylinders the engine has. Two needle pulses indicate a four-cylinder; three pulses, a six-cylinder; and four pulses identify the engine as an eight-cylinder model. Engine ID codes appear at the beginning of the engine-running segment only.

Diagnostic codes can also be retrieved using an analog volt-ohmmeter, a scan tool, or Ford star tester. When a service code is reported on the analog voltmeter for a function test, it represents itself as a pulsing or sweeping movement of the voltmeter (Figure 27–34). Therefore, a single-digit number of three is reported by three needle pulses (sweeps). However, as previously stated, a service code is represented by a two-digit number, such as 2-3. As a result, the self-test service code of 2-3 appears on the voltmeter as two needle pulses (sweeps). Then, after a 2-second pause, the needle pulses (sweeps) three times. To activate the self-test mode, two jumper wires (about 6 inches long each) with male spade terminals and a voltmeter are needed (Figure 27–35).

FIGURE 27–34 Reading an analog voltmeter and determining the service code.

FIGURE 27–35 Checking a self-diagnostic connector with jumper wires and a voltmeter.

CUSTOMER CARE

You have finished servicing the engine electronic control system and are ready to deliver the vehicle to the customer. This is a good time to make a final check of the electronic system. What you do not want to do is to release a car and then have the customer bring it back a few hours later because something is not right. ∎

◆ Start the engine. Does the check engine light stay on? If so, you go through the process of checking for diagnostic codes.

◆ If the MIL goes out, then listen to the engine. Does it sound normal? Do all the instruments and accessories work like they are supposed to?

◆ If everything seems okay here, take it for a test drive. Does it run right? Do all the systems work? Drive it for several miles, not just around the block. Does the MIL come on? If there is a problem, it may take a few miles for the computer to detect it and store a code. This is why a customer often notices nothing for the first several miles after taking delivery of the car.

◆ If no problems show up by the time you have finished the test drive, it is a safe bet the car is okay.

OBD-II STANDARDS

The purpose of OBD-II was to provide standard service procedures without the use of dedicated special tools. To accomplish this goal, manufacturers needed to change many aspects of their electronic control systems. Since 1994 manufacturers have been producing some models that meet this new standard. By 1997, all new car models will meet these mandates. According to the guidelines of OBD-II, all vehicles will have:

◆ A universal diagnostic test connector, known as the data link connector (**DLC**), with dedicated pin assignments.

◆ A standard location for the DLC. It must be under the dash on the driver's side of the vehicle and must be visible.

◆ A standard list of diagnostic trouble codes (**DTC**s).

◆ Vehicle identification must be automatically transmitted to the scan tool.

◆ Stored trouble codes must be able to be cleared from the computer's memory with the scan tool.

◆ The ability to record, and store in memory, a snapshot of the operating conditions that existed when a fault occurred.

◆ The ability to store a code whenever something goes wrong that affects exhaust quality.

◆ A standard glossary of terms, acronyms, and definitions (Figure 27–36) must be used for all components in the electronic control systems.

The primary advantage of the snapshot feature is the ability to look at the existing conditions when a code was set. This will be especially valuable for diagnosing intermittent problems. Whenever a code is set, a record of all related activities will be stored in memory. This allows the technician to look at the action of sensors and actuators when the code was set. This helps identify the cause of the problem.

The standard DLC (Figure 27–37) is a 16-pin connector. The connector is "D"-shaped and has guide keys that allow the scan tool to be installed one way only. Using a standard connector design and by designating the pins, allows data retrieval with any scan tool designed for OBD-II.

The connector pins are arranged in two rows and are numbered consecutively. Seven of the sixteen pins have been assigned by the OBD-II standard. The remaining nine pins can be used by the individual manufacturers to meet their needs and desires.

The DLC is designed only for scan tool use. You cannot jump across any of the terminals to display codes on an instrument panel or other indicator lamp. The warning light (MIL), is only used to inform the driver that the vehicle should be serviced soon. It also informs a technician that the computer has set a trouble code.

Many of the trouble codes from an OBD-II system will mean the same thing regardless of manufacturer. However, some of the codes will pertain only to a particular system or will mean something different with each system. The DTC is a five-character code with both letters and numbers (Figure 27–38). This is called the alphanumeric system. The first character

J1930 Terminology List

NOTE: Certain Ford Component names have been changed in this Service Manual to conform to Society of Automotive Engineers (SAE) directive J1930.

SAE J1930 standardizes automotive component names for all vehicle manufacturers.

New Term	New Acronyms/ Abbreviations	Old Acronyms/ Term
Accelerator Pedal	AP	– Accelerator
Air Cleaner	ACL	– Air Cleaner
Air Conditioning	A/C	– A/C – Air Conditioning
Barometric Pressure	BARO	– BP – Barometric Pressure
Battery Positive Voltage	B+	– BATT+ – Battery Positive
Camshaft Position	CMP	– Camshaft Sensor
Carburetor	CARB	– CARB Carburetor
Continuous Fuel Injection	CFI	– Continuous Fuel Injection
Charge Air Cooler	CAC	– After Cooler – Intercooler
Closed Loop	CL	– EEC
Closed Throttle Position	CTP	– CTP – Closed Throttle Position
Clutch Pedal Position	CPP	– CES – CIS – Clutch Engage Switch – Clutch Interlock Switch
Continuous Trap Oxidizer	CTOX	– CTO
Crankshaft Position	CKP	– CPS – VRS – Variable Reluctance Sensor
Data Link Connector	DLC	– Self-Test Connector
Diagnostic Test Mode	DTM	– Self-Test Mode
Diagnostic Trouble Code	DTC	– Self-Test Code
Distributor Ignition	DI	– CBD – DS – TFI – Closed Bowl Distrbutor – Duraspark Ignition – Thick Film Ignition
Early Fuel Evaporation	EFE	– EFE – Early Fuel Evaporation

FIGURE 27–36 A list of SAE J1930 terms.

J1930 Terminology List

New Term	New Acronyms/ Abbreviations	Old Acronyms/ Term
Electrically Erasable Programmable Read Only Memory	EEPROM	– E2PROM
Electronic Ignition	EI	– DIS – EDIS – Distributorless Ignition System – Electronic Distributorless Ignition System
Engine Coolant Level	ECL	– Engine Coolant Level
Engine Coolant Temperature	ECT	– ECT – Engine Coolant Temperature
Engine Control Module	ECM	– ECM – Engine Control Module
Engine Speed	RPM	– RPM – Revolutions Per Minute
Erasable Programmable Read Only Memory	EPROM	– EPROM – Erasable Programmable Read Only Memory
Evaporative Emission	EVAP	– EVP Sensor – EVR Solenoid
Exhaust Gas Recirculation	EGR	– EGR – Exhaust Gas Recirculation
Fan Control	FC	– EDF – Electro-Drive Fan
Flash Electrically Erasable Programmable Read Only Memory	FEEPROM	– FEEPROM – Flash Electrically Erasable Programmable Read Only Memory
Flash Erasable Programmable Read Only Memory	FEPROM	– FEPROM – Flash Erasable Programmable Read Only Memory
Flexible Fuel	FF	– FCS – FFS – FFV – Fuel Compensation Sensor – Flex Fuel Sensor
Fourth Gear	4GR	– Fourth Gear
Fuel Pump	FP	– FP – Fuel Pump
Generator	GEN	– ALT – Alternator
Ground	GND	– GND – Ground
Heated Oxygen Sensor	HO2S	– HEGO – Heated Exhaust Gas Oxygen Sensor
Idle Air Control	IAC	– IAC – Idle Air Bypass Control

FIGURE 27–36 *Continued*

J1930 Terminology List

New Term	New Acronyms/ Abbreviations	Old Acronyms/ Term
Idle Speed Control	ISC	– Idle Speed Control
Ignition Control Module	ICM	– DIS Module – EDIS Module – TFI Module
Indirect Fuel Injection	IFI	– IDFI – Indirect Fuel Injection
Inertia Fuel Shutoff	IFS	– Inertia Switch
Intake Air Temperature	IAT	– ACT – Air Charge Temperature
Knock Sensor	KS	– KS – Knock Sensor
Malfunction Indicator Lamp	MIL	– CEL – "CHECK ENGINE" Light – "SERVICE ENGINE SOON" Light
Manifold Absolute Pressure	MAP	– MAP – Manifold Absolute Pressure
Manifold Differential Pressure	MDP	– MDP – Manifold Differential Pressure
Manifold Surface Temperature	MST	– MST – Manifold Surface Temperature
Manifold Vacuum Zone	MVZ	– MVZ – Manifold Vacuum Zone
Mass Air Flow	MAF	– MAF – Mass Air Flow
Mixture Control	MC	– Mixture Control
Multiport Fuel Injection	MFI	– EFI – Electronic Fuel Injection
Non-Volatile Random Access Memory	NVRAM	– NVM – Non-Volatile Memory
On-Board Diagnostic	OBD	– Self-Test – On-Board Diagnostic
Open Loop	OL	– OL – Open Loop
Oxidation Catalytic Converter	OC	– COC – Conventional Oxidation Catalyst
Oxygen Sensor	O2S	– EGO
Park/Neutral Position	PNP	– NDS – NGS – TSN – Neutral Drive Switch – Neutral Gear Switch – Transmission Select Neutral
Periodic Trap Oxidizer	PTOX	– PTOX – Periodic Trap Oxidizer

FIGURE 27–36   *Continued*

J1930 Terminology List

New Term	New Acronyms/ Abbreviations	Old Acronyms/ Term
Power Steering Pressure	PSP	– PSPS – Power Steering Pressure Switch
Powertrain Control Module	PCM	– ECA – ECM – ECU – EEC Processor – Engine Control Assembly – Engine Control Module – Engine Control Unit
Programmable Read Only Memory	PROM	– PROM – Programmable Read Only Memory
Pulsed Secondary Air Injection	PAIR	– MPA – PA – Thermactor II – Managed Pulse Air – Pulse Air
Random Access Memory	RAM	– RAM – Random Access Memory
Read Only Memory	ROM	– ROM – Read Only Memory
Relay Module	RM	– RM – Relay Module RM
Scan Tool	ST	– GST – NGS – Generic Scan Tool – New Generation STAR Tester – Enhanced Scan Tool OBD II ST
Secondary Air Injection	AIR	– AM – CT – MTA – Air Management – Conventional Thermactor – Managed Thermactor Air – Thermactor
Sequential Multiport Fuel Injection	SFI	– SEFI – Sequential Electronic Fuel Injection
Service Reminder Indicator	SRI	– SRI – Service Reminder Indicator
Smoke Puff Limiter	SPL	– SPL – Smoke Puff Limiter
Supercharger	SC	– SC – Supercharger
Supercharger Bypass	SCB	– SCB – Supercharger Bypass
System Readiness Test[1]	SRT[1]	– –

FIGURE 27–36   *Continued*

J1930 Terminology List

New Term	New Acronyms/ Abbreviations	Old Acronyms/ Term
Thermal Vacuum Valve	TVV	– Thermal Vacuum Switch
Third Gear	3GR	– Third Gear
Three Way Catalytic Converter	TWC	– TWC – Three Way Catalytic Converter
Three Way + Oxidation Catalytic Converter	TWC+OC	– TWC & COC – Dual Bed – Three Way Catalyst and Conventional Oxidation Catalyst
Throttle Body	TB	– TB – Throttle Body
Throttle Body Fuel Injection	TBI	– CFI – Central Fuel Injection – EFI
Throttle Position	TP	– TP – Throttle Position
Torque Converter Clutch	TCC	– CCC – CCO – MCCC – Converter Clutch Control – Converter Clutch Override – Modulated Converter Clutch Control
Transmission Control Module	TCM	– 4EAT Module
Transmission Range	TR	– PRNDL
Turbocharger	TC	– TC – Turbocharger
Vehicle Speed Sensor	VSS	– VSS –Vehicle Speed Sensor
Voltage Regulator	VR	– VR – Voltage Regulator
Volume Air Flow	VAF	– VAF – Volume Air Flow
Warm-Up Oxidation Catalytic Converter	WU-OC	– WV-OC – Warm-up Oxidation Catalytic Converter
Warm-Up Three Way Catalytic Converter	WU-TWC	– WU-TWC – Warm-up Three Way Catalytic Converter
Wide Open Throttle	WOT	– Full Throttle – WOT – Wide Open Throttle

FIGURE 27–36 *Continued*

PINS 9-16

FIGURE 27–37   Standard diagnostic connector (DLC) for OBD-II systems. *Courtesy of Ford Motor Company*

of the code is a letter. This defines the system in which the code was set. Currently, there are four possible first-character codes: "B" for body, "C" for chassis, "P" for powertrain, and "U" for undefined. The U-codes are designated for future use.

The second character is a number. This defines the code as being a mandated code or a special manufacturer code. This number will either be a "0," "1," "2," or "3." A "0" code means the fault is defined or mandated by OBD-II. A "1" code means the code is

manufacturer specific. Codes of "2" or "3" are designated for future use.

The third through fifth characters are numbers. These describe the fault. The third character of a powertrain code tells you where the fault occurred. The remaining two characters describe the exact condition that set the code.

Many of the same test procedures for non-OBD-II systems used to find the exact problem or to set the computer are also used for OBD-II systems.

⚠ *WARNING!*

Static electricity, as mentioned earlier, can damage the calibration units. Do not open the package until you have grounded it and are ready to install it. Never touch the terminals on the part. ■

The SAE J2012 standards specify that all DTCs will have a five-digit alphanumeric numbering and lettering system. The following prefixes indicate the general area to which the DTC belongs:

1. P — power train
2. B — body
3. C — chassis

The first number in the DTC indicates who is responsible for the DTC definition.

1. 0 — SAE
2. 1 — manufacturer

The third digit in the DTC indicates the subgroup to which the DTC belongs. The possible subgroups are:

0 — Total system
1 — Fuel-air control
2 — Fuel-air control
3 — Ignition system misfire
4 — Auxiliary emission controls
5 — Idle speed control
6 — PCM and I/O
7 — Transmission
8 — Non-EEC power train

The fourth and fifth digits indicate the specific area where the trouble exists. Code P1711 has this interpretation:

P — Power train DTC
1 — Manufacturer-defined code
7 — Transmission subgroup
11 — Transmission oil temperature (TOT) sensor and related circuit

FIGURE 27–38   OBD-II trouble codes and their meanings.

CASE STUDY

Trouble code indicates that the computer is faulty (Chrysler code 53, Ford code 15, and General Motors code 54.)

Computer modules seldom fail unless something on the vehicle puts an excess load on the unit. Therefore, you should never install a replacement computer without finding what caused it to fail. Otherwise, the replacement module could also be destroyed.

Once it has been determined that the computer should be replaced, follow these precautions.

1. Make sure the ignition key is turned off.
2. Disconnect the battery ground cable and remove the fuse. It is necessary to eliminate all possibilities of static or stray voltage when you connect the new unit.
3. Disconnect the harness and remove the attaching bolts. Then, remove the computer unit.
4. Separate the multi-pin connector carefully from the computer itself, then remove the computer.
5. Some computers have removable calibration units that must be transferred to the new computer before installation.

Before installing the new computer, follow the step-by-step instructions for measuring the resistance between particular pins on the wiring harness. Computers rarely fail from internal problems. If any of the resistances do not match, test the subcircuits.

KEY TERMS

Actuator	Keep-alive memory
Adder	LM
ALDL	Look-up table
ASD	MIL
CEL	OBD-II
DLC	PFE
DTC	Sensor
Hard fault	Strategy
J1930	

SUMMARY

- The four major advantages of using electronic engine controls in a vehicle are better emissions, mileage, performance (power and driveability), and protection (durability).
- A typical electronic control system is made up of sensors, actuators, computer, and related wiring.
- Most input sensors are variable resistance/reference types, switches, and thermistors.
- The computer and its processors are the heart of the computerized engine control system.
- System strategy is a plan of how the computer will respond to all possible engine conditions. It is stored in the computer's permanent memory.
- The fail safe or limp-in mode allows the engine to operate if the computer loses a major input signal. The computer substitutes an input value for the lost sensor or input.
- Control loops are the cycles by which a process can be controlled by information received from input sensors, data computer processing, and out of specific commands to the output actuators.
- The three important control loops are the spark control system, fuel control system, and emission control system.
- Logical troubleshooting can involve either microcomputer logic flow, technician's logical diagnosis, or both.
- Electronic control components can be checked by visual inspection, ohmmeter and voltmeter checks, and by substitution of known good parts.
- Most computerized engine control systems have self-diagnostic capabilities. By entering a self-test mode, the computer is able to evaluate the condition of the entire electronic engine control system, including itself.
- The purpose of OBD-II was to provide: a universal diagnostic test connector with dedicated pin assignments, a standard location for the DLC, a standard list of diagnostic trouble codes (DTCs), automatic vehicle identification to the scan tool, the ability to clear all stored trouble codes with the scan tool, the ability to record (and store in memory) a snapshot of the operating conditions that existed when a fault occurred, the ability to store a code whenever something goes wrong and affects exhaust quality, and a standard glossary of terms, acronyms, and definitions that must be used for all components in the electronic control systems.

TECH MANUAL

The following procedures are included in Chapter 27 of the *Tech Manual* that accompanies this book:

1. *Connect a scan tool to an imported vehicle.*
2. *Retrieve codes from a Ford product.*
3. *Retrieve codes from a GM product.*
4, *Retrieve codes from a Chrysler product.*

REVIEW QUESTIONS

1. What advantages does the use of PROM chips offer?

2. What are self-diagnostics?

3. Describe the difference between an open and closed loop operation.

4. What devices may be involved in activating self-diagnosis and reading trouble codes?

5. Explain the use and importance of system strategy and look-up tables in the computerized control system.

6. When removing a PROM chip, Technician A uses a special removal tool. Technician B is careful not to touch the chip's legs. Who is correct?
   a. Technician A   c. Both A and B
   b. Technician B   d. Neither A nor B

7. Technician A says an oxygen sensor can be either a variable resistor or voltage-producing sensor. Technician B says an oxygen sensor is a thermistor sensor. Who is correct?
   a. Technician A   c. Both A and B
   b. Technician B   d. Neither A nor B

8. Technician A says the oxygen sensor provides the major input during the open loop mode. Technician B says the coolant temperature sensor controls open loop mode operation. Who is correct?
   a. Technician A   c. Both A and B
   b. Technician B   d. Neither A nor B

9. Which of the following inputs tells the computer the make-up of the exhaust gas?
   a. MAP sensor
   b. high gear switch
   c. oxygen sensor
   d. throttle position sensor

10. All of the following statements about feedback control are correct except ____.
    a. sensor input data are sent to the computer
    b. computer output is used to energize solenoids and other electrically controlled devices
    c. the computer changes output in response to input data
    d. computer output signals are fed back into the computer as input data

11. Technician A says electronic engine control problems are usually caused by defective sensors. Technician B says most sensors are output devices that can be checked with an ohmmeter. Who is correct?
    a. Technician A   c. Both A and B
    b. Technician B   d. Neither A nor B

12. Self-diagnostic systems provide ____.
    a. computer codes that can be read on the dashboard
    b. computer codes that can be read on a tester
    c. both a and b
    d. neither a nor b

13. Technician A says the power module in a Chrysler system is responsible for controlling the injector and ignition ground circuit. Technician B says the logic module is responsible for supplying the ground to the automatic shutdown relay. Who is correct?
    a. Technician A   c. Both A and B
    b. Technician B   d. Neither A nor B

14. Technician A says a code 11 on a Ford EEC-IV diagnostic system is referred to as a dynamic response code. Technician B says a code 10 indicates that all the parts are repaired correctly. Who is correct?
    a. Technician A   c. Both A and B
    b. Technician B   d. Neither A nor B

15. A computer is capable of doing all of the following except ____.

a. receive input data

b. process input data according to a program and monitor output action

c. control the vehicle's operating conditions

d. store data and information

16. The self-diagnostic feature of computer-controlled ignition systems displays ____ to identify trouble areas.

a. trouble codes

b. engine rpm

c. torque specifications

d. all of the above

17. Which of the following memory circuits is used to store trouble codes and other temporary information?

a. read only memory

b. programmed read only memory

c. random access memory

d. all of the above

18. When a sensor failure occurs in a computer control system, the computer enters a(n) ____.

a. fail safe or limp-in mode

b. open loop mode of operation

c. closed loop mode of operation

d. none of the above

19. Which of the following are used to identify hard faults?

a. on-demand codes

b. keep-alive memory codes

c. dynamic response codes

d. fast codes

20. Technician A says vehicles that do not have MAP or BARO sensors may use a vacuum sensor to provide engine load and speed change information. Technician B says the vacuum sensor tells the computer when vacuum is applied to the EGR valve. Who is correct?

a. Technician A

b. Technician B

c. Both A and B

d. Neither A nor B

SECTION 5

MANUAL TRANSMISSIONS AND TRANSAXLES

Transmission/transaxles, drive axles, and differentials, perform the important task of manipulating the power produced by the engine and routing it to the driving wheels of the vehicle. Precision machined and fitted gearsets and shafts change the ratio of speed and power between the engine and drive axles. The flow of power is controlled through a manually operated clutch and shift lever.

Transmission/transaxle service requires sound diagnostic skills plus the ability to work with intricate gearing and linkages. The material covered in Section 5 corresponds to the ASE certification test on manual drivetrain and axles.

WE ENCOURAGE
PROFESSIONALISM

THROUGH TECHNICIAN
CERTIFICATION

CLUTCHES *côn số*

28

OBJECTIVES

◆ **Describe the various clutch components and their functions.** ◆ **Name and explain the advantages of the different types of pressure plate assemblies.** ◆ **Name the different types of clutch linkages.** ◆ **List the safety precautions that should be followed during clutch servicing.** ◆ **Explain how to perform basic clutch maintenance.** ◆ **Name the six most common problems that occur with clutches.** ◆ **Explain the basics of servicing a clutch assembly.**

The clutch is located between the transmission and engine where it provides a mechanical coupling between the engine's flywheel and the transmission's input shaft. The driver operates the clutch through a linkage that extends from the passenger compartment to the **bell housing** (also called the clutch housing) between the engine and the transmission.

All manual transmissions require a clutch to engage or disengage the transmission. If the vehicle had no clutch and the engine was always connected to the transmission, the engine would stop every time the vehicle was brought to a stop. The clutch allows the engine to idle while the vehicle is stopped. It also allows for easy shifting between gears. (Of course, all of this applies to manual transaxles as well.)

The clutch engages the transmission gradually by allowing a certain amount of slippage between the transmission's input shaft and the flywheel. Figure 28–1 shows the components needed to do this: the flywheel, clutch disc, pressure plate assembly, clutch release bearing (or throwout bearing), and the clutch fork.

OPERATION

The basic principle of engaging a clutch is demonstrated in Figure 28–2. The flywheel and the pressure plate are the drive or driving members of the clutch. The driven member connected to the transmission input shaft is the **clutch disc**, also called the **friction**

Flywheel

Clutch disc

Clutch cover

Clip

Clutch release fork

Release bearing

Clutch release bearing hub

Clip

FIGURE 28–1 Major parts of a clutch assembly. *Courtesy of Ford Motor Company*

FIGURE 28–2 When the clutch is engaged, the driven member is squeezed between the two driving members. The transmission is connected to the driven member. *Courtesy of General Motors Corporation*

FIGURE 28–3 Parts of a clutch disc.

disc. As long as the clutch is disengaged (clutch pedal depressed), the drive members turn independently of the driven member, and the engine is disconnected from the transmission. However, when the clutch is engaged (clutch pedal released), the pressure plate moves in the direction of the arrows and the clutch disc is bound between the two revolving drive members and forced to turn at the same speed.

Flywheel

The **flywheel**, an important part of the engine, is also the main driving member of the clutch. It is normally made of nodular cast iron, which has a high graphite content to lubricate the engagement of the clutch. Welded to or pressed onto the outside diameter of the flywheel is the starter ring gear. The starter ring gear is replaceable on most flywheels. The large diameter of the flywheel allows for an excellent gear ratio of the starter drive to ring gear, which provides for ample engine rotation during starting. The rear surface of the flywheel is a friction surface machined very flat to ensure smooth clutch engagement. The flywheel also provides some absorption of torsional vibration of the crankshaft. It further provides the inertia to rotate the crankshaft through the four strokes.

The flywheel has two sets of bolt holes drilled into it. The inner set is used to fasten the flywheel to the crankshaft, and the outer set provides a mounting plate for the pressure plate assembly. A bore in the center of the flywheel and crankshaft holds the **pilot bushing**, which supports the front end of the transmission input shaft and maintains alignment with the engine's crankshaft. Sometimes a ball or roller needle bearing is used instead of a pilot bushing.

Clutch Disc

The clutch disc receives the driving motion from the flywheel and pressure plate assembly and transmits

that motion to the transmission input shaft. The parts of a clutch disc are shown in Figure 28–3.

There are two types of friction facings. Molded friction facings are preferred because they withstand greater pressure plate loading force without damage. Woven friction facings are used when additional cushioning action is needed for clutch engagement. Until recently, the material that was molded or woven into facings was predominantly asbestos. Now, because of the hazards associated with asbestos, other materials such as paper-base and ceramics are being used instead. Particles of cotton, brass, rope, and wire are added to prolong the life of the clutch disc and provide torsional strength.

Grooves are cut across the face of the friction facings. This promotes clean disengagement of the driven disc from the flywheel and pressure plate; it also promotes better cooling. The facings are riveted to wave springs, also called **cushioning springs**, which cause the contact pressure on the facings to rise gradually as the springs flatten out when the clutch is engaged. These springs eliminate chatter when the clutch is engaged and also reduce the chance of the clutch disc sticking to the flywheel and pressure plate surfaces when the clutch is disengaged. The wave springs and friction facings are fastened to the steel disc.

The clutch disc is designed to absorb such things as crankshaft vibration, abrupt clutch engagement, and driveline shock. Torsional coil springs allow the disc to rotate slightly in relation to the pressure plate while they absorb the torque forces. The number and tension of these springs is determined by engine torque and vehicle weight. Stop pins limit this torsional movement to approximately 3/8 inch.

Pilot Bushing

The purpose of the pilot bushing or bearing is to support the outer end of the transmission's input shaft. This shaft is splined to the clutch disc and transmits power from the engine (when the clutch is engaged) to the transmission. The transmission end of the input shaft is supported by a large bearing in the transmission case. Because the input shaft extends unsupported from the transmission, a pilot bushing is used to keep it in position. By supporting the shaft, the pilot bushing keeps the clutch disc centered in the pressure plate.

Pressure Plate Assembly

The purpose of the pressure plate assembly is twofold. First, it must squeeze the clutch disc onto the flywheel with sufficient force to transmit engine torque efficiently. Second, it must move away from the clutch disc so the clutch disc can stop rotating, even though the flywheel and pressure plate continue to rotate.

Basically, there are two types of pressure plate assemblies: those with coil springs and those with a **diaphragm spring**. Both types have a steel cover that bolts to the flywheel and acts as a housing to hold the parts together. In both, there is also the pressure plate, which is a heavy, flat ring made of cast iron. The assemblies differ in the manner in which they move the pressure plate toward and away from the clutch disc.

Coil Spring Pressure Plate Assembly A coil spring pressure plate assembly, shown in Figure 28–4, uses coil springs and release levers to move the pressure plate back and forth. The springs exert pressure to hold the pressure plate tightly against the clutch disc. This forces the clutch disc against the flywheel. The release levers release the holding force of the springs. There are usually three of them. Each one has two pivot points. One of these pivot points attaches the

FIGURE 28–5 Release levers remove the coil spring's pressure on the pressure plate. *Courtesy of Ford Motor Company*

lever to a pedestal cast into the pressure plate and the other to a release lever yoke bolted to the cover (Figure 28–5). The levers pivot on the pedestals and release lever yokes to move the pressure plate through its engagement and disengagement operations. To disengage the clutch, the release bearing pushes the inner ends of the release levers forward toward the flywheel. The release lever yokes act as fulcrums for the levers and the outer ends of the release levers move backward, pulling the pressure plate away from the clutch disc. This action compresses the coil springs and disengages the clutch disc from the driving members.

When the clutch is engaged, the release bearing moves backward toward the transmission. Without this force against the release levers, the coil springs are able to push the pressure plate and clutch disc against the flywheel with sufficient force to resist slipping. The following are common advantages of all pressure plate assemblies that use coil springs.

◆ They cleanly disengage the clutch at high engine speeds because of the high force exerted by the pressure plate springs.
◆ They offer great flexibility and can be used on various applications since the coil springs can be changed to increase or decrease pressure plate holding force.

Diaphragm Spring Pressure Plate Assembly The diaphragm spring pressure plate assembly relies on a cone-shaped diaphragm spring between the pressure

FIGURE 28–4 Parts of a coil spring pressure plate.

FIGURE 28–6   Diaphragm spring pressure plate assembly.

plate and the pressure plate cover to move the pressure plate back and forth. The diaphragm spring (sometimes called a Belleville spring) is a single, thin sheet of metal that works in the same manner as the bottom of an oil can. The metal yields when pressure is applied to it. When the pressure is removed, the metal springs back to its original shape. The center portion of the diaphragm spring is slit into numerous fingers that act as release levers (Figure 28–6).

During clutch disengagement, these fingers are moved forward by the release bearing. The diaphragm spring pivots over the fulcrum ring (also called the pivot ring), and its outer rim moves away from the flywheel. The retracting springs pull the pressure plate away from the driven disc and disengage the clutch.

When the clutch is engaged, the release bearing and the fingers of the diaphragm spring move toward the transmission. As the diaphragm pivots over the pivot ring, its outer rim forces the pressure plate against the clutch disc so the clutch is engaged to the flywheel.

Diaphragm spring pressure plate assemblies have the following advantages over other types of assemblies.

◆ Compactness
◆ Less weight
◆ Fewer moving parts to wear out
◆ Little pedal effort required from the operator
◆ Provide a balanced force around the pressure plate so rotational unbalance is reduced
◆ Clutch disc slippage is less likely to occur. Mileage builds because the force holding the clutch disc to the flywheel does not change throughout its service life.

Clutch Release Bearing

The **clutch release bearing**, also called a **throwout bearing**, is usually a sealed, prelubricated ball bearing (Figure 28–7). Its function is to smoothly and quietly move the pressure plate release levers or diaphragm spring through the engagement and disengagement process.

The release bearing is mounted on an iron casting called a hub, which slides on a hollow shaft at the front of the transmission housing. This hollow shaft, shown in Figure 28–8, is part of the transmission bearing retainer.

To disengage the clutch, the release bearing is moved forward on its shaft by the **clutch fork**. As the release bearing contacts the release levers or diaphragm spring of the pressure plate assembly, it begins to rotate with the rotating pressure plate assembly. As the release bearing continues forward, the

FIGURE 28–7   Typical clutch release bearing.

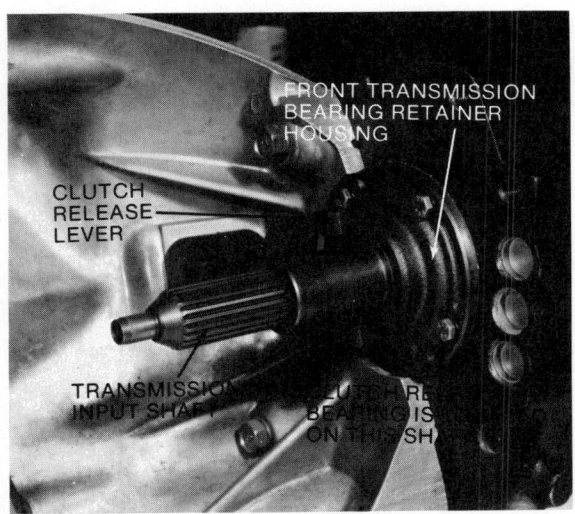

FIGURE 28–8 The clutch release bearing assembly slides on the hollow shaft of the front transmission bearing retainer housing.

FIGURE 28–9 Clutch fork and throwout bearing location in the bell housing. *Courtesy of Nissan Motors*

clutch disc is disengaged from the pressure plate and flywheel.

To engage the clutch, the release bearing slides to the rear of the shaft. The pressure plate moves forward and traps the clutch disc against the flywheel to transmit engine torque to the transmission input shaft. Once the clutch is fully engaged, the release bearing is normally stationary.

Rotating Release Bearing Self-adjusting clutch linkages, used on many vehicles, apply just enough tension to the clutch control cable to keep a constant light pressure against the release bearing. As a result, the release bearing is kept in contact with the release levers or diaphragm spring of the rotating pressure plate assembly. The release bearing rotates with the pressure plate.

Clutch Fork

The clutch fork is a forked lever that pivots on a ball stud located in an opening in the bell housing (Figure 28–9). The forked end slides over the hub of the release bearing and the small end protrudes from the bell housing and connects to the clutch linkage and clutch pedal. The clutch fork moves the release bearing and hub back and forth during engagement and disengagement.

Clutch Linkage

The clutch linkage is a series of parts that connects the clutch pedal to the clutch fork. It is through the clutch linkage that the operator controls the engagement and disengagement of the clutch assembly smoothly and with little effort.

Clutch linkage can be mechanical or hydraulic. Mechanical clutch linkage can be divided into two types: shaft and lever linkage, and cable linkage.

Shaft and Lever Linkage The shaft and lever clutch linkage consists of the various shafts, levers, adjustable rods, and pivots that transmit clutch pedal motion to the clutch fork (Figure 28–10). A rod connects the clutch pedal to the lever and shaft assembly. When the upper lever is moved by the clutch pedal, the shaft rotates and moves the lower lever, which is connected to a pushrod that is attached to the clutch fork. The linkage assembly is located between the chassis and bell housing, near the lower rear part of the engine block. These linkages are not commonly used on modern vehicles, simply because there are so many wear points.

Cable Linkage A cable linkage can perform the same controlling action as the shaft and lever linkage but with fewer parts. The clutch cable system does not take up much room. It also has the advantage of flexible installation so it can be routed around the power brake and steering units. These advantages help to make it the most commonly used clutch linkage.

The clutch cable (Figure 28–11) is made of braided wire. The upper end is connected to the top of the clutch pedal arm, and the lower end is fastened to the clutch fork. It is designed with a flexible outer housing that is fastened at the fire wall and the clutch housing.

When the clutch pedal is pushed to the disengaged position, it pivots on the pedal shaft and pulls the inner cable through the outer housing. This action moves the clutch fork forward to disengage the clutch. The pressure plate springs and springs on the clutch pedal provide the force to move the cable back when the clutch pedal is released.

SELF-ADJUSTING CLUTCH Self-adjusting clutch mechanisms monitor clutch pedal play and automatically adjust it when necessary.

FIGURE 28–10 Shaft and lever clutch linkage. _Courtesy of Ford Motor Company_

Usually the self-adjusting clutch mechanism is a ratcheting mechanism located at the top of the clutch pedal behind the dash panel (Figure 28–12). The ratchet is designed with a pawl and toothed segment, and a pawl tension spring is used to keep the pawl in contact with the toothed segment. The pawl allows the toothed segment to move in only one direction in relation to the pawl.

The clutch cable is guided around and fastened to the toothed segment, which is free to rotate in one direction (backwards) independently of the clutch pedal. The tension spring pulls the toothed segment backwards.

When the clutch cable develops slack due to stretching and clutch disc wear, the cable is adjusted automatically when the clutch is released. The ten-

FIGURE 28–11 Typical clutch cable system.

FIGURE 28–12 Ratchet-type automatic clutch adjusting mechanism. *Courtesy of Ford Motor Company*

sion spring pulls the toothed segment backwards and allows the pawl to ride over to the next tooth. This effectively shortens the cable. Actually, the cable is not really shortened; but the slack has been reeled in by the repositioning of the toothed segment. This self-adjusting action takes place automatically during the clutch's operational life.

Hydraulic Clutch Linkage Frequently, the clutch assembly is controlled by a hydraulic system (Figure 28–13). In the hydraulic clutch linkage system, hydraulic (liquid) pressure transmits motion from one sealed cylinder to another through a hydraulic line. Like the cable linkage assembly, the hydraulic

linkage is compact and flexible. Cable linkages also allow engineers to place the release fork anywhere that gives them more flexibility in body design. In addition, the hydraulic pressure developed by the master cylinder decreases required pedal effort and provides a precise method of controlling clutch operation. Brake fluid is commonly used as the hydraulic fluid in hydraulic clutch systems.

A hydraulic clutch master cylinder is shown in Figure 28–14. Its pushrod moves the piston and primary cup to create hydraulic pressure. The snap ring restricts the travel of the piston. The secondary cup at the snap ring end of the piston stops hydraulic fluid from dripping into the passenger compartment. The piston return spring holds the primary cup and piston in the fully released position. Hydraulic fluid is stored in the reservoir on top of the master cylinder housing.

The slave cylinder body has a bleeder valve to bleed air from the hydraulic system for efficient clutch linkage operation (Figure 28–15). The cylinder body is threaded for a tube and fitting at the fluid entry port. Rubber seal rings are used to seal the hydraulic pressure between the piston and the slave cylinder walls. The piston retaining ring is used to restrict piston travel to a certain distance. Piston travel is transmitted by a pushrod to the clutch fork. The pushrod boot keeps contaminants out of the slave cylinder.

When the clutch pedal is depressed, the movement of the piston and primary cup develops hydraulic pressure that is displaced from the master cylinder, through a tube, into the slave cylinder. The

FIGURE 28–13 Typical hydraulic clutch linkage arrangement. *Courtesy of Nissan Motors*

A. Pushrod and boot
B. Piston
C. Primary cup
D. Snap ring
E. Secondary cup
F. Piston return spring
G. Master cylinder housing
H. Hydraulic fluid reservoir and bolt

FIGURE 28–14   Parts of a hydraulic clutch master cylinder. *Courtesy of General Motors Corporation*

A. Slave cylinder body
B. Bleeder valve
C. Fluid entry port
D. Piston seal rings
E. Piston
F. Piston retaining ring
G. Pushrod
H. Pushrod boot

FIGURE 28–15   Parts of a clutch slave cylinder. *Courtesy of General Motors Corporation*

slave cylinder piston movement is transmitted to the clutch fork, which disengages the clutch.

When the clutch pedal is released, the primary cup and piston are forced back to the engaged position by the master cylinder piston return spring. External springs move the slave cylinder pushrod and piston back to the engaged position. Fluid pressure returns through the hydraulic tubing to the master cylinder assembly. There is no hydraulic pressure in the system when the clutch assembly is in the engaged position.

CLUTCH SERVICE SAFETY PRECAUTIONS

When servicing the clutch, exercise the following precautions.

- Always wear eye protection when working underneath a vehicle.
- Remove asbestos dust only with a special, approved vacuum collection system or an approved liquid cleaning system.
- Never use compressed air or a brush to clean off asbestos dust.
- Follow all federal, state, and local laws when disposing of collected asbestos dust or liquid containing asbestos dust.
- Never work under a vehicle that is not raised on a hoist or supported by safety or jack stands.
- Use jack stands and special jacks to support the engine and transmission.
- Have a helper assist in removing the transmission.
- Be sure the work area is properly ventilated, or attach a ventilating hose to the vehicle's exhaust system when an engine is to be run indoors.
- Do not allow anyone to stand in front of or behind the automobile while the engine is running.
- Set the emergency brake securely and place the gearshift in neutral when running the engine of a stationary vehicle.
- Avoid touching hot engine and exhaust system parts. Whenever possible, let the vehicle cool down before beginning to work on it.

CLUTCH MAINTENANCE

All clutches require checking and adjustment of linkage at regular intervals. Vehicles with external clutch linkage require periodic lubrication. These maintenance procedures are explained in this section.

USING SERVICE MANUALS

Service Manuals include adjustment procedures and instructions for clutch removal, inspection, installation, and troubleshooting. They may also offer information to aid in clutch release bearing distress analysis. ■

Clutch Linkage Adjustment

Except for systems with self-adjusting mechanisms, the release bearing should not touch the pressure plate release levers when the clutch is engaged (pedal up). Clearance between these parts prevents premature clutch plate, pressure plate, and release bearing wear. As the clutch disc wears and becomes thinner, this clearance changes.

Clearance can be ensured by adjusting the clutch linkage so the pedal has a specified amount of play, or **free travel**. Free travel is the distance a clutch pedal moves when depressed, before the clutch fork begins to move the release bearing.

To check pedal play, use a tape measure or ruler. Place the tape measure or ruler beside the clutch pedal and the end against the floor of the vehicle and note the reading (Figure 28–16). Then, depress the clutch pedal just enough to take up the pedal play and note the reading again. The difference between the two readings is the amount of pedal play.

Adjustment should be performed when pedal play is not correct or when the clutch does not engage or disengage properly. To adjust clutch pedal play, refer to the manufacturer's service manual for the correct procedure and adjustment point locations. Often pedal play can be increased or decreased by turning a threaded fastener located either under

FIGURE 28–16 Checking clutch pedal play. *Courtesy of Chrysler Corporation*

the dash at the clutch pedal or where the linkage attaches to the clutch fork.

SHOP TALK

Normally clutch condition will dictate the amount of clutch pedal free play there is. However, there will always be free play with hydraulic clutch systems. ■

Clean the linkage with a shop towel and solvent, if necessary, before checking it and replacing any damaged or missing parts or cables. Check hydraulic linkage systems for leaks at the clutch master cylinder, hydraulic hose, and slave cylinder. Then, adjust the linkage to provide the manufacturer's specified clutch pedal play.

External Clutch Linkage Lubrication

External clutch linkage should be lubricated at regular intervals, such as during a chassis lubrication. Refer to the vehicle's service manual to determine the proper lubricant. Many clutch linkages use the same chassis grease that is used for suspension parts and U-joints. Lubricate all the sliding surfaces and pivot points in the clutch linkage (Figure 28–17). The linkage should move freely after lubrication.

On vehicles with hydraulic clutch linkage, check the clutch master cylinder reservoir fluid level. It should be approximately 1/4 inch from the top of the reservoir. If it must be refilled, use approved brake fluid. Also, since the clutch master cylinder does not consume fluid, check for leaks in the master cylinder, connecting flexible line, and slave cylinder, if the fluid is low.

CLUTCH PROBLEM DIAGNOSIS

Check and attempt to adjust the clutch pedal play before attempting to diagnose any clutch problems. If the friction lining of the clutch is worn too thin, the clutch cannot be adjusted successfully. The most common clutch problems are described here.

Slippage

Clutch slippage is a condition in which the engine overspeeds without generating any increase in torque to the driving wheels. It occurs when the clutch disc is not gripped firmly between the flywheel and the pressure plate. Instead, the clutch disc slips between these driving members. Slippage can occur during initial acceleration or subsequent shifts, but it is usually most noticeable in higher gears.

Clutch cable

Rod and lever   Cable   Hydraulic

FIGURE 28–17   All of the clutch linkage lubrication points are marked with an arrow. *Courtesy of Nissan Motors*

One way to check for slippage is by driving the vehicle. Normal acceleration from a stop and several gear changes indicate whether the clutch is slipping.

Slippage also can be checked in the shop. Check the service manual for correct procedures. A general procedure for checking clutch slippage follows. Be sure to follow the safety precautions stated earlier.

With the parking brake on, disengage the clutch. Shift the transmission into third gear, and increase the engine speed to about 2,000 rpm. Slowly release the clutch pedal until the clutch engages. The engine should stall immediately.

If it does not stall within a few seconds, the clutch is slipping. Safely raise the vehicle and check the clutch linkage for binding and broken or bent parts. If no linkage problems are found, the transmission and the clutch assembly must be removed so the clutch parts can be examined.

SHOP TALK

Severe or prolonged clutch slippage causes grooving or heat damage to the pressure plate and/or flywheel. ■

Clutch slippage can be caused by an oil-soaked or worn disc facing, warped pressure plate, weak diaphragm spring, or the release bearing contacting and applying pressure to the release levers.

Drag and Binding

If the clutch disc is not completely released when the clutch pedal is fully depressed, clutch drag occurs. Clutch drag causes gear clash, especially when shifting into reverse. It can also cause hard starting because the engine attempts to turn the transmission input shaft.

To check for clutch drag, start the engine, depress the clutch pedal completely, and shift the transmission into first gear. Do not release the clutch. Then, shift the transmission into neutral and wait 5 seconds before attempting to shift smoothly into reverse.

It should take no more than 5 seconds for the clutch disc, input shaft, and transmission gears to come to a complete stop after disengagement. This period, called the clutch spindown time, is normal and should not be mistaken for clutch drag.

If the shift into reverse causes gear clash, raise the vehicle safely and check the clutch linkage for binding, broken, or bent parts. If no problems are found in the linkage, the transmission and clutch assembly must be removed so that the clutch parts can be examined.

Clutch drag can occur as a result of a warped disc or pressure plate, a loose disc facing, a defective release lever, or incorrect clutch pedal adjustment that results in excessive pedal play.

Binding can result when the splines in the clutch disc hub or on the transmission input shaft are damaged or when there are problems with the release levers.

Chatter

A shaking or shuddering that is felt in the vehicle as the clutch is engaged is known as clutch **chatter**. It usually occurs when the pressure plate first contacts the clutch disc and stops when the clutch is fully engaged.

To check for clutch chatter, start the engine, depress the clutch completely, and shift the transmission into first gear. Increase engine speed to about 1,500 rpm, then slowly release the clutch pedal and check for chatter as the pedal begins to engage. Do not release the pedal completely, or the vehicle might jump and cause serious injury. As soon as the clutch is partially engaged, depress the clutch pedal immediately and reduce engine speed to prevent damage to the clutch parts.

Usually clutch chatter is caused by liquid leaking onto the clutch and contaminating its friction surfaces. This results in a mirrorlike shine on the pressure plate or a glazed clutch facing. Oil and clutch hydraulic fluid leaks can occur at the engine rear main bearing seal transmission input shaft seal, clutch slave cylinder, and hydraulic line. Other causes of clutch chatter include broken engine mounts, loose bell housing bolts, and damaged clutch linkage.

During disassembly, check for a warped pressure plate or flywheel, hot spots on the flywheel, a burned or glazed disc facing, and worn input shaft splines. If the chattering is caused by an oil-soaked clutch disc and no other parts are damaged, then the disc alone needs to be replaced. However, the cause of the oil leak must also be found and corrected.

Pedal Pulsation

Pedal pulsation is a rapid up-and-down movement of the clutch pedal as the clutch disengages or engages. This pedal movement usually is minor, but it can be felt through the clutch pedal. It is not accompanied by any noise. Pulsation begins when the release bearing makes contact with the release levers.

To check for pedal pulsation, start the engine, depress the clutch pedal slowly until the clutch just begins to disengage, and then stop briefly. Resume depressing the clutch pedal slowly until the pedal is depressed to a full stop.

On many vehicles, minor pulsation is considered normal. If pulsation is excessive, the clutch must be removed and disassembled for inspection.

Pedal pulsations can result from the misalignment of parts. Check for a misaligned bell housing or a bent flywheel. Inspect the clutch disc and pressure plate for warpage. Broken, bent, or warped release levers also create misalignment.

CUSTOMER CARE

If you repair a vehicle with clutch slippage, tactfully inform the customer about the different poor driving habits that can cause this problem. These habits include riding the clutch pedal and holding the vehicle on an incline by using the clutch as a brake. ■

Vibration

Clutch vibrations, unlike pedal pulsations, can be felt throughout the vehicle, and they occur at any clutch pedal position. These vibrations usually occur at normal engine operating speeds (more than 1,500 rpm).

There are several possible sources of vibration that should be checked before disassembling the clutch to inspect it. Check the engine mounts and the crankshaft damper pulley. Look for any indication that engine parts are rubbing against the body or frame.

Accessories can also be a source of vibration. To check them, remove the drive belts one at a time. Set the transmission in neutral, and securely set the emergency brake. Start the engine and check for vibrations. Do not run the engine for more than 1 minute with the belts removed.

If the source of vibration is not discovered through these checks, the clutch parts should be examined. Be sure to check for loose flywheel bolts, excessive flywheel runout, and pressure plate cover balance problems.

Noises

Many clutch noises come from bushings and bearings. Pilot bushing noises are squealing, howling, or trumpeting sounds that are most noticeable in cold weather. These bushing noises usually occur when the pedal is being depressed and the transmission is in neutral. Release bearing noise is a whirring, grating, or grinding sound that occurs when the clutch pedal is depressed and stops when the pedal is fully released. It is most noticeable when the transmission is in neutral, but it also can be heard when the transmission is in gear.

CLUTCH SERVICE

A prerequisite for removing and replacing the clutch in a vehicle is removing the driveline or drive shafts and transmission or transaxle.

Removing the Clutch

After raising the vehicle on a hoist, clean excessive dirt, grease, or debris from around the clutch and transmission. Then, disconnect and remove the clutch linkage. Cable systems need to be disconnected at the transmission.

On rear-wheel-drive automobiles, remove the driveline and the transmission. In some cases the bell housing is removed with the transmission. In others, it is removed after the transmission is removed.

On front-wheel-drive vehicles with transaxles, any parts that interfere with transaxle removal must be removed first. These parts might include drive axles, parts of the engine, brake and suspension system or body parts. Check the service manual for specific instructions.

INSTALLING AND ALIGNING A CLUTCH DISC

P16–1 The removal and replacement of a clutch assembly can be completed while the engine is in or out of the car. The clutch assembly is mounted to the flywheel, which is mounted to the rear of the crankshaft.

P16–2 Before disassembling the clutch, make sure alignment marks are present on the pressure plate and flywheel.

P16–3 The attaching bolts should be loosened before removing any of the bolts. With the bolts loosened, support the assembly with one hand while using the other to remove the bolts. The clutch disc will be free to fall as the pressure plate is separated from the flywheel. Keep it intact with the pressure plate.

P16–4 The surface of the pressure plate should be inspected for signs of burning, warpage, and cracks. Any faults normally indicate that the plate should be replaced.

P16–5 The surface of the flywheel should also be carefully inspected. Normally the flywheel surface can be resurfaced to remove any defects. The pilot bushing or bearing should also be inspected.

P16–6 The new clutch disc is placed into the pressure plate as the pressure plate is moved into its proper location. Make sure the disc is facing the correct direction. Most are marked to indicate which side should be seated against the flywheel surface.

P16–7 Install the pressure plate according to the alignment marks made during disassembly.

P16–8 Install the attaching bolts, but do not tighten. Then install the clutch alignment tool through the hub of the disc and the pilot bearing. This will center the disc on the flywheel.

P16–9 With the disc aligned, tighten the attaching bolts according to the procedures outlined in the service manual

FIGURE 28–18 Check for pressure plate warpage.
Courtesy of Ford Motor Company

The clutch assembly is accessible after the bell housing has been removed. Use an approved vacuum collection system or an approved liquid cleaning system to remove asbestos dust and dirt from the clutch assembly.

Photo Sequence 16 on page 732, outlines the typical procedure for replacing a clutch disc and pressure plate. Always refer to the manufacturer's recommendations for bolt torque specifications prior to reinstalling the assembly.

While disassembling the clutch, follow these guidelines.

◆ Check the bell housing, flywheel, and pressure plate for signs of oil leaks.
◆ Carefully examine each part for wear, discoloration, and damage.
◆ Check the flywheel for signs of burning or excessive wear.
◆ When measuring the lining thickness of a bonded clutch disc, measure the total thickness of the facing or lining. To measure the wear of a riveted lining, measure the material above the rivet heads.
◆ Keep grease off the frictional surfaces of the clutch disc, flywheel, and pressure plate.
◆ Check the pressure plate surface for warpage by laying a straightedge across the surface and inserting a feeler gauge between the surface and the straightedge (Figure 28–18). Compare the measurement against the specifications given in the service manual.
◆ Check the release levers of the pressure plate for uneven wear or damage.
◆ Check the release bearing by turning it with your fingers and making sure it rotates freely.
◆ Check the clutch for damage.
◆ Lubricate the clutch fork pivot points, the inside of the release bearing hub, and the linkages.
◆ After the clutch assembly has been reinstalled, check the clutch pedal free travel.

CASE STUDY

A customer brings in a car that develops a harsh scratching noise and becomes quite difficult to shift gears. The symptoms become more apparent when shifting into first gear.

Since trouble of this sort can be caused by a defective synchronization mechanism in the transmission as well as a problem with the clutch, a series of tests is called for. First, the technician disengages the clutch and shifts quickly from neutral to reverse in idling condition. If no gear noise resulted, the technician would know there is sufficient disengagement of the clutch. But instead, gear noise does occur, so the technician performs the next test by shifting to reverse after 5 seconds of clutch disengagement. If no gear noise results, the technician knows the transmission is defective or there is excessive clutch drag torque. Gear noise does occur, so the technician performs the next test by shifting between neutral and reverse several times, after having disengaged the clutch for 5 seconds. If no gear noise results, the technician knows the problem is a stuck clutch disc. Since gear noise does occur, the technician knows the clutch is not completely disengaging.

KEY TERMS

Bell housing
Chatter
Clutch disc
Clutch fork
Clutch release bearing
Clutch slippage
Cushioning springs

Diaphragm spring
Flywheel
Free travel
Friction disc
Pilot bushing
Throwout bearing

SUMMARY

◆ The clutch, located between the transmission and the engine, provides a mechanical coupling between the engine flywheel and the transmission's input shaft. All manual transmissions and transaxles require a clutch.
◆ The flywheel, an important part of the engine, is also the main driving member of the clutch.
◆ The clutch disc receives the driving motion from the flywheel and pressure plate assembly and transmits that motion to the transmission input shaft.

- The twofold purpose of the pressure plate assembly is to squeeze the clutch disc onto the flywheel and move away from the clutch disc so the disc can stop rotating. There are basically two types of pressure plate assemblies: those with coil springs and those with a diaphragm spring.
- The clutch release bearing, also called a throwout bearing, smoothly and quietly moves the pressure plate release levers or diaphragm spring through the engagement and disengagement processes.
- The clutch fork moves the release bearing and hub back and forth. It is controlled by the clutch pedal and linkage.
- Clutch linkage can be mechanical or hydraulic. Mechanical linkage is divided into two types: shaft and lever linkage, and cable linkage.
- The self-adjusting clutch is a clutch cable linkage that monitors clutch pedal play and automatically adjusts it when necessary.
- It is important that certain precautions are exercised when servicing the clutch. Clutch maintenance includes linkage adjustment and external clutch linkage lubrication.
- Slippage occurs when the clutch disc is not gripped

firmly between the flywheel and the pressure plate. It can be caused by an oil-soaked or worn disc facing, warped pressure plate, weak diaphragm spring, or the release bearing contacting and applying pressure to the release levers.
- Clutch drag occurs if the clutch disc is not completely released when the clutch pedal is fully depressed. It can occur as a result of a warped disc or pressure plate, a loose disc facing, a defective release lever, or incorrect clutch pedal adjustment that results in excessive pedal play.
- Chatter is a shuddering felt in the vehicle when the pressure plate first contacts the clutch disc and it stops when the clutch is fully engaged. Usually chatter is caused when liquid contaminates the friction surfaces.
- Pedal pulsation is a rapid up-and-down movement of the clutch pedal as the clutch disengages or engages. It results from a misalignment of parts.
- Clutch vibrations can be felt throughout the vehicle, and they occur at any clutch pedal position. Sources of clutch vibrations include loose flywheel bolts, excessive flywheel runout, and pressure plate cover balance problems.

TECH MANUAL

The following procedures are included in Chapter 28 of the *Tech Manual* that accompanies this book:

1. Troubleshoot clutch assembly.

2. Inspect and adjust clutch linkage.

3. Inspect a clutch assembly.

REVIEW QUESTIONS

1. Name two types of friction facings. *molded / woven*

2. List the two advantages of coil spring pressure plate assemblies. *uses coil spring / release lever to move PP back forth*

3. What is another name for the diaphragm spring? *belleville spring*

4. Name three types of clutch linkages. *shaft and lever / cable / hydraulic clutch*

5. What is used to measure clutch pedal play? *tape measure — ruler*

6. The clutch, or friction, disc is connected to the _____.

   a. engine crankshaft
   b. transmission input shaft *(circled)*
   c. transmission output shaft
   d. transmission counter shaft

7. Torsional coil springs in the clutch disc _____.

   a. cushion the driven disc engagement rear to front
   b. are the mechanical force holding the pressure plate against the driven disc and flywheel
   c. absorb the torque forces
   d. are located between the friction rings

8. Fulcrum rings are found in the _____.

   a. diaphragm pressure plate
   b. coil spring pressure plate
   c. driven disc between the friction facings
   d. release bearing

9. Which of the following is probably *not* the cause of a vibrating clutch?

   a. excessive crankshaft end play
   b. out-of-balance pressure plate assembly
   c. excessive flywheel runout
   d. loose flywheel bolts

10. When a rotating release bearing is installed in a clutch assembly, the release bearing is ____.
    a. stationary when the clutch is fully engaged
    b. rotating when the clutch is fully engaged
    c. stationary when the engine is operating with clutch engaged
    d. stationary during clutch effective travel

11. When the clutch pedal is released on a hydraulic clutch linkage, the ____.
    a. master cylinder piston is released by spring tension
    b. master cylinder piston is released by hydraulic pressure
    c. slave cylinder is released by hydraulic pressure
    d. slave cylinder piston does not move

12. When the clutch is disengaged, the power flow stops at the ____.
    a. transmission input shaft
    b. driven disc hub
    c. pressure plate and flywheel
    d. torsion springs

13. While discussing the purpose of a clutch pressure plate, Technician A says the pressure plate assembly squeezes the clutch disc onto the flywheel. Technician B says the pressure plate moves away from the clutch disc so the disc can stop rotating. Who is correct?
    a. Technician A
    b. Technician B
    c. Both A and B
    d. Neither A nor B

14. Insufficient clutch pedal clearance results in ____.
    a. gear clashing while shifting transmission
    b. a noisy front transmission bearing
    c. premature release bearing failure
    d. premature pilot bearing failure

15. Technician A says an oil-soaked clutch disc can cause clutch chatter. Technician B says clutch chatter can be caused by loose bell housing bolts. Who is correct?
    a. Technician A
    b. Technician B
    c. Both A and B
    d. Neither A nor B

16. When making a clutch adjustment, it is necessary to ____.
    a. measure clutch pedal free travel
    b. lubricate the clutch linkage
    c. check hydraulic fluid level
    d. place the transmission in reverse

17. Technician A says clutch slippage is most noticeable in higher gears. Technician B says clutch slippage is not noticeable in lower gears. Who is correct?
    a. Technician A
    b. Technician B
    c. Both A and B
    d. Neither A nor B

18. Technician A says clutch drag can cause hard starting. Technician B says clutch drag has no effect on starting. Who is correct?
    a. Technician A
    b. Technician B
    c. Both A and B
    d. Neither A nor B

19. The surface of the pressure plate contacts the ____.
    a. transmission main shaft
    b. throwout bearing
    c. clutch disc
    d. flywheel

20. While discussing different abnormal clutch noises, Technician A says pilot bushing noises are most noticeable in cold weather and usually occur when the pedal is being depressed and the transmission is in neutral. Technician B says release bearing noise is most noticeable when the transmission is in neutral and occurs when the clutch pedal is depressed and stops when the pedal is fully released. Who is correct?
    a. Technician A
    b. Technician B
    c. Both A and B
    d. Neither A nor B

MANUAL TRANSMISSIONS AND TRANSAXLES

29

OBJECTIVES

◆ *Explain the design characteristics of the gears used in manual transmissions and transaxles.* ◆ *Explain the fundamentals of torque multiplication and overdrive.* ◆ *Describe the purpose, design, and operation of synchronizer assemblies.* ◆ *Describe the purpose, design, and operation of internal and remote gearshift linkages.* ◆ *Explain the operation and power flows produced in typical manual transmissions and transaxles.*

The transmission or transaxle is a vital link in the power train of any modern vehicle. The purpose of the transmission or transaxle is to use gears of various sizes to give the engine a mechanical advantage over the driving wheels. During normal operating conditions, power from the engine is transferred through the engaged clutch to the input shaft of the transmission or transaxle. Gears in the transmission or transaxle housing alter the torque and speed of this power input before passing it on to other components in the power train. Without the mechanical advantage the gearing provides, an engine can generate only limited torque at low speeds. Without sufficient torque, moving a vehicle from a standing start would be impossible.

In any engine, the crankshaft always rotates in the same direction. If the engine transmitted its power directly to the drive axles, the wheels could be driven only in one direction. Instead, the transmission or transaxle provides the gearing needed to reverse direction so the vehicle can be driven backward.

TRANSMISSION VERSUS TRANSAXLE

Vehicles are propelled in one of three ways: by the rear wheels, by the front wheels, or by all four wheels. The type of drive system used determines whether a conventional transmission or a transaxle is used.

Vehicles propelled by the rear wheels normally use a transmission. Transmission gearing is located within an aluminum or iron casting called the transmission **case** assembly (Figure 29–1). The transmis-

sion case assembly is attached to the rear of the engine, which is normally located in the front of the vehicle. A drive shaft links the output shaft of the transmission with the differential and drive axles located in a separate housing at the rear of the vehicle (Figure 29–2). The differential splits the driveline power and redirects it to the two rear drive axles, which then pass it on to the wheels. For many years, rear-wheel-drive systems were the conventional method of propelling a vehicle.

Front-wheel-drive vehicles are propelled by the front wheels. For this reason, they must use a drive design different from that of a rear-wheel-drive vehicle. The transaxle is the special power transfer unit commonly used on front-wheel-drive vehicles. A transaxle combines the transmission gearing, differ-

FIGURE 29–1 Typical five-speed manual transmission, with the mainshaft (speed) gears, countershaft cluster gears, and shaft forks visible through the case cutaway. *Courtesy of Ford Motor Company*

FIGURE 29–2 Location of typical rear-wheel-drive power train components. *Courtesy of Chrysler Corporation*

ential, and drive axle connections into a single case aluminum housing located in front of the vehicle (Figure 29–3). This design offers many advantages. One major advantage is the good traction on slippery roads due to the weight of the power train components being directly over the driving axles of the vehicle. It is also more compact and lighter than the transmission of a RWD vehicle.

Four-wheel-drive vehicles typically use a transmission and transfer case. The transfer case mounts on the side or back of the transmission. A chain or gear drive inside the transfer case receives power from the transmission and transfers it to two separate drive shafts. One drive shaft connects to a differential on the front drive axle. The other drive shaft connects to a differential on the rear drive axle.

Most manual transmissions and transaxles are constant mesh, fully synchronized units. Constant mesh means that whether or not the gear is locked to

the output shaft, it is in mesh with its counter gear. All gears rotate in the transmission as long as the clutch is engaged. Fully synchronized means the unit uses a mechanism of brass rings and clutches to bring rotating shafts and gears to the same speed before shifts occur. This promotes smooth shifting. In a vehicle equipped with a four-speed manual shift transmission or transaxle, all four forward gears are synchronized. Reverse gearing may or may not be synchronized, depending on the type of transmission/transaxle.

GEARS

The purpose of a gear in a manual transmission or transaxle is to transmit rotating motion. Gears are normally mounted on a shaft, and they transmit rotating motion from one parallel shaft to another.

Gears and shafts can interact in one of three ways: the shaft can drive the gear; the gear can drive the shaft; or the gear can be free to turn on the shaft. In this last case, the gear acts as an idler gear.

Sets of gears can be used to multiply torque and decrease speed, increase speed and decrease torque, or transfer torque and leave speed unchanged.

Gear Design

Figure 29–4 illustrates the basic names of major gear tooth parts. **Gear pitch** is a very important factor in gear design and operation. Gear pitch refers to the number of teeth per given unit of pitch diameter. A simple way of determining gear pitch is to divide the number of teeth by the pitch diameter of the gear. For example, if a gear has 36 teeth and a 6-inch pitch diameter, it has a gear pitch of 6 (Figure 29–5). The

Transaxle
Input cluster shaft
Mainshaft
Driving axle
Engine
Driving axle
Pinion gear
Differential
Ring gear

FIGURE 29–3 Location of typical front-wheel-drive power train components.

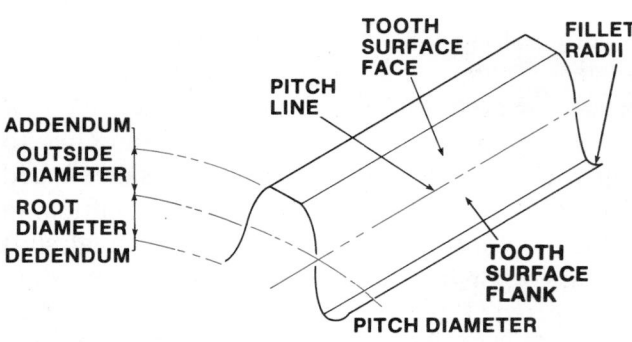

FIGURE 29–4   Basic names of major gear tooth parts.

FIGURE 29–5   Determining gear pitch.

FIGURE 29–6   Spur gears have teeth cut straight across the gear edge, parallel to the shaft.

FIGURE 29–7   Helical gears have teeth cut at an angle to the gear's axis of rotation.

important fact to remember is that gears must have the same pitch to operate together. A 5-pitch gear meshes only with another 5-pitch gear, a 6-pitch only with a 6-pitch, and so on.

Spur Gears   The **spur gear** is the simplest gear design used in manual transmissions and transaxles. As shown in Figure 29–6, spur gear teeth are cut straight across the edge parallel to the gear's shaft. During operation, meshed spur gears have only one tooth in full contact at a time.

Its straight tooth design is the spur gear's main advantage. It minimizes the chances of popping out of gear, an important consideration during acceleration/deceleration and reverse operation. For this reason, spur gears are often used for the reverse gear.

The spur gear's major drawback is the clicking noise that occurs as teeth contact one another. At higher speeds, this clicking becomes a constant whine. Quieter gears, such as the helical design, are often used to eliminate this gear whine problem.

🔧 SHOP TALK

When a small gear is meshed with a much larger gear, as shown in Figure 29–6, the small gear is often called a pinion or pinion gear, regardless of its tooth design. ∎

Helical Gears   A **helical gear** has teeth that are cut at an angle or are spiral to the gear's axis of rotation (Figure 29–7). This allows two or more teeth to mesh at the same time. This distributes tooth load and produces a very strong gear. Helical gears also run more quietly than spur gears because they create a wiping action as they engage and disengage the teeth on another gear. One disadvantage is that helical teeth on a gear cause the gear to move fore or aft (axial thrust) on a shaft, depending on the direction of the angle of the gear teeth. This axial thrust must be absorbed by thrust washers and other transmission gears, shafts, or the transmission case.

Helical gears can be either righthanded or lefthanded, depending on the direction the spiral appears to go when the gear is viewed face-on. When mounted on parallel shafts, one helical gear must be righthanded and the other lefthanded. Two gears with the same direction spiral do not mesh in a parallel mounted arrangement.

External and Internal Gear Teeth   Spur and helical gears having teeth cut around their outer edge are called **external gears**. When the teeth of two external gears are meshed, the direction of rotation is reversed as the gears turn (Figure 29–8). In other words, the driven or output gear rotates in the opposite direction of the drive or input gear. An internal gear has teeth around its inside diameter. When an external gear and an internal gear are meshed and rotate, they do so in the same direction.

Idler Gears

An **idler gear** is a gear that is placed between a drive gear and a driven gear. Its purpose is to transfer motion from the drive gear to the driven gear without changing the direction of rotation. It can do this because all three gears have external teeth (Figure 29–9).

FIGURE 29–8 Externally meshed gears rotate in opposite directions.

Idler gears are used in reverse gear trains to reverse the directional rotation of the output shaft. In all forward gears, the output shaft rotates in the opposite direction as the input shaft. With the placement of an idler gear, the input and output shafts now rotate in the same direction. This allows the vehicle drive wheels to turn backward.

Gear Ratios

As mentioned earlier, only gears with matching pitches can be meshed together. The speeds at which two meshed gears turn depend on the number of teeth on each gear. If both gears are the same size (same number of teeth), then the speed of both gears is equal (Figure 29–10A). If the driving gear is smaller (fewer teeth) than the driven gear, the speed of the driven (output) gear decreases (Figure 29–10B). However, when the driving gear is larger (more teeth) than the driven (output) gear, the speed of the driven gear increases (Figure 29–10C).

To calculate the speed of either gear, multiply the number of teeth on one gear by the speed of that gear. Divide that number by the number of teeth on the other gear.

For example, calculate the speed of the driven gear when the driving gear has 45 teeth and is rotat-

FIGURE 29–9 An idler gear is used to transfer motion without changing rotational direction.

INPUT SPEED = OUTPUT SPEED
A

INPUT SPEED GREATER THAN OUTPUT SPEED
B

INPUT SPEED LESS THAN OUTPUT SPEED
C

FIGURE 29–10 (A) When gears of equal size are meshed, output speed equals input speed. (B) A small gear driving a large gear reduces output speed. (C) A large gear driving a small gear increases output speed. In all cases, the output gear rotates in the opposite direction of the input gear.

ing at 200 rpm, while the driven gear has 75 teeth. The formula follows.

$$\frac{\text{Teeth on driven gear}}{\text{Teeth on driving gear}} = \frac{\text{rpm of driving gear}}{\text{rpm of driven gear}}$$

Putting in the known data leads to

$$\frac{75}{45} = \frac{200}{x} \text{ Therefore,}$$

$$x = \frac{45 \times 200}{75} = \frac{9,000}{75}$$

$$x = 120 \text{ rpm of driven gear}$$

The input speed of 200 rpm is reduced to an output speed of 120 rpm. The relationship of input and output speeds is stated in a gear ratio. This gear ratio can be calculated in a number of ways depending on the data that is known. One method is to divide the speed of the driving (input) gear or shaft by the speed of the driven (output) gear or shaft. In the given example, this results in

$$\frac{200 \text{ rpm}}{120 \text{ rpm}} = 1.66 : \text{gear ratio}$$

The gear ratio can also be found by dividing the number of teeth on the driven gear (d) by the number of teeth on the driving gear (D). Again, in the sample problem, this leads to

$$\frac{d}{D} = \frac{75 \text{ driven gear teeth}}{45 \text{ driving gear teeth}} = 1.66 : \text{gear ratio}$$

This means the driven (output) gear is rotating 1.66 times slower than the driving (input) gear.

Speed Versus Torque A rotating gear also produces a rotational force known as torque. Torque is calculated by multiplying the applied force by its distance from the centerline of rotation. A simple example of this law of physics is demonstrated whenever a torque wrench is used. As shown in Figure 29–11, when a force of 10 pounds is applied perpendicular to the centerline of the bolt's rotation at a distance 1 foot from this centerline, 10 foot-pounds of torque are generated at the centerline of rotation. The torque wrench acts as a lever to apply this force.

Meshed gears use this same leverage principle to transfer torque. If two gears in mesh have the same number of teeth, they rotate at the same speed, and the input gear transfers an equal amount of torque to the output gear (Figure 29–12A).

It has already been explained that when a driven gear is larger than its driving gear, output speed decreases. But how is torque affected?

Figure 29–12B illustrates a small gear with 12 teeth driving a large gear with 24 teeth. This results in a gear ratio of 2:1 with the output speed being half of the input speed.

FIGURE 29–12 Gear teeth are actually a series of levers used to transfer torque. (A) If gears are the same size, output torque equals input torque. (B) When the input gear is smaller than the output gear, output torque increases.

In this example, torque at the input shaft of the driving gear is 10 foot-pounds. The distance from the centerline of this input shaft to the gear teeth is 1 foot. This means the driving gear transfers 10 pounds of force to the teeth of the larger driven gear. The distance between the teeth of the driven gear and the centerline of its output shaft is 2 feet. This means the torque at the output shaft is 10 pounds × 2 feet, or 20 foot-pounds. Torque has doubled.

The amount of torque increase from a driving gear to a driven gear is directly proportional to the speed decrease. When speed is halved, torque doubles.

Review the previous example. With a gear ratio of 1.66:1, the driven gear is rotating 1.66 times slower than the driving gear, but it is producing 1.66 times the torque of the driven gear. If torque at the driving gear input is 100 foot-pounds, torque at the driven gear output is 1.66 × 100 foot-pounds, or 166 foot-pounds.

Most manual transmission gearing is speed reducing/torque increasing. In some transmissions, the top gear is a 1:1 gear ratio in which speed and torque are transferred directly from the input to the output shaft. In most cases, the top gear is an overdrive gear combination. This means it is a speed-increasing/torque-reducing gearing.

Overdrive gear ratios are stated using a decimal

FIGURE 29–11 A torque wrench is a good example of how rotational force or torque is generated.

point, such as 0.85:1. This means that for every 0.85 times the input shaft rotates, the output shaft rotates one complete revolution. However, output torque is only 0.85 of input torque. This is because speed and torque are opposite.

Reverse Gear Ratios

Reverse gear ratios involve two driving gears and two driven gears:

- the input gear is driver #1
- the idler gear is driven #1
- the idler gear is also driver #2
- the output gear is driven #2

If the input gear has 20 teeth, the idler gear has 28 teeth and the output gear has 48 teeth. However, since a single idler gear is used, the teeth of it are not used in the calculation of gear ratio. The idler gear merely transfers motion from one gear to another. The calculations for determining reverse gear ratio with a single idler gear follow.

$$\text{Reverse gear ratio} = \frac{\text{driven \# 2}}{\text{driver \#1}}$$
$$= \frac{48}{20}$$
$$= 2.40$$

If the gear set uses two idler gears (one with 28 teeth and the other with 40 teeth), the gear ratio involves three driving gears and three driven gears:

- the input gear is driver #1
- the #1 idler gear is driven #1
- the #1 idler gear is also driver #2
- the #2 idler gear is driven #2
- the #2 idler gear is also driver #3
- the output gear is driven #3

The ratio of this gearset would be calculated as follows:

$$\text{Reverse gear ratio} = \frac{\text{driven \#1} \times \text{driven \# 2} \times \text{driven \# 3}}{\text{driver \#1} \times \text{driver \# 2} \times \text{driver \# 3}}$$
$$= \frac{28 \times 40 \times 48}{20 \times 28 \times 40}$$
$$= \frac{53,760}{22,400}$$
$$= 2.40$$

TRANSMISSION/TRANSAXLE DESIGN

The internal components of a transmission or transaxle consist of a parallel set of metal shafts on which

FIGURE 29–13 Simplified view of major transmission shafts and gearsets in a three-speed transmission.

meshing gearsets of different ratios are mounted (Figure 29–13). By moving the shift lever, gear ratios can be selected to generate different amounts of output torque and speed.

The gears are mounted or fixed to the shafts in a number of ways. They can be internally splined or keyed to a shaft. Gears can also be manufactured as an integral part of the shaft. Gears that must be able to freewheel around the shaft during certain speed ranges are mounted to the shaft using bushings or bearings.

The shafts and gears are contained in a transmission or transaxle case or housing. The components of this housing include the main case body, side or top cover plates, extension housings, and bearing retainers (Figure 29–14). The metal components are bolted together with gaskets providing a leak-proof seal at all joints. The case is filled with transmission fluid to provide constant lubrication and cooling for the spinning gears and shafts.

Transmission Features

Although they operate in a similar fashion, the layout, components, and terminology used in transmissions and transaxles are not exactly the same.

A transmission has three specific shafts: the input shaft, the **countergear** shaft, and the mainshaft or output shaft (Figure 29–15). The clutch gear is an integral part of the transmission's input shaft and always rotates with the input shaft.

The counter gear is actually several gears machined out of a single piece of steel. The counter gear may also be called the countergear or **cluster gear**.

The counter gear mounts on roller bearings on the countershaft. The countershaft is pinned in place and does not turn. Washers control the amount of end play of the unit in the transmission case (Figure 29–16).

The main gears on the main shaft or output shaft transfer rotation from the counter gears to the output shaft. The main gears are also called speed gears. They are mounted on the output shaft using roller bearings. Speed gears freewheel around the output

FIGURE 29–14 Typical four-speed manual transmission case components. *Courtesy of Ford Motor Company*

FIGURE 29–15 Internal parts of a four-speed transmission (shown in neutral), excluding shift forks. Power flows from the input shaft to the countershaft and back to the output shaft. *Courtesy of Ford Motor Company*

FIGURE 29–16 Components of a typical counter shaft gear or cluster gear assembly. *Courtesy of Chrysler Corporation*

FIGURE 29–17 Components of a typical mainshaft or output shaft. *Courtesy of Mazda*

shaft until they are locked to it by the engagement of their shift **synchronizer** unit (Figure 29–17).

Power flows from the transmission **input shaft** to the **clutch gear**. The clutch gear meshes with the large counter gear of the counter gear cluster. This cluster gear is now rotating. Since the cluster gear is meshed with the speed gears on the mainshaft, the speed gears are also turning.

There can be no power output until one of the speed gears is locked to the mainshaft. This is done by activating a shift fork, which moves its synchronizer to engage the selected speed gear to the mainshaft. Power travels along the counter gear until it reaches this selected speed gear. It then passes through this gear back to the mainshaft and out of the transmission to the driveline.

Transaxle Features

Transaxles use many of the design and operating principles found in transmissions. But because the transaxle also contains the differential gearing and drive axle connections, there are major differences in some areas of operation. Figure 29–18 illustrates the interior of a four-speed manual transaxle. This transaxle uses fully synchronized, constant mesh helical gears on all forward speeds and spur gears for reverse.

A transaxle has two separate shafts—an input shaft and an output shaft. The input shaft is the driving shaft. It is normally located above and parallel to the output shaft. The output shaft is the driven shaft. The transaxles main (speed) gears freewheel around the output shaft unless they are locked to the shaft by their synchronizer assembly. The main speed gears are in constant mesh with the input shaft drive gears. The drive gears turn whenever the input shaft turns.

ITEM	DESCRIPTION
1.	MAINSHAFT
2.	INPUT CLUSTER GEAR SHAFT
3.	4TH SPEED GEARS
4.	3RD SPEED GEARS
5.	2ND SPEED GEARS
6.	REVERSE GEARS
7.	REVERSE IDLER GEAR
8.	1ST SPEED GEARS
9.	MAIN SHAFT PINION GEAR
10.	DIFFERENTIAL OIL SEALS
11.	CV SHAFTS
12.	DIFFERENTIAL PINION GEARS
13.	DIFFERENTIAL SIDE GEARS
14.	FINAL DRIVE RING GEAR
15.	1ST/2ND SYNCHRONIZER
16.	3RD/4TH SYNCHRONIZER

FIGURE 29–18 Exploded view of a typical four-speed manual transaxle. *Courtesy of Ford Motor Company*

The names used to describe transaxle shafts vary between manufacturers. The service manuals of some vehicles refer to the input shaft as the mainshaft and the output as the driven pinion or drive shaft. Others call the input shaft and its gears the input gear cluster and refer to the output shaft as the mainshaft. For clarity, this text uses the terms input gear cluster for the input shaft and its drive gears, and **pinion shaft** for the output shaft.

A pinion gear is machined onto the end of the transaxle's pinion shaft. This pinion gear is in constant mesh with the differential ring gear located in the lower portion of the transaxle housing. Because the pinion gear is part of the pinion shaft, it must rotate whenever the pinion shaft turns. With the pinion rotating, engine torque flows through the ring gear and differential gearing to the drive shafts and driving wheels.

SYNCHRONIZERS

The synchronizer performs a number of jobs vital to transmission/transaxle operation. Its main job is to bring components that are rotating at different speeds to one synchronized speed. A synchronizer ensures that the pinion shaft and the speed gear are rotating at the same speed. The second major job of the synchronizer is to actually lock these components together. The end result of these two functions is a clash-free shift. In transaxles, a synchronizer can have another important job. When spur teeth are cut into the outer sleeve of the synchronizer, the sleeve can act as a reverse idler gear and assist in producing the correct direction of rotation for reverse operation.

In modern transmissions and transaxles, all forward gears are synchronized. One synchronizer is placed between the first and second gears on the pinion shaft. Another is placed between the third and fourth gears on the **mainshaft**. If the transmission has a fifth gear, it is also equipped with a synchronizer. Reverse gear is not normally fitted with a synchronizer. A synchronizer requires gear rotation to do its job and reverse is selected with the vehicle at a stop. In some older transmissions, or truck transmissions, both reverse and first gears may be unsynchronized.

Synchronizer Design

Figure 29–19 illustrates the most commonly used synchronizer—a **block** or **cone synchronizer**. The synchronizer sleeve surrounds the synchronizer assembly and meshes with the external splines of the clutch hub. The clutch hub is splined to the transmission pinion shaft and is held in position by a snap ring. A few transmissions use pin-type synchronizers.

FIGURE 29–19 Exploded view of a blocker ring-type synchronizer assembly.

The synchronizer sleeve has a small internal groove and a large external groove in which the shift fork rests. Three slots are equally spaced around the outside of the clutch hub. Inserts fit into these slots and are able to slide freely back and forth. These inserts, sometimes referred to as **shifter plates**, are designed with a ridge in their outer surface. Insert springs hold the ridge in contact with the synchronizer sleeve internal groove.

The synchronizer sleeve is precisely machined to slide onto the clutch hub smoothly. The sleeve and hub sometimes have alignment marks to ensure proper indexing of their splines when assembling to maintain smooth operation.

Brass or bronze synchronizing **blocker rings** are positioned at the front and rear of each synchronizer assembly. Each blocker ring has three notches equally spaced to correspond with the three insert keys of the hub. Around the outside of each blocker ring is a set of beveled clutching teeth, which is used for alignment during the shift sequence. The inside of the blocker ring is shaped like a cone. This coned surface is lined with many sharp grooves.

The cone of the blocker ring makes up only one-half of the total cone clutch. The second or matching half of the cone clutch is part of the gear to be synchronized. As shown in Figure 29–20, the shoulder of the speed gear is cone shaped to match the blocker ring. The shoulder also contains a ring of beveled clutching teeth designed to align with the clutching teeth on the blocker ring.

Operation

When the transmission is in neutral or reverse, the first/second and third/fourth synchronizers are in their neutral position and are not rotating with the pinion shaft. Gears on the mainshaft are meshed with their countershaft partners and are freewheeling around the pinion shaft at various speeds.

FIGURE 29–20 Gear shoulder and blocker ring mating surfaces.

To shift the transmission into first gear, the clutch is disengaged and the gearshift lever is placed in first gear position. This forces the shift fork on the synchronizer sleeve toward the first speed gear on the pinion shaft. As the sleeve moves, the inserts also move because the insert ridges lock the inserts to the internal groove of the sleeve.

The movement of the inserts forces the blocking ring's coned friction surface against the coned surface of the first speed gear shoulder. When the blocking ring and gear shoulder come into contact, the grooves on the blocker ring cone cut through the lubricant film on the first speed gear shoulder and a

metal-to-metal contact is made (Figure 29–21). The contact generates substantial friction and heat. This is one reason bronze or brass blocker rings are used. A nonferrous metal such as bronze or brass minimizes wear on the hardened steel gear shoulder. This frictional coupling is not strong enough to transmit loads for long periods. As the components reach the same speed, the synchronizer sleeve can now slide over the external clutching teeth on the blocking ring and then over the clutching teeth on the first speed gear shoulder. This completes the engagement. Power flow is now from the first speed gear, to the synchronizer sleeve, to the synchronizer clutch hub, to the main output shaft, and out to the driveline.

To disengage the first speed gear from the pinion shaft and shift into second speed gear, the clutch must be disengaged as the shift fork is moved to pull the synchronizer sleeve and disengage it from the first gear. As the transmission is shifted into second gear, the inserts again lock into the internal groove of the sleeve. As the sleeve moves forward, the forward blocking ring is forced by the inserts against the coned friction surface on the second speed gear shoulder. Once again, the grooves on the blocker ring cut through the lubricant on the gear shoulder to

SYNCHRONIZER IN NEUTRAL POSITION BEFORE SHIFT

A

DURING SYNCHRONIZATION—BLOCKING RING AND GEAR SHOULDER CONTACTING

B

SHIFT COMPLETED—COLLAR LOCKS DRIVEN GEAR TO HUB AND SHAFT

C

FIGURE 29–21 (A) Block or cone-type synchronizer in the neutral position; (B) initial contact of the blocking ring and gear shoulder; and (C) final engagement as the synchronizer sleeve locks the driven speed gear to the synchronizer hub and output shaft.

FIGURE 29–22   Interior view of a five-speed overdrive transmission. Three separate shift rail/shift fork/synchronizer combinations control first/second, third/fourth, and fifth/reverse shifting. *Courtesy of Ford Motor Company*

generate a frictional coupling that synchronizes the gear and shaft speeds. The shift fork can then continue to move the sleeve forward until it slides over the blocker ring and gear shoulder clutching teeth, locking them together. Power flow is now from the second speed gear, to the synchronizer sleeve, to the clutch hub, and out through the pinion shaft.

GEARSHIFT MECHANISMS

Figure 29–22 illustrates a typical transmission shift linkage for a five-speed transmission. As you can see, there are three separate shift rails and forks. Each shift rail/shift fork is used to control the movement of a synchronizer, and each synchronizer is capable of engaging and locking two speed gears to the mainshaft. The shift rails transfer motion from the driver controlled gearshift lever to the shift forks. The **shift forks** are semicircular castings connected to the shift rails with split pins. The shift fork rests in the groove in the synchronizer sleeve and surrounds about one-half of the sleeve circumference.

The gearshift lever is connected to the shift forks by means of a gearshift linkage. Linkage designs vary between manufacturers but can generally be classified as being internal or remote.

Internal gearshift linkage controls are positioned at the side of or on top of the transmission/transaxle housing. They are most often used in console (floor) mounted, rear-wheel-drive applications.

Internal Linkage Design

Figure 29–23 illustrates an exploded view of an internal gearshift assembly in a four-speed transmission.

When the driver selects a specific gear range, the hooked end of the shift lever fits into the notch in the selected gear gate. The gates and shift forks are held to **shift rails** with pins. Any movement of the shift lever is transferred to the selected gate, rail, and fork.

To hold the shift rail in position and prevent other rails from moving, a special locking system is used. As shown in Figure 29–24, the shift rails are designed with detent and interlock notches. Each shift rail has a detent ball that drops into the detent areas on the shift rail as a gear selection is made. This effectively locks the gear into position. There is also a detent notch for neutral. For example, when a shift from first to second gear is made, the detent ball moves from the first gear detent notch on the first/second rail to the second gear notch on the rail. A spring is used to hold the ball firmly in the notch and lock the transmission in second gear. At the same time the first to second shift is being made, the interlock pin moves out of its notch on the first/second shift rail. The interlock pin now rides on the outside diameter of the first/second rail until it is forced into the third/fourth interlock notch. The seated interlock pin holds the third/fourth rail, stopping it from moving. The only way the third/fourth rail can be moved is to return the first/second rail to the neutral position. When this is done, the interlock pin drops into place, permitting third/fourth shift rail movement.

Remote Linkage Design

Remote gearshift linkages must be used when the shifting lever cannot or is not positioned at the transmission/transaxle location. A remote linkage can be divided into two parts: the external section required

FIGURE 29-23 Typical internal shift linkage design. *Courtesy of Chrysler Corporation*

FIGURE 29-24 Shift rails installed on an internal linkage. *Courtesy of Ford Motor Company*

to transmit motion from the remote gearshift lever location to the transmission or transaxle, and the internal, which includes all linkage components contained inside the transmission/transaxle housing.

FIGURE 29-25 Remote gearshift showing linkage, selector rod, and stabilizer (stay bars). *Courtesy of Ford Motor Company*

The external section of a remote linkage can consist of rods (Figure 29-25) or cables (Figure 29-26), which transmit motion to the control shaft that is connected to the internal components inside the housing.

As shown in Figure 29-27, the control shaft passes through the transmission/transaxle housing. The internal end of the control shaft is connected to the selector block. The crosswise slot on the selector block operates the outer guide lever. The lengthwise slot on the selector block transfers rotary action from the control shaft to the inner guide lever. The movement of these parts results in the movement of the guide shaft selector block, which engages the proper shift fork to move the required synchronizer.

TRANSMISSION POWER FLOW

The following sections describe the power flow paths in a typical four-speed manual transmission.

Neutral

Neutral power flow is illustrated in Figure 29-28. The input shaft rotates at engine speed whenever the clutch is engaged. The clutch gear is mounted on the input shaft and rotates with it. The clutch gear meshes with the counter gear, which rotates around the countershaft.

The counter gear transfers power to the speed gears on the mainshaft. However, since speed gears one, two, three, and four are not locked to the mainshaft when the transmission is in neutral, they cannot transfer power to the mainshaft. The mainshaft does not turn, and there is no power output to the driveline.

All gear changes pass through the neutral gear position. When changing gears, one speed gear is disengaged, resulting in neutral, before the chosen gear is engaged. This is important to remember when diagnosing hard-to-shift problems.

FIGURE 29–26 Cable-type external gearshift linkage used in a transaxle application. *Courtesy of Chrysler Corporation*

1 REVERSE GEARSHIFT LEVER
2 GUIDE LEVERS (2)
3 CONTROL SHAFT BOOT
4 CONTROL SHAFT OIL SEAL
5 CONTROL SHAFT
6 SELECTOR BLOCK
7 SELECTOR BLOCK
8 GUIDE SHAFT
9 INNER GUIDE LEVER
10 OUTER GUIDE LEVER
11 CROSS SLOT

FIGURE 29–27 Interior linkage components used for a remote gearshift setup. *Courtesy of Ford Motor Company*

KEY
1 CLUTCH GEAR
2 3-4 SYNCHRONIZER
3 3RD GEAR
4 2ND GEAR
5 1-2 SYNCHRONIZER SLEEVE
6 1-2 SYNCHRONIZER
7 1ST SPEED GEAR
8 MAINSHAFT
9 COUNTERGEAR 1ST GEAR
10 COUNTERGEAR REVERSE GEAR
11 COUNTERGEAR 2ND GEAR
12 COUNTERGEAR 3RD GEAR
13 COUNTERSHAFT GEAR
14 REVERSE IDLER GEAR ASSEMBLY

FIGURE 29–28 Four-speed transmission power flow—neutral. *Courtesy of Volvo Car Corporation*

First Gear

First gear power flow is illustrated in Figure 29–29. Power or torque flows through the input shaft and clutch gear to the counter gear. The counter gear rotates. The first gear on the cluster drives the first speed gear on the mainshaft. When the driver selects first gear, the first/second synchronizer moves to the rear to engage the first speed gear and lock it to the mainshaft. the first speed gear drives the main (output) shaft, which transfers power to the driveline. A typical first speed gear ratio is 3:1 (three full turns of

the input shaft to one full turn of the output shaft). So, if the engine torque entering the transmission is 220 foot-pounds it is multiplied three times to 660 foot-pounds by the time it is transferred to the driveline.

Second Gear

When the shift from first to second gear is made, the shift fork disengages the first/second synchronizer

SEE KEY IN FIGURE 29–28

FIGURE 29–29 Four-speed transmission power flow—first gear. *Courtesy of Volvo Car Corporation*

SEE KEY IN FIGURE 29–28

FIGURE 29–31 Four-speed transmission power flow—third gear. *Courtesy of Volvo Car Corporation*

SEE KEY IN FIGURE 29–28

FIGURE 29–30 Four-speed transmission power flow—second gear. *Courtesy of Volvo Car Corporation*

SEE KEY IN FIGURE 29–28

FIGURE 29–32 Four-speed transmission power flow—fourth gear. *Courtesy of Volvo Car Corporation*

from the first speed gear and moves it until it locks the second speed gear to the mainshaft. Power flow is still through the input shaft and clutch gear to the counter gear. However, now the second counter gear on the cluster transfers power to the second speed gear locked on the mainshaft. Power flows from the second speed gear through the synchronizer to the mainshaft (output shaft) and driveline (Figure 29–30).

In second gear, the need for vehicle speed and acceleration is greater than the need for maximum torque multiplication. To meet these needs, the second speed gear on the mainshaft is designed slightly smaller than the first speed gear. This results in a typical gear ratio of 2.2:1, which reflects a drop in torque and an increase in speed.

Third Gear

When the shift from second to third gear is made, the shift fork returns the first/second synchronizer to its neutral position. A second shift fork slides the third/fourth synchronizer until it locks the third speed gear to the mainshaft. Power flow now goes through the third gear of the counter gear to the third speed gear, through the synchronizer to the mainshaft, and driveline (Figure 29–31).

Third gear permits a further decrease in torque and increase in speed. As you can see, the third speed gear is smaller than the second speed gear. This results in a typical gear ratio of 1.7:1.

Fourth Gear

In fourth gear, the third/fourth synchronizer is moved to lock the clutch gear on the input shaft to the mainshaft. This means power flow is directly from the input shaft to the mainshaft (output shaft) at a gear ratio of 1:1 (Figure 29–32). This ratio results in maximum speed output and no torque multiplication. Fourth gear has no torque multiplication because it is used at cruising speeds to promote maximum fuel economy. The vehicle is normally downshifted to lower gears to take advantage of torque multiplication and acceleration when passing slower vehicles or climbing grades.

Reverse

In reverse gear, it is necessary to reverse the direction of the mainshaft (output shaft). This is done by introducing a reverse idler gear into the power flow path. The idler gear is located between the countershaft reverse gear and the reverse speed gear on the main-

FIGURE 29–33 Components of a typical reverse idler gear assembly. *Courtesy of Chrysler Corporation*

SEE KEY IN FIGURE 29–28

FIGURE 29–34 Four-speed transmission power flow—reverse gear. *Courtesy of Volvo Car Corporation*

shaft. The idler assembly is made of a short drive shaft independently mounted in the transmission case parallel to the countershaft. The idler gear may be mounted near the mid-point of the shaft (Figure 29–33).

In other transmissions, there are two separate idler gears, one near each end of the shaft. As shown in Figure 29–15, the reverse speed gear may be an independent gear located at the rear of the mainshaft. In the transmission shown in Figure 29–34, the reverse speed gear is actually the external tooth sleeve of the first-second synchronizer.

When reverse gear is selected, both synchronizers are disengaged. In the transmission shown in Figure 29–34, the shifting linkage moves the reverse idler gear into mesh with the first/second synchronizer sleeve. Power flows through the input shaft and clutch gear to the countershaft. From the countershaft, it passes to the reverse idler gear, where it changes rotational direction. It then passes to the first/second synchronizer sleeve. Rotational direction is again reversed. From the sleeve, power passes to the mainshaft and driveline. In the transmission shown in Figure 29–15, selecting reverse slides the reverse speed gear forward until it meshes the gear

idler gear. Power flows from the input shaft and clutch gear to the countershaft. It then passes through the front idler gear (direction change), rear idler gear, rear speed gear (direction change), and out through the mainshaft to the driveline.

FIVE-SPEED OVERDRIVE

As discussed earlier, when a large gear drives a smaller gear, an overdrive condition occurs. The large driving gear may rotate three-quarters of a revolution while the smaller driven gear rotates one full turn. Overdrive permits an engine speed reduction at higher cruising speeds. Because the engine (rpm) is running slower, fuel economy is greater. However, engine torque also drops, so power is sacrificed for better mileage.

Overdrive gears are usually located in the transmission housing. Figure 29–22 illustrates a five-speed overdrive transmission. The gear ratio of this fifth gear is 0.87:1. The reverse gear train is designed with spur-type gearing. Unlike the four-speed transmission covered earlier, reverse shifting in this transmission is controlled by a synchronizer. As you can see, this synchronizer is also used to control engagement of fifth gear overdrive.

Power flows for first, second, third, fourth, and fifth gears are similar to those in the four-speed transmission described earlier. In each case, a shift fork moves the appropriate synchronizer to lock the required speed gear to the mainshaft. Power flows through the input shaft to the counter gear, and back through the mainshaft to the driveline.

When reverse gear is selected, the fifth/reverse synchronizer is moved by the fifth/reverse shift rail and shift fork. The synchronizer locks the reverse gear to the mainshaft. The clockwise rotation of the input shaft and clutch gear drive the counter gear in a counterclockwise direction. The reverse idler gearing is driven clockwise by the counter gear. The clockwise turning reverse idler gear drives the reverse speed gear, synchronizer, mainshaft, and driveline counterclockwise. The vehicle can then back up.

TRANSAXLE POWER FLOWS

The following sections describe power flow for the gear ranges of the transaxle shown in Figure 29–16. The direction of rotation used in this example would be as viewed from the vehicle's right front fender looking into the engine compartment.

Neutral

When the transaxle is placed in neutral, the engaged clutch drives the input shaft and gear cluster assembly in a clockwise direction. The first/second and third/fourth synchronizers on the pinion shaft are not engaged, so the pinion shaft gears are not locked to the pinion shaft. The pinion shaft and the pinion gear do not turn, so there is no output to the transaxle differential ring gear.

First

In first gear, the first/second synchronizer engages the first speed gear to the pinion shaft, locking it to the pinion shaft. The cluster's first gear, rotating clockwise, drives the first speed gear and the pinion shaft in a counterclockwise direction. The counterclockwise turning pinion on the end of the pinion shaft drives the differential ring gear, differential gearing, drive shafts, and wheels in a clockwise direction (Figure 29–35).

Second

As the shift from first to second gear is made, the first/second synchronizer disengages the first speed gear on the pinion shaft and engages the second speed gear. With the second speed gear locked to the pinion shaft, power flow is shown in Figure 29–36. As you can see, power flow and direction is similar to first gear with the exception that flow is now through the second speed gear and synchronizer to the pinion shaft and pinion.

Third

With the clutch disengaged, the first/second synchronizer sleeve disengages from the second speed gear on the pinion shaft and returns to its midway or neutral position between the first and second speed gears. As

FIGURE 29–36 Four-speed transaxle power flow—second gear. *Courtesy of Ford Motor Company*

the driver moves the shift lever from its second gear position through neutral to the third gear position, the gear lever inside the transaxle housing moves from the first/second synchronizer position to the third/fourth synchronizer position. It engages the third/fourth synchronizer and locks it to the third speed gear on the pinion shaft. Power flow is then through the third speed gear to the synchronizer and pinion shaft to the pinion gear and differential ring gear (Figure 29–37).

FIGURE 29–35 Four-speed transaxle power flow—first gear. *Courtesy of Ford Motor Company*

FIGURE 29–37 Four-speed transaxle power flow—third gear. *Courtesy of Ford Motor Company*

FIGURE 29–38 Four-speed transaxle power flow—fourth gear. *Courtesy of Ford Motor Company*

FIGURE 29–39 Four-speed transaxle power flow—reverse gear. *Courtesy of Ford Motor Company*

Fourth

The action of the shift lever moves the third/fourth synchronizer sleeve away from the pinion shaft third speed gear and toward the fourth speed gear, locking it to the pinion shaft. Power flow for fourth gear is shown in Figure 29–38.

Reverse

When the shift lever is placed in reverse, the reverse idler gear shifts into mesh with the input cluster reverse gear and the reverse speed gear. The reverse speed gear is the sleeve of the first/second synchronizer. To act as the reverse speed gear, the synchronizer sleeve is designed with spur teeth machined around its outside edge.

The reverse idler gear changes the direction of rotation of the pinion shaft reverse speed gear so that the vehicle backs up. Reverse power flow is illustrated in Figure 29–39.

Like transmissions, some transaxles have five forward speeds. Normally, fourth and fifth gears for smaller cars have overdrive ratios. These high gear ratios compensate for very low final drive gear ratios. Low final drive ratios provide great torque multiplication, which is needed to safely accelerate with a small engine.

FINAL DRIVE GEARS AND OVERALL RATIOS

All vehicles use a differential to provide an additional gear reduction (torque increase) above and beyond what the transmission or transaxle gearing can produce. This is known as the **final drive gear**.

In a transmission equipped vehicle, the differential gearing is located in the rear axle housing. In a transaxle, however, the final reduction is produced by the final drive gears housed in the transaxle case.

The final drive gears consist of the pinion shaft pinion gear and the large differential ring gear. The fact that the driving pinion gear is much smaller than the driven ring gear leaves no doubt that there is substantial gear reduction and torque multiplication in the final drive gears. A typical final drive ratio in a transaxle is 3.78:1. This is calculated by dividing the number of teeth on the driving ring gear (68) by the number of teeth on the driven pinion gear (18): 68 ÷ 18 = 3.78.

To obtain the overall gear ratio or the final gear reduction at the drive axles and drive wheels, the final gear ratio is multiplied by the gear ratio generated by the input cluster and pinion shaft gears for each gear range.

For example, first gear cluster and pinion shaft gears produce a gear ratio of 3.16:1. When multiplied by the final drive ratio of 3.78:1, the overall ratio is 3.16 × 3.78 = 11.94:1. This means driving torque at the drive axles and wheels is 11.94 times greater than engine torque at the input shaft.

Use Table 29–1 for troubleshooting transmission/transaxle problems.

TABLE 9–1 TRANSMISSION/TRANSAXLE TROUBLESHOOTING CHART

Problem	Possible Cause	Remedy
Gear clash when shifting from one gear to another	1. Clutch adjustment incorrect 2. Clutch linkage or cable binding 3. Clutch housing misalignment 4. Lubricant level low or incorrect lubricant 5. Gearshift components or synchronizer blocker rings worn or damaged	1. Adjust clutch. 2. Lubricate or repair as necessary. 3. Check runout at rear face of clutch housing. Correct runout. 4. Drain and refill transmission/transaxle and check for lubricant leaks if level was low. Repair as necessary. 5. Remove, disassemble, and inspect transmission/transaxle. Replace worn or damaged components as necessary.
Clicking noise in any one gear range	1. Damaged teeth on input or intermediate shaft gears (transaxles) or damaged teeth on the counter gear, or cluster gear assembly, or output shaft gears (transmissions)	1. Remove, disassemble, and inspect unit. Replace worn or damaged components as necessary.
Does not shift into one gear	1. Gearshift internal linkage or shift rail assembly worn, damaged, or incorrectly assembled 2. Shift rail detent plunger worn, spring broken, or plug loose 3. Gearshift lever worn or damaged 4. Synchronizer sleeves or hubs damaged or worn	1. Remove, disassemble, and inspect transmission/transaxle cover assembly. Repair or replace components as necessary. 2. Tighten plug or replace worn or damaged components as necessary. 3. Replace gearshift lever. 4. Remove, disassemble, and inspect unit. Replace worn or damaged components.
Locked in one gear—cannot be shifted out of that gear	1. Shift rails worn or broken, shifter fork bent, setscrew loose, center detent plug missing or worn 2. Broken gear teeth on countershaft gear input shaft, or reverse idler gear 3. Gearshift lever broken or worn, shift mechanism in cover incorrectly assembled or broken, worn or damaged gear train components	1. Inspect and replace worn or damaged parts. 2. Inspect and replace damaged part. 3. Disassemble transmission/transaxle. Replace damaged parts of assemble correctly.
Slips out of gear	1. Clutch housing misaligned 2. Gearshift offset lever nylon insert worn or lever attachment nut loose 3. Gearshift mechanisms, shift forks, shift rail, detent plugs, springs, or shift cover worn or damaged 4. Clutch shaft or roller bearings worn or damaged 5. Gear teeth worn or tapered, synchronizer assemblies worn or damaged, excessive end play caused by worn thrust washers or output shaft gears 6. Pilot bushing worn	1. Check runout at rear face of clutch housing. 2. Remove gearshift lever and check for loose offset lever nut or worn insert. Repair or replace as necessary. 3. Remove, disassemble, and inspect transmission cover assembly. Replace worn or damaged components as necessary. 4. Replace clutch shaft or roller bearings as necessary. 5. Remove, disassemble, and inspect transmission/transaxle. Replace worn or damaged components as necessary. 6. Replace pilot bushing.

TABLE 9–1 *(CONT.)*

Problem	Possible Cause	Remedy
Vehicle moving—rough growling noise isolated in transmission/transaxle heard in all gears	1. Intermediate shaft front or rear bearings worn or damaged (transaxle) or output shaft rear bearing worn or damaged (transmission)	1. Remove, disassemble, and inspect transmission/transaxle. Replace damaged components as necessary.
Rough growling noise when engine operating with transmission/transaxle in neutral	1. Input shaft front or rear bearings worn or damaged (transaxle) or input shaft bearing, countergear, or countershaft bearings worn or damaged (transmission)	1. Remove, disassemble, and inspect transmission/transaxle. Replace damaged components as necessary.
Vehicle moving—rough growling noise in transmission—noise heard in all gears, except direct drive	1. Output shaft pilot roller bearings	1. Remove, disassemble, and inspect transmission. Replace damaged components as needed.
Transmission/transaxle shifts hard	1. Clutch adjustment incorrect 2. Clutch linkage binding 3. Shift rail binding 4. Internal bind in transmission/transaxle caused by shift forks, selector plates, or synchronizer assemblies 5. Clutch housing misalignment 6. Incorrect lubricant	1. Adjust clutch. 2. Lubricate or repair as necessary. 3. Check for mispositioned roll pin, loose cover bolts, worn shift rail bores, worn shift rail, distorted oil seal, or extension housing not aligned with case. Repair as necessary. 4. Remove, disassemble, and inspect unit. Replace worn or damaged components as necessary. 5. Check runout at ear of clutch housing. Correct runout. 6. Drain and refill.

CUSTOMER CARE

Just because the technician gets a little dirty in the course of a repair, does not mean the vehicle should, too. Treat every car that enters the shop with the utmost care and consideration. Scratches from belt buckles or tools and grease smears on the steering wheel, upholstery, or carpeting are inexcusable, and a sure way of losing business. Always use fender, seat, and floor covers when the job requires them. Check your hands for cleanliness before driving a vehicle or operating the windows and dash controls. ∎

CASE STUDY

A regular customer brings a recently-purchased 1989 Mustang GT into the shop. The used car was bought just two months ago. The customer's main complaint is that the car gets extremely poor gas mileage. The customer states that the car runs well and has plenty of power, but it seems to use much more fuel than he had anticipated it would.

The technician takes the car out for a test drive. The car runs very well. In fact, the car accelerates much quicker than the technician experienced in similar cars. Knowing the customer, the technician knows the complaint is legitimate. Therefore, she begins to think of the possible

causes for poor fuel mileage. Because the engine runs well, it is unlikely that an engine problem is the cause unless the engine has been modified. Another possible cause is a fuel leak. After a detailed visual inspection, the technician finds no evidence of modifications or fuel leaks.

The technician decides to road test the car again. This time she notices a problem with the speedometer. It seems to be reading much higher speeds than the car is actually travelling. To verify this, she drives the car onto the freeway and observes the odometer and the mileage markers along the side of the road. The speedometer is in error. It records speeds that are higher than actual speeds and measures a mile well before completing an actual mile.

Odometer error was causing the owner to perceive that the gas mileage was very poor. But why is the odometer in error? Another careful visual inspection is conducted. This time attention is paid to the transmission and the rear axle. Sealing compound is present around the outside of the differential housing. This indicates that the unit has been disassembled. She rotates the rear wheels while observing the drive shaft. Doing so, she is able to closely determine the final drive gear ratio. Comparing her findings to the specifications listed in the service manual, she finds that the gear ratio is much higher numerically than the standard gear ratio. She concludes that the gears had been changed for better performance and that is what caused the error in the speedometer.

The technician contacts the owner and explains what she has found. She gives the owner two options to correct the problem. Either he should replace the gears with gears of the standard ratio or have the transmission's speedometer gear replaced with one that matches the final drive gear. Because the latter is less costly, the owner elects to change the speedometer gear.

KEY TERMS

Block synchronizer	Helical gear
Blocker rings	Idler gear
Case	Input shaft
Cluster gear	Mainshaft
Clutch gear	Pinion shaft
Cone synchronizer	Shift forks
Countergear	Shift rails
External gear	Shifter plate
Final drive gear	Spur gear
Gear pitch	Synchronizer

SUMMARY

- A transmission or transaxle uses meshed gears of various sizes to give the engine a mechanical advantage over its driving wheels.
- Transaxles contain the gear train plus the differential gearing needed to produce the final gear ratios. Transaxles are commonly used on front-wheel-drive vehicles.
- Transmissions are normally used on rear-wheel-drive vehicles.
- Gears in the transmission/transaxle transmit power and motion from an input shaft to an output shaft. These shafts are mounted parallel to one another.
- Spur gears have straight cut teeth, while helical gears have teeth cut at an angle. Helical gears run without creating gear whine.
- When a small gear drives a larger gear, output speed decreases but torque (power) increases.
- When a large gear drives a smaller gear, output speed increases but torque (power) decreases.
- When two external tooth gears are meshed and turning, the driven gear rotates in the opposite direction of the driving gear.
- Synchronizers bring parts rotating at different speeds to the same speed for smooth clash-free shifting. The synchronizer also locks and unlocks the driven (speed) gears to the transmission/transaxle output shaft.
- Idler gears are used to reverse the rotational direction of the output shaft for operating the vehicle in reverse.
- In typical five-speed transmission shift linkage, there are three separate shift rails and forks. Each shift rail/shift fork is used to control the movement of a synchronizer.
- Gear ratios indicate the number of times the input drive gear is turning for every turn of the output driven gear. Ratios are calculated by dividing the number of teeth on the driven gear by the number of teeth on the drive gear. You can also use the rpm speeds of meshed gears to calculate gear ratios.
- A gear ratio of less than one indicates an overdrive condition. This means the driven gear is turning faster than the drive gear. Speed is high, but output torque is low.
- All vehicles use a gearset in a differential to provide additional gear reduction (torque increase) above and beyond what the transmission or transaxle gearing can produce.

TECH MANUAL

The following procedures are included in Chapter 29 of the *Tech Manual* that accompanies this book:

1. Check fluid level in a transmission.

2. Check fluid level in a transaxle.

3. Inspect and adjust shift linkage.

4. Inspect and diagnose a transmission/transaxle.

REVIEW QUESTIONS

1. What determines whether a conventional transmission or a transaxle is used?

2. Explain the relationship between output speed and torque.

3. What is the special function the synchronizer performs in some transaxles?

4. Define final drive gear.

5. Explain the role of shift rails and shift forks in the operation of transmissions and transaxles.

6. Gears can ____.
   a. transfer speed and torque unchanged
   b. decrease speed and increase torque
   c. increase speed and increase torque
   d. all of the above

7. The number of gear teeth per unit of measurement of the gear's diameter (such as teeth/inch) is known as gear ____.
   a. ratio   c. size
   b. pitch   d. load

8. Which of the following gear ratios shows an overdrive condition?
   a. 2.15:1   c. 0.85:1
   b. 1:1   d. none of the above

9. Which type of gear develops the problem of gear whine at higher speeds?
   a. spur gear   c. both a and b
   b. helical gear   d. all of the above

10. Technician A says in a conventional transmission, the speed gears freewheel around the mainshaft until they are locked to it by the appropriate synchronizer. Technician B says speed gears are an integral part of the countershaft. Who is correct?
   a. Technician A   c. Both A and B
   b. Technician B   d. Neither A nor B

11. When an idler gear is placed between the driving and driven gear, the driven gear ____.
   a. rotates in the same direction as the driving gear
   b. rotates in the opposite direction of the driving gear
   c. remains stationary
   d. causes the driven gear to rotate faster

12. The component used to ensure that the mainshaft (output shaft) and main (speed) gear to be locked to it are rotating at the same speed is known as a ____.
   a. synchronizer   c. shift fork
   b. shift linkage   d. transfer case

13. Technician A says the counter gear or cluster gear is actually several gears machined out of a single piece of steel. Technician B says the counter gear is driven by the clutch gear and drives the mainshaft speed gears. Who is correct?
   a. Technician A   c. Both A and B
   b. Technician B   d. Neither A nor B

14. In a transaxle, the pinion gear on the pinion shaft meshes with the ____.
   a. reverse idler gear
   b. differential ring gear
   c. countershaft drive gear
   d. input gear

15. Which of the following gearshift linkage types mounts to the top or side of the transmission/transaxle housing?
   a. internal   c. remote
   b. external   d. synchronized

16. Technician A says a gear ratio can be determined by dividing the number of teeth in the driven gear by the number of teeth in the drive gear. Technician B says the gear ratio can be determined by dividing the rpm of the driven gear by the rpm of the drive gear. Who is correct?
   a. Technician A   c. Both A and B
   b. Technician B   d. Neither A nor B

17. Which of the following gear ratios generates the highest torque or power output?

    a. 0.85:1   **c.** 5.23:1

    b. 2.67:1   **d.** 11.12:1

18. Technician A says the speeds at which two meshed gears turn depend on the number of teeth on each gear. Technician B says if the driving gear has fewer teeth than the driven gear, the speed of the driven gear increases. Who is correct?

    a. Technician A   **c.** Both A and B

    b. Technician B   **d.** Neither A nor B

19. Technician A says a gear reduction results in an increase of gear speed. Technician B says a speed reduction results in a decrease in torque. Who is correct?

    a. Technician A   **c.** Both A and B

    b. Technician B   **d.** Neither A nor B

20. Technician A says if a single idler gear is used to obtain reverse gear, the size and number of teeth of the idler gear must be used to calculate gear ratios. Technician B says an idler gear is often used for reverse gear because it causes the output shaft to rotate in the reverse direction of the input shaft. Who is correct?

    a. Technician A   **c.** Both A and B

    b. Technician B   **d.** Neither A nor B

OBJECTIVES

◆ **Perform a visual inspection of transmission/transaxle components for signs of damage or wear.** ◆ **Check transmission oil level correctly, detect signs of contaminated oil, and change oil as needed.** ◆ **Describe the steps taken to remove and install transmissions/transaxles including the equipment and safety precautions used.** ◆ **Identify common transmission problems, and their probable causes and solutions.** ◆ **Describe the basic steps and precautions taken during transmission/transaxle disassembly, cleaning, inspection, and reassembly procedures.**

When properly operated and maintained, a manual transmission/transaxle normally lasts the life of the vehicle without a major breakdown. All units are designed so the internal parts operate in a bath of oil circulated by the motion of the gears and shafts. Some units also use a pump to circulate oil to critical wear areas that require more lubrication than the natural circulation provides.

Maintaining good internal lubrication is the key to long transmission/transaxle life. If the amount of oil falls below minimum levels, or if the oil becomes too dirty, problems result.

UPPER LEVEL

LOWER LEVEL

FIGURE 30–1 Example of typical underhood gear oil dipstick location and level readings. *Courtesy of Subaru of America*

LUBRICANT CHECK

The transmission/transaxle gear oil level should be checked at the intervals specified in the service manual. Normally, these range from every 7,500 to 30,000 miles. For service convenience, many units are now designed with a dipstick and filler tube accessible from beneath the hood (Figure 30–1). Check the oil with the engine off and the vehicle resting on level grade. If the engine has been running, wait 2 to 3 minutes before checking the gear oil level.

Some vehicles have no dipstick. Instead, the vehicle must be placed on a lift, and the oil level checked through the **fill plug** opening on the side of the unit (Figure 30–2). Clean the area around the plug before loosening and removing it. Insert a finger or bent rod into the hole to check the level. The oil may be hot.

FIGURE 30–2 Typical drain plug location on transaxle case. *Courtesy of Subaru of America*

API CLASSIFICATION	SAE VISCOSITY NO. AND APPLICABLE TEMPERATURE					
	(°F)	-30	0	30	60	90
	(°C)	-34	-18	0	16	32
GL-4					90	
				85W		
GL-5			80W			
		75W-90				

FIGURE 30–3 Typical transmission/transaxle gear oil classification and viscosity range data. *Courtesy of Subaru of America*

Lubricant should be level with, or not more than 1/2 inch below the fill hole. Add the proper grade lubricant as needed using a filler pump.

Manual transmission/transaxle lubricants in use today include single and multiple viscosity gear oils, engine oils, and automatic transmission fluid. Always refer to the service manual to determine the correct lubricant and viscosity range for the vehicle and operation conditions (Figure 30–3).

Lubricant Replacement

Transmission/transaxle lubricant should be changed at the manufacturer's specified intervals. Typical intervals are 24,000 or 30,000 miles or every two years. Vehicles used for towing trailers, off-road operation, or continuous stop-and-go driving may require shorter change intervals.

Drive the vehicle to warm the lubricant before placing the vehicle on the hoist. Clean and remove the drain plug and allow the lubricant to drain into a clean catch pan. Inspect the lubricant for metal particles, which may appear as a shiny, metallic color in the lubricant. Large amounts of metal particles indicate severe bearing, synchronizer, gear, or housing wear.

Once all lubricant has drained, replace the washer or apply a recommended sealant to the threads on the drain plug and replace it. Tighten the drain plug to the recommended torque. Fill the transmission or transaxle with the proper lubricant.

DIAGNOSING PROBLEMS

Service manuals list the most common problems associated with manual transmissions and transaxles. Proper diagnosis involves locating the exact source of the problem. Many problems that seem transmission/transaxle related may actually be caused by problems in the clutch driveline or differential. Check these areas along with the transmission/transaxle, particu-

larly if you are considering removing the transmission/transaxle for service.

Visual Inspection

Visually inspect the transmission/transaxle at regular intervals. Perform the following checks.

1. Check for lubricant leaks at all gaskets and seals. The transmission rear seal at the driveline is particularly prone to leakage.
2. Check the case body for signs of porosity that show up as leakage or seepage of lubricant.
3. Push up and down on the unit. Watch the transmission mounts to see if the rubber separates from the metal plate. If the case moves up, but not down, the mounts require replacement.
4. Move the clutch and shift linkages around and check for loose or missing components. Cable linkages should have no kinks or sharp bends, and all movement should be smooth.
5. Transaxle drive axle boots should be checked for cracks, deformation, or damage.
6. The constant velocity joints on transaxle drive axles should be thoroughly inspected.

Transmission Noise

Most manual transmission/transaxle complaints center around noise in the unit. Once again, be certain the noise is not coming from other components in the drivetrain. Unusual noises may also be a sign of trouble in the engine or transmission mounting system. Improperly aligned engines, improperly torqued mounting bolts, damaged or missing rubber mounts, cracked brackets, or even a stone rattling around inside the engine compartment can create noises that appear to be transmission/transaxle related.

SHOP TALK

If during the test drive you hear a noise you suspect is coming from inside the transmission/transaxle, bring the vehicle to a stop. Disengage the clutch. If the noise stops with the engine at idle and the clutch disengaged, it is likely the noise is inside the unit. ∎

Once you have eliminated all other possible sources of noise, concentrate on the transmission/transaxle unit. Noises from inside the transmission/transaxle may indicate worn or damaged bearings, gear teeth, or synchronizers. A noise that changes or disappears in different gears can indicate a specific problem area in the transmission.

CAUTION:

When the transmission/transaxle is in gear and the engine is running, the driving wheels and related parts turn. Avoid touching moving parts. Severe physical injury can result from contact with spinning drive axles and wheels. ∎

The type of noise detected may also help indicate the problem.

Rough, Growling Noise

This can be a sign of several problems in a transaxle or transmission depending on when it occurs. If the noise occurs when the transaxle is in neutral and the engine running, the problem may be the input shaft roller bearings. The input shaft is supported on either end by tapered roller bearings, and these are the only bearings in operation when the transaxle is in neutral (Figure 30–4). In early stages, the problem should not cause operational difficulties; but left uncorrected, it grows worse until the bearing race or rolling element fractures. Solving the problem involves transaxle disassembly and bearing replacement.

When the vehicle is moving, both the input and mainshaft (output shaft) are turning in the transaxle. If the noise occurs in forward and reverse gears, but not in neutral, the output or mainshaft bearings are the likely failed component. Replacement is the solution.

In transmissions, the problem is also bearing related. If the rough growling noise occurs when the engine is running, the clutch engaged, and the transmission in neutral, the front input shaft bearing is likely at fault. Rough growling when the vehicle is moving in all gears indicates faulty counter gear bearings or countershaft-to-cluster assembly needle bearings. If the problem occurs in all gears except direct drive, the bearing at the rear of the transmission input shaft may be at fault. This bearing supports the pilot journal at the front of the transmission output shaft. In all forward gears except direct drive, the input shaft and output shaft turn at two different speeds. In reverse, the two shafts turn in opposite

ITEM	DESCRIPTION
1.	MAINSHAFT
2.	INPUT CLUSTER GEAR SHAFT
3.	4TH SPEED GEARS
4.	3RD SPEED GEARS
5.	2ND SPEED GEARS
6.	REVERSE GEARS
7.	REVERSE IDLER GEAR
8.	1ST SPEED GEARS
9.	5TH SPEED GEAR DRIVESHAFT
10.	5TH SPEED GEAR
11.	5TH GEAR DRIVESHAFT PINION GEAR
12.	MAINSHAFT PINION GEAR
13.	DIFFERENTIAL OIL SEALS
14.	CV SHAFTS
15.	DIFFERENTIAL PINION GEARS
16.	DIFFERENTIAL SIDE GEARS
17.	FINAL DRIVE RING GEAR
18.	1ST/2ND SYNCHRONIZER
19.	3RD/4TH SYNCHRONIZER
20.	5TH SYNCHRONIZER

TAPERED ROLLER BEARINGS
DIFFERENTIAL OIL SEALS

FIGURE 30–4   Roller bearing and oil seal location in a typical transaxle. *Courtesy of Ford Motor Company*

directions. In direct drive, the two shafts are locked together and this bearing does not turn. If the growling noises stop during direct drive operation, the rear input shaft bearing may be at fault. Disassembly, inspection, and replacement of damaged parts is needed.

Clicking or Knocking Noise

Normally, the helical gears used in modern transmissions/transaxles are quiet because the gear teeth are constantly in contact. (When spur cut gear teeth are found in the reverse gearing, clicking or a certain amount of **gear whine** is normal, particularly when backing up at faster speeds.)

Clicking or whine in forward gear ranges may indicate worn helical gear teeth. This problem may not require immediate attention.

Chipped or broken teeth are dangerous because the loose parts can cause severe damage in other areas of the transmission/transaxle. Broken parts are usually indicated by a rhythmical knocking sound, even at low speeds. Complete disassembly, inspection, and replacement of damaged parts is the solution to this problem.

Gear Clash

Gear clash is indicated by a grinding noise during shifting. The noise is the result of one gearset remaining partly engaged while another gearset attempts to turn the mainshaft. Gear clash can be caused by incorrect clutch adjustment or binding of clutch or gearshift linkage. Damaged, worn, or defective synchronizer blocker rings can cause gear clash as can use of an improper gear lubricant.

Hard Shifting

If the shift lever is difficult to move from one gear to another, check the clutch linkage adjustment. Hard shifting may also be caused by damage inside the transmission/transaxle, or by a lubricant that is too thick. Common hard shifting includes badly worn bearings and damaged clutch gears, control rods, shift rails, shift forks, and synchronizers.

Jumping out of Gear

If the car jumps out of gear into neutral, particularly when decelerating or going down hills, first check the shift lever and internal gearshift linkage. Excessive clearance between gears and the input shaft or badly worn bearings can cause jumping out of gear. Other internal transmission/transaxle parts to inspect are the clutch pilot bearing, gear teeth, shift forks, shift rails, and springs or detents.

Locked in Gear

If a transmission or transaxle locks in one gear and cannot be shifted, check the gearshift lever linkage for misadjustment or damage. Low lubricant level can also cause needle bearings, gears, and synchronizers to seize and lock up the transmission.

If these checks do not resolve the problem, the transmission or transaxle must be removed from the vehicle and disassembled. After disassembly, inspect the internal counter gear, clutch shaft, reverse idler, shift rails, shift forks, and springs or detents for damage. Also, check for worn support bearings.

USING SERVICE MANUALS

A service manual is absolutely necessary when performing any type of transmission/transaxle disassembly work. Not only does the manual clearly illustrate all components and their disassembly procedure, it also lists many vital specifications, such as shaft and gear thrust (side) clearances, synchronizer ring and cone clearances, and bolt torque values. Special service tools, such as transmission service stands, oil seal presses, bearing replacers, shaft removers, pullers, and installing tools are also illustrated and explained. ∎

TRANSMISSION/TRANSAXLE REMOVAL

If the transmission or transaxle must be removed from the vehicle for service or overhaul, always follow the specific removal procedures listed in the vehicle service manual.

PROCEDURES
Removing the Transmission/Transaxle

1. Disconnect the ground terminal of the battery.
2. Support and raise the vehicle on a hoist or safety jack stands.
3. Drain the transmission/transaxle lubricant.
4. On transmissions, make a mark on the drive shaft-to-flange connection at the rear axle assembly. Disconnect the drive shaft at the rear axle and tape the U-joint bearings in place to prevent the loss of bearings or the entry of dirt.

(continued)

5. Slide the drive shaft from the transmission output shaft and inspect.

6. On transaxles, remove the drive axles from the transaxle. This involves removing the wheel, brake, and other suspension components needed to access the drive shafts. Support the drive axles by tying them to the underbody with wire hangers.

7. Remove the rod and lever, cable, or hydraulic clutch linkage (Figure 30–5).

8. Remove the speedometer cable that connects to the transmission or transaxle. The speedometer cable housing may also be screwed or bolted to the housing. Disconnect the cable and use wire to keep it out of the way.

9. Remove all wiring, hoses, and cords from the transmission, such as the backup light switch connector near the shift lever (Figure 30–6), the ground wire, and any hoses for four-wheel-drive/front-wheel-drive changeovers. If the starter is mounted on the transmission /transaxle housing, disconnect all wiring and remove the starter.

10. Remove the shift linkage and shift lever assembly as needed. This may require working inside and under the vehicle.

11. Remove the emergency brake linkages if they block access to the transmission.

12. With transaxles, remove any brake or suspension system parts that block access to the transaxle.

13. Remove any exhaust system components that block access to the transmission or transaxle. This may involve disconnecting the header pipe from the exhaust manifold and removing hangers and straps as needed.

14. Attach the hoist to the appropriate lifting points on the housing (Figure 30–7). In many cases a special lifting bracket is bolted to the housing to provide the point.

15. Remove the transmission cross member that supports the transmission and engine after making certain the engine and transmission are safely and securely supported with a transmission jack or jack stands (Figure 30–8).

16. Remove the transmission/transaxle attaching bolts.

17. Move the transmission/transaxle straight out of the clutch assembly.

18. Clean the excess dirt from the housing and place the transmission/transaxle on a suitable workbench.

FIGURE 30–5 Disconnecting the clutch cable from the transaxle housing connection. *Courtesy of Subaru of America*

BACKUP LIGHT SWITCH

FIGURE 30–6 Location of typical backup light switch and wiring harness connection. *Courtesy of Ford Motor Company*

WIRE ROPE

FIGURE 30–7 Attaching the lifting hoist cable to the lifting bracket on the transmission/transaxle. *Courtesy of Subaru of America*

FIGURE 30–8 Typical transmission jack used to support the unit during removal from the vehicle. *Courtesy of Chrysler Corporation*

1 DRIVE PINION
2 WASHER
3 1ST DRIVEN GEAR
4 REVERSE DRIVEN GEAR
5 SYNCHRONIZER RING
6 SYNCHRONIZER SPRING
7 SYNCHRONIZER HUB INSERT
8 SYNCHRONIZER HUB
9 GEAR THRUST SPACER 2
10 2ND DRIVEN GEAR
11 3RD DRIVEN GEAR
12 GEAR THRUST SPACER
13 GEAR THRUST SPACER KEY
14 SYNCHRONIZER SLEEVE
15 4TH DRIVEN GEAR
16 WASHER
17 BALL BEARING
18 SNAP RING
19 5TH DRIVEN THRUST PLATE
20 5TH DRIVEN GEAR BUSHING
21 5TH DRIVEN GEAR
22 INSERT GUIDE
23 WASHER
24 DRIVE PINION COTTER
25 DRIVE PINION RETAINER
26 SNAP RING OUTER
27 MAINSHAFT
28 WASHER
29 5TH DRIVE GEAR
30 LOCK WASHER
31 LOCK NUT
32 SPRING PIN
33 REVERSE IDLER GEAR SHAFT
34 REVERSE IDLER GEAR
35 WASHER

FIGURE 30–9 Exploded view of typical transaxle shafts, gearsets, and synchronizer assemblies. *Courtesy of Subaru of America*

CLEANING AND INSPECTION

Disassembly and overhaul procedures can vary greatly between transmission/transaxle models, so always follow the exact steps outlined in the service manual. Figure 30–9 illustrates an exploded view of the internal components of a five-speed transaxle.

In some cases the countershaft must be removed before the input and mainshaft. In other cases, the mainshaft is removed with the extension housing. It may be removed through the shift cover opening. To avoid difficulty in disassembly, follow the recommended sequence. A **gear puller** (Figure 30–10) or hydraulic press is often needed to remove gears and synchronizer assemblies from transmission/transaxle pinion shafts.

Bearing removal and installation procedures require that the force applied to remove or install the bearing should always be placed on the tight bearing race. In some cases, the inner race is tight on the shaft, while in others it is the outer race that is tight in its bore. Removal or installation force should be applied to the tight race. Serious damage to the bearing can result if this practice is not followed.

Use a soft-faced hammer or a brass drift and ball peen hammer if tapping is required. Never use excessive force or hammering.

During assembly of the transmission, never attempt to force parts into place by tightening the front bearing retainer bolts or extension housing bolts. All parts must be fully in place before tightening any bolts. Check for free rotation and shifting. New gaskets and seals should always be used.

The following are some general cleaning and inspection guidelines that result in quality workmanship and service.

1. Wash all parts, except sealed ball bearings and seals, in solvent. Brush or scrape all dirt from the parts. Remove all traces of old gasket. Wash roller bearings in solvent; dry them with a clean cloth, never with compressed air.

2. Inspect the front of the transmission case for nicks or burrs that could affect its alignment with the flywheel housing. Remove all nicks and burrs with a fine stone (cast-iron casing) or fine file (aluminum casing).

3. Replace any cover that is bent or distorted. If there are vent holes in the case, make certain they are open.

4. Inspect ball bearings by holding the outer ring stationary and rotating the inner ring several times. Inspect the raceway of the inner ring from both sides for pits and spalling. Light particle indentation is acceptable wear, but all other types of wear merit replacement of the bearing assembly. Next, hold the inner ring stationary and rotate the outer ring. Examine the outer ring raceway for wear and replace as needed.

5. Examine the external surfaces of all bearings. Replace the bearings if there are radial cracks on the front and rear faces of the outer or inner rings, cracks on the outside diameter or outer ring, or deformation or cracks in the ball cage.

6. Lubricate the cleaned bearing raceways with a light coat of oil. Hold the bearing by the inner ring in a vertical position. Spin the outer ring several times by hand. If roughness or vibration is felt, or the outer ring stops abruptly, replace the bearing.

7. Replace any roller bearings that are broken, worn, or rough. Inspect their respective races. Replace them as needed.

FIGURE 30–11
Details of typical synchronizer. *Courtesy of Subaru of America*

8. Replace the counter (cluster) gear if its gear teeth are chipped, broken, or excessively worn. Replace the countershaft if the shaft is bent, scored, or worn. Also, inspect the bore for the countershaft. If the bore is excessively worn or damaged, the needle bearings will not seat properly against the shaft.

9. Replace the reverse idler gear or sliding gear if its teeth are chipped, worn, or broken. Replace the idler gear shaft if it is bent, worn, or scored.

10. Replace the input shaft and gear if its splines are damaged or if the teeth are chipped, worn, or damaged. If the roller bearing surface in the bore of the gear is worn or rough, or if the cone surface is damaged, replace the gear and the gear rollers.

11. Replace all main or speed gears that are chipped, broken, or worn.

12. Check the synchronizer sleeves for free movement on their hubs. Alignment marks (if present) should be properly indexed (Figure 30–11).

13. Inspect the synchronizer blocking rings for widened index slots, rounded clutch teeth, and smooth internal surfaces. Remember, the blocking rings must have machined grooves on their internal surfaces to cut through lubricant (Figure 30–12). Units with worn, flat grooves must be replaced.

FIGURE 30–10 Pullers are often used to remove bearings and gears.

FIGURE 30–12 Grooves on the internal surface of the synchronizer blocker ring must be sharp.

FIGURE 30–13 The clearance between the synchronizer blocker ring and the gear's clutching teeth must meet specifications.

FIGURE 30–14 An arbor press is often used to press gears and bearings onto the shaft during reassembly. *Courtesy of Chrysler Corporation*

Also, check the clearance between the block ring and gear clog teeth against service manual specifications (Figure 30–13).

14. Replace the speedometer drive gear if its teeth are stripped or damaged. Install the correct size replacement gear.
15. Replace the output shaft if there is any sign of wear or if any of the splines are damaged.
16. Inspect the bushings and seal in the extension housing, and replace if worn or damaged. The bushing and seal should be replaced once the extension housing has been reinstalled on the transmission.
17. Replace the seal in the input shaft bearing retainer.
18. Replace the seals on the cam shafts.

REASSEMBLY/REINSTALLATION OF TRANSMISSION/TRANSAXLE

Transmission/transaxle reassembly and reinstallation procedures are basically the reverse of disassembly. Once again, refer to the service manual for any special procedures. New parts are installed as needed, and new gaskets and seals are always used.

Serviceable gears are pressed onto the main shaft using special press equipment (Figure 30–14). Separate needle bearings should be held in place with heavy grease so shafts can be inserted into place. During reassembly, measure shaft end play. Adjust it to specifications with shims, spacers, or snap rings of different thicknesses. All fasteners are tightened to the manufacturer's torque specifications.

Soft-faced mallets can be used to tap shafts and other parts into place. After reassembly, secure the transmission to a transmission jack with safety chains and raise it into place. Before the transmission is reinstalled, inspect and service the clutch as necessary.

Reinstallation into the vehicle is basically the reverse of removal procedures outlined earlier.

CUSTOMER CARE

Lack of telephone skills costs many shops business. Every time you talk to a potential customer on the telephone, it is a one-to-one selling opportunity with no distractions. The customer is seeking professional help to solve a problem with a vehicle. Mishandling the all-important first minute of the conversation generates a bad impression of the shop and its ability to do a good job.

Always use a pleasant voice when talking on the phone. Pay attention to what the customer is saying and how he or she is saying it. The words being said and the tone of voice being used are the only contact you have with the other person. Do not allow your attention to wander.

Have a prepared response ready for the first part of the conversation. Keep an outline of this script and a sales lead sheet handy at the phone at all times. Make it a habit to pick up a pen and lead sheet whenever you answer the phone.

The following points should always be covered in any conversation.

1. Greet the customer pleasantly. State the name of the shop, your name, and ask who is calling.
2. Write down the customer's name immediately on the lead sheet. Use it frequently during the conversation.
3. Ask how you can help the customer. Find out what the vehicle seems to be doing. Find out the year and model of the car and when it was last serviced.
4. Do not make the diagnosis over the phone. You might state some general areas where the problem

may be occurring, but clearly state that a thorough inspection is needed before any diagnosis or estimates can be made.

5. Ask the customer to bring the vehicle in for inspection. You want the opportunity to inspect the vehicle so you can perform all needed service.

6. Ask the customer when is a convenient time to bring in the car. Mark down the time, and repeat it to the customer so there is no misunderstanding.

7. Ask the customer if directions are needed to the shop. Give simple, complete directions if needed. Once again, it is easiest to have these written down based on some key landmarks or major streets in your area.

8. Repeat your name. Tell the customer to ask for you when bringing in the car. If you will not be available, give the name of a co-worker. Be sure to inform that person.

9. If the customer is new, ask how he or she heard of your shop. Jot the response down on the lead sheet. This data is often useful in setting up and evaluating sales programs. Thank the customer for calling. ∎

CASE STUDY

A customer complains that his rear-wheel-drive, manual transmission vehicle is experiencing intermittent operating noise, particularly when the vehicle is "just warming up." On the test drive, the technician notices a low growling noise in the lower gear ranges. The noise disappears at cruising speeds in high (fourth) gear.

The technician returns to the shop and places the vehicle on a lift for further inspection. The driveline, differential, clutch, and wheel bearings all appear to be in good condition. This confirms that the problem is transmission related. The technician suspects a damaged bearing at the rear of the unit's input shaft. This bearing supports the pilot journal at the front of the transmission's output shaft. In all forward gear ranges except direct drive, the input and output shafts turn at different speeds. In reverse gear they turn in opposite directions; but in direct drive (fourth gear in this case), the two shafts are locked together by a synchronizer and turn at the same speed. This relieves the operating pressure placed on the input shaft rear bearing, thus eliminating the growling noise.

The only way this problem can be corrected is to disassemble the transmission, clean, examine, and replace any damaged components. The teardown confirms the technician's diagnosis. The roller bearings are cracked and disintegrating. The pilot journal on the output shaft is also slightly damaged. The shaft is sent to a machine shop where it is undercut and fitted with a press-on steel bushing to return it to the manufacturer's specified diameter. The roller bearings are then replaced and the unit reassembled. While the unit is apart, all components are cleaned and examined closely for damage and wear. The oil-cutting grooves on the first/second synchronizer are dull and flat. Although the customer has not yet experienced jumping out of gear problems in these gear ranges, the technician shows the customer the worn synchronizer and explains the problem it could cause in the near future. He strongly suggests replacement at this time and the customer agrees to this additional work.

KEY TERMS

Fill plug	Gear puller
Gear clash	Gear whine

SUMMARY

- Proper lubrication is vital to long transmission/transaxle life. The transmission gear oil must be checked and changed at manufacturer's suggested intervals.
- Metal particles or shavings in the gear oil indicate extensive internal wear or damage.
- The first step in diagnosing transmission/transaxle problems is to confirm that the problem exists inside the unit. Clutch and driveline problems may often appear to be transmission/transaxle problems.
- The initial visual inspection should include checks for lubricant leakage at gaskets and seals, transmission mount inspection, clutch and gearshift linkage checks, and drive axle and CV joint inspection.
- Rough growling noise inside the transmission/transaxle housing is an indication of bearing problems.
- A clicking noise may indicate excessive gear tooth wear. Rhythmical knocking is a sign of loose or broken internal components.
- Gear clash occurs when one gearset remains partially engaged when a second gearset attempts to turn the mainshaft.

◆ Hard shifting can be caused by shift linkage problems, improper lubricant, or worn internal components, such as bearings, gears, shift forks, or synchronizers.

◆ Jumping out of gear can be caused by a poorly adjusted shift linkage, excessive clearance between gears, or badly worn bearings.

◆ Low lubricant levels, poorly adjusted shift linkages, or damaged internal components can result in transmission/transaxle lockup.

◆ Always follow service manual recommendations for removing the transmission/transaxle from the vehicle and disassembling it.

◆ Use recommended bearing pullers, gear pullers, and press equipment to remove and install gears and synchronizers on shafts.

◆ Clean and inspect all parts carefully, replacing worn or damaged components. Never force components in place during reassembly. Follow all clearance specifications listed in the service manual.

◆ Always use new gaskets and seals during reassembly.

TECH MANUAL

The following procedures are included in Chapter 30 of the *Tech Manual* that accompanies this book:

1. Check fluid level in a transmission.

2. Check fluid level in a transaxle.

3. Inspect and adjust shift linkage.

4. Inspect and diagnose a transmission/transaxle.

REVIEW QUESTIONS

1. After draining gear oil from a transaxle, the technician notices the oil has shiny, metallic particles on it. What does this indicate?

2. List at least five separate checks that should be made during the visual inspection of the transmission/transaxle.

3. List at least three causes of noise that are not transmission related but may appear to be.

4. What tool is often needed to remove gears and synchronizer assemblies from the transmission/transaxle mainshaft?

5. When removing or installing bearings, where should force be applied?

6. Technician A says transmission/transaxle gaskets and seals can be reused if they show no signs of tears or excessive wear. Technician B says these items should always be replaced if the unit is disassembled. Who is correct?

   a. Technician A   c. Both A and B
   b. Technician B   d. Neither A nor B

7. Gear clash is a grinding noise that occurs most often during shifting when ____.

   a. gears involved in the shift are chipped or broken

   b. one gearset remains partially engaged while another gearset tries to turn the mainshaft

   c. there is excess clearance between the input shaft and mainshaft gears

   d. bearings seize and lock on the mainshaft

8. A rough, growing noise from a transaxle in neutral with the engine operating and the clutch engaged is a likely indication that there is a problem in the ____.

   a. transaxle input shaft bearings
   b. transaxle main (intermediate) shaft bearings
   c. first/second synchronizer assembly
   d. pinion and ring gear interaction

9. A clicking noise during transmission/transaxle operation may be an indication of ____.

   a. worn mainshaft (input shaft) bearings
   b. faulty synchronizer operation
   c. failed oil seals
   d. worn, broken, or chipped gear teeth

10. Low lubricant levels are the most likely cause of ____.

   a. gear clash
   b. hard shifting
   c. gear lockup or seizure
   d. gear jump out

11. Using a lubricant that is thicker than service manual specifications can lead to ____.

   a. gear jump out   c. gear lockup
   b. hard shifting   d. gear slippage

12. During a test drive, a noise that appears to be transmission related disappears when the driver brings the vehicle to a stop and disengages the clutch with the engine at idle. Technician A says this indicates the noise is most likely coming from inside the transmission. Technician B says the problem is most likely not transmission related. Who is correct?
    a. Technician A   c. Both A and B
    b. Technician B   d. Neither A nor B

13. When is a gear whine or excessive clicking considered normal?
    a. at high cruising speeds
    b. when backing up at higher speeds
    c. when coasting with the clutch disengaged
    d. never

14. Technician A says spinning cleaned bearings with compressed air is a fast, convenient way of drying them. Technician B says this can damage the bearing and should never be done. Who is correct?
    a. Technician A   c. Both A and B
    b. Technician B   d. Neither A nor B

15. A poorly adjusted shift linkage can cause which of the following problems?
    a. gear clash   c. gear jump out
    b. hard shifting   d. all of the above

16. Technician A says the transmission rear seal at the driveline is particularly prone to leakage. When Technician B pushes up and down on the transmission, he says the mounts require replacement because the case moves up and down. Who is correct?
    a. Technician A   c. Both A and B
    b. Technician B   d. Neither A nor B

17. Noise occurs in forward and reverse gears, but not in neutral. Technician A says the output shaft bearing is the likely failed component. Technician B says the mainshaft bearing is the likely failed component. Who is correct?
    a. Technician A   c. Both A and B
    b. Technician B   d. Neither A nor B

18. A rough growling occurs when a vehicle is moving in any gear. Technician A says the rear input shaft bearing may be at fault. Technician B says this condition indicates the counter gear bearings may be faulty. Who is correct?
    a. Technician A   c. Both A and B
    b. Technician B   d. Neither A nor B

19. A car jumps out of gear into neutral, particularly when decelerating or going down hills. Technician A checks the shift lever and internal gearshift linkage first. Technician B says the clutch pilot bearing could be the problem. Who is correct?
    a. Technician A   c. Both A and B
    b. Technician B   d. Neither A nor B

20. While diagnosing a noise from a transmission, Technician A says the noise is caused by something internal if it is most noticeable during a test drive. Technician B says the noise is caused by the clutch if it disappears when the clutch is disengaged. Who is correct?
    a. Technician A   c. Both A and B
    b. Technician B   d. Neither A nor B

DRIVE AXLES AND DIFFERENTIALS

31

OBJECTIVES

◆ *Name and describe the components of a front-wheel-drive axle.* ◆ *Describe the operation of a front-wheel-drive axle.* ◆ *Differentiate between the various types of constant velocity joints, including inboard, outboard, fixed, plunge, ball-type, and tripod.* ◆ *Diagnose problems in CV joints.* ◆ *Perform preventive maintenance on CV joints.* ◆ *Explain the difference between CV joints and universal joints.* ◆ *Name and describe the components of a rear-wheel-drive axle.* ◆ *Describe the operation of a rear-wheel-drive axle.* ◆ *Explain the function and operation of a differential and drive axles.* ◆ *Describe the various differential designs including complete, integral carrier, removable carrier, and limited slip.* ◆ *Describe the three common types of driving axles.* ◆ *Explain the function of the main driving gears, drive pinion gear, and ring gear.* ◆ *Describe the operation of hunting, nonhunting, and partial nonhunting gears.* ◆ *Describe the different types of axle shafts and axle shaft bearings.*

The drive axle assembly transmits torque smoothly and efficiently from the engine and transmission to drive the vehicle's wheels. The purpose of a drive axle is to change the direction of the power flow, multiply torque, and allow different speeds between the two drive wheels. Drive axles are used for both front-wheel- and rear-wheel-drive vehicles (Figure 31–1).

FRONT-WHEEL-DRIVE (FWD) AXLES

Front-wheel-drive axles, also called axle shafts and front-drive shafts, transfer engine torque generally from the transaxle differential to the front wheels. One of the most important components of FWD axles

is the constant velocity (**CV**) **joint**. These joints are used to transfer uniform torque and a constant speed while operating through a wide range of angles.

On front- or four-wheel-drive cars, operating angles of as much as 40 degrees are common (Figure 31–2). The drive axles must transmit power from the engine to the front wheels that have to drive, steer, and cope with the severe angles caused by the up-and-down movement of the vehicle's suspension. To accomplish this, these cars must have a compact joint that ensures the driven shaft is rotated at a constant velocity, regardless of angle. CV joints not only need to bend, they also must permit the length of the axle assembly to change as the wheel travels up and down.

FIGURE 31–1 Both front-wheel- and rear-wheel-drive axles must transmit engine torque smoothly to the vehicle's driving wheels.

FIGURE 31–2 Front-wheel-drive shaft angles.

HALF SHAFT AND CV JOINTS ROTATE AT APPROXIMATELY 1/3 THE SPEED OF CONVENTIONAL REAR-WHEEL-DRIVE SHAFTS AND DO NOT CONTRIBUTE TO VIBRATION PROBLEMS.

FIGURE 31–3 Front-wheel-drive axles for a typical transaxle. On some vehicles, the shorter shaft is solid steel and the longer shaft is tubular.

TYPES OF CV JOINTS

To satisfy the needs of different applications, constant velocity (CV) joints come in a variety of styles. The different types of joints can be referred to by position (inboard or outboard), by function (fixed or plunge,) or by design (ball-type or tripod).

Inboard and Outboard Joints

In front-wheel-drive drivetrains, two CV joints are used on each half shaft (Figure 31–3). The joint nearer the transaxle is the inner or **inboard joint**, and the one nearer the wheel is the outer or **outboard joint**. In a rear-wheel-drive vehicle with independent rear suspension (**IRS**), the joint nearer the differential can also be referred to as the inboard joint. The one closer to the wheel is the outboard joint.

Fixed and Plunge Joints

CV joints can also be categorized by function. They are either **fixed** (meaning they do not plunge in and out to compensate for changes in length) or are a **plunge joint** (one that is capable of in-and-out movement).

In front-wheel-drive applications, the inboard joint is also a plunge joint. The outboard joint is a fixed joint. Both joints do not have to plunge if one can handle the job. Further, the outboard joint must also be able to handle much greater operating angles necessary for steering (up to 40 degrees).

In rear-wheel-drive applications with independent rear suspension, one joint on each axle shaft can be fixed and the other a plunge, or both can be plunge joints. Since the operating angles are not as great because the wheels do not have to steer, plunge joints can be used at either or both ends of the axle shafts.

Ball-Type Joints

CV joints are also classified by design. The two basic varieties are **ball-type** and **tripod-type** joints. Both types are used as either inboard or outboard joints, and both are available in fixed or plunge designs.

Fixed CV Joints The **Rzeppa** or fixed ball-type joint consists of an inner ball race, six balls, a cage to position the balls, and an outer housing (Figure 31–4). Tracks machined in the inner race and outer housing allow the joint to flex. The inner race and outer hous-

FIGURE 31-4 Rzeppa ball-type fixed CV joint.

FIGURE 31-6 Exploded view of a disc-type CV joint.

ing form a ball-and-socket arrangement. The six balls serve both as bearings between the races and the means of transferring torque from one to the other.

If viewed from the side, the balls within the joint always bisect the angle formed by the shafts on either side of the joint regardless of the operating angle (Figure 31–5). This reduces the effective operating angle of the joint by half and virtually eliminates all vibration problems. Just as the output speed between two bevel gears is always equal, so is the output velocity of the joint—thus the description, constant velocity. The cage helps to maintain this alignment by holding the six balls snugly in its windows. If the cage windows become worn or deformed over time, the resulting play between ball and window typically results in a clicking noise when turning. It is important to note that the opposing balls in a Rzeppa CV joint always work together as a pair. Heavy wear in the tracks of one ball almost always results in identical wear in the tracks of the opposing ball.

Another ball-type joint is the dish-style CV joint (Figure 31–6), which is used predominantly on Volkswagen as well as on many German rear-wheel-drive models. Its design is very similar to the Rzeppa joint.

Plugging Ball-Type Joints There are two basic styles of plunging ball-type joints: the **double-offset** design that uses a cylindrical outer housing with straight grooves and the cross groove joint, which is a more compact design with a flat, doughnut-shaped outer housing and angled grooves.

The double-offset joint (Figure 31–7) is typically used in applications that require higher operating angles (up to 25 degrees) and greater plunge depth (up to 2.4 inches). This type of joint can be found at the inboard position on some front-wheel-drive half shafts as well as on the propeller shaft of some four-wheel-drive shafts.

The **cross groove joint** (Figure 31–8) has a much flatter design than any other plunge joint. It is used at the inboard position on front-wheel-drive half shafts or at either end of a rear-wheel-drive independent rear suspension axle shaft.

The feature that makes this joint unique is its ability to handle a fair amount of plunge (up to 1.8 inches) in a relatively short distance. The inner and

FIGURE 31-5 In a Rzeppa CV joint, the balls bisect the joint angle.

FIGURE 31-7 Double-offset CV joint.

FIGURE 31-8 Cross groove joint.

FIGURE 31–9 Inner tripod plunge-type joints: closed housing and open housing.

outer races share the plunging motion equally so less overall depth is needed for a given amount of plunge. The cross groove can handle operating angles up to 22 degrees.

Tripod CV Joints

As with ball-type CV joints, tripod joints come in two varieties: plunge and fixed.

Tripod Plunging Joints Tripod plunging joints (Figure 31–9) consist of a central drive part or tripod (also known as spider). This has three trunnions fitted with spherical rollers on needle bearings and an outer housing (sometimes called a tulip because of its three-lobed, flowerlike appearance). On some tripod joints, the outer housing is closed, meaning the roller tracks are totally enclosed within it. On others, the tulip is open and the roller tracks are machined out of the housing.

Tripod joints are most commonly used as front-wheel-drive inboard plunge joints. Other tripod plunge-type joints are shown in Figure 31–10.

Fixed Tripod Joints The fixed tripod joint (Figure 31–11) is sometimes used as the outboard joint in front-wheel-drive applications. In this design, the trunnion is mounted in the outer housing and the three roller bearings turn against an open tulip on the input shaft. A steel spider holds the joint together.

The fixed tripod joint has a more angular capability. The only major difference from a service standpoint is that the fixed tripod joint cannot be removed from the drive shaft or disassembled because of the way it is manufactured. The complete joint and shaft assembly must be replaced if the joint goes bad.

FRONT-WHEEL-DRIVE APPLICATIONS

In a typical front-wheel-drive application, two CV joints are used on each half shaft. The outboard joints can be fixed Rzeppa or tripod, and the inner ones plunging tripod, double-offset, or cross groove joints (Figure 31–12).

Front-wheel-drive half shafts can be solid or tubular, of equal or unequal length (Figure 31–13A), and come with or without damper weights. Equal length shafts (Figure 31–13B) are used in some vehicles to help reduce torque steer (the tendency to steer to one side as engine power is applied). In these applications, an intermediate shaft is used as a link from the transaxle to one of the half shafts. This intermediate shaft can use an ordinary Cardan universal joint (described later in this chapter) to a yoke at the transaxle. At the outer end is a support bracket and bearing assembly. Looseness in the bearing or bracket can create vibrations. These items should be included in any

FIGURE 31–10 Different designs of tripod plunge joints. *Courtesy of Chrysler Corporation*

inspection of the drivetrain components. The small damper weight, called a **torsional damper**, that is sometimes attached to one half shaft serves to dampen harmonic vibrations in the drivetrain and to stabilize the shaft as it spins, not to balance the shaft.

Regardless of the application, outer joints typically wear at a higher rate than inner joints, because of the increased range of operating angles to which they are subjected. Inner joint angles may change only 10 to 20 degrees as the suspension travels through jounce and rebound. Outer joints can undergo changes of up to 40 degrees in addition to jounce and rebound as the wheels are steered (see Figure 31–2). That, combined

FIGURE 31–11 Tripod fixed CV joint.

FIGURE 31–12 Typical CV joint combinations on front-wheel-drive half shafts.

FIGURE 31–13 (A) Unequal length front-wheel-drive half shafts; (B) equal length front-wheel-drive half shafts with intermediate shaft. _Courtesy of Ford Motor Company_

with more flexing of the outer boots, is why outer joints have a higher failure rate. On average, nine outer CV joints are replaced for every inner CV joint. That does not mean the technician should overlook the inner joints. They wear too. Every time the suspension travels through jounce and rebound, the inner joints must plunge in and out to accommodate the different arcs between the driveshafts and suspension. Tripod inner joints tend to develop unique wear patterns on each of the three rollers and their respective tracks in the housing, which can lead to noise and vibration problems.

CV JOINT SERVICE

With proper service, CV joints can have a long life, despite having to perform extremely difficult jobs in hostile environments. They must endure extreme heat and cold and survive the shock of hitting pot holes at

high speeds. Fortunately, high torque loads during low-speed turns and many thousands of high-speed miles normally do not bother the CV joint. It is relatively trouble-free unless damage to the boot or joint goes unnoticed.

All CV joints are encased in a protective rubber (neoprene, natural or silicone) or thermoplastic (Hycrel) boot (Figure 31–14). The job of the boot is to retain grease and keep dirt and water out. The boots also pump grease through the joint as they flex with the movement of the suspension. The importance of the boot cannot be overemphasized, because without its protection, the joint does not survive. For all practical purposes, a CV joint is lubed for life. Once packed with grease and installed, it requires no further maintenance. A loose or missing boot clamp, a slit, tear, or even a small puncture in the boot itself, allows grease to leak out and water or dirt to enter. Consequently, the joint is destroyed.

CV joint

Drive shaft

Boot clamp

Boot

Boot clamp

Stub shaft

FIGURE 31–14 Typical CV joint boot assembly.

SHOP TALK

It takes only 8 hours of driving with a torn boot to destroy a CV joint. ∎

Outer joints in front-wheel-drive vehicles tend to wear somewhat faster than inner joints due to the added motions of steering. By the time the outer joint produces noticeable wear symptoms, the inner joint might be on the verge of needing replacement. The decision as to whether to replace both joints when the half shaft is removed depends on the circumstances. If the vehicle has low miles and joint failure is the result of a defective boot, there is no reason to replace both joints. On a high-mileage vehicle where the bad joint has actually just worn itself out, it might be wise to save the expense and inconvenience of having the half shaft removed twice for CV joint replacement.

CV joints failure is usually preceded by various noticeable symptoms. If these signs are ignored, the results of complete failure could be very serious. For example, if an outer joint seizes due to loss of lubricant, it can cause loss of steering control. If the joint breaks, the half shaft or axle shaft could drop out of the car. Because of these possibilities, any symptom of a potential CV joint problem should be properly investigated and the appropriate service performed.

CUSTOMER CARE

There has been some confusion about towing a front-wheel-drive vehicle. It is correct for you to advise your customer that CV joints require only one special towing precaution. If a front-wheel-drive car requires towing, tell your customer to be sure that the tow-truck operator does not use J-hooks on the half shaft or lower control arms. The hooks can bend the half shafts or slide along the shafts or arms and rip the boots. Position the hooks on the subframe or

cross member only. In fact, it is a good idea to point out these surfaces to your customer. ∎

Diagnosis and Inspection

Any noise in the engine, drive axle, steering, or suspension is a good reason for a thorough inspection of the vehicle. A road test on a smooth surface is a good place to begin. The test should include driving at average highway speeds, some sharp turns, acceleration, and coasting. Look and listen for the following signs.

◆ A popping or clicking noise when turning signals a worn or damaged outer joint. The condition can be aggravated by putting the car in reverse and backing in a circle. If the noise gets louder, the outer joints should be replaced.

◆ A clunk during accelerating, decelerating, or when putting the transaxle into drive can be caused by excessive play in the inner joint of front-wheel-drive applications or from CV joints. A clunking noise when putting an automatic transmission into gear or when starting out from a stop usually indicates excessive play in an inner or outer joint. Be warned, though, that the same kind of noise can also be produced by excessive back-lash in the differential gears and transmission.

◆ A humming or growling noise is sometimes due to inadequate lubrication in either the inner or outer CV joint. It is more often due to worn or damaged wheel bearings, a bad intermediate shaft bearing on equal-length half shaft transaxles, or worn shaft bearings within the transmission.

◆ A shudder or vibration when accelerating is often caused by excessive play in either the inboard or outboard joints but more likely the inboard plunge joint. These kinds of vibrations can also be caused by a bad intermediate shaft bearing on transaxles with equal-length half shafts. On front-wheel-drive vehicles with transverse-mounted engines, this kind of vibration can also be caused by loose or deteriorated engine/transaxle mounts. Be sure to inspect the rubber bushings in the upper torque strap on these engines to rule out this possibility. A vibration or shudder that increases with speed or comes and goes at a certain speed may be the result of excessive play in an inner or outer joint. A bent drive shaft can cause the same condition. Note, however, that some shudder could also be inherent to the vehicle.

◆ A cyclic vibration that comes and goes between 45 and 60 mph may lead the technician to think there is a wheel that is out of balance. Though liquid inside a tire (from using an aerosol tire sealer) can sometimes create a cyclic vibration, as a rule an out-of-balance wheel produces a continuous vibration. A more likely cause is a bad inner tripod CV joint. The vibration occurs because one of the three roller tracks has become dimpled or rough. Every time the tripod roller on the bad track hits the rough spot, it creates a little jerk in the driveline that the driver feels as a cyclic vibration.

◆ If a noise is heard while driving straight ahead but it ceases while turning, the problem is usually not a defective outer CV joint but a bad front wheel bearing. Turning changes the side load on the bearing, which may make it quieter than before.

◆ A vibration that increases with speed is rarely due to CV joint problems or front-wheel-drive half shaft imbalance. An out-of-balance tire or wheel, an out-of-round tire or wheel, or a bent rim are the most likely causes. It is possible that a bent half shaft, as the result of collision or towing damage, could cause the vibration. A missing damper weight could also be the culprit.

The spin test is useful for determining which of the CV joints is the problem. Put the vehicle on a lift. Make sure to raise the drive wheels clear of the rack. Support the lower control arm bushing, then spin the front tires until the noise is heard. Engine power can be used to perform this test, but the speed should never exceed 30 mph.

![warning icon] **WARNING!**

Use extreme caution to avoid touching the wheels when the power is on. Also, before making a spin test, check the shop service manual. Some manufacturers do not recommend this test on their front-wheel-drive cars and rear-wheel-drive vehicles with independent rear suspensions. If the chassis is raised and the wheel spun at high speed, the joint or boot could be damaged. ∎

CHECK LUBRICANT FOR CONTAMINATION BY RUBBING IT BETWEEN TWO FINGERS. ANY GRITTY FEELING INDICATES A CONTAMINATED CV JOINT.

FIGURE 31–16   Check for contaminated grease.

Begin the CV joint inspection (Figure 31–15) by checking the condition of the boots. Splits, cracks, tears, punctures, or thin spots caused by rubbing call for immediate boot replacement. If the boot appears rotted, this indicates improper greasing or excessive heat, and it should be replaced. Squeeze all boots. If any air escapes, replace the boot. Also replace any boots that are damaged.

If the inner boot appears to be collapsed or deformed, venting it (allowing air to enter) might solve the problem. Place a round-tipped rod between the boot and drive shaft. This equalizes the outside and inside air and allows the boot to return to its normal shape.

Make sure all boot clamps are tight. Missing or loose clamps should be replaced. If the boot appears loose, slide it back and inspect the grease inside for possible contamination (Figure 31–16). A milky or foamy appearance indicates water contamination. A gritty feeling when rubbed between the fingers indicates dirt. In most cases, a water- or dirt-contaminated boot should be replaced.

The drive shafts should be checked for signs of contact or rubbing against the chassis. Rubbing can be a symptom of a weak or broken spring or engine mount, as well as chassis misalignment. On front-

CHECK CARDAN JOINT.

CHECK BEARING AND BRACKET ASSEMBLY.

CHECK BOOTS AND CLAMPS.

CHECK BOOTS AND CLAMPS.

CHECK FOR SEAL LEAKS.

CHECK INTERMEDIATE SHAFT BEARING.

FIGURE 31–15   Inspection points for front-wheel-drive vehicles.

wheel-drive transaxles with equal-length half shafts, inspect the intermediate shaft U-joint, bearing, and support bracket for looseness by rocking the wheel back and forth and watching for any movement. Oil leakage around the inner CV joints indicates a faulty transaxle shaft seal. To replace the seal, the half shaft must be removed.

A quick check for possible wear in the outer joint of front-wheel-drive vehicles can be made by putting the car in reverse and driving in a circle. Clicking noises indicate worn outer joints. Alternately accelerating and decelerating in reverse while driving straight can reveal worn inner plunge joints. A bad joint clunks or shudders.

FIGURE 31–17 CV joint kit with special grease and components. *Courtesy of Perfect Circle/Dana*

CUSTOMER CARE

The most important responsibility an automotive technician has is diagnosing problems. To do this, you must know exactly what is wrong. Many service complaints arise when the wrong part is replaced or repaired. These problems are created when the wrong diagnosis is made. For this reason, it's important to keep in mind that the customer's complaint may be used as a very helpful guide to determine the cause of the problem. ■

Obtaining CV Repair Parts CV replacement parts are available as follows.

1. Complete shaft replacement. Most aftermarket part suppliers offer a complete line of original equipment drive shafts for front-wheel-drive cars. These shafts come fully assembled and ready for installation. This repair method eliminates the need to tear down and rebuild an old shaft.
2. CV joint service kits and boot seals. Most service kits that are available from parts suppliers contain the following.
   ◆ CV joint
   ◆ Boot
   ◆ Special grease for lubrication (Various joints require different amounts of grease; the correct quantity is packed in each kit.)
   ◆ Attachment parts

Part manufacturers also produce a line of complete boot sets for each application, including all the components supplied in the service kit except the CV joint itself.

Old boots should never be reused when replacing a CV joint. In most cases, failure of the old joint is caused by some deterioration of the old boot. Reusing an old boot on a new joint usually leads to the quick destruction of the joint.

Replacement boots are packaged with new clamps and the appropriate type and amount of grease for the joint. CV joints require a special high-temperature, high-pressure grease.

Substituting any other type of grease may lead to premature failure of the joint. Be sure to use all the grease supplied in the joint or boot kit (Figure 31–17).

The same rule applies to the clamps. Use only those clamps supplied with the replacement boot. Follow the directions for positioning and securing them. Photo Sequence 17 shows the procedure for removing a typical drive axle and replacing a CV joint boot. Always refer to the service manual for the exact service procedure.

USING SERVICE MANUALS

The diagnosis and service chart shown in Table 31–1 is a combination of several different service manual charts. This gives an idea of the types of front-wheel drivetrain problems that can occur. A diagnosis chart shows the technician what to look for when a certain type of problem occurs. ■

PREVENTIVE MAINTENANCE

Lubricant is the most important key to a long life of the CV joint. Without lubrication it is rendered ineffective, just like other high-speed mechanical devices that transfer power and motion, including engines, transmissions, and axles. Any condition that starves the CV joint for lubrication causes serious failure. In addition, water entering the boot areas (due to boot breakage, punctures, or improper tightening of the clamps) can wash lubricant out of the CV joint in a short period of time.

REMOVING AND REPLACING A CV JOINT BOOT

P17–1   Removing the axle from the car begins with the removal of the wheel cover and the wheel hub cover. The hub nut should be loosened before raising the car and removing the wheel and tire assembly.

P17–2   After the car is raised and the wheel is removed, the hub nut can be unscrewed from the shaft.

P17–3   The brake line holding clamp must be loosened from the suspension.

P17–4   The ball joint must be separated from the steering knuckle assembly. To do this, first remove the ball joint retaining bolt. Then, pry down on the control arm until the ball joint is free.

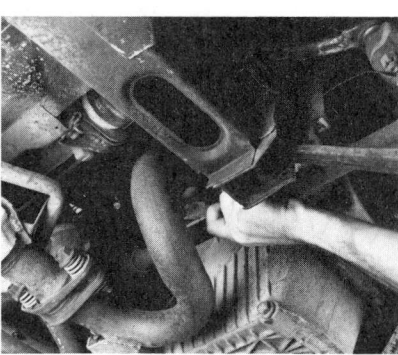

P17–5   The inboard joint can be pulled free from the transaxle.

P17–6   A special tool is normally needed to separate the axle shaft from the hub. This allows the axle to be removed from the car.

P17–7   The axle shaft should be mounted in a soft-jawed vise for work on the joint. Pieces of wood on either side of the axle work well to secure the axle without damaging it.

P17–8   Begin boot removal by cutting and discarding the boot clamps.

P17-9 Scribe a mark on the axle to indicate the boot's position on the shaft. Then, move the boot off the joint.

P17-10 Remove the circlip and separate the joint from the shaft.

P17-11 Slide the old boot off the shaft.

P17-12 Wipe the axle shaft clean and install the new boot onto the shaft.

P17-13 Place the boot into its proper location on the shaft and install a new clamp.

P17-14 Using a new circlip, reinstall the joint onto the shaft. Pack joint grease into the joint and boot. The entire packet of grease that comes with a new boot needs to be forced into the boot and joint.

P17-15 Pull the boot over the joint and into its proper position. Use a dull screwdriver to lift the boot up, to purge it of any air that may be trapped, and to correct any collapsing of the boot.

P17-16 Install the new large boot clamp and reinstall the axle into the car. Tighten the hub nut after the wheels have been reinstalled and the car is sitting on the ground.

TABLE 31–1 PROBLEM DIAGNOSIS AND SERVICE FOR FRONT-WHEEL DRIVELINE

Problem	Possible Cause	Corrective Remedy
Vibrations in steering wheel at highway speeds	Front-wheel balance	Front-wheel unbalance is felt in the steering wheel. Front wheels must be balanced.
Vibrations throughout vehicle	Worn inner CV joints	Worn parts of the inner CV joint not operating smoothly.
Vibrations throughout vehicle at low speed	Bent axle shaft	Axle shaft does not operate on center of axis, thus vibration develops.
Vibrations during acceleration	Worn or damaged outer or inner CV joints	CV joints not operating smoothly due to damage or wear on parts.
	Fatigued front springs	Sagged front springs are causing the inner CV joint to operate at too great an angle, causing vibrations.
Grease dripping on ground or sprayed on chassis parts	Ripped or torn CV joint boots	Front-wheel-drive CV joints are immersed in lubricant. If the CV joint boot has a rip or is torn, lubricant leaks out. Condition must be corrected as soon as possible.
Clicking or snapping noise heard when turning curves and corners	Worn or damaged outer CV joint	Worn parts are clicking and noisy as loading and unloading on CV joint takes place.
	Bent axle shaft	Irregular rotation of the axle shaft causing a snapping, clicking noise.

The special grease package included with each CV joint has a three-fold purpose: to properly lubricate the joint, to protect against exposure to extreme heat and cold, and to prevent boot rot.

CV Joint Servicing

The following are some pointers that should be kept in mind when servicing CV joints.

◆ Never jerk or pull on the drive shaft when removing the drive shaft on a vehicle with tripod inner joints. Doing so may pull the joint apart, allowing the needle bearings to fall out of the roller. Pull on the inner housing, and support the outer end of the shaft until the shaft is completely out.

◆ Always torque the hub nuts to the vehicle manufacturer's specifications. This is absolutely necessary to properly preload the wheel bearings. Do not guess. The specifications can vary from 75 to 235 foot-pounds.

◆ Never use an impact wrench to loosen or tighten axle hub nuts. Doing so may damage the wheel bearings as well as the CV joints.

◆ On vehicles with antilock brakes, use care to protect the wheel speed sensor and tone ring on the outer CV joint housings. If misaligned or damaged during joint replacement, it can cause wheel speed sensor problems.

◆ Always recheck the alignment after replacing CV joints. Marking the camber bolts is not enough; camber can be off as much as 3/4 degree due to differences between the size of the camber bolts and their holes.

CV Shaft and Rubber Boot Care Tips The rubber boots need special care when you are servicing the CV joints, engine, or transaxle. The following tips might save you trouble later.

◆ Always support the control arm when doing on-the-car balancing of the front wheels (Figure 31–18) to avoid high-speed operation at a steep half shaft angle. Off-the-car balancing might be a wiser choice.

FIGURE 31–18 Correctly supported control arm.

- Do not use half shafts as lift points for raising a car.
- Use a plastic or metal shield over rubber boots to protect them from accidental tool damage when performing other wheel, brake, suspension, or steering system maintenance.
- Clean only with soap and water.
- Avoid boot contact with gasoline, oil, or degreaser compounds.

USING SERVICE MANUALS

The exact procedures for performing service operations vary from vehicle to vehicle, but the included steps can be used as general guidelines. While specific installation instructions are provided with all replacement CV joints, boot kits, and drive shafts, they also can be found in the service manual as well. Figures 31–19 and 31–20 illustrate how the service manual details the assembly and disassembly procedures for both the inner and outer CV joints. ∎

Rear-Wheel-Drive Axles

Starting at the front or transmission end of the rear-wheel-drive shaft, there is a slip yoke, universal joint, drive axle yoke, and drive shaft (Figure 31–21, page 785). At the rear or differential end, there is another drive axle yoke and a second universal joint connected to the differential pinion flange.

In addition to these basic components, some drivetrain systems employ a center carrier bearing for added support (Figure 31–22, page 785). Large cars with long drive shafts often use a double U-joint arrangement, called a constant velocity U-joint, to help minimize driveline vibrations. A U-joint should not be confused with the type of CV joint found on front-wheel-drive vehicles, which is described previously in this chapter. The function of these various components follows.

SLIP YOKE The most common **slip** or **sliding yoke** design (Figure 31–23, page 785) features an internally splined, externally machined bore that lets the yoke rotate at transmission output shaft speed and slide at the same time (hence the name slip yoke). While the need for rotation is obvious, without the linear flexibility, the drive shaft would bend like a bow the first time the suspension jounced.

DRIVE SHAFT AND YOKES The drive shaft is nothing more than an extension of the transmission output shaft. The drive shaft, which is usually made from seamless steel tubing, transfers engine torque from the transmission to the rear driving axle. The

yokes, which are either welded or pressed onto the shaft, provide a means of connecting two or more shafts together. At the present time, limited numbers of vehicles are equipped with fiber composite—reinforced fiberglass, graphite, and aluminum—drive shafts. The advantages of the fiber composite drive shaft are weight reduction, torsional strength, fatigue resistance, easier and better balancing, and reduced interference from shock loading and torsional problems. Some drive shafts are fitted with a torsional damper to reduce torsional vibrations.

The drive shaft, like any other rigid tube, has a natural vibration frequency. If one end was held tightly, it would vibrate at its own frequency when deflected and released. It reaches its natural frequency at its critical speed. Critical drive shaft speed depends on the diameter of the tube and its length. Diameters are as large as possible and shafts as short as possible to keep the critical speed frequency above the driving speed range. It should be remembered that since the drive shaft generally turns three to four times faster than the tires, proper drive shaft balance is required for vibration-free operation.

Several different methods have been designed to reduce the effects of vibrations and noise transfer. One example is a drive shaft with cardboard liners that strengthen the drive shaft's axial length (See page 786 for Figure 31–24A, B, and C). Drive shaft performance has also been improved by placing biscuits (Figure 31–24B) between the drive shaft and cardboard liner. These biscuits are simply rubber inserts that reduce noise transfer within the drive shaft. The tube-in-tube construction, illustrated in Figure 31–24C is another method of reducing drive shaft problems. This design eliminates much of the vibration and also reduces the clicking sound heard when the driveline is stressed with directional rotation changes. What makes the design different is that the input driving yoke has an input shaft that fits inside the hollow drive shaft. Rubber inserts are bonded to the outside diameter of the input shaft and to the inside diameter of the drive shaft.

As discussed later in this chapter, there are several methods of balancing drive shafts and drive axles. One of the most common techniques employed by vehicle manufacturers to reduce vibrations is to balance the drive shaft by welding balance weights to the outside diameter.

OPERATION OF U-JOINTS

The **U-joint** allows two rotating shafts to operate at a slight angle to each other. The original joint was developed in the sixteenth century by a French mathematician named Cardan. In 1902, Clarence Spicer modi-

1.

CAGE AND INNER RACE TILTED FOR BALL REMOVAL

WOODEN DOWEL

CAGE

BALL

DUST SEAL

2.

INNER RACE

BALL

CAGE

NOTE: SHARP EDGES ON SCREWDRIVER SHOULD BE BLUNTED TO PREVENT SCRATCHING OF FINISHED SURFACES.

SCREWDRIVER

BALL

CAGE

DUST SEAL

3.

CAGE

PIVOT CAGE AND INNER RACE SO THAT CAGE WINDOWS ARE ALIGNED WITH LANDS OF OUTER RACE. LIFT OUT CAGE AND INNER RACE

LAND

WINDOWS

OUTER RACE

CAGE WINDOW

OUTER RACE LAND

OUTBOARD CV JOINT OUTER RACE

DUST SEAL

4.

TURN INNER RACE 90 DEGREES POSITION LAND THROUGH CAGE WINDOW — ROTATE IN

INNER RACE LAND

CAGE WINDOW

5.

TO ASSEMBLE, ALIGN OUTER RACE LAND AND CAGE WINDOW

CAGE WINDOW

CAGE

OUTER RACE LAND

OUTER RACE

INNER RACE

FIGURE 31–19 Service manual instructions for an inner CV joint. *Courtesy of Ford Motor Company*

FIGURE 31–20 Service manual instructions for an outer CV joint. *Courtesy of Ford Motor Company*

(continued)

7.

8.

9.

10.

11.

12.

FIGURE 31–20 *(Continued)*

FIGURE 31–21 Hotchkiss rear-wheel driveline.

FIGURE 31–23 Typical slip or sliding yoke assembly.

FIGURE 31–22 Center carrier bearing is added to a long drive shaft for additional support.

fied Cardan's invention for the purpose of transmitting engine torque to an automobile's rear wheels. By joining two shafts with U-shaped forks (called yokes) to a pivoting cruciform member, the problem of torque transfer through a connection that also needed to compensate for slight angular variations was eliminated.

There are three operating U-joint considerations that automotive engineers must keep in mind when designing rear-wheel drivelines: speed variations, phasing of U-joints, and canceling angles.

Speed Variations

Although simple in appearance (Figure 31–25), the universal joint is more intricate than it seems. This is because its natural action is to speed up and slow down twice in each revolution when operating at an angle. The rate of speed varies, depending on the steepness of the U-joint angle.

The universal joint **operating angle** is derived by taking the difference between the transmission installation angle and the drive shaft installation angle. For instance, in Figure 31–26 a true horizontal centerline is drawn through the transmission. To align better with the rear axle, the transmission is installed at an angle 5 degrees off the true horizontal line. The drive shaft installation angle is 8 degrees off the true horizontal. The difference between the transmission installation angle and the drive shaft installation angle is 3 degrees. Therefore, the universal joint operating angle is 3 degrees. When the universal joint is operating at an angle, the driven yoke speeds up and slows down twice during each drive shaft revolution. This acceleration and deceleration of the universal joint is known as speed variation or fluctuation.

The four speed changes are not normally visible during rotation. They might be felt as torsional vibra-

FIGURE 31–24   (A) Drive shaft with cardboard liner for strength; (B) drive shaft with rubber biscuit inserts to reduce noise; (C) tube-in-tube drive shaft eliminates vibration and noise.

FIGURE 31–25   Exploded view of Cardan universal joint.

tions due to improper installation, steep or unequal operating angles, and high speeds.

This is more easily understood after examining the universal joint action. A universal joint is a coupling between two shafts not in direct alignment, usually with changing relative positions. It would be logical to assume the entire unit simply rotates. This is true only for the universal joint's input yoke.

FIGURE 31–26   U-joint action.

An ellipse is merely a compressed form of the circle. The output yoke's circular path looks like an ellipse because it can be viewed at an angle instead of straight on. This effect can be obtained when a coin is rotated by the fingers. The height of the coin stays the same even though the sides seem to get closer together.

This might seem to be a merely visual effect, but it is more than that. The U-joint rigidly locks the circular action of the input yoke to the elliptical action of the output yoke. The result is similar to what would happen when changing a clock face from a circle to an ellipse. Figure 31–27 shows that 12, 3, 6, and 9 o'clock are the same, but in between the time reading changes. At 2 o'clock on the circle, it is 2:20 on the ellipse.

Like the hands of a clock, the input yoke turns at a constant speed in its true circular path. The output yoke, operating at an angle to the other yoke, completes its path in the same amount of time. However, its speed varies, or is not constant, compared to the input.

Speed variation is more easily visualized when looking at the travel of the yokes by 90-degree quadrants (Figure 31–28). The input yoke rotates at a steady or constant speed through the complete 360-degree turn. The output yoke quadrants alternate between shorter and longer distance travel than the input yoke quadrants. When one point of the output yoke covers the shorter distance in the same amount of time, it must travel at a slower rate. Conversely, when traveling the longer distance (but only 90 degrees) in the same amount of time, it must move faster.

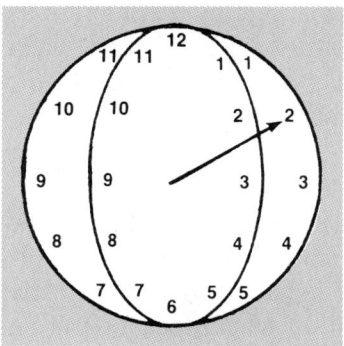

FIGURE 31–27   The face of a clock illustrates the elliptical action of the yokes.

FIGURE 31–28 This graph shows typical yoke speed vibrations.

Because the average speed of the output yoke through the four 90-degree quadrants (360 degrees) equals the constant speed of the input yoke during the same revolution, it is possible for the two mating yokes to travel at different speeds. The output yoke is falling behind and catching up constantly, like a racer on an irregular track. The resulting acceleration and deceleration produces a fluctuating torque and torsional vibrations. This acceleration and deceleration is characteristic of all Cardan universal joints. The steeper the U-joint angle, the greater the fluctuations in speed. Conversely, the smaller the angle, the less the speed change.

Phasing of Universal Joints

Speed variations must be canceled at exactly the same point in drive shaft rotation. The two driving yokes at opposite ends of the drive shaft must be at the same point of rotation.

Single-piece drive shafts have the universal joint yokes welded into position when they are manufactured. On a two-piece drive shaft, a technician might encounter problems if care is not exercised, because the center universal joint must be disassembled to replace the center support bearing. The center driving yoke is splined to the front drive shaft. If the yoke's position on the drive shaft is not indicated in some manner, the yoke could be installed in a position that is out of phase. Manufacturers use different methods of indexing the yoke to the shaft. Some use aligning arrows (Figure 31–29). Others machine a master spline that is wider than the others. The yoke and shaft cannot be reassembled until the master spline is aligned properly. When there are no indexing marks, the technician should always index the

FIGURE 31–29 Arrows are placed on the driving and driven parts of the drive shaft to maintain alignment.

yoke to the drive shaft before disassembling the universal joint. This saves time in the reassembly procedure. Indexing requires only a light hammer and center punch to mark the yoke and drive shaft.

Canceling Angles

Vibrations can be reduced by using canceling angles (Figure 31–30). Carefully examine the illustration, and note that the operating angle at the front of the drive shaft is offset by the one at the rear of the drive shaft. When the front universal joint accelerates, causing a vibration, the rear universal joint decelerates, causing a vibration. The vibrations created by

FIGURE 31–30 Canceling angles reduce vibrations.

the two joints oppose and dampen the vibrations from one to the other. The use of canceling angles provides a smoother drive shaft operation.

TYPES OF U-JOINTS

There are three common types of U-joint designs.

1. Single U-joints retained by either an inside or outside snap ring.
2. Coupled U-joints commonly called the double-Cardan constant velocity joints.
3. U-joints held in the yoke by U-bolts or lock plates.

Single Universal Joint

The single **Cardan/Spicer** universal joint is also known as the cross or four-point joint. These two names aptly describe the single Cardan, since the joint itself forms a cross, with four machined trunnions or points equally spaced around the center of the axis. Needle bearings used to abate friction and provide smoother operation are set in bearing cups. The trunnions of the cross fit into the cup assemblies and the cup assemblies fit snugly into the driving and driven universal joint yokes. Universal joint movement takes place between the trunnions, needle bearings, and bearing cups (Figure 31–31). No movement should take place between the bearing cup and the hole in the universal joint yoke. The fit between the hole in the yoke and the bearing cups is known as a press-fit. Retaining rings hold the bearing cups in place in the universal joint yoke.

Replacing a single U-joint requires that the technician know more than the make and model of the vehicle. It might be necessary to know the type of U-joint and the yoke span to obtain the proper replacement part (Figure 31–32).

Spicer Style In this single U-joint design (Figure 31–33A) an outside snap ring fits into a groove mach-

FIGURE 31–32   (A) Outside yoke span and (B) inside yoke span.

ined in the outer end of the yoke. The bearing cups for this style are machined to accommodate the snap ring.

Mechanics or Detroit/Saginaw Style In this design (Figure 31–33B), an inside snap ring or C-clip fits into a groove machined in the bearing cup on the side closer to the grease seal. When installed, the clip rests against the machined inside portion of the yoke. The snap ring in the **Detroit/Saginaw style** is injected nylon. That is, the snap rings are retained by nylon injected into the retaining ring grooves.

Cleveland Style In an attempt to combine U-joints to obtain more coverage, the **Cleveland style** is used for some applications. The bearing cups for this U-joint are machined to accommodate either Spicer or Mechanics style snap rings. If a replacement U-joint comes with both style clips, use the clips that pertain to your application.

FIGURE 31–31   Components involved in U-joint movement.

FIGURE 31–33   (A) Spicer style U-joint and (B) mechanics or Detroit style U-joint.

USING SERVICE MANUALS

In addition to the technician knowing how to read a service manual, it is also important to know the ins and outs of aftermarket catalogs and similar literature. This helps to identify the correct type of joint used in a particular vehicle. ■

Double-Cardan Universal Joint

Most often installed in front-engine rear-wheel-drive luxury automobiles, the **double-Cardan** universal joint smoothly transmit torque regardless of the operating angle of the driving and driven members. It is, therefore, classified as a constant velocity universal joint. Observe the left and right universal joint centerlines (Figure 31–34). They bisect the angle made by the input driving and the output driven universal joint. Constant velocity operation is the result.

The double-Cardan universal joint is made up of two Cardan universal joints linked together by a coupling yoke. A centering ball socket is inside the coupling yoke between the two universal joints. This ball and socket maintain an axial relationship between the two universal joints. The ball joint divides the universal joint operating angle into two equal parts, so each universal joint operates at half of the operating angle. Since the two universal joints operate at the same angle, vibrations and fluctuations in speed from the front joint are nullified by the vibrations and fluctuations in speed from the rear universal joint. The canceling angles produce a smooth transfer of engine torque. The double-Cardan joint is often a vital part of a two-piece drive axle shaft (Figure 31–35).

Other U-Joint Retaining Methods

There are several methods of retaining the U-joint in its position. The methods shown in Figure 31–36 are most common.

FIGURE 31–34 Double-Cardan constant speed universal joint's centerline bisects the angle at the ball socket.

⬤ CAUTION:

Extreme care should be taken when working around a rotating drive shaft. Severe injury can result from touching a moving shaft. Never attempt to stop the spinning shaft by hand. It can cause serious physical injury. ■

FIGURE 31–35 Two-piece drive shaft and double-Cardan joints. *Courtesy of Chrysler Corporation*

FIGURE 31–36   Various retaining methods for U-joints.

DIAGNOSIS OF DRIVE SHAFT AND U-JOINT PROBLEMS

A failed U-joint or damaged drive shaft can exhibit a variety of symptoms. A clunk that is heard when the transmission is shifted into gear is the most obvious. You can also encounter unusual noise, roughness, or vibration.

To help differentiate a potential drivetrain problem from other common sources of noise or vibration, it is important to note the speed and driving conditions at which the problem occurs. As a general guide, a worn U-joint is most noticeable during acceleration or deceleration and is less speed sensitive than an unbalanced tire (commonly occurring in the 30 to 60 mph range) or a bad wheel bearing (more noticeable at higher speeds). Unfortunately, it is often very difficult to accurately pinpoint drivetrain problems with only a road test. Therefore, expand the undercar investigation by putting the vehicle up on the lift where it is possible to get a good view of what is going on underneath.

CUSTOMER CARE

To some customers, a little noise might be easier to live with than the cost of a differential teardown. On the other hand, repairs now may be less

extensive than later. The best method is to go over all the options in detail and let the customer decide. This goes for most other vehicle problems as well. ■

The first problem most likely encountered is an undercar fluid leak. If there is a lot of lube escaping from the pinion shaft seal, the drivetrain noise could be caused by a bad pinion bearing. To confirm the problem, start the engine, put the transmission in gear, and listen at the carrier. If the bearing is noisy, it is necessary to make one of those difficult judgment calls. If the bearing sounds fine but the pinion seal is still leaking, suggest an on-the-car seal replacement.

On some vehicles, seal replacement is a simple procedure that involves removing the pinion flange and replacing the seal. However, always refer to the service manual for the correct procedure and note any special precautions that may be given.

At the other end of the driveline, inspect the extension housing seal the same way. If it is leaking, the seal itself can be easily replaced. Check the extension housing bushing. That is the most likely reason the seal went bad in the first place. Once the yoke is removed, an internal expanding bearing/bushing puller makes short work of bushing replacement. Before pushing the slip yoke back in after the new seal is installed, make sure the machined surface of the bore is free of scratches, nicks, and grooves that could damage the seal. For that added margin of safety, a little transmission lube or white grease on the lip of the seal helps the parts slide in easily.

If the seals pass the test, continue driveline examination by inspecting the U-joint's grease seals for signs of rust, leakage, or lubrication breakdown. Also, check for excessive joint movement by firmly grasping and attempting to rotate the coupling yokes back and forth in opposite directions. If any perceptible trunnion-to-bearing movement is felt, the joint should be replaced.

The runout of the drive shaft should also be checked. If there is excessive runout, determine the cause and make the necessary repairs. If the runout is fine, check the phasing of the joints and their angle. To check their operating angle, use an inclinometer. This instrument, when attached to the drive shaft, will display the angle of the drive shaft along any point. Your finding from this test should be compared to specifications. Normally if the angles are wrong, the rear axle has moved in its mounting.

As a final diagnosis inspection point, check the entire length of the drive shaft for excess undercoating, dents, missing weights, or other damage that could cause an imbalance and result in a vibration. If no damage is found, the drive shaft should be removed and its balance checked by a specialty shop.

DIFFERENTIALS

The differential is a geared mechanism located between the driving axles of a vehicle. Its job is to direct power flow to the driving axles. Differentials are used in all types of power trains: rear-wheel-drive, front-wheel-drive, and four-wheel-drive.

On a front-wheel-drive car or truck, the differential is normally an integral part of the transaxle assembly located at the front of the vehicle. Depending on whether the engine is mounted transversely or longitudinally, the transaxle differential design and operation vary (Figure 31–37). With a transverse-mounted

FIGURE 31–38 Four-wheel-drive drivetrain based on a rear-wheel-drive design. *Courtesy of Mitsubishi Motor Sales of America, Inc.*

FIGURE 31–37 There are two basic transaxle differential design variations: (A) with transverse mounted engine, engine crankshaft centerline and axle centerline are on the same plane; (B) with longitudinal mounted engine, differential must change power flow 90 degrees, as with rear-wheel drive. *Courtesy of Chrysler Corporation*

engine, the crankshaft centerline and drive axle are on the same plane. With a longitudinal-mounted power plant, the differential must change the power flow 90 degrees.

On rear-wheel-drive vehicles, the differential is part of the rear assembly. It is located in the rear axle housing or carrier. A driveline running beneath the vehicle from front to rear connects the transmission with the differential gearing. Four-wheel-drive vehicles have differentials on both their front and rear axles. A transfer case mounted to the side or back of the transmission splits the power between two drive shafts or lines. One runs to the front drive axle and the other runs to the rear drive axle (Figure 31–38). Differentials at the front and rear axles redirect power flow to all wheels. Some full-time four-wheel-drive systems employ a third differential. This interaxle differential is located in the transfer case between the front and rear drive axles (Figure 31–39). The interaxle differential allows the two drivelines to rotate at different speeds, which improves vehicle handling and reduces component wear.

FIGURE 31–39 The interaxle differential is located in the transfer case between the front- and rear-drive axles.

FIGURE 31–40 The differential is needed because the rear wheels turn at different speeds when turning a corner.

Differential Functions

The differential actually performs several functions. It allows the drive wheels to rotate at different speeds when negotiating a turn or curve in the road (Figure 31–40) and redirects the engine torque from the drive shaft to the rear drive axles. The drive shaft turns in a motion that is perpendicular to the rotation of the drive wheels. The differential assembly redirects the torque so that the drive shafts turn in a motion that is parallel with the rotation of the drive wheels.

The differential also splits torque between the drive axles. Each drive wheel receives an equal amount of torque. The torque delivered to the wheels is no greater than the torque required by the wheel with the least amount of traction. If one wheel begins to slip, it requires much less torque to turn it. Less torque is then delivered to the wheel that is not slipping. In such a situation, unless the differential is a limited-slip design, the vehicle loses traction.

The drive gears of a differential are also sized to provide a gear reduction, or a torque multiplication. Differentials with a low (numerically high) gear ratio allow for fast acceleration and good pulling power. Differentials with high gear ratios allow the engine to run slower at any given speed, resulting in better fuel conservation.

Differential Components

The components of commonly used differentials are shown in Figure 31–41. There are several other basic

FIGURE 31–41 A typical differential design. *Courtesy of Toyo Kogyo Co., Ltd.*

design arrangements. However, the one most commonly used design features pinion/ring gears and a **pinion shaft**. The latter is a spiral bevel gear that is mounted on an input (pinion) shaft. The shaft is mounted in the front end of the carrier and supported by two or three bearings. An overhung pinion gear is supported by two tapered bearings spaced far enough apart to provide the needed leverage to rotate the ring gear and drive axles (Figure 31–42). A straddle-mounted pinion gear rests on three bearings: two tapered bearings on the front support the input shaft and one roller bearing is fitted over a short shaft extending from the rear end of the **pinion gear** (Figure 31–43).

The pinion gear meshes with a **ring gear**. The ring gear is a ring of hardened steel with curved teeth on one side and threaded holes on the other. The ring

FIGURE 31–42 Overhung-type of drive pinion mount.

FIGURE 31–43 A straddle-mounted drive pinion gear. The drive pinion is straddled between two tapered rollers and a straight roller bearing. These three bearings hold the drive pinion in mesh with the ring gear. *Courtesy of Ford Motor Company*

gear is bolted to the differential case. When the pinion gear is rotated by the drive shaft, the ring gear is forced to rotate, turning the differential case and axle shafts. In most automotive applications, there are two pinion gears mounted on a straight shaft. On heavier trucks, the differential contains four pinion gears mounted on a cross-shaped spider. The pinion shafts are mounted in holes in the case (or in matching grooves in the case halves) and are secured in place with a lock bolt or retaining rings.

The teeth on the drive pinion contact the ring gear at either the same, or different, places after several revolutions of the ring gear. There are three terms that describe the tooth contact: hunting gearset, nonhunting gearset, and partial nonhunting gearset.

HUNTING GEARSET When one drive pinion gear tooth contacts every ring gear tooth after several revolutions, the gearset is **hunting**. In other words, the drive pinion hunts out each ring gear tooth. A typical hunting gearset may have 9 drive pinion teeth and 37 ring gear teeth. The rear-axle ratio for this combination would be 4.11:1.

NONHUNTING GEARSET When one drive pinion gear tooth contacts only certain ring gear teeth, the gearset is **nonhunting**. A typical nonhunting gearset may have 10 drive pinion teeth and 30 ring gear teeth. The rear-axle ratio for this combination would be 3.00:1. For every revolution of the ring gear, each drive pinion tooth would contact the same 3 ring gear teeth. The drive pinion gear teeth do not hunt out all ring gear teeth.

PARTIAL NONHUNTING GEARSET The difference between nonhunting and **partial nonhunting** gearsets is the amount of ring gear teeth that are contacted. On a partial nonhunting gearset, one drive pinion tooth contacts six ring gear teeth instead of three. During the first revolution of the ring gear, one drive pinion tooth contacts three ring gear teeth. During the second revolution of the ring gear, the drive pinion tooth contacts three different ring gear teeth. During every other ring gear revolution, one drive pinion tooth contacts the same ring gear teeth. A typical partial nonhunting gearset may have 10 drive pinion teeth and 35 ring gear teeth. The rear-axle ratio for this combination would be 3.50:1. The number of teeth on the drive pinion and ring gear determine whether the gearset is hunting, nonhunting, or partial nonhunting. Knowing the type of gearset is important in diagnosing ring and pinion problems.

A **hypoid gear** is similar to a spiral bevel gear (Figure 31–44). The hypoid gear contacts more than one tooth at a time. The hypoid gear also makes con-

FIGURE 31–44 (A) Spiral bevel differential gears and (B) hypoid gears. *Courtesy of Ford Motor Company of Canada, Ltd.*

tact with a sliding motion. This sliding action, however, is smoother than that of the spiral valve gear, resulting in quieter operation. The biggest difference is that in a hypoid gear, the centerlines of the ring and pinion gears do not match. A centerline is an imaginary line that connects the axis of one part to the axis of another part. For example, when the drive pinion is set in the middle of the right gear, the centerlines of each gear meet. To determine this, draw a line from the center, or axis, of the drive-pinion-gear shaft. Then, locate the centerline of the ring gear. The centerlines should meet on spur-type bevel gears. Using hypoid gears, the drive pinion gear is placed lower in the differential. The drive pinion meshes with the ring gear at a point below its centerline.

When hypoid gears mesh during operation, they do so with a sliding action. The teeth tend to wipe lubricant from the face of the gears, resulting in eventual damage. Differentials require the use of extreme pressure-type lubricants. The additives in this type of lubricant allow the lubricant to withstand the wiping action of the gear teeth without separating from the gear face.

The differential also contains two side gears (Figure 31–45). The inside bore of the side gears is splined and mates with splines on the ends of the

FIGURE 31–45 Hypoid ring and pinion assembly with side gears. *Courtesy of Ford Motor Company*

drive axles. The differential pinion gears and side gears are in constant mesh. The pinion gears are mounted on a pinion gear shaft, which is mounted in the differential casing. As the casing turns with the ring gear, the pinion shaft and gears also turn. The pinion gears deliver torque to the side gears.

When the pinion and ring gear are manufactured, the faces of the gear teeth are machined to provide smooth mating surfaces. The pinion gear and ring gear are always matched to provide a good mesh. Pinion gears and the ring gear should always be installed as a set. Otherwise, the mismatched gearset might operate noisily. A matched gearset code is etched in each drive pinion and ring gearset.

Rear Axle Housing and Casing The differential in a rear-drive vehicle is housed in the rear axle housing, or carrier. The axle housing also contains the two drive axle shafts (Figure 31–46). There are two types of axle housings found on modern automobiles: the removable carrier and the integral carrier. The removable carrier axle housing is open on the front side. Because it resembles a banjo, it is often called a banjo housing. The backside of the housing is closed to seal out dirt and contaminants and keep in the differential lubricant. The differential is mounted in a carrier assembly that can be removed as a unit from the axle housing (Figure 31–47). Removable carrier

FIGURE 31–46 In a typical rear end, the drive axles are enclosed in metal tubes connected to the differential housing. *Courtesy of Ford Motor Company*

FIGURE 31–47 A typical removable carrier axle housing. *Courtesy of Ford Motor Company*

axle housings are most commonly used today on trucks and other heavy-duty vehicles.

The **integral axle** housing is most commonly found on late-model cars and light trucks (Figure 31–48). A cast-iron carrier forms the center of the axle housing. Steel axle tubes are pressed into both sides of the carrier to form the housing. The housing and carrier have a removable rear cover that allows access to the differential assembly. Because the carrier is not removable, the differential components must be removed and serviced separately. In addition to providing a mounting place for the differential, the axle housing also contains brackets for mounting suspen-

sion components, such as control arms, leaf springs, and coil springs.

GEAR REDUCTION When a smaller gear drives a larger gear, the larger gear turns slower. This is known as **speed** or **gear reduction**. The smaller drive pinion gear may turn only about two-and-a-half times the ring gear speed. This difference between the speed of the drive pinion gear and the ring gear is known as the rear-axle ratio. Most rear-axle ratios appear with decimals, such as: 2.43:1, 3.08:1, or 4.11:1. In a differential, the smaller gear is the drive pinion gear and the larger gear is the ring gear.

FIGURE 31–48 Integral-carrier differential exploded view. *Courtesy of Ford Motor Company*

INCREASING TORQUE A gear reduction increases torque.

🔧 SHOP TALK

By using the rear-axle ratio as a guideline, you can tell how much gear reduction there is. This is expressed by the torque ratio. If the rear-axle ratio is 3.00:1, the torque ratio is just the opposite, or 1:3.00. This means the torque at the ring gear has been increased three times. ∎

Differential Operation

The amount of power delivered to each driving wheel by the differential is expressed as a percentage. When the vehicle moves straight ahead, each driving wheel rotates at 100 percent of the case speed. When the vehicle is turning, the inside wheel might be getting 90 percent of the case speed. At the same time, the outside wheel might be getting 110 percent of the differential action.

Power flow through the differential begins at the drive pinion yoke or companion flange (Figure 31–49). The Companion flange accepts torque from the rear U-joint and is attached to the drive pinion gear, which transfers torque to the ring gear. As the ring gear turns, it turns the carrier and the pinion shaft. The differential pinion gears transfer torque to the side gears to turn the driving axles. The differential pinion gears determine how much torque goes to each driving axle. The pinion gears can move with the carrier, and they can rotate on the pinion shaft.

When drive shaft torque is applied to the input shaft and drive pinion, the shaft rotates in a direction that is perpendicular to the vehicle's drive axles. When this rotary motion is transferred to the ring gear, the torque flow changes direction and becomes parallel to the axles and wheels. Because the ring gear is bolted to the differential case, the case must rotate with the ring gear. The pinion gear shaft mounted in the casing must also rotate with the case and the ring gear. The pinions turn end over end. Gears do not rotate on the pinion shaft when both driving wheels are turning at the same speed. They rotate end over end as the differential case rotates. Because the pinions are meshed with both side gears, the side gears rotate and turn the axle shafts. The ring gear, differential gears, and axle shafts turn together without variation in speed as long as the vehicle is moving in a straight line.

When a vehicle turns into a curve or negotiates a turn, the wheels on the outside of the curve must travel a greater distance than the wheels on the inside

FIGURE 31–49 (A) Basic differential, (B) differential action when the vehicle is turning a corner, (C) differential action when the vehicle is moving straight.

of the curve. The outer wheels must then rotate faster than the inside wheels. This would be impossible if the axle shafts were locked solidly to the ring gear. However, the differential allows the outer wheels and axle shaft to increase in speed and the inner wheels and axle to slow down. This prevents the skidding and rapid tire wear that would otherwise occur. The differential action also makes the vehicle much easier to control while turning. (The differential also allows the wheels on opposite ends of the axle to rotate at different speeds to compensate for uneven road conditions and slightly mismatched tires.)

For example, when a car makes a sharp right-hand turn, the left-side wheels, axle shaft, and side gear must rotate faster than the right-side wheels, axle shaft, and side gear. The left side of the axle must speed up and the right side must slow down. This is possible because the pinions to which the side gears are meshed are free to rotate on the pinion shaft. The increased speed of the left-side wheels causes the side gear to rotate faster than the differential case. This causes the pinions to rotate and walk around the side gear. As the pinions turn to allow the left-side gear to increase speed, a reverse action—known as a reverse walking effect—is produced on the right-side gear. It slows down an amount that is inversely proportional to the increase in the left-side gear.

LIMITED SLIP DIFFERENTIALS

As mentioned earlier in this chapter, driveline torque is evenly divided between the two rear drive axles by the differential. As long as the tires grip the road providing a resistance to turning, the drivetrain forces the vehicle forward. When one tire encounters a slippery spot on the road, it loses traction, resistance to rotation drops, and the wheel begins to spin. Because resistance has dropped, the torque value delivered to both drive wheels also drops. The wheel with good traction is no longer driven. If the vehicle is stationary in this situation, only the wheel over the slippery spot rotates. When this is occurring, the differential case is driving the differential pinion gears around the stationary side gear.

This situation places stress on the differential gears. When the wheel spins because of traction loss, the speed of some of the differential gears increases greatly while others remain idle. The amount of heat developed increases rapidly, lube film breaks down, metal-to-metal contact occurs, and the parts are damaged. If spinout is allowed to continue long enough, the axle could break down completely.

Other failures can occur during spinout. If a spinning wheel is subjected to grabbing on a firm surface, a shock impact occurs. If the shock is severe enough, broken gear teeth or shaft fracturing can result. A fatigue failure can start if the shock is only great enough to damage the gear or shaft material.

To overcome these problems, differential manufacturers have developed the **limited slip** differential (Figure 31–50). While the limited slip differentials are manufactured under such names as sure-grip, no-spin, positraction, or equal-lock, there are really only two types: the clutch pack and the brake cone.

FIGURE 31–50 A normal differential transmits more power to the wheel with less traction.

Clutch Packs

The clutch pack limited slip differential (Figure 31–51) uses two sets of clutch plates and friction discs to prevent normal differential action. The friction discs are steel plates with an abrasive coating on both sides. The discs are splined internally to mate with external splines on the hub of the side gears. Steel plates without friction linings are placed between the friction discs. These plates have tangs that fit into the grooves in the differential case.

When installed in the differential, the discs are connected to the side gears and the plates are locked to the case. There is one set of clutch plates between each side gear and the differential case.

Pressure is kept on the clutch packs by springs. Either an S-shaped spring or coil springs are placed

FIGURE 31–51 Clutch discs with friction facings are separated by steel shims in this limited slip differential. Notice the four preload springs.

between the side gears. Those differentials using coil springs also have a set of spring retainers against which the springs bear. The springs (or spring) keep pressure against the side gear and the clutch pack.

As long as the clutch friction discs maintain their grip on the steel plates, the differential side gears are locked to the differential case. The case and drive axles rotate at the same speed which prevents one set of wheels from spinning on a slippery pavement or spinning momentarily faster when operating on uneven roads.

The clutch plates are designed to slip when a predetermined torque value is reached. This enables the car or truck to negotiate turns in a normal manner. The high torque caused by the wheels on the outside radius of a turn or curve rotating faster than the gear support case and differential causes the plates in the clutch pack to slip, allowing the side gear to increase in speed and the pinions to walk around the side gear in normal differential fashion.

Brake Cones

The most common limited slip differential in late-model vehicles employs two cone-shaped friction components to lock the side gears to the differential case (Figure 31–52). The cones are located between the side gears and the case and are splined to the side gear hubs. The exterior surface of the cones is coated with a friction material that grabs the inside surface of the case. The friction surface on the cones has a coarse spiral thread to provide a passage for lubricant. Four to six coil springs mounted in thrust plates between the side gears maintain a preload on the cones.

FIGURE 31–53 Some vehicles have an antiskid sensor, part of a safety braking system, attached to the differential carrier. *Courtesy of Ford Motor Company*

The operation of the cone system is essentially the same as the clutch-plate system. The cones are forced against the carrier and squeezed or compressed. At this point, the cone rotates with the carrier and locks up both axles.

Some vehicles have an antiskid sensor (part of the braking system) attached to the differential carrier for extra nonskid protection during braking (Figure 31–53).

CUSTOMER CARE

Remind your customer that the drive shaft, transmission, and rear (drive) axle should give trouble-free service if they are maintained at intervals recommended in the service manual. Be sure to check this out with your customer.

Maintenance includes inspecting the level of and changing the gear lubricant, and lubricating the universal joints if they are equipped with zerk or grease fittings (Figure 31–54). Most modern universal joints are of the extended life design, meaning they are sealed and require no periodic lubrication. However, it is wise to inspect the joints for hidden grease plugs or fittings, initially. Also, inspect the driveline for abnormal looseness, whenever the car is serviced.

In general, rear axles use either SAE 80 or 90 weight gear oil for lubrication, meeting API GL-4 or GL-5 specifications. This is stated on the top of the can. In the case of limited-slip rear axles, it is very important that the proper gear lube be used. The wrong lubricant can damage the clutch packs and cause grabbing or chattering on turns. If this condition exists, try draining the oil and refilling with the proper gear lube before having it serviced. ■

FIGURE 31–52 Cone-type limited slip differential. Notice the positions of the cones, thrust plates, thrust washers, and preload springs. *Courtesy of Ford Motor Company*

A common source of operation noise comes from the tires. To make sure the noises identified during

FIGURE 31–54 Some drive shaft U-joints are equipped with grease (zerk) fittings. Lubricate these with a grease gun.

FIGURE 31–55 Three types of rear drive axles: (A) semi-floating; (B) three-quarter floating; (C) full-floating axle assemblies.

the test drive are not caused by the tire tread patterns and tread wear, drive the car on various types of road surfaces (asphalt, concrete, and packed dirt). If the noise changes with the road surfaces, it means the tires are the cause of the noise.

Another way to isolate tire noises is to coast at speeds under 30 mph. If the noise is still heard, the tires are probably the cause. Drive axle and differential noises are less noticeable at these speeds. Accelerate and compare the sounds to those made while coasting. Drive axle and differential noises change. Tire noise remains constant.

Sometimes it is difficult to distinguish between axle bearing noises and noises coming from the differential. Differential noises often change with the driving mode whereas axle bearing noises are usually constant. The sound of the bearing noise usually increases in speed and loudness as vehicle speed increases.

AXLE SHAFTS

The purpose of the axle shaft is to transfer driving torque from the differential assembly to the vehicle's driving wheels. There are two types of axles: dead and drive or live.

DEAD AXLE The **dead axle** does not drive a vehicle. It merely supports the vehicle load and provides a mounting place for the wheels. In automotive operation, dead axles are usually on trailers and tandem-type axle vehicles.

DRIVE OR LIVE AXLE The main purpose of the drive or **live axles** is to transfer torque from the differential to each driving wheel. Depending on the design, rear axles can also help carry the weight of the vehicle or even act as part of the suspension. Most driving axles are enclosed in a housing. This housing is usually of a three-piece design. The two axle housings are pressed into the differential housing and then welded in place. Welding the three pieces together makes the axle housings and differential housing a single unit. A variation of the driving axle is the open axle shaft. In this design, the axle

shaft is not enclosed in a housing. Instead, it is part of the suspension system and moves up and down with changing road conditions.

Three types of driving axles are commonly used (Figure 31–55): semifloating, three-quarter floating, and full-floating. All three use axle shafts that are splined to the differential side gears. The combination of the driving axles and the differential is known as the final drive (Figure 31–56). At the wheel ends, the axles can be attached in any one of a number of ways. This attachment depends on the type of axle used. The differences between the three types actually lie in the manner in which the shafts are supported on bearings and the way they are attached to the wheel hubs.

Semifloating Axle Shafts

Semifloating axles help to support the weight of the vehicle. The differential assembly is supported by

FIGURE 31–56 The drive pinion gear and differential ring gear are known collectively as the final drive gears. The final drive gears and differential assembly are housed in the transaxle housing. *Courtesy of Chrysler Corporation*

FIGURE 31–57   Semifloating axle shaft in axle housing with ball-type axle bearing. If this axle shaft breaks, the axle shaft comes out of the axle housing. *Courtesy of Chrysler Corporation*

tapered roller bearings and the axle housing. The semifloating axle shafts are not affected by stresses associated with the differential's operation (Figure 31–57).

The inner ends of the axle shafts are splined to the axle side gears. The axle shafts transmit only driving torque and are not acted upon by other forces. Therefore, the axle shafts are said to be floating.

The driving wheels are bolted to the outer ends of the axle shafts. The outer axle bearings are located between the axle shaft and axle housing. This type of axle has a bearing pressed into the end of the axle housing that supports the axle shaft. The axle shaft is held in place with either a bearing retainer belted to a flange on the end of the axle housing or by a C-shaped washer that fits into grooves machined in the splined end of the shaft. A flange on the wheel end of the shaft is used to attach the wheel.

When semifloating axles are used to drive the vehicle, the axle shafts push on the shaft bearings as they rotate. This places a driving force on the axle housing, springs, and vehicle chassis moving the vehicle forward. The axle shaft takes bending stresses associated with turning corners and curves, skidding, bent or wobbling wheels, as well as the weight of the vehicle. In the semifloating axle arrangement, if the axle shaft breaks, the driving wheel comes away from or out of the axle housing.

Three-Quarter Floating Axle

The wheel bearing on a **three-quarter floating** axle is on the outside of the axle housing instead of inside the housing as in the semifloating axle. The wheel hubs are bolted to the end of the axle shaft and are supported by the bearing. In this arrangement, the axle shaft does not support the weight of the vehicle.

It is transferred through the wheel hub and bearing to the axle housing. Three-quarter floating axles are found on older vehicles and some trucks.

Full-Floating Axle Shafts

Most heavy commercial vehicles use a **full-floating** axle shaft to accommodate the higher vehicle loads. This design is similar to the three-quarter floating axle except that two bearings rather than one are used to support the wheel hub. These are pressed over the outside of the axle housing and carry all of the stresses caused by torque loading and turning. The wheel hubs are bolted to flanges on the outer end of each axle shaft.

In operation, the axle shaft transmits only the driving torque. The driving torque from the axle shaft rotates the axle flange, wheel hub, and rear driving wheel. The wheel hub forces its bearings against the axle housing to move the vehicle. The stresses caused by turning, skidding, and bent or wobbling wheels are taken by the axle housing through the wheel bearings. If a full-floating axle shaft should break, it can be removed from the axle housing. Because the rear wheels rotate around the rear axle housing the disabled vehicle can be towed to a service area for replacement of the axle shaft. This is considered by many technicians to be an advantage of the full-floating axle design.

Independently Suspended Axles

This type of rear driving axle system is found mostly on European automobiles. The driving axles are usually open instead of being enclosed in an axle housing.

The two most common suspended rear driving axles are the DeDion axle system and the swing axle system.

FIGURE 31–58 DeDion rear suspension on Chevrolet Corvette. Notice the universal joints at each end of the driving axles.

DeDION AXLE SYSTEM The **DeDion axle** system (Figure 31–58) resembles a driveline. The driving axle resembles a drive shaft, with U-joints at each end of the axles. A slip joint is attached to the inboard, or innermost, U-joint. The outboard, or outermost, U-joint is connected to the driving wheel. This allows the driving axle to move up and down as it rotates.

SWING AXLE SYSTEM On automobiles with **swing axles**, the driving axles can be open or enclosed. An axle fits into the differential by way of a ball-and-socket system that allows the axle to pivot up and down. As the axle pivots, the driving wheel swings up and down. A typical swing axle assembly is shown in Figure 31–59. This system best describes the drive axles of a front-wheel-drive vehicle.

Axle Shaft Bearings

The axle shaft bearing supports the vehicle's weight and reduces rotational friction. In an axle mount, radial and thrust loads are always present on the axle shaft bearing when the vehicle is moving. Radial bearing loads act at 90 degrees to the axle shaft's center of axis. **Radial loading** is always present whether or not the vehicle is moving.

FIGURE 31–59 Swing axle assembly. *Courtesy of Volkswagen of America, Inc.*

Thrust loading acts on the axle bearing parallel with the center of axis. It is present on the driving wheels, axle shafts, and axle bearings when the vehicle turns corners or curves.

There are three designs of axle shaft bearings used in semifloating axles.

◆ Ball-type bearing (Figure 31–60A)
◆ Straight-roller bearing (Figure 31–60B)
◆ Tapered-roller bearing (Figure 31–60C)

The bearing load of primary concern is axle shaft end thrust. When a vehicle moves around a corner, centrifugal force acts on the vehicle body, causing it to lean to the outside of the curve. The vehicle's chassis does not lean because of the tires' contact with the road's surface. As the body leans outward, a thrust load is placed on the axle shaft and axle bearing. Each type of axle shaft bearing handles axle shaft end thrust differently.

Normally, the way the axles are held in the housing is quite obvious after the rear wheels and brake assemblies have been removed. If the axle shaft is held in by a retainer and three or four bolts, it is not necessary to remove the differential cover to remove the axle. Most ball- and tapered-roller bearing supported axle shafts are retained in this manner. To remove the axle, remove the bolts that hold the retainer to the backing plate, then pull the axle out. Normally, the axle shaft slides out without the aid of a puller. Sometimes a puller is required.

A tapered-roller bearing supported axle shaft does not use a retainer to secure it. Rather, a C-washer is used to retain the axle shaft. This C-washer is located inside the differential, and the differential cover must be removed to gain access to it. To remove this type

A Bearing retainer plate — Bearing retainer ring — Oil seal collar — Oil seal — Axle shaft bearing

B Axle housing — Bearing — Seal — Axle shaft

C Bearing — Wheel hub — Bearing — Axle housing — Sleeve nuts retain bearing — Axle shaft

FIGURE 31–60
(A) Semifloating axle shaft supported by a ball-type bearing. (Axle shaft bearing is located inside axle housing.) (B) Straight-roller bearing and axle shaft installed in axle housing. (C) Tapered-roller drive axle bearing and related parts.

of axle, first remove the wheel, brake drum, and differential cover. Then, remove the differential pinion shaft retaining bolt and differential pinion shaft. Now push the axle shaft in and remove the C-washer. The axle can now be pulled out of the housing.

Ball bearings are lubricated with grease packed in the bearing at the factory. An inner seal, designed to keep the gear oil from the bearing, rides on the axle shaft just in front of the retaining ring. This type of bearing also has an outer seal to prevent grease from spraying onto the rear brakes. Ball-type axle bearings are pressed on and off the axle shaft. The retainer ring is made of soft metal and is pressed onto the shaft against the wheel bearing. Never use a torch to remove the ring. Rather, drill into it or notch it in several places with a cold chisel to break the seal. The ring can then be slid off the shaft easily. Heat should not be used to remove the ring because it can take the temper out of the shaft and thereby weaken

it. Likewise, a torch should never be used to remove a bearing from an axle shaft.

Roller axle bearings are lubricated by the gear oil in the axle housing. Therefore, only a seal to protect the brakes is necessary with these bearings. These bearings are typically pressed into the axle housing and not onto the axle. To remove them, the axle must first be removed and then the bearing pulled out of the housing. With the axle out, inspect the area where it rides on the bearing for pits or scores. If any are present, replace the axle.

Tapered-roller axle bearings are not lubricated by gear oil. They are sealed and lubricated with wheel grease. This type of bearing uses two seals and must be pressed on and off the axle shaft using a press. After the bearing is pressed onto the shaft, it must be packed with wheel bearing grease. After packing the bearing, install the axle in the housing. Shaft end play must be checked. Use a dial indicator and adjust the end play to the specifications given in the service manual. If the end play is not within specifications, change the size of the bearing shim.

The installation of new axle shaft seals is recommended whenever the axle shafts have been removed. Some axle seals are identified as being either right or left side. When installing new seals, make sure to install the correct seal in each side. Check the seals or markings of right or left or for color coding.

USING SERVICE MANUALS

The driveline can create some especially difficult diagnostic problems. The driveline easily picks up vibrations and noises from other parts of the vehicle. What may seem to be a driveline problem can actually be a suspension or wire problem. For this reason, the test drive is important. A test drive does not mean hopping into a vehicle and driving it around the block. Certain procedures are necessary.

The test drive may call for a fast start or a slow start from a dead stop. Driving at low speeds and at highway speeds is necessary. Speeds should be varied. Acceleration tests from steady cruising speeds should include both mild and hard applications of power. Note what happens during any of these speeds or during speed changes. A tachometer can be helpful. Most vehicles, however, are not equipped with tachometers.

Before the test drive, check out the appropriate service manual test-drive chart (Figure 31–61). Note that different problems occur at different speeds. Some problems that seem to come from the driveline actually come from other parts of the vehicle. Also, notice that when the problem appears at different speeds, the cause of the problem changes.

The four modes of driving given in most service manuals should be checked out for driving-axle and differential problems. For the drive mode, accelerate

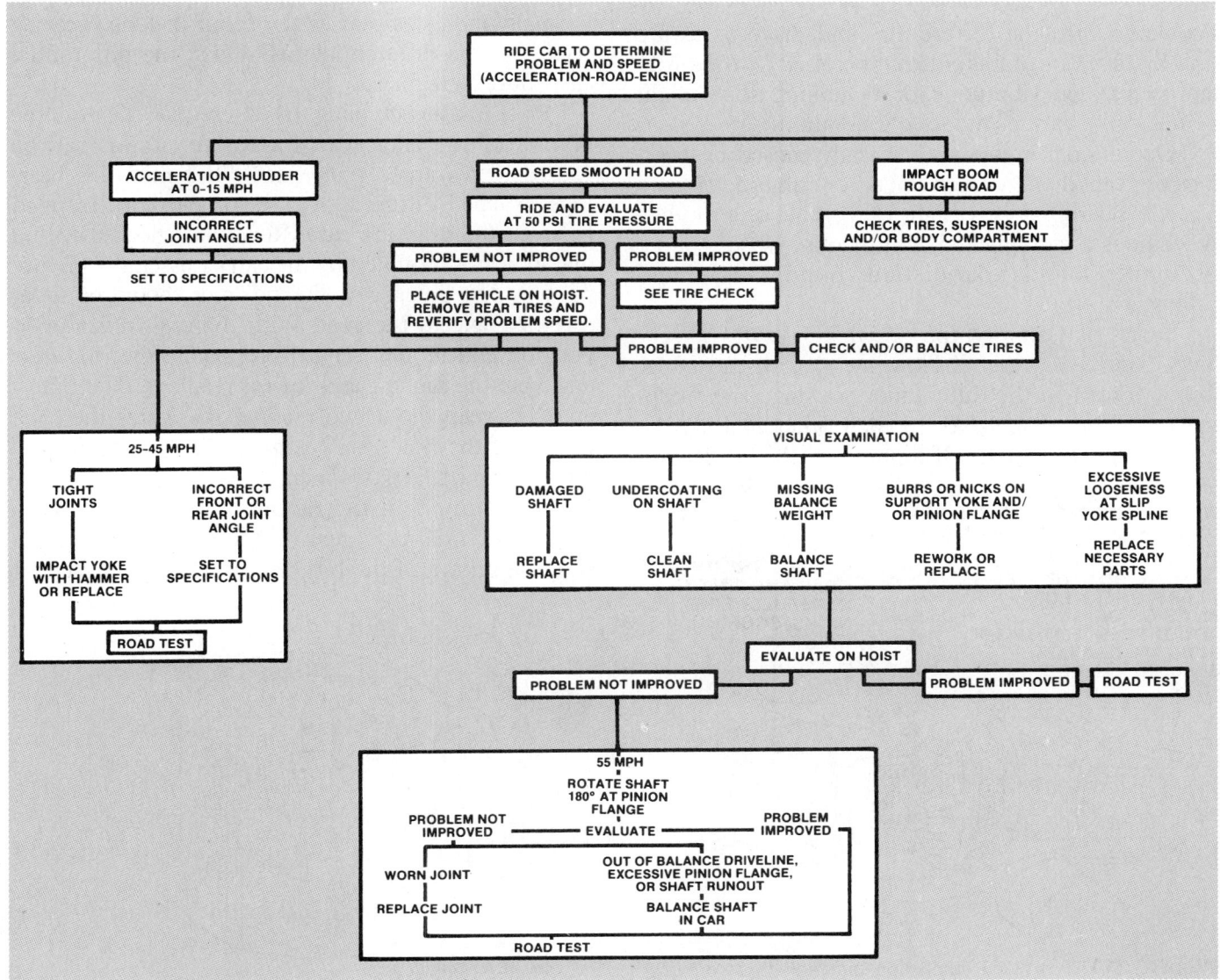

FIGURE 31–61 Service manual test-drive chart.

the vehicle. The throttle must be depressed enough to apply sufficient engine torque. In the cruise mode, vehicle speed must be constant. This means the throttle must be applied at all times. The speed must be held at a predetermined rpm on a level road. For the coast mode, take your foot off the throttle. Let the vehicle coast down from a specific speed. The float mode is a controlled deceleration. Back off the throttle gradually and continually. Do not brake or accelerate during this mode.

Remember that driving safely is always an important consideration. Jackrabbit starts, hard cornering, or sudden braking should be avoided. Driving conditions other than normal can worsen a problem or create a new one. Carelessness during the test drive can result in an accident. Remember, you are responsible for someone else's vehicle. Drive only in a manner that is required to diagnose the problem. ■

SERVICING THE DIFFERENTIAL

Problems with the differential and drive axles are usually first noticed as a leak or noise. As the problem progresses, vibrations, or a clunking noise might be felt in the various modes of operation.

Operational noises are generally caused by bearings or gears that are worn, loose, or damaged (Figure 31–62). Bearing noises might be a whine or a rumble. A whine is a high-pitched, continuous "whee" sound. A rumble sounds like distant thunder—low and rolling.

Gears can also whine or emit a howl—a very loud, continuous sound. Howling is often caused by low lubricant in the differential housing. The meshing teeth scrape metal from each other and can be heard in all gear ranges. If topping off the lubrication

level does not alleviate the howling noise, then the drive pinion and ring gear must be replaced.

Front-wheel-drive differentials are normally an integral part of the transaxle. To service them, the transaxle must be removed and disassembled. Most of the procedures for servicing a rear-wheel-drive differential apply to front-wheel-drive differentials. To service a differential from a removable carrier, the differential must be removed from the housing. Differentials from integral carriers are serviced in the housing.

A highly important step in the procedure for disassembling any differential is a careful inspection of each part as it is removed. The differential bearings should be looked at and felt to determine if there are any defects or evidence of damage.

After the ring and pinion gears have been inspected and before they have been removed from the assembly, check the side play. Using a screwdriver, attempt to move the differential case assembly laterally. Any movement is evidence of side play. Side play normally indicates that as the result of loose bearing cones on the differential case hubs, the differential case must be replaced.

Prior to disassembling the differential, measure the runout of the ring gear. Excessive runout can be caused by a warped gear, worn differential side bearings, warped differential case, or particles trapped between the gear and case. Runout is checked with a dial indicator mounted on the carrier assembly (Figure 31–63). The plunger on the indicator should be set at a right angle to the gear. With the dial indicator in position and its dial set to zero, rotate the ring gear and note the highest and lowest readings. The difference between these two readings indicates the total runout of the ring gear. Normally, the maximum permissible runout is 0.004 inch.

To determine if the runout is caused by a damaged differential case, remove the ring gear and measure the runout of the ring gear mounting surface on

VISUALLY INSPECT ALL THE GEARS AND OTHER PARTS FOR WEAR AND DAMAGE.

TURN THE DRIVE SHAFT BY HAND TO ROTATE THE GEARS. CHECK FOR ANY SIGN OF ROUGHNESS THAT MIGHT INDICATE GEAR OR BEARING DAMAGE.

INSPECT THE RING GEAR AND PINION CAREFULLY FOR NICKS, SCORING, OR WEAR.

FIGURE 31–62 Visual inspection can verify that worn or damaged gears or bearings are the cause of abnormal noises.

DIAL INDICATOR

FIGURE 31–63 Measuring ring gear backface runout.

FIGURE 31–64 Marking the drive shaft and its mating flange.

the differential case. Runout should not exceed 0.004 inch. If runout is greater than that, the case should be replaced. If the runout was within specifications, the ring gear is probably warped and should be replaced. A ring gear is never replaced without replacing its mating pinion gear.

Some ring gear assemblies are comprised of an excitor ring, used in antilock brake systems. This ring is normally pressed onto the ring gear hub and can be removed after the ring gear is removed. If the ring gear assembly is equipped with an excitor ring, carefully inspect it and replace it if it is damaged.

Prior to disassembling the differential unit, the drive shaft must be removed. Before disconnecting it from the pinion's companion flange, locate the shaft to pinion alignment marks. If they are not evident, make new ones (Figure 31–64). This avoids assembling the unit with the wrong index, which can result in driveline vibration.

When disassembling a differential, keep the right and left differential shims, cups, and caps separated (Figure 31–65). If any of these parts are reused, they must be installed on the same side as they were originally located.

When installing a ring gear onto the differential case, make sure the bolt holes are aligned before pressing the gear in place. While pressing the gear, pressure should be evenly applied to the gear. Likewise, when tightening the bolts, always tighten them in steps and to the specified torque. These steps reduce the chances of distorting the gear.

Examine the gears to locate any timing marks on the gearset that indicate where the gears were lapped by the manufacturer. Normally, one tooth of a pinion gear is grooved and painted, while the ring gear has a notch between two painted teeth. If the paint marks are not evident, locate the notches. Proper timing of the gears is set by placing the grooved pinion tooth between the two marked ring gear teeth. Some gearsets have no timing marks. These gears are hunting gears and do not need to be timed.

Whenever the ring and pinion gears or the pinion or carrier bearings are replaced, pinion gear depth, bearing preload, and the ring and pinion gear tooth patterns must be checked and adjusted. This holds true for all types of differentials except most front-wheel-drive differentials that use helical-cut gears and taking tooth patterns is not necessary. Nearly all other final drive units use hypoid gears that must be properly adjusted to ensure a quiet operation.

Pinion gear depth is adjusted with shims that are placed in the housing. The thickness of the drive pinion rear bearing shim controls the depth of the mesh between the pinion and ring gear. To determine and set pinion depth a special tool is normally used to select the proper pinion shim (Figure 31–66). Always follow the procedures in the service manual when setting up the tool and determining the proper shim.

Pinion bearing **preload** is set by tightening the pinion nut until the desired number of inch-pounds is required to turn the shaft. Tightening the nut crushes the collapsible pinion spacer, which maintains the desired preload. Never overtighten and then loosen the pinion nut to reach the desired torque reading. Tightening and loosening the pinion nut damages the collapsible spacer. It must then be replaced. For the exact procedures and specifications for bearing pre-

FIGURE 31–65 While disassembling a differential, keep all parts separated according to the side from which they were removed.

FIGURE 31–66 Selecting the correct pinion shim for proper pinion gear depth.

load, refer to the service manual. Incorrect bearing preload can cause differential noise.

It is recommended that a new pinion seal be installed whenever the pinion shaft is removed from the differential. To install a new seal, thoroughly lubricate it and press it in place with an appropriate seal driver.

Backlash of the gearset is adjusted at the same time as the side bearing preload. Side bearing preload limits the amount the differential is able to move laterally in the axle housing. Adjusting backlash sets the depth of the mesh between the ring and pinion gear teeth. Both of these are adjusted by shim thickness or by the adjustments made by the side bearing adjusting nuts (Figure 31–67).

Always refer to the procedures given in the service manual before proceeding to adjust preload and backlash. A typical procedure for measuring and adjusting backlash and preload involves rocking the ring gear and measuring its movement with a dial indicator (Figure 31–68). Compare measured backlash with the specifications. Make the necessary adjustments. Then recheck the backlash at four points equally spaced around the ring gear.

The pattern of gear teeth determines how quietly two meshed gears run. The pattern also describes where on the faces of the teeth the two gears mesh. The pattern should be checked during teardown for gear noise diagnosis, after adjusting backlash and side bearing preload, or after replacing the drive pinion and setting up the pinion bearing preload. The terms commonly used to describe the possible pat-

Dial indicator

FIGURE 31–68 Mount a dial indicator and measure the ring gear-to-pinion backlash at three or four locations around the ring gear. The variation between readings should be no more than 0.006 inch.

terns on a ring gear and the necessary corrections are shown in Figure 31–69.

To check the gear tooth pattern, paint several ring gear teeth with nondrying Prussian blue, ferric oxide, or red or white lead-marking compound. White marking compound is preferred by many technicians because it tends to be more visible than the others. Use a box wrench on the ring gear bolts to rotate the ring gear so the painted teeth contact the pinion gear. Move it in both directions enough to get a clearly defined pattern (Figure 31–70). Examine the pattern on the ring gear and make the necessary corrections.

Most new gearsets purchased today come with a pattern prerolled on the teeth. This pattern provides the quietest operation for that gearset. Never wipe this pattern off or cover it up. When checking the

FIGURE 31–67 This drawing shows the direction of movement when adjusting the ring gear and pinion gear. Shims are used to position the pinion gear, and bearing adjusting nuts are used to position the ring gear.

FIGURE 31–69 Commonly used terms describing the possible patterns on a ring gear and the necessary corrections. *Courtesy of Ford Motor Company*

FIGURE 31–70 Area where grease, red lead, or ferric oxide is rubbed off ring gear is contact pattern. It must be centrally located on teeth. Note typical methods of correcting patterns. *Courtesy of Cadillac Motor Car Division, General Motors Corporation*

pattern on a new gearset, coat only half of the ring gear with the marking compound and compare the pattern with the prerolled pattern.

DIAGNOSING DIFFERENTIAL NOISES

If a whining is heard when turning corners or rounding curves, the problem might be damaged differential pinion gears and pinion shaft. This is caused when the inside diameter of the differential pinions and the outside diameter of the differential pinion shaft is scored and damaged. The damage is usually caused by allowing one driving wheel to revolve at high speeds while the opposite wheel remains stationary.

Another gear noise that is common in differentials is the chuckle. A chuckle is a low "heh-heh" sound that occurs when gears are worn to the point where there is excessive clearance between the pinion gear and the ring gear. Chuckle sounds occur most often in the decelerating mode, particularly below 40 mph. As the vehicle decelerates, the chuckle also slows and can be heard all the way to a stop.

A knock or clunk is caused by excessive wear or loose or broken parts. A knock is a repetitious rapping sound that occurs during all phases of driving but is most noticeable during acceleration and deceleration when the gears are loaded. A clunk is a sharp, loud noise caused by one part hitting another. Unlike a knock, a clunk can be felt as well as heard. Clunks are generally caused by loose parts striking each other.

Limited slip clutch packs or cones that need servicing might be heard as a chatter or a rapid clicking noise that creates a vibration in the vehicle. Chattering is usually noticed when rounding a corner. A change of differential lubricant sometimes corrects this problem. After draining the oil, replace it with the manufacturer's suggested lubricant. Road test the vehicle again.

To make sure the noise heard during the test drive is coming from the differential, stop the vehicle and shift the transmission into neutral. Run the engine at various rpm levels. If the noise is heard during this procedure, it is caused by a problem somewhere other than in the differential.

CASE STUDY

A customer brings his subcompact, front-wheel-drive car into the shop complaining of recurring noise in the front wheels. The noise is most noticeable when the car is making turns. The owner states he had a similar complaint a few months ago and the shop had replaced an outer CV-joint. This corrected the problem until recently. The customer suspects the same joint went bad again and demands the shop replace it, free of charge, because it is obvious the replacement joint was defective.

The service writer records the information from the customer and tells him he will be notified as soon as the problem is diagnosed. As soon as the customer leaves, the service writer looks up the customer's file and finds a CV-joint had been replaced two months ago.

The service writer gives the repair order to the technician, along with the old repair order. The technician begins the diagnostic procedure with a test drive to verify the complaint. From the test drive and a visual inspection, the technician concludes that the same CV-joint is faulty. What could cause the joint to fail so soon? Was the replacement joint defective? Was the replacement joint installed incorrectly? Is some other fault causing the joints to fail? No matter what the answer, it seems the customer will not be charged for this repair. Also, it is likely the technician will not get paid for the repair.

Upon disassembly of the axle, the technician finds the joint's lubricant to be contaminated with metal shavings and moisture. A thorough inspection of the boot reveals no tears or punctures. While inspecting the boot, it is noticed that the inner end of the boot moves freely on the axle shaft. The technician knows then what had caused the contamination and resulting premature failure of the joint.

When installing the replacement joint and boot, the technician failed to properly tighten the inner boot clamp. This allowed lubricant to leak from and water to enter the boot. A new joint and boot is installed on the axle. The technician verifies the repair by a test drive. The replacement joint took care of the noise. Before releasing the car back to the owner, the technician rechecks the position and tightness of the boot clamps. The customer is called and is told what had happened. Although the customer is not happy about the mistake, he appreciates the honesty of the technician. Two months later he returns to the shop for an oil change. He has been a regular customer since.

KEY TERMS

Backlash	Nonhunting
Ball-type joint	Operating angle
Cardan/Spicer joint	Outboard joint
Cleveland style joint	Partial nonhunting
Cross groove joint	Pinion gear
CV joint	Pinion gear depth
Dead axle	Pinion shaft
DeDion axle	Plunge joint
Detroit/Saginaw style joint	Preload
	Radial loading
Double-Cardan joint	Ring gear
Double-offset joint	Rzeppa joint
Fixed joint	Semifloating
Full-floating	Sliding yoke
Gear reduction	Slip yoke
Hunting	Speed reduction
Hypoid gear	Swing axle
Inboard joint	Three-quarter floating
Integral axle	Thrust loading
IRS	Torsional damper
Limited slip	Tripod-type joint
Live axle	U-joint

SUMMARY

- Front-wheel-drive axles generally transfer engine torque from the transaxle differential to the front wheels.
- Constant velocity (CV) joints provide the necessary transfer of uniform torque and a constant speed while operating through a wide range of angles.
- In front-wheel-drive drivetrains, two CV joints are used on each half shaft. The different types of joints can be referred to by position (inboard or outboard), function (fixed or plunge), or design (ball-type or tripod).
- Front-wheel-drive half shafts can be solid or tubular, of equal or unequal length, and with or without damper weights.
- Most problems with front-wheel-drive systems are noted by noise and vibration.
- Lubricant is the most important key to a long life for the CV joint.
- The U-joint is a flexible coupling located at each end of the drive shaft between the transmission and the pinion flange on the drive axle.
- The U-joint allows two rotating shafts to operate at a slight angle to each other, which is most important in rear-wheel-drive vehicles.
- There are three common types of U-joint designs: single U-joints, coupled U-joints, and yoke U-joints.

◆ A failed U-joint or damaged drive shaft can exhibit a variety of symptoms. A clunk that is heard when the transmission is shifted into gear is the most obvious. You can also encounter unusual noise, roughness, or vibrations.

◆ A differential is a geared mechanism located between the driving axles of a vehicle. Its job is to direct power flow to the driving axles. Differentials are used in all types of power trains.

◆ The differential performs several functions. It allows the drive wheels to rotate at different speeds when negotiating a turn or curve in the road, and the differential drive gears redirect the engine torque from the drive shaft to the rear drive axles.

◆ While there are several basic designs of differentials, most feature pinion/ring gears and a pinion shaft.

◆ The differential in rear-wheel-drive vehicles is housed in the axle housing, or carrier.

◆ The purpose of the axle shaft is to transfer driving torque from the differential assembly to the vehicle's driving wheels.

◆ There are three types of driving axles commonly used: semifloating, three-quarter floating, and full-floating.

◆ The axle shaft bearing supports the vehicle's weight and reduces rotational friction.

◆ Problems with the differential and drive axles are usually first noticed as a leak or noise. As the problem progresses, vibrations or a clunking noise might be felt in various modes of operation.

TECH MANUAL

The following procedures are included in Chapter 31 of the *Tech Manual* that accompanies this book:

1. *Inspect and replace CV joints.*
2. *Inspect and replace U-joints.*
3. *Measure and adjust drive pinion depth.*
4. *Measure and adjust backlash.*
5. *Measure and adjust bearing preload.*

REVIEW QUESTIONS

1. Name the three ways in which CV joints can be classified.

2. What type of axle housing resembles a banjo?

3. What type of axle merely supports the vehicle load and provides a mounting place for the wheels?

4. What type of floating axle has one wheel bearing per wheel on the outside of the axle housing?

5. How are problems with the differential and drive axles usually first noticed?

6. The use of constant velocity joints is restricted to ____.

   a. front-wheel-drive vehicles
   b. rear-wheel-drive vehicles
   c. rear-wheel-drive vehicles with independent rear suspension
   d. none of the above

7. In front-wheel drivetrains, the CV joint nearer the transaxle is the ____.

   a. inner joint
   b. inboard joint
   c. outboard joint
   d. both a and b

8. A CV joint that is capable of in and out movement is a ____ joint.

   a. plunge
   b. fixed
   c. inboard
   d. outboard

9. Technician A says a gear tooth pattern identifies ring gear runout. Technician B says gear patterns are not accurate if there is excessive ring gear runout. Who is correct?

   a. Technician A
   b. Technician B
   c. Both A and B
   d. Neither A nor B

10. The double-offset joint is typically used in applications that require ____.

   a. higher operating angles and greater plunge depth
   b. lower operating angles and lower plunge depth
   c. higher operating angles and lower plunge depth
   d. lower operating angles and greater plunge depth

11. Which type joint has a flatter design than any other?
    a. double-offset
    c. cross groove
    b. disc
    d. fixed tripod

12. What is useful for determining which CV joint is the problem?
    a. squeeze test
    c. swerve test
    b. chassis test
    d. spin test

13. The single Cardan/Spicer universal joint is also known as the ____.
    a. cross joint
    c. both a and b
    b. four-point joint
    d. neither a nor b

14. The drive shaft component that provides a means of connecting two or more shafts together is the ____.
    a. pinion flange
    c. yoke
    b. U-joint
    d. biscuit

15. Large cars with long drive shafts often use a double-U-joint arrangement called a ____.
    a. Spicer style U-joint
    b. constant velocity U-joint
    c. Cleveland style U-joint
    d. none of the above

16. Which type of driving axle supports the weight of the vehicle?
    a. semifloating
    b. three-quarter floating
    c. full-floating
    d. none of the above

17. Technician A says limited slip differential clutch packs are designed to slip when the vehicle turns a corner. Technician B says a special additive is placed in the hypoid gear lubricant to promote clutch pack slippage on corners. Who is correct?
    a. Technician A
    c. Both A and B
    b. Technician B
    d. Neither A nor B

18. Technician A says side bearing preload limits the amount the differential is able to move laterally in the axle housing. Technician B says adjusting backlash sets the depth of the mesh between the ring and pinion gears' teeth. Who is correct?
    a. Technician A
    c. Both A and B
    b. Technician B
    d. Neither A nor B

19. Technician A says a hunting gearset is one in which one drive pinion gear tooth contacts only certain ring gear teeth. Technician B says a partial nonhunting gearset is one in which one pinion tooth contacts only six ring gear teeth. Who is correct?
    a. Technician A
    c. Both A and B
    b. Technician B
    d. Neither A nor B

20. Which of the following describes the double-Cardan universal joint?
    a. It is most often installed in front-engine rear-wheel-drive luxury automobiles.
    b. It is classified as a constant velocity U-joint.
    c. A centering ball socket is inside the coupling yoke between the two universal joints.
    d. All of the above.

SECTION 6

AUTOMATIC TRANSMISSIONS AND TRANSAXLES

Many vehicles are equipped with automatic transmissions or transaxles. These systems perform the same job as standard or manual shift units, but they do so in quite a different manner. A torque converter replaces the clutch as the link between the engine and transmission/transaxle gearing. The planetary or Ravigneaux gear trains found in automatic units generate speed and torque using a completely different set of operating principles. Finally, the hydraulic and electronic control systems used to initiate shifting are unique to automatic transmissions/transaxles.

This section also covers four- and all-wheel-drive systems, which are becoming a standard feature on many vehicles.

The information found in Section 6 corresponds to materials covered on the ASE certification test on automatic transmissions/transaxles.

WE ENCOURAGE
PROFESSIONALISM

THROUGH TECHNICIAN
CERTIFICATION

AUTOMATIC TRANSMISSIONS AND TRANSAXLES

32

OBJECTIVES

◆ Explain the basic design and operation of standard and lockup torque converters. ◆ Describe the design and operation of a simple planetary gearset and Simpson gear train. ◆ Name the major types of planetary gear controls used on automatic transmissions and explain their basic operating principles. ◆ Describe the construction and operation of common Simpson gear train-based transmissions and transaxles. ◆ Describe the construction and operation of common Ravigneaux gear train-based transmissions. ◆ Describe the construction and operation of Ford AXOD and General Motors' 4T60 (THM 440-T4) transaxles that use planetary gearsets in tandem. ◆ Describe the construction and operation of Honda automatic transmissions that use helical gears in constant mesh. ◆ Describe the design and operation of the hydraulic controls and valves used in modern transmissions and transaxles. ◆ Explain the role of the following components of the transmission control system: pressure regulator valve, throttle valve, governor assembly, manual valve, shift valves, and kickdown valve. ◆ Identify the various pressures in the transmission, state their purpose, and tell how they influence the operation of the transmission. ◆ Explain the advantages of using electronic controls for transmission shifting. ◆ Briefly describe what determines the shift characteristics of each selector lever position. ◆ Identify the input and output devices in a typical electronic control system and briefly describe the function of each.

Many rear-wheel-drive and four-wheel-drive vehicles are equipped with automatic transmissions (Figure 32–1). Automatic transaxles, which combine an automatic transmission and final drive assembly in a single unit, are used on front-wheel-drive, all-wheel-drive, and some rear-wheel-drive vehicles (Figure 32–2).

An automatic transmission or transaxle selects gear ratios according to engine speed, power train load, vehicle speed, and other operating factors. Little effort is needed on the part of the driver, because both upshifts and downshifts occur automatically. A driver-operated clutch is not needed to change gears, and the vehicle can be brought to a stop without shifting to neutral. This is a great convenience, particularly in stop-and-go traffic. The driver can also manually select a lower forward gear, reverse, neutral, or park. Depending on the forward range selected, the transmission can provide engine braking during deceleration.

The most widely used automatic transmissions and transaxles have three forward speeds and neutral, reverse, and park positions. Four-speed units

that offer an **overdrive** fourth gear have become increasingly popular. Overdrive occurs when less than one full revolution of the transmission's input shaft produces one full revolution at the output shaft. The purpose of overdrive is to improve fuel economy and reduce engine speed and noise. Most new automatics also feature a lockup torque converter.

Until recently, all automatic transmissions were controlled by hydraulics. However, many new systems now feature computer-controlled operation of the torque converter and transmission. Based on input data supplied by electronic sensors and switches, the computer sets the torque converter's operating mode, controls the transmission's shifting sequence, and in some cases regulates transmission oil pressure.

TORQUE CONVERTER

Automatic transmissions use a fluid clutch known as a torque converter to transfer engine torque from the engine to the transmission.

The torque converter operates through hydraulic force provided by automatic transmission fluid often

FIGURE 32–1 Interior view of a typical rear-wheel-drive transmission. *Courtesy of Ford Motor Company*

simply called transmission oil. The torque converter changes or multiplies the twisting motion of the engine crankshaft and directs it through the transmission.

The torque converter automatically engages and disengages power from the engine to the transmission in relation to engine rpm. With the engine running at the correct idle speed, there is not enough fluid flow for power transfer through the torque converter. As engine speed is increased, the added fluid flow creates sufficient force to transmit engine power through the torque converter assembly to the transmission.

Design

Torque converters, or T/Cs, are either one-piece, welded units that cannot be dismantled for repair, or they are bolt-together units that can be broken down for servicing. The torque converter, located between the engine and transmission, is a sealed, doughnut-shaped unit that is always filled with automatic transmission fluid.

A special **flex plate**, sometimes called a flex disc, is used to mount the torque converter to the crankshaft (Figure 32–3). The purpose of the flex plate is to transfer crankshaft rotation to the shell of the torque converter assembly. The flex plate bolts to a flange machined on the rear of the crankshaft and to mounting pads located on the front of the torque converter shell.

The flex plate also carries the starter motor ring gear. A flywheel is not required because the mass of the torque converter and flex disc acts like a flywheel to smooth out the intermittent power strokes of the engine.

Components

A standard torque converter consists of three elements (Figure 32–4): the pump assembly, often called an impeller, the stator assembly, and the turbine.

The **impeller** assembly is the input (drive) member. It receives power from the engine. The **turbine** is the output (driven) member. It is applied to the forward clutch of the transmission and to the turbine shaft assembly. The **stator** assembly is the reaction member or torque multiplier. The stator is supported on a roller race, which operates as an overrunning clutch and permits the stator to rotate freely in one direction and lock up in the opposite direction.

T/C EXTERIOR The exterior of the torque converter shell is shaped like two bowls standing on end, facing each other. To support the weight of the torque converter, a short stubby shaft projects forward from the front of the torque converter shell and fits into a pocket at the rear of the crankshaft. At the rear of the torque converter shell is a hollow shaft with notches or flats at one end, ground 180 degrees apart. This shaft is called the pump drive hub. The notches or

RANGE	GEAR	DIRECT CLUTCH	INTERMEDIATE BAND	FORWARD CLUTCH	LO-REVERSE CLUTCH	ROLLER CLUTCH
P - N						
D	1st			APPLIED		HOLDING
	2nd		APPLIED	APPLIED		
	3rd	APPLIED		APPLIED		
2	1st			APPLIED		HOLDING
	2nd		APPLIED	APPLIED		
1	1st			APPLIED	APPLIED	HOLDING
R	REVERSE	APPLIED			APPLIED	

FIGURE 32–2 Interior view of a typical transaxle. *Courtesy of Chevrolet Division, General Motors Corporation*

FIGURE 32–3 The torque converter mounts to the engine crankshaft using a flex plate or disc. *Courtesy of Ford Motor Company*

FIGURE 32–4 A torque converter's major internal parts are its impeller, turbine, and stator. *Courtesy of Ford Motor Company*

flats drive the transmission pump assembly. At the front of the transmission within the pump housing is a pump bushing that supports the pump drive hub and provides rear support for the torque converter assembly.

T/C INTERIOR The impeller forms one section of the torque converter shell. The impeller has numerous curved blades that rotate as a unit with the shell. It turns at engine speed, acting like a pump to start the transmission oil circulating within the torque converter shell.

While the impeller is positioned with its back facing the transmission housing. The turbine is positioned with its back to the engine. The curved blades of the turbine face the impeller assembly.

The turbine blades have a greater curve than the impeller blades. This helps eliminate oil turbulence between the turbine and impeller blades that would slow impeller speed and reduce the converter's efficiency.

The stator is located between the impeller and turbine. It redirects the oil flow from the turbine back into the impeller in the direction of impeller rotation with minimal loss of speed or force. The side of the stator blade with the inward curve is the concave side. The side with an outward curve is the convex side.

Basic Operation

Transmission oil is used as the medium to transfer energy in the T/C. Figure 32–5A illustrates the T/C impeller or pump at rest. Figure 32–5B shows it being driven. As the pump impeller rotates, centrifugal force throws the oil outward and upward due to the curved shape of the impeller housing.

The faster the impeller rotates, the greater the centrifugal force becomes. In Figure 32–5B, the oil is simply flying out of the housing and is not producing any work. To harness some of this energy, the turbine assembly is mounted on top of the impeller (Figure 32–5C). Now the oil thrown outward and upward from the impeller strikes the curved vanes of the turbine, causing the turbine to rotate. (There is no direct mechanical link between the impeller and turbine.) An oil pump driven by the converter shell and the engine continually delivers oil under pressure into the T/C through a hollow shaft at the center axis of the rotating torque converter assembly. A seal prevents the loss of fluid from the system.

FIGURE 32–5 Fluid travel inside the torque converter: (A) fluid at rest in impeller/pump, (B) fluid thrown up and outward by spinning pump, and (C) fluid flow harnessed by turbine and redirected back into the pump.

The turbine shaft is located within this hollow shaft. As mentioned earlier, the turbine shaft is splined to the turbine and transfers power from the torque converter to the transmission's main drive shaft. Oil leaving the turbine is directed out of the torque converter to an external oil cooler and then to the transmission's oil sump or pan.

With the transmission in gear and the engine at idle, the vehicle can be held stationary by applying the brakes. At idle, engine speed is slow. Since the impeller is driven by engine speed, it turns slowly creating little centrifugal force within the torque converter. Therefore, little or no power is transferred to the transmission.

When the throttle is opened, engine speed, impeller speed, and the amount of centrifugal force generated in the torque converter increase dramatically. Oil is then directed against the turbine blades, which transfer power to the turbine shaft and transmission.

Types of Oil Flow

Two types of oil flow take place inside the torque converter: rotary and vortex flow (Figure 32–6). **Rotary oil flow** is the oil flow around the circumference of the torque converter caused by the rotation of the torque converter on its axis. **Vortex oil flow** is the oil flow occurring from the impeller to the turbine and back to the impeller.

Figure 32–7 also shows the oil flow pattern as the speed of the turbine approaches the speed of the impeller. This is known as the **coupling point**. The turbine and the impeller are running at essentially the same speed. They cannot run at exactly the same speed due to slippage between them. The only way they can turn at exactly the same speed is by using a lockup clutch to mechanically tie them together.

As mentioned earlier, the stator is a small, wheel-like assembly positioned between the impeller and turbine. The stator has no mechanical connection to either the impeller or turbine but fits between the outlet of the turbine and the inlet of the impeller so all the oil returning from the turbine to the impeller must pass through the stator.

The stator mounts through its splined center hub to a mating stator shaft, often called a ground sleeve. The stator freewheels when the impeller and turbine reach the coupling stage.

The stator redirects the oil leaving the turbine back to the impeller, which helps the impeller rotate more efficiently (Figure 32–8). Torque converter mul-

FIGURE 32–7   Rotary flow is at its greatest at the coupling stage.

A

B

FIGURE 32–8   (A) Without a stator, fluid leaving the turbine works against the direction in which the impeller or pump is rotating. (B) With a stator in its locked (noncoupling) mode, fluid is directed to help push the impeller in its rotating direction.

FIGURE 32–6   Rotary and vortex oil flow in the torque converter.

tiplication can only occur when the impeller is rotating faster than the turbine.

A stator is either a rotating or fixed type. Rotating stators are more efficient at higher speeds because there is less slippage when the impeller and turbine reach the coupling stage.

Overrunning Clutch

An **overrunning clutch** keeps the stator assembly from rotating when driven in one direction and permits overrunning (rotation) when turned in the opposite direction. Rotating stators generally use a roller-type overrunning clutch that allows the stator to freewheel (rotate) when the speed of the turbine and impeller reach the coupling point.

The roller clutch (Figure 32–9) is designed with a movable inner race, rollers, accordion (apply) springs, and outer race. Around the inside diameter of the outer race are several cam-shaped pockets. The rollers and accordion springs are located in these pockets.

As the vehicle begins to move, the stator stays in its stationary or locked position because of the difference between the impeller and turbine speeds. This locking mode takes place when the inner race rotates counterclockwise. The accordion springs force the rollers down the ramps of the cam pockets into a wedging contact with the inner and outer races.

As vehicle road speed increases, turbine speed increases until it approaches impeller speed. Oil exiting the turbine vanes strikes the back face of the stator, causing the stator to rotate in the same direction as the turbine and impeller. At this higher speed, clearance exists between the inner stator race and hub. The rollers at each slot of the stator are pulled around the stator hub. The stator freewheels or turns as a unit.

If the vehicle slows, engine speed also slows along with turbine speed. This decrease in turbine speed allows the oil flow to change direction. It now strikes the front face of the stator vanes, halting the turning stator and attempting to rotate it in the opposite direction.

As this happens, the rollers jam between the inner race and hub, locking the stator in position. In a stationary position, the stator now redirects the oil exiting the turbine so torque is again multiplied.

LOCKUP TORQUE CONVERTER

A lockup torque converter eliminates the 10 percent slip that takes place between the impeller and turbine at the coupling stage of operation. The engagement of a clutch between the engine crankshaft and the turbine assembly has the advantage of improving fuel economy and reducing torque converter operational heat and engine speed.

There are two types of lockup torque converters. The centrifugal lockup clutch (**CLC**) was installed in Ford Motor Company C-5 automatic transmissions during the early 1980s. The piston lockup clutch (**PLC**) is the type installed in most automatic transmissions.

Centrifugal Lockup Clutch (CLC)

As shown in Figure 32–10, the principle part added to the torque converter is the clutch and damper assembly located between the torque converter shell and turbine assembly.

The clutch and damper assembly looks like a manual transmission clutch disc. At its center is an internally splined hub meshing with an externally splined hub on the turbine assembly. The clutch and damper assembly drive the turbine when the lockup clutch is engaged. Outward from the internally splined hub is the coasting one-way overrunning clutch. This sprag-type clutch connects the clutch and damper assembly to the turbine hub when the engine is driving the vehicle. When the vehicle is decelerating or coasting, the coasting clutch overruns and disconnects the turbine from the torque converter shell. This clutch is considered a safety factor during an emergency stop because the engine will not stall.

Midway from the center of the clutch and damper assembly are six coil torsional springs that absorb the shock associated with the torque converter locking action. Collectively, the torsional coil springs are called an absorption unit. Placed around the outside edge of the clutch and damper assembly are several shoe assemblies called centrifugal clutch shoes. Each shoe is mounted on a spring sensitive to centrifugal force and faced with a friction material pad.

With the vehicle stopped, the torque converter shell drives the impeller using fluid to rotate the turbine and turbine shaft hydraulically (Figure 32–11).

FIGURE 32–9 Typical roller-type overrunning clutch.

FIGURE 32–10   In a centrifugal lockup torque converter, a clutch and damper assembly is positioned between the turbine and the torque converter shell. It uses a coasting overrunning sprag-type clutch. *Courtesy of Ford Motor Company*

FIGURE 32–11   (A) With the vehicle stopped, the torque converter shell drives the impeller, turbine, and turbine shaft. (B) As turbine speed increases, friction shoes engage to drive the overrun clutch and turbine shaft. *Courtesy of Ford Motor Company*

As turbine speed and centrifugal force increase the centrifugal clutch, the shoes are thrown outward and expand to contact the inside diameter of the torque converter shell (Figure 32–11B). Power flows from the inside surface of the torque converter shell to the expanded centrifugal clutch shoe, clutch, and damper assembly to drive the turbine hub and turbine shaft.

In the lockup mode, there is no hydraulic operation. The drive is strictly mechanical. If the driver requires an increase in vehicle speed, increased impeller speed raises vortex flow and produces some torque multiplication. A friction-modified automatic transmission fluid permits the centrifugal clutch shoes to slip when extra torque is needed. When the demand for torque has been satisfied, the centrifugal clutch shoes resume driving the interior of the torque converter shell, reestablishing lockup torque converter action.

Piston Lockup Clutch (PLC)

The other type of lockup torque converter has a piston clutch located between the front of the turbine and the interior front face of the shell (Figure 32–12). Its main components are a piston plate and damper assembly and a clutch friction ring. The friction ring is bonded to the piston plate and damper assembly, in many cases. The second part of the damper assembly is made of several coil springs designed into the piston plate to transmit driving torque and absorb shock.

In piston-type lockup torque converters, the front section of the turbine shaft is drilled lengthwise allowing fluids to be supplied to and drained from the chamber between the front side of the piston plate and damper assembly and torque converter shell.

Whereas a centrifugal lockup clutch is operated by engine speed, the piston lockup clutch is controlled by hydraulic valve action or, more precisely, by computer. The computer control is superior because information about the engine, fuel, ignition, vacuum, and operating temperature is fed into the computer so engagement is closely monitored to take place at exactly the right time as it relates to engine operation.

SHOP TALK

The Chrysler lockup clutch friction facings float between the torque converter shell and the pressure plate and piston assembly. Chrysler does not have an absorption unit. It relies instead on the fluid in the torque converter to cushion lockup clutch engagement. ◼

To provide for piston clutch control, Chrysler adds a three-valve module to its standard transmission valve body (Figure 32–13). The lockup valve is controlled by fluid pressure produced by the transmission's governor assembly called **governor pressure**. When vehicle road speed is high enough, governor pressure forces the lockup valve to move against coil spring tension. The moving over of the lockup valve permits fluid pressure to move to the **fail-safe** valve. The purpose of the fail-safe valve is to prevent lockup clutch engagement until the transmission is in third gear. Third gear fluid pressure moves the fail-safe valve, which allows fluid pressure to flow to the switch valve. The purpose of the switch valve is to direct fluid pressure, called **line pressure**, between the turbine shaft and the stator support to fill the torque converter. When the torque converter is filled, fluid flows out from the space around the periphery of the impeller and turbine to the rear of the piston plate and damper assembly. This fluid flow acts on the rear surface of the piston plate and moves it forward to bring the piston plate and friction ring into contact with the torque converter shell. When the piston plate engages, the clutch friction ring forms a fluid pressure seal with the torque converter shell. This seal stops fluid pressure from leaking to the turbine shaft. A fluid leak in this area decreases the fluid pressure that keeps the clutch engaged. The fluid in the torque converter does not circulate but remains there to act as the torque converter coolant and lubricant throughout the lockup engagement.

FIGURE 32–12 Piston lockup clutch components and oil flow. *Courtesy of Ford Motor Company*

FIGURE 32–13 Control valve operation to produce direct lockup clutch engagement in Chrysler piston lockup torque converter. *Courtesy of Chrysler Corporation*

FIGURE 32–14 Planetary gear configuration is similar to the solar system, with the sun gear surrounded by the planetary pinion gears. The ring gear surrounds the complete gearset.

Forced Disengagement

While in the lockup mode, the driver might want to accelerate rapidly. By opening the throttle, pressure increases, stroking the fail-safe valve to block line pressure to the lockup valve. Spring tension moves the switch valve, directing fluid pressure to the front (disengaged) side of the piston plate and damper assembly) side of the piston plate and damper assembly. The torque converter then returns to conventional operation.

PLANETARY GEARS

All automatic transmissions rely on planetary gearsets to transfer power and multiply engine torque to the drive axle. Compound gearsets combine two simple planetary gearsets so load can be spread over a greater number of teeth for strength and also to obtain the largest number of gear ratios possible in a compact area.

A simple planetary gearset consists of three parts: a sun gear, a carrier with planetary pinions mounted to it, and an internally toothed ring gear or annulus. The **sun gear** is located in the center of the assembly (Figure 32–14). It can be either a spur or helical gear design. It meshes with the teeth of the planetary pinion gears. Planetary pinion gears are small gears fitted into a framework called the planetary carrier. The planetary carrier can be made of cast iron, aluminum, or steel plate and is designed with a shaft for each of the planetary pinion gears. (For simplicity, planetary pinion gears are called **planetary pinions**.)

Planetary pinions rotate on needle bearings positioned between the planetary carrier shaft and the planetary pinions. The carrier and pinions are considered one unit—the mid-size gear member.

The planetary pinions surround the sun gear's center axis and they themselves are surrounded by the **annulus** or **ring gear**, which is the largest part of the simple gearset. The ring gear acts like a band to hold the entire gearset together and provide great strength to the unit. To help remember the design of a simple planetary gearset, use the solar system as an example. The sun is the center of the solar system with the planets rotating around it; hence, the name planetary gearset.

How Planetary Gears Work

Each member of a planetary gearset—the sun gear, pinion gear carrier, and ring gear—can spin (revolve) or be held at rest. Power transfer through a planetary gearset is only possible when one of the members is held at rest, or if two of the members are locked together.

Any one of the three members can be used as the driving or input member. At the same time, another member might be kept from rotating and thus becomes the held or stationary member. The third member then becomes the driven or output member.

			TABLE 32–1 LAWS OF SIMPLE PLANETARY GEAR OPERATION		
Sun Gear	**Carrier**	**Ring Gear**	**Speed**	**Torque**	**Direction**
1. Input	Output	Held	Maximum reduction	Increase	Same as input
2. Held	Output	Input	Minimum reduction	Increase	Same as input
3. Output	Input	Held	Maximum increase	Reduction	Same as input
4. Held	Input	Output	Minimum increase	Reduction	Same as input
5. Input	Held	Output	Reduction	Increase	Reverse of input
6. Output	Held	Input	Increase	Reduction	Reverse of input
7. When any two members are held together, speed and direction are the same as input. Direct 1:1 drive occurs.					
8. When no member is held or locked together, output cannot occur. The result is a neutral condition.					

Depending on which member is the driver, which is held, and which is driven, either a torque increase or a speed increase is produced by the planetary gearset. Output direction can also be reversed through various combinations.

Table 32–1 summarizes the basic laws of simple planetary gears. It indicates the resultant speed, torque, and direction of the various combinations available. Also, remember that when an external-to-external gear tooth set is in mesh, there is a change in the direction of rotation at the output. When an external gear tooth is in mesh with an internal gear, the output rotation for both gears is the same.

MAXIMUM FORWARD REDUCTION With the ring gear stationary and the sun gear turning clockwise, the sun gear rotates the planetary pinions counterclockwise on their shafts (Figure 32–15). The small sun gear (driving) rotates several times, driving the mid-size planetary carrier one complete revolution, resulting in the most gear reduction or the maximum torque multiplication that can be achieved in one planetary gearset. Input speed is high, but output speed is low.

MINIMUM FORWARD REDUCTION In this combination the sun gear is stationary and the ring gear

FIGURE 32–15 Maximum forward reduction (greatest torque, lowest speed) is produced with the sun gear as input, ring gear stationary, and carrier as output.

FIGURE 32–16 Minimum forward reduction (good torque, medium-to-high speed) is produced with the ring gear as input, the sun gear stationary, and the carrier as output.

rotates clockwise (Figure 32–16). The ring gear drives the planetary pinions clockwise and walks around the stationary sun gear. The planetary pinions drive the planetary carrier in the same direction as the ring gear—forward. This results in more than one turn of the input as compared to one complete revolution of the output. The result is torque multiplication. The planetary gearset is operating in a forward reduction with the large ring gear driving the small planetary carrier. Therefore, the combination produces minimum forward reduction.

MAXIMUM OVERDRIVE With the ring gear stationary and the planetary carrier rotating clockwise (Figure 32–17), the three planetary pinion shafts push against the inside diameter of the planetary pinions. The pinions are forced to walk around the inside of the ring gear, driving the sun gear clockwise. In this combination, the mid-size planetary carrier is rotating less than one turn and driving the smaller sun gear at a speed greater than the input speed. The result is overdrive with maximum speed increase.

SLOW OVERDRIVE In this combination, the sun gear is stationary and the carrier rotates clockwise (Figure 32–18). As the carrier rotates, the pinion shafts push against the inside diameter of the pinions

FIGURE 32–17 Maximum overdrive (lowest torque, greatest speed) is produced with the carrier as input, ring gear stationary, and sun gear as output.

FIGURE 32–18 Slow overdrive (lower torque, greater speed) is produced with the carrier as input, sun gear stationary, and ring gear as output.

and they are forced to walk around the held sun gear. This drives the ring gear faster and the speed increases. The carrier turning less than one turn causes the pinions to drive the ring gear one complete revolution in the same direction as the planetary carrier and a slow overdrive occurs.

SLOW REVERSE Here the sun gear is driving the ring gear with the planetary carrier held stationary (Figure 32–19). The planetary pinions, driven by the sun gear, rotate counterclockwise on their shafts. While the sun gear is driving, the planetary pinions are used as idler gears to drive the ring gear counterclockwise. This means the input and output shafts are operating in the opposite or reverse direction to

FIGURE 32–20 Fast reverse (opposite output direction, great torque, low speed) is produced with the ring gear as input, carrier stationary, and sun gear as output.

provide a reverse power flow. Since the driving sun gear is small and the driven ring gear is large, the result is slow reverse.

FAST REVERSE For fast reverse, the carrier is held, but the sun gear and ring gear reverse roles, with the ring gear now being the driving member and the sun gear driven (Figure 32–20). As the ring gear rotates counterclockwise, the pinions rotate counterclockwise as well, while the sun gear turns clockwise. In this combination, the input ring gear uses the planetary pinions to drive the output sun gear. The sun gear rotates in reverse to the input ring gear, providing fast reverse.

DIRECT DRIVE In the direct drive combination, both the ring gear and the sun gear are input members (Figure 32–21). They turn clockwise at the same speed. The internal teeth of the clockwise turning ring gear try to rotate the planetary pinions clockwise as well. But the sun gear, which rotates clockwise, tries to drive the planetary pinions counterclockwise. These opposing forces lock the planetary pinions against rotation so the entire planetary gearset rotates as one complete unit. This ties together the input and output members and provides a direct drive.

NEUTRAL OPERATION When no member is held stationary or locked, there is input into the gearset, but no output. The result is a neutral condition (Figure 32–22).

FIGURE 32–19 Slow reverse (opposite output direction, greatest torque, lowest speed) is produced with the sun gear as input, planetary carrier stationary, and the ring gear as output.

FIGURE 32–21 Direct drive is produced if any two gearset members are locked together.

FIGURE 32–22 With no held or stationary member, there can be no output. The result is a neutral condition.

PLANETARY GEAR CONTROLS

The following are helpful tips for remembering the basics of simple planetary gearset operation.

♦ When the planetary carrier is the drive (input) member, the gearset produces an overdrive condition. Speed increases, torque decreases.
♦ When the planetary carrier is the driven (output) member, the gearset produces a forward direction. Speed decreases, torque increases.
♦ When the planetary carrier is held, the gearset produces a reverse.

Certain parts of the planetary gear train must be held while others must be driven to provide the needed torque multiplication and direction for vehicle operation. Planetary gear controls is the general term used to describe transmission bands, servos, and clutches.

Transmission Bands

A **band** is a braking assembly positioned around a stationary or rotating drum. The band brings a drum to a stop by wrapping itself around the drum and holding it. The band is hydraulically applied by a servo assembly. Connected to the drum is a member of the planetary gear train. The purpose of a band is to control the planetary gear train by holding the drum and connecting planetary gear member stationary. Bands provide excellent holding characteristics and require a minimum amount of space within the transmission housing.

When a band closes around a rotating drum, a wedging action takes place to stop the drum from rotating. The wedging action is known as self-energizing action. It is explained later in this chapter.

There are two types of bands used in automatic transmissions: single wrap and **double wrap**. A thick steel **single wrap** band (Figure 32–23A) is used to hold gear train components driven by high output engines. Self-energizing action is low because of the rigidity of the band's design. Thinner steel bands are

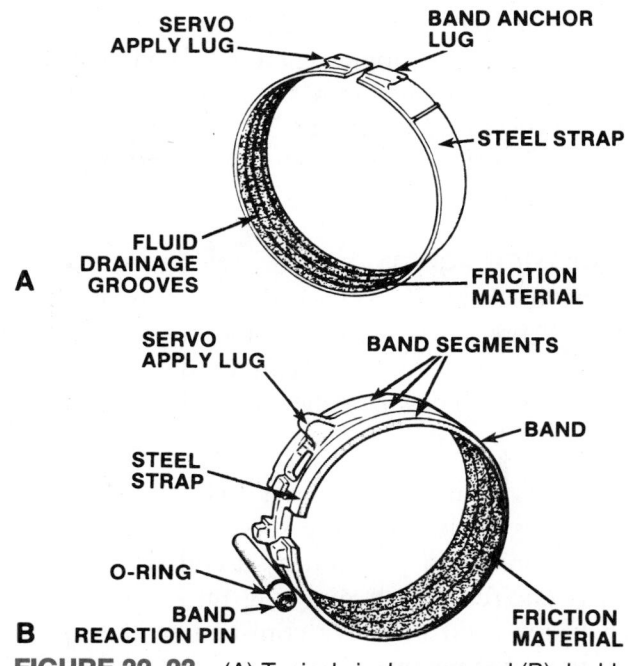

FIGURE 32–23 (A) Typical single-wrap and (B) double-wrap transmission band designs. *Courtesy of Chrysler Corporation*

not able to provide a high degree of holding power, but because of the flexibility of design, self-energizing action is stronger and provides more apply force.

Band lugs are either spot welded or cast as a part of the band assembly. The purpose of the lugs is to connect the band with the servo through the actuating (apply) linkage or the band anchor (reaction) at the opposite end.

SHOP TALK

A holding planetary control unit is also called a reaction unit because it holds a gear train member stationary, reacting to rotation. ∎

The band's steel strap is designed with slots or holes to release fluid trapped between the drum and the applying band.

A typical band is designed to be larger in diameter than the drum it surrounds. This design promotes self-disengagement of the band from the drum when servo apply force is decreased to less than servo release spring tension. A friction material resembling automobile brake lining is bonded to the inside diameter of the band.

The double wrap band is a circular external contracting band normally designed with two or three segments (parts) illustrated in Figure 32–23B. As the band closes, the segments align themselves around the drum and provide a cushion.

The steel body of the double wrap band may be thin or thick steel strapping material. Modern automatic transmissions use thin single or double wrap bands for increased efficiency. Double wrap bands made with heavy thick steel strapping are required for high output engines.

Transmission Servos

The **servo** assembly converts hydraulic pressure into mechanical pressure that applies the band around a drum, holding it stationary. Simple and compound servos are used to engage bands in modern transmissions.

Simple Servo In a simple servo (Figure 32–24), the servo piston fits into the servo cylinder and is held in the released position by a coil spring. The piston is encircled by a seal ring made of rubber, which keeps fluid pressure confined to the apply side of the servo piston.

In the illustration (but not on all servo designs), the piston pushrod is drilled through the center, which permits fluid pressure to be directed to the apply side of the servo piston. The piston pushrod locates in the band apply strut, which is indexed with the band apply lug. At the opposite end of the band is the anchor strut and adjustment screw. They receive the engagement force of a band.

To apply a band, fluid pressure is directed down the servo pushrod to the apply side of the servo piston. The servo piston strokes through the servo cylinder, compresses the servo coil spring, and develops servo apply force. As the servo piston and pushrod stroke the servo cylinder, they force the apply lever and strut against the band lug. The band tightens around the rotating drum. The rotating drum comes to a stop and is held stationary by the band.

When servo apply force is released, the servo coil spring forces the servo piston to stroke back up the

FIGURE 32–25 Typical compound servo design. *Courtesy of Ford Motor Company*

servo cylinder to the released position. With the servo apply force removed, the band springs free and permits drum rotation.

Compound Servos A compound servo (Figure 32–25) has a cylinder that is cast as part of the transmission housing. The servo piston located nearest the front of the transmission uses cast-iron seal rings capable of withstanding the heat generated by the torque converter and engine.

When the compound servo is applied, fluid pressure flows through the hollow piston pushrod to the apply side of the servo piston. The piston moves inward, compressing the servo coil spring and forcing the pushrod to move one end of the band toward the adjusting screw and anchor. The band tightens around the rotating drum and brings it to a stop. If the drum was stationary, the band would apply, holding the drum tight and unable to revolve. The apply of the compound servo piston is much like the simple servo, but there the similarity ends.

Fluid pressure is applied to the release side of the servo piston when the band is to be released. To release the compound servo, fluid pressure is admitted to the release side of the servo piston. Line pressure on either side of the servo piston balances out. The force of the servo spring causes the release of the servo piston.

Transmission Clutches

In contrast to a band, which can only hold a planetary gear member, transmission clutches, either overrunning or multiple-disc, are capable of both holding and driving members.

Overrunning Clutches When applied to transmission operation, the overrunning clutch is broadened to a holder or driver. Both sprag and roller overrunning clutches can be applied to either the holding or driving application.

FIGURE 32–24 Typical simple servo design. *Courtesy of Ford Motor Company*

For example, when the turbine shaft and inner race rotate, the accordion apply springs force the rollers down their ramps and engage both the inner and outer races. Power flow passes from the inner race through the roller to the outer race, driving the low reverse sun gear and direct clutch splines at turbine shaft speed.

Should the turbine shaft decelerate and rotate slower than the driven race, the overrunning clutch rollers in an overrun mode disengage from the driving race. The low reverse sun gear and direct clutch are disengaged from the turbine shaft.

Multiple-Disc Clutches A **multiple-disc clutch** uses a series of hollow friction discs to transmit torque or apply braking force. The discs have internal teeth that are sized and shaped to mesh with splines on the clutch assembly hub. In turn, this hub is connected to a planetary gear train component so gearset members receive the desired braking or transfer force when the clutch is applied or released.

DESIGN Multiple-disc clutches have a large drum-shaped housing that can be either a separate casting or part of the existing transmission housing (Figure 32–26). This drum housing holds all other clutch components: the cylinder, hub, piston, piston return springs, seals, pressure plate, **clutch pack** (including friction plates), and snap rings.

The cylinder in a multiple-disc clutch is very shallow when compared to an engine cylinder. The hub of the cylinder acts as a guide for piston travel.

The piston is made of cast aluminum or a steel stamping with a seal ring groove around the outside diameter. A seal ring seats in the groove. This rubber seal retains fluid pressure used to stroke the piston engaging the clutch pack. The piston return springs overcome the reduced fluid pressure in the clutch and move the piston to the disengaged position when clutch action (holding or transfer) is no longer needed.

The clutch pack consists of normal clutch plates, friction discs, and one very thick plate known as the pressure plate (Figure 32–27). The pressure plate has tabs around the outside diameter to mate with the channels in the clutch drum (Figure 32–28). It is held in place by a large snap ring. The stroking piston forces the engaging clutch pack against the fixed pressure plate. Because the pressure plate cannot move or deflect, it provides the reaction to the engaging clutch pack.

Clutch plates must be perfectly flat, and although the surface of the plate might appear smooth, it is specifically machined to promote a coefficient of friction to help transmit engine torque.

The friction discs are sandwiched between the clutch plates and pressure plate. Friction discs are designed with a steel core plate center with friction material bonded to either side. Asbestos was once the universal friction material used, but because it is hazardous to human health, cellular paper fibers, graphites, and ceramics are now being used as friction materials.

FIGURE 32–27 The clutch pack is made of friction discs and clutch plates. *Courtesy of Chrysler Corporation*

FIGURE 32–26 Exploded view of multiple-disc clutch assembly. *Courtesy of Ford Motor Company*

FIGURE 32–28 Channels in the clutch drum receive the tabs of the clutch plates. *Courtesy of Chrysler Corporation*

COOLING During clutch engagement, friction takes place and develops heat between the clutch plates and friction discs. The transmission fluid absorbed by the paper-based friction material transfers heat from the discs to the plates. The plates then transfer the heat to the drum housing where it can be cooled by the surrounding transmission fluid. Operating temperatures can reach 1,100°F, so clutch disc cooling is an important design consideration in transmission manufacturing.

To help with this cooling and provide other performance advantages, friction disc surfaces are normally grooved.

Planetary Control Terminology

Table 32–2 is a crossover chart listing the names the different manufacturers call the same planetary gear control. On some four-speed transaxles, the terminology changes because the gear train arrangement changes.

Chrysler refers to the planetary controls by their location in the transaxle or transmission housing. To help eliminate confusion, this test follows Chrysler's logical approach. Chrysler calls the clutch engaged for all forward speeds the rear clutch. The band at the front of the transaxle is the front kickdown band engaged in second gear and also in downshift from third to second gear, which is also known as the passing gear. The front clutch in the transaxle is engaged in reverse and high or third gear. The band located at the rear of the transaxle housing is known as the low and reverse band. It is engaged when the gear selector lever is placed in reverse or manually shifted to first or low gear. The overrunning clutch engages only in low gear or, if the vehicle speed is low enough, on a three to one downshift for rapid torque multiplication.

TABLE 32–2 PLANETARY CONTROL TERMINOLOGY CROSSOVER CHART		
Chrysler	**Ford**	**General Motors**
Front clutch	Reverse and high clutch	Direct clutch
Rear clutch	Forward clutch	Forward clutch
Front kickdown band	Intermediate band	Intermediate band
Low and reverse rear band	Low and reverse band or clutch	Low and reverse band or clutch
Overrunning clutch	One-way clutch	Low roller clutch

PLANETARY GEAR TRAIN

Automatic transmissions use several simple planetary gearsets tied together to generate the required gear ratios and direction needed for optimum performance. When several simple gearsets work as a unit, they are known as a gear train. The most common gear train used in automatic transmissions is the **Simpson gear train**.

The Simpson gear train consists of two simple planetary gearsets that share a common sun gear. This common sun gear ties the two gearsets together and allows the output of one gearset to become the input of the other (Figure 32–29).

In a Simpson gear train, both the forward ring gear and the common sun gear can be connected to the transmission input shaft using two separate multiple-disc clutches. Although the sun gear rotates around the output shaft, it is not connected to the output shaft. The sun gear and the rear carrier can be held. The sun gear is held stationary by either a band or a multiple-disc clutch, which locks the sun gear to the transmission housing.

In manually selected low gear, the rear carrier is held by either a band or multiple-disc clutch. In both cases, there is also an overrunning clutch that prevents backward rotation of the carrier while allowing forward rotation. When the drive position is selected, the overrunning clutch only holds while the transmission is in low gear.

FIGURE 32–29 Simpson planetary gear train shown without its planetary controls.

The forward carrier and the rear ring gear are splined to the transmission output shaft. To make this connection, the output shaft extends through the hollow sun gear to reach the forward carrier.

CHRYSLER TORQUEFLITE TRANSMISSIONS

Chrysler Corporation introduced the Torqueflite transmission in 1956. This transmission was the first modern 3-speed automatic transmission with a torque converter and the first to use the Simpson 2-planetary compound gear train. Nearly all Torqueflite-based transmissions and transaxles use a rotor-type oil pump and all use a Simpson gear train.

There are two basic versions of the 3-speed Torqueflite transmission: the A-904 and the A-727. The 904 is the light-duty version, while the 727, is the heavy-duty version. The A-998 and A-999 transmissions are newer versions of the A-904. In 1978, the basic Torqueflite transmission was modified for use as a FWD transaxle. Torqueflite transaxles contain the same basic parts as the A-904 transmission, except a transfer shaft, final drive gears, and a differential unit have been added to the assembly.

All the Torqueflite-based transmissions and transaxles, used today, have two multiple disc clutches, an overrunning clutch, two servos and bands, and two planetary gearsets to provide three forward gear ratios and a reverse ratio. The two multiple-disc clutches are called the front and rear clutch packs. The servos and bands are also referred to by their location, front and rear, or by their function, kickdown and low/reverse.

Power flow through Torqueflite transmissions occurs by the engagement and disengagement of the clutches and bands. Refer to the clutch and band application chart Figure 32–30, while reading through the power flow.

Power Flow in Park/Neutral The power inputs the transmission through the turbine of the torque converter. When the gear selector is in park and neutral, the power flow ends at the front and rear clutches because neither are applied; therefore, no power is applied to the output shaft. When the selector is placed in park, a parking pawl is mechanically moved by the linkage and locks the parking gear to the transmission case. The parking gear is on the outer circumference of the governor support.

Power Flow in Reverse When the gear selector is placed into reverse, the front clutch is applied and engages the input shell and the sun gear. The rear band is also applied and holds the rear planetary carrier. The front clutch drives the sun gear in a clockwise direction. Because the rear planet carrier is held, the sun gear drives the rear planet gears in a counterclockwise direction. The rotation of the planet gears drives the rear ring gear and the output shaft in a counterclockwise direction, resulting in reverse gear with gear reduction.

Power Flow in First Gear When the gear selector is moved to the drive position, fully automatic shifting with three gear ranges is available. The shift points are determined by vehicle speed and load. When the transmission is operating in first gear, the rear clutch is applied and serves as the input member for the planetary gearset. Because the rear clutch is applied, input torque flows from the turbine of the torque converter through the input shaft to the rear clutch, which drives the front ring gear in a clockwise direction.

The front planetary carrier is splined to the output shaft and is, therefore, held by the weight of the vehicle and the drive wheels. This causes the ring gear to drive the front planet gears in a clockwise direction. The pinion gears, which are in mesh with

GEAR SELECTOR POSITION	OPERATING GEAR	REAR CLUTCH	REAR BAND	FRONT BAND	FRONT CLUTCH	ONE-WAY CLUTCH
P-Park	None					
R-Reverse	Reverse		x		x	
N-Neutral	None					
D-Drive	1st gear	x				x
	2nd gear	x		x		
	3rd gear	x			x	
2-Man. 2nd	1st gear	x				x
	2nd gear	x		x		
1-Man. 1st	1st gear	x	x			

FIGURE 32–30 Clutch and band application chart for typical Chrysler transmissions.

the sun gear, rotate it counterclockwise. The rotation of the common sun gear causes the rear planet pinion gears to rotate in a clockwise direction. The planet gears cause the rear ring gear and the output shaft to turn in a clockwise direction.

The rear planet carrier is held by the overrunning clutch whenever the engine's torque is driving the planetary unit. During coast or deceleration, the weight of the vehicle and its momentum drive the planetary units through the output shaft. This causes the rear carrier to rotate clockwise and release the one-way clutch. This results in a neutral condition and doesn't allow for engine braking.

When the gear selector is placed in manual low (1), the rear band and clutch are applied. The overrunning clutch holds the rear planet carrier, as does the rear band. The band holds the carrier during deceleration when the one-way clutch freewheels, this does allow for engine braking during coasting.

Power Flow in Second Gear When the gear selector is in drive, the transmission will automatically shift from first to second gears when the vehicle speed has reached a particular point and some load is overcome. The rear clutch remains applied and the front band engages to hold the sun gear stationary. The input shaft causes the front ring gear to rotate clockwise. Because the sun gear is held, the planet gears walk around the sun gear and drive the front planetary carrier and output shaft in a clockwise, but speed-reduced, direction.

The rear planetary set is effective during this gear because the rear planet carrier is rotating clockwise. This allows the one-way clutch to freewheel, thereby providing a neutral condition in the rear planetary gearset.

Power Flow in Third Gear Third gear is a direct drive gear. When the transmission shifts into third, both the front and rear clutches become inputs for the planetary gearsets. This locks the gearsets into direct drive. Whenever two members of a gearset are locked together, the pinion gears are unable to rotate on their individual shafts and the planetary gearset is locked. In this transmission, the two members that are locked together are the front ring gear and the sun gear.

Add-On Overdrive Chrysler's A-500 and A-518, which are four-speed automatic transmissions, are used exclusively in the mid-size Dodge Dakota and full-size Dodge RAM pick-ups and vans. Fourth gear is provided by a separate planetary gearset and controlled by an overdrive clutch, direct clutch, and overrunning clutch in the overdrive assembly attached to the rear of the transmission. In overdrive, the output ratio is 0.69 to 1.

Overdrive or fourth gear operation is controlled by a manually operated overdrive switch on the instrument panel. The electrical overdrive switch and the single board engine controller (**SBEC**) controls the overdrive solenoid on the valve body.

These transmissions have extra long extension housings that hold the additional planetary gearset. An additional shaft was also added to the basic three-speed models. This shaft serves as the output shaft. The three-speed output shaft became an intermediate shaft linking the output from the Simpson gear train to the overdrive assembly.

Power flow through the first three gears is the same as other Torqueflite transmissions. However, to control the operation of the overdrive planetary, two multiple-disc clutches (direct and overdrive clutches) and a one-way overrunning clutch is used. The intermediate shaft is locked to the output shaft whenever the one-way clutch is locked. This locking results in bypassing the overdrive planetary and provides for direct drive.

The direct clutch locks the sun and ring gears together to prevent freewheeling of the overrunning clutch during coasting and deceleration. This provides for engine braking. The spring used in the direct clutch assembly is a heavy tension single-coil spring that applies great holding force onto the clutch discs.

The intermediate shaft also drives the planetary carrier of the overdrive gearset. When the transmission shifts from third to fourth gear, the overdrive clutch piston moves the clutch's hub to relieve the spring tension on the direct clutch assembly. It also applies pressure to the overdrive clutch, which locks the sun gear to the transmission case. With the sun gear held, the planet carrier forces the ring gear and output shaft to rotate in an overdrive condition.

FORD SIMPSON GEAR TRAIN TRANSMISSIONS

Ford Motor Company has five basic transmissions that use the Simpson gear train and are quite similar to each other: the C-3, C-4, C-5, C-6, and A4LD. The A4LD is a 4-speed, whereas the others are 3-speeds. All of these units use a gear and crescent-type oil pump as the source of all hydraulic pressures.

The A4LD is a modified version of the C-3. Its housing was enlarged and an additional planetary gearset was added to provide for an overdrive fourth gear. The A4LD was the first electronically controlled Ford automatic transmission.

GEAR SELECTOR POSITION	OPERATING GEAR	FORWARD CLUTCH	LOW/REVERSE BAND	INTERMEDIATE BAND	HIGH/REVERSE CLUTCH	ONE-WAY CLUTCH
P-Park	None					
R-Reverse	Reverse		x		x	
N-Neutral	None					
D-Drive	1st gear	x				x
	2nd gear	x		x		
	3rd gear	x			x	
L2-Man. 2nd	2nd gear	x		x		
L1-Man. 1st	1st gear	x	x			

FIGURE 32–31 Clutch and band application chart for a Ford C-6 transmission.

The gear train for the first three speeds of these transmissions is identical except for the C-6, which uses a low/reverse clutch instead of the low/reverse band used by the other models.

In appearance, these transmissions are similar and all have a separate and removable extension housing. The major external difference between the models is the size and the reinforcements of the case. The bell housings of the C-3, C-4, and C-5 are removable from the transmission case, whereas the bell housing of the C-6 is part of the case's casting.

To control planetary gear action, these transmissions use two multiple-disc clutches, two bands, and one overrunning clutch. The two clutches are referred to as the high, front, or reverse/high and the rear or forward clutches. The two bands are the intermediate, front, or kickdown and low/reverse or rear units. Again the exception to this is the C-6, which uses a clutch in place of a band for low and reverse. See Figure 32–31 for the band and clutch application chart for a C-6 transmission.

The power flow through Ford transmissions with a Simpson gear train is similar to that of the power flow through a Chrysler Torqueflite transmission.

Add-On Overdrive The A4LD transmission consists of a torque converter, planetary gear train, three multiple disc clutch packs, three bands, a one-way clutch, and hydraulic control system. The housing of a C-3 was enlarged and an additional planetary gearset was added to provide for an overdrive fourth gear. The additional planetary gearset was added in front of the normal 3-speed Simpson gear train. Input from the torque converter passes through the overdrive planetary gearset (Figure 32–32) before it reaches the Simpson gearset. To control planetary action of the overdrive gearset, the A4LD uses an overdrive band, overdrive clutch, and an overdrive one-way clutch.

The overdrive band holds the overdrive sun gear to provide for fourth gear overdrive. The overdrive clutch locks the overdrive sun gear to the overdrive planetary carrier to provide for engine braking while the transmission is operating in drive. The overdrive one-way roller clutch locks the input from the torque converter's turbine shaft directly to the input shaft of the Simpson gear train and provides direct drive through the planetary gearset by locking the carrier to the ring gear.

Direct drive through the overdrive planetary unit is present whenever the transmission is operating in

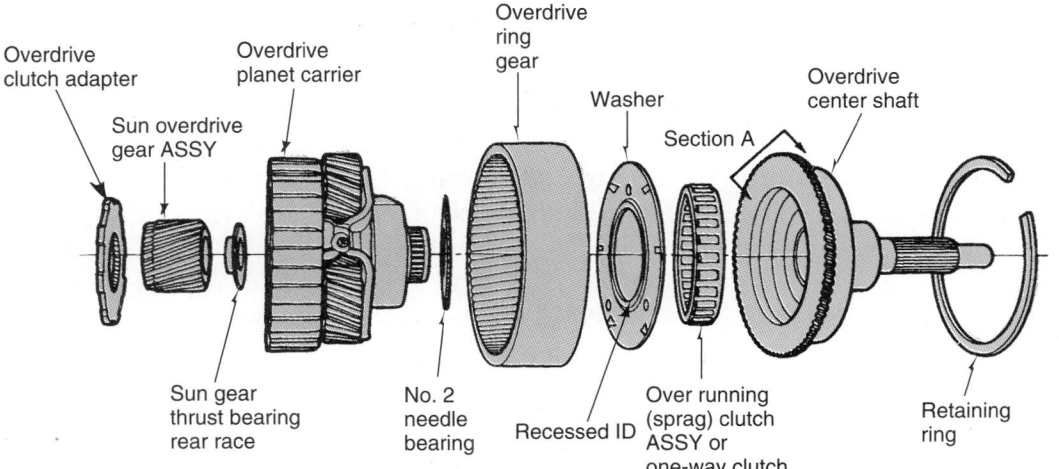

FIGURE 32–32 Add-on planetary gearset that provides fourth gear. *Courtesy of Ford Motor Company*

first, second, third, or reverse gears. During these conditions, all input power flows through the overdrive one-way clutch, also the overdrive clutch is applied to provide for engine braking.

When overdrive is selected, the overdrive band is applied and holds the sun gear. The overdrive clutch is released and the planet carrier becomes the input member driving the ring gear at an overdrive ratio of approximately 0.75:1.

GENERAL MOTORS' SIMPSON GEAR TRAIN TRANSMISSIONS

Most General Motors' transmissions and transaxles are based on the Simpson gear train. The turbo hydramatic (THM) 375, 400, and 475 transmissions are heavy-duty transmissions generally used in full-sized RWD cars and trucks. The 425 is based on the same design as the others but had been modified for use in FWD vehicles with a longitudinally placed engine. The 3L80 (THM 400) was introduced in 1964 and has been used by all divisions of General Motors, as well as by many different manufacturers, such as Jaguar and Rolls-Royce.

The THM 250, 250C, 350, 350C, and 375B transmissions are 3-speed units. The 250 and 250C are light-duty, the 350 and 350C are medium-duty, and the 375B is a heavy-duty version of the 350. On THM transmissions and transaxles, the suffix C means the unit is equipped with a lock-up torque converter.

The primary difference between a 250 and 350 transmission is a 250 uses a band as the second gear holding device, and a 350 uses a band plus a multiple-disc clutch and a one-way roller clutch as holding devices during second gear operation.

The 200, 200C, 200-4R, 325, and 325-4L are light- to medium- duty transmissions. The 200, 200C, and 325 are 3-speed units and the 200-4R and 325-4L have four forward speeds. The 200 series are used in RWD vehicles and the 325 series are used in FWD models. The 325 replaced the 425 in FWD Buick Riviera, Cadillac Eldorado, and Oldsmobile Toronado models.

The 325 and 425 transmissions are not classified as transaxles because the differential and final drive gears are not built into the transmission case, rather a separate final drive unit is bolted to the transmission to drive the front wheels.

The turbine shaft of the torque converter in a 325 and 425 transmission is splined to a drive sprocket. This drive sprocket rotates with the turbine shaft and drives a multiple-link chain that connects the drive sprocket to a driven sprocket. The driven sprocket is connected to the transmission's input

shaft. This arrangement allows engine torque to take a 90-degree turn before it reaches the gear train. After the input shaft, the internal components are identical to a 200 or 3L80 transmission.

The 3T40 (THM 125 and 125C) are 3-speed automatic transaxles designed for light-duty use. The 3T40 housing is a one-piece aluminum casting with the case cover and oil pan bolted to it. The bell housing is integral with the transaxle case. The torque converter does not directly drive the transaxle, rather the turbine shaft drives two sprockets and a chain, which transfers engine torque to the gear train. This transfer is necessary because the gear train is positioned behind and below the centerline of the crankshaft.

Most General Motors' transmissions and transaxles are fitted with gear-type oil pumps. Exceptions to this are late-model 4L30/4L80 (THM 200-4R) and 4L60 (THM 700-R4) transmissions, which use a variable displacement vane-type oil pump. The 3T40 models also use a vane-type oil pump, which is mounted to the valve body and is driven indirectly, through a drive shaft, by the torque converter.

Although there are differences between the various models of General Motors' transmissions with a Simpson gear train, most use three multiple-disc clutches, one band, and a single one-way roller clutch to provide the various gear ratios. Each clutch is applied hydraulically and released by several small coil springs (Figure 32–33). Two exceptions to this should be noted. The 350/350C has four multiple-disc clutches instead of three. The 200/200C uses a waved spring for clutch release in place of small coil springs.

Power Flow The power flow through General Motors' transmissions with a Simpson gear train is similar to that of the power flow through a Chrysler Torqueflite transmission. There are some slight variations within the different model types, but these are dependent upon the operating characteristics of each model. The chart in Figure 32–34 shows the clutch and band applications for one of General Motors' most commonly used transaxle, the 3T40.

Add-On Overdrive The 4L30/4L80 and 325-4L use the same multiple-disc clutches as the 200 but also have two additional clutches—the overrun clutch and fourth clutch. Each of these clutches is applied hydraulically. The forward, direct, and fourth clutches are released by several small coil return springs and the drive and low/reverse clutches are released by wave plate springs.

The 4L60 is a fully automatic transmission consisting of two planetary gearsets, five multiple-disc clutches, one sprag clutch, one roller clutch, and a band. (Refer to the clutch and band application

FIGURE 32–33 Most multiple-disc clutch assemblies in General Motors' transmissions are released by several small coil springs. *Courtesy of the Hydra-Matic Division, General Motors Corporation*

GEAR SELECTOR POSITION	OPERATING GEAR	DIRECT CLUTCH	FORWARD CLUTCH	LOW & REVERSE CLUTCH	INTERMEDIATE BAND	LOW ROLLER CLUTCH
D	1st gear		x			x
	2nd gear		x		x	
	3rd gear	x	x			
2	1st gear		x			x
	2nd gear		x		x	
1	1st gear		x	x		x
R	Reverse	x		x		

FIGURE 32–34 Clutch and band application chart for a 3T40 transmission.

chart, Figure 32–35 for more details.) These provide four forward gears, including an overdrive. The five multiple-disc clutches are applied hydraulically and released by several small coil springs. The 4L60 has a one-piece case casting that incorporates the bell housing. The extension housing is a separate casting bolted to the rear of the case.

OTHER SIMPSON-BASED TRANSMISSIONS

There are many different automatic transmissions that are based on the basic Simpson gear train. Most

have similar power flows and major components. The primary differences between most of the transmissions is in the nomenclature and holding devices used by the different manufacturers. The following transmissions are presented to illustrate the similarities of all Simpson-based transmissions and to expose you to some of the nomenclature used by the manufacturers.

Nissan Motor Company Transmissions A widely used Nissan RWD transmission is the L4N71B/ E4N71B series. These transmissions provide four forward gears through the use of a Simpson gearset and

GEAR SELECTOR POSITION	OPERATING GEAR	2-4 BAND	REVERSE INPUT CLUTCH	OVERRUN CLUTCH	FORWARD CLUTCH	FORWARD SPRAG CLUTCH	3-4 CLUTCH	LOW ROLLER CLUTCH	LOW/ REVERSE CLUTCH
OD	1st gear				x	x		x	
	2nd gear	x			x	x			
	3rd gear				x	x	x		
	Overdrive								
D	1st gear			x	x	x		x	
	2nd gear	x		x	x	x			
	3rd gear			x	x	x	x		
2	1st gear			x	x	x		x	
	2nd gear	x		x	x	x			
R	Reverse		x						x

FIGURE 32–35   Clutch and band application chart for a 4L60 transmission.

an additional planetary unit mounted in front of the Simpson (Figure 32–36). The primary difference between the "L" and the "E" is that the E-model provides converter lock-up in third and fourth gear.

These transmissions use four multiple-disc clutches, two servos and bands, and a one-way clutch to provide for the different ranges of gears. The direct clutch is applied in all gears except overdrive. Its pur-

FIGURE 32–36   Exploded view of a Nissan L4N71B Simpson-based transmission. *Courtesy of Nissan Motors*

pose is to bypass the overdrive planetary gearset and transfer engine torque to the Simpson gearset. The forward or rear clutch is applied in all forward gears. The high/reverse (front) clutch is applied in reverse gear and third and fourth gears. The low/reverse clutch is applied in reverse and in manual low. This clutch serves as a brake and allows for engine braking during manual low operation. All of these clutches except the low/reverse unit are released by several small coil springs. The low/reverse unit utilizes a belleville-type spring for greater clamping pressures.

The bands and the one-way clutch are used as holding members. The second band is applied only in second gear. The overdrive band is applied only when the transmission is operating in fourth gear. The one-way clutch is locked during first gear operation but freewheels and is ineffective during deceleration or coasting. The bands are externally adjustable. Refer to Figure 32–37, the clutch and band application chart, for more details on power flow.

Toyota Motors Transmissions Many different transmissions and transaxles have been used by this manufacturer. One of the most common is the A-140E/A-140L, used in the Camry and Celica models. This transaxle combines a 3-speed transmission with an overdrive assembly. The A140E is used on Camry and Celica models, whereas the A140L is used on the Celica GT-S. The primary differences between the L and E type transaxles are the main valve body, operat-

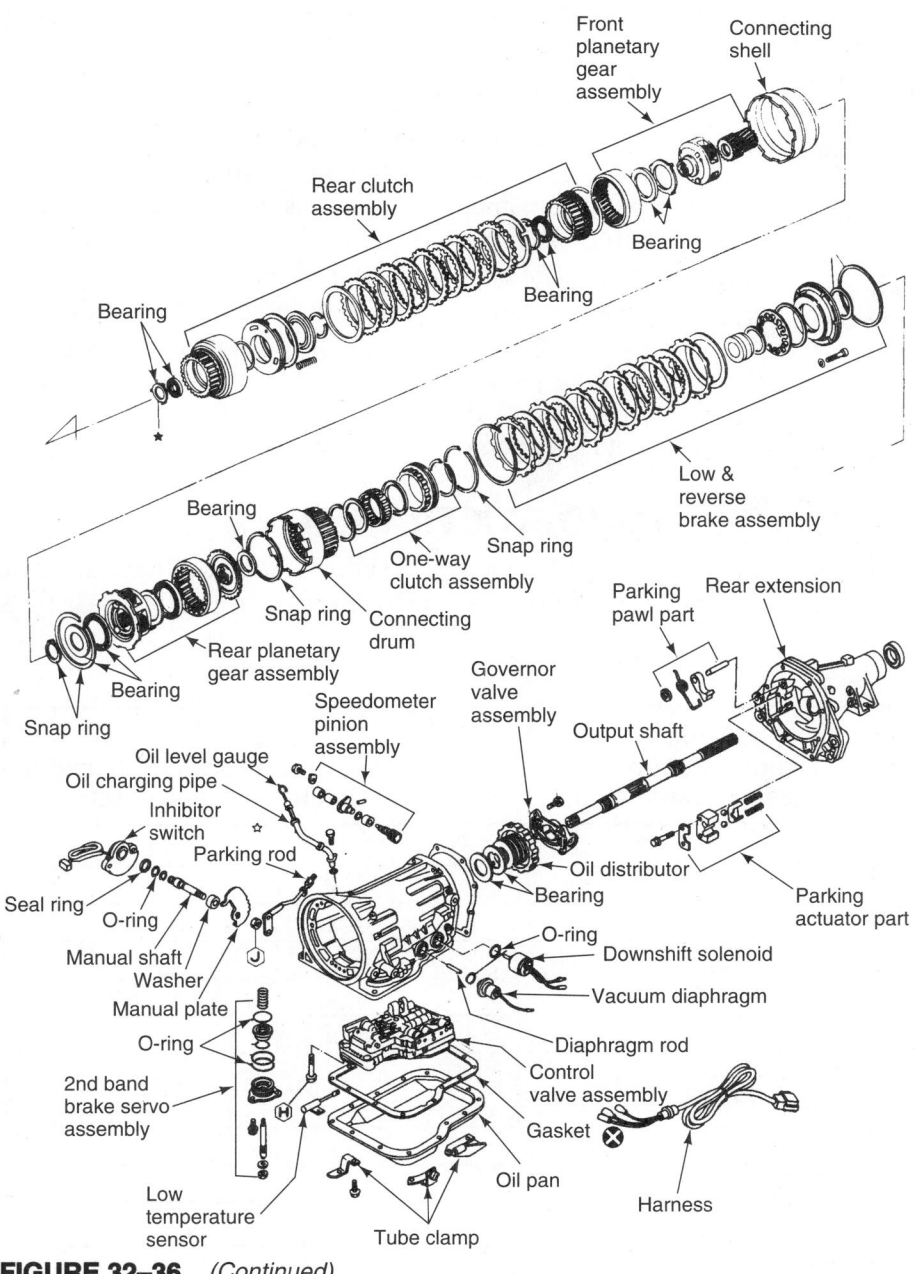

FIGURE 32–36 *(Continued)*

GEAR SELECTOR POSITION	OPERATING GEAR	REAR CLUTCH	ONE-WAY CLUTCH	BAND	FRONT CLUTCH	LOW & REVERSE BAND
D	1st gear	x	x			
	2nd gear	x		x		
	3rd gear	x			x	
2	2nd gear	x		x		
1	1st gear	x	x			x
R	Reverse				x	x

FIGURE 32–37   Clutch and band application chart for a Nissan L4N71B transmission.

ing mechanism, and electronic control. The E is referred to an electronic controlled transaxle (ECT). The ECT is different from the oil pressure control transaxle (A140L) in that it is controlled by a microprocessor located behind the glove box. The A140L uses an electronic overdrive solenoid system.

Although these transaxles are electronically controlled, the basis for operation is a Simpson gear train in line with a single overdrive planetary gearset. The transaxles uses four multiple-disc clutches, two band and servo assemblies, and three one-way clutches to provide the various gear ranges.

Refer to the clutch and band application chart given in Figure 32–38 for details on the power flow through this transmission.

RAVIGNEAUX GEAR TRAIN

The **Ravigneaux gear train**, like the Simpson gear train, provides gear reductions, overdrives, direct drive, and reverse combination. It offers the following advantages:

- Torque loading capacity is increased due to greater tooth contact area.
- It is a very compact unit in comparison to the Simpson gear train.
- It can have the large sun gear, planetary carrier, or ring gear as the output member.

The Ravigneaux gear train uses two sun gears, one small and one large, and two sets of planetary pinion gears, three long pinions and three short pinions. The planetary pinion gears rotate on their own shafts, which are fastened to a common planetary carrier. The small sun gear is meshed with the short planetary pinion gears. These short pinions act as idler gears to drive the long planetary pinion gears. The long planetary pinion gears mesh with the large sun gear and the ring gear. A single ring gear surrounds the complete assembly.

FORD ATX TRANSAXLE

The Ford ATX is a 3-speed automatic transaxle that uses a Ravigneaux planetary gear train. The gear-type

GEAR SELECTOR POSITION	OPERATING GEAR	OD CLUTCH	FORWARD CLUTCH	DIRECT CLUTCH	2ND COAST BAND	2ND COAST DRUM	1ST & REVERSE BRAKE	OD ONE-WAY CLUTCH	#1 ONE-WAY CLUTCH	#2 ONE-WAY CLUTCH
D-Drive	1st gear	x	x					x		x
	2nd gear	x	x			x		x	x	
	3rd gear	x	x	x		x		x		
	Overdrive		x	x		x				
2-Second	1st gear	x	x					x		x
	2nd gear	x	x		x	x		x	x	
	3rd gear	x	x	x		x		x		
L-Low	1st gear	x	x				x	x		x
	2nd gear	x	x		x	x		x	x	
R	Reverse	x		x			x			
N/P	Neutral	x								

FIGURE 32–38   Clutch and band application chart for a Toyota A140 transmission.

GEAR SELECTOR POSITION	OPERATING GEAR	FRONT BAND	TOP-GEAR CLUTCH	2ND GEAR CLUTCH	REVERSE CLUTCH	ONE-WAY CLUTCH
P-Park	None					x
R-Reverse	Reverse		x		x	x
N-Neutral	None					x
D-Drive	1st gear	x				x
	2nd gear	x		x		
	3rd gear		x	x		
2-Man. 2nd	1st gear	x				x
	2nd gear	x		x		
1-Man. 1st	1st gear	x	x			x

FIGURE 32–39 Clutch and band application chart for a Ford ATX transaxle.

oil pump is driven indirectly by the torque converter. Because the oil pump is located at the opposite end of the transaxle, as is the torque converter, a drive shaft is used to rotate the oil pump.

The transaxle has been continuously updated and modified to fit different applications. The most obvious changes made to the transaxle are the torque converter. The ATX has been available with three different designs of torque converters: the conventional three-element converter, a converter with centrifugal lock-up, and a split-torque converter.

The original ATX transaxles were equipped with a **splitter gear** torque converter. This unit contained a planetary gearset that divided the delivery of input torque. Part of the torque is transmitted mechanically and the remainder by fluid force on the torque converter's turbine. In second gear, 62 percent of the torque is transmitted mechanically, while in third gear 93 percent is mechanically transmitted. In low gear and reverse, full engine torque is transmitted by normal converter fluid flow.

The split-torque converter is used in Escort and Lynx ATX transaxles and in the transaxles of 1984-86 Tempo and Topaz models. The ATX used in the Taurus and Sable models used a centrifugally locking torque converter. By 1988, all ATX transaxles used in the Tempo, Topaz, Taurus, and Sable models were equipped with a conventional fluid-linked torque converter.

The small sun gear of the ATX gear train is called the reverse sun gear and is meshed with the short pinion gears. The short pinion gears serve as idler gears between the reverse sun gear and the long pinion gears. The large sun gear is called the forward sun gear and it meshes with the long planetary pinion gears. The short pinion gears are meshed with the long gears and both sets of pinions can rotate on their own shafts held by the carrier. The planetary carrier serves as the output for the gear train. The ring gear surrounds the other members of the planetary gearset. The long pinions are in constant mesh with the short pinions, the forward sun gear, and the ring gear.

The ATX is equipped with three multiple-disc clutches, one band, and a one-way roller clutch. The parking gear is located on the output gear of the final drive assembly.

Refer to the clutch and band application chart given in Figure 32–39 while reading through the power flow of this transaxle.

Power Flow in Neutral When the gear selector is placed into neutral or park, the one-way clutch locks the input from the torque converter's turbine shaft to the sun gear. Since no other clutch or band is applied, power does not flow through the gear train. When the gear selector is in park, the parking gear is locked to the transaxle case by the parking pawl.

Power Flow in First Gear The one-way roller clutch locks and allows the reverse sun gear to be driven by the turbine shaft. The reverse sun gear drives the short pinion gears in a counterclockwise direction. The short pinions, in turn, drive the long pinion gears in a clockwise direction. The long pinions walk around the forward sun gear, which is held stationary by the front brake band and drive the planet carrier and final drive clockwise. The top gear clutch is applied in manual low to provide for engine braking.

Power Flow in Second Gear Engine torque is transmitted through the planet carrier to the applied second gear clutch, which locks the intermediate shaft to the ring gear. The front brake band is also applied and holds the forward sun gear. The turning of the ring gear causes the long pinion gears to rotate clockwise and walk around the forward sun gear. This action drives the planetary carrier and final drive clockwise.

GEAR SELECTOR POSITION	OPERATING GEAR	INTER-MEDIATE CLUTCH	INTER-MEDIATE ONE-WAY CLUTCH	OVER-DRIVE BAND	REVERSE CLUTCH	FORWARD CLUTCH	PLANETARY ONE-WAY	LOW/REVERSE BAND	DIRECT CLUTCH
OD	1st gear					x	x		
	2nd gear	x	x			x			
	3rd gear	x				x			x
	4th gear	x		x		x			x
3	1st gear					x	x		
	2nd gear	x	x			x			
	3rd gear	x				x	x		x
1	1st gear					x		x	
	2nd gear	x	x	x		x			
R	Reverse				x			x	

FIGURE 32–40 Clutch and band application chart for a Ford AOD transmission.

Power Flow in Third Gear When operating in third gear, the second gear clutch of the ATX remains applied and locks the intermediate shaft to the ring gear. The top gear clutch is also applied and locks the reverse sun gear to the turbine shaft. Since the planetary gear train has two inputs, direct drive results. By allowing input on both the reverse sun gear and the ring gear, the long and short pinion gears are trapped between the ring gear and reverse sun gear. The planetary carrier is the output.

Power Flow in reverse While operating in reverse gear, the ATX applies the reverse clutch, which holds the ring gear. The applied top gear clutch and one-way clutch lock the reverse sun gear to the turbine shaft. The clockwise rotation of the sun gear causes the short pinion gears to rotate in a counterclockwise direction. The short pinion gears drive the long pinion gears in a clockwise direction; however, since the ring gear is held, the planetary carrier is forced to rotate in a counterclockwise direction. The carrier drives the final drive and the vehicle moves in reverse.

FORD AOD TRANSMISSION

With the introduction of the AOD transmission, Ford became the first manufacturer to offer an automatic transmission with a built-in overdrive. The AOD is a 4-speed transmission that uses the Ravigneaux gear train.

Another feature of the AOD is the split-torque-type torque converter. This arrangement consists of two input shafts driven by the converter. One of these shafts relays torque into the transmission through the normal hydraulic action of a converter and the other shaft provides a mechanical link from the engine to the gear train when the transmission is operating in third and fourth gears.

The AOD uses the common ring gear as the output member. Two sun gears are used, a small one called the forward sun gear and a larger one called the reverse sun gear. The planetary gearset has two sets of planetary pinion gears, three long and three short ones. The planetary pinion gears are able to rotate on their own shafts while sharing the common planetary carrier.

The AOD uses four multiple-disc clutches, two one-way clutches, and two bands to obtain the various gear ranges. (See Figure 32–40, the clutch and band application chart.) The forward sun gear is driven by the turbine shaft when the forward clutch is applied. The reverse sun gear is driven by the turbine input shaft when the reverse clutch is applied and is held, during overdrive, by the overdrive band. The reverse sun gear also can be held by applying the intermediate clutch in second, third, and fourth gears.

The single planetary carrier assembly can be held by either the low/reverse band or the low one-way clutch. The long pinion gears are in constant mesh with the ring gear, the reverse sun gear, and the short pinion gears. The short pinion gears are in constant mesh with the forward sun gear and the long pinions. The short pinions do not mesh with the ring gear but can drive it through the long pinion gears. The ring gear is splined to a flange on the output shaft and the ring gear is always the output member.

Input Devices The AOD uses a torque converter that splits power flow from the engine. The converter drives two input shafts to provide both a hydraulic and mechanical input into the transmission. A typical input shaft from the converter's turbine hydraulically drives the forward clutch drum. An additional input shaft linked to the converter cover mechanically links the output of the engine to the direct clutch (Figure

Direct
drive
shaft

Front
pump

FIGURE 32–41 Because the AOD is equipped with a split-torque converter, it has an additional input shaft that is attached to the converter cover and passes through the center of the pump. *Courtesy of Ford Motor Company*

32–41). The amount of input from either or both sources varies according to the operating gear. When the transmission is operating in first, second, and reverse gears, 100 percent of the input is delivered hydraulically by the turbine shaft. When operating in third gear, the gear train receives approximately 40 percent of its input from the turbine shaft and 60 percent is delivered through the mechanical linkage. In fourth gear, all of the input to the gear train is through the mechanical linkage.

Regardless of the input into the transmission, the gear train receives power through the application of the forward, direct, or reverse clutches, which serve as the input devices for the gear train.

GENERAL MOTORS' 3L30 TRANSMISSION

The 3L30 (THM 180/180C) is a 3-speed automatic transmission that uses the Ravigneaux compound planetary gearset. Three multiple-disc clutches, referred to as the second, third, and reverse or the intermediate/high, direct, and reverse clutches; one band, and a single one-way (sprag) clutch are used to

provide for the various gear ratios. Each clutch is hydraulically applied and released by several small coil springs when hydraulic pressure is routed away from the bore of the clutch's piston. This General Motors' transmission uses a gear-type oil pump.

The planet carrier is the output member of the gearset. The power flow through the gears is identical to that of the Ford ATX, except the location of the planetaries is reversed. (See Figure 32–42 for clutch and band applications throughout the operating gear ranges.)

PLANETARY GEARSETS IN TANDEM

Rather than relying on the use of a compound gearset, some automatic transmissions use two simple planetary units in series. In this type of arrangement, gearset members are not shared; instead, the holding devices are used to lock different members of the planetary units together. Normally, the front planetary carrier is locked to the rear ring gear and the front ring gear is locked to the rear planetary carrier. Two common transaxles use this planetary gear arrangement, General Motors' 4T60 (THM 440-T4) and the Ford AXOD. Both of these will be covered in detail, although they are both quite similar in design and power flow.

4T60 TRANSAXLE

General Motors' 4T60 was the first domestically produced 4-speed automatic transaxle built for FWD vehicles. Overdrive fourth gear is obtained by using the same planetary units as are used for the first three speeds, instead of adding a planetary unit just for overdrive.

Although the gear train is based on two simple planetary gearsets operating in tandem, the combination of the two planetary units does function much like a compound unit. The two tandem units do not share a common member, rather certain members are locked together or are integral with each other. The

GEAR SELECTOR POSITION	OPERATING GEAR	ONE-WAY CLUTCH	INTERMEDIATE/ HIGH CLUTCH	DIRECT CLUTCH	REVERSE CLUTCH	LOW/ INTERMEDIATE BAND
Drive	1st gear	x				x
	2nd gear		x			x
	3rd gear		x	x		x
2	2nd gear		x			x
Low	1st gear	x		x		x
R	Reverse	x		x	x	

FIGURE 32–42 Clutch and band application chart for a 3L80 transmission.

FIGURE 32–43 Engine torque is delivered to a 4T60 transaxle through a sprocket and drive link assembly. *Courtesy of the Hydra-Matic Division, General Motors Corporation*

front planetary carrier is locked to the rear ring gear and the front ring gear is locked to the rear planetary carrier. The transaxle houses a third planetary unit, which is used only as the final drive unit and not for overdrive.

The 4T60 uses a variable-displacement vane-type oil pump and four multiple-disc clutches, two bands and two one-way clutches, to provide the various gear ranges. One of the one-way clutches is a roller clutch; the other is a sprag. The four multiple-disc clutches are released by several small coil springs when hydraulic pressure is diverted from the clutch's piston.

Input Devices Engine torque is transferred to the transaxle through the torque converter and a sprocket and drive link assembly (Figure 32–43). The torque converter does not directly drive the gear train of the transaxle, rather the converter drives a sprocket that is linked, by a drive chain, to an input sprocket at the gear train. This arrangement allows the gear

train to be positioned away from the centerline of the engine's crankshaft.

Input through the gear train is controlled by the input clutch, input one-way clutch, and second clutch. The input clutch and the input one-way clutch drive the front sun gear.

Refer to the clutch and band application chart, Figure 32–44, while reading through the power flow of this transmission.

Power Flow While operating in first gear, the input is received through the front sun gear, which is locked to and drives the rear ring gear. The 1-2 band is applied and holds the rear sun gear. This forces the rear carrier to be driven by the rear ring gear at a speed reduction and a ratio of 2.92:1 (Figure 32–45).

Input for second gear operation is received by the front planetary carrier when the second clutch is applied. Since the rear ring gear is an integral part of the front planetary carrier, the two rotate at the same

GEAR SELECTOR POSITION	OPERATING GEAR	4TH CLUTCH	REVERSE BAND	2ND CLUTCH	3RD CLUTCH	3RD ROLLER CLUTCH	INPUT CLUTCH	INPUT SPRAG CLUTCH	1-2 BAND
D	1st gear						x	x	x
	2nd gear			x			x		x
	3rd gear			x	x	x			
	Overdrive	x		x	x				
3	3rd gear			x	x	x	x	x	
2	2nd gear			x			x		x
Low	1st gear				x	x	x	x	x
R	Reverse		x				x	x	

FIGURE 32–44 Clutch and band application chart for a 4T60 transaxle.

FIGURE 32–45 Power flow through first gear. *Courtesy of the Hydra-Matic Division, General Motors Corporation*

speed and in the same direction. The rear sun gear is held stationary by the one-way clutch; therefore, the rear planetary carrier rotates around it at a gear reduction ratio of 1.57:1 (Figure 32–46).

Third gear offers direct drive. Input is received by the gear train through the front sun gear by the application of the third clutch. The second clutch is still applied and directs input through the front planetary

Drive Range—
Second Gear

Input
clutch on

Second
clutch on

Input
sprang
overrunning

1–2
band on

Driving (input)

Held

Driven (output)

Reaction gear set

Output to
final drive

Second
clutch
housing

Second
clutch
piston

Apply
ring
and
return
spring

Wave
plate

Second
clutch
plates

Reverse
reaction
drum

Input carrier
and reaction
internal gear

FIGURE 32–46 Power flow through second gear. *Courtesy of the Hydra-Matic Division, General Motors Corporation*

carrier. Since two of the three planetary members are rotating at the same speed, the ring gear is forced to rotate with them. The ring gear drives the rear planetary carrier at the same speed and direct drive results (Figure 32–47).

In fourth gear, the second clutch remains applied and input is received through the front planetary carrier. The fourth clutch is also applied and it holds the front sun gear. This causes the front ring gear to rotate around the carrier at a speed greater than input speed. Since the rear planetary carrier is connected to the front ring gear, the output from the gearsets is an overdrive with a ratio of 0.70:1 (Figure 32–48).

Reverse operation is achieved by holding the front planetary carrier with the reverse band. With the carrier held, the input on the front sun gear causes the front ring gear to rotate in the opposite direction. Because the front ring gear is locked to the rear

carrier, the output of this gear combination is in the opposite direction as the input and at a ratio of 2.38:1 (Figure 32–49).

AXOD TRANSAXLE

The AXOD 4-speed transaxle relies on two simple planetary units that operate in tandem. The planetary carriers of each planetary unit are locked to the other planetary unit's ring gear. Each planetary set has its own sun gear and set of planetary pinion gears. There are no transmissions used by Ford that have any similarity to the AXOD, rather the similarity lies with the construction and operation of the THM 4T60.

The AXOD combines an automatic transmission and differential into a single unit designed for FWD vehicles. The transmission is a fully automatic unit with four forward speeds, one reverse, neutral, and park. The AXOD uses four multiple-disc clutches,

Drive range third gear

| Second clutch on | Third clutch on |
| | Third roller clutch holding |

Driving

Holding sun gear from turning faster

Driven at turbine speed

Third roller clutch

Driven (output)

Input gear set

Driving (input)

Output to final drive

Third clutch housing

Third clutch piston

Return spring assembly

Third clutch plates

Third roller clutch cam

Third roller clutch

Third roller clutch race

Input sun gear

FIGURE 32–47 Power flow through third gear. *Courtesy of the Hydra-Matic Division, General Motors Corporation*

two band assemblies, and two one-way clutches to control the operation of the planetary gearset. Output from the planetary units is through the rear planetary carrier and front ring gear.

All of the multiple-disc clutches are hydraulically applied and released by several small coil springs when hydraulic pressure is diverted from the clutch's piston. For more insight on the operation of the AXOD, refer to the clutch and band application chart (Figure 32–50).

Input Devices Like the 4T60, the AXOD torque converter does not directly drive the gear train of the transaxle. The converter drives a sprocket, which is connected by a chain to a sprocket on the input shaft of the gear train.

Input to the gear train is received by the front sun gear, the front planetary carrier, or rear ring gear. The forward clutch, low one-way clutch, direct one-way clutch, and intermediate clutch serve as the input devices.

HONDA'S NONPLANETARY BASED TRANSAXLE

The Honda CA, F4, and G4 transaxles are used in many Honda and Acura cars. These transmissions are rather unique in that they do not use a planetary gearset to provide for the different gear ranges. Constant-mesh helical and square-cut gears (Figure 32–51, page 844) are used in a manner similar to that of a manual transmission.

These transaxles have a main shaft and counter shaft on which the gears ride. To provide the four forward and one reverse gear, different pairs of gears are locked to the shafts by hydraulically controlled clutches (Figure 32–52, page 845). Reverse gear is obtained through the use of a shift fork, which slides

FIGURE 32–48 Power flow through fourth gear. *Courtesy of the Hydra-Matic Division, General Motors Corporation*

the reverse gear into position. The power flow through these transaxles is also similar to that of a manual transaxle.

Four multiple-disc clutches, the sliding reverse gear, and a one-way clutch are used to control the gears. These are designated by the gear they activate: first gear clutch, first gear one-way clutch, second gear clutch, third gear clutch, fourth gear clutch, and reverse gear. Refer to the clutch and band application chart (Figure 32–53, page 845) for details on the power flow through this transaxle.

HYDRAULIC SYSTEM

A hydraulic system uses a liquid to perform work. In an automatic transmission, this liquid is automatic transmission fluid (**ATF**). Automatic transmission fluid is one of the most complex fluids produced by the petroleum industry for the automobile.

ATF performs several jobs. It transmits engine torque as in the torque converter, controls valve body operation, and operates planetary controls such as in multiple-disc clutches, band and servo mechanisms. It also lubricates shaft bushings, thrust washers and bearings, and planetary gear train assemblies. ATF smoothly develops the action between the automatic transmission fluid and multiple-disc clutch friction discs and clutch plates, as well as between rotating drums and stationary bands. It acts as a cooling agent and transfers heat at the transmission cooler assembly while trying to operate the automatic transmission within the desired temperature range. Finally, ATF interacts with all the existing chemicals found in the automatic transmission and those developed as a result of operating extremes.

Hydraulic Principles

An automatic transmission uses ATF fluid pressure to control the action of the planetary gearsets. This fluid pressure is regulated and directed to change gears automatically through the use of various pressure regulators and control valves.

Reverse

Input clutch on

Reverse band on

Input sprag holding

Driving (input)

Held

Driven (output)

Input gear set

Drive sprocket

Converter

Turbine shaft

Link assembly

Held

Driven sprocket

Second clutch housing

Reverse band

Input housing and shaft

Input clutch plates

Input sprag

Input sun gear

Reverse reaction drum

Held

Input carrier

Input internal gear

Final drive shaft

FIGURE 32–49 Power flow through reverse gear. *Courtesy of the Hydra-Matic Division, General Motors Corporation*

GEAR SELECTOR POSITION	OPERATING GEAR	LOW/ INTERMEDIATE BAND	OVERDRIVE BAND	FORWARD CLUTCH	INTER- MEDIATE CLUTCH	DIRECT CLUTCH	REVERSE CLUTCH	LOW ONE-WAY CLUTCH	DIRECT ONE-WAY CLUTCH
OD	1st gear	x		x				x	
	2nd gear	x		x	x				
	3rd gear			x	x	x			x
	Overdrive		x		x	x			x
D	1st gear	x		x				x	
	2nd gear	x		x	x			x	
	3rd gear			x	x	x			
Low	1st gear			x		x		x	x
R	Reverse			x			x	x	

FIGURE 32–50 Clutch and band application chart for a Ford AXOD transaxle.

① **2ND GEAR COLLAR**
② **THRUST NEEDLE BEARING**
③ **SECONDARY SHAFT 2ND GEAR**
④ **NEEDLE BEARINGS**
⑤ **THRUST NEEDLE BEARING**
⑥ **2ND GEAR COLLAR**
⑦ **1ST/2ND CLUTCH ASSEMBLY**
⑧ **O-RINGS** Replace.
⑨ **SECONDARY SHAFT**
⑩ **SEAL RINGS**
⑪ **THRUST NEEDLE BEARING**
⑫ **NEEDLE BEARING**
⑬ **SECONDARY SHAFT 1ST GEAR**
⑭ **DISTANCE COLLAR 5 mm**
⑮ **COTTAR 29 mm**
⑯ **COTTAR RETAINER**
⑰ **CIRCLIP**
⑱ **LOCK WASHER** Replace.
⑲ **REVERSE SHIFT FORK**
⑳ **COUNTERSHAFT REVERSE GEAR**
㉑ **NEEDLE BEARING**
㉒ **COUNTERSHAFT REVERSE GEAR COLLAR**
㉓ **REVERSE SELECTOR HUB**
㉔ **REVERSE SELECTOR**
㉕ **COUNTERSHAFT 4TH GEAR**
㉖ **NEEDLE BEARING**

㉗ **4TH GEAR COLLAR**
㉘ **DISTANCE COLLAR 46 mm**
㉙ **COUNTERSHAFT 3RD GEAR**
㉚ **THRUST NEEDLE BEARING**
㉛ **ONE-WAY CLUTCH**
㉜ **COUNTERSHAFT 1ST GEAR**
㉝ **NEEDLE BEARING**
㉞ **THRUST WASHER**
㉟ **1ST GEAR COLLAR**
㊱ **1ST HOLD CLUTCH ASSEMBLY**
㊲ **O-RINGS** Replace.
㊳ **COUNTERSHAFT**
㊴ **SNAP RING**
㊵ **COLLAR**
㊶ **THRUST NEEDLE BEARING**
㊷ **COUNTERSHAFT 4TH/REVERSE GEAR**
㊸ **NEEDLE BEARINGS**
㊹ **THRUST NEEDLE BEARING**
㊺ **4TH GEAR COLLAR**
㊻ **3RD/4TH CLUTCH ASSEMBLY**
㊼ **3RD GEAR COLLAR**
㊽ **THRUST NEEDLE BEARING**
㊾ **NEEDLE BEARING**
㊿ **MAINSHAFT 3RD GEAR**

�51 **THRUST NEEDLE BEARING**
�52 **O-RINGS** Replace.
�53 **MAINSHAFT**
�54 **SEAL RINGS 31 mm**
�55 **SEAL RING 25 mm**
�56 **NEEDLE BEARING**
�57 **SET RING 23 mm**
�58 **REVERSE IDLER SHAFT HOLDER**
�59 **STEEL BALL**
�60 **SPRING**
�64 **NEEDLE BEARING**
�65 **DIFFERENTIAL OIL SEAL** Replace.
�66 **THRUST SHIM**
�67 **BEARING OUTER RACE**
�68 **CIRCLIPS**
�69 **TRANSMISSION HOUSING BALL BEARINGS**
㊀ **COUNTERSHAFT 2ND GEAR**
�71 **REVERSE IDLER GEAR**
�72 **DIFFERENTIAL ASSEMBLY**
�73 **BEARING OUTER RACE**
�74 **DIFFERENTIAL OIL SEAL** Replace.
㊋ **TORQUE CONVERTER HOUSING**

FIGURE 32–51 Exploded view of Honda's automatic transaxle which uses constant-mesh helical gears instead of planetary gearsets. *Courtesy of American Honda Motor Company, Inc.*

FIGURE 32–52 Arrangement of gears and reaction devices in a typical Honda transaxle. *Courtesy of American Honda Motor Company, Inc.*

GEAR SELECTOR POSITION	OPERATING GEAR	1ST CLUTCH	1ST ONE-WAY CLUTCH	2ND CLUTCH	3RD CLUTCH	4TH CLUTCH	REVERSE GEAR
D4	1st gear	x	x				
	2nd gear	x		x			
	3rd gear	x			x		
	4th gear	x				x	
D3	1st gear	x	x				
	2nd gear	x		x			
	3rd gear	x			x		
2	2nd gear	·		x			
R	Reverse					x	x

FIGURE 32–53 Clutch and band application chart for a Honda CA/F4/G4 transaxle.

More than 300 years ago, a French scientist named Blaise Pascal discovered the basic principles that pertain to all hydraulic systems. His work resulted in **Pascal's law**. It states, "Pressure exerted on a confined liquid or fluid is transmitted undiminished and equally in all directions and acts with equal force on all areas."

Figure 32–54 shows two cylinders that differ in size. In cylinder A the piston has an area of 1 square inch. The area of the piston in cylinder B is 10 square inches. The piston in cylinder A is being moved by 1 pound. A pressure of 1 pound is exerted on every square inch of the piston in cylinder B. The area of piston B is 10 square inches. Total pressure exerted on piston B is 10 × 10 pounds per square inch.

This example shows how fluids can be used to increase work force. Fluids work well in increasing force because they are perfect conductors of pressure. Fluids cannot be compressed. Therefore, when a piston in a cylinder moves ahead and displaces fluid, that fluid is distributed equally on the load piston's surface.

Hydraulics are used to engage planetary gear controls. A typical hydraulic application is the servo

FIGURE 32–54 Hydraulics can be used to increase work force. *Courtesy of Chrysler Corporation*

FORCE = $\pi r^2 \times psi$
= $3.14 \times 3 \times 3 \times 70$
= 1979 POUNDS

FIGURE 32–56 Using hydraulics to increase work in a multiple-disc clutch. *Courtesy of Chrysler Corporation*

assembly (Figure 32–55). The fluid pressure in the servo is 70 psi. The output force exerted by the servo is 880 pounds. Remember this servo output force is further multiplied by the servo mechanical linkage and the natural self-energizing action of the band to stop and hold a planetary member from rotating.

A multiple-disc clutch assembly also makes use of increasing force by using hydraulics (Figure 32–56). If the fluid pressure in the automatic transmission is 70 psi, the force applying the clutch pack is 1979 pounds.

If the clutch assembly is designed with a belleville spring having a mechanical advantage of 1.25:1, the clutch engagement force would change. The new engagement force would be $1.25 \times 1{,}979 = 2{,}747$ pounds, engaging the clutch pack.

To form a complete, working hydraulic system, the following elements are needed: fluid reservoir, pressure source, control valving, and output devices.

The automatic transmission reservoir is the transmission oil pan. Transmission fluid is drawn from the pan and returned to it. The pressure source in the system is the oil pump. The valve control body contains control valving to regulate or restrict the pressure and flow of fluid within the transmission. Output devices are the servos or clutches operated by hydraulic pressure.

PUMPS

The transmission pump is driven by the torque converter shell at engine speed. The purpose of the pump is to create fluid flow and pressure in the system. Pump pressure is a variable pressure, depending on engine speed from idle to full throttle. At some speeds, pump pressure exceeds transmission requirements and must be controlled by the pressure regulator valve.

Three types of oil pumps are installed in automatic transmissions: the gear, rotor, and vane. The **gear-type pump** is the most commonly used (Figure 32–57).

Many people misunderstand the concept of how pumps move liquids. It is often thought that the action of a pump sucks liquid in, but this is not true. What actually happens during pump operation is that the liquid moves from an area of high pressure (atmospheric pressure) to an area of low pressure (below atmospheric pressure).

The spinning pump generates a low pressure area at its inlet chamber. A vent in the transmission admits atmospheric pressure to the transmission oil pan or sump. This higher atmospheric pressure act-

FORCE = $\pi r^2 \times psi$
= $3.14 \times 2 \times 2 \times 70 = 880$ POUNDS

FIGURE 32–55 Calculating the output force developed by a servo assembly. *Courtesy of Chrysler Corporation*

FIGURE 32–57 Operation of a gear-type pump.

ing on the transmission fluid in the oil pan forces the fluid into the low pressure area of the pump at its inlet chamber. The fluid is picked up by the pump gears, which move it to the pump's outlet chamber. Here the fluid is squeezed out of the pump.

VALVE BODY

The **valve body** can be best understood as the control center of an automatic transmission (Figure 32–58). The purpose of the valve body is to sense the load on

DETENT BALL AND SPRING

MANUAL LEVER ASSEMBLY

WASHER

E-CLIP

SEAL

THROTTLE LEVER ASSEMBLY

SWITCH VALVE

SWITCH VALVE SPRING

LINE PRESSURE REGULATOR SPRING

LINE PRESSURE REGULATOR VALVE

THROTTLE VALVE

THROTTLE VALVE SPRING

KICKDOWN VALVE

MANUAL VALVE

KICKDOWN DETENT

LINE PRESSURE ADJUSTING SCREW ASSEMBLY

THROTTLE PRESSURE ADJUSTING SCREW

SPRING RETAINER AND ADJUSTING SCREW BRACKET

FIGURE 32–58 Typical valve body assembly. *Courtesy of Chrysler Corporation*

FIGURE 32–59 Worm tracks are the fluid passages in the valve body. *Courtesy of Chrysler Corporation*

the vehicle's engine and drivetrain and the operator's driving requirements.

The valve body is machined from aluminum or iron castings. Many precisely machined holes are located in the valve body to accommodate the various valves.

The valve body is made of two or three main parts. Valve bodies and related parts are bolted together and the bolts set to specifications with a torque wrench.

Some valve bodies are bolted directly to the transmission housing so the valve body becomes a part of the housing assembly. Internally, the valve body has many fluid passages called **worm tracks** (Figure 32–59).

VALVES

The purpose of a valve is to start, stop, or direct and regulate fluid flow. Generally in most valve bodies, three types of valves are used: check ball, poppet, and, most commonly, the spool.

Check Ball Valve

The **check ball valve** is a ball that operates on a seat located on the valve body. The check ball operates by having a fluid pressure or manually operated linkage force it against the ball seat to block fluid flow (Figure 32–60). Pressure on the opposite side unseats the check ball. Check balls and poppet valves can be designed to be normally open, which allows free flow of fluid pressure, or normally closed, which blocks fluid pressure flow.

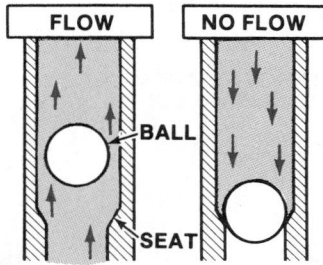

FIGURE 32–60 Operation of a check ball valve. *Courtesy of Chrysler Corporation*

FIGURE 32–61 Check ball valve operating with two seats. *Courtesy of Chrysler Corporation*

Check balls can be seated while directing fluid flow. Other applications of the check ball have two seats to check and direct fluid flow from two directions, being seated and unseated by pressures from either source shown in Figure 32–61.

Pressure Relief Valve Check ball valves can be used as **pressure relief valves** to relieve excessive fluid pressure. The check ball is held against its seat by spring tension that is stronger than the fluid pressure. When the fluid pressure overcomes the spring tension, the check ball is forced off its seat, which relieves excess pressure. As soon as the opposing fluid pressure is relieved, the spring tension forces the check ball back onto its seat.

Poppet Valve

A **poppet valve** (Figure 32–62) can be a ball or a flat disc. In either case the poppet valve acts to achieve its purpose, which is to block fluid flow. Often the poppet valve has a stem to guide the valve's operation. The stem normally fits into a hole acting as a guide to the valve's opening and closing. Poppet valves tend to pop open and close, hence their name.

Poppet valves close against a valve seat. In some applications fluid pressure holds the valve closed or seated. When the stem of the poppet valve is pushed, the valve pops open, permitting fluid flow. When the opening force on the stem is released, the poppet valve closes, blocking fluid flow.

FIGURE 32–62 Typical poppet valve operation. *Courtesy of Chrysler Corporation*

FIGURE 32–63 Components of a spool valve assembly. *Courtesy of Chrysler Corporation*

FIGURE 32–64 Forces acting on the reaction area of the spool valve can be mechanical linkage, spring tension, or fluid pressure. *Courtesy of Chrysler Corporation*

Spool Valve

The most frequently used valve in the valve body is the **spool valve**. A spool valve (Figure 32–63) looks similar to a sewing thread spool. The large circular parts of the valve are called the spools. There are a minimum of two spools per valve. Each spool of the assembly is connected by a stem. The stem is not a precisely machined part of the valve. Adjoining spools and the valve stem form a space called the valley. Valleys form a fluid pressure chamber between the spools and valve body bore. Fluid flow can be directed into other passages depending on the spool valve and valve body design.

Precisely machined around the periphery of each valve spool is the valve land. The land is the part of the spool valve assembly that rides on a very thin film of fluid in the valve body bore. The land must be treated very carefully because any damage, even a small score or scratch, can impair smooth valve operation. As the spool valve moves, the land covers (closes) or uncovers (opens) ports in the valve body.

The vertical part of each spool valve forms an area called the reaction area. Forces acting against the reaction area to move the spool valve (Figure 32–64) include spring tension, fluid pressure, or mechanical linkage.

All valve bodies are designed with ports to support spool valve operation. Each spool valve has a fluid inlet port. Aligning with the spool valve's valley, but not necessarily in direct alignment with the inlet port, is the outlet port. If fluid pressure builds excessively, the spool valve moves to open the exhaust port that protects the system's parts. Each spool valve area has a vent to prevent buildup of fluid between the valve assembly and valve body. Since fluids are incompressible, fluid buildup would hinder valve travel.

PRESSURE REGULATOR VALVE

When a spool valve cycles back and forth between the open and the exhaust positions, it is called a regulating valve. An automatic transmission uses a positive displacement oil pump. As the pump delivers, fluid pressure rises uncontrollably until the pump stalls from extremely high pressure. This condition is aggravated by high engine speeds that drive the pump faster to deliver more fluid. To prevent this stalling, the pump has a pressure regulator valve located in the valve body that maintains a basic fluid pressure. A simple pressure regulation circuit is illustrated in Figure 32–65. Fluid pressure flows from the pump to the pressure regulator valve, which is held in position by coil spring tension. Pressure regulator valve movement to the exhaust position is controlled by calibrated coil spring tension.

The three steps of pressure regulation operation are charging the torque converter, exhausting fluid pressure, and establishing a balanced condition.

When fluid pressure reaches normal baseline pressure (usually about 60 psi), fluid enters at the top of the regulator valve, forcing it down against coil spring tension. The outlet port opens, which permits fluid flow to charge (fill) the torque converter. The torque converter pressure regulator valve is usually a spring-loaded spool type. Torque converter pressure is developed from line pressure at the pressure regulator valve. The torque converter pressure regulator valve has several spools and lands so when different oil pressures are applied, converter pressure varies in proportion to torque requirements. Converter pressure transmits torque and keeps transmission fluid

FIGURE 32–65 Basic pressure regulator circuit. *Courtesy of Ford Motor Company*

circulating into and out of the torque converter, which reduces the formation of air bubbles and aids cooling. The exception to this is when the torque converter is operating in the lockup mode.

In the second stage, the pressure regulator valve is forced down against spring tension by fluid pressure to uncover the exhaust port. Fluid pressure not needed for transmission operation is exhausted into the pump inlet circuit.

With fluid pressure acting at one end and coil spring tension at the opposite end, the pressure regulator valve takes a balanced position. While the coil spring tension controls pressure, the valve adjusts itself automatically to the pressure, which forces it downward. The pressure regulator valve's new position might have one of the spool's lands partially covering the inlet port.

Increasing Pressure

There are times in the automatic transmission's operation when fluid pressure must be increased above its baseline pressure. This increase is needed to hold bands and clutches more tightly and to raise the point at which shifting takes place. Increasing pressure above normal line pressures allows operational load flexibility, such as when towing trailers.

There are two methods used to monitor vehicle and engine load: vacuum modulation and throttle pressure. A **vacuum modulator** measures fluctuating engine vacuum to sense the load placed on the engine and drivetrain. The modulator is normally a small canister that is threaded or push-fit into the transmission housing. A rubber tube connects the canister to the intake manifold of the engine. The canister itself has two chambers divided by a diaphragm (Figure 32–66). The chamber closest to the transmission housing is open to atmospheric pressure, and the second chamber is closed to atmospheric pressure. The closed chamber contains a coil spring trapped between the diaphragm and the end of the canister. The open chamber holds a pushrod connecting the diaphragm to the modulator valve.

Vacuum Modulator Operation

When a vehicle is placed under a heavy load, the driver opens the throttle. This reduces vacuum in the intake manifold and the closed chamber or the vacuum modulator. With reduced vacuum, the coil spring tension releases to move the diaphragm, pushrod, and modulator valve. The modulator valve opens, allowing line pressure to flow through the modulator valve to the booster valve at the pressure regulator valve. The modulator pressure acting on the booster valve assists the pressure regulator valve coil spring in pushing the regulator valve up against the line pressure at the top of the pressure regulator valve. Line pressure continues to increase until the pressure on the regulator valve overcomes the pressure regulator valve spring tension and modulator (auxiliary) pressure. The pressure regulator valve opens the

FIGURE 32–66 A vacuum modulator is a small canister divided into two separate chambers by a diaphragm. *Courtesy of Ford Motor Company*

FIGURE 32–67 Throttle pedal movement is connected to the fuel injection or carburetor bell crank. Bell crank movement is then transferred to the transmission throttle lever by a second throttle cable. *Courtesy of the Hydra-Matic Division, General Motors Corporation*

exhaust port at a new boosted line pressure. This new pressure holds planetary controls tightly to resist slippage and raise automatic shift points.

Throttle Pressure

Vacuum modulators are found on older vehicles. Newer vehicles use throttle valve pressure to increase line pressure. **Throttle valve** pressure develops when line pressure passes through the throttle valve valley to become throttle pressure. Throttle pedal movement is carried through the throttle linkage to control the operation of the throttle valve (Figure 32–67).

When the pedal is depressed (opened), the throttle valve opens to produce throttle pressure, which is directed to the pressure regulator throttle plug (Figure 32–68). It helps the pressure regulator valve spring hold the pressure regulator valve in position to close the exhaust port. This results in increased pressure.

When the pedal is released (closed), the throttle valve partially closes. This decreases throttle pressure at the throttle valve plug, resulting in a reduction of line pressure.

Relay Valve

The direction of line pressure flow is directed by a relay valve. A **relay valve** is a spool-type valve with

FIGURE 32–68 Throttle pressure directed to the pressure regulator throttle plug helps the coil spring close the exhaust valve. *Courtesy of the Hydra-Matic Division, General Motors Corporation*

several spools, lands, and reaction areas. It is held in one position in the valve body bore by coil spring tension, auxiliary fluid pressure, or a mechanical force. Auxiliary fluid pressure or mechanical force can oppose coil spring tension to move the relay valve to a new position. In the new position, the valley of the relay valve aligns with interconnecting ports. Fluid pressure flows from an inlet port across the relay valve valley to the outlet port. When a relay valve is in one position, it blocks fluid flow. When moved to an alternative position, fluid is directed through to the outlet port.

Shift Valve One application of the relay valve is a **shift valve**. A shift valve usually operates in one of two positions—either downshifted or upshifted. In operation, throttle pressure, which is high, is acting on one reaction area of a shift valve (Figure 32–69). Throttle pressure and light coil spring tension act and hold the valve in the downshifted position. In this position, fluid pressure is blocked from flowing to one of the planetary gear controls.

As vehicle speed increases, a device on the transmission output shaft, called the governor, develops a pressure, called governor pressure. Governor pressure is directed to the opposite reaction area of the shift valve. With increasing vehicle speed, governor pressure increases to overcome coil spring tension and throttle pressure. Governor pressure moves the shift valve to the upshifted position. In this position (Figure 32–70) the inlet and outlet ports are in the same valley area of the shift valve. Fluid pressure flows across the shift valve valley, out of the outlet port, and through the connecting worm tracks to engage the planetary controls for the next higher gear.

If the vehicle operator pushes down on the throttle pedal, the throttle valve opens wider and throttle pressure increases. Throttle pressure is higher than governor pressure. The high throttle pressure and coil spring tension force the shift valve to move to

FIGURE 32–70 Governor pressure moves the shift valve to an upshift position. *Courtesy of Chrysler Corporation*

the downshifted position against governor pressure. The transmission automatically downshifts to the next lower gear. The shift valve blocks fluid pressure at the inlet port, which prevents the planetary controls from operating for an upshift. The automatic downshifting of the transmission is often referred to as a passing gear or **kickdown**. A kickdown valve (Figure 32–71) is often used to generate additional kickdown pressure from line pressure. This ensures that the downshift is made quickly and positively.

Manual Valve

The **manual valve** is a spool valve operated manually by the vehicle operator and gear selector linkage. When the operator selects the gear position, the gear selector linkage positions the manual valve in the valve body. The manual valve directs line pressure to the correct combination of circuits, which produces the range desired for the driver's requirements (Figure 32–72). For example, if the drive range is

FIGURE 32–71 A kickdown valve is used to assist the throttle valve in making fast, smooth downshifts at WOT. *Courtesy of Chrysler Corporation*

FIGURE 32–69 A shift valve is a relay valve. Throttle pressure and coil spring tension hold the shift valve in the downshift position. *Courtesy of Chrysler Corporation*

FIGURE 32–72 The manual valve is operated by the gear selector linkage to direct line pressure to the required circuits needed to produce the selected gear or range of gears. In this case there are four manual outlets. *Courtesy of Chrysler Corporation*

selected, the gear selector linkage is placed in a position that allows fluid pressure at the inlet port to flow across the manual valve valley passing through the outlet port to charge the forward circuit. Control areas of the forward circuit are the governor, rear clutch, and accumulator. The various transmission controls and circuitry that drive the vehicle forward make up the forward circuit. If the gear selector is moved to the reverse position, the manual valve is moved to open the reverse inlet and outlet ports to charge the rear servo and front clutch and move the vehicle in reverse.

GOVERNOR ASSEMBLY

The **governor** assembly is a very important part of the transmission control system (Figure 32–73). The purpose of the governor assembly is to sense vehicle road speed and send a fluid pressure signal to the transmission valve body to either upshift or permit the transmission to downshift. The governor assembly is located on the transmission output shaft and is influenced by increases and decreases in output shaft speed. When output shaft speed decreases, governor pressure decreases. Governor pressure decreases to a point less than throttle pressure and coil spring tension. As a result, high throttle pressure and coil spring tension force the shift valve to the downshifted position. Fluid inlet passages are now blocked by the 1-2 shift valve land, which stops fluid flow from stroking the 2-3 shift valve and preventing the engagement of the upshift planetary controls. The 1-2 shift valve remains in the downshifted position. With the transmission shift valve in this position, the transmission pulls away from a stop in first gear. As vehicle speed increases, the transmission output shaft speed increases, resulting in more governor pressure to automatically upshift the transmission.

SHOP TALK

There are two simple rules to remember regarding throttle and governor pressures. First, throttle pressure delays the transmission upshift and forces the downshift. Secondly, governor pressure upshifts the transmission and permits the downshift. ■

HYDRAULIC CIRCUITS

To provide a practical review of the valve body's operation, the following sections examine the 3-speed transaxle with computer-controlled lockup torque converter that is installed in Chrysler front-wheel-drive vehicles. This transaxle and valve body are not highly sophisticated, but it is a good example of general, fundamental valve body operation and the control of various fluid pressures. The hydraulic circuits for each gear selector position is explained using flow charts, accompanied by the torque converter's lockup clutch controls and operation along with schematic diagrams of transaxle power flows. The flow charts and transaxle diagrams bring together the hydraulic controls and mechanical operation, that combined, give transaxle operation.

Preceding the explanation for each flow chart, note the gear range, torque converter mode, planetary controls engaged, approximate vehicle speed, and throttle position. Be sure to read the flow indica-

FIGURE 32–73 Typical governor assembly. *Courtesy of Chrysler Corporation*

FIGURE 32–74 Fluid flows in the neutral gear range. *Courtesy of Chrysler Corporation*

tion and pressure chart to establish the parameters for valve body and transaxle operation.

Gear Range: Neutral and Park
Gear Selector Position: N and P
Throttle Position: 0 to 10 psi (Approximately closed)

Pump pressure leaves the transmission pump and is directed to the pressure regulator valve and manual valve (Figure 32–74). At the pressure regulator valve, pump pressure is regulated to become line pressure. Line pressure enters the pressure regulator valve and leaves as converter pressure, flowing to the switch valve. The switch valve allows line pressure to enter the torque converter. Converter pressure circulates from the switch valve to fill the torque converter and returns to the switch valve to become cooling and lubrication pressure.

From the pressure regulator valve, line pressure flows to the manual valve. From the manual valve, line pressure seats #9 check ball and flows around #8 check ball to stop at the land of the closed throttle valve. Throttle pressure is low because the throttle valve is not open. Line pressure flows to the accumulator to cushion the engagement of the planetary controls when the gear selector is moved to D or R ranges. The accumulator is basically a hydraulic shock absorber designed to absorb the shock of engaging planetary controls.

In neutral, line pressure is established by the pressure regulator valve and flows to the manual valve and throttle valve.

Gear Range: D First Gear
Selector Position: D
Torque Converter Mode: Unlock
Planetary Controls Engaged: Rear Clutch; Overrunning Clutch
Approximate Speed: 8 mph
Throttle Position: Half Throttle

In Figure 32–75, pressure between the manual valve and pressure regulator valve is considered to be line pressure. This line pressure circulates to the switch valve. Since the switch valve is held in the torque converter unlocked position line pressure flows no further.

LINE PRESSURE Beginning at the first manual valve outlet #1, line pressure seats #9 check ball flows past #8 check ball to enter the throttle valve and establish throttle pressure. Line pressure also flows to the pressure regulator valve to regulate pressure. Line pressure strokes the accumulator piston against coil spring tension, cushioning the engagement of the rear clutch.

At outlet port #2 of the manual valve, line pressure charges (fills) the worm track, which engages the rear clutch and flows to the governor assembly. When the rear clutch is engaged and the governor assembly is filled with line pressure, the forward circuit is ready to drive the vehicle forward.

THROTTLE PRESSURE As line pressure passes through the valley of the throttle valve, it becomes throttle pressure. Throttle pressure circulates around the kickdown valve valley. With throttle pressure at

FIGURE 32–75 In drive range first gear, the rear clutch and overrunning clutch are engaged. *Courtesy of Chrysler Corporation*

the kickdown valve, a very quick downshift response to full-throttle operation is provided. Throttle pressure is directed to the pressure regulator throttle plug. It acts on the throttle plug, compressing the throttle plug spring. The result is that the pressure regulator valve closes the exhaust port, which results in a line pressure (boost) increase.

Throttle pressure moves to act on the spring end of the 1-2 shift valve. The throttle pressure and coil spring tension work together to hold the shift valve and governor plug in the downshifted position against governor pressure. Throttle pressure passes #5 check ball, which is acting on the spring end of the 2-3 shift valve. From the 2-3 shift valve, throttle pressure flows to hold the shuttle valve throttle plug against its stop in the valve body.

GOVERNOR PRESSURE Governor pressure developed from line pressure leaves the governor assembly terminating at the shuttle valve spool land.

Governor pressure also acts on the 2-3 and 1-2 shift valve governor plugs. Because the vehicle is traveling at 8 mph, governor pressure is not strong enough to overcome throttle pressure and spring tension at the opposite end of the shift valves. Therefore, the transmission stays downshifted in drive range first gear.

CONVERTER PRESSURE From the pressure regulator valve, converter pressure is directed to the converter pressure control valve. From the converter pressure control valve, converter pressure flows through the switch valve valley and enters the torque converter turbine shaft to keep the lockup piston disengaged. Converter pressure entering between the impeller and turbine fills the torque converter. Converter pressure flows back to the switch valve and enters the cooler to become cooler pressure. When cooler pressure returns to the transmission, it cools and lubricates transmission parts.

Drive Range: D Second Gear

Gear Selector Position: D

Torque Converter Mode: Unlock

Planetary Controls Engaged: Rear Clutch; Front Kickdown Band

Approximate Vehicle Speed: 15 mph

Throttle Position: Half Throttle

Line pressure leaving the area between the pressure regulator valve and manual valve develops throttle pressure and torque converter control pressure.

Referring to the manual valve (Figure 32–76), line pressure leaves the #1 outlet port, seating #9 check ball. Line pressure passing #8 check ball moves to the throttle valve to become throttle valve pressure. From the #1 outlet, line pressure also flows to the pressure regulator valve, regulating line pressure. Line pressure from the same circuit flows to the accumulator, opposing line pressure and spring tension. The accumulator cushions the engagement of the intermediate band.

From the #2 manual valve outlet, fluid moves to the upshifted 1-2 shift valve. Line pressure flows to engage the rear clutch, then around the #7 check ball, through the governor screen to the governor assembly.

From the 1-2 shift valve, line pressure circulates to the shuttle valve and bypass valve through the restriction, or around the #6 check ball to operate the front servo. When the front servo piston strokes in the cylinder, the front kickdown band engages around the front clutch drum.

FIGURE 32–76 In drive range second gear, the rear clutch and front kickdown band are applied. *Courtesy of Chrysler Corporation*

THROTTLE PRESSURE The throttle pedal is in the half-open position, developing throttle pressure, which is directed to the kickdown valve. Throttle pressure is also directed to the throttle plug of the pressure regulator valve. Throttle pressure moving the throttle plug forces it against the throttle plug spring tension. The action of the throttle plug removes some of the opposition to the pressure regulator valve spring, resulting in a boost in line pressure. Throttle pressure moves to the 1-2 shift valve where it is blocked by the upshifted valve's spool land. After seating the #5 check ball, throttle pressure and coil spring tension pushes on the 2-3 shift valve reaction area and moves it to the downshifted position against governor pressure. Throttle pressure leaves the 2-3 shift valve to hold the shuttle valve throttle plug against its seat.

SHOP TALK

In drive range second gear, the 1-2 shift valve is upshifted while the 2-3 shift valve is downshifted. ■

GOVERNOR PRESSURE Governor pressure leaves the rotating governor assembly and flows to the shuttle valve throttle plug. Governor pressure also acts on the governor plugs of the two shift valves. Vehicle speed and governor pressure are high enough to overcome throttle valve pressure and coil spring tension at the 1-2 shift valve. Governor pressure forces the 1-2 shift valve to move against throttle pressure. Therefore, throttle pressure is blocked from acting on the shift valve reaction area.

CONVERTER PRESSURE Converter pressure flow is the same as in first gear.

Drive Range: D Third Gear

Gear Selector Position: D

Torque Converter Mode: Unlock

Planetary Controls Engaged: Rear Clutch; Front Clutch

Approximate Vehicle Speed: 25 mph

Throttle Position: Half Throttle

Drive range third gear is covered in two parts. The first explains the hydraulic operation to shift the transmission into third gear. The second part introduces the sensors and controls affiliated with engine computer operation and torque converter lockup clutch control. (To this point, in drive range first and second gears, the torque converter clutch has been unlocked.)

LINE PRESSURE Line pressure between the manual and pressure regulator valves is directed to the throttle valve and switch valve (Figure 32–77). Start at the #1 manual valve outlet where line pressure seats #9 check ball and circulates to the throttle valve. With the throttle valve open, throttle pressure is developed. In this circuit, pump pressure flows to the pressure regulator valve to develop line pressure, which, in this circuit, also operates the accumulator.

From the #2 manual valve outlet, line pressure charges the forward circuit, engages the rear clutch, and enters the governor assembly to produce governor pressure.

Line pressure also flows from the #2 manual valve outlet to circulate around the valley of the upshifted 1-2 shift valve and then around the valley of the 2-3 shift valve to the restriction above the shuttle valve. This restriction biases line pressure to the shuttle and by-pass valves. Line pressure leaves the shuttle and by-pass valve area and moves to the release side of the front servo and the front clutch. The feed line to the front clutch has a restriction that causes pressure to build on the release side of the front servo, which disengages the front kickdown band. Line pressure flowing through the front clutch feed restriction engages the front clutch for third gear direct drive operation.

THROTTLE PRESSURE With throttle valve open, throttle pressure flows to the kickdown valve, throttle plug of the pressure regulator valve, 1-2 and 2-3 shift valves, and the shuttle valve throttle plug. At the 2-3 shift valve, throttle pressure and coil spring tension are opposed by increasing governor pressure.

GOVERNOR PRESSURE Governor pressure leaves the governor to move the shuttle valve, opening line pressure circuits. The shuttle valve's movement buries the coil spring in the hollow shuttle valve throttle plug. The governor pressure has moved the 1-2 and 2-3 shift valves to the upshifted position, directing line pressure to engage the front clutch and hold the front servo released during third gear operation.

Torque Converter Controls and Pressure

The lockup torque converter clutch assembly is controlled by the engine computer. The engine computer energizes the torque converter relay, which sends 12 volts to the lockup solenoid. When the engine computer receives electronic signals from the different sensors confirming the requirements for lockup have been met, lockup clutch engagement begins.

These sensors include an engine coolant sensor, vehicle speed sensor, engine vacuum sensor, and throttle position sensor.

FIGURE 32–77 Drive range third gear with the lockup torque converter clutch disengaged and front and rear clutches engaged. *Courtesy of Chrysler Corporation*

Lockup Relay

The lockup relay is energized when the engine computer grounds the circuit. The lockup relay sends 12 volts to energize the lockup solenoid.

Lockup Solenoid

A solenoid is a device capable of converting electrical energy into mechanical force. When applied to the automatic transaxle lockup solenoid, the check ball is held off its seat by fluid pressure. The unseated check ball prevents line pressure from building until it is high enough to move the switch valve against switch valve spring tension.

When the lockup solenoid is electrically energized by a signal from the engine computer and lockup relay, the check ball is seated by the lockup solenoid (Figure 32–78), stopping the exhaust of line pressure. Line pressure builds up on the reaction area of the switch valve and moves it against spring tension to begin lockup engagement.

CONVERTER PRESSURE CONTROL VALVE

SOLENOID

LINE PRESSURE BLOCKED.

COOLER

SWITCH VALVE

TORQUE CONVERTER

FIGURE 32–78 When the lockup solenoid is energized, the check ball seats and line pressure builds, forcing the switch valve into the lockup position. *Courtesy of Chrysler Corporation*

Drive Range: D Third Gear

Gear Selector Position: D

Torque Converter Mode: Locked

Planetary Controls Engaged: Rear Clutch; Front Clutch

Approximate Vehicle Speed: 40 mph

Throttle Position: Half Throttle

In drive range third gear lockup, the transaxle operates in the same manner as third gear unlock. The focus of attention is on the torque converter lockup clutch control system.

Lockup Clutch Engagement

The coolant sensor reports to the computer that the engine has reached a temperature of at least 150°F. The vehicle speed sensor located on the speedometer cable sends an electronic signal to the computer, which reports that vehicle speed is above 40 mph. Since the vehicle is traveling at engagement speed, the throttle must be open (driver's foot on throttle). The vacuum transducer reports to the computer via electronic signal that engine vacuum is above 4 inches and within 22 inches. Based on these inputs, the computer energizes the clutch relay and lockup solenoid to move the solenoid check ball on its seat. The lockup solenoid check ball stops the lockup solenoid from exhausting line pressure. The increasing line pressure forces the switch valve to move against the coil's spring tension. Line pressure from the switch valve is directed to the pump drive hub and stator support to fill the torque converter with fluid. Fluid in the torque converter during lockup operation resides there to become the cooling and lubricating pressure. Line pressure flows from the impeller and turbine to fill the space behind the torque converter clutch piston and force engagement.

Drive Range: Reverse Gear

Gear Selector Position: R

Torque Converter Mode: Unlock

Planetary Controls Engaged: Low and Reverse Rear Band; Front Clutch

Approximate Vehicle Speed: 5 mph

Throttle Position: Part Throttle

Line pressure from a manual valve outlet not used before circulates through a bypass around the manual valve valley. Line pressure circulates to the low and reverse servo and front clutch (Figure 32–79). During the process of engaging the low and reverse servo and

front clutch, the #4 and #3 check balls are seated by line pressure.

LINE PRESSURE Line pressure from between the pressure regulator and manual valve circulates around the pressure regulator valve. After flowing through a restriction to seat #8 check ball, line pressure enters the throttle valve, which produces line-to-throttle pressure. With the throttle valve open, throttle pressure charges the kickdown valve and strokes the throttle plug to its extreme left position at the pressure regulator valve. Line pressure from the manual valve does not flow to the pressure regulator valve to oppose spring tension. The pressure regulator valve coil spring pushes the pressure regulator valve over to close the exhaust port. Line pressure builds to approximately 200 to 300 psi. You may wonder why line pressure must be increased so much in reverse gear. The planetary control units engaged in reverse are the front clutch and the low and reverse rear band. The front clutch, unlike the rear clutch, does not have a belleville spring. The belleville spring multiplies clutch piston apply force on the clutch pack, which reduces possible slippage. Therefore, to keep the front clutch from slipping when moving the vehicle from a stop, reverse line pressure is increased. The concept of increasing line pressure in reverse is common in many automatic transaxles and transmissions.

THROTTLE PRESSURE Throttle pressure circulates to the shift valve area to keep both the 1-2 and 2-3 shift valves downshifted. Throttle pressure also keeps the shuttle valve throttle plug against its seat in the valve body.

CONVERTER PRESSURE In reverse, the transaxle needs the torque multiplication of vortex flow to start the vehicle moving from a stop. Therefore, the switch valve maintains the position and holds the torque converter piston in the unlocked position.

LINE TO THROTTLE PRESSURE This pressure is derived from line pressure and becomes the new throttle pressure.

USING SERVICE MANUALS

Before beginning to service a transaxle or transmission, have the service manual and latest service bulletins on the bench for ready reference. Many service manual publishers have complete volumes dedicated to automatic transmissions and

FIGURE 32–79   Reverse line pressure is increased to keep the front clutch, which has no Belleville spring, from slipping. The front clutch and the low reverse bands are engaged. *Courtesy of Chrysler Corporation*

transaxles. These volumes contain detailed information on domestic and imported transmissions and transaxles.   ■

ELECTRONIC CONTROLS

In many vehicles, automatic transmissions and transaxles are electronically controlled (Figure 32–80). Shifting and torque converter lockup are regulated by a computer with programmed logic and in response to input sensors and switches. The electronic system controls these two operations by means of solenoid-operated valves. The precision of this type of control produces optimum driveability. Electronic control is superior because information about the engine, fuel, ignition, vacuum, and operating temperature is fed into the computer so shifting and lockup are closely monitored to take place at exactly the right time.

Electronic Control of Torque Converter Lockup

The electronically controlled lockup torque converter improves fuel economy by eliminating converter slip like other lockup converters. It also prevents lockup from occurring in engine modes where noise, vibration, or harshness concerns are most evident.

A computer is used to control the converter clutch solenoid based on the input from several sensors placed around the engine. The computer turns on the converter clutch solenoid (Figure 32–81) to move a valve that allows fluid pressure to engage the converter clutch. When the computer de-energizes the converter clutch solenoid, the converter clutch disengages.

The system operates in the following manner. The engine operates for more than 5 minutes and the engine coolant temperature sensor reports 150°F. Engagement could take place if all the other sensors agree. However, the vehicle operates in congested traffic at speeds varying from 15 to 35 mph and the

INPUTS

INFORMATION SENSORS

A. PRESSURE SWITCH MANIFOLD
   (PSM)
B. TRANSMISSION INPUT SPEED
   SENSOR (TISS)
C. TRANSMISSION OUTPUT SPEED
   SENSOR (TOSS)
D. TRANSMISSION FLUID
E. ENGINE COOLANT TEMPERATURE
   SENSOR (CTS)
F. THROTTLE POSITION SENSOR (TPS)
G. ENGINE SPEED SENSOR
H. BRAKE SWITCH
I. A/C REQUEST SWITCH

ELECTRONIC CONTROLLERS

● POWERTRAIN CONTROL
   MODULE (PCM) OR
   TRANSMISSION CONTROL
   MODULE (TCM)

● ASSEMBLY LINE DIAGNOSTIC LINK
   (ALDL)

OUTPUTS

**ELECTRONICALLY CONTROLLED
TRANSMISSION COMPONENTS**

1. SHIFT SOLENOID "A"
2. SHIFT SOLENOID "B"
3. PULSE WIDTH MODULATED TCC
   SOLENOID (PWM)
4. VARIABLE FORCE MOTOR

FIGURE 32–80   An electronic automatic transmission. *Courtesy of the Hydra-Matic Division, General Motors Corporation*

converted clutch engagement speed is approximately 40 mph. Under these operating conditions, the vehicle speed sensor reports that the vehicle speed is too low for clutch converter engagement. In addition, the throttle position sensor reports to the computer the unsteady, up and down movement of the throttle. The computer interprets this as a reason not to engage the converter clutch. The brake switch also opens periodi-

cally. Thus, the computer does not energize the clutch solenoid to engage the converter clutch.

If the vehicle breaks out of congested traffic and is travelling at a steady higher speed, the speed sensor reports that the vehicle is at a speed higher than converter clutch engagement speed. The throttle position sensor reports that the throttle is in a steady position in favor of engagement, and the brake switch is closed because the driver's foot is not on the brake pedal. When the computer scans all the sensors and determines that all sensor and switch signals favor engagement, it energizes the converter clutch solenoid and the converter clutch is engaged for lockup operation.

Electronically Controlled Shifting

When shifting of the automatic transmission is controlled by a computer, input signals for engine and road speed, manifold vacuum, engine operating temperature, gear selection, throttle position, and other factors are fed to the computer. The computer produces output signals that activate relays, which in

FIGURE 32–81   A converter clutch solenoid. *Courtesy of the Hydra-Matic Division, General Motors Corporation*

turn, operate electrical solenoid valves. Instead of hydraulic pressures and springs, the motion of the solenoids controls the position of the valves. When activated, a solenoid moves its valve to control fluid pressure in a valve body.

For the computer in an electronic control system to determine when to start a gear change, it must be able to refer to **shift schedules** that it has stored in its memory. A shift schedule contains the actual shift points to be used by the computer according to the input data it receives from the sensors. Shift schedule logic chooses the proper shift schedule for the current conditions of the transmission. It uses the shift schedule to select the appropriate gear, then determines the correct shift schedule or pattern that should be followed.

The first input a computer looks at to determine the correct shift logic, is the position of the gear shift lever. All shift schedules are based on the gear selected by the driver. The choices of shift schedules are limited by the type and size of engine that is coupled to the automatic transmission. Each engine/transmission combination has a different set of shift schedules. These schedules are coded by selector lever position and current gear range, and use throttle angle and vehicle speed as primary determining factors. The computer also looks at different temperature, load, and engine operation inputs for more information.

The shift schedules set the conditions that need to be met for a change in gears. Since the computer frequently reviews the input information, it can make quick adjustments to the schedule if needed and as needed. The result of the computer's processing of this information and commanding outcomes according to a logical program is optimum shifting of the automatic transmission. This results in improved fuel economy and overall performance.

The electronic control systems used by the manufacturers differ with the various transmission models and the engines to which they are attached. The components in each system and the overall operation of the system also varies with the different transmissions. However, all operate in a similar fashion and use basically the same parts.

CHRYSLER TRANSMISSIONS

Late-model Chrysler A-500/A-518 transmissions and the transaxles used in most Chrysler/Mitsubishi vehicles rely on electronics to control the shifting into overdrive gear. Electronics are also involved in the control of the converter clutch in all late-model Chrysler transmissions.

The A-500 and A-518 transmissions are fully automatic units with an overdrive attached to the rear of the transmission. The first through third gear shifts are controlled hydraulically through apply devices in the main body of the transmission.

Fourth gear operation is controlled by a manually operated overdrive switch on the instrument panel, center console, or shift lever. The overdrive switch is wired into a circuit with an overdrive solenoid, located on the valve body, and the single board engine controller (SBEC). The torque converter clutch lockup solenoid is also wired into this circuit. The overdrive switch prevents a shift into fourth gear when the switch is off. Therefore, the operation of the torque converter clutch is also inhibited when the overdrive switch is off.

The shift from third to fourth gears is electronically controlled and hydraulically activated by the SBEC. The SBEC controls the overdrive solenoid using information received from several sensors.

Chrysler A-604/41TE Controls The A-604/41TE transaxle is an electronically controlled 4-speed transaxle. The transaxle uses hydraulically operated clutches, which are controlled by the transaxle controller. The controller receives information from various inputs and controls a solenoid assembly through the electronic automatic transaxle (**EATX**) relay. The solenoid assembly consists of four solenoids (Figure 32–82) that control hydraulic pressure to four of the five clutches in the transaxle and to the lockup clutch of the torque converter.

FIGURE 32–82 Location of solenoid assembly on a Chrysler A-604 transaxle. *Courtesy of Chrysler Corporation*

The controller has an adaptive learning characteristic that learns the release rate and application rate of various transaxle components during various operating conditions. Adaptive learning allows the controller to compensate for wear and other events that might occur and cause the normal shift programming to be inefficient.

The controller may receive information from two different sources: directly from a sensor, or through a twisted-pair bus circuit, which connects all of the vehicle computer systems (Figure 32–83). This modulated bi-directional bus system is called Chrysler collision detection (**CCD**) bus and allows the various computers in the vehicle to share information.

When the controller receives an ignition run from the ignition switch, it performs a series of circuit and relay checks. If a problem is found, the controller will provide voltage to the EATX relay, which causes its contacts to close. This sends voltage to the solenoid assembly.

Direct battery voltage is supplied to the controller. If the controller loses source voltage, the transaxle will enter into **limp-in** mode. The transaxle will also enter into limp-in if the controller senses a transmission failure. At this point, a fault code will be stored in the memory of the controller and the transaxle will remain in limp-in until the transaxle is repaired. While in limp-in, the transaxle will operate only in park, neutral, reverse, and second gears. The transaxle will not upshift or downshift. This allows the vehicle to be operated, although its efficiency and performance is hurt.

The solenoids are controlled by the controller, which sends voltage to the EATX relay. The EATX relay, in turn, sends voltage to the solenoid assembly. The controller also completes the ground circuit of the solenoids when a particular solenoid should be activated. The controller also monitors the operation of the solenoids through inputs from low-reverse, 2-4 pressure, and overdrive switches. These switches are located in the solenoid assembly and inform the controller when a hydraulic circuit is open.

FIGURE 32–83 Schematic of the electronic control system used by Chrysler transaxles. Note the CCD bus link. *Courtesy of Chrysler Corporation*

Inputs The direct inputs are those sensors that provide information to the controller and do not use the CCD bus circuit. The CCD bus inputs use the bus circuit to supply the controller and other computers with information.

Typical CCD bus inputs used by the transaxle controller are from an ambient or battery temperature sensor, brake switch, coolant temperature sensor (CTS), and manifold absolute pressure (MAP) sensor. Other information, such as engine and body identification, the SBEC's target idle speed, and speed control operation are not the result of monitoring by sensors, rather these have been calculated or determined by the SBEC and made available on the bus. The ambient or battery temperature sensor monitors intake air temperature. The SBEC uses the temperature of intake air and current flow to calculate the temperature of the battery. The SBEC uses this temperature calculation to estimate transaxle fluid temperature.

The brake switch is used to disengage the torque converter clutch when the brakes are applied. Its input has little to do with the up and down shifting of gears. The input from the CTS is critical to the operation of the transaxle. If the engine's coolant temperature is cold, the controller may delay upshifts to improve driveability. The controller may also lock the converter clutch in second or third gear if the coolant temperature rises. The MAP sensor keeps the controller informed of changes in engine load.

Although engine speed information is available at the bus, the controller receives this signal directly from the distributor pick-up coil or crank angle sensor. With the direct feed, any time delay at the bus circuit is avoided and the controller is aware of current engine speeds.

Other direct inputs to the controller include battery voltage, selector lever positions, throttle position, turbine shaft speed, output shaft speed, and information from the low-reverse, overdrive, and 2-4 pressure switches at the solenoid assembly. The output shaft and turbine shaft speed sensors are magnetic pick-up type sensors that generate an AC voltage.

The controller processes these inputs and selects the proper shift schedule for the transaxle. The controller will then control the power feed to the solenoid assembly through the EATX relay and the ground circuit of the solenoids to force upshifts and downshifts. The controller will also activate the back-up lamp relay based on these inputs.

42LE Controls The 42LE four-speed transaxle, released in 1994 by Chrysler for use in the their New Yorker, Intrepid, LHS, and Vision models, also uses

fully adaptive controls. Like the 41TE, this transaxle uses hydraulically applied clutches to shift gear but controls the hydraulics electronically.

The hydraulics of the transaxle provide for the control of torque converter fluid flow and oil cooler flow, the regulation of mainline pressure, and the movement of the manual shift valve. Fluid flow to the various apply devices is directly controlled by the solenoids. The basic hydraulic system also includes a logic-controlled solenoid switch valve, which locks out first gear when second, direct, or overdrive gears are engaged. This solenoid switch also redirects fluid to the torque converter lockup clutch. To regain access to first gear, a special sequence of solenoid commands from the control unit must be used to unlock and move the solenoid switch. This prevents the engagement of first gear when other gears are engaged (Figure 32–84).

The solenoids act directly on steel poppet and ball valves. Two of the solenoid valves are normally-venting and the other two are normally-applying. This combination allows for a fault mode of operation. If electrical power to the transaxle is lost, the transaxle will only provide second gear in all forward drive ranges.

There are three pressure switches that give input to the transaxle controller. They are all located within the solenoid assembly. One speed sensor reads input speed at the turbine shaft and another speed sensor reads output speed. The third sensor monitors the position of the manual shift valve.

Engine speed, throttle position, temperature, engine load, and other typical engine-related inputs are also used by the controller to determine the best shift points. Many of these inputs are available through multiplexing and are inputted from the common bus.

The **adaptive learning** takes place as the controller reads input and output speeds over 140 times per second. The controller responds to each new reading. This learning process allows the transaxle controller to make adjustments to its program so quality shifting always occurs.

The basic shift logic of the controller allows the releasing apply device to slip slightly during the engagement of the engaging apply device. Once the apply device has engaged and the next gear is driven, the releasing apply device is pulled totally away from its engaging member and the transmission is fully into its next gear. This allows for smooth shifting into all gears. The adaptive learning capability of the transaxle controller allows for this smooth shifting throughout the life of the transmission. The controller learns the characteristics of the transaxle and changes its programming accordingly.

FIGURE 32–84 Oil circuit for direct drive in a 42LE transaxle. Notice how often the fluid flow to low gear is blocked off. *Courtesy of Chrysler Corporation*

FORD MOTOR COMPANY TRANSMISSIONS

The circuitry and components used by Ford Motor Company to control their transmissions varies with transmission models and applications. Although there are some similarities across models, the common systems should be looked at individually.

Ford AOD-E Controls The AOD-E is a fully automatic four-speed transmission with electronic shifting, torque converter control, and line pressure controls. This transmission is identical to an AOD except it no longer uses a split-torque converter and its operation is controlled by the electronic engine control's (EEC) electronic control assembly (ECA). Input sensors provide information to the ECA, which, in turn, controls actuators. Actuators control transmission operation.

The engine control system consists of the ECA, sensors, switches, and solenoids. It also has self-diag-

nostic capabilities. The engine sensors supply the ECA with the information necessary to determine engine operating conditions, through voltage signals. The ECA will then send out electrical signals to control air/fuel ratio, idle speed, emission controls, ignition timing, and transmission solenoids.

The ECA uses logic to control shift scheduling, shift feel, and converter lockup, and relies on information from the engine control system, through such sensors as the MAP and TPS, as well as information from the transmission to determine the optimum shift timing. Information about the operation of the transmission is received by the ECA through signals from an output shaft sensor (OSS), vehicle speed sensor (VSS), transmission oil temperature (TOT) sensor, and a manual lever position sensor (**MLPS**).

The transmission control system uses four solenoids for control of operation. One solenoid, the **MCCC** solenoid, is used for modulated converter clutch control. Another, the **EPC** solenoid, is used to

FIGURE 32–85   Typical variable force solenoid or motor. *Courtesy of the Hydra-Matic Division, General Motors Corporation*

control hydraulic pressures throughout the transmission. The remaining two solenoids are shift solenoids.

The EPC solenoid replaces the conventional TV cable setup to provide changes in pressure in response to engine load. This solenoid is a variable force solenoid (**VFS**) and contains a spool valve and spring (Figure 32–85). To control fluid pressure, the ECA sends a varying signal to the solenoid. This varies the amount the solenoid will cause the spool valve to move. When the solenoid is off, the spring tension keeps the valve in place to maintain maximum pressure. As more current is applied to the solenoid, the solenoid moves the spool valve more, which moves to uncover the exhaust port more, thereby causing a decrease in pressure (Figure 32–86). The shift solenoids offer four possible on/off combinations to control fluid to the various shift valves.

Ford AXOD-E Controls

The AXOD-E is an electronically controlled four-speed transaxle. Shift control solenoids provide gear changes and are controlled by the ECA, as is the converter lockup clutch solenoid. Five solenoids are mounted on the AXOD-E valve body to control transmission functions. One solenoid, the MCCC solenoid, is used for modulated converter clutch control. Another, the EPC solenoid, is used to control hydraulic pressures throughout the transmission. The remaining three solenoids are shift solenoids.

The EPC solenoid replaces the conventional TV cable setup to provide changes in pressure in response to engine load. This solenoid is a variable force solenoid and contains a spool valve and spring. To control fluid pressure, the ECA sends a varying signal to the solenoid. This varies the amount the solenoid will cause the spool valve to move. When the solenoid is

FIGURE 32–86   The EPC solenoid controls hydraulic pressures throughout the transmission by controlling the current going to the solenoid. *Courtesy of the Hydra-Matic Division, General Motors Corporation*

off, the spring tension keeps the valve in place to maintain maximum pressure. As more current is applied to the solenoid, the solenoid moves the spool valve more, which moves to uncover the exhaust port more, thereby causing a decrease in pressure.

The shift solenoids offer many possible on/off combinations to control fluid to the various shift valves. These solenoids are on/off solenoids that are normally off and in the open position. Being open, the solenoid valves allow line pressure to the bore of the shift valve and keep the shift valve closed. When the shift solenoids are energized, they block the line pressure and exhaust line pressure from the valve. This allows the shift valve to open. A summary of the shift solenoid activity follows.

Selector Position	Gear	Solenoid		
		#1	#2	#3
OD	First Gear	OFF	ON	OFF
	Second Gear	ON	ON	OFF
	Third Gear	OFF	OFF	ON
	Fourth Gear	ON	OFF	ON
D (Drive)	First Gear	OFF	ON	OFF
	Second Gear	ON	ON	OFF
	Third Gear	OFF	OFF	OFF
1	First Gear	OFF	ON	OFF
	Second Gear	OFF	OFF	OFF
R	Reverse	OFF	ON	OFF
P or N	Park/Neutral	OFF	ON	OFF

Ford A4LD Controls The A4LD is a four-speed automatic transmission with a lockup torque converter. The engine control system controls the operation of the lockup converter clutch and the operation of a shift solenoid for third to fourth gear shifting. Prior to 1987, 3-4 shift was done hydraulically. In 1987, a electronic 3-4 shift solenoid was added.

This solenoid is normally off and permits line pressure flow through the solenoid valve, which inhibits the 3-4 shift. When the ECA receives information that the time is right to allow the 3-4 shift, the solenoid is energized and the inhibitor oil is exhausted. This allows the hydraulic shift valve to make the shift.

Ford 4EAT Controls The 4EAT is a four-speed transaxle that is controlled both electronically and hydraulically. Input signals from sensors are sent to the 4EAT control module, the Mazda electronic control system (MECS), which controls the appropriate gear range, shift timing, and converter clutch lockup timing. The 4EAT control module has self-diagnostic capabilities, a fail-safe mode, and a warning code display for the main input sensors and solenoid valves. Four solenoid valves are located in the valve body. These redirect fluid flow and cause shifting and converter lockup. The 4EAT can be operated in manual or automatic shift mode. Manual shifting can be selected by the driver through a switch located on the center console. When the switch is in the NORM position, the transmission automatically shifts gears to achieve maximum fuel economy. Some model cars have a switch that allows the driver to select in and out of a POWER range. Selection of the POWER range, causes a delay in the shift timing to provide for maximum acceleration.

GENERAL MOTORS' TRANSMISSIONS

General Motors is using several different transmission models in their current line of automobiles. Although these transmissions are significantly different in design and operation, most of the electronically controlled units are controlled in the same way. A look at some of the more commonly used transmissions should provide an accurate description of all General Motors' electronic-controlled transmission systems.

4L80-E Controls The 4L80-E was introduced in 1991 and is based on the same design as a THM 400 with a THM 200-R4 overdrive assembly and with an electronic control system. All automatic upshifts and downshifts are electronically controlled by the powertrain control module (PCM) for gasoline engines or the transmission control module (TCM) for diesel engines.

Park, neutral, and drive ranges are hydraulically controlled according to the position of the manual shift valve, as are selector-operated, forced downshifts. The PCM/TCM also has a self-diagnostic mode that is capable of storing transmission fault codes. The PCM is programmed to adjust its operating parameters in response to changes within the system, such as component wear. As component wear and shift overlap times increase, the PCM adjusts line pressure by controlling the VFM to maintain proper shift timing calibrations.

A variable force motor (**VFM**) controlled by the PCM is used to change line pressure in response to engine speed and vehicle load. By responding to current operating conditions, the VFM is able to match shift timing and feel with the current needs of the vehicle. The lockup converter is hydraulically applied and electrically controlled through a pulse width modulated (**PWM**) solenoid (Figure 32–87) and the PCM/TCM.

CUSTOMER CARE

Vehicles with a 4L80-E transmission should have their transmission fluid changed on a regular basis as stated in the owner's manual. These transmissions use aluminum valves in the valve body, instead of steel valves. This makes the valves subject to damage if the ATF contains metallic particles. The periodic fluid changes can prevent serious damage. ■

Operation Once the PCM has processed the input signals, it controls transmission operation through two on/off solenoids, a pulse width modulated sole-

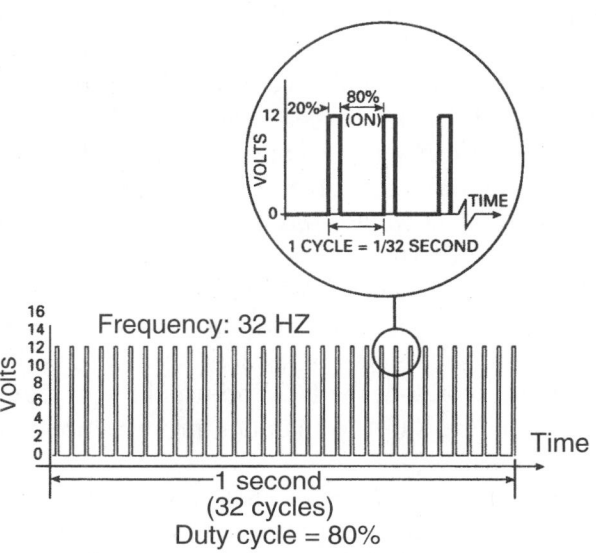

FIGURE 32–87 (Top) A typical PWM solenoid. (Bottom) The signal representing the control or ordered duty cycle from the computer. *Courtesy of the Hydra-Matic Division, General Motors Corporation*

noid, and a variable force motor located in the valve body. The two shift solenoids are attached to the valve body and are normally open. There are four possible on/off combinations of the solenoids, which determine fluid pressure flow to the shift valves in the valve body.

The shift solenoids receive voltage through the ignition switch and are grounded through the PCM. When a solenoid is energized by the PCM, a check ball held in place by the solenoid plunger blocks the fluid pressure feed. This closes the exhaust passage and causes signal fluid pressure to increase. When the solenoid is de-energized, fluid pressure moves the check ball and plunger off the check ball seat. This allows fluid to flow past the check ball and exhaust through the solenoid, decreasing signal pressure.

The PWM is a normally closed valve installed in the valve body. It controls the position of the TCC apply valve. When the solenoid is off, TCC signal fluid exhausts and the converter clutch remains released. Once the solenoid is energized, the plunger moves the metering ball to allow TCC signal fluid to pass to the TCC regulator valve. The PCM cycles the PWM solenoid on and off 32 times per second but varies the length of time it is energized in each cycle, or 1/32 second. The VFM is an electro-hydraulic actuator made of a variable force solenoid and a regulating valve. The VFM is installed in the valve body and controls main line pressure by moving a pressure regulator valve against spring pressure. The VFM operates by a constantly changing current from the PCM. The PCM turns the solenoid on and off 292.5 times per second but varies the solenoid's duty cycle. When the duty cycle is zero, line pressure is at maximum. Under normal operating conditions, the PCM pulses the VFM about every 10 seconds to either 100 percent duty cycle or 0 percent duty cycle. This prevents the VFM valve from sticking in any given position due to contamination. The torque signal compensator valve spring prevents major fluctuations in line pressure by absorbing the pulsations caused by the temporary full duty of the solenoid.

4T60-E Controls The 4T60-E transaxle is a four-speed automatic transmission with electronically controlled shifting and converter lockup. The torque converter clutch is controlled by two electronic solenoids, one for apply and release and the other to control the feel of the apply and release of the TCC. Some 4T60-E transaxles use a PWM solenoid to control converter lockup. The operation of this transaxle is very similar to the 4L80-E transmission. The transaxle relies on the energizing and de-energizing of two solenoids to cause a change of gears. A summary of the solenoid activity and power flow is shown in Figure 32–88.

The primary inputs for transmission operation are from the throttle position sensor, vehicle speed sensor, engine coolant temperature sensor, manifold air pressure sensor, and from the cruise control, brake, low gear pressure, and fourth gear pressure switches. With this information, the PCM is able to calculate the optimum time for gear changes.

On some models, the PCM is also connected to one or more other computers, which operate the climate control system, antilock brake system, driver information center, and supplemental restraint system. Through multiplexing, these computers are able to share information and use common input sensors.

RANGE	GEAR	A SOLENOID	B SOLENOID	4TH CLUTCH	REVERSE BAND	2ND CLUTCH	3RD CLUTCH	3RD ROLLER CLUTCH	INPUT CLUTCH	INPUT SPRAG	FORWARD BAND	1/2 SUPPORT ROLLER CLUTCH	2/1 BAND
P-N		ON	ON						*	*			
D	1st	ON	ON						APPLIED	HOLDING	APPLIED	HOLDING	
	2nd	OFF	ON			APPLIED			*	OVERRUN	APPLIED	HOLDING	
	3rd	OFF	OFF			APPLIED	APPLIED	HOLDING			APPLIED	OVERRUN	
	4th	ON	OFF	APPLIED		APPLIED	*	OVERRUN			APPLIED	OVERRUN	
D	3rd	@OFF	@OFF			APPLIED	APPLIED	HOLDING	APPLIED	HOLDING	APPLIED	OVERRUN	
	2nd	@OFF	@ON			APPLIED			*	OVERRUN	APPLIED	HOLDING	
	1st	@ON	@ON						APPLIED	HOLDING	APPLIED	HOLDING	
2	2nd	@OFF	@ON			APPLIED			*	OVERRUN	APPLIED	HOLDING	APPLIED
	1st	@ON	@ON						APPLIED	HOLDING	APPLIED	HOLDING	APPLIED
1	1st	@ON	@ON				APPLIED	HOLDING	APPLIED	HOLDING	APPLIED	HOLDING	APPLIED
R	REVERSE	ON	ON		APPLIED				APPLIED	HOLDING			

*APPLIED BUT NOT EFFECTIVE

@ THE SOLENOID'S STATE FOLLOWS A SHIFT PATTERN WHICH DEPENDS UPON VEHICLE SPEED AND THROTTLE POSITION. IT DOES NOT DEPEND UPON THE SELECTED GEAR.

ON = SOLENOID ENERGIZED

OFF = SOLENOID DE-ENERGIZED

FIGURE 32–88   Range reference chart for a 4T60-E transaxle. *Courtesy of the Chevrolet Division, General Motors Corporation*

HONDA TRANSMISSIONS

The electronic control system of Honda automatic transmissions consists of the transmission control module (TCM), sensors, and four solenoid valves (Figure 32–89). Shifting and converter lockup are electronically controlled. Activating a shift solenoid valve changes modulator pressure, causing a shift valve to move. This allows pressurized fluid to flow through a line to engage the appropriate clutch and its corresponding gearset. Converter lockup is controlled by the action of the other two solenoid valves.

By receiving information from its input sensors, the TCM calculates the required gear changes and energizes or de-energizes the shift solenoids. A summary of the solenoid activity follows.

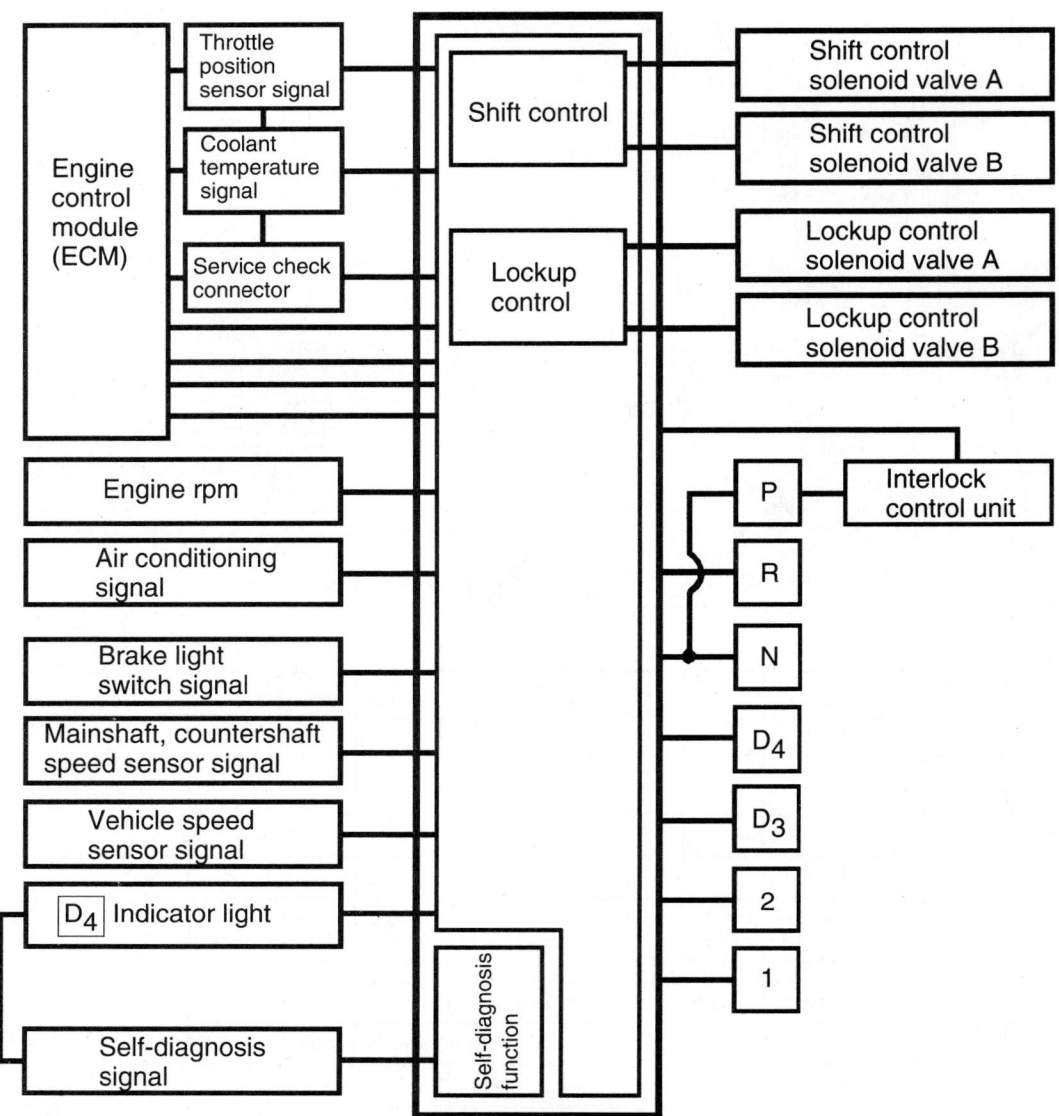

FIGURE 32–89 Schematic of Honda's electronically controlled transaxle. *Courtesy of American Honda Motor Company, Inc.*

Selector Lever Position	Operating Gear	"A" Solenoid	"B" Solenoid
D4	First Gear	OFF	ON
	Second Gear	ON	ON
	Third Gear	ON	OFF
	Fourth Gear	OFF	OFF
D3	First Gear	OFF	ON
	Second Gear	ON	ON
	Third Gear	ON	OFF
2	Second Gear	ON	ON
1	First Gear	ON	OFF
R	Reverse	ON	OFF

The TCM receives information about the throttle position, engine coolant temperature, engine speed, A/C on/off, brake on/off, vehicle speed, and the speed of the transaxle's counter shaft. Based on this information and the shift schedule and logic in the TCM, the transaxle is shifted to meet the current operating requirements of the vehicle.

OTHER COMMON TRANSMISSIONS

Saturn Transmissions Although Saturn is a division of General Motors Corporation, they do not use normal corporation transaxles. Saturn vehicles use an electronically controlled four-speed automatic transmission with a shift mode select function. This mode switch allows the driver to select NORMAL mode or PERFORMANCE mode. When the switch is depressed, it provides a signal to the powertrain control module (PCM), which adjusts shift points and lockup timing for the selected mode.

The transaxle relies on five solenoid valves, controlled by the PCM, to regulate shift timing, feel, and TCC application. Two solenoids are used as shift solenoids. They control the delivery of fluid to the manual shift valve. A solenoid is also used to control line pressure. This solenoid operates on a duty cycle controlled by the PCM. Its purpose is to regulate line pressure according to engine running conditions and engine torque. An additional solenoid is used to provide for engine braking during coasting. This solenoid operates when the vehicle is slowing down and the throttle is closed. The other solenoid controls the operation of the lockup converter clutch.

If an electrical circuit problem occurs, the CHECK ENGINE SOON or SHIFT TO D2 light may come on or start flashing. The PCM will store fault codes or information flags in its memory. A stored fault code indicates the PCM has detected a fault in the engine or transaxle circuits. Information flags help diagnose current or intermittent trouble codes.

The primary inputs to the PCM for transaxle operation are ATF temperature, brake on/off, an ignition signal, selected mode, selector lever position, torque converter turbine speed, and vehicle speed. Both the turbine speed and vehicle speed sensors are PM generators.

The ATF temperature sensor is a thermistor mounted in the line pressure port. The PCM supplies a 5-volt reference signal to the ATF temperature sensor through a resistor inside the PCM and uses a signal line to measure voltage. Signal voltage will be high when transaxle fluid is cold and it will be low when the ATF is warm.

Toyota Transmissions Toyota led the way into electronically controlled automatic transmissions. Their transmission model, the A-140E, was the first fully electronic transmission. This transaxle is actually a 3-speed unit with an add-on fourth or overdrive gear. The functions of the transaxle are controlled by a microprocessor located behind the glove box. The control module receives input signals from the water temperature sensing switch, throttle position switch and the shift pattern selector switch. The water temperature sensing switch does not allow the transaxle to shift into overdrive until coolant has reached a minimum of 122°F. The throttle switch is located at the throttle body and the shift pattern switch is located at the instrument panel and is used for various dri-

ving conditions. The module receives signals from two speed sensors; one is located at the speedometer and the other at the transaxle. The back-up lamp/neutral safety switch signals the module for starting and back-up lamp circuits. The module controls and sends output signals to the stop and back-up lamps. The module also controls two shift solenoids, located within the transaxle. A summary of the solenoid activity follows.

Selector Lever Position	Operating Gear	#1 Solenoid	#2 Solenoid
Drive	First gear	On	Off
	Second gear	On	On
	Third gear	Off	On
	Overdrive	Off	Off
2—Second	First gear	On	Off
	Second gear	On	On
	Third gear	Off	On
L—Low	First gear	On	Off
	Second gear	On	On

Since the introduction of the A-140 with electronic controls, Toyota has added these controls to several other automatic transmissions. The A-240E/A-340E are four-speed transaxles with electronically controlled shifting. Gear changes are determined by an electronically controlled transmission (ECT) computer, which activates solenoids in the valve body. One of the two different driving modes (NORMAL or POWER) can be selected by the driver. The transaxle shift points are changed by the computer depending on mode selected. The transmission is fitted with a lockup torque converter.

The A-340H is a modified version of the A-340E. It has been modified for four-wheel-drive and has a hydraulically operated transfer case mounted to the rear of the transmission. The transmission is still a 4-speed unit and gear changes are still determined by an ECT computer.

Nissan Transmissions Nissan uses different transaxles and transmissions in their vehicles. Most have electronically controlled converter clutches. All RE4F02A-based transaxles also have electronic shift controls. Shifting is controlled by a transmission control unit. This microprocessor operates, primarily, in response to throttle position and vehicle speed. Based on inputs, the microprocessor provides the appropriate shift schedule for the current operating conditions. The control unit also has a fail-safe feature, which allows the vehicle to be driven even if an important input fails.

This system relies on two shift solenoids, which are controlled by the control unit. In addition to these solenoids, two other solenoids are incorporated into the system. One of these solenoids, called the timing solenoid, provides for smooth downshifting. The other, called the line pressure solenoid, provides for smooth upshifting. Both of these solenoids control the engagement and disengagement of the transmission's apply units. The system has a fifth solenoid, which is used to control converter lockup clutch activity.

The control unit relies on inputs from various sensors: a throttle position sensor, mode switch inhibitor switch, throttle valve switch, fluid temperature switch, revolution sensor, and vehicle speed sensor. Based on the throttle position and vehicle speed, the control unit is able to calculate the load on the engine. This information is then used to control the timing solenoid and the shift solenoids.

The driver can select between three driving modes: POWER, COMFORT, or AUTO. The mode switch is located near the gearshift lever. When POWER is selected, the timing for downshifting and upshifting is set for higher speeds. This mode was designed for rapid acceleration or operating under heavy loads. Normal shift patterns are followed when the mode selector is in the COMFORT position. This mode is designed to achieve maximum fuel economy. The AUTO mode is a mixture between the COMFORT and the POWER modes. Most of the time, the control unit will control the shifts in a normal way. However, if the throttle is quickly opened, the shift pattern will switch to the POWER mode.

The control unit activates the shift solenoids according to the shift schedule it selected in response to the signals received by its inputs. The shift solenoids are simple on/off solenoids. When the solenoid is energized, line pressure flows to the appropriate shift valve. One solenoid controls fluid flow to the 2-3 shift valve. The other solenoid activates the 1-2 or 3-4 shift valve through the 2-3 valve. In other words, the position of the first shift valve determines where fluid flow will be directed when the second solenoid is activated. When only the first solenoid is energized, the transaxle will operate in second gear. When both are energized, the transaxle will operate in first gear.

CASE STUDY

A *"fast-lube" business has recently been faced with numerous complaints from customers who had their transmission fluid and filters changed. All of these customers owned late-model Ford products and have a common complaint of overly harsh shifting.*

Concerned about these complaints, the owner reviews the files of each of these customers. He finds something else the cars have in common. All were refilled with type F transmission fluid. The owner wonders if the fluid was faulty. After doing some research, he finds that late-model Ford products call for Mercon fluid, which has special friction modifiers in it to allow for smoother shifting.

This could be the cause of the complaints. The owner contacts one of the customers and requests that the car be brought in. The fluid is drained and the Mercon fluid is put in. The car is returned to the customer. The transmission now operates normally. All of the other customers are contacted and scheduled for the same procedure. The shop owner realizes that the money saved on buying type F fluid from a surplus distributor was more than lost. Not only did he lose what he paid for the fluid, he also risked losing his customers. The correct type fluid should always be used in an automatic transmission.

KEY TERMS

Adaptive learning	Kickdown
Annulus	Limp-in
ATF	Line pressure
Band	Manual valve
CCD	MCCC
Check ball valve	MLPS
CLC	Multiple-disc clutch
Clutch pack	Overdrive
Coupling point	Overrunning clutch
Double wrap	Pascal's law
EATX	Planetary pinions
EPC	PLC
Fail-safe	Poppet valve
Flex plate	Pressure relief valve
Gear-type pump	PWM
Governor	Ravigneaux gear train
Governor pressure	Relay valve
Impeller	Ring gear

Rotary oil flow
SBEC
Servo
Shift schedule
Shift valve
Simpson gear train
Single wrap
Splitter gear
Spool valve
Stator

Sun gear
Throttle valve
Turbine
Vacuum modulator
Valve body
VFM
VFS
Vortex oil flow
Worm tracks

SUMMARY

- The torque converter is a fluid clutch used to transfer engine torque from the engine to the transmission. It automatically engages and disengages power transfer from the engine to the transmission in relation to engine rpm. It consists of three elements: the impeller (input), turbine (output), and stator (torque multiplier). Two types of oil flow take place inside the torque converter: rotary and vortex flow. An overrunning clutch keeps the stator assembly from rotating in one direction and permits overrunning when turned in the opposite direction.

- A lockup torque converter eliminates the 10 percent slip that takes place between the impeller and turbine at the coupling stage of operation. There are two types: centrifugal lockup clutch and the more popular piston lockup clutch.

- Planetary gearsets transfer power and generate torque from the engine to the drive axle. Compound gearsets combine two simple planetary gearsets so that load can be spread over a greater number of teeth for strength and also to obtain the largest number of gear ratios possible in a compact area. A simple planetary gearset consists of a sun gear, a carrier with planetary pinions mounted to it, and an internally toothed ring gear.

- Planetary gear controls include transmission bands, servos, and clutches. A band is a braking assembly positioned around a drum. There are two types: single wrap and double wrap. Simple and compound servos are used to engage bands. Transmission clutches, either overrunning or multiple-disc, are capable of both holding and driving members.

- The most common gear train used in automotive transmissions is the Simpson gear train. It consists of two simple planetary gearsets that share a common sun gear.

- The basic Torqueflite transmission was modified for use as a FWD transaxle and contain the same basic parts as the A-904 transmission, with the

addition of a transfer shaft, final drive gears, and a differential unit.

- All the Torqueflite-based transmissions and transaxles have two multiple-disc clutches, an overrunning clutch, two servos and bands, and two planetary gearsets to provide three forward gear ratios and a reverse ratio.

- The A-500 and A-518 are four-speed automatic transmissions with the first three forward gear ratios the same as the A-904 and A-727 Loadflite units and fourth gear provided for by a separate planetary gearset and controlled by an overdrive clutch, direct clutch, and overrunning clutch.

- Ford Motor Company has many transmissions that use the Simpson gear train and are quite similar to each other, including the C-3, C-4, C-5, C-6, and A4LD. The gear trains for the first three speeds of Ford transmissions are controlled by two multiple-disc clutches, two bands, and one overrunning clutch. The exception to this is the C-6, which uses a clutch in place of a band for low and reverse.

- Most General Motors' transmissions and transaxles are based on the Simpson gear train and use three multiple-disc clutches, one band, and a single one-way roller clutch to provide the various gear ratios.

- The 4L60 is a fully automatic transmission consisting of two planetary gear sets, five multiple-disc clutches, one sprag clutch, one roller clutch, and a band.

- The Nissan L4N71B/E4N71B series has four forward gears through a Simpson gearset and an additional planetary unit mounted in front of the Simpson. These transmissions use four multiple-disc clutches, two servos and bands, and a one-way clutch.

- The Ford ATX is a 3-speed automatic transaxle that uses a Ravigneaux planetary gear train. The original ATX transaxles were equipped with a splitter gear torque converter.

- The AOD uses four multiple-disc clutches, two one-way clutches, and two bands to obtain the various gear ranges.

- General Motors' 3L30 is a 3-speed automatic that uses the Ravigneaux compound planetary gearset and three multiple-disc clutches, one band, and a single one-way (sprag) clutch are used to provide for the various gear ratios.

- The KM 170/171/172 uses three multiple-disc clutches, a band, and a one-way clutch to provide the various gear ranges.

- In the 4T60, the two tandem planetary units do not share a common member, rather the front planetary carrier is locked to the rear ring gear and the front ring gear is locked to the rear planetary carrier.

◆ The AXOD 4-speed transaxle has the planetary carriers of each planetary unit locked to the other planetary unit's ring gear. Each planetary set has its own sun gear and set of planetary pinion gears.

◆ The AXOD uses four multiple-disc clutches, two band assemblies, and two one-way clutches to control the operation of the planetary gearset.

◆ The Honda CA, F4, and G4 transaxles use constant-mesh helical and square-cut gears controlled by four multiple-disc clutches, a sliding reverse gear, and a one-way clutch to control the gears.

◆ An automatic transmission uses ATF fluid pressure to control the action of the planetary gearsets. This fluid pressure is regulated and directed to change gears automatically through the use of various pressure regulators and control valves. To form a complete working hydraulic system, the following elements are needed: fluid reservoir (transmission oil pan), pressure source (oil pump), control valving (valve control body), and output devices (servos and clutches).

◆ The transmission pump is driven by the torque converter shell at engine speed. The purpose of the pump is to create fluid flow and pressure in the system. Excessive pump pressure is controlled by the pressure regulator valve. Three types of oil pumps are installed in automatic transmissions: the gear, rotor, and vane. The gear type is the most popular.

◆ The valve body is the control center of the automatic transmission. It is made of two or three main parts. Internally, the valve body has many fluid passages called worm tracks.

◆ The purpose of a valve is to start, stop, or to direct and regulate fluid flow. Generally, in most valve bodies used in automatic transmissions, three types of valves are used: check ball, poppet, and most commonly, the spool.

◆ To prevent stalling, the automatic transmission pump has a pressure regulator valve located in the valve body. It maintains a basic fluid pressure. The valve's movement to the exhaust position is controlled by calibrated coil spring tension. The three stages of pressure regulation are charging the torque converter, exhausting fluid pressure, and establishing a balanced position. There are times when fluid pressure must be increased above its baseline pressure.

◆ The purpose of the governor assembly is to sense vehicle road speed and send a fluid pressure signal to the transmission valve body to either upshift or permit the transmission to downshift.

Throttle pressure delays the transmission upshift and forces the downshift.

◆ A shift schedule contains the actual shift points to be used by the computer according to the input data it receives from the sensors. Its logic chooses the proper shift schedule for the current conditions of the transmission.

◆ Fourth gear on late-model Chrysler transmissions is controlled by a manually operated overdrive switch on the instrument panel, center console, or shift lever. The overdrive switch is wired into a circuit with an overdrive solenoid, located on the valve body, and the single board engine controller. The torque converter clutch lockup solenoid is also wired into this circuit. The overdrive switch prevents a shift into fourth gear when the switch is off.

◆ The A-604/41TE transaxle is an electronically controlled 4-speed transaxle. The transaxle uses hydraulically operated clutches, which are controlled by the transaxle controller. The controller receives information from various inputs and controls a solenoid assembly through the electronic automatic transaxle relay. The solenoid assembly consists of four solenoids that control hydraulic pressure to four of the five clutches in the transaxle and to the lockup clutch of the torque converter.

◆ The controller may receive information from two different sources: directly from a sensor, or through a twisted-pair bus circuit, which connects all of the vehicle computer systems. This modulated bi-directional bus system is called the Chrysler collision detection bus and allows the various computers in the vehicle to share information.

◆ If the controller loses source voltage or senses a transaxle problem, the transaxle will enter into limp-in mode. While in limp-in, the transaxle will operate only in park, neutral, reverse, and second gears. This allows the vehicle to be operated, although its efficiency and performance are hurt.

◆ Adaptive learning allows the controller to compensate for wear and other events that might occur and cause the normal shift programming to be inefficient.

◆ The Chrysler 42LE four-speed transaxle also uses fully adaptive controls. Like the 41TE, this transaxle uses hydraulically applied clutches to shift gears but controls the hydraulics electronically.

◆ There are three pressure switches that give input to the transaxle controller. They are all located within the solenoid assembly.

◆ The AOD-E is identical to an AOD except it no longer uses a split-torque converter and its operation is controlled by the electronic engine control's ECA, which relies on information from the engine control system, as well as information from the transmission to determine the optimum shift timing.

◆ The transmission control system uses four solenoids for control of operation. One solenoid, the MCCC solenoid, is used for modulated converter clutch control. Another, the EPC solenoid, is used to control hydraulic pressures throughout the transmission. The remaining two solenoids are shift solenoids.

◆ The AXOD-E is an electronically controlled 4-speed transaxle. Shift control solenoids provide gear changes and these solenoids are controlled by the ECA, as is the converter lockup clutch solenoid. Five solenoids are mounted on the AXOD-E valve body to control transmission functions.

◆ The A4LD is a 4-speed automatic transmission with a lockup torque converter. The engine control system controls the operation of the lockup converter clutch and the operation of a shift solenoid for third to fourth gear shifting.

◆ The 4EAT is controlled both electronically and hydraulically. Four solenoid valves are located in the valve body. These redirect fluid flow and cause shifting and converter lockup.

◆ The 4L80-E's PCM is programmed to adjust its operating parameters in response to changes within the system, such as component wear. As component wear and shift overlap times increase, the PCM adjusts line pressure by controlling the VFM to maintain proper shift timing calibrations.

◆ A variable force motor controlled by the PCM is used to change line pressure in response to engine speed and vehicle load.

◆ The PCM controls transmission operation through two on/off solenoids, a pulse width modulated solenoid, and a variable force motor located in the valve body.

◆ The 4T60-E transaxle is an electronically controlled shifting transmission with converter lockup. The torque converter clutch is controlled by two electronic solenoids, one for apply and release and the other to control the feel of the apply and release of the TCC.

◆ The electronic control system in Honda automatic transmissions consists of the transmission control module, sensors, and four solenoid valves.

◆ Saturn vehicles use an electronically controlled 4-speed automatic transmission with a shift mode select function. This mode switch allows the driver to select NORMAL mode or PERFORMANCE mode. The transaxle relies on five solenoid valves, controlled by the PCM, to regulate shift timing, feel, and TCC application.

◆ Toyota's A-140E was the first fully electronic transmission. A control module controls two shift solenoids, located within the transaxle. Gear changes are determined by a computer that activates solenoids in the valve body. One of the two different driving modes (NORMAL or POWER) can be selected by the driver.

◆ Nissan's RE4F02A-based transaxles also have electronic shift controls. This system relies on two shift solenoids, which are controlled by the control unit. In addition to these solenoids, two other solenoids are incorporated into the system. One of these solenoids, called the timing solenoid, provides for smooth downshifting. The other, called the line pressure solenoid, provides for smooth upshifting. Both of these solenoids control the engagement and disengagement of the transmission's apply units. The system has a fifth solenoid, which is used to control converter lockup clutch activity.

TECH MANUAL

The following procedures are included in Chapter 32 of the *Tech Manual* that accompanies this book:

1. Perform pressure tests.

2. Perform stall test.

3. Perform lock-up converter system tests.

4. Replace fluid and filter.

5. Adjust transmission bands.

REVIEW QUESTIONS

1. Explain the difference between rotary and vortex fluid flow in a torque converter.

2. What component keeps the stator assembly from rotating when driven in one direction and permits rotation when turned in the opposite direction?

3. When an external gear tooth is in mesh with an internal gear, what is the direction of output rotation for one gear when the other is turned?

4. Name the two types of bands used in automatic transmissions.

5. List three purposes of automatic transmission fluid.

6. In the coupling stage of conventional torque converter operation, ____.
   a. both the impeller and turbine are turning at essentially the same speed
   b. both the stator and turbine are stationary
   c. both the stator and impeller are stationary
   d. the stator freewheels or turns as a unit
   e. both a and d

7. To achieve a slow overdrive in a simple planetary gearset, the ____.
   a. sun gear must be the input member
   b. ring gear must be the input member
   c. planetary carrier must be the input member
   d. ring gear must be held

8. In a simple planetary gearset, when the planetary carrier is held, the gearset produces a ____.
   a. reverse
   b. direct drive
   c. fast overdrive
   d. forward reduction

9. Overrunning clutches are capable of ____.
   a. holding a planetary gear member stationary
   b. driving a planetary gear member
   c. both a and b
   d. neither a nor b

10. Technician A says a Simpson gearset is two planetary gearsets that share a common sun gear. Technician B says a Ravigneaux gearset has two sun gears, two sets of planet gears, and a common ring gear. Who is correct?
    a. Technician A
    b. Technician B
    c. Both A and B
    d. Neither A nor B

11. Technician A says shift solenoids direct fluid flow to and away from the various apply devices in the transmission. Technician B says shift solenoids are used to mechanically apply a friction band or multiple-disc clutch assembly. Who is correct?
    a. Technician A
    b. Technician B
    c. Both A and B
    d. Neither A nor B

12. When the pressure regulator valve begins to operate, the first part to be charged with line pressure is the ____.
    a. torque converter
    b. forward clutch assembly
    c. manual valve
    d. governor assembly

13. To boost transmission line pressure, throttle pressure assists the ____.
    a. pressure regulator valve coil spring
    b. pressure regulator valve
    c. modulator valve
    d. governor valve

14. What is necessary for lockup engagement to take place?
    a. The lockup solenoid check ball must be off its seat and the switch valve held up by the spring tension.
    b. The lockup solenoid must be energized with the check ball on its seat and the switch valve held down by line pressure.
    c. The lockup check ball must be off its seat and the switch valve held down by the line pressure.
    d. The solenoid must have the check ball seated and the switch valve held up by spring tension.

15. Technician A says the electronically controlled lockup torque converter improves fuel economy. Technician B says it prevents lockup from occurring during certain engine modes. Who is correct?
    a. Technician A
    b. Technician B
    c. Both A and B
    d. Neither A nor B

16. Technician A says the turbine is positioned with its back facing the transmission housing. Technician B says the turbine shaft transfers power flow to the mainshaft of the transmission. Who is correct?
    a. Technician A
    b. Technician B
    c. Both A and B
    d. Neither A nor B

17. Technician A says rotary oil flow is the oil flow around the circumference of the torque converter caused by the rotation of the torque converter on its axis. Technician B says the centrifugal lockup clutch is the type installed in most automatic transmissions. Who is correct?
    a. Technician A
    b. Technician B
    c. Both A and B
    d. Neither A nor B

18. Technician A says Chrysler refers to the planetary controls by their location in the transaxle or transmission housing. Technician B says the Simpson gear train is used in most automatic transmissions installed in North American automobiles. Who is correct?
    a. Technician A
    b. Technician B
    c. Both A and B
    d. Neither A nor B

19. Technician A says the planetary carriers of each planetary unit are locked to the other planetary unit's ring gear in an AXOD transaxle. Technician B says in an AXOD, each planetary set has its own sun gear and set of planetary pinion gears. Who is correct?
    a. Technician A
    b. Technician B
    c. Both A and B
    d. Neither A nor B

20. Technician A says throttle position is an important input in most electronic shift control systems. Technician B says vehicle speed is an important input for most electronic shift control systems. Who is correct?
    a. Technician A
    b. Technician B
    c. Both A and B
    d. Neither A nor B

AUTOMATIC TRANSMISSION/ TRANSAXLE SERVICE

33

OBJECTIVES

◆ *Check, diagnose, and change the transmission fluid level.* ◆ *List possible causes of oil leaks.* ◆ *Explain how to check and adjust the gear selector linkage.* ◆ *Explain how to adjust the throttle cable.* ◆ *Describe the procedure for adjusting a front kickdown band.* ◆ *Explain how a vacuum modulator and governor are serviced.* ◆ *Describe how to perform a road test analysis accurately.* ◆ *Explain when and how pressure tests are performed.* ◆ *Explain the basics of computer and solenoid valve tests.*

Automatic transmission diagnosis and service is a highly specialized field of automotive work. Entire books cannot cover all the variables offered by the different manufacturers. However, half of all automatic transmission problems result from improper fluid levels, fluid leaks, vacuum leaks, or electrical malfunctions.

Changing fluid and filters and adjusting gear selector, throttle cable, and downshift linkages are also easily accessible service jobs that can be routinely performed by knowledgeable technicians.

Typical automatic transmission diagnostic steps may include the use of manufacturers' diagnostic guides, input from the customer, fluid and linkage checks, electrical checks, stall testing, road testing, and pressure testing.

USING SERVICE MANUALS

The diagnostic guides supplied by the automobile manufacturers provide a logical step-by-step plan to solve transmission problems. A section of a typical guide is shown in Figure 33–1. ■

Diagnostic sheets, such as the one shown in Figure 33–2, are extremely helpful in accurately recording all useful information during testing and troubleshooting.

FIGURE 33–1 Section of a typical manufacturer's troubleshooting diagnostic chart.

MULTI-CHECK

Fluid Check		Minor Adjustment Diagnosis
LEVEL	**CONDITION**	☐ Check Shift Linkage or Cable
☐ OK	☐ Normal	☐ Check Engine Idle Speed (RPM)
☐ Low ____	☐ Contaminated	☐ Check Engine Performance
☐ High	☐ Varnished	☐ Check Vacuum Hose/Cable Connections
	☐ Burnt Odor	

Initial Engagement

Park:	3rd:
Reverse:	2nd:
Neutral:	1st:
Drive:	

Driving Conditions

1st:

2nd:

3rd:

4th:

5th:

Reverse:

TCC Engagement:	Passing Gear:

Noises/Vibrations:

Minor Adjustment Checks and Tests Performed

☐ Check Vacuum
☐ Check Modulator / Modulator Pin
☐ Check TV/ Detent Linkage or Cable
☐ Check Band Adjustments
☐ Check Shift Linkage/ Cable
☐ Check Mounts
☐ Check Final Drive / Drive Axle / U Joints / CV Joints

☐ Fluid Retention
☐ Speedometer   ☐ OK ☐ NG
AS REQUIRED:
☐ Check External Electrical Controls and Internal Solenoid(s)
☐ Perform Hydraulic Pressure Test

Sump:	☐ Normal	☐ EF	☐ Water	☐ EM	☐ Varnish	☐ Center Remarks

Center Remarks

FIGURE 33–2 Typical transmission diagnostic checklist. *Courtesy of AAMCO Tools*

CUSTOMER CARE

Before taking on the responsibility of repairing an automatic transmission, be sure you have a competent knowledge of transmission design, operation, and diagnostic procedures. There are many horror stories told by customers about dollars wasted on reconditioned transmissions when all that was needed was something as simple as topping off the transmission fluid or adjusting the gear selector linkage or throttle cable. ∎

AUTOMATIC TRANSMISSION FLUID

ATF can be a petroleum-based, partially synthetic, or totally synthetic-based oil. All domestic automobile manufacturers require a petroleum-based fluid in their automatic transmissions; however, some imported vehicles require the use of a partially synthetic fluid.

ATF is a compound liquid that also includes special additives, which allow the lubricant to better meet the flow and friction requirements of an automatic transmission. ATF is normally dyed red, primarily to help distinguish it from engine oil when determining the source of fluid leaks.

Petroleum-based ATF typically has a clear red color and will darken when it is burnt or become milky when contaminated by water. Synthetic ATF is normally a darker red than petroleum-based fluid. Synthetic fluids tend to look and smell burnt after normal use; therefore, the appearance and smell of these fluids is not a good indicator of the fluid's condition.

The various chemicals added to ATF ensure the durability and overall performance of the fluid. Zinc, phosphorous, and sulfur are commonly added to reduce friction. Detergent additives are added to ATF to help keep the transmission parts clean. Also added are dispersants that keep contaminants suspended in the fluid so they can be trapped by the filter.

All certified types and brands of ATF have been tested to ensure they meet the criteria set by the manufacturers. Some of these test standards apply to all types of ATF, such as oxidation resistance, corrosion and rust inhibition, flash and flame points, and resistance to foaming. Other standards are specific for a particular fluid rating or type.

Because some chemicals used in the composition of transmission fluid may adversely react with the fibers or synthetic materials used in the seals of the transmission, the compatibility of the fluids with specific transmissions is also tested. Incompatibility can result in external and internal transmission fluid leaks due to deterioration, swelling, and/or shrinking of the seals.

All brands of ATF are also tested for their **miscibility** or compatibility with other brands of ATF. Although the different brands of transmission fluids must meet the same set of standards, they may differ in their actual chemical composition and be incompatible with others. There should be no fluid separation, color change, or chemical breakdown when two different brands of ATF are mixed together. This level of compatibility is important to the service life of a transmission as it allows for the maintenance of fluid levels without the worry of switching to or mixing different brands of fluid.

Recommended Applications There are several ratings or types of ATF available, each type is designed for a specific application. The different classifications of transmission fluid have resulted from the inclusion of new or different additives, which enhance the operation of the different transmission designs. Each automobile manufacturer specifies the proper type of ATF that should be used in their transmissions. Both the design of the transmission and the desired shift characteristics are considered when a specific ATF is chosen.

To reduce wear and friction inside a transmission, most commonly used transmission fluids are mixed with **friction modifiers**. Fluid types A, CJ, H, DEXRON, and MERCON have friction modifiers added to the ATF. Transmission fluids with these additives allow for the use of lower clutch and band application pressures, which, in turn, provide for a very smooth feeling shift. Transmission fluids without a friction modifier, such as Types F and G, tend to have a firmer shift because higher clutch and band application pressures are required to avoid excessive slippage during gear changes.

If an ATF without friction modifiers is used in a transmission designed for friction modified fluid, the service life of the transmission is not normally affected. However, firmer shifting will result and the driver might not welcome this change in shifting quality. Transmission durability is affected by using friction modified fluid in a transmission designed for non-modified fluids. This incorrect use of fluid will cause slippage, primarily when the vehicle is working under a load. Any amount of slippage can cause the clutches and bands to wear prematurely. Also, because of the high heat generated by the slippage, the fluid may overheat and lose some of its lubrication and cooling qualities, which could cause the entire transmission to fail.

The formulation of an ATF must also be concerned with the viscosity of the fluid. Although the fluids are not selected according to viscosity numbers, proper flow characteristics of the fluid are important in operation of a transmission. If the viscosity is too low, the chances of internal and external leaks increase, parts can prematurely wear due to a lack of adequate lubrication, system pressure will be reduced, and overall control of the hydraulics will be less affective. If the viscosity is too high, internal friction will increase resulting in a greater chance of building up sludge, hydraulic operation will be sluggish, and the transmission will require more engine power for operation.

Nearly all manufacturers recommend the use of **Dexron**-II ATF in their automatic transmissions. This type of ATF has been developed through the years to meet the needs of the newer transmissions. The series or classification of the fluid is designated by a progressing alphabetical suffix. Dexron-IIE is currently the preferred fluid for all Hydra-Matic transmissions and transaxles and many other transmissions. It replaces Dexron-II and is recommended wherever Dexron-II was previously specified. It may be used in all General Motors' automatic transmissions produced since 1949. It may be mixed, in any ratio, in a transmission already filled with Dexron-II

without draining or flushing. Both fluids are fully compatible and may be substituted when necessary. Dexron-IIE has the following advantages over other Dexron-II fluids: improved antifoaming characteristics, improved low temperature flow, and improved high temperature oxidation stability.

Some manufacturers recommend the use of other types of fluid, but normally list Dexron-II has a secondary choice. Fluid recommendations from Ford Motor Company have changed several times through the years. These recommendations will vary according to the vehicle in which a particular transmission is installed or the year in which the transmission was manufactured. Typically Type F ATF is recommended for all 1976 and earlier Ford automatic transmissions. **Mercon** is the preferred fluid for 1983-87 Ford products, although Dexron-II is a secondary choice for some transmissions. The use of Mercon is a warranty requirement for all 1988 and later Ford automatic transmissions.

Chrysler Corporation vehicles, such as some Eagle and Jeep models, also have Mercon as the recommended ATF. Most other Chrysler vehicles should use Dexron-II. Chrysler does recommend the use of their own formulated fluid, Mopar ATF Plus (7176), in some of their automatics equipped with a lockup torque converter.

Fluid Service The ATF level should be checked at regular mileage and time intervals. The dipstick is located on the transmission housing at the end of the engine opposite the belts and pulleys.

Make sure the vehicle is level. On most automobiles, the ATF level can be checked accurately only when the transmission is at operating temperature. For most vehicles, the engine must be running and the shift lever placed in either park or neutral, as specified by the vehicle manufacturer, with the parking brake applied. Markings on a dipstick indicate add levels, plus full levels for fluid when cool, warm, or hot (Figure 33–3).

Some dipsticks have readings on both sides. Others have readings on only one side. On some vehicles with automatic transaxles, the cold fluid level might be higher than the hot fluid level. Refer to the manufacturer's service manual and service bulletins for specific information.

To check the fluid level, start the engine and bring it to operating temperature. Remove the dipstick and wipe it clean with a lint-free cloth or paper towel. Reinsert the dipstick fully. Remove it again and note the reading.

LOW FLUID LEVELS If the fluid level is low and off the crosshatch section of the dipstick, the problem could be external fluid leaks. Low fluid levels cause a variety of problems. The condition allows air to be drawn into the pump inlet circuit. Aeration of the fluid causes slow pressure buildup and low fluid pressures, contributing to slipping automatic shifts.

Air in the fluid pressure regulator valve can cause a buzzing action and noise as it tries to regulate pump pressure. The most probable cause of low fluid levels is an external fluid leak.

HIGH FLUID LEVELS High fluid levels cause the rotating planetary gears and parts to churn up the fluid and admit air-developing foam. This condition is very similar to low fluid level. Aerated fluid can cause overheating, fluid oxidation, which contributes to varnish buildup, and interference with normal spool valve, clutch, and servo operation.

Diagnosing Transmission Fluid

Uncontaminated automatic transmission fluid is pinkish or red in color. A dark brownish or blackish color or a burnt odor indicate overheating. If the fluid has overheated, the ATF and the filter must be changed and the transmission inspected. A milky color can indicate that engine coolant is leaking into the transmission cooler in the radiator outlet tank.

Bubbles on the dipstick indicate the presence of air. The bubbles usually are caused by a high-pressure leak.

Wipe the dipstick on absorbent white paper. Look at the fluid stain. Dark particles in the fluid indicate band or clutch material. Silvery metal particles indicate excessive wear on metal parts or housings. Varnish or gum deposits on a dipstick indicate the need to change the ATF and the transmission filter.

Changing Transmission/Transaxle Fluid

Change the fluid when the engine and transmission or transaxle are at normal operating temperatures. Contaminants flow out more completely when the fluid is warm.

FIGURE 33–3 Typical transaxle dipstick indicating proper ATF levels at various operating temperatures. *Courtesy of Chrysler Corporation*

FIGURE 33–4 Removing the transmission pan drain plug.

On most units, it is necessary to remove the oil pan to drain the fluid. Some transmission pans on recent vehicles include a drain plug (Figure 33–4). After draining, the pan must be removed for inspection and to replace the filter.

Check the bottom of the oil pan for deposits and metal particles. A small amount of blackish deposits from transmission clutches and bands and a few small metal particles are normal. Large amounts of deposits or metal particles indicate major damage to friction materials or metal parts in the transmission. Clean the inside of the pan with solvent and blow it dry with compressed air.

A filter or screen is usually attached to the valve body (Figure 33–5). Filters are made of paper or fabric, and may be held in place by screws, clips, or bolts (Figure 33–6). A filter kit contains a new filter and a transmission pan gasket.

Screens are removed in the same way as filters. Some transmissions have valves and springs between the valve body and screen. Do not loosen or remove valves or springs. Clean the screen with fresh solvent and a stiff brush.

Remove any traces of the old gasket on the case housing and oil pan by scraping with a gasket scraper or putty knife. Do not damage the sealing surface of the housing or oil pan. Refill with the recommended type and amount of new ATF. Be careful not to overfill.

The steps involved in a typical automatic transmission fluid and filter change are illustrated in Photo Sequence 18.

FIGURE 33–5 Typical location of an oil screen.

PERFORMING AN AUTOMATIC TRANSMISSION FLUID AND FILTER CHANGE

P18–1   To begin the procedure for changing automatic transmission fluid and filter, raise the car on a lift. Before working under the car, make sure it is safely positioned on the lift.

P18–2   Locate the transmission pan. Remove any part that may interfere with the removal of the pan.

P18–3   Position the oil drain pan under the transmission pan. A large diameter drain pan helps prevent spills.

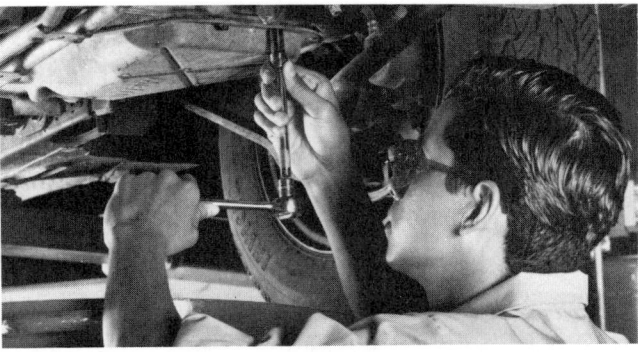

P18–4   Loosen all of the pan bolts and remove all but three. This will cause fluid to flow out around the pan into the drain pan.

P18–5   Supporting the pan with one hand, remove the remaining bolts and pour the fluid from the transmission pan into the drain pan.

P18–6   Carefully inspect the transmission pan and the residue in it. The condition of the fluid is often an indication of the condition of the transmission and serves as a valuable diagnostic tool.

P18–7 Remove the old pan gasket and wipe the transmission pan clean with a lint-free rag.

P18–9 Before continuing, compare the old filter and pan gasket with the new ones.

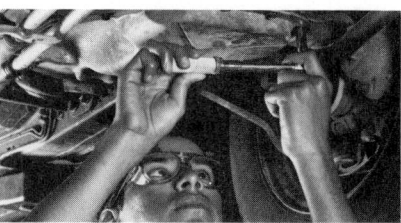

P18–11 Install the attaching bolts and tighten them to the recommended specifications. Read the specifications for installing the filter and pan carefully. Some transmissions require torque specifications of inch-pounds rather than the typical foot-pounds.

P18–8 Unbolt the fluid filter from the transmission's valve body. Keep the drain pan under the transmission while doing this. Additional fluid may leak out of the filter or valve body.

P18–10 Install the new filter into the valve body and tighten the attaching bolts to proper specifications. Lay the new pan gasket over the sealing surface of the pan and move the pan into place.

P18–12 With the pan tightened, lower the car. Start the engine, with the parking brake applied and your foot on the brake pedal. Move the shift lever through the gears. This allows the fluid to circulate throughout the entire transmission. After the engine reaches normal operating temperature, check the transmission fluid level and correct it if necessary

SHOP TALK

Automatic transmission fluids are classified as either nonfriction modified or friction modified. Nonfriction modified fluids, such as General Motors' Dexron® (used in both General Motors' and Chrysler units) and Ford's Type F are not compatible with modern lockup torque converters and automatic transmissions.

Friction modified fluids were introduced in the late 1970s and are compatible with modern transmission/transaxle designs. These include General Motors' Dexron® II, Ford's Mercon®, and Chrysler's ATF fluids. Ford Mercon® fluid can be used in transmissions originally designed for Ford's CJ and Type H friction modified fluids.

Always use the exact automatic transmission fluid type specified in the vehicle service manual. ■

Oil Leaks

There are many possible sources for ATF leakage. One of these, the pump seal, can be replaced only if the transmission is removed from the vehicle.

Leaks caused by worn or defective gaskets or seals are repaired by replacing the defective part. The transmission need not be removed for this service. Follow the manufacturer's replacement instructions.

Case porosity, tiny holes caused by trapped air bubbles during the casting process, can occur. Leakage of ATF through the cap can be seen and felt. Case

FIGURE 33–6 Removing a transaxle filter with a Torx® driver. *Courtesy of Chrysler Corporation*

porosity may be repaired using an epoxy-type sealer. All traces of oil must be removed before attempting this repair, which may require transmission removal.

GEAR SELECTOR LINKAGE CHECK

Proper adjustment of the gear selector or manual linkage is important in order to have the manual valve fluid inlet and outlets properly aligned in the valve body. If the manual valve does not align with the inlet and outlets, line pressure could be lost to an open circuit.

A neutral safety switch permits starter engagement only in park or neutral gear selector positions. If the neutral safety switch is suspect, refer to the vehicle's service manual for proper testing procedures. The gear selector positions must correspond to the range selected in the transaxle.

PROCEDURES
Checking Gear Selector Linkage

1. Move the gear selector into the park position.
2. Turn the ignition key to the start position. If the starter operates in this position, the adjustment is correct.
3. Slowly move the gear selector to the neutral position and let the gear selector drop into the notch.
4. Repeat the engine start test. If the starter operates when the ignition key is in the start position, the gear selector linkage is properly adjusted. If the starter does not engage, the gear selector linkage must be adjusted.

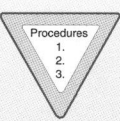

PROCEDURES
Adjusting Gear Selector Linkage

1. Place the gear selector in the park position.
2. Loosen the clamp bolt on the gear selector cable bracket at the transaxle housing (Figure 33–7).
3. Move the transaxle shift lever to the front detent position. The shift lever is in the detent position when it clicks as the roller seats in the detent recess.
4. Move the gear selector cable to achieve the correct adjustment.
5. With the gear selector cable in the cable clamp, tighten the cable clamp bolt to the manufacturer's specifications as found in the service manual.
6. Recheck the gear selector linkage adjustment. The starting motor should engage only in park and neutral positions.
7. With the ignition key turned on, place the gear selector lever in reverse. The backup lights should be on if the circuit is complete.

THROTTLE CABLE LINKAGE CHECK

The throttle cable connects the throttle pedal to the transmission/transaxle valve body throttle valve, which makes throttle pressure. Throttle pressure signals the engine load and torque required and is opposed by governor pressure. Throttle pressure affects the speed at which shifting occurs.

PROCEDURES
Throttle Cable Adjustment

1. To adjust the throttle cable, the engine must be at operating temperature and off the warm-up fast idle.
2. Check engine idle speed with a reliable tachometer. Idle speed specifications are located in the vehicle's service manual. Proper engine idle speed avoids harsh engagements when the gear selector is moved to reverse or drive positions. Low idle speed creates a variety of engagement problems.
3. Refer to Figure 33–8 and loosen the throttle cable bracket bolt.

FIGURE 33–7 Typical gear selector control linkage for a transaxle. *Courtesy of Chrysler Corporation*

4. Check the alignment of the cable bracket with the tabs to the transaxle housing.
5. Tighten the bracket bolts to the manufacturer's specifications.
6. The throttle cable is held in position in the throttle cable bracket by the cross-lock, an automatic locking device that keeps the throttle cable properly adjusted. Most vehicles using throttle cables have some type of automatic cable-locking device. For the correct procedure for throttle cable adjustment and the operation of the automatic cable-locking device, refer to the vehicle's service manual.
7. To release the cross-lock's hold on the throttle cable, pull upward on the cross-lock.
8. Be sure the throttle cable slides freely in the cross-lock.
9. With the throttle cable sliding freely in the cross-lock, hold the cable against the throttle cable stop. With the throttle cable in contact with its stop, release the cross-lock.
10. Move the throttle control level through its full travel from one end to the other. With the throttle level and throttle cable moving freely, press the cross-lock down and trap the throttle cable in position. The throttle cable is now adjusted.

Figure 33–9 illustrates a typical self-adjusting throttle cable used on some front-wheel- and rear-wheel-drive vehicles.

FIGURE 33–8 Throttle linkage adjustment bracket. *Courtesy of Chrysler Corporation*

FIGURE 33–9 Automatic throttle cable adjuster. *Courtesy of Chevrolet Motor Division, General Motors Corporation*

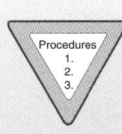

PROCEDURES

Adjusting a Self-Adjusting Throttle Cable

1. Press in the readjust tab.
2. Move the sliding part back through the fitting until the slider stops against the fitting.
3. Release the readjust tab.
4. Open the carburetor level to the wide-open throttle position, which automatically adjusts the throttle cable.
5. Release the carburetor lever. The throttle cable is adjusted.

FIGURE 33–10 Front kickdown band adjusting screw and locknut. *Courtesy of Chrysler Corporation*

BAND ADJUSTMENT

Slippage during shifting can indicate the need for band adjustment. Adjusting transmission bands may or may not be part of a scheduled maintenance program for the vehicle. Many transmissions have no provisions for adjusting bands. In other cases, the adjustment procedure involves draining the transmission fluid and removing the oil pan. Figure 33–10 shows a front kickdown band adjustment being made.

PROCEDURES

Adjusting the Band

1. Loosen the band adjusting bolt locknut.
2. Back off the locknut approximately five turns.
3. Rotate the adjusting screw in the transaxle housing. Be sure it is free to turn and does not interfere with the torque specification.
4. Use an inch-pound torque wrench and socket to tighten the adjusting bolt to 72 inch-pounds or the specified torque.
5. After reaching the specified torque, back out the adjusting screw the specified number of turns indicated in the vehicle's service manual for that particular model transmission/transaxle.
6. Tighten the adjuster bolt locknut.

VACUUM MODULATOR SERVICE

The vacuum modulator usually is screwed or clamped into place at the side or rear of the transmission.

Improper shifting can be caused by a defective vacuum modulator or by defective or missing modu-

FIGURE 33–11 A damaged vacuum line in the modulator circuit can cause improper shifting.

lator vacuum connectors (Figure 33–11). Engine vacuum leaks can produce the same symptoms. Follow the diagnostic procedure outlined in the manufacturer's service manual to determine the exact cause.

A repeated low fluid level in the transmission with no visible external leaks and the sudden appearance of excessive blue-white smoke from the tailpipe usually indicates a ruptured diaphragm in the modulator. To check for this condition, pull the vacuum hose off the modulator connection. If ATF is present in the hose, the vacuum modulator must be replaced.

Clean the area around the modulator with solvent. Then disconnect the vacuum hose. The modulator itself is either unscrewed or unclamped from the transmission housing and removed carefully. Special tools might be necessary. Take care that the modulator valve does not fall out during this removal. Then install the new replacement unit. Refer to the manufacturer's service manual for more complete replacement procedures.

FIGURE 33–12 Example of governor held in place with a retaining clamp.

GOVERNOR SERVICE

Improper shift points can be caused by a malfunction in the governor or governor drive gear system.

Although all governors are mounted internally, some require removal of the extension housing or oil pan for access.

Another type of governor is serviced by removing an external retaining clamp and then removing the unit (Figure 33–12). Follow the manufacturer's recommended diagnostic and service procedures.

ROAD TESTING

Road testing is exceedingly important when troubleshooting automatic transaxle and transmission problems. The objective of the road test is to confirm the customer's complaint. It is always wise to have the customer accompany the diagnostician on a road test to confirm the malfunction. The road test allows for the opportunity to check the transaxle or transmission operation for slipping, harshness, incorrect upshift speeds, and incorrect downshifts.

DIAGNOSING ACCURATELY

The secret of an accurate diagnosis is knowing what planetary controls are applied in a particular gear range. The rear clutch is engaged in both D range first gear and manual first gear #1 on the gear selector. The overrunning clutch is engaged in D range first gear and the low and reverse rear band in manual first gear.

If the transaxle slips in D range first gear but not in manual first gear, the overrunning clutch must be slipping. Similarly, if the transaxle slips in any two forward gear ranges, the rear clutch is the slipping planetary control unit. Using the same procedure, the rear clutch and front clutch are engaged in D range

third gear. If there is slippage in this range, either the front clutch or rear clutch is slipping. By selecting another gear range that does not use one of these two units, the planetary control slippage can be determined. If the transaxle also slips in reverse, the front clutch is slipping. If the transaxle does not slip in reverse, the rear clutch is slipping. This process of eliminating the various planetary controls can be used to detect any planetary unit that slips and to confirm proper operation of the good units.

Although road testing analysis can help to identify slipping units, the actual cause of the slip or malfunction usually cannot be decided. Nearly any slipping condition can be caused by leaking hydraulic circuits or sticking spool valves in the valve body. When hydraulic circuits leak within the transmission/transaxle housing, they are referred to as internal leaks.

PRESSURE TESTING

A road test enables the technician to determine which apply devices might not be working properly. For example, a slipping band might be detected. The next step is to find what caused the band to slip.

The problem might be mechanical—improper band adjustment or a worn friction lining. However, low hydraulic pressure could have caused the band to slip and wear out. A valve in the valve body could be stuck or leaking. Just replacing the worn-out band would not solve the problem. If the sticking valve is not found and replaced, the new band would soon slip and wear out.

A **pressure test** checks hydraulic pressures in the transmission by using gauges that are attached to the transmission. The transmission is shifted into a specific gear, and the engine is run at a recommended speed while pressure readings are recorded. Pressure readings reveal possible problems in the oil pump, governor, and throttle circuits.

Pressure test openings, or ports, are located on the transmission case (Figure 33–13). After removing a plug, a fitting can be screwed into the port. The pressure gauge connects to the fitting. In addition, a tachometer and vacuum gauge might be required. The use of a combination tester, shown in Figure 33–14, makes the procedure easier. Consult the manufacturer's service manual for the recommended gauge or for reading more than one pressure gauge at the same time, in addition to a vacuum gauge. To perform a pressure test correctly, refer to the proper service manual.

When conducting pressure tests on different transmissions, all of the following steps might be necessary. However, some manufacturers might omit one

FIGURE 33–13 Pressure testing ports on the side of a transaxle. *Courtesy of Chrysler Corporation*

FIGURE 33–14 Typical combination pressure test equipment. *Courtesy of Ford Motor Company*

or more of the steps. Other procedures might replace some steps with alternate, or different, ones. Additional steps might be required.

PROCEDURES
Pressure Testing

1. Start the engine and let it warm to normal operating temperature. Then shut it off.
2. Connect a tachometer to the engine according to the manufacturer's instructions.
3. Have a helper inside the vehicle start the engine and operate the transmission, accelerator, and brake controls.
4. Safely raise the vehicle on a hoist to a comfortable working height.
5. Connect pressure gauges to the specified test ports.

6. Use a T-fitting and vacuum tubing to connect a vacuum gauge with a shutoff or bleed-down valve to the vacuum modulator line.

⬤ CAUTION:

If the pressure test procedures or equipment require you to be under the vehicle while the test is performed, be extremely careful. The driveline and drive wheels turn for most tests. Contact with the spinning driveline or wheels can cause serious physical injury. Always wear eye protection while working under a car. ■

7. Start the engine. Move the selector lever to the first test position. Run the engine at the specified rpm. Take readings from the gauges, and write them down. Move the transmission controls as specified, and note the readings or change in readings. Make notes of the pressures or pressure changes.
8. Slow the engine and press gently on the service brakes to stop the spinning wheels and driveline. Shut off the engine.
9. Attach the pressure gauges and vacuum gauge to the proper pressure ports for the next test.
10. Start the engine. Move the gearshift lever to the next test position. Run the engine at the specified rpm. Take pressure readings as specified. Slow the engine, and press gently on the service brakes to stop the spinning wheels and driveline.
11. Repeat the steps for each test procedure. Make notes of all pressure readings and vacuum readings obtained for each test.

Analyzing Pressure Test Readings
Charts in the manufacturers' service manual list correct specifications for the pressure tests, as well as possible causes of incorrect readings. Refer to the service manual to determine the causes of pressure readings other than as specified.

Air Pressure Tests
The source of a transmission hydraulic problem can be difficult to locate. If road testing and pressure testing have indicated a slipping clutch or band, air pressure tests can be made. Air pressure tests can determine whether the problem is in the apply device or in the valve body that supplies hydraulic pressure.

After the valve body has been removed, air pressure is applied to the case holes and passages leading to the apply devices. Correct operation of servos and clutches can be heard and felt. Air pressure tests are done during overhaul disassembly to locate leaking seals. Air pressure tests are also done during reassembly to check for proper clutch and servo operation.

Filtered, moisture-free compressed air of 40 psi is normally used for the test. Air pressure of up to 90 psi can be used if it is difficult to hear the clutches apply. An air blowgun with a conical rubber nozzle is used to apply the air pressure (Figure 33–15).

Some manufacturers recommend the use of special metal plates that bolt to the transmission to seal the case apply passages (Figure 33–16). The metal plate and gasket are bolted to the case. Identification of the holes is stamped into the plate. Air is applied through the plate holes.

FIGURE 33–15   Air pressure tests are performed using an air blowgun with a conical rubber nozzle.

FIGURE 33–16   Installing the air pressure plate service tool. *Courtesy of Ford Motor Company*

PROCEDURES

Conducting Air Pressure Tests

1. Safely raise the vehicle on a hoist.
2. Drain the transmission oil and remove the oil pan.
3. Remove the filter.
4. Remove the valve body.
5. Refer to the manufacturer's service manual to identify the fluid passages. Attach special plates and gaskets as necessary. Torque the plate attaching screws to the manufacturer's specifications.
6. Apply air pressure to the servo and clutch apply passages and listen for 5 to 10 seconds. Listen for hissing, which indicates air leakage from faulty seals.

CAUTION:

Compressed air can blow liquids or metal chips into your eyes, causing serious physical injury or blindness. Always wear safety glasses or goggles when working with compressed air. ■

7. Release air pressure and reapply. Listen for thuds or thunks. If you cannot hear a servo operate, watch to see if the band tightens and loosens properly as air pressure is applied and released. Repair or replace apply devices during overhaul as necessary.

Computer and Solenoid Valve Tests

Refer to the manufacturer's service manual procedures for specific transmission computer tests. Be aware that improper test procedures can damage or destroy computer units immediately.

Specific tests for input and output signals are made. Special hand-held computer testers might be required. If input signals are correct and output signals are incorrect, the computer unit must be replaced.

Solenoid valves are tested by removing the electrical connector. Then the resistance of the solenoid coil can be checked between the connector and ground. Another way of testing a solenoid is to apply current with a small jumper wire to the disconnected solenoid valve. Correct operation can be heard or felt when the solenoid moves sharply. Refer to the manufacturer's service manuals and service bulletins for specific tests.

CASE STUDY

A customer complains of delayed and harsh shifting.

The knowledgeable technician realizes this problem results from high throttle pressure caused by a lack of engine vacuum at the vacu-

um modulator (closed) chamber. He seeks to determine why the engine vacuum is not reaching the modulator chamber. The technician begins by connecting a vacuum gauge to the end of the steel vacuum pipe between the intake manifold and the vacuum modulator. With the engine operating and the transmission in neutral, he checks the vacuum gauge reading. It is within specifications, so he rapidly accelerates the engine for a moment. Because the vacuum gauge needle drops rapidly at acceleration and returns immediately upon release of the throttle, the technician knows that the steel vacuum pipe is not plugged or restricted. Next, the technician uses a hand-held vacuum pump to check the steel pipe for pinholes. The hand-held pump is connected to the intake manifold end of the steel piping. The steel piping is disconnected at the vacuum modulator and the end of the steel piping is blocked. Then the technician operates the vacuum pump to pump up vacuum. Because a vacuum reading is shown on the vacuum pump and it holds steady, the technician knows there are no pinholes in the steel piping. Finally, he examines the rubber tubing that connects the steel piping to the vacuum modulator and finds it is porous. The technician replaces the connector tubing and the problem is corrected.

KEY TERMS

Case porosity
Dexron
Friction modifiers

Mercon
Miscibility
Pressure test

SUMMARY

- The ATF level should be checked at regular mileage and time intervals. When the fluid is checked, the vehicle should be level and running and the transmission should be at operating temperature.
- Both low fluid levels and high fluid levels can cause aeration of the fluid, which, in turn, can cause a number of transmission problems.
- Uncontaminated automatic transmission fluid is pinkish or red in color and it has no dark or metallic particles suspended in it.
- The fluid should be changed when the engine and transmission or transaxle are at normal operating temperatures. After draining the fluid, the pan should be inspected and the filter replaced.

- If ATF is leaking from the pump seal, the transmission must be removed from the vehicle so the seal can be replaced. Other worn or defective gaskets or seals can be replaced without removing the transmission. Case porosity may be repaired using an epoxy-type sealer.
- Proper adjustment of the gear selector or manual linkage is important to have the manual valve fluid inlet and outlets properly aligned in the valve body. If the manual valve does not align with the inlet and outlets, line pressure could be lost to an open circuit.
- The throttle cable connects the throttle pedal's movement to the transaxle valve body throttle valve, which produces throttle pressure. The throttle cable is held in position in the throttle cable bracket by the cross-lock, an automatic locking device that keeps the throttle cable properly adjusted.
- Slippage during shifting can indicate the need for band adjustment.
- Improper shifting can be caused by a defective vacuum modular or by defective or missing modulator vacuum connectors. A repeated low fluid level in the transmission with no visible external leaks and the sudden appearance of excessive blue-white smoke from the tailpipe usually indicates a ruptured diaphragm in the modulator.
- Improper shift points can be caused by a malfunction in the governor or governor drive gear system.
- The road test gives the technician the opportunity to check the transaxle or transmission operation for slipping, harshness, incorrect upshift speeds, and incorrect downshift.
- Accurate diagnosis depends on knowing what planetary controls are applied in a particular gear range. Although road testing analysis can help to diagnose slipping units, the actual cause of the slip or malfunction usually cannot be decided.
- A pressure test checks hydraulic pressures in the transmission by using gauges that are attached to the transmission. Pressure readings reveal possible problems in the oil pump, governor, and throttle circuits.
- Air pressure tests can determine whether the problem is in the apply device or in the valve body that supplies hydraulic pressure.
- If a computer's input signals are correct and its output signals are incorrect, the computer must be replaced. Solenoid valves can be checked by measuring their resistance, or by applying a current to it and listening and feeling for its movement.

TECH MANUAL

The following procedures are included in Chapter 33 of the *Tech Manual* that accompanies this book:

1. Perform pressure tests.

2. Perform stall test.

3. Perform lock-up converter system tests.

4. Replace fluid and filter.

5. Adjust transmission bands.

REVIEW QUESTIONS

homework

1. What is the most probable cause of a low fluid level?

2. What does milky colored ATF indicate?

3. What do varnish or gum deposits on the dipstick indicate?

4. What switch permits starter engagement only in park or neutral gear selector positions?

5. What is a probable cause of a repeated low fluid level in the transmission with no visible external leaks and the sudden appearance of excessive blue-white smoke from the tailpipe?

6. Technician A says automatic transmission fluid smells burned if there is a burned-out planetary control unit. Technician B says all automatic transmission fluid smells burned after approximately 50 miles of operation. Who is correct?

   a. Technician A   c. Both A and B
   b. Technician B   d. Neither A nor B

7. What type of test is used to evaluate the application of servos and clutches?

   a. air pressure   c. both a and b
   b. hydraulic pressure   d. neither a nor b

8. Half of all automatic transmission problems result from _____.

   a. improper fluid levels
   b. fluid leaks and vacuum leaks
   c. electrical malfunctions
   d. all of the above

9. When should the ATF level be checked on most vehicles?

   a. when the engine is cool
   b. when the engine is at operating temperature and the engine is off
   c. when the engine is at operating temperature and the engine is on
   d. it does not matter

10. Technician A says low fluid levels can lead to aeration of the fluid. Technician B says high fluid levels cause aeration of the fluid. Who is correct?

    a. Technician A   c. Both A and B
    b. Technician B   d. Neither A nor B

11. Technician A changes the ATF when the engine and transmission are cool. Technician B checks the bottom of the oil pan, finds a few small metal particles, and concludes everything is normal. Who is correct?

    a. Technician A   c. Both A and B
    b. Technician B   d. Neither A nor B

12. Technician A says the pump seal can be replaced without removing the transmission from the vehicle. Technician B says case porosity may be repaired using an epoxy-type sealer. Who is correct?

    a. Technician A   c. Both A and B
    b. Technician B   d. Neither A nor B

13. Technician A says throttle pressure influences the vehicle speed at which automatic shifts take place. Technician B says throttle pressure is opposed by governor pressure. Who is correct?

    a. Technician A   c. Both A and B
    b. Technician B   d. Neither A nor B

14. Which of the following is true?

    a. The cross-lock keeps the gear selector linkage properly adjusted.
    b. The cross-lock keeps the throttle cable properly adjusted.
    c. The cross-lock keeps the front kickdown band properly adjusted.
    d. None of the above.

15. Technician A says engine vacuum leaks can produce the same symptoms as a defective vacuum modulator. Technician B says the vacuum modulator is located inside the transmission. Who is correct?

    a. Technician A   c. Both A and B
    b. Technician B   d. Neither A nor B

16. Improper shifting can be caused by ____.
    a. a defective vacuum modulator
    b. a malfunction in the governor
    c. both a and b
    d. neither a nor b

17. Technician A says a prerequisite to accurate road testing analysis is knowing what planetary controls are applied in a particular gear range. Technician B says all slipping conditions can be traced to a leaking hydraulic circuit. Who is correct?
    a. Technician A
    b. Technician B
    c. Both A and B
    d. Neither A nor B

18. Pressure readings reveal possible problems in which of the following?
    a. oil pump
    b. governor
    c. throttle circuits
    d. all of the above

19. What level of compressed air is usually used for the air pressure test?
    a. 40 psi
    b. 60 psi
    c. 80 psi
    d. 90 psi

20. Technician A says if input signals are correct and output signals are incorrect, the computer unit must be replaced. Technician B tests a solenoid by checking the voltage between the solenoid's connector and ground. Who is correct?
    a. Technician A
    b. Technician B
    c. Both A and B
    d. Neither A nor B

OBJECTIVES

♦ *Identify the advantages of four- and all-wheel drive.* ♦ *Name the major components of a conventional four-wheel-drive system.* ♦ *Name the components of a transfer case.* ♦ *State the difference between the transfer, open, and limited slip differentials.* ♦ *State the major purpose of locking/unlocking hubs.* ♦ *Name the five shift lever positions on a typical 4WD vehicle.* ♦ *Understand the difference between four- and all-wheel drive.* ♦ *Know the purpose of a viscous clutch in all-wheel drive.*

Four-wheel-drive (**4WD**) and all-wheel-drive (**AWD**) systems can dramatically increase a vehicle's traction and handling ability in rain, snow, and off-road driving. Considering that the vehicle's only contact with the road is the small areas of the tires, driving and handling is vastly improved if the work load is spread out evenly among four wheels rather than two.

Factors such as the side forces created by cornering and wind gusts have less effect on vehicles with four driving wheels. The increased traction also makes it possible to apply greater amounts of energy through the drive system. Vehicles with 4WD and AWD can maintain control while transmitting levels of power that would cause two wheels to spin either on take off or while rounding a curve. The improved traction of 4WD and AWD systems allows the use of tires narrower than those used on similar 2WD vehicles. These narrow tires are less expensive. They also tend to cut through snow and water rather than hydroplane over it.

Four-wheel-drive vehicles can transfer large amounts of horsepower through the drivelines without fear of drivetrain damage. This is not necessarily true of front-wheel-drive vehicles and all-wheel-drive vehicles (both of which use transaxles).

Both 4WD and AWD systems add initial cost and weight. With most passenger cars, the weight problem is minor. A typical 4WD system adds approximately 170 pounds to a passenger car. An AWD system adds even less weight. The additional weight in larger 4WD trucks can be as much as 400 pounds or more.

The systems also add initial cost to the vehicle. Vehicles equipped with 4WD and AWD require special service and maintenance not performed on 2WD vehicles. However, the slight disadvantages of 4WD and AWD are heavily outweighed by the traction and performance these systems offer. Their popularity is increasing at a rapid rate, and technicians must be prepared to diagnose and repair these systems.

4WD VERSUS AWD

Due to the many names manufacturers give their drive systems, it is often difficult to clearly define the difference between 4WD and AWD.

In this text, 4WD systems are those having a separate **transfer case** (Figure 34–1A). They also give the driver the choice of operating in either 2WD or 4WD through the use of a shift lever or shift button. The **locking hubs** used in 4WD systems can be either manual or automatic locking. Finally, a 4WD system may or may not use an **interaxle differential** or **viscous clutch** to distribute driving power to its front and rear drivelines.

All-wheel-drive systems differ in several major ways (Figure 34–1B). They do not have a separate transfer case. All-wheel-drive systems use a front-wheel-drive transaxle equipped with a viscous clutch, center differential, or transfer clutch. The viscous clutch, center differential, or transfer clutch transfers power from the transaxle to a rear driveline and rear axle assembly. All-wheel-drive systems do not give the driver the option of selecting 2WD or 4WD modes. The system operates in continuous 4WD.

FIGURE 34–1 (A) Four-wheel drive compared to (B) all-wheel drive. *Courtesy of Chrysler Corporation*

FOUR-WHEEL-DRIVE SYSTEMS

The typical truck or utility 4WD vehicle contains the following components (Figure 34–2): a front-mounted, longitudinally positioned engine; the transmission (either manual or automatic); two driveline shafts (front and rear); front and rear axle assemblies; and the transfer case.

The heart of most conventional four-wheel-drive vehicles is the transfer case, which is usually mounted to the side or the back of the transmission (Figure 34–3). A chain or gear drive within the case receives the power flow from the transmission and transfers it to two separate drive shafts leading to the front and rear axles.

A selector switch or shifter located in the driving compartment (Figure 34–4) controls the transfer case so power is directed to the axles as the driver desires. Power can be directed to all four wheels, two wheels, or no wheels (neutral). On many vehicles, the driver is also given the option of low four-wheel-drive range for extra traction in especially rough conditions such as deep snow or mud.

The driveline from the transfer case shafts run to differentials at the front and rear axles. As on two-wheel-drive vehicles, these axle differentials are used to compensate for road and driving conditions by adjusting the rpm to opposing wheels. For example, the outer wheel must roll faster in a turn than the inner wheel during a turn because it has more ground to cover. To permit this action, the differential cuts back the power delivered to the inner wheel and boosts the amount of power delivered to the outer wheel.

U-joints are used to couple the driveline shafts with the differentials and transfer cases on all these vehicles. U-joints can also be used on some vehicles to connect the rear axle and wheels. Normally, however, rear axles are simply bolted to the wheel hubs.

The coupling between front wheels and axles is normally done with U-joints on heavy-duty vehicles and with CV (constant velocity) joints on lightweight vehicles (Figure 34–5). Generally, half axles or half shafts with CV joints are found on four-wheel-drive passenger cars. They can also be found on a number of passenger vans and on mini pickups and trucks.

TRANSMISSION

REAR
DRIVE
SHAFT

REAR AXLE
ASSEMBLY

TRANSFER
CASE

FRONT
DRIVE
SHAFT

FRONT DRIVE AXLE

FIGURE 34–2 Truck-type four-wheel drivetrain based on a rear-wheel-drive design.

TRANSMISSION GEARSHIFT LEVER

TRANSFER GEARSHIFT LEVER

DUST COVER
RETAINING PLATE

GEARSHIFT
LEVER
COVER

MANUAL TRANSMISSION
AND TRANSFER ASSEMBLY

BELLHOUSING COVER

FIGURE 34–3 Transmission and transfer case for four-wheel drive. *Courtesy of Mitsubishi Motor Sales of America, Inc.*

LEVER

2WD STOP VEHICLE ENGAGE 4WD

LOCKPIN

FIGURE 34–4 The 2WD and 4WD selector can be simply a lever on the dash to engage or disengage the four-wheel drive. *Courtesy of Chrysler Corporation*

On 4WD systems adapted from front-wheel-drive systems, a separate front differential and driveline are not needed. The front wheels are driven by the transaxle differential of the base model. A **power take-off** is added to the transaxle to transmit power to the rear wheels in four-wheel drive. This takeoff gearing is housed in a transfer case mounted to the transaxle housing. The gearing connects to a rear driveline and rear axle assembly that includes the rear differential.

TRANSFER CASE

In a 4WD vehicle, as mentioned earlier, the transfer case delivers power to both the front and rear assemblies. Two drive shafts normally operate from the transfer case, one to each drive axle.

CV joints

U-joints

FIGURE 34–5   CV joint and U-joint locations on a 4WD.

The transfer case itself is constructed similar to a standard transmission. It uses shift forks to select the operating mode, plus splines, gears, shims, bearings, and other components found in manual and automatic transmissions. The outer case of the unit is made of cast iron or aluminum. It is filled with lubricant (oil) that cuts friction on all moving parts. Seals hold the lubricant in the case and prevent leakage around shafts and yokes. Shims set up the proper clearance between the internal components and the case.

Driveline Windup

It must be kept in mind that vehicles with two driving axles have different gear ratios between the front and rear driving axles, resulting in a pull-push action. The result of having the two axle ratios is a phenomenon called **driveline windup**. Driveline windup can be explained by associating the driveline to a torsion bar. The driveline twists up when both driving axles are rotating at different speeds, pushing and pulling the vehicle on hard, dry pavement. Also remember that neither the front nor rear axle has any compensating factor for speed and gear ratio differences between the front and rear driving axles.

Driveline windup can cause handling problems, particularly when rounding turns on dry pavement. This is because the front axle wheels must travel farther than the rear axle wheels when rounding a curve. On wet or slippery roads, the front and rear wheels slide enough to prevent damage to the driveline components. However, this may not be the case on dry surfaces. This is why many older 4WD systems that do not include components to dissipate driveline windup can only be safely driven on wet or slippery surfaces.

Interaxle Differentials The most common method of dissipating driveline windup is to include a third

or interaxle differential in the transfer case gearing (Figure 34–6).

The front and rear drivelines are connected to the interaxle differential inside the transfer case. Just as a drive axle differential allows for different left and right drive axle shaft speeds, the interaxle differential allows for different front and rear driveline shaft speeds (Figure 34–7). The driveline windup, developed as a result of different front and rear axle gear ratios, is dissipated by the interaxle differential.

While the interaxle differential solves the problem of driveline windup during turns, it also lowers performance in poor traction conditions. This is because the interaxle differential will tend to deliver more power to the wheels with the least traction. The result is increased slippage, the exact opposite of what is desired.

To counteract this problem, some interaxle differentials are designed much like a limited slip differential. They use a multiple-disc clutch pack to maintain a predetermined amount of torque transfer before the differential action begins to take effect. Other systems, such as the one shown in Figure 34–6, use a cone braking system rather than a clutch pack. However, the end result is the same. Power is supplied to both axles regardless of the traction encountered.

Most systems also give the driver the option of locking the interaxle differential in certain operating modes. This eliminates the differential action altogether. However, the interaxle differential should only be locked while driving in slippery conditions.

LOCKING/UNLOCKING HUBS

Most 4WD systems on trucks and utility vehicles use front-wheel drive hubs that can be disengaged from the front axle when the vehicle is operating in the 2WD mode. When unlocked in 2WD, the front wheels still turn, but the entire front drivetrain, including the front axles, the front differential, the front drive shaft, and certain internal transfer case components, stop turning (Figure 34–7). This helps reduce wear to these items.

The front hubs must be locked during 4WD operation. Some front hub designs lock automatically. Others require the driver to get out and turn a lever or knob at the center of each front wheel (Figure 34–8). Figures 34–9 and 34–10 illustrate the components in lock manual and automatic locking hubs. By locking the hubs, the wheels turn with the axle for the most traction. When unlocked, the wheels are free to spin at different rotational speeds, such as when cornering. The tires scrub on the pavement if the hubs are locked, causing them to wear faster, so they should only be locked when venturing

FIGURE 34–6 Four-wheel-drive transfer case with integral differential and cone brakes for limited slip.

off-road or under other low-traction situations, such as heavy rain, snow, or ice.

The disadvantage of the self-locking hub is that power cannot be applied to the wheels in reverse. This can be a big disadvantage if the vehicle gets stuck and backing up is the only way out. To unlock the automatic type, stop the car, disengage the four-wheel drive, and back up about 3 feet. Often these hubs unlock immediately when the four-wheel drive is disengaged, without the need to back up.

The latest development in hubs is the fully automatic type. Once four-wheel drive is engaged, they lock automatically when power is applied, either forward or reverse. That is, power can be applied in either forward or reverse direction once locked.

Axle Disconnects

Some 4WD vehicles are equipped with ordinary front wheel hubs, but have a vacuum-operated axle disconnect shift mechanism (Figure 34–11). The vacuum motor moves a splined collar to connect or disconnect one of the front axle drive shafts from the front differential. The axle shafts and differential continue to turn. However, the ring gear, pinion, and

FIGURE 34–7 Speed of drive shaft controlled by transfer case.

FIGURE 34–8 Rotating handle locks the hub.

front drive axle remain stationary. This reduces wear to these major components. This system is used on both trucks and passenger cars.

CONVENTIONAL 4WD OPERATING MODES

The typical five-position shift pattern of a conventional 4WD gearbox is as follows (Figure 34–12).

2WD Two-wheel-drive range. In this high-range mode, the gear ratio is at 1 to 1. Both of the output shafts revolve at the same rate as the transmission output shaft.

HI LOCK Four-wheel-drive high range with transfer case differential locked up (part-time, high-traction mode). A straight 1 to 1 gear ratio.

4WD Four-wheel-drive high range with transfer case differential not locked up (full-time, all-surface mode). A straight 1 to 1 gear ratio.

N—NEUTRAL Both front and rear axles are disengaged from the power train and the vehicle may be towed without uncoupling the propeller shafts. However, torque is not transferred to the front axle assembly.

LO LOCK Four-wheel-drive low range with transfer case differential locked up. This mode of operation has a gear ratio generally at 2:1 (although it may go as high as 26:1), which cuts the road speed in half. Thus, the vehicle can be operated in 4WD low range over difficult obstacles and through mud, snow, and sand with the engine running up in its power band but with relatively slow vehicle speed.

The transfer case shift pattern is usually marked on the shifter knob. Manufacturers use different patterns and designations for the various gear positions. On some vehicles, an indicator light is located on the dash panel to show the driver which mode of operation the vehicle is in. When the indicator lamp is not lit, it usually indicates the vehicle is 2WD or neutral.

WARNING!

Four-wheel-drive vehicles featuring hi lock and lo lock should not be operated on dry, hard surfaces. Such an operation causes tire scuffing and driveline damage. ∎

FIGURE 34–9 Manual locking front hub components and engagement knob. *Courtesy of Mitsubishi Motor Sales of America, Inc.*

FIGURE 34–10 Automatic front hub components. *Courtesy of Mitsubishi Motor Sales of America, Inc.*

One system on the market contains a transfer case that does not have a low-range position. The transmission includes a low-geared sixth-speed position, which can only be engaged when the transfer case is in the four-wheel-drive mode. In fact, there are single-speed transfer cases available that permit the operator to employ either 2WD or 4WD through a simple gear train. In one position, the gear train permits the power flow to the rear driveline only. An integral main drive gear in the transfer case (driven by the transmission output shaft) provides power to the rear driveline at all times. In addition, it is in mesh with an idler gear on a short auxiliary shaft. The idler gear, in turn, meshes with a front-axle drive gear to rotate the front driveline when in the 4WD mode. Or, the front-axle drive gear is moved out of mesh with the idler gear when the 2WD mode is desired.

On some models, particularly more recent ones, the shift to 4WD can be accomplished while the vehicle is moving (shifting on-the-fly). Most vehicles must be stopped before the change can be made. Also, the shift into a four-wheel-drive low mode normally requires that the vehicle is stopped first.

Some of the power on-the-fly systems feature a magnetic clutch on the transfer case that speeds up the front drive shaft, differential, and axles to the same speed as the transmission (Figure 34–13). At the instant the speed is synchronized, an electric motor on the transfer case completes the shaft, smoothly and quietly. The operator cannot damage the system because it does not shift until the speeds are synchronized.

The newest of all 4WD systems is the automatic design. While there are several different systems on

FIGURE 34–11 Axle disconnect mechanism using a vacuum-operated shifter. *Courtesy of Chrysler Corporation*

the market, one of the more commonly used systems has a microprocessor to control the interaxle differential, thus providing varying amounts of torque to the front and rear driving wheels. That is, in a fraction of a second, a computer device senses the difference in wheel speeds and engages a clutch-type device to begin driving the rear wheels. When the wheel speeds are equal again, the system reverts to front drive.

4WD PASSENGER CARS

While most 4WD trucks and utility vehicles are design variations of most basic rear-wheel-drive vehicles, most passenger cars featuring 4WD were developed from a front-wheel-drive base model.

As mentioned at the beginning of this chapter, they feature a transaxle and differential that drive the front wheels, plus some type of mechanism for connecting the transaxle to a rear driveline. In many cases this is a simple clutch type engagement.

4WD passenger cars normally differ from heavier-duty 4WD trucks and vehicles in several other ways. First, there is no separate transfer case; any gearing needed to transfer power to the rear driveline is usually contained in the transaxle housing or small bolt on extension housing. Four-wheel-drive passenger cars do not use front wheel locking hubs. Since the cars do not have lockout hubs, traction is not quite as good in the worst conditions and tire wear

FIGURE 34–13 Magnetic clutch that synchronizes the shaft speeds before allowing the shift. *Courtesy of Ford Motor Company*

not so severe should the driver forget to take the car out of four-wheel drive. Interaxle differentials are also very uncommon.

Most passenger cars with 4WD are not designed for the rigors of off-road driving, in which clearance over rocks and debris is needed. For simple road driving there is no clearance or durability problems. As with 4WD trucks, the passenger car 4WD mode should not be used on dry pavement due to increased tire and drivetrain wear.

Limited Slip and Open Differentials

To help compensate for the lack of locking hubs many 4WD passenger cars use limited slip or open differential designs for the front and rear differentials. These systems allow enough differential slippage to substantially reduce wheel scrubbing and driveline windup.

A limited slip differential (LSD) uses a friction clutch to join the right and left rear axle shafts to the differential case. This system ensures that most power is supplied where the traction is greatest. It permits the inner and outer wheels to rotate at different speeds when turns are made, just as in general differentials.

In addition, the LSD provides these features. When one front and one rear wheel, which are diago-

FIGURE 34–12 The power flow through transfer case in 2H, 4H, and 4L modes. *Courtesy of Chrysler Corporation*

nal to each other, slip on snow-covered roads and driving force cannot be delivered, or when one rear wheel is caught in a ditch and runs idle, the LSD delivers strong torque to the other wheel so the vehicle can run normally. Even if the vehicle bumps with one rear wheel off the road, such as when driving on rough terrain, gravel, or snow-covered roads, the LSD ensures easy straightforward driveability by its limited differential function.

Other systems use an open differential. Here the greatest power is supplied where there is the least resistance. This is an excellent system for fuel economy and gear wear in full-time, four-wheel drive, but it does not provide the true traction advantages of four-wheel drive. For example, the greatest power would be supplied to the slipping wheels (least resistance) on icy road conditions when it is actually needed at the wheels facing the most resistance (for example, where the greatest traction is).

USING SERVICE MANUALS

Because of the various four-wheel-drive systems in use, it is essential that the undercar technician carefully study and understand that particular vehicle's service manual. ∎

Systems using an open differential have a drive mode on the selector, which permits the differential to be locked up in such conditions. This causes the drivetrain to function the same as a part-time four-wheel-drive system. The power is distributed equally to all the wheels. Vehicles should not be driven in this mode, except under poor road conditions, for the same reasons that part-time systems should be used only when needed.

CUSTOMER CARE

Advise your customer that wear on 4WD systems is much greater than on a two-wheel-drive transaxle or transmission. This is especially true if drivers leave the four-wheel drive engaged on dry pavement. Some car makers warn that abuse of the system is not covered under the warranty. ∎

SERVICING 4WD VEHICLES

Components of 4WD vehicles can be serviced in basically the same manner as the identical components of a 2WD vehicle. Before doing any servicing,

FIGURE 34–14 U-joints, slip joints, and CV joints on four-wheel-drive drivetrains should be lubed regularly to prevent premature failure.

however, it is necessary to give the undercar a complete inspection. Pay particular attention to the steering dampers, steering linkage, wheel bearing, ball joints, coil springs, and radius arm bushings.

The U-joints, slip joints, or CV joints on a 4WD drivetrain that must be lubed on a regular basis are shown in Figure 34–14. To service the drive shafts on a four-wheel-drive vehicle, use the general instructions given earlier for a cross universal joint. A four-wheel drive simply uses two drive shafts instead of one.

Servicing the Transfer Case

As with all automobile servicing procedures, be sure to check the manufacturer's service manual for specific transfer case repair and overhaul procedures. It gives details for the particular make and model of transfer case to be worked on.

CAUTION:

When removing and working on a transfer case, be sure to support it on a transmission jack or safety stands. The unit is heavy and if dropped, it could cause part damage and personal injury. ∎

When removing the transfer case, disconnect and remove all driveline or propeller shaft assemblies. Be sure to mark the parts and their relative positions on their yokes so the proper driveline balance can be maintained when reassembled. Disconnect the linkage to the transfer case shift lever. Also disconnect wires to switches for 4WD dash indicator lights, if used. Remove all fasteners holding the case and move it away from the transaxle or transmission.

Once the transfer case has been removed from the vehicle and safely supported, take off the case cover and disconnect any electrical connections. Visually inspect for any oil leaks. Then carefully

FIGURE 34–15 Check the chain drive for stretch. *Courtesy of Mitsubishi Motor Sales of America, Inc.*

loosen and drive out the pins that hold the shift forks in place. Remove the front output shafts and chain drive or gearsets from the case. Keep in mind that some cases use chain drives while others use spur or helical cut gearsets to transfer torque from the transaxle or transmission to the output shafts. Planetary gearsets provide the necessary gear reductions in some transfer cases. Photo Sequence 19 shows the procedure for disassembling a Warner 13-56 transfer case, which is a commonly used unit.

Clean and carefully inspect all parts for damage and wear. Check the slack in the chain drive by following the procedure given in the service manual (Figure 34–15). Replace any defective parts. It may be necessary to measure the shaft assembly end play. If excessive, new snap rings and shims may be used to correct the situation.

When reassembling the transfer case, the procedure is essentially the reverse of the removal. Be sure to use new gaskets between the covers when reassembling the unit. Photo Sequence 20 shows the procedure for reassembling a Warner 13-56 transfer case.

CUSTOMER CARE

It is very important to remind your customers that the fluid level in a transfer case must be checked at recommended time intervals. (Check the service manual.) It is wise to show your customers where the transfer case fill plug is located and how to remove it. Also tell them the lubricant should be almost even with the fill hole. Always refer to the service manual for recommended transfer case lubricants. Many transfer cases require extreme pressure (EP) lubricants as used in differentials and in some manual transmissions. ■

ALL-WHEEL-DRIVE SYSTEMS

All-wheel-drive systems do not give the driver the option of 2WD or 4WD. They always drive all wheels. All-wheel-drive vehicles are usually passenger cars that are not designed for off-road operation. The all-wheel-drive-vehicle is designed to increase vehicle performance in poor traction situations, such as icy or snowy roads, and in emergencies. All-wheel drive gives the vehicle operator maximum control in adverse operating conditions by biasing the driving torque to the axle with driving traction. The advantage of all-wheel drive can be compared to walking on snowshoes. Snowshoes prevent the user from sinking into the snow by spreading the body weight over a large surface. All-wheel-drive vehicles spread the driving force over four wheels when needed rather than two wheels. When a vehicle travels over the road, the driving wheels transmit a tractive force to the road's surface. The ability of each tire to transmit tractive force is a result of vehicle weight pressing the tire into the road's surface and the coefficient of friction between the tire and the road. If the road's surface is dry and the tire is dry, the coefficient of friction is high and four driving wheels are not needed. If the road's surface is wet and slippery, the coefficient of friction between the tire and road is low. The tire loses its coefficient of friction on slippery road surfaces, which could result in loss of control by the operator. Unlike a two-wheel-drive vehicle, an all-wheel-drive vehicle spreads the tractive effort to all four driving wheels. In addition to spreading the driving torque, the all-wheel-drive vehicle biases the driving torque to the axle that has the traction only when it is needed.

Viscous Clutch

The viscous clutch is used in the driveline of vehicles to drive the axle with low tractive effort, taking the place of the interaxle differential. In existence for several years, the viscous clutch is installed to improve the mobility factor under difficult driving conditions. It is similar in action to the viscous clutch described for the cooling system fan. The viscous clutch in AWD is a self-contained unit. When it malfunctions, it is simply replaced as an assembly. The viscous clutch assembly is very compact, permitting installation within a front transaxle housing. Viscous clutches operate automatically while constantly transmitting power to the axle assembly as soon as it becomes necessary to improve driving wheel traction. This action is also known as biasing driving torque to the axle with tractive effort. The viscous clutch assembly is designed similarly to a multiple-disc clutch with alternating driving and driving plates (Figure 34–16, page 907).

TYPICAL PROCEDURE FOR DISASSEMBLING A WARNER 13-56 TRANSFER CASE

P19–1   If not previously drained, remove the drain plug and allow the oil to drain, then reinstall the plug. Loosen the flange nuts.

P19–2   Remove two output shaft yoke nuts, washers, rubber seals, and output yokes from the case.

P19–3   Remove the four-wheel-drive indicator switch from the cover.

P19–4   Remove the wires from the electronic shift harness connector.

P19–5   Remove the speed sensor retaining bracket screw, bracket, and sensor.

P19–6   Remove the bolts securing the electric shift motor and remove the motor.

P19–7   Note the location of the triangular shaft in the case and the triangular slot in the electric motor.

P19–8   Loosen and remove the front case to rear case retaining bolts.

P19–9   Separate the two halves by prying between the pry bosses on the case.

(continued)

P19–10 Remove the shift rail for the electric motor.

P19–11 Pull the clutch coil off the main shaft.

P19–12 Pull the 2WD/4WD shift fork and lock-up assembly off the main shaft.

P19–13 Remove the chain, driven sprocket, and drive sprocket as a unit.

P19–14 Remove the main shaft with the oil pump assembly.

P19–15 Slip the high-low range shift fork out of the inside track of the shift cam.

P19–16 Remove the high-low shift collar from the shift fork.

P19–17 Unbolt and remove the planetary gear mounting plate from the case.

P19–18 Pull the planetary gearset out of the mounting plate.

TYPICAL PROCEDURE FOR REASSEMBLING A WARNER 13-56 TRANSFER CASE

P20–1 Install the input shaft and front output shaft bearings into the case.

P20–2 Apply a thin bead of sealer around the ring gear housing.

P20–3 Install input shaft with planetary gear set and tighten retaining bolts to specifications.

P20–4 Install high-low shift collar into shift fork.

P20–5 Install high-low shift assembly into case.

P20–6 Install main shaft with oil pump assembly into case.

P20–7 Install drive and driven sprockets and chain into position in the case.

P20–8 Install shift rails.

P20–9 Install the 2WD/4WD shift fork and lock-up assembly onto the main shaft.

(continued)

P20–10   Install the clutch coil onto the main shaft.

P20–11   Clean the mating surface of the case.

P20–12   Position the shafts and tighten the case halves together. Tighten attaching bolts to specifications.

P20–13   Apply a thin bead of sealer to the mating surface of the electric shift motor.

P20–14   Align the triangular shaft with the motor's triangular slot.

P20–15   Install the motor over the shaft, wiggle the motor to ensure that it is fully seated on the shaft.

P20–16   Tighten the motor's retaining bolts to specifications.

P20–17   Reinstall the wires into the connector and connect all electric sensors.

P20–18   Install the companion flanges' seal, washer and nut. Then tighten the nut to specifications

FIGURE 34–16 Typical viscous clutch assembly. *Courtesy of Volkswagen of America, Inc.*

The viscous clutch parts fit inside a drum that is completely sealed. The clutch pack is made up of alternating steel driving and driven plates. One set of steel plates is splined internally to the clutch assembly hub. The second set of clutch plates is splined externally to the clutch drum. The clutch housing is filled with a small quantity of air and special silicone fluid with the purpose of transmitting force from the driving plates to the driven plates.

Based on practical experience, vehicles operating with this clutch transmit power automatically, smoothly, and with the added benefit of the fluid being capable of dampening driveline shocks. When a difference in speed of 8 percent exists between the input shaft driven by the driving axle with tractive effort, the clutch plates begin shearing (cutting) the special silicone fluid. The shearing action causes heat to build within the housing very rapidly, which results in the silicone fluid stiffening. The stiffening action causes a locking action between the clutch plates to take place within approximately one-tenth second. The locking action results from the stiff silicone fluid becoming very hard for the plates to shear. The stiff silicone fluid transfers power flow from the driving to the driven plates. The driving shaft is then connected to the driven shaft through the clutch plates and stiff silicone fluid.

The viscous clutch has a self-regulating control. When the clutch assembly locks up, there is very little, if any, relative movement between the clutch plates. Because there is little relative movement, silicone fluid temperature drops, which reduces pressure within the clutch housing. But as speed fluctuates between the driving and driven members, heat increases, causing the silicone fluid to stiffen. Speed differences between the driving and driven members regulate the amount of slip in a viscous clutch driveline. The viscous clutch takes the place of the interaxle differential, biasing driving torque to the normally undriven axle during difficult driving conditions.

The viscous clutch is also used in some part-time 4WD vehicles, replacing the transfer case.

Center Differential AWD

One of the more recent AWD designs features a center differential to split the power between the front and rear axles (Figure 34–17). On the manual transmission model, the driver can lock the center differential with a switch. On the automatic transmission model, the center differential locks automatically, depending on which transaxle range the driver selects and whether or not there is any slippage between front and rear wheels.

Electronically Controlled AWD

Electronically controlled all-wheel drive is found in several import four-speed automatic overdrive transaxles designed with lockup torque converters. These vehicle drivetrains are designed with a front transaxle

FIGURE 34–17 AWD system using a center differential. A conventional transfer case is not needed. *Courtesy of Porsche-Audi*

FIGURE 34–18   Schematic of the electrically controlled AWD transaxle. *Courtesy of Ford Motor Company*

and two front drive shafts (each with its constant velocity universal joints). The rear drive shaft extends from the transaxle extension to the rear axle drive pinion and ring gear, two rear-drive shafts, universal joints, and driving wheels (Figure 34–18). Remember, there must be some type of interaxle differential in full-time, all-wheel drivelines.

The FWD transaxle has the same features. The torque converter is complete with impeller, turbine, stator, and lockup clutch. The turbine shaft drives the various engaged planetary controls and planetary gears to achieve the gear range selected. The interesting area of the transaxle is the output to the rear driving axle. In this area on Figure 34–18, locate the transaxle reduction drive shaft, reduction driving gear, transfer clutch, and rear drive shaft. The reduction gearset transfers torque to the front-axle drive pinion, ring gear, differential, drive shafts, and driving wheels.

At the rear of the transaxle immediately behind the reduction gearset is the multiple-disc transfer clutch. The design of this transfer clutch acts as the driveline interaxle differential, permitting the difference in front- and rear-axle speeds. The secret to the operation of this all-wheel-drive design is the method of controlling transfer clutch operation.

Strategically placed around the vehicle are sensors that monitor front- and rear-axle speeds, engine speed, and load on the engine and driveline. Information from the sensors is reported to the transmission computer unit called the transmission control unit (TCU). The TCU controls a solenoid called the duty sole-

noid that operates on a duty (jitter) cycle controlling the fluid flow that engages the transfer clutch. The duty solenoid pulses, cycling on and off very rapidly, which develops a controlled slip condition. Driveline windup is dissipated when the clutch pack disengages, acting like an interaxle differential to the full-time, all-wheel driveline. The result of the operation of the transmission control unit and the duty solenoid is that the transfer clutch operates like an interaxle differential to a power split from 95 percent front-wheel drive and 5 percent rear-wheel drive to 50 percent front-wheel drive and 50 percent rear-wheel drive. This power split takes place so rapidly that the vehicle operator is not aware of a traction problem.

CASE STUDY

A four-wheel-drive pickup truck is brought into the shop. There is a severe vibration through the truck when it is traveling at road speeds. New wheels and tires were recently installed on the truck. The new wheels and tires are drastically oversized. Lift kits were installed by the owner to provide the necessary tire clearance. The owner would like the alignment checked and the wheels balanced.

The technician carefully balances and aligns the wheels. He takes the truck for a test drive to veri-

fy the repair. The truck still has a harsh vibration. It seems to get worse as speed increases. A bent wheel or bad wheel bearing or hub is suspected.

After returning to the shop, he measures the runout and checks the play of each wheel. Finding nothing wrong, he carefully checks the roundness of the tires. While doing so on the rear tires, he discovers the cause of the problem. When the lift kit was installed, the operating angle of the rear U-joint was affected. As the drive shaft turns, it hesitates slightly. This hesitation is caused by a binding of the U-joint.

The technician informs the owner of the cause and suggests that the lift kits be removed or the drive shaft operating angle be corrected.

KEY TERMS

AWD
Driveline windup
4WD
Interaxle differential

Locking hubs
Power takeoff
Transfer case
Viscous clutch

SUMMARY

◆ The importance of excellent traction and the benefits of four-wheel- and all-wheel-drive systems become readily apparent in snow or heavy rain.
◆ The heart of most conventional 4WD systems is the transfer case.

◆ One main function of the transfer case is to prevent driveline windup.
◆ The interaxle is placed in the transfer case to operate in the same fashion as the differentials at the axles. The only difference is that the transfer differential controls the speed of the drivelines instead of the axles.
◆ Many vehicles require that the front hubs be in a locked condition to operate as 4WD vehicles. This lockup may be made either manually or automatically.
◆ With the four-wheel drive disengaged at the transmission or transaxle, the disengaged front or rear wheels are still forced to turn the axles, differential, and drive shafts. To avoid this, hubs that lock or unlock disconnect everything from the wheels back to the transfer case.
◆ On 4WD vehicles with on-the-fly shifting, it is not necessary to come to a complete stop when changing operational modes.
◆ Components of 4WD vehicles can be serviced in basically the same manner as the identical components on a 2WD vehicle.
◆ All-wheel-drive vehicles use a viscous clutch, rather than a transfer case, to drive the axle with low tractive effort
◆ Electronically controlled all-wheel-drive vehicles can be found on some vehicles with four-speed automatic overdrive transaxles.

TECH MANUAL

The following procedures are included in Chapter 34 of the *Tech Manual* that accompanies this book:

1. Inspect and replenish the lubricant in a transfer case.
2. Replace wheel lock hub.
3. Replace an output shaft seal and bushing.

homework

REVIEW QUESTIONS

1. What is the main advantage of all-wheel drive?
2. Name the three main driveline components that are added to a 2WD vehicle to make it a 4WD vehicle. transfer case / interaxle / drive differential shaft
3. Describe the purpose of a viscous clutch.
4. What is the purpose of the interaxle differential?
5. What is the disadvantage of the self-locking hub?

6. Tractive effort is defined as a ____.
   a. driving force where a driving gear meshes with a driven gear
   b. place where the clutch disc makes contact with the flywheel and pressure plate
   c. driving force in which the wheel contacts the road's surface
   d. driving force at the wheel
7. Which type of differential does not provide the true traction advantages of four-wheel drive?
   a. transfer
   b. limited slip
   c. open
   d. none of the above

8. Which shift position is used full-time for all surfaces?

   a. 4WD
   b. hi lock
   c. lo lock
   d. none of the above

9. How does a viscous clutch assembly work? Why is it used in AWD systems?

10. What results from having different axle ratios on the front and rear of a 4WD vehicle, when it is operating in 4WD?

    a. poor handling on dry surfaces
    b. driveline windup
    c. mechanical damage to the driveline
    d. all of the above

11. In full-time, four-wheel-drive vehicles all four wheels are ____.

    a. constantly receiving an equal amount of power
    b. constantly open to receiving power
    c. receiving power when the driver asks for it
    d. all of the above

12. Technician A says driveline windup, when referring to a four-wheel-drive vehicle, results from different gear ratios between the front and rear axles. Technician B says most 4WD vehicles use an interaxle differential in the transfer case to eliminate the problem. Who is correct?

    a. Technician A
    b. Technician B
    c. Neither A nor B
    d. Both A and B

13. The transfer clutch in the all-wheel-drive automatic transaxle takes the place of the ____.

    a. transmission
    b. reduction gears
    c. torque converter
    d. interaxle differential

14. In a typical all-wheel-drive automatic transaxle, the transfer clutch is controlled by the ____.

    a. transmission control unit operating the pressure regulator valve
    b. engine computer controlling line pressure to the various clutches in the transmission
    c. transmission control unit and the duty solenoid
    d. front axle speed sensor and the vehicle speed sensor

15. Technician A says some AWD systems have a center differential. Technician B says some AWD vehicles have a viscous clutch. Who is correct?

    a. Technician A
    b. Technician B
    c. Neither A nor B
    d. Both A and B

16. In a viscous clutch, when the silicone fluid is heated, it ____.

    a. becomes a very thin fluid
    b. boils to a vapor
    c. thickens to a solid mass
    d. stiffens

17. When servicing transfer cases, all of the following are correct, except ____.

    a. it must be supported on a transmission jack or safety stands
    b. all transfer cases have both a chain drive and a planetary gearset
    c. visual inspections for leaks and damage are necessary
    d. follow the manufacturer's recommendations for lubricants

18. Which of the following is an advantage of four-wheel drive?

    a. It weighs less.
    b. It requires less maintenance.
    c. Tires cost less.
    d. None of the above.

19. The viscous clutch is used to ____.

    a. engage engine torque to the transmission
    b. improve mobility when driving conditions become difficult
    c. drive both rear driving wheels when a vehicle is stuck
    d. drive the rear axle assembly

20. The primary differences between a AWD and 4WD driveline is (are) that the AWD has ____.

    a. a center differential
    b. a transfer case
    c. a differential unit at both axles
    d. all of the above

SECTION 7 SUSPENSIONS

A vehicle's tires, wheels, and suspension and steering systems provide the contact between the driver and the road. They allow the driver to safely maneuver the vehicle in all types of conditions as well as to ride in comfort and security.

Once straightforward mechanical systems, suspension and steering systems have become increasingly sophisticated. Computer technology has made possible features such as variable ride qualities and active and adaptive suspensions. Four-wheel steering is now a reality. The electronic controls, air systems, and solenoids that operate this new technology require special servicing techniques.

The information found in Section 7 corresponds to materials covered on the ASE certification test on suspension and steering.

WE ENCOURAGE
PROFESSIONALISM

THROUGH TECHNICIAN

TIRES AND WHEELS

35

OBJECTIVES

◆ *Describe basic wheel and hub design.* ◆ *Recognize the basic parts of a tubeless tire.* ◆ *Explain the differences between the three types of tire construction in use today.* ◆ *Explain the tire ratings and designations in use today.* ◆ *Describe why certain factors affect tire performance, including inflation pressure, tire rotation, and tread wear.* ◆ *Remove and install a wheel and tire assembly.* ◆ *Dismount and remount a tire.* ◆ *Repair a damaged tire.* ◆ *Describe the differences between static balance and dynamic balance.* ◆ *Balance wheels both on and off a vehicle.* ◆ *Describe the three popular types of wheel hub bearings.*

Tire and wheel assemblies provide the only connection between the road and the vehicle. Tire design has improved dramatically during the past few years and modern tires require increased attention to achieve their full potential of extended service and correct ride control. Tire wear that is uneven or premature is usually a good indicator of problems in the steering and suspension system. Tires, therefore, become not only a good diagnostic aid to a technician, but they can also be clear evidence to the customer of the need to service the front-end.

WHEELS

Wheels are made of either stamped or pressed steel discs riveted or welded together. They are also available in the form of aluminum or magnesium rims that are die-cast or forged. Magnesium wheels are commonly referred to as mag wheels, although they are commonly made of an aluminum alloy. Aluminum wheels are lighter in weight when compared with the stamped steel type.

Near the center of the wheel are mounting holes that are designed to fit tapered mounting nuts (**lug nuts**) that center the wheel over the hub. The rim has a hole for the **valve stem** and a **drop center** area designed to allow easy tire removal and installation. **Wheel offset** is the vertical distance between the centerline of the rim and the mounting face of the disc. The offset is considered positive if the centerline of the rim is inboard of the mounting face and negative if outboard of the mounting face. The amount and

type of offset is critical because changing the wheel offset changes the loading on the front suspension loading as well as the scrub radius.

The wheel is bolted to a **hub**, either by lug bolts that pass through the wheel and thread into the hub, or by studs that protrude from the hub. In the case of studs, special lug nuts are required. Some vehicles employ left-hand threads (which turn counterclockwise to tighten) on the driver's side, and right-hand threads (which turn clockwise to tighten) on the passenger's side. Other cars use right-hand threads on both sides.

Wheel size is designated by rim width and rim diameter (Figure 35–1). Rim width is determined by measuring across the rim between the flanges. Rim

FIGURE 35–1 Wheel dimensions important to tire replacement.

FIGURE 35–2 Safety rim. Note safety ridge on each side of wheel that retains tire in case of a flat or blowout (ruptured tire). *Courtesy of Chrysler Corporation*

FIGURE 35–3 Typical tubeless tire installation and valve. *Courtesy of Chrysler Corporation*

diameter is measured across the bead seating areas from the top to the bottom of the wheel. Some rims have safety ridges near their lips. In the event of a tire blowout, these ridges tend to keep the tire from moving into the dropped center and from coming off the wheel (Figure 35–2).

Replacement wheels must be equal to the original equipment wheels in load capacity, diameter, width, offset, and mounting configuration. An incorrect wheel can affect wheel and bearing life, ground and tire clearance, or speedometer and odometer calibrations.

TIRES

The primary purpose of tires is to provide traction. Tires also help the suspension absorb road shocks, but this is a side benefit. They must perform under a variety of conditions. The road might be wet or dry; paved with asphalt, concrete, or gravel; or there might be no road at all. The car might be traveling slowly on a straight road, or moving quickly through curves or over hills. All of these conditions call for special requirements that must be present, at least to some degree, in all tires.

In addition to providing good traction, tires are also designed to carry the weight of the vehicle, withstand side thrust over varying speeds and conditions, and transfer braking and driving torque to the road.

Tube and Tubeless Tires

Early vehicle tires were solid rubber. These were replaced with pneumatic tires, which are filled with air.

There are two basic types of pneumatic tires: those that use inner tubes and those that do not. The latter are called **tubeless tires** and are about the only type used on passenger cars today. A tubeless tire has a soft inner lining that keeps air from leaking between the tire and rim (Figure 35–3). This inner lining can often form a seal around a nail or other object that punctures the tread. A self-sealing tire holds in air even after the object is removed. A tubeless tire air valve has a central core that is spring-loaded to allow air to pass inward only, unless the pin is depressed. If the core becomes defective, it can be unscrewed and replaced. The airtight cap on the end of the valve provides extra protection against valve leakage. A tubeless tire is mounted on a special rim that retains air between the rim and the tire casing when the tire is inflated.

Figure 35–4 shows a cutaway view of a typical tubeless tire. The basic parts are shown. The cord body or casing consists of layers of rubber-impregnated cords, called **plies**, that are bonded into a solid unit. Typically tires are made of 2, 4, or 8 plies; thus, the reference to 2-, 4-, and 8-ply tires. The character of the plies determines a tire's strength, handling, ride, amount of road noise, traction, and resistance to fatigue, heat, and bruises. The **bead** is the portion of the tire that helps keep it in contact with the rim of the wheel. It also provides the air seal on tubeless tires. The bead is constructed of a heavy band of steel wire wrapped into the inner circumference of the tire's ply structure. The **tread**, or crown, is the portion of the tire that comes in contact with the road surface. It is a pattern of grooves and ribs that provides traction. The grooves are designed to drain off water, while the ribs grip the road surface. Tread thickness varies with tire quality. On some tires, small cuts, called **sipes**, are molded into the ribs of

1. CAP tread
2. Tread base
3. Nylon wound aquachannel breaker
4. Two-ply nylon wound breaker
5. Two steel-cord plies
6. Two rayon-carcass plies
7. Double nylon bead reinforcement
8. Bead filler
9. Bead core

FIGURE 35–4 Typical tubeless tire. *Courtesy of SAE International*

rough roads. Nylon cord tires generally give a slightly harder ride than rayon, especially for the first few miles after the car has been parked, but offer greater toughness and resistance to road damage. Polyester and fiberglass tires offer many of the best qualities of rayon and nylon but without the disadvantages. They run as smoothly as rayon tires but are much tougher. They are almost as tough as nylon but give a much smoother ride. Steel is tougher than fiberglass or polyester, but it gives a slightly rougher ride because the steel cord does not give under impact as do fabric plies. Amarid and kevlar cords are lighter than steel cords and, pound for pound, stronger than steel.

Types of Tire Construction

There are three types of tire construction in use today (Figure 35–5). They are bias ply, belted bias ply, and radial ply tires.

BIAS PLY TIRES The oldest tire currently in use is the **bias ply**. It has a body of fabric plies that runs alternatively at opposite angles to form a crisscross design. The angle varies from 30 to 38 degrees with the centerline of the tire and has an effect on high-speed stability, ride harshness, and handling. Generally speaking, the lower the cord angle, the better the high-speed stability but also the harsher the ride. Bias ply tires usually are available in 2- or 4-ply.

BELTED BIAS PLY TIRES **Belted bias ply** tires are similar to the bias ply, except two or more belts run the circumference of the tire under the tread. This construction gives strength to the sidewall and greater stability to the tread. The belts reduce tread motion during contact with the road, thus improving tread life. Plies and belts of various combinations of rayon,

the tread. These sipes open as the tire flexes on the road, offering additional gripping action, especially on wet road surfaces. The **sidewalls** are the sides of the tire body. They are constructed of thinner material than the tread to offer greater flexibility.

The tire body and belt material can be made of rayon, nylon, polyester, fiberglass, steel, or the newest synthetics—amarid or kevlar. Each has its advantages and disadvantages. For instance, rayon and cord tires are low in cost and give a good ride but do not have the inherent strength needed to cope with long high-speed runs or extended periods of abusive use on

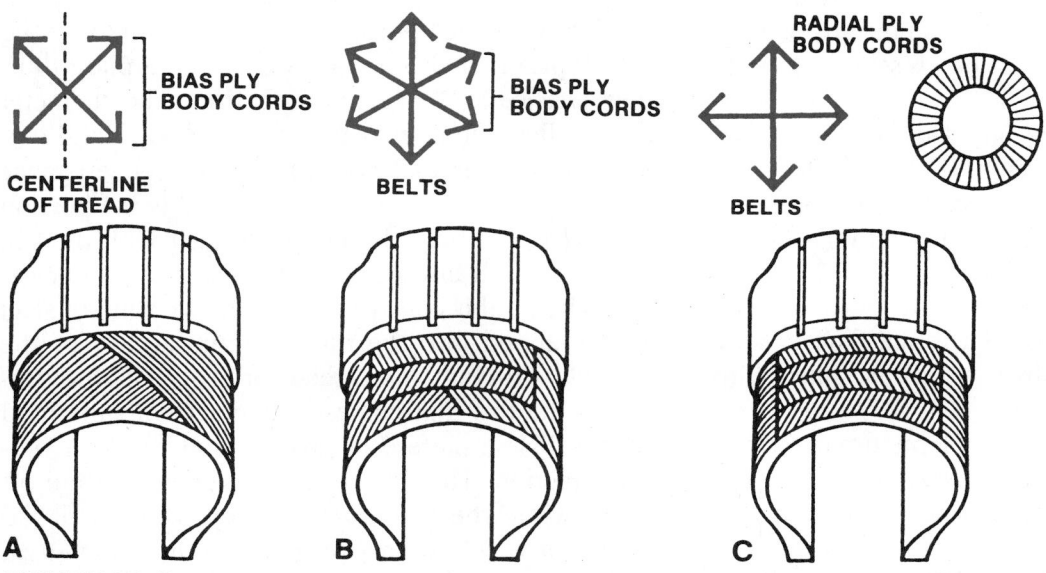

FIGURE 35–5 Three types of tire construction: (A) bias ply; (B) belted bias ply; and (C) radial ply.

RADIAL   **BIAS-PLY**

FIGURE 35–6 A radial tire's highly flexible sidewalls give maximum tread contact area during fast, hard turning.

nylon, polyester, fiberglass, and steel are used with belted bias construction. Belted bias ply tires generally cost more than conventional bias ply tires but last up to 40 percent longer.

RADIAL PLY TIRES Radial ply tires have body cords that extend from bead to bead at an angle of about 90 degrees—"radial" to the tire circumferential centerline—plus two or more layers of relatively inflexible belts under the tread. This construction of various combinations of rayon, nylon, fiberglass, and steel gives greater strength to the tread area and flexibility to the sidewall (Figure 35–6). The belts restrict tread motion during contact with the road, thus improving tread life and traction. Radial ply tires also offer greater fuel economy, increased skid resistance, and more positive braking.

Although the newer synthetics are being used more frequently in radial tires, steel is still the most popular belt material. Bias ply and belted bias are available in all cord materials mentioned earlier, except amarid and kevlar. Nonradial belts are usually of the same material as the sidewalls.

Specialty Tires

Specialty tires reflect the advances made in the conventional tire field. Special snow and mud tires are available in all three construction types. Studded tires provide superior traction on ice; however, they are slowly disappearing from the tire market because their performance in dry weather is poor. In addition, in the last few years many states have outlawed their use because they damage roads.

The present trend in specialty tire manufacturing is toward all-season or all-weather tires. The all-season tire, however, is a compromise and might not perform as well as specialty tires under certain circumstances. Their use has not eliminated the twice-a-year tire change for many northern motorists.

CUSTOMER CARE

Advise your customer that the use of tire chains is not recommended by most tire manufacturers. In case of emergency, or where required by law, chains can be used if they are the proper size for the tires and are installed tightly (no slack) with their ends securely restrained. Follow the chain manufacturer's instructions. Drive slowly. If any contact of the chains against the vehicle is heard, stop and retighten the chains. Use only SAE Class C tire chains. Use of other chains can damage the vehicle. ∎

Compact Spare Tires A compact spare tire is designed to reduce weight and provide more luggage room. There are several types used today.

HIGH-PRESSURE MINI SPARE The high pressure (60 psi) mini-spare tire is the one most commonly used. This small, temporary tire should not be used for extended mileage or for speeds above 50 mph. Check the pressure in the spare tire at least monthly. If it is in use, check the pressure when the vehicle has been stopped at least 3 hours and driven less than 1 mile. Do not reduce the pressure when the tire is hot. Use a tire gauge to check the pressure and maintain 60 psi.

SPACE-SAVER SPARE This type of tire must be blown up with a special compressor that operates off the cigarette lighter electrical unit. Inflate the tire to 35 psi. Before installing it on the vehicle, make sure it looks like a road tire with no folds in the sidewalls.

LIGHTWEIGHT SKIN SPARE The skin spare is designed to provide additional luggage room and a lightweight, easy-to-use spare tire. This type of spare is a normal type bias ply with a reduced tread depth to provide an estimated tread life of 2,000 miles. It is for emergency use only and has a maximum speed capability of 50 mph. Maintain the cold inflation pressure as specified on the vehicle's tire pressure decal.

CUSTOMER CARE

Be sure to warn your customer that the mini, space-saver, skin, or similar type of compact spare should be used only temporarily for an emergency. It should never be used as a regular tire. Any continuous load use of the temporary compact spare might result in tire failure, loss of vehicle control, and injury to the vehicle's occupants. ∎

High-Performance (Speed-Rated) Tires In recent years, the so-called high-performance tire has made an increasing appearance on cars driven in the United States. Many drivers do not care if they actually use

TABLE 35–1 SPEED RATINGS	
Symbol	**Maximum Speed**
F	50 mph
G	56 mph
J	62 mph
K	68 mph
L	75 mph
M	81 mph
N	87 mph
P	93 mph
Q	100 mph
R	106 mph
S	112 mph
T	118 mph
U	124 mph
H	130 mph
V	149 mph
Z	+149 mph

High-performance tires, like all tires, eventually have to be replaced. In some European countries, the replacement tire must have, by law, the same speed rating as the OE tire. Although it is not the law in the United States, trading down in speed ratings would probably not be a good idea. Optimum performance and, perhaps, even safe handling might be sacrificed.

The speed ratings are currently set by the Economic Commission using the European passenger car tire regulation R-30. While United States tire makers use the testing procedures established by this association, there are no minimum standards to which they must comply.

Tire Ratings and Designations

Tires are rated by their profile, ratio, size, and load range. **Tire profile** is the relation of its cross-section height (from tread to bead) compared to the cross-section width (from sidewall to sidewall). Today, this ratio is also known as **series**.

For many years, the accepted profile ratio for standard bias ply passenger car tires was approximately 83. This meant the tire was 83 percent as high as it was wide. Since the introduction of bias belted and radial ply construction, lower profile tires and ratios of 78, 70, 60, or even 50 have become popular (Figure 35–7). The lower the number, the wider the tire. For instance, a 50-series tire is quite low and fat, being only 50 percent as high as it is wide. Most new cars are equipped with 80-, 78-, 75-, or 70-series tires.

Prior to 1967, tire sizes were designated by a series of numbers, such as 7.75–15 or 9.50–15. The first number (9.50) referred to the cross-section width, in

the speed capabilities of the tire, just as long as the performance is there. In fact, many of their cars are not capable of these higher speeds. A comparison of the Porsche 928S4 and Ford Probe GT points this out.

The Porsche has a top speed of 165 mph. The Probe GT tops out at 120 mph. Yet, both are equipped with V-rated tires (up to 149 mph; see Table 35–1). While the Porsche can certainly use the V-rated tire, the Probe is using it strictly for handling, and, of course, image.

FIGURE 35–7   The aspect ratio (profile ratio) of a tire is its cross-sectional height compared to its cross-sectional width expressed in percentage figures.

TABLE 35-2 WIDTH/LOAD LETTER STANDARDS
V—650 pounds
W—710 pounds
Y—770 pounds
Z—830 pounds
A—900 pounds
B—980 pounds
C—1050 pounds
D—1120 pounds
E—1190 pounds
F—1280 pounds
G—1380 pounds
H—1510 pounds
J—1580 pounds
K—1620 pounds
L—1680 pounds
M—1780 pounds
N—1880 pounds

TABLE 35-3 LOAD RANGES		
Rating	**Ply Rating**	**Maximum psi**
B	4	32
C	6	36
D	8	40

inches, of an inflated tire, and the second number (15) was the rim diameter. Then tire sizes were noted by alpha-numerics.

In the standard alpha-numeric system, the width/load letter scale starts at *V* and runs through *Z*, then takes up with *A* and runs through *N*. Typically the wider the tire, the more weight it is designed to carry. Table 35–2 shows the maximum weight each tire size can carry when inflated to 24 psi. As inflation is increased, so is the tire's carrying capacity up to a usual maximum of 35 psi.

In the alpha-numeric system, the tire letter size is followed by a number to indicate the tire's approximate profile ratio, followed by the rim diameter. For example, a tire designated as F78-15 means it belongs to the 78 series and fits a 15-inch rim. Radial ply tires use the same designation but have an *R* inserted in the number, such as FR78-14.

The half alpha-numeric, half metric system gives the tire's width in millimeters but gives its rim diameter in inches, such as 195R-15. Although the profile ratio is usually omitted in part-metric designations, a few manufacturers designate the tire series, such as 185-70-14. The *70* stands for a 70-series tire. In 1977, *P* metric tires were introduced.

In P195/75R14, *P* identifies passenger car tire. If this designation is followed by *M*, *S*, or *MS*, the tire's tread is rated for use in mud, snow, or both. The width in millimeters is 195. The height-to-width ratio is 75. *R* identifies radial construction. The rim diameter is 14.

All metric system measurements are now being given along with a standard translation. A typical metric tire shows its width in millimeters, its inflation pressure in kilopascals (kPa), and its load capacity in kilograms (kg). One kilopascal equals 6.895 psi. A typical all-metric radial size is 190/65R-390. It fits a 390-mm diameter wheel.

Additionally, the letters *B*, *C*, or *D*, might appear on the sidewall, separate from the tire designation coding. These are holdovers from the old load-rating system, which replaced the still older ply system (Table 35–3). Load range B is the lightest design, suited to passenger car use. Load range C is in between, while load range D is heavy-duty. It is best for trucks and off-road vehicles.

The newer tires have abandoned the load range system replacing it with SL and XL for standard load and extra load. Standard load falls between load ranges B and C. XL is a little heavier duty than load range D.

Federal law requires that all tires carry designations (Figure 35–8) indicating size, load range, maximum load, maximum inflation pressure in pounds per square inch, number of plies under the tread and the sidewalls, manufacturer's name, tubeless or tube construction, radial construction (if a radial tire), and United States Department of Transportation (DOT) symbol indicating confirmation to applicable federal standards. Adjacent to the DOT symbol is a tire identification number. The first two characters identify the tire manufacturer. The remaining characters identify size, type, date of manufacture, and whether the tires are tubeless or tube-type.

In addition, DOT requirements mandate that tires must have the uniform tire quality grading system (UTQGS) molded into their sidewalls. As shown in Figure 35–9, this consumer comparison information includes tread wear, traction, temperature, and the tire performance criteria (**TPC**) specification number.

TREADWEAR The **treadwear grade** is a comparative rating based on the wear rate of the tire when tested under controlled conditions on a specified government test course. For example, a tire graded 160 would wear twice as well on the government course as a tire graded 80.

FIGURE 35–8   All tire sidewalls carry this information. *Courtesy of Oldsmobile Division, General Motors Corporation*

TRACTION The wet-weather traction grades are, from highest to lowest, A, B, and C. These represent the tire's ability to stop on wet pavement as measured under controlled conditions on specified government test surfaces of asphalt and concrete. The federal government warns consumers not to choose tires that earn only a C traction rating, no matter what other ratings they have. They have poor traction on wet roads.

TEMPERATURE The resistance to a high-temperature grading system also uses an A, B, and C rating. The C grade indicates the tire meets DOT's present standards for temperature resistance and is acceptable. Tires that earn A and B temperature resistance ratings are still better.

TPC SPECIFICATION NUMBER On most vehicles equipped with radial tires, a TPC specification number is molded into the sidewall. This indicates the tire meets rigid size and performance standards developed for that particular automobile. It ensures the combination of endurance, handling, load capacity, ride, and traction on wet, dry, and snow-covered surfaces.

Tire Placard

The tire placard, or safety compliance certification label, is generally found on the driver's door jamb. It includes recommended maximum vehicle load, tire size (including spare), and correct cold tire inflation for the specific vehicle (Figure 35–10). Never use this information for other cars.

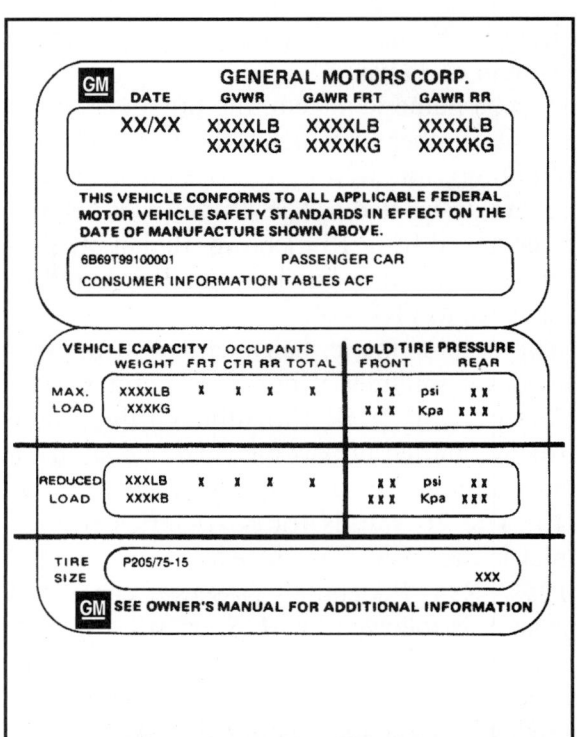

FIGURE 35–10   Typical tire placard. *Courtesy of Cadillac Motor Car Division, General Motors Corporation*

FIGURE 35–9   Uniform tire quality grading system.

CUSTOMER CARE

Be sure to tell your customer to stay within the gross vehicle weight rating (**GVWR**) and the front and rear gross axle weight rating (**GAWR**) when loading a vehicle. The GVWR and GAWR are shown on the safety compliance certification label or tie placard. These limits represent the designed capacity of the vehicle, not merely of the tires. When towing a trailer, the allowable passenger and cargo load must be reduced by an amount equal to the trailer tongue load on the trailer hitch. Station wagon loads should be distributed as far forward as possible. Vehicles equipped with luggage racks do not have a vehicle load capacity greater than specified on the tire placard. When carrying heavier-than-normal loads, the tire pressure should be increased but never to an extent greater than load range. ■

Combining Tire Types

As a general rule, tires should be replaced with the same size designation or an approved optional size as recommended by the auto or tire manufacturer. In addition to following the vehicle manufacturer's recommendations for tire size, type, inflation pressures, and rotation patterns, the following points should be observed.

1. Never mix size or construction types on the same axle.
2. Tires on the same axle should be of approximately equal tread depth.
3. All tires on station wagons and all other vehicles used for trailer towing should be of the same size, type, and load rating.
4. New tires should be installed in pairs on the same axle. When replacing only one tire, it should be paired with the tire having the most tread to equalize braking traction.
5. If radial tires are used on the car, combine them with radial snow tires on the driving wheels.
6. Snow tires should be of a size and type equivalent to the other tires on the vehicle; otherwise, the safety and handling of the vehicle might be adversely affected.
7. If any doubt exists as to combining tires on the same vehicle, use Table 35–4 as a guide.

TABLE 35–4 TIRE COMBINATIONS

Construction	Series (Profile)	Bias on Front (Read down for rear)			Belted Bias on Front (Read down for rear)			Radial on Front (Read down for rear)			
		78 Series	70 Series	60/50 Series	78 Series	70 Series	60/50 Series	Metric	78 Series	70 Series	60/50 Series
Bias on Rear (Read across for front)	Conventional (83 Series)	A	NO	NO	A	NO	NO	NO	NO	NO	NO
	78 Series	P	A	NO	A	NO	NO	NO	NO	NO	NO
	70 Series	A	P	NO	A	A	NO	NO	NO	NO	NO
	60/50 Series	A	A	P	A	A	A	NO	NO	NO	NO
Belted Bias on Rear (Read across for front)	78 Series	A	A	NO	P	A	NO	NO	NO	NO	NO
	70 Series	A	A	NO	A	P	NO	NO	NO	NO	NO
	60/50 Series	A	A	A	A	A	P	NO	NO	NO	NO
Radial on Rear (Read across for front)	Metric	A	A	NO	A	A	NO	P	A	A	NO
	78 Series	A	A	NO	A	A	NO	A	P	A	NO
	70 Series	A	A	NO	A	A	NO	A	A	P	NO
	60/50 Series	A	A	A	A	A	A	A	A	A	P

P: Preferred applications. For best all-around car handling, performance tires of the same size and construction should be used on all wheel positions.

A: Acceptable but not preferred applications. Consult the car owner's manual and do not apply if vehicle manufacturer recommends against this application.

NO: Not recommended.

SHOP TALK

Tires larger or smaller than originally installed might affect the accuracy of the speedometer calibration. It might be necessary to change the speedometer drive gears when tire size has been changed. Check the vehicle's service manual for details. ∎

Tire Care

To maximize tire performance, inspect for signs of improper inflation and uneven wear, which can indicate a need for balancing, rotation, or front suspension alignment. Tires should also be checked frequently for cuts, stone bruises, abrasions, blisters, and objects that might have become imbedded in the tread. More frequent inspections are recommended when rapid or extreme temperature changes occur, or where road surfaces are rough or occasionally littered with debris.

To clean tires, use a mild soap and water solution only. Rinse thoroughly with clear water. Do not use any caustic solutions or abrasive materials. Never use steel wool or wire brushes. Avoid gasoline, paint thinner, and similar materials having a mineral oil base. These materials are harmful to the tires and eventually discolor the whitewalls and raised letters.

Inflation Pressure A properly inflated tire (Figure 35–11A) gives the best tire life, riding comfort, handling stability, and gas mileage for normal driving conditions. Too little air pressure can result in tire squeal, hard steering, excessive tire heat, abnormal tire wear, and increased fuel consumption by as much as 10 percent. An underinflated tire (Figure 35–11B) shows

TABLE 35–5 INFLATION PRESSURE CONVERSION (KILOPASCALS TO psi)			
kPa	psi	kPa	psi
140	20	215	31
145	21	220	32
155	22	230	33
160	23	235	34
165	24	240	35
170	25	250	36
180	26	275	40
185	27	310	45
190	28	345	50
200	29	380	55
205	30	415	60

Conversion: 6.9 kPa = 1 psi

maximum wear on the outside edges of the tread. There is little or no wear in the center. Conversely, an overinflated tire (Figure 35–11C) shows its wear in the center of the tread and little wear on the outside edges. A higher tire inflation pressure than recommended can cause a hard ride, tire bruising, and rapid wear at the center of the tire.

Many inflation pressures given on OE import vehicles use kilopascals (kPa) rather than psi. Table 35–5 converts kPa to psi.

CUSTOMER CARE

Be sure to tell your customer that radial tires have a distinctive bulge (Figure 35–12) that gives the appearance of an underinflated tire. This is normal and air should not be added to make a radial tire look as inflated as a bias or bias-belted tire. Inflate a radial to the recommended pressure only. Do not overinflate. ∎

Tire Rotation To equalize tire wear, most car and tire manufacturers recommend the tires be rotated. Remember that front and rear tires perform different

A TREAD CONTACT WITH ROAD

B TREAD CONTACT WITH ROAD

C TREAD CONTACT WITH ROAD

FIGURE 35–11 Effects of inflation on tires.

NONRADIAL TIRE INFLATED APPEARANCE

RADIAL TIRE BULGE

FIGURE 35–12 Tire profile on a nonradial tire as compared to a radial tire.

jobs and can wear differently, depending on driving habits and the type of vehicle. In a RWD vehicle, for instance, the front tires usually wear along the outer edges, primarily because of the scuffing and slippage encountered in cornering. The rear tires wear in the center because of acceleration thrusts. To equalize wear, it is recommended that tires be rotated as illustrated in Figure 35–13. Bias ply and bias-belted tires should be rotated about every 6,000 miles. Radial tires should be initially rotated at 7,500 miles and then at least every 15,000 miles thereafter. Many auto shops keep a record of tire rotation periods so they can notify their customers when it should be done next.

When snow tires are installed, the regular tread tires on the rear should be moved to the front and the front tires stored. When snow tires are removed, install the stored tires on the rear. Do not rotate studded tires. Always remount them in their original positions.

When storing tires, lay them flat on a clean, dry, oil-free floor. Keep them away from ozone, which comes from the electrical sparking frequently produced by electric motors. Store them in the dark. Direct sunlight is hard on tires.

FIGURE 35–14 Tread wear indicators.

FIGURE 35–15 Checking tread depth.

Tread Wear Most tires used today have built-in tread wear indicators to show when they need replacement. These indicators appear as 1/2-inch wide bands when the tire tread depth wears to 1/16 inch (Figure 35–14). When the indicators appear in two or more adjacent grooves, at three locations around the tire, or when cord or fabric is exposed, tire replacement is recommended.

If the tires do not have tread wear indicators, a tread depth indicator (Figure 35–15) quickly shows in 32nds of an inch how much tire tread is left. When only 2/32 inch is left, it is time to replace the tire.

CUSTOMER CARE

It is good public relations to explain or, better still, to show a customer how to remove the tire/wheel assembly. This is especially true in the case of wheelcovers equipped with an antitheft locking system. The lock bolt for each wheelcover is located behind the hub ornament. A special key wrench is required to pry off the center hub ornament and remove the lock bolt (Figure 35–16). To allow for service in the event the customer's key has been misplaced, a master key set is available at the new car dealership.

In recent years more and more wheels are being equipped with antitheft wheel lugs (one per wheel). The key has a circular keyway that is matched to the female slot in the antitheft wheel lug nut (Figure 35–17). To remove or install the antitheft wheel lug nut, insert the special key into the slot of the lug nut. Place the lug nut wrench on the key. While applying pressure on the key, remove or install the lug nut. ■

FIGURE 35–13 Rotation for radial and bias-belted tires.

LOCKING WIRE COVER MUST BE PROPERLY INSTALLED BEFORE INSTALLING LOCK BOLT.

FIGURE 35–16 Antitheft wire wheelcovers. *Courtesy of Ford Motor Company*

FIGURE 35–17 Circular keyway fits female slot of antitheft wheel lug nut. *Courtesy of Ford Motor Company*

Tire Repair The most common tire repair problem is a puncture. When properly done, a repaired tire can be put back in service safely and without fear of the leak recurring. Service punctures in the tread area only (Figure 35–18). Never attempt to service punctures in the tire's shoulders or sidewalls. In addition, do not service any tire that has sustained the following damage.

FIGURE 35–18 Repair areas of (A) bias and belted bias, and (B) radial tires.

- ◆ Bulges or blisters
- ◆ Ply separation
- ◆ Broken or cracked beads
- ◆ Fabric cracks or cuts
- ◆ Wear to the fabric or visible wear indicators
- ◆ Punctures larger and 1/4-inch diameter

⚠ *WARNING!*

Tire sealants injected through the valve stem can produce wheel rust and tire imbalance. ■

To locate a puncture in a tire, inflate it to the maximum inflation pressure marked on the tire. Then, submerge the tire/wheel assembly in a tank of water or sponge it with a soapy water solution. The water bubbles at the exact spot of the leak.

Mark the location of the leak with a crayon so it can be easily found once the tire is removed from the wheel. Also place a crayon mark to identify the valve stem location so the original tire balance and tire runout can be maintained when the tire is remounted.

The proper procedure for dismounting and remounting a tire is illustrated in Photo Sequence 21. Do not use hand tools or tire irons alone to change a tire because they might damage the beads or wheel rim. When mounting or dismounting tires on vehicles using aluminum or wire spoke wheels, contact the tire changer manufacturer about the accessories required to protect the wheel's finish.

Once the tire is off the wheel and the cause of the puncture is removed, the tire can be permanently serviced from the inside using a combination service plug and vulcanized patch. While the service kit manufacturer's instructions should always be followed, there are some general procedures that help to make a good, permanent patch. (Since so few vehicles still use tube-type tires, their repair is not covered in this book.)

The following methods are the most popular types of tire repair.

PLUG REPAIR The head-type plug (Figure 35–19) is the most popular method. Place a plug slightly larger than the size of the puncture hole in the eye of the insertion tool. Wet both the plug and insertion tool with vulcanizing fluid.

While holding and stretching the long end of the plug, insert it into the puncture hole from inside the tire. The plug must extend above both the tread and inner liner surface. If the plug pops through, discard it and repeat the insertion procedure. Once the insertion tool has been removed, trim off the plug 1/32

PHOTO SEQUENCE 21

DISMOUNTING AND MOUNTING A TIRE ON A WHEEL ASSEMBLY

P21–1 A typical tire changer.

P21–2 Dismounting the tire from the wheel begins with releasing the air, removing the air valve core, and unseating the tire from the rim. The machine does the unseating. The technician merely guides the operating lever.

P21–3 Once both sides of the tire are unseated, place the assembly onto the machine.

P21–4 Depress the pedal that clamps the wheel to the tire machine.

P21–5 Lower the machine's arm into position on the tire and wheel assembly.

P21–6 Insert the tire iron between the tire and wheel. Depress the pedal that causes the wheel to rotate. This will free the tire from the wheel.

P21–7 After the tire is totally free from the rim, remove the tire.

(continued)

P21–8 To prepare the wheel for the mounting of a new tire, use a wire brush to remove all of the dirt and rust from the sealing surface.

P21–9 Rubber compound should be liberally applied to the bead area of the new tire.

P21–10 Place the tire onto the wheel assembly and lower the arm onto the assembly. As the wheel rotates, the tire will be forced over the rim.

P21–11 After the tire is completely over the rim, install the air ring over the tire. Activate this to seat the tire against the wheel.

P21–12 Reinstall the air valve core and inflate the tire to the recommended pressure.

FIGURE 35–19 Plug for a radial tire.

inch above the inner liner surface. Do not pull on the plug while cutting.

COLD PATCH REPAIR When using a cold patch, carefully remove the backing from the patch. Spread vulcanizing fluid on the punctured area. Let it dry, then center the patch base over the punctured area. Run a stitching tool over the patch to help bind it to the tire.

⚠️ **WARNING!**

When repairing radial tires, use only a patch specially approved for that application. These special patches have arrows that must be lined up parallel to the radial plies. ∎

HOT PATCH REPAIR A hot tire patch application is similar to a cold patch. The difference is that the hot patch is clamped over the puncture and heat is applied to the patch to make it adhere.

SHOP TALK

When mounting new tires, always install new valve stems. The life of tire rubber is close to the life of the valve stem rubber. Most stems are the snap-in type. These are installed from inside the wheel with a pulling tool. Make sure the stem is properly seated. Another style of stem has a retaining nut that must be removed when pulling off the old stem. Be sure to completely tighten the new nut. ■

Installation of Tire/Wheel Assembly on the Vehicle

A wheel should be carefully inspected each time a tire is to be mounted on it. The major causes of wheel failure are improper maintenance, overloading, age, and accidents, including pot hole damage. Wheels must be replaced when they are bent, dented, or heavily rusted, have leaks or elongated bolt holes, and have excessive **lateral** or **radial runout**. Wheels with a lateral or radial runout greater than the recommended specification can cause high-speed vehicle vibration. Stones wedged between the wheel and disc brake rotor or drum can unbalance the wheel. Remember that wobble or shimmy caused by a damaged wheel eventually damages the wheel bearings. Also, check the lug nuts to be sure they are set according to the torque given in the vehicle's service manual. Loose lug nuts can cause shimmy and vibration and can also distort the stud holes in the wheels.

WARNING!

Steel wheel repairs that use welding, heating, or peening are not approved. The use of an inner tube is not an acceptable repair for leaky wheels or tubeless tires. ■

Before reinstalling a tire/wheel assembly on a vehicle, inspect the wheel bearings as described later in this chapter, then clean the axle/rotor flange and wheel bore with a wire brush or steel wool. Coat the axle pilot flange with disc brake caliper slide crease or an equivalent. Place the wheel on the hub. Install the locking wheelcover pedestal (if used) and lug nuts, and tighten them alternately to draw the wheel evenly against the hub. They should be tightened to a specified torque and sequence (Figure 35–20) to avoid distortion. Many tire technicians snug up the lug nuts. Then when the car is lowered to the floor, they use a torque wrench for the final tightening.

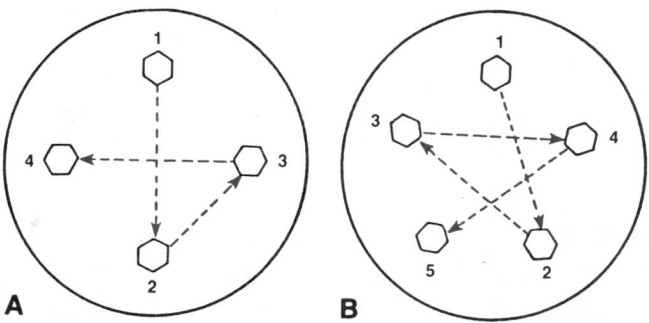

FIGURE 35–20 Lug nut tightening sequence for (A) four-bolt wheel and (B) five-bolt wheel.

WARNING!

Overtorqueing of the lug nuts is the most common cause of disc brake rotor distortion. Also, an overtorqued lug distorts the threads of the lug and could lead to premature failure. ■

Be sure the wheels and hub are clean. To clean aluminum wheels, use a mild soap and water solution and rinse thoroughly with clear water. Do not use a steel wool abrasive cleaner or strong detergent containing high alkaline or caustic agents because they might damage the protective coating and cause discoloration. Once the vehicle is on the ground, check and adjust the air pressure in all tires.

TIRE/WHEEL RUNOUT

A tire that is off center is said to run out. This is known as radial runout or eccentricity. One that wobbles side to side is said to have lateral runout. If a tire with some built-in runout is mismatched with a wheel's runout, the resulting total runout can exceed the ability of the balance weights to correct the problem. For this reason, part of a wheel balance check should be a check for excessive runout. Sometimes tires or wheels can be remounted to lessen or correct runout problems.

To avoid false readings caused by temporary flat spots in the tires, check runout only after the vehicle has been driven. Visually inspect the tire for abnormal bulges or distortions. The extent of runout should be measured with a dial indicator. All measurements should be made on the vehicle with the tires inflated to recommended load inflation pressures and with the wheel bearing adjusted to specification.

Measure tire radial runout at the center and outside ribs of the tread face (Figure 35–21). Measure tire lateral runout just above the buffing rib on the sidewall. Mark the high points of lateral and radial runout for future references. On bias or belted bias

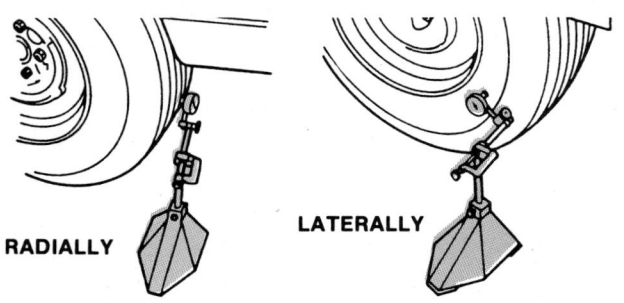

RADIALLY   **LATERALLY**

FIGURE 35–21   Using a dial indicator to measure tire runout.

4. Use a clean rag to remove all sanding dust.
5. With the wheel at room temperature, apply a generous portion of silicone rubber sealer to the leak area.
6. Use a spatula or similar tool and spread the sealer over the entire area, forming a thin coat.
7. Allow to cure for approximately 6 hours before remounting the tire.

tires, radial runout must not exceed 0.104 inch and lateral runout must not exceed 0.099 inch. On radial ply tires, radial runout must not exceed 0.081 inch and lateral runout must not exceed 0.099 inch.

If total radial or lateral runout of the tire exceeds specified limits, it is necessary to check wheel runout to determine whether the wheel or tire is at fault. Wheel radial runout is measured at the wheel rim just inside the wheelcover retaining nibs. Wheel lateral runout is measured at the wheel rim bead flange just inside the curved lip of the flange. Wheel radial runout should not exceed 0.035 inch and wheel lateral runout should not exceed 0.040 inch. Mark the high points of radial and lateral runout for future reference.

If total tire runout, either lateral or radial, exceeds the specified limit but wheel runout is within the specified limit, it might be possible to reduce runout to an acceptable level. This is done by changing the position of the tire on the wheel so the previously marked high points are 180 degrees apart.

If an air leak is suspected due to wheel damage, use the following procedure before considering wheel replacement.

PROCEDURES
Repairing Air Leaks

1. Remove the tire and wheel assembly, and inspect the wheel for structural damage. If none exists, go on to step 2. If the wheel is damaged, replace it.
2. With the tire mounted on the wheel, locate the leak as described earlier. Mark the location. Check the complete wheel for possible additional leaks. After all leaks are marked, dismount the tire.
3. On the inside of the rim, use about #80 grit sandpaper on the area of the leak to thoroughly remove all contamination. Score the surface of the wheel to improve sealer adhesion.

TIRE/WHEEL ASSEMBLY SERVICE

For most tire/wheel service, the assembly must first be removed from the vehicle. The wheel and the tire must be separated whenever tires are placed or repaired. The rear wheel drum or disc brake rotor is usually attached to studs on the rear axle shaft hub flange. The wheel and tire mounts on the same rear axle shaft flange studs and is held against the hub and drum or rotor by the wheel nuts.

Tire/Wheel Balance

Proper front-end alignment allows the tires to roll straight without excessive tread wear. The wheels can go out of alignment from striking raised objects or pot holes. Misalignment subjects the tires to uneven and/or irregular wear. An out-of-balance condition can also cause increased wear on the ball joints, as well as deterioration of shock absorbers and other suspension components.

Should an inspection show uneven or irregular tire wear, wheel alignment and balance service is a must. Wheel balancing distributes weights along the wheel rim that counteract heavy spots in the wheels and tires and allow them to roll smoothly without vibration. There are two types of wheel imbalance: static and dynamic.

Static Balance   **Static balance** is the equal distribution of weight around the wheel. Wheels that are statically unbalanced cause a bouncing action called **wheel tramp**. This condition eventually causes uneven tire wear. As the name implies, static balance is balancing a wheel at rest. This is done by adding a compensating weight. Static balance is achieved when the wheel does not rotate by itself regardless of the position in which it is placed on its axis. This is true whether the wheel is mounted vertically, as on a spindle or balancer shaft, or horizontally, as on a bubble-type balancer.

A statically unbalanced wheel tends to rotate by itself until the heavy portion is down. To balance against the heavy portion, a weight is attached to the wheel directly opposite the heavy area. Some technicians place the weight on the inside of the wheel. Others place the weight on the outside of the wheel. Still others recommend placing two equal weights, one on each side of the wheel, opposite the heavy area.

There are many static balancers commonly used. The simplest is the bubble balancer. This design features a movable flange that rests on a point. A round sight glass filled with liquid containing a bubble rides with the flange. The bubble indicates whether the flange is level. When the tire/wheel assembly is placed on the flange, any static imbalance makes it tilt and moves the bubble off center. Lead wheel balance weights are then placed on the wheel where the bubble points to counteract the imbalance and center the bubble on the sight glass. When balance weights are used in pairs, the total balance-correcting weight is divided in half. One half is installed on the back of the wheel, the other half on the front. This weight-splitting method leaves the wheel's dynamic balance or imbalance unchanged. Many equipment manufacturers recommend static balancing a wheel at equal distances from the center of the light area. The balance weights are normally hammered on with their holding tabs between the tire head and rim. Mag wheels require the use of tape weights to balance them.

Dynamic Balance **Dynamic balance** is the equal distribution of weight on each side of the centerline. When the tire spins, there is no tendency for the assembly to move from side to side. Wheels that are dynamically unbalanced can cause **wheel shimmy** and a wear pattern (Figure 35–22). Dynamic bal-

FIGURE 35–23 Static unbalance causes wheel tramp.

ance, simply stated, is balancing a wheel in motion. Once a wheel starts to rotate and is in motion, the static weights try to reach the true plane of rotation of the wheel because of the action of centrifugal force. In an attempt to reach the true plane of rotation when there is an imbalance, the static weights force the spindle to one side.

At 180 degrees of wheel rotation, static weights kick the spindle in the opposite direction. The resultant side thrusts cause the wheel assembly to wobble or wiggle (Figure 35–23). When severe enough, as already mentioned, it causes vibration and front-wheel shimmy.

To correct dynamic unbalance, equal weights are placed 180 degrees opposite each other, one on the inside of the wheel and one on the outside, at the point of unbalance. This corrects the couple action or wiggle of the wheel assembly. Also, note that dynamic balance is obtained, while static balance remains unaffected.

The most commonly used dynamic wheel balancer requires that the tire/wheel assembly be taken off and mounted on the balancer's spindle (Figure 35–24). The machine spins the entire assembly to indicate the heavy spot with a strobe light or other device. Two tests must be done, one for static and one for dynamic imbalance. One set of weights is placed to correct for static imbalance, and others are placed to correct for dynamic imbalance. Sometimes proper positioning of the static balance weights also corrects dynamic imbalance.

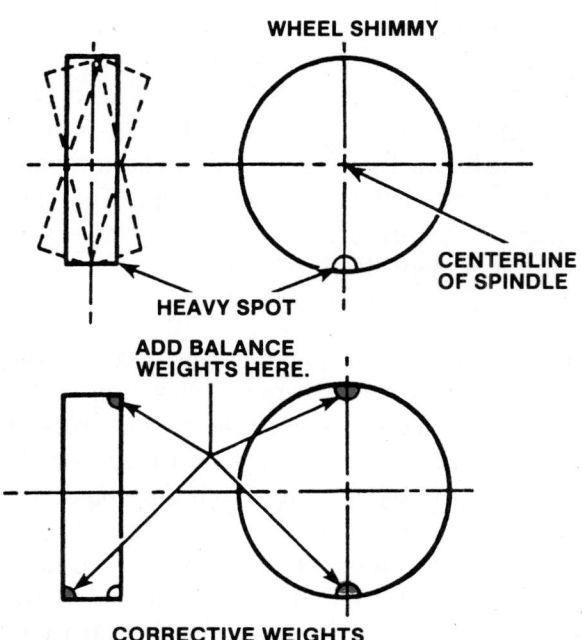

FIGURE 35–22 Dynamic unbalance causes wheel shimmy.

FIGURE 35–24 Tire/wheel assembly mounted on balancer's spindle. *Courtesy of Hunter Engineering Company*

FIGURE 35–25 Exploded view of a typical front wheel assembly for RWD vehicle. Safety washer, used between outer bearing and spindle nut, is found on all cars. It must always be in place. *Courtesy of Ford Motor Company*

There are several electronic dynamic/static balancer units available that will permit balancing while the wheel and tire are on the car. A switch on the console sets the machine for either static or dynamic balancing. When the wheel balancing assembly is mounted for static balancing, it rotates until the heavy spot falls to the bottom. Weights are added to balance the assembly.

In the dynamic balance mode, the wheel assembly is rotated at high speed. Observing the balance scale, the operator reads out the amount of weight that has to be added and the location where the weights should be placed.

Wheel Bearings

There are several types of wheel bearing arrangements for both driving and nondriving wheels.

Front Wheel Hubs Traditionally, the front wheel hub bearing for driven and nondriven wheels incorporated two bearings (Figure 35–25). They were usually of the separable type and, therefore, were comprised of four components. This arrangement required periodic bearing lubrication and adjustment.

In the early 1970s, the automotive industry began to show more interest in compactness and reduced mass. To meet future demands, especially for driven wheels, a unit in which both bearing rings were flanged was studied. The outer ring became a stiff structural member and thus permitted a simplification of the hub carrier. The hub was eliminated as the rotating inner ring flange took over its function. Design and assembly were simplified and there was a consequent savings in weight and space. Because the bearing rings are rigid, bearing geometry is precisely controlled.

There are three popular hub units (Figure 35–26).

HUB UNIT 1 This unit is a double-row, angular contact ball bearing with a two-part inner ring. The bearing has the correct axial clearance when mounted. Therefore, no adjustment is required and there is no risk of preloading the bearing. The contact angle of 32 degrees gives a large distance between the pressure centers of the bearing and reduces sensitivity to tilting movements. An added benefit is good axial carrying capacity, which is particularly important during cornering conditions. A tapered roller bearing version is available for use in which radial space restricts the fitting of the ball bearing type. This unit has a higher radial carrying capacity but is more sensitive to misalignment. Both ball and roller types are designed for compact FWD cars.

HUB UNIT 2 This unit is a double-row, angular contact ball bearing with a two-part inner ring and a flanged outer ring. The contact angle is 32 degrees. It is designed for outer ring rotation and incorporates the function of the wheel hub, having a spigot for centering the wheel and the brake drum or disc. Since a hub cap provides protection, there is no need for an outboard seal. This unit was designed for FWD vehicles that are somewhat larger than those using hub unit 1.

A

B

C

FIGURE 35–26 Examples of ready-to-mount units: (A) hub unit 1, (B) hub unit 2, and (C) hub unit 3. *Courtesy of SKF USA, Inc.*

HUB UNIT 3 This unit, designed primarily for mid-sized FWD cars, is a double-row, angular contact ball bearing with a correct angle of 32 degrees. Both inner and outer rings have been shaped to take over the functions of the other. The inner ring is extended on the outside to provide a flange and spigot. The bore is also splined, which enables hub unit 3 to

completely replace the conventional driven wheel hub. The extremely stiff outer ring is also flanged and is provided with bolt holes for attachment to the steering knuckle. Therefore, it becomes a structural part of the suspension. Because the bearing outer ring is self-supporting, the steering knuckle can be designed for fatigue strength rather than for stiffness. The CV-joint shaft no longer needs to be designed to hold the bearing assembly together. Its only requirement is to transmit torque, and it can be locked in the inner ring by a retaining ring.

Some early European sports models featured a so-called quick-change hub assembly. While this is similar to the standard disc type, it has a wire spoke center that slides into a splined hub and is retained by a single quick release or knock-off spinner nut. The wheel and tire assembly can be changed merely by removing this nut. The wheel then pulls off. To replace, merely reverse the procedure. This quick-change design requires special hubs.

Rear Hubs Most RWD axle bearings are of the straight roller bearing design (Figure 35–27), in which the drive axle shaft serves as the bearing race. Some rear wheel axle bearings are of the ball or tapered roller bearing type. Figures 35–28 and 35–29 show typical rear bearing designs.

A popular 4WD design is the so-called detachable rear axle hub (Figure 35–30). In this design, the hub is secured to the tapered axle end by means of a nut and key. The key fits into a groove cut in both the hub and axle. The key is used to prevent the hub from slipping on the axle.

FIGURE 35–27 Straight roller-type rear-axle bearing-and-seal arrangement. Notice the absence of a separate inner bearing race. Rollers run directly on the axle shaft. *Courtesy of Oldsmobile Division, General Motors Corporation*

FIGURE 35–28 Typical rear wheel bearing assembly for a FWD vehicle. *Courtesy of Ford Motor Company*

FIGURE 35–29 Exploded view of 4WD wheel hub and bearing assembly. *Courtesy of Ford Motor Company*

FIGURE 35–30 Detachable rear axle wheel hub. Hub is kept from turning on tapered axle end by a key. *Courtesy of Chrysler Corporation*

WARNING!

Never drive or move a vehicle with the wheel nuts loosened. Such an action could damage the wheel. ■

Wheel Bearing Grease Specification The grease for wheel bearings should be smooth textured, consist of soaps and oils, and be free of filler and abrasives. Recommended are lithium complex (or equivalent) soaps, or solvent-refined petroleum oils. Additives could be added to inhibit corrosion and oxidation. The grease should be noncorrosive to bearing parts, with no chance of separating during storage or use.

Using the correct amount of lube is also essential. Failure to maintain proper lubrication might result in bearing damage, causing a wheel to lock (Figure 35–31). To lubricate a bearing, force grease around the outside of the bearing and between the rollers,

FIGURE 35–31 Wheel bearing lubrication.

cone, and cage. Also, pack grease into the wheel hub. The depth of the grease should be level with the inside diameter of the cup.

Oil Lubrication Since it is thinner than grease, oil needs more frequent service intervals. Generally, oil is used to lubricate bearings in high-temperature and/or high-speed applications. It is primarily used on heavy-duty fleet, automotive, and agricultural vehicles.

Bearing Troubleshooting Wheel bearings are designed for longevity. Their life expectancy, based on metal fatigue, can usually be calculated if general operating conditions are known. Bearing failures not caused by normal material fatigue are called premature failures. The causes can range from improper lubrication or incorrect mounting, to poor condition of the shaft housing or bearing surfaces.

When servicing, replacing, or installing wheel bearings, always follow the procedure given in the service manual.

CASE STUDY

A customer wishes to purchase new tires for a sports car. The original size tire for the car is P235 VR60-15. He receives an estimate for purchasing four new tires of the same size and made by the same manufacturer. He is hesitant to spend that amount of money on replacement tires. He then asks for an estimate on a variety of alternative tires. The cost of the same tire from different tire manufacturers varies. A slightly narrower tire, e.g., P215 VR60-15, costs slightly less than the original size tire. Lower speed rated tires, e.g. H-series, cost considerably less. The customer is inclined to go with the H-series tire. Is he making the correct decision?

Although it is unlikely the customer will travel at 150 mph, the original tires for that car were rated at these speeds. Speed ratings not only indicate the top speed the tire can safely run, they also indicate the amount of heat they can withstand. A tire rated at 150 mph can withstand more heat than a tire rated at 130 mph. The V-series tires would be a safer tire for that car. Therefore, if the vehicle's manufacturer installed a V-series tire, so should the customer.

This same logic is true for not changing the width of the tires. The car was built and the alignment specifications set for a particular width tire. Therefore, the customer should be advised not to switch to narrower tires.

The only possible way the customer can save money on buying replacement tires for his car is to change brands. However, all the features of the OE tires should be compared to the features and specifications of the other brands. As a technician, you should be able to give sound advice based on a knowledge of tires.

KEY TERMS

Bead
Belted bias ply
Bias ply
Drop center
Dynamic balance
GAWR
GVWR
Hub
Lateral runout
Lug nuts
Plies
Radial ply
Radial runout
Series

Sidewalls
Sipes
Static balance
Tire profile
TPC
Tread
Treadware grade
Tubeless tires
Valve stem
Wheel
Wheel offset
Wheel shimmy
Wheel tramp

SUMMARY

◆ Wheels are made of either stamped or pressed steel discs riveted or welded into a circular shape or are die-cast or forged aluminum or magnesium rims.

◆ The primary purpose of tires is to provide traction. They also are designed to carry the weight of the vehicle, withstand side thrust over varying speeds and conditions, transfer braking and driving torque to the road, and absorb much of the road shock from surface irregularities.

◆ Pneumatic tires are of two types: those that use inner tubes and those that do not. The latter are called tubeless tires and are about the only type used on passenger cars.

◆ There are three types of tire construction in use today: bias ply, belted bias ply, and radial ply.

◆ Tires are rated by their profile, ratio, size, and load range.

◆ Tire construction affects both dimensions and ride characteristics, creating differences that can seriously affect vehicle handling.

◆ To maximize tire performance, inspect for signs of improper inflation and uneven wear, which can indicate a need for balancing, rotation, or alignment. Tires should also be checked frequently for cuts, bruises, abrasions, blisters, and stones or other objects that might have become imbedded in the tread.

◆ A properly inflated tire gives the best tire life, riding comfort, handling stability, and even gas mileage during normal driving conditions.

◆ To equalize tire wear, most car and tire manufacturers recommend the tires be rotated. It must be remembered that front and rear tires perform different jobs and can wear differently, depending on driving habits and the type of vehicle.

◆ Most tires used today have built-in tread wear indicators to show when tires need replacement.

◆ There are three popular methods of tire repair: head-type plug, cold patch repair, and hot patch repair.

◆ There are two types of wheel balancing: static and dynamic.

◆ The front wheel hubs on ball or tapered roller bearings are lubricated by wheel bearing grease.

◆ Rear wheels are bolted to integral or detachable hubs.

TECH MANUAL

The following procedures are included in Chapter 35 of the *Tech Manual* that accompanies this book:

1. Inspect tires for inflation and wear.

2. Remove and install front wheel bearings on a RWD vehicle.

3. Balance a tire and wheel assembly (off the vehicle).

REVIEW QUESTIONS

1. How is a modern tire wheel constructed? What materials are used?

2. Define dynamic and static wheel balance.

3. How is the tire load rating designated?

4. Which of the following statements concerning tires is incorrect?

   a. The main job of tires is to provide traction.

   b. Uneven tire wear is usually the first good indicator of alignment problems.

   c. The bead is the portion of the tire that comes in contact with the road surface.

   d. The inner tube tire was used exclusively before the 1960s.

5. Generally speaking, the lower the cord angle on a bias ply tire, the ____.

   a. worse the high-speed stability

   b. better the high-speed stability

   c. smoother the ride

   d. b and c

6. Series is another name for a tire's ____.

   a. size   c. bead

   b. load range   d. profile

7. The three belting systems available for today's tires are ____.

   a. steel, nylon, and woven

   b. lateral, cut, and block

   c. cut, folded, and woven

   d. folded, straight ahead, and turning

8. Technician A equips a four-wheel-drive vehicle with radial tires on the rear wheels only. Technician B equips a four-wheel-drive vehicle with radial tires on all four wheels. Who is correct?
   a. Technician A
   b. Technician B
   c. Both A and B
   d. Neither A nor B

9. Which of the following statements concerning inflation pressure is incorrect?
   a. Once a tire is hot, its pressure drops 4 psi or more.
   b. All inflation pressures indicate cold inflation.
   c. A hot tire should never be held.
   d. Pressure recommendations are normally specified for light load and maximum load.

10. Where does an overinflated tire show its wear?
    a. in the center of the tread
    b. on the outside edges
    c. both a and b
    d. neither a nor b

11. Which of the following is a major cause of wheel failure?
    a. overloading
    b. age
    c. improper maintenance
    d. all of the above

12. Technician A uses tire sealant injected through the valve stem to repair a tire punctured in the tread area. Technician B uses tire sealant injected through the valve stem to repair a tire punctured in the sidewall. Who is correct?
    a. Technician A
    b. Technician
    c. Both A and B
    d. Neither A nor B

13. Technician A says you can drive on a temporary spare tire indefinitely, as long as you are careful. Technician B says there are strict limitations on how fast and how far you may drive on a temporary spare tire. Who is correct?
    a. Technician A
    b. Technician
    c. Both A and B
    d. Neither A nor B

14. Most information about a car's tires can be found on the ____.
    a. engine block
    b. tire placard
    c. undercarriage of the vehicle
    d. steering wheel

15. A tire that wobbles from side to side is said to have ____.
    a. radial runout
    b. lateral runout
    c. eccentric runout
    d. none of the above

16. Technician A says tire rotation is done to even out wear on the front and rear tires. Technician B says tire wear is always greatest on the rear wheels. Who is correct?
    a. Technician A
    b. Technician
    c. Both A and B
    d. Neither A nor B

17. All of the following statements is true except ____.
    a. a cold patch should be stitched to the inner surface of the carcass.
    b. a tread puncture less than 1/4 inch in diameter is repairable.
    c. wheel balancing is required only when new tires are installed.
    d. for best results, punctures should be repaired from inside the tire.

18. All of the following statements are correct except ____.
    a. belts are reinforcing materials that encircle the tire under the tread
    b. the carcass of a tire is made up of plies, layers of cloth, and rubber
    c. most tread patterns are designed to work well on both wet and dry roads
    d. the bead is the decorative pattern at the outer edge of the tread

19. Which of the following statements about sidewall marking is correct?
    a. aspect ratio, or profile, indicates a grading for tread life.
    b. important information and safety warnings are indicated.
    c. the UTQG rating indicates maximum safe inflation pressure and load.
    d. section width is the distance between the tread and the bead.

20. All of the following statements are correct except ____.
    a. tire inflation pressure directly affects traction
    b. recommended tire pressure for front and rear tires may be different
    c. recommended tire pressure are often lower than maximum pressures
    d. recommended tire pressure is molded into the sidewall of the tire

SUSPENSION SYSTEMS

36

OBJECTIVES

◆ *Name the different types of springs and how they operate.* ◆ *Name the advantages of ball joint suspensions.* ◆ *Explain the important differences between sprung and unsprung weight with regard to suspension control devices.* ◆ *Identify the functions of shock absorbers and struts, and describe their basic construction.* ◆ *Identify the components of a MacPherson strut system and describe their functions.* ◆ *Identify the functions of bushings and stabilizers.* ◆ *Perform a general front suspension inspection.* ◆ *Check chassis height measurements to specifications.* ◆ *Identify the three basic types of rear suspensions and know their affects on traction and tire wear.* ◆ *Identify the various types of springs, their functions, and locations in the rear axle housing.* ◆ *Describe the advantages and operation of the three basic electronically controlled suspension systems: level control, adaptive, and active.* ◆ *Explain the function of electronic suspension components including air compressors, sensors, control modules, air shocks, electronic shock absorbers, and electronic struts.* ◆ *Explain the basic towing, lifting, jacking, and service precautions that must be followed when servicing air springs and other electronic suspension components.*

The suspension system performs a very complicated function. It must keep the wheel lined up with the axis and direction of travel of the vehicle, provide steering control for the driver under all road conditions, and help the vehicle ride smoothly and comfortably.

To provide a rigid structural foundation for the vehicle body and a solid anchorage for the suspension system, a frame of some type is essential. As detailed in a previous chapter, there are two basic frames in common use today.

CONVENTIONAL FRAME CONSTRUCTION In the conventional body-over-frame construction, the frame is the vehicle's foundation. The body and all major parts of a vehicle are attached to the frame. It must provide the support and strength needed by the assemblies and parts attached to it. In other words, the frame is an independent, separate component because it is not welded to any of the major units of the body shell.

UNIBODY CONSTRUCTION This type of construction has no separate frame. The body is constructed in such a manner that the body parts themselves supply the rigidity and strength required to maintain the structural integrity of the car. The uni-

body design significantly lowers the base weight of the car, and that in turn increases gas mileage capabilities.

SUSPENSION SYSTEM COMPONENTS

Most automotive suspension systems have the same basic components and operate similarly. Their differences are found in the method in which the basic components are arranged.

Springs

The spring is the core of nearly all suspension systems. It is the component that absorbs shock forces while maintaining correct riding height. If the spring is worn or damaged, the other suspension elements shift out of their proper positions and are subject to increased wear. The increased effect of shock impairs the vehicle's handling.

Various types of springs are used in suspension systems—coil, torsion, bar, leaf (both mono and multi-leaf types) (Figure 36–1) and air springs. Springs are rubber mounted to reduce road shock and noise.

Automotive springs are generally classified by the amount of deflection exhibited under a specific load.

FIGURE 36–1   Various types of automotive springs.

COIL SPRING

AIR SPRING

SINGLE-LEAF (MONO-) SPRING

TORSION BAR SPRING

MULTILEAF SPRING

JOUNCE

SUSPENSION MOVES UPWARD TOWARD FRAME.

A

REBOUND

SUSPENSION MOVES DOWNWARD FROM FRAME.

B

FIGURE 36–2   (A) Upward and (B) downward suspension movement.

This is referred to as the **spring rate**. According to the law of physics, a force (weight) applied to a spring causes it to compress in direct proportion to the force applied. When that force is removed, the spring returns to its original position if not overloaded. Remember that a heavy vehicle requires stiffer springs than a lightweight car.

The springs take care of two fundamental vertical actions: jounce and rebound. **Jounce** occurs when a wheel hits a bump and moves up (Figure 36–2A). When this happens, the suspension system acts to pull in the top of the wheel, maintaining an equal distance between the two front wheels and preventing a sideways scrubbing action as the wheel moves up and down. **Rebound** occurs when the wheel hits a dip or hole and moves downward (Figure 36–2B). In this case, the suspension system acts to move the wheel in at both the top and bottom equally, while maintaining an equal distance between the wheels.

The spring goes back and forth from jounce to rebound. Each time jounce and rebound become smaller and smaller. This is caused by friction of the spring's molecular structure and the suspension pivot joints. A **shock absorber** is added to each suspension to dampen and stop the motion of the spring after jounce.

All of the vehicle's weight supported by the suspension system is known as **sprung weight**. The weight of those components not supported by the springs is known as **unsprung weight**. The vehicle's body, frame, engine, transmission, and all of their components are considered sprung weight. Undercar parts classified as unsprung weight include the steering knuckles and rear axle assemblies (but not always the differentials). Keep

in mind that, in general, the lower the ratio of unsprung weight to sprung weight, the better the vehicle's ride will be.

Coil Springs   Two basic designs of coil springs are used: linear rate and variable rate. **Linear rate** springs characteristically have one basic shape and a consistent wire diameter. All linear springs are wound from a steel rod into a cylindrical shape with even spacing between the coils. As the load is increased, the spring is compressed and the coils twist (deflect). As the load is removed, the coils flex (unwind) back to the normal position. The amount of load necessary to deflect the spring 1 inch is the spring rate. On linear rate springs this is a constant rate, no matter how much the spring is compressed. For example, 250 pounds compress the spring 1 inch and 750 pounds compress the spring 3 inches. Spring rates for linear rate springs are normally calculated between 20 and 60 percent of the total spring deflection.

Since heavy-duty springs are designed to carry 3 to 5 percent greater loads than regular duty springs,

FIGURE 36-3 Comparison of regular and heavy-duty coil springs.

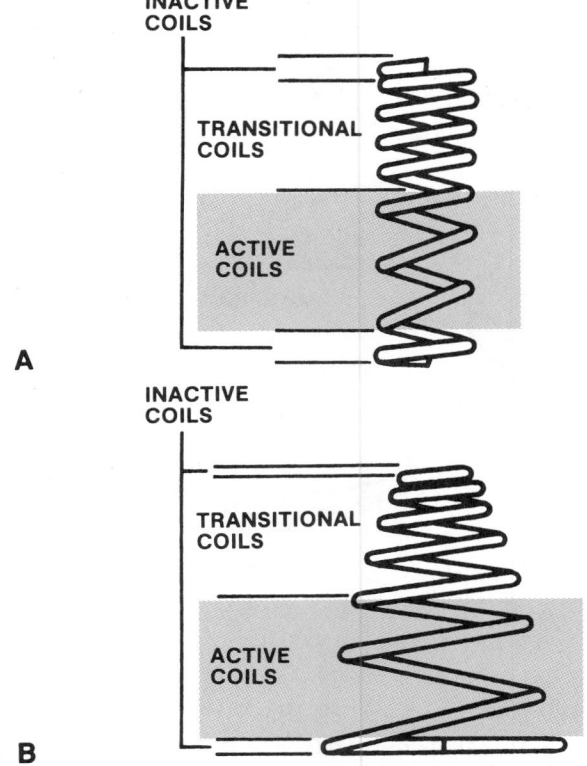

FIGURE 36-4 (A) Progressive rate coil; (B) cone-type variable rate coil spring.

they are somewhat different (Figure 36-3). The first difference that can be noticed is wire diameter. On heavy-duty springs, wire diameter can be up to 0.100 inch greater than the regular-duty spring for the same application.

The other difference is free length. A heavy-duty spring is up to 2-1/2 inches shorter than a regular-duty spring for the same application. The important factor to remember is load-carrying capabilities.

Variable rate spring designs are characterized by a combination of wire sizes and shapes. The most commonly used variable rate springs have a consistent wire diameter, are wound in a cylindrical shape, and have unequally spaced coils. This type of spring is called a progressive rate coil spring.

The design of the coil spacing gives the spring three functional ranges of coils: inactive, transitional, and active (Figure 36-4). Inactive coils are usually the end coils and introduce force into the spring. Transitional coils become inactive as they are compressed to their point of maximum load-bearing capacity. Active coils work throughout the entire range of spring loading. Theoretically in this type of design, at stationary loads the inactive coils are supporting all of the vehicle's weight. As the loads are increased, the transitional coils take over until they reach maximum capacity. Finally, the active coils carry the remaining overload. This allows for automatic load adjustment while maintaining vehicle height.

Another common variable rate design uses tapered wire to achieve this same type of progressive rate action. In this design, the active coils have a large wire diameter and the inactive coils have a small wire diameter.

The latest designs of variable rate springs deviate from the old cylindrical shape. These include the truncated cone, the double cone, and the barrel spring. The major advantage of these designs is the ability of the coils to nest, or bottom out, within each other without touching, which lessens the amount of space needed to store the springs in the vehicle.

Unlike a linear rate spring, a variable rate spring has no predictable standard spring rate. Instead, it has an average spring rate based on the load of a predetermined spring deflection. This makes it impossible to compare a linear rate spring to a variable rate spring. Variable rate springs, however, handle a load of up to 30 percent over standard rate springs in some applications.

SERVICING COIL SPRINGS A technician must know how to check and replace coil springs, select the proper replacement, and recommend the proper size and type of spring to the customer.

The first step in coil spring selection is to check for the original equipment part number. This is usually on a tag wrapped around the coil. In many instances, this tag falls off before replacement is necessary. If a set of aftermarket springs has been installed, the part number might be stamped on the end of the coil. Next, check to see what type of ends the coil springs have. There are three types of ends used in automotive applications (Figure 36-5): full wire open, tapered wire closed, and pigtail. Springs with full wire open ends are cut straight off and sometimes flattened or ground into a D or square shape. Tapered wire closed ends are wound to ensure squareness and ground into a taper at the ends. Pigtail ends are wound into a smaller diameter at the end.

FIGURE 36–5 Three types of coil spring ends.

The final step is to check the application in the catalog. To do this, it is necessary to know the make, year, model, body style, engine size (number of cylinders), and if the vehicle is equipped with air-conditioning. In some cases, it is also good to know the type of transmission, seating capacity, and other specifics that add extra weight to the vehicle. In most catalogs, springs are listed by vehicle application in two sections: front and rear.

CUSTOMER CARE

When making a recommendation as to which type of spring a customer should use, keep in mind that linear rate designs are normally found in regular, heavy-duty, and sport suspension packages. Regular-duty linear rate springs are a close replacement for the original spring found in the vehicle. They might replace as many as thirty different original equipment (OE) springs in the same vehicle. These are selected on the basis of tire and wheel packages, suspension packages, and optional equipment. Extra heavy-duty cargo linear rate springs offer increased load-carrying capabilities under constant loads. Two common examples of this are trailer towing and salespeople's vehicles. Variable rate designs are normally found when automatic load leveling is desired under increased loads and space savings are necessary, as in front-wheel-drive vehicles. Variable rate springs allow the suspension to maintain correct vehicle height under changing loads and give increased load-carrying capabilities over heavy-duty springs. Be sure to choose the correct spring for the intended use. ∎

Leaf Springs Although leaf springs were the first type of suspension spring used on automobiles, today they are generally found only on light-duty trucks, vans, and some passenger cars. There are three basic types of leaf springs: multiple leaf, monoleaf, and fiber composite.

MULTIPLE-LEAF SPRINGS Multiple-leaf springs consist of a series of flat steel leaves that are bundled together and held with clips or by a bolt placed slightly ahead of the center of the bundle (Figure 36–6). One leaf, called the **main leaf**, runs the entire length of the spring. The next leaf is a little shorter and attaches to the main leaf. The next leaf is shorter yet and attaches to the second leaf, and so on. This system allows almost any number of leaves to be used to support the vehicle's weight. It also gives a progressively stiffer spring. The spring easily flexes

6. Spring bolt
7. Frame bolt
8. Washers
9. Nut
10. Washers
11. Nut
12. Shackle
13. Spring assembly
14. Washer
15. U-bolt nut
16. Anchor plate
17. Nut
18. U-bolts
19. Washer
20. Bolt
21. Bushing

FIGURE 36–6 Leaf springs and related hardware. *Courtesy of Chevrolet Motor Division, General Motors Corporation*

over small distances for minor bumps. The farther the spring is deflected, the stiffer it gets. The more leaves and the thicker and shorter the leaves, the stronger the spring. It must be remembered that as the spring flexes, the ends of the leaves slide over one another. This sliding could be a source of noise and can also produce friction. These problems are reduced by interleaves of zinc and plastic placed between the spring's leaves. As the multiple leaves slide, friction produces a harsh ride as the spring flexes. This friction also dampens the spring motion.

Multiple-leaf springs have a curve in them. This curve, if doubled, forms an ellipse. Thus, leaf springs are sometimes called semi-elliptical or quarter-elliptical. The semi or quarter refers to how much of the ellipse the spring actually describes. The vast majority of leaf springs are semi-elliptical.

Leaf springs are commonly mounted at right angles to the axle. In addition to absorbing blows from road forces, they also serve as suspension locators by fixing the position of the suspension with respect to the front and rear of the vehicle. A centering pin is frequently used to ensure that the axle is correctly located. If a spring is broken or misplaced, the axle might be mislocated and the alignment impaired.

The front eye of the main leaf at either end of the axle is attached to a bracket on the frame of the vehicle with a bolt and bushing connection. The rear eye of the main leaf is secured to the frame with a shackle, which permits some fore and aft movement in response to physical forces of acceleration, deceleration, and braking.

MONOLEAF SPRINGS Monoleaf or single-leaf springs are usually the tapered plate type with a heavy or thick center section tapering off at both ends. This provides a variable spring rate for a smooth ride and good load-carrying ability. In addition, single-leaf springs do not have the noise and static friction characteristic of multiple-leaf springs.

FIBER COMPOSITE SPRINGS While most leaf springs are still made of steel, recent years have shown the **fiber composite** types increasing in popularity. Some automotive people call them plastic springs in spite of the fact that the springs contain no plastic at all. They are made of fiberglass, laminated and bonded together by tough polyester resins. The long strands of fiberglass are saturated with resin and bundled together by wrapping (a process called filament winding) or squeezed together under pressure (compression molding).

Fiber composite leaf springs are incredibly lightweight and possess some unique ride control charac-

teristics. Conventional monoleaf steel springs are real heavyweights, tipping the scale at anywhere from 25 to 45 pounds apiece. Some multiple-leaf springs can weigh almost twice as much. A fiber composite leaf spring is a featherweight by comparison, weighing a mere 8 to 10 pounds. As every performance enthusiast knows, springs are dead weight. Reducing the weight of the suspension not only reduces the overall weight of the vehicle but also reduces the sprung mass of the suspension itself. This reduces the spring effort and amount of shock control that is required to keep the wheels in contact with the road. The result is a smoother riding, better handling, and faster responding suspension, which is exactly the sort of thing every performance enthusiast wants.

Other advantages of using fiber composite springs include the following.

- A quieter ride. A fiber composite spring does not resonate or transmit sound like a steel spring. In fact, it actually dampens noise.
- A smoother ride. Because fiber composite springs use a one-piece monoleaf design, there is no rubbing friction like there is between the leaves in a multiple-leaf steel spring.
- No spring sag. All steel springs sag with age, whether leaves or coils. Spring sag affects ride height, which in turn alters wheel alignment, handling, steering, and braking. A weak spring can load the suspension unevenly, allowing the wheel under the weak spring to lose traction when accelerating or braking. According to the manufacturers of fiber composite springs, there is no sag with age.
- Less body roll. In applications where the leaf springs are mounted sideways (transversely), the spring also acts like a sway bar to limit body sway and roll when cornering (Figure 36–7). This load transfer characteristic also permits softer than normal spring rates to be used for a smoother ride.

With fiber composite leaf springs, there is little or no danger of the spring suddenly snapping. The laminated layers create a built-in fail-safe mechanism for keeping the spring intact should a problem arise (Figure 36–8).

Air Springs Another type of spring, an air spring, is used in an air-operated microprocessor-controlled system that replaces the conventional coil springs with air springs to provide a comfortable ride and automatic front and rear load leveling. This system, fully described later in this chapter, uses four air springs to carry the vehicle's weight. The air springs are located in the same positions as coil springs are usually found. Each spring consists of a reinforced rubber bag pres-

FIGURE 36–7 Typical transversely mounted monoleaf spring. *Courtesy Vette Brakes and Products, Inc.*

FIGURE 36–8 The manner in which a fiber composite spring bends dictates that there is no danger of it suddenly snapping. Laminated layers create a built-in safe mechanism for keeping the spring intact should a problem arise. *Courtesy of Vette Brakes and Products, Inc.*

surized with air. The bottom of each air bag is attached to an inverted pistonlike mount that reduces the interior volume of the air bag during jounce (Figure 36–9). This has the effect of increasing air pressure inside the spring as it is compressed, making it progressively stiffer. Thus a vehicle equipped with an electronic air suspension system is able to provide a comfortable street ride, about a third softer than conventional coil springs. At the same time, its variable spring rate helps absorb bumps and protect against bottoming.

Torsion Bar Suspension System

Torsion bars serve the same function as coil springs. In fact, they are often described as straightened-out coil springs. Instead of compressing like coil springs, a torsion bar twists and straightens out on the recoil. That is, as the bar twists, it resists up-and-down movement. One end of the bar—made of heat-treated alloy spring steel—is attached to the vehicle frame. The other end is attached to the lower control arm (Figure 36–10). When the wheel moves up and down, the lower control arm is raised and lowered. This twists the torsion bar, which causes it to absorb road shocks. The bar's natural resistance to twisting quickly restores it to its original position, returning the wheel to the road.

When torsion bars are manufactured, they are prestressed to give them fatigue strength. Because of directional prestressing, torsion bars are directional. The torsion bar is marked either right or left to identify on which side it is to be used.

A torsion bar can store a significantly higher maximum amount of energy than either an equally stressed coil or leaf spring. The shorter and thicker the rod is, the stiffer the torsion bar. Because torsion bars use less space than either coil or leaf springs, they are usually found on the front suspension, although a few cars have them at the rear. They are easily adjusted for riding height by changing the preload at the anchored end. (Preload is the weight on the springs while the car is at rest.)

In a conventional torsion bar suspension, the torsion bar runs from front to rear (Figure 36–11A). Either an A-arm or a single inner bushing control arm with a strut rod is used for the lower control arm. Torsion bars can be used to adjust vehicle riding height. They are not interchangeable from side to side, because the direction of the twisting (or torsion) is different between the left and right sides.

In a transverse torsion bar system—the latest in torsion bar suspension—the bar is mounted from side to side and runs across the width of the chassis

Bearing/cup
washer

Rebound
plate

Actuator
assembly

Rebound cup

Upper mount
assembly

Radial ball
bearing

"O" ring
retainer

Jounce plate/
"o" ring retainer

"O" rings

Jounce
bumper
(micro-cellular
poly urethane)

Solenoid
valve and
filter assembly

Rebound | Compression

Flow
path
soft
mode
only

Clip-solenoid
valve

Flow
path
soft
mode
only

Air spring
assembly

Gas

Flow
path
soft
mode
only

Shock strut
assembly

Shield

Anti-skid
brake
sensor
bracket

Stabilizer
bar bracket

Oil

Locator
tab

← View this
direction

FIGURE 36–9 Air springs are used on some late-model cars. They are especially adaptable to automatic leveling systems. *Courtesy of Ford Motor Company*

RIDE HEIGHT ADJUSTMENT SCREW

FIXED TO CONTROL ARM

FRONT SPINDLE

FRAME

BUSHING MOUNT

BALL JOINTS

BAR TWISTS WITH CAR'S WEIGHT.

ADJUSTMENT LEVER FIXED TO BAR

BUSHING

FIGURE 36–10 Torsion bar.

back to the control arm (Figure 36–11B). This eliminates the need for a strut rod or A-arm.

Because the torsion bar is connected to the lower control arm, the lower ball joint is the load carrier. A shock absorber is connected between the lower control arm and the frame to damp the twisting motion of the torsion bar.

Shock Absorbers

Shock absorbers damp or control motion in a vehicle. If unrestrained, springs continue expanding and contracting after a blow until all the energy is absorbed (Figure 36–12). Not only would this lead to a rough and unstable—perhaps uncontrollable—ride after consecutive shocks, it would also create a great deal

FIGURE 36–11 (A) Torsion bar suspension using bars mounted parallel with frame. (B) Torsion bars on this modern suspension mount crosswise in the car. Both can be adjusted to change vehicle height. *Courtesy of Moog Automotive*

of wear on the suspension and steering systems. Shock absorbers prevent this. Despite their name, they actually dampen spring movement instead of absorbing shock. As a matter of fact, in England and almost everywhere else but the United States, shock absorbers are referred to as **dampers**.

Today's conventional shock absorber is a velocity-sensitive hydraulic damping device. The faster it moves, the more resistance it has to the movement (Figure 36–13). This allows it to automatically adjust to road conditions. A shock absorber works on the principle of fluid displacement on both its compression (jounce) and extension (rebound) cycles. A typical car shock has more resistance during its extension cycle than its compression cycle. The extension cycle controls motions of the vehicle body spring weight. The compression cycle controls the same motions of the unsprung weight. This motion energy is converted into heat energy and dissipated into the atmosphere.

FIGURE 36–12 (A) Series of spring oscillations occurs as shown when not controlled by the shock absorber. (B) Notice the reduced number and severity of oscillations when controlled by the shock absorber.

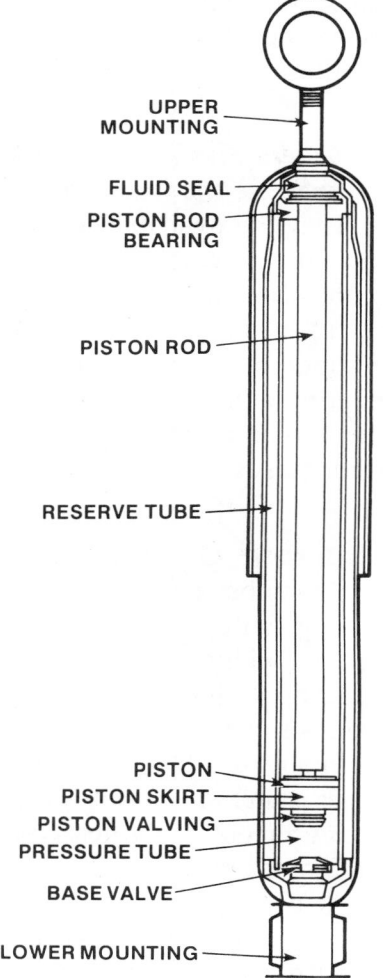

FIGURE 36–13 Cross section of a conventional shock absorber.

Shock absorbers can be mounted either vertically or at an angle. Angle mounting of shock absorbers improves vehicle stability and dampens accelerating and braking torque.

Conventional hydraulic shocks are available in two styles: the single-tube and double-tube shock. The vast majority of domestic shocks are double tubed. While they are a little heavier and run hotter than the single-tubed type, they are easier to make. The double-tube shock has an outer tube that completely covers the inner tube. The area between the tubes is the oil reservoir. A compression valve at the bottom of the inner tube allows oil to flow between the two tubes. The piston moves up and down inside the inner tube.

In a single **monoshock**, there is a second floating piston near the bottom of the tube. When the fluid volume increases or decreases, the second piston moves up and down, compressing the reservoir. The fluid does not move back and forth between a reservoir and the main chamber. There are no other valves in a single-tube shock besides those in the main piston. The second piston prevents the oil from splashing around too much and getting air bubbles in it. Air in the shock oil is detrimental. Air, unlike oil, is compressible and slips past the piston easily. When this happens, the result is a shock that offers poor vehicle control on bumpy roads.

In addition to these conventional hydraulic shocks, there are a number of others the technician may encounter.

Shock-Assist Shock Absorbers Shock-assist shock absorbers can be used to increase the load-carrying capacity of the springs. They are available for the front or rear suspension. They resemble a conventional shock absorber with a coil spring fitted to it. An upper spring mount is fastened to the upper shock tube and a lower spring mount is attached to the lower shock tube. The spring is mounted between. The spring is under some tension in its normal curb height position and compresses when the shock absorber compresses.

Gas-Charged Shock Absorbers On rough roads, the passage of fluid from chamber to chamber becomes so rapid that foaming can occur. Foaming is simply the mixing of the fluid with any available air. Since aeration can cause a skip in the shock's action, engineers have sought methods of eliminating it. One is the spiral groove reservoir, the shape of which breaks up bubbles. Another is a gas-filled cell or bag (usually nitrogen) that seals air out of the reservoir so the shock fluid can only contact the gas.

Gas-charged shock absorbers (Figure 36–14) operate on the same hydraulic fluid principle as conventional shocks. It uses a piston and oil chamber

FIGURE 36–14 Gas-pressure damped shocks operate like conventional oil-filled shocks. Gas is used to keep oil pressurized, which reduces oil foaming and increases efficiency under severe conditions. (A) Gas-charged shock for strut. (B) Conventional style gas-charged shock. (C) Gas-charged, self-leveling shock. *Courtesy of Volvo Car Corporation*

similar to other shock absorbers. Instead of a double tube with a reserve chamber, it has a dividing piston that separates the oil chamber from the gas chamber. The oil chamber contains a special hydraulic oil, and the gas chamber contains either freon or nitrogen gas under pressure equal to approximately 25 times atmospheric pressure.

As the piston rod moves downward in the shock absorber, oil is displaced, just as it is in a double-tube shock. This oil displacement causes the divided piston to press upon the gas chamber. The gas is compressed and the chamber reduces in size. When the piston rod returns, the gas pressure returns the dividing piston to its starting piston. Whenever the static pressure of the oil column is held at approximately 100 to 360 psi (depending on the design), the pressure decreases behind the piston and, so, cannot be high enough for the gas to escape from the oil column. As a result, a gas-filled shock absorber operates without aeration.

🔧 SHOP TALK

Some high-pressure gas-charged shocks are monotube shocks with fluid and gas in separate chambers. The gas is charged to 360 psi. Its basic design does not allow the valving range needed for a more responsive ride over a broad range of road conditions. The high-pressure gas charge can provide a harsh ride under normal driving conditions and is usually found on small trucks. ∎

Air Shock Systems There are two basic adjustable air shock systems: manual fill and automatic load-leveling. The manual fill system can be ordered on new vehicles or can be installed on almost any vehicle manufactured without it.

There are several different types of manual fill air shock systems available. One common manual fill air shock system uses a high-speed, direct current (DC) motor to transfer a command signal that is manually selected from the driver's seat. The selective ride feature is accomplished by the physical movement of a drive rod that can rotate approximately 90 degrees to open or close calibrated fluid passages built into the lower section of the shock body. The relative ease of installation allows the technician to find a rather straightforward approach to servicing. Basic multimeter voltage and resistance values can be adapted for use on most systems.

In another manual air system, the shock absorber is the only active part. These units are inflated through air valves mounted at the rear of the vehicle. Air lines run between the shocks and the valve. A tire air pressure pump is used to fill the shocks to bring the rear of the vehicle to the desired height.

A two-stage vacuum-operated air compressor is sometimes used in some manual fill systems. In this type of system, the diaphragm forces the piston toward the reservoir. Fresh air is drawn in through a check valve. The air is compressed in the second stage cylinder and forced through another check valve into the reservoir. The reverse stroke forces air from the first stage cylinder through the hollow cylinder into the second stage cylinder. The compressor piston cycles (moves back and forth) until the pressure built up in the reservoir is equal to the pressure generated by the piston in the second stage cylinder. When this point is reached, a balanced condition exists. The compressor does not operate until some air has been used by the system.

Some import cars use a lever-activated air shock. In this manual fill system, the piston, chamber, and reservoir are encased in a box that is fastened securely to the vehicle's body. The piston is connected to an overtravel arm extending from the box to the suspension. When the suspension moves downward, the overtravel lever opens an intake valve so compressed air can enter the shock absorber (Figure 36–15). These lever shocks help to minimize the amount of unsprung weight.

Shock Absorber Ratio Most shock absorbers are valved to offer roughly equal resistance to suspension movement upward (jounce) and downward (rebound). The proportion of a shock absorber's ability to resist these movements is indicated by a numerical formula. The first number indicates jounce resistance. The second indicates rebound resistance. For example, passenger cars with normal suspension requirements use shock absorbers valued at 50/50 (50% jounce/50% rebound). Drag racers, on the other hand, use shocks valued at about 90/10. Small vehicles, because of their light weight and soft springs, require more control in both jounce and rebound in the shock absorbers. Damping rates within the shock absorbers are controlled by the size of the piston, the size of the orifices, and the closing force of the values.

It is important to keep in mind that the shock absorber ratio only describes what percent of the shock absorber's total control is compression and what percent is extension. Two shocks with the same ratio can differ greatly in their control capacity. This is one reason the technician must be sure correct replacement shocks are installed on the vehicle.

ELECTRONICALLY CONTROLLED SHOCK ABSORBERS Electronically adjusted shock absorbers are one step above manually adjustable shocks. They are basically remote control shocks that allow the driver to select a soft, medium, or firm ride by pressing a button on the instrument panel. When activated, variable shock damping is accomplished by

FIGURE 36–15 Typical lever-type shock absorber.

varying the size of the metering orifices inside the shock absorber. This is done by rotating a control rod inside the shock by using a small electric actuator motor mounted on the tip of the shock. This control rod varies the size of the metering orifices, which, in turn, changes the shock rate from firm to medium to soft. The speed at which this occurs is usually less than half a second.

This type of electronically controlled shock can be used alone as a driver-controlled device or it can be part of a computer-controlled suspension system. In a computer-controlled system, the shock is activated based on input from various vehicle sensors. Computer-controlled suspensions are discussed later in this chapter.

MacPHERSON STRUT SUSPENSION COMPONENTS

The **MacPherson strut** suspension is dramatically different in appearance from the traditional independent front suspension (Figure 36–16), but similar components operate in the same way to meet suspension demands.

The MacPherson strut suspension's most distinctive feature is the combination of the main elements into a single assembly. It typically includes the spring, upper suspension locator, and shock absorber. It is mounted vertically between the top arm of the steering knuckle and the inner fender panel (Figure 36–17).

Domestic struts have taken two forms—a concentric coil spring around the strut itself (Figure 36–18) and a spring located between the lower control arm and the frame (Figure 36–19, page 947). The location of the spring on the lower control arm, not on the strut as in a conventional MacPherson strut sys-

FIGURE 36–16 Typical coil independent front suspension (IFS) system. *Courtesy of Sealed Power Corporation*

tem, allows minor road vibrations to be absorbed through the chassis rather than be fed back to the driver through the steering system. This system is called modified MacPherson suspension.

Struts

The core element of the suspension is the strut. With its cylindrical shape and protruding piston rod, it looks quite similar to the conventional shock absorber. In fact, the strut provides the damping function of the shock absorber, in addition to serving to locate the spring and to fix the position of the suspension.

The shock-damping function is accomplished differently on various types of struts. None of them uses a separate shock absorber as the traditional front suspension does. Some versions are designed so the damper can be independently serviced.

Struts fall into two broad categories: sealed and serviceable units. A sealed strut is designed so the top closure of the strut assembly is permanently sealed. There is no access to the shock absorber cartridge inside the strut housing and no means of replacing the cartridge. Therefore, it is necessary to replace the entire strut unit. A serviceable strut is designed so the cartridge inside the housing, which provides the shock-absorbing function, can be replaced with a new cartridge. Serviceable struts use a threaded body nut in place of a sealed cap to retain the cartridge.

The shock absorber device inside a serviceable strut is generally wet. This means the shock absorber contains oil that contacts and lubricates the inner wall of the strut body. The oil is sealed inside the strut by the body nut, O-ring, and piston rod seal. Servicing a wet strut with the equivalent components involves a thorough cleaning of the inside of the strut body, absolute cleanliness, and great care in reassembly (including replenishing the strut with oil).

Cartridge inserts were developed to simplify servicing wet struts. The insert is a factory-sealed replacement for the strut shock absorber. The replacement cartridge is simply substituted for the original shock absorber cartridge and retained with the body nut.

Most OE domestic struts are serviced by replacement of the entire unit. There is no strut cartridge to replace. Sealed OE units can also be serviced by replacement with an aftermarket unit that permits future servicing by cartridge replacement.

The use of the strut reduces suspension space and weight requirements. By mounting the bottom of the strut assembly to the steering knuckle, the upper control arm and ball joint of the traditional suspension are eliminated. In place of the ball joint, the upper mount, which is bolted to the fender panel, is the load-carrying member on MacPherson suspensions.

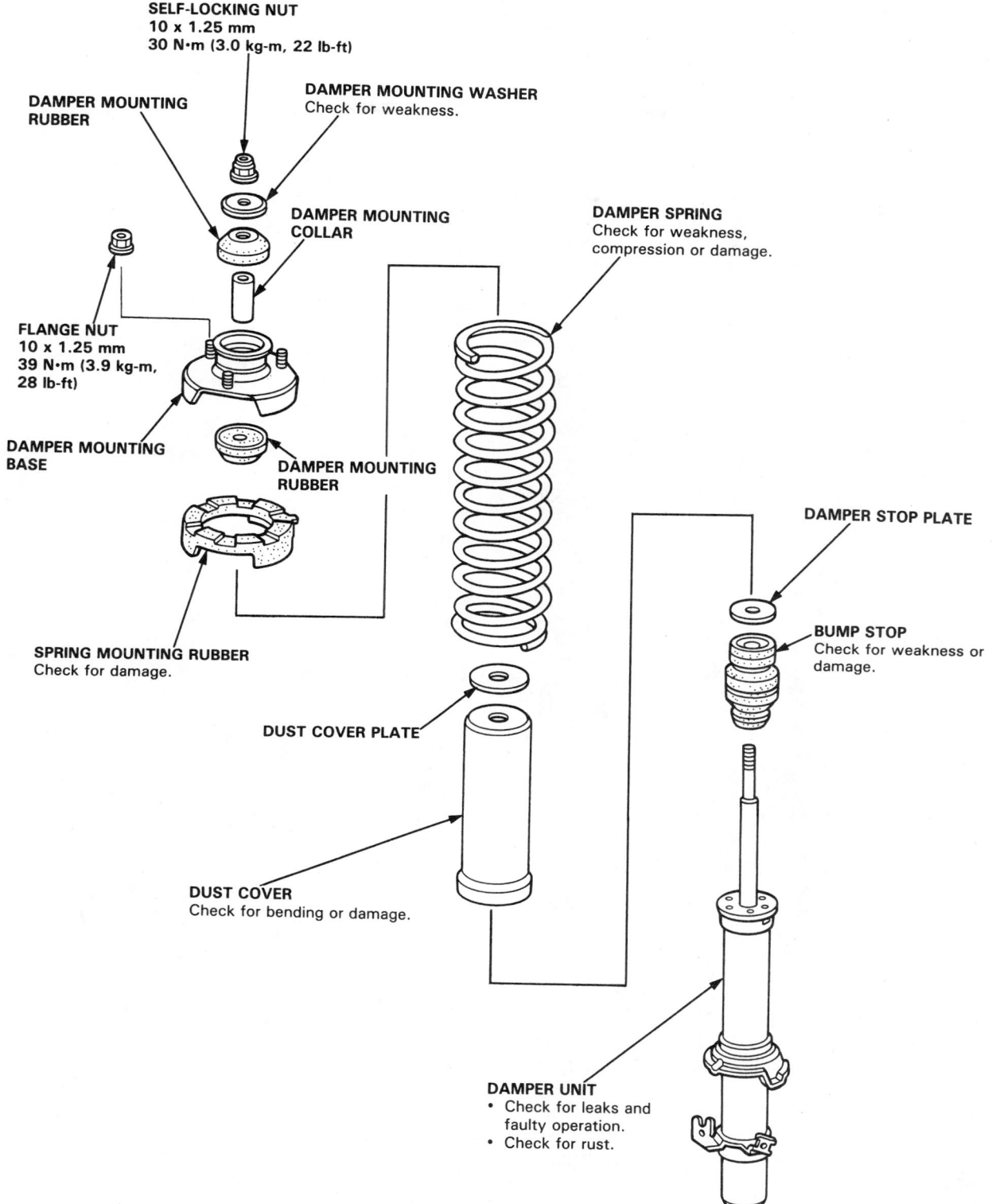

SELF-LOCKING NUT
10 x 1.25 mm
30 N·m (3.0 kg-m, 22 lb-ft)

DAMPER MOUNTING RUBBER

DAMPER MOUNTING WASHER
Check for weakness.

DAMPER MOUNTING COLLAR

DAMPER SPRING
Check for weakness, compression or damage.

FLANGE NUT
10 x 1.25 mm
39 N·m (3.9 kg-m, 28 lb-ft)

DAMPER MOUNTING BASE

DAMPER MOUNTING RUBBER

DAMPER STOP PLATE

BUMP STOP
Check for weakness or damage.

SPRING MOUNTING RUBBER
Check for damage.

DUST COVER PLATE

DUST COVER
Check for bending or damage.

DAMPER UNIT
• Check for leaks and faulty operation.
• Check for rust.

FIGURE 36–17 MacPherson strut with replaceable shock absorber (dampener) cartridge. *Courtesy of American Honda Motor Company, Inc.*

Lower Suspension Components

The suspension's lower mounting position continues to be the frame, as on the traditional suspension, because the lower control arm and ball joint are retained (Figure 36–20). As on those suspensions, the control arm serves as the lower locator for the suspension.

MacPherson strut suspensions continue to use sway, or stabilizer, bars. On models with single-bushing control arms, strut rods or the sway bar can be fastened to the control arm to provide lateral stability.

The lower **ball joint** is a friction or steering ball joint and is used to stabilize the steering and to retard

1. Strut mount cover
2. Nut
3. Nut
4. Strut mount
5. Spring seat
6. Spring upper insulator
7. Bumper
8. Spring
9. Spring lower insulator
10. Strut
11. Nut
12. Wheel bearing seal
13. Nut
14. Pin
16. Hub and bearing assembly
17. Disc brake splash shield
18. Bolt
19. Washer
20. Drive shaft nut
21. Washer
22. Rotor
23. Steering knuckle
24. Disc brake caliper
25. Bolt
26. Cover
27. Bolt
28. Lower ball joint
29. Rivet
30. Insulator
31. Washer
32. Bolt
33. Lower control arm
34. Bushing
35. Bolt
36. Bolt
37. Support
38. Bolt
39. Nut
40. Bolt
41. Washer
42. Drive shaft
43. Spacer
44. Nut
45. Stabilizer shaft
46. Nut
47. Insulator
48. Clamp

FIGURE 36–18 Typical MacPherson front suspension. *Courtesy of Oldsmobile Division, General Motors Corporation*

FIGURE 36–19 Modified MacPherson suspension has the spring mounted separately from the strut. *Courtesy of Ford Motor Company*

FIGURE 36–20 Lower suspension components. *Courtesy of Sealed Power Corporation*

shimmy. The only exception is on modified MacPherson suspensions. In this design, the ball joint becomes the load bearer; the upper mount becomes the steering component.

Springs

Coil springs are used on all strut suspensions. A mounting plate welded to the strut serves as the lower spring seat. The upper seat is bolted to the strut piston rod. A bearing or rubber bushing in the upper mount permits the spring and strut to turn with the motion of the wheel as it is steered.

INDEPENDENT FRONT SUSPENSION

Front suspension systems are fairly complex. They have somewhat contradictory jobs. They must keep the wheels rigidly positioned and at the same time allow them to steer right and left. In addition, because

of weight transfer during braking, the front suspension system absorbs most of the braking torque. While accomplishing this, it must provide good ride and stability characteristics.

As stated earlier in this chapter, most independent front suspension systems have the same basic components and basically operate in the same manner as already described. These systems differ only in the way the components are arranged. The first independent system (known as knee action suspension) was the parallelogram design. It consisted of upper and lower control arms, called A arms, that were hinged to the car with pins or bushings at the frame and at the top and the bottom of the spindle support (Figure 36–21). The earlier vertical pivot pin or kingpin that enabled the wheels to turn was the only carryover from the solid conventional axle.

In the early systems, the upper and lower control arms were the same length. As the vehicle bounced along bumpy roads, this design kept wheel camber, or pitch as it was called then, at a fixed relationship. It was felt this was necessary to maintain steering

FIGURE 36–21 Parallelogram suspension.

FIGURE 36–22 Short-long arm suspension.

control. A detrimental side effect of this design was that the tire's contact with the road was constantly changing, causing serious tire wear problems due to the scuffing action.

A later design changed all this. In it, the upper control arm was shorter than the lower (Figure 36–22). With the upper arm pivoting in a shorter arc, the top of the wheel moved in and out slightly but the tire's road contact remained constant. Far from making the vehicle unstable, this configuration actually improved steering control. At last, independent suspension achieved both improved comfort and rideability without sacrificing tire life. The design was so successful it was incorporated into many vehicles worldwide.

Short-Long Arm and Double-Wishbone Suspensions

The unequal length control arm or short-long arm (**SLA**) suspension system has been common on domes-

FLANGE NUT
10 x 1.25 mm
39 N·m (3.9 kg-m, 28 lb-ft)

SELF-LOCKING NUT
10 x 1.25 mm
30 N·m (3.0 kg-m, 22 lb-ft)
Replace.

SELF-LOCKING NUT
12 x 1.25 mm
65 N·m (6.5 kg-m, 47 lb-ft)
Replace.

UPPER ARM

CASTLE NUT
10 x 1.25 mm
40−48 N·m (4.0−4.8 kg-m, 29−35 lb-ft)

DAMPER UNIT

DAMPER FORK

COIL SPRING

STABILIZER SHAFT

SELF-LOCKING NUT
8 x 1.25 mm
19 N·m (1.9 kg-m, 14 lb-ft)
Replace.

DAMPER PINCH BOLT
(SELF-LOCKING BOLT)
10 x 1.25 mm
44 N·m (4.4 kg-m, 32 lb-ft)

SELF-LOCKING NUT
12 x 1.25 mm
65 N·m (6.5 kg-m, 47 lb-ft)
Replace.

SELF-LOCKING BOLT
12 x 1.25 mm
55 N·m (5.5 kg-m, 40 lb-ft)

SELF-LOCKING BOLT
12 x 1.25 mm
105 N·m (10.5 kg-m, 76 lb-ft)

SELF-LOCKING BOLT
10 x 1.25 mm
45 N·m (4.5 kg-m, 33 lb-ft)

LOWER ARM

RADIUS ROD

SELF-LOCKING NUT
12 x 1.25 mm
44 N·m (4.4 kg-m, 32 lb-ft)
Replace.

CASTLE NUT
10 x 1.25 mm
40−48 N·m (4.0−4.8 kg-m, 29−35 lb-ft)

CALIPER BRACKET MOUNTING BOLT
12 x 1.25 mm
110 N·m (11 kg-m, 80 lb-ft)

SPINDLE NUT
24 x 1.5 mm
250 N·m (25 kg-m, 181 lb-ft)
Replace.
NOTE: After tightening, use a drift to stake the spindle nut shoulder against the spindle.

CASTLE NUT
12 x 1.25 mm
50−60 N·m (5.0−6.0 kg-m, 36−43 lb-ft)

FIGURE 36–23 A FWD double-wishbone suspension system. *Courtesy of American Honda Motor Company, Inc.*

tic-made vehicles for many years. Each wheel is independently connected to the frame by a steering knuckle, ball joint assemblies, and upper and lower control arms. The SLA system is often called the **A-frame** wishbone system.

The **double-wishbone** suspension system can also be used in FWD applications (Figure 36–23). The components are not subjected to the side loads that are generated by car braking, cornering, and accelerating. This means the FWD double-wishbone can be tuned to provide firm but soft ride without taking away any of the car's built-in handling characteristics. The basic configuration of FWD double-wishbone suspension borrows heavily from the similar suspension systems used on Formula One racing cars.

The function and operation of the essential components of SLA systems are the wheel spindle assembly, control arms, ball joints, shock absorbers, and springs, among others.

A **wheel spindle** assembly consists of a wheel spindle and a steering knuckle (Figure 36–24). A wheel spindle is connected to the wheel through wheel bearings. The wheel spindle is the point at which the wheel hub and wheel bearings are connected. A **steering knuckle** is connected to control arms. In most cases, a steering knuckle and wheel spindle are forged to form a single piece.

Control Arms The upper and lower **control arms** on the traditional independent front suspension (**IFS**) function primarily as locators. They fix the position of the system and its components relative to the vehicle. They are attached to the frame with bushings that permit the wheel assemblies to move up and down separately in response to irregularities in the road surface. The outer ends are connected to the wheel assembly with ball joints (Figure 36–25) inserted through each arm into the steering knuckle.

FIGURE 36–25 Typical ball joint assembly.

FIGURE 36–26 The single pivot is lighter and requires less space than the wishbone type.

There are two types of control arms: the wishbone or double-pivot control arm, and the single-pivot or single-bushing control arm (Figure 36–26). The wishbone offers greater lateral stability than the single-pivot arm. The single-pivot is lighter and requires less space than the wishbone but also requires modifications in suspension design to compensate for the reduced lateral stability. Those modifications are discussed further later in this chapter.

Ball Joints The ball joints connect the steering knuckle to the control arms, allowing the steering knuckle to pivot between the control arms when the car is steered. They also permit up and down movement of the control arm.

Ball joints can be grouped into two classifications: load-carrying and nonload-carrying or stabilizing type. The load-carrying or loaded ball joint supports the vehicle weight. It is mounted in the control arm of an independent front suspension system on which the

FIGURE 36–24 Typical wheel spindle assembly.

FIGURE 36–27 The load-carrying ball joint supports the vehicle weight.

FIGURE 36–29 Wear-indicator load-carrying ball joints.

coil spring is seated or to which the torsion bar spring is attached as shown in Figure 36–27. These units are designed so the weight of the vehicle holds the ball stud and its bearing surface into close contact.

Load-carrying ball joints come in two versions: compression loaded or tension loaded. Compression ball joints are designed to carry loads that bear down on top of the ball stud (Figure 36–28A). Because of this, most joint wear occurs where the head of the ball stud presses into its seat. Compression ball joints are used in suspensions in which the coil spring mounts over the upper control arm.

Tension joints carry a load that tries to pull the joint apart (Figure 36–28B). Wear occurs in this joint in the area where the shoulder of the ball stud pulls against its seat. The lower ball joint on a short-long

arm suspension, where the spring sits on the lower control arm, is a tension joint. Tension joints are also found on modified MacPherson strut suspensions, where the springs sit on the lower control arm rather than the strut.

Some load-carrying ball joints have built-in wear indicators on the grease fitting. As the joint wears, the grease fitting recedes into the housing. When the shoulder of the fitting is flush with the housing, the joint needs replacing (Figure 36–29).

The nonload-carrying ball joint is used for the upper ball joint on short-long arm suspensions. The spring seats on the lower arm or the lower ball joint on suspensions in which the spring is over the upper control arm. It is also used as the lower ball joint on MacPherson strut suspensions when the spring is mounted around the strut. Because it does not carry weight, it is preloaded to keep it tight and to provide resistance for improved steering stability. Any play in a nonload-carrying ball joint means it should be replaced.

Coil Springs As described previously in this chapter, the most commonly used spring on front suspensions is the coil spring. Most traditional suspensions have coil springs mounted between the control arms. However, some designs mount them on top of the upper control arm, seating them between the surface of the arm and a projecting arm of the frame (Figure 36–30).

Other Front System Components In addition to shock absorbers, other suspension control devices include bushings, stabilizer or sway bars, and strut rods. In the design of these suspension control devices, the difference between sprung and unsprung weight is important.

Bushings Rubber or polyurethane bushings are found on many suspension components, such as the control arms (Figure 36–31), radius arms, and strut rods (Figure 36–32). They make good suspension system pivots, minimize the number of lubrication points, and allow for slight assembly misalignments.

FIGURE 36–28 Two types of friction ball joints.

FIGURE 36–30 The upper ball-joint is the load-carrying joint in this system because of the position of the spring.

Bushings help to absorb road shock, allow some movement, and reduce noise entering the vehicle.

Suspension bushings can deteriorate fairly rapidly, causing tire wear. They are a common cause of misalignment. Replacement bushings come in two basic varieties: stock and performance. The latter are usually made of a high grade polyurethane material and are sold primarily as an upgrade to improve handling response and ride control.

FIGURE 36–31 Control arm bushings.

FIGURE 36–32 Single-bushing control arm with strut rod.

The harder urethane bushings eliminate unwanted compliance or give in the suspension. When hard cornering overtaxes stock bushings and causes them to deflect excessively, undesirable chamber changes occur in the front wheels that result in excessive outer shoulder wear on the tires. Compliance also slows down the action of the sway bar when cornering, which has a significant impact on the vehicle's road holding ability and steering stability (especially in cross winds). Firmer bushings can also help reduce torque steer in front-wheel-drive cars. Torque steer is the tendency to pull to one side (usually to the right) under hard acceleration. It is more of a problem on FWD cars with unequal length drive shafts because the wheel with the shorter shaft (usually the left side) gets more torque than the one with the longer shaft. There is enough give in the suspension that the left wheel tries to pull ahead of the right, throwing wheel alignment off enough to make the car pull to the right.

The procedures for checking bushings and the methods for replacing them are given in service manuals.

Stabilizers A variety of devices are used with the basic suspension components to provide additional stability. One of the most common is the **sway bar**, which is also known as the **antisway bar** or stabilizer. This is a metal rod running between the opposite lower control arms. As the suspension at one wheel responds to the road surface, the sway bar transfers a similar movement to the suspension at the other wheel. For example, if the right wheel is drawn down by a dip in the road surface, the sway bar is drawn with it creating a downward draw on the left wheel as well. In this way, a more level ride is produced. Sway or lean during cornering is also reduced.

If both wheels go into a jounce, the sway bar simply rotates in its insulator bushings. It is a different matter when only one wheel goes into jounce. The stabilizer bar twists, just like a torsion bar, to lift the frame and the opposite suspension arm. This action reduces body roll.

The sway bar can be a one-piece, U-shaped rod fastened directly into the control arms with rubber bushings, or it can be attached to each control arm by a separate sway bar link (Figure 36–33). The arm is held to the links with nuts and rubber bushings and is also mounted to the frame in the center with rubber bushings. If the sway bar is too large, it causes the vehicle to wander. If it is too small, it has little effect on stability.

On suspensions that use single-housing lower control arms instead of wishbone types, the sway bar can also be used to add lateral stability to the control

FIGURE 36–33 Sway bar, or stabilizer bar, controls sway and stabilizes front suspension.

arm. **Strut rods** are used on models that do not use the sway bar like this. They are attached to the arm and frame with bushings, allowing the arm a limited amount of forward and backward movement. Strut rods are directly affected by braking forces and road shocks, and their failure can quickly lead to failure of the entire suspension system.

GENERAL FRONT-SUSPENSION INSPECTION

To minimize the chance of performing an unnecessary service, the following preliminary or general inspections should be made.

1. Check all tires for proper inflation pressure.
2. Check the tires for telltale indications of improper front-end alignment, wheel and tire imbalance, and physical defects or damage.
3. Check the vehicle for optional suspension equipment, such as that provided for heavy-duty applications or trailer towing packages. They have a firmer ride quality.
4. Check vehicle attitude for evidence of overloading or sagging. Be sure the chassis height is correct.
5. Raise the vehicle off the floor. Grasp the upper and lower surfaces of the tire and shake each front wheel to check for worn wheel bearings.
6. Check front suspension ball joints and mounts for looseness, wear, and damage.
7. Check the steering gear mountings, steering linkage, and steering connections for looseness, binding, or damage.
8. Check the shock absorbers or shock struts for the condition of their attaching parts.
9. Also check shocks or struts for proper action or leakage.

If, in the course of making these checks, damaged or worn parts are found, replace them.

SHOP TALK

Before visual inspection or suspension height measurements can be performed, the vehicle must be on a level surface. Tires must be at recommended pressures; gas tank must be full; and there should be no passenger or luggage compartment load. Beginning at the rear bumper, jounce the car up and down several times. Proceed to the front bumper and repeat, releasing during same cycle as rear jounce. ■

Chassis Height Specifications

A quick overall visual inspection detects any obvious sag from front to rear or from side to side. Under the car, at the level of the two ends of the control arms, check for out-of-level, damaged, or worn rubber bumpers, or shiny or worn spring coils. All indicate weak coil springs.

A more accurate inspection reveals less obvious problems by measuring heights at specific points on each side of the suspension system.

USING SERVICE MANUALS

For the most accurate measurement of chassis height, use the service manual to check against the manufacturer's recommendations for the specific model. Photo Sequence 22 shows the typical procedure for checking vehicle ride height. Be careful, the measurement points vary from one model to another even if manufactured by the same company. When coil spring wear is suspected, it might be necessary to load the vehicle to the manufacturer's suggested capacities and measure at the designated points. ■

FRONT SUSPENSION COMPONENT SERVICING

As is the case in all sections of this text, specific troubleshooting procedures are given in detail in the *Tech Manual*. However, the following is information on servicing the major components or assemblies of front suspension systems.

Coil Springs

The never-ending twisting and untwisting of the coil spring (or the torsion bar) lead to inevitable loss of elasticity and spring sag. Coil springs, then, require replacement because they sag in service. A sagged coil spring upsets vehicle trim height resulting in upset wheel alignment angles, steering angles, headlight aiming, braking distribution, riding quality, tire tread life, shock life, and U-joint life.

TYPICAL PROCEDURE FOR MEASURING FRONT AND REAR CURB RIDING HEIGHT

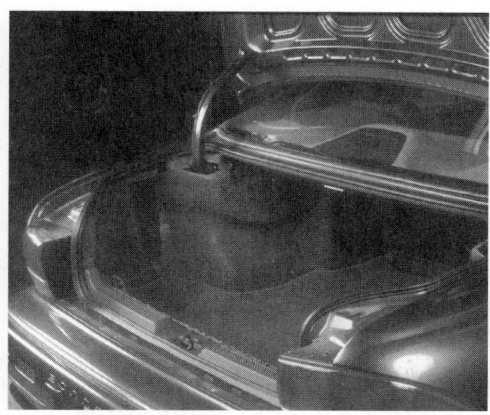

P22–1 Check the trunk for extra weight.

P22–2 Check the tires for normal inflation pressure.

P22–3 Park the car on a level shop floor or alignment rack.

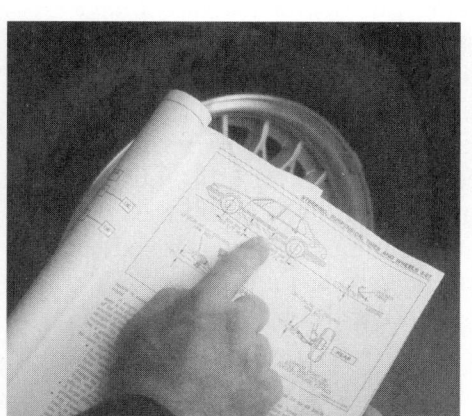

P22–4 Find the vehicle manufacturer's specified curb riding height measurement locations in the service manual.

P22–5 Measure and record the right front curb riding height.

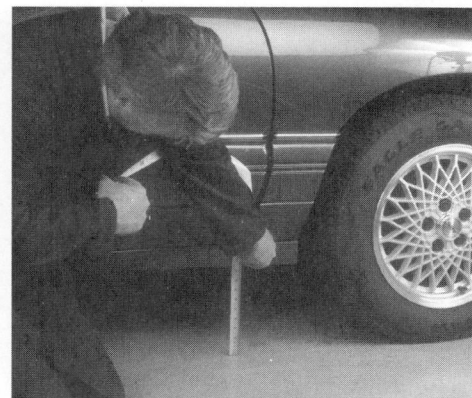

P22–6 Measure and record the left front curb riding height.

P22–7 Measure and record the right rear curb riding height.

P22–8 Measure and record the left rear curb riding height.

P22–9 Compare the measurement results to the specified curb riding height in the service manual.

FIGURE 36–34 Spring compressor tool used to contain the coil spring for removal or installation. *Courtesy of Ford Motor Company*

Coil springs also break. Downsized cars are often forced to carry the same loads as their larger counterparts, mostly because people and their hauling needs did not down-size along with the cars.

⬤ CAUTION:

The coil spring exerts a tremendous force on the control arm. Before you disconnect either control arm from the knuckle for any service operation, contain the spring with a spring compressor to prevent it from flying out and causing injury. ■

Removing a Spring To remove a coil spring, raise and support the vehicle by its frame. Let the control arm hang free. Remove wheels, shock absorbers, and stabilizer links. Disconnect the outer tie-rod ends from their respective arms.

Unload the ball joints with a roll-around floor jack. Jack under the lower control arm from the opposite side of the vehicle. This allows the jack to roll back when the control arm is lowered. Position the jack as close to the lower ball joint as possible for maximum leverage against the spring.

The spring is ready for the installation of the spring compressor (Figure 36–34). There are many different types of spring compressors. One type uses a threaded compression road that fits through two plates, an upper and lower ball nut, a thrust washer, and a forcing nut. The two plates are positioned at either end of the spring. The compressing rod fits through the plates with a ball nut at either end. The upper ball nut is pinned to the rod. The thrust washer and forcing nut are threaded onto the end of the rod. Turning the forcing nut draws the two plates together and compresses the spring.

In some cases, it is necessary to break the tapers of both upper and lower ball joints so the steering knuckle can be moved to one side (Figure 36–35). If the vehicle is equipped with a strut rod, this must be disconnected at the lower control arm. Push the control arm down until the spring can be removed. If necessary, a pry bar can be used to remove the spring from its lower seat. Remove the spring and compressor.

FIGURE 36–35 When this tool is expanded, it forces the ball joint stud out of the steering knuckle taper. *Courtesy of American Honda Motor Company Inc.*

If the same spring is to be reinstalled, leave the compressor in position. If a new spring is to be used, slowly release the pressure on the tool by backing off the forcing nut. Compress the new spring prior to installing it.

Torsion Bars

Torsion bars are subjected to many of the same conditions affecting coil springs. Periodic adjustment of the torsion bars is necessary to maintain the proper height. Replacement is sometimes necessary because of breakage. It should be noted that the bars are not interchangeable from side to side.

Height inspection and measurements for vehicles with torsion bar suspensions are the same for coil springs. However, sagging can usually be corrected by adjusting the bars. Procedures for adjusting torsion bars are given in the service manual.

Ball Joints

Begin ball joint inspection by determining if the vehicle is equipped with wear indicator-type load-carrying ball joints. This information can be found in a manufacturer's ball joint specification chart or the vehicle's service manual. If the vehicle is not equipped with wear indicator-type ball joints, proceed to unload the load carriers.

When the coil spring is on the lower control arm, raise the vehicle by jacking under the control arm as close to the ball joint as possible. This gives the maximum amount of leverage against the spring. The ball joint is unloaded when the upper strike out bumper is not in contact with the control arm or frame. A quick check for looseness can be made by using a pry bar between the tire and the ground. To find out if the ball joint is loose beyond manufacturer's specifications, use an accurate measuring device. The following checking procedures demonstrate the use of a dial indicator. The dial indicator is a precision instrument and should be handled carefully to prevent damage. The mounting procedure for the checking tool might vary depending on the style of ball joint used on the vehicle. Manufacturer's tolerances can be axial (vertical), radial (horizontal), or both. To conduct these checks, follow these procedures.

TYPICAL RADIAL CHECK For a radial check, attach a dial indicator to the control arm of the ball joint being checked. Position and adjust the plunger of the dial indicator against the edge of the wheel rim nearest to the ball joint being checked. Slip the dial ring to the zero marking. Move the wheel in and out and note the amount of ball joint radial looseness registered on the dial (Figure 36–36). The procedure for checking the radial movement of a lower ball joint on

FIGURE 36–36 Typical mounting of dial indicator for a radial check. *Courtesy of Moog Automotive*

a MacPherson strut front suspension is shown in Photo Sequence 23.

TYPICAL AXIAL CHECK For an axial check, first fasten the dial indicator to the control arm, then clean off the flat on the spindle next to the ball joint stud nut. Position the dial indicator plunger on the flat of the spindle and depress the plunger approximately 0.350 inch. Turn the lever to tighten the indicator in place. Pry the bar between the floor and tire. Record the reading (Figure 36–37).

FIGURE 36–37 Typical mounting of dial indicator for an axial check. *Courtesy of Moog Automotive*

PHOTO SEQUENCE 23

TYPICAL PROCEDURE FOR MEASURING THE LOWER BALL JOINT RADIAL MOVEMENT ON A MacPHERSON STRUT FRONT SUSPENSION

P23–1 Raise the front suspension with a floor jack and place jack stands under the chassis at the vehicle's lift points.

P23–2 Grasp the front tire at the top and bottom and rock the tire inward and outward while a co-worker visually checks for movement in the front wheel bearing. If there is movement, adjust or replace the wheel bearing.

P23–3 Position a dial indicator against the inner edge of the rim at the bottom. Preload and zero the dial indicator.

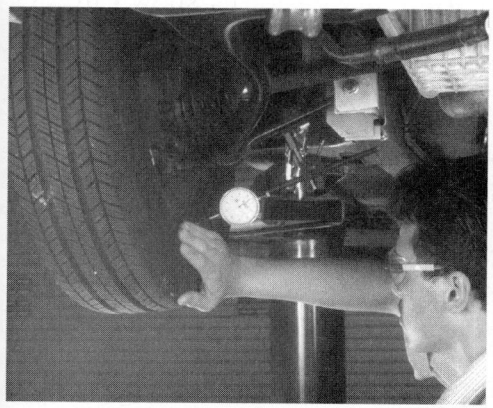

P23–4 Grasp the bottom of the tire and pull outward.

P23–5 With the tire held outward, read the dial indicator.

P23–6 Push the bottom of the tire inward and be sure the dial indicator reading is zero. Adjust the dial indicator as required.

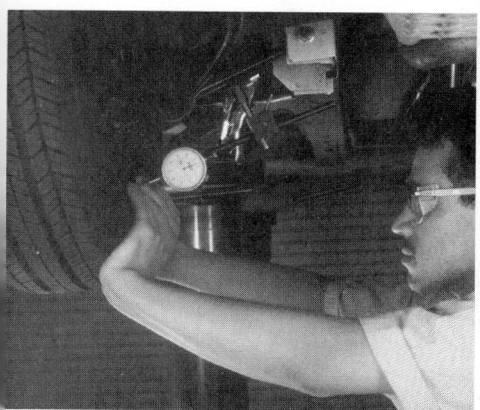

P23–7 Grasp the bottom of the tire and pull outward.

P23–8 With the tire held in this position, read the dial indicator.

P23–9 If the dial indicator reading is more than specified, replace the lower ball joint.

If the ball joint looseness reading on the dial indicator exceeds manufacturer's specifications, the ball joint should be replaced.

When the load-carrying ball joints are on the upper control arm (spring mounted on the upper arm), raise the vehicle by its frame using support tools to unload the ball joints and hold them in their normal position. To determine the condition of the nonload-carrying (or follower) ball joint, vigorously push and pull on the tire, while watching the ball joint for signs of movement. Refer to the manufacturer's specifications for tolerances.

INSPECTION OF WEAR INDICATORS Wear indicator-type ball joints must remain loaded to check for wear. The vehicle should be checked with the suspension at curb height. The most common type has a small diameter boss, which protrudes from the center of the lower housing. As wear occurs internally, this boss recedes very gradually into the housing. When it is flush with the housing, the ball joint should be replaced. To remove and install a ball joint, follow the procedure given in the service manual.

Control Arm Bushings

If the bushings, which attach the arms to the frame, are not in good condition, precise wheel alignment settings cannot be maintained.

Visually inspect each rubber bushing for signs of distortion, movement, off-center condition, and presence of heavy cracking. Check metal bushings for noise and loose seals.

To remove the control arm bushings, raise the vehicle and support the frame on safety jack stands. Remove the wheel assembly. Install a spring compressor on the coil spring.

Disconnect the ball joint studs from the steering knuckle as described previously. Remove the bolts attaching the control arm assembly to the frame and remove the control arm.

Old bushings are pressed out of the control arm. A C-clamp tool can be used to remove the bushing. The C-clamp is installed over the bushing. An adapter is selected to fit on the bushing and push the bushing through the control arm. Turning the handle on the C-clamp pushes the bushing out of the control arm.

New bushings can be installed by driving or pressing. Adapters are available for the C-clamp tool to install the new bushings. After the correct adapters are selected, position the bushing and tool on the control arm as shown in Figure 36–38. Turning the C-clamp handle pushes the bushing into the control arm. When installing new bushings, make sure they are driven in straight. A poor installation could enlarge the hole in the control arm.

Some older vehicles use a bushing that is all metal instead of a metal-rubber combination. These are removed and replaced in the same way as the rubber and metal type just described.

Once the new bushings are started into the control arm, measure and mark the center between mounting holes and center the control arm. Now, alternately press in the bushings on each side, keeping the reference marks aligned. This ensures the shaft is not off center, causing binding. End cap nuts or bolts should not be torqued until the vehicle is at curb height and the suspension has been bounced and allowed to settle out.

Rebolt the control arm and tighten the bolts to specifications, then install the coil spring into position. Install the ball joint studs into the control arms. Remove the coil spring compressor. Install the wheel assembly and lower the car. Road test the car, retighten all bolts, and set wheel alignment.

Strut Rod Bushings

Except in the case of accidental damage, the strut rod itself is rarely replaced. Rather, it is the bushing that wears, deteriorates, and needs replacement.

Sway Bar Bushings

These bushings anchor the sway bar securely to the vehicle frame and the control arms on each side. The condition of the bushings affects the performance of the bar. Visual inspection of mounting bushings indicates if the bushings are worn, have taken a permanent set, or are possibly missing.

Shock Absorbers

A shock absorber that is functioning properly ensures vehicle stability, handling, and rideability. Most motorists fail to notice gradual changes in the operation of their cars as a result of worn shock absorbers. Some common indications of shock absorber failure follow.

◆ Steering and handling more difficult
◆ Braking not smooth
◆ Excessive bouncing after stops

FIGURE 36–38 Removing a control-arm bushing. *Courtesy of Ford Motor Company*

◆ Unusual tire wear patterns, especially cupping
◆ Springs bottom out

Vibrations set up by a worn shock absorber can cause premature wear in many of the undercar systems. They can cause wear in the front and rear component parts of the suspension system, the linkage component parts of the steering system, and the U-joints and motor or transmission mounts of the driveline. Also, vibrations can cause unnatural wear patterns on the tires.

A shock absorber can be bench tested. First, turn it up in the same direction it occupies in the vehicle. Then, extend it fully. Next, turn it upside down and fully compress it. Repeat this operation several times. Install a new shock absorber if a lag or skip occurs near mid-stroke of the shaft's change in travel direction, or if the shaft seizes at any point in its travel, except at the ends. Also, install a new shock absorber if noise, other than a switch or click, is encountered when the stroke is reversed rapidly, if there are any leaks, or if action remains erratic after purging air.

When removing and installing shock absorbers, be sure to follow the aftermarket manufacturer's instructions or those given in the service manual.

MacPherson Strut Suspension

The MacPherson strut suspension system is based on a triangular design. The strut shaft is a structural member that does away with the upper control arm bushings and the upper ball joint. Since this shaft is also the shock absorber shaft, it receives a tremendous amount of force vertically and horizontally. Therefore, this assembly should be inspected very closely for leakage, bent shaft, and poor damping.

To remove and replace the MacPherson strut, proceed as shown in Photo Sequence 24.

REAR-SUSPENSION SYSTEMS

There are three basic types of rear suspensions: live-axle, semi-independent, and independent. There are distinct designs of each, but the types of components and the principles involved are the same as on front suspension systems described earlier in this chapter. Live-axle suspensions are found on rear-wheel-drive (RWD) trucks, vans, and many four-wheel-drive (4WD) passenger cars. Semi-independent systems are used on front-wheel-drive (FWD) vehicles. Independent suspensions can be found on both RWD and FWD vehicles, as well as 4WD cars.

LIVE-AXLE REAR SUSPENSION SYSTEMS

This traditional rear-suspension system consists of springs used in conjunction with a live-axle (one in which the differential axle, wheel bearings, and brakes act as a unit). The springs are either of leaf or coil type.

Leaf Spring Live-Axle System

Two springs—either multiple-leaf or monoleaf—are mounted at right angles to the axle and, along with the shock absorbers, are positioned below the rear axle housing. The front of the two springs is attached to brackets on the vehicle's frame by a bolt and bushing inserted through the eyes of the springs. While the bushing allows the spring to move, it isolates the rest of the vehicle from noisy road vibrations.

The center of each leaf spring is connected to the rear axle housing with U-bolts. Rubber bumpers are located between the rear axle housing and frame or unit body to dampen severe shocks. The rear eye pivot bushings are held to the frame with shackles, which attach to the springs by a bolt and bushing (Figure 36–39).

The advantage to this live-axle suspension system is that the leaf springs act as excellent axle locators. The springs allow for the up-and-down movement of the axle and wheels; but, at the same time, the springs prevent them from wandering. Therefore, control arms are not required with leaf springs.

There are some disadvantages to the live-axle suspension system. First, this design has a large amount of unsprung weight. Another drawback is the instability caused by the use of a solid axle. Since both rear wheels are connected to the same axle, movement up or down by one wheel affects the other. Consequently, poor traction results because both wheels are pushed out of alignment with the road. Under severe acceleration, this type of suspension is subject to **axle tramp**, a rapid up-and-down jumping of the rear axle due to the torque absorption of the leaf springs. This condition can break spring mounts and shock absorbers and cause premature wear of wheel bearings. Axle tramp is reduced by mounting shock absorbers on the opposing sides (front and back) of the axle. Some heavy-duty vehicles have two-stage springs that allow the vehicle to ride comfortably with both a light or heavy load.

Coil Spring Live-Axle System

Some vehicles use two coil springs at the rear with a live rear axle. Because coil springs can only support weight and have little axle-locating capabilities, such vehicles need forward and lateral control arms or links. This type of suspension is called the link-type rigid axle.

The coil springs, located between the brackets on the axle housing and the vehicle body or frame, are held in place by the weight of the vehicle and some-

REMOVING AND REPLACING A MacPHERSON STRUT

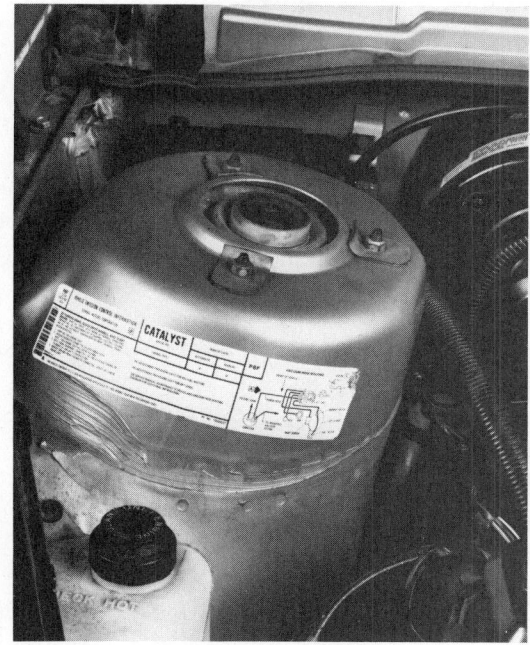

P24–1 The top of the strut assembly is mounted directly to the chassis of the car.

P24–3 With the top strut bolts or nuts removed, raise the car to a working height. It is important that the car be supported on its frame and not on its suspension components.

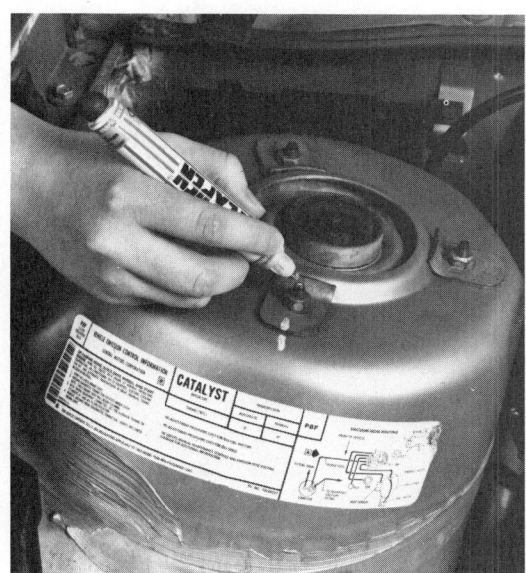

P24–2 Prior to loosening the strut to the chassis bolts, scribe alignment marks on the strut bolts and the chassis.

P24–4 Remove the wheel assembly. The strut is accessible from the wheel well after the wheel is removed.

P24–5 Remove the bolt that fastens the brake line or hose to the strut assembly.

(continued)

P24–6 Remove the strut to steering knuckle bolts.

P24–8 Install the strut assembly into the proper type spring compressor. Then compress the spring until it is possible to safely loosen the retaining bolts.

P24–9 Remove the old strut assembly from the spring and install the new strut. Compress the spring to allow for reassembly and tighten the retaining bolts.

P24–7 Support the steering knuckle with wire and remove the strut assembly from the car.

P24–10 Reinstall the strut assembly into the car. Make sure all bolts are properly tightened and in the correct locations.

times by the shock absorbers (Figure 36–40). The control arms are usually made of channeled steel and mounted with rubber bushings. Accelerating, driving, and braking torque are transmitted through three or four control arms, depending on the design. Two forward links are always used, but either one or two lateral links can be found on individual models. **Trailing arms** mount to the underside of the axle, and run forward at a 90-degree angle to the axle to brackets on the car frame. Rubber bushings are used at mounting locations to permit up-and-down movement of the arms, and to reduce noise and the effect of shock.

Some rear axle assemblies are connected to the body by two lower control arms and a tracking bar. A single torque arm is used in place of upper control arms and is rigidly mounted to the rear axle housing at the rear and through a rubber bushing to the transmission at the front.

Live-Axle Suspension System Servicing

Typical service to both coil-spring and leaf-spring systems include the replacement of shock absorbers or springs. Bushings, shackles, or control arms do not need replacement frequently. Always follow the procedures outlined in the service manual whenever servicing the rear suspension.

FIGURE 36–39 Exploded view of leaf-spring rear suspension.

FIGURE 36–40 Typical live-axle suspension with coil springs.

SEMI-INDEPENDENT SUSPENSION

This system is used on many front-wheel-drive models. On some, the suspension position is fixed by an axle beam, or cross member, running between two trailing arms (Figure 36–41). Although there is a solid connection between the two halves of the suspension because of the axle beam, the beam twists as the wheel assemblies move up and down. The twisting action not only permits semi-independent suspension movement, but it also acts as a stabilizer. Frequently, a separate shock and spring trailing arm system is also used. In either an integrated or separate shock system, each rear wheel is independently suspended by a coil spring.

A coil spring and shock absorber-strut assembly are ordinarily used with this suspension system. The bottom of the strut is mounted to the rear end of the trailing arm. The top is mounted to the reinforced inner fender panel. Braking torque is transmitted through the trailing control arms and struts. The arms and struts also maintain the fore and aft, and lateral positioning of the wheels. A tracking bar is also used on some trailing arm suspension systems (Figure 36–42). The tracking bar helps to reduce sidesway movement of the axle.

Semi-Independent Suspension System Servicing

As in most rear system servicing, the first step is to remove the shock absorber. It is important to remember not to remove both shock absorbers at one time.

FIGURE 36–41 One design of a semi-independent rear suspension. *Courtesy of Chrysler Corporation*

FIGURE 36–42 Tracking bar of rear suspension used to reduce sideway movement.

Suspending the rear axle at full length could result in damage to the brake lines and hoses. The servicing of a semi-independent suspension system usually involves the removal and reinstallation of shock absorbers, springs, insulators, and control arm bushings. Follow the procedures given in the vehicle's service manual.

⚠️ *WARNING!*

When removing the rear springs, do not use a twin-post hoist. The swing arc tendency of the rear-axle assembly when certain fasteners are removed might cause it to slip from the hoist. Perform this operation on the floor if necessary. ∎

INDEPENDENT SUSPENSION

Independent suspensions can be found in large numbers on both FWD and RWD vehicles. The introduction of independent rear suspensions was brought about by the same concerns for improved traction ride that prompted the introduction of independent front suspensions. If the wheels can move separately on the road, traction and ride is improved.

Independent coil-spring rear suspensions can have several control arm arrangements. For example, A-shaped control arms are sometimes employed. When the wide bottom of a control arm is toward the front of the car and the point turns in to meet the upright, they are called trailing arms (Figure 36–43). When the entire A-shaped control arms are mounted at an angle, they are known as semitrailing control arms (Figure 36–44). This design is used on many sports cars. Coil springs are used between the control arm and the vehicle body. The control arms pivot on a cross member and are attached at the other end to a spindle. A shock absorber is attached to the spindle or control arm.

Some vehicles use a rear suspension system that uses a lower control arm and open driving axles. A cross member supports the control arms, while the tops of the shock absorbers are mounted to the body. The springs are set in seats at the bottom and top of the cross member.

FIGURE 36–43 Trailing arms are often used with independent rear suspensions.

FIGURE 36–44 Semitrailing control arms.

A few European cars employ only lower control arms, but substitute a wishbone-shaped subframe for the upper control arms. Two torque arms transfer the

rear-end torque to the subframe. In fact, many imports are now featuring rear double-wishbone suspension (Figure 36–45). Torque loads create bushing and control arm deflection during braking, cornering, acceleration, and deceleration. It is interesting to note this rear suspension system allows for a small amount of toe-in change to enhance straight line stability. The

FIGURE 36–45 A double-wishbone type rear suspension. *Courtesy of Honda Motor Company, Inc.*

DAMPER MOUNTING NUT
10 x 1.25 mm
39 N·m (3.9 kg-m, 28 lb-ft)

FLANGE NUT
10 x 1.25mm
30 N·m (3.0 kg-m, 22 lb-ft)

FLANGE BOLT
10 x 1.25 mm
39 N·m (3.9 kg-m, 28 lb-ft)

UPPER ARM

DAMPER UNIT

COIL SPRING

SELF-LOCKING NUT
8 x 1.25 mm
13 N·m (1.3 kg-m, 9 lb-ft)
Replace.

KNUCKLE

CASTLE NUT
10 x 1.25 mm
44 N·m (4.4 kg-m, 32 lb-ft)

SELF-LOCKING BOLT
12 x 1.25 mm
65 N·m (6.5 kg-m, 47 lb-ft)

SELF LOCKING NUT
10 x 1.25mm
55 N·m (5.5 kg-m, 40 lb-ft)
Replace.

LOWER ARM

FLANGE BOLT
10 x 1.25 mm
55 N·m (5.5 kg-m, 40 lb-ft)

TRAILING ARM

SELF-LOCKING NUT
8 x 1.25 mm
13 N·m (1.3 kg-m, 9 lb-ft)
Replace.

SPINDLE NUT
22 x 1.5 mm
185 N·m (18.5 kg-m, 134 lb-ft)
Replace.
NOTE: After tightening, use a drift to stake the spindle nut shoulder against the spindle.

SELF-LOCKING NUT
10 x 1.25 mm
36 N·m (3.6 kg-m, 26 lb-ft)
Replace.

SELF-LOCKING NUT
10 x 1.25 mm
36 N·m (3.6 kg-m, 26 lb-ft)
Replace.

SELF-LOCKING NUT
12 x 1.25 mm
65 N·m (6.5 kg-m, 47 lb-ft)
Replace.

FLANGE BOLT
12 x 1.25mm
65 N·m (6.5 kg-m, 47 lb-ft)

FLANGE BOLT
10 x 1.25
55 N·m (5.5 kg-m, 40 lb-ft)

FIGURE 36–46 MacPherson strut rear suspension. *Courtesy of Toyota Motor Corporation*

toe-in change during cornering leads to quicker and more responsive turning. The rear suspension system can also be tuned to ensure minimal dive under braking and minimal squat under acceleration.

Currently, struts are replacing conventional shock absorbers in rear independent suspension systems. One of the latest strut rear suspension designs used by car manufacturers is shown in Figure 36–46.

On this type system, the spindle is used to secure the strut, the outer ends of two of the four control arms, the rear ends of the tie-rods, and a rear wheel. The control arms contain bushings of different sizes at their outer ends. The ends with the smaller bushings attach near the body centerline. The ends with the larger bushings attach at the spindle. (When replacing control arms, it is mandatory that offsets at their outer ends and the flanges on the arms face in the direction prescribed in the manufacturer's service manual.) This system is also called the nonmodified MacPherson strut system.

The modified MacPherson strut rear suspension is very common for vehicles with front-wheel drive (Figure 36–47). Study the illustration carefully. Note

Front of vehicle

FIGURE 36–47 Modified MacPherson strut rear suspension. *Courtesy of Ford Motor Company*

the major components on each side of the vehicle are modified MacPherson shock strut, lower control arm, tie-rod, and wheel spindle. A coil spring mounts between the lower control arm and the body cross member/side rail. The spindle, in addition to supporting the rear wheel, is used as an attaching location for the outer end of the control arm and the rear end of the tie-rod. The inner end of the control arm attaches to the cross member. The forward end of the tie-rod attaches to the side rail.

Another rear strut design uses a **Chapman strut** (Figure 36–48). It is similar to the modified MacPherson strut. The difference between the two struts is the MacPherson strut is involved directly in the car's steering system. The Chapman strut is not. In addition, the Chapman strut can be used with con-

FIGURE 36–48 Independent rear suspension system that uses Chapman struts. *Courtesy of Nissan Motors*

ventional springs, often a leaf-type spring. It frees the Chapman strut of load-carrying duties so it can concentrate on providing exact wheel location and shock absorbing functions.

Rear leaf-spring suspension systems are used on many vehicles with conventional rear drives. These leaf springs are generally mounted longitudinally in the same manner as described earlier in this chapter for live-axle systems. A few leaf-spring systems, however, employ springs mounted transversely. Both multiple-leaf and monoleaf or single-leaf can be used. The transverse leaf spring is mounted to the differential housing rather than the vehicle frame as in the longitudinal installation. The transversely mounted spring's eyes are connected to the wheel spindle assemblies.

Rear shock absorbers or shock struts have the same service limitations as those used on the front of the vehicle. They cannot be adjusted, refilled, or repaired. The procedure for inspecting rear shocks or shock struts is similar to previously mentioned front-end parts inspection. Repetition is not necessary.

Servicing Independent Suspension Systems

Most of the servicing techniques for rear independent suspension systems—except coil, control arm, and strut removal and installation—are similar to other front and rear suspension parts. They have been covered earlier in this chapter. Of course, check the service manual for all inspection and repair techniques of the vehicle's independent rear system.

Servicing Rear Coil Spring Raise the vehicle on a frame contact hoist or position jack stands under the frame forward of the rear-axle assembly. This allows the shock absorbers to fully extend. Place a floor jack under the center of the rear-axle housing and support the weight of the rear axle, but do not lift the vehicle off the jack stands. Disconnect the lower end of the shock absorber. Then, lower the floor jack until all of the coil spring force is relieved. If a coil spring positioner is used, remove it from the center of the coil spring. The coil spring can usually be removed from the vehicle at this time by lifting it from its spring seat. If the springs are to be used again, mark or tag each one so it can be returned to its original location. When a replacement is needed, always replace coil springs in pairs. This ensures equal height.

To install a spring, place the insulator on top of the coil spring and position the spring on the spring seat. The end of the top coil must be positioned to line up with the recess in the spring seat. Jack up the rear axle housing so the spring is properly seated at the lower end and the shock absorbers line up. Reconnect the shock absorbers.

There are some definite advantages to working on one spring at a time. First of all, the assembled side of the vehicle helps support the disassembled side. It also keeps the parts aligned and eliminates the possibility of putting the parts on the wrong side of the vehicle.

Servicing Rear Control Arms To remove the upper rear control arms from the vehicle, remove the bolts passing through the control arms at the frame and at the axle ends. Usually the rear coil spring does not have to be removed for this. Service one side of the vehicle at a time. This simplifies realigning the parts during assembly. On a serviceable control arm, replace the control arm bushings by removing the defective bushing with an appropriate puller. Properly position the new bushing and press it into place in the same manner it is done on front suspensions. Position the repaired control arm on the vehicle and loosely install the bolts. Repeat the service on the other control arm if necessary. Properly torque the nuts and bolts once the vehicle's entire weight is on the springs again.

The coil springs must be removed to service the lower rear control arms. Again, one side of the vehicle should be serviced at a time. Once the vehicle is properly supported and the springs are dismantled, remove the nuts and bolts that pass through the control arm. Remove the control arm from the vehicle and service it in the same way as the upper control arm.

Check the service manual to see if there is an adjustment for the driveline working angle. If none is specified, torque the control arm bolts to specification while the full vehicle weight is on the rear axle. This sets neutral bushing tension at normal curb height.

When there is a driveline working angle adjustment, adjust the angle before torquing the control arm bolts. After the rear suspension has been serviced, always check the working angle of the universal joints on the drive shaft. This minimizes the possibility of driveline vibration.

Servicing Struts (Modified) The independent rear suspension system shown in Figure 36–47 is a typical modified MacPherson strut design. The following applies to components that are replaced individually or as an assembly.

◆ The strut upper mounting is separately serviceable.
◆ The strut is not repairable and must be replaced as an assembly.
◆ Lower control arm bushings are not serviceable. They must be replaced with a lower control arm and bushing assembly.

◆ Tie-rod bushings can be serviced separately at both the forward and rear locations. However, if the tie-rod requires replacement, new bushings must be installed in the spindle at the same time.

◆ Coil springs are serviceable. If a rear coil spring is replaced, the upper spring insulator must also be replaced.

Photo Sequence 24 (page 959) procedures basically can be followed when removing and installing rear struts.

ELECTRONICALLY CONTROLLED SUSPENSIONS

All of the suspension systems covered up to this point are known as passive systems. Vehicle height and damping depend on fixed nonadjustable coil springs, shock absorbers, or MacPherson struts (Figure 36–49A). When weight is added, the vehicle lowers as the springs are compressed. Air adjustable shock absorbers may provide some amount of ride height and ride firmness flexibility, but there is no way to vary this setting during operation. Passive systems can be set to provide a soft, firm, or compromise ride. Vehicle body motion and tire traction vary due to road conditions and turning and braking forces. Passive systems have no way of adjusting to these changes.

Advances in electronic sensor and computer control technology have led to a new generation of suspension systems. The simplest systems are level control systems that use electronic height sensors to control an air compressor linked to air adjustable shock absorbers (Figure 36–49B).

FIGURE 36–49 (A) Conventional passive suspension compromises handling because of static spring rates and shock valving. (B) A computer-controlled adaptive suspension system constantly adapts to changing road and driving conditions.

More advanced adaptive suspensions are capable of altering shock damping and ride height continuously. Electronic sensors provide input data to a computer. The computer adjusts air spring and shock damping settings to match road and driving conditions.

The most advanced computer-controlled suspension systems are true active suspensions. These systems are hydraulically, rather than air controlled. They use high pressure hydraulic actuators to carry the vehicle's weight rather than conventional springs or air springs.

The unique feature of an active suspension is that it can be programmed to respond almost perfectly to various operating conditions. For example, by raising the height of the outside actuators and lowering the inside actuators when going around a curve, the vehicle can be made to lean into a curve, much like a motorcycle. Active systems using hydraulic actuators are presently used on a limited number of high-performance vehicles. Most manufacturers are introducing various adaptive suspension systems that rely on pneumatically actuated air springs and dampers.

Adaptive Suspensions

Adaptive suspensions use electronic shock absorbers with variable valving. In some cases, variable air spring rates are used to adapt the vehicle's ride characteristics to the prevailing road conditions or driver demands.

Electronic sensors monitor factors such as vehicle height, vehicle speed, steering angle, braking force, door position, shock damping status, engine vacuum, throttle position, and ignition switching. A computer is used to analyze this input and switch the suspension into a preset operating mode that matches exiting conditions. Some systems are fully automatic. Others allow the driver to select the ride mode.

At present, adaptive suspensions are less costly and complicated than hydraulically controlled active suspensions. However, they do have some limitations. Although they can reduce body roll, adaptive suspensions cannot eliminate it like true active systems. Adaptive systems also experience a slight delay in their reaction time, although some systems can change shock valving in as little as 150 microseconds.

System Components Although designs and components vary between manufacturers, Figure 36–50 illustrates the layout and parts of a popular adaptive suspension system. It employs four air springs that support the vehicle load at the front and rear wheels (Figure 36–51). The air spring membrane is similar to a tire in construction. A solenoid valve and filter assembly allows clean air to be added or released

FIGURE 36–50 Typical electronic air suspension system. *Courtesy of Ford Motor Company*

from the air spring. Adding or removing air changes the ride height of the vehicle.

The airflow to the springs is controlled by the interaction of the air compressor, system sensors, computer control module, and solenoid valves. All of the air-operated parts of the system are connected by nylon tubing.

COMPRESSOR The compressor supplies the air pressure for operating the entire system. It is often a positive displacement single piston pump powered by a 12-volt DC motor. A regenerative air dryer is attached to the compressor output to remove moisture from the air before it is delivered to the air springs. The compressor is operated through the use of an electric relay controlled by the computer module.

SENSORS Vehicle height sensors can be rotary Hall-effect sensors that enable the computer to more accurately measure ride height as well as to compensate for road variations. This prevents the vehicle from bottoming out when crossing over railroad tracks or similar road irregularities.

Advanced systems also read the steering angle by using a photo diode and shutter location inside the steering column. This allows the system to firm up the suspension when the vehicle is turning. The system also reads engine vacuum or throttle position to stiffen the suspension when the vehicle is accelerating. A brake sensor allows the system to

compensate for front nose dive during hard braking. Some systems use a special G-sensor to sense sudden acceleration or braking. Other adaptive systems use a yaw sensor to pick up body roll when cornering.

ELECTRONIC SHOCK ABSORBERS Many adaptive suspension systems use electronically controlled shock absorbers that feature variable shock damping. The degree of damping is controlled by the computer based on input from the vehicle speed, steering angle, and braking sensors. As explained earlier in this chapter, variable shock damping is accomplished by varying the size of the metering orifices inside the shock. A small actuating motor mounted on top of the shock absorber rotates a control rod that alters the size of the metering orifices.

The latest advancement in adaptive suspension technology is the use of real time shock damping. These systems use solenoid-actuated shocks, rather than the motor driven shocks. Solenoids allow almost instantaneous valving changes. This means the suspension can react to bumps and body motions as they happen. Real time adaptive systems deliver most of the handling advantages of a full active suspension without increased vehicle weight and power drain. With these systems, changes to shock valving as little as 10 milliseconds is possible when bumps are encountered.

FIGURE 36-51 Typical components of an air spring assembly. *Courtesy of Ford Motor Company*

ELECTRONIC STRUTS Some systems use an electronically controlled strut in place of the air spring and shock absorber (Figure 36–52). Design and operation is similar to electronic shock absorbers. A valve selector or variable orifice located inside the strut controls fluid pressure in the suspension system based on input from many sensors and commands from the system's control module.

Some variable damping suspension systems use air or gas rather than a fluid. At speeds up to 40 mph, the orifice is fully open and provides full flow (Figure 36–53). From 40 to 60 mph, the orifice is in the normal position and flow is restricted. At speeds more than 60 mph, or when the vehicle is accelerating or braking, the variable orifice is shifted to the firm position.

The use of a variable orifice in the damper control, coupled with the deflected disc valving, provides optimum fluid flow control for both rebound and jounce strokes. In the comfort mode, the selector is set to allow fluid flow primarily through the large selector orifice to achieve minimum damping forces.

While in the normal mode, the unit is set to balance fluid flows between the small selector orifice and the deflected disc valving to provide moderate damping forces. Under conditions in which the firm mode is needed, the selector is rotated to its firm or blocked position and fluid flows entirely through the deflected disc valving.

The damper control also can raise or lower the vehicle's height. This action also improves the car aerodynamic characteristics at highway speed. As speed increases, the suspension reduces the vehicle's height and the front end angles downward. This action tends to reduce wind resistance for greater stability and better gas mileage. As the vehicle slows, the suspension brings the body up to its normal height and level position.

COMPUTER CONTROL MODULE A microcomputer-based module controls the air compressor motor (through a relay), the compressor vent solenoid, and the four air spring solenoids. The computer module also controls operation of electronic shock

FIGURE 36–52   Computer command ride strut. Four electronically controlled struts are used on many adaptive suspension systems. Based on input from the computer, the valving selector shifts the variable by-pass orifice to a comfort, normal or firm setting. *Courtesy of Oldsmobile Division, General Motors Corporation*

FIGURE 36–53   CCR damper fluid flow. The use of a variable orifice in the strut, coupled with the deflected disc valving, provides optimum fluid flow control for both rebound and jounce strokes.

absorber actuating motors and electronic strut valving selectors. The control module receives input from all system sensors.

The computer module also has the capability of performing diagnostic tests on the system. It has a pre-programmed routine for properly fitting air springs after servicing. The module also controls the dash-mounted system warning light.

Electrical power to operate the basic air suspension system is distributed by the main body wiring harness. Each wiring harness involved has a special function in the typical air suspension system.

⚠️ WARNING!

The compressor relay, compressor vent solenoid, and all air spring solenoids have internal diodes for electrical noise suppression and are polarity sensitive. Care must be taken when servicing these components not to switch the battery feed and ground circuits or component damage results. When charging the battery, the ignition switch must be in the off position, if the air suspension switch is on, or damage to the air compressor relay or motor may occur. However, use of a battery charger while performing the diagnostic test or air spring fill option is acceptable. Set to a rate to maintain but not damage the vehicle battery. ■

ELECTRONIC LEVELING CONTROL Adaptive suspension systems are capable of adjusting the suspension system during operation. Less complicated electronic level control systems are used on many large and mid-size vehicles.

These systems do not use a computer module. In most cases, height sensors are the only types of sensors used. These height sensors sense when passenger weight or cargo is added to or removed from the vehicle (Figure 36–54). The height sensors control two basic circuits. The compressor relay coil grounds circuits that activate the compressor. The exhaust solenoid coil grounds circuits that vent air from the system.

To prevent falsely actuating the compressor relay or exhaust solenoid circuits during normal ride motions, the sensor circuitry provides an 8- to 15-second delay before either circuit can be completed.

In addition, the typical sensor electronically limits compressor run time or exhaust solenoid energized time to a maximum of approximately 3 1/2 minutes. This time limit function is necessary to prevent con-

FIGURE 36–54 Electronic level control system. *Courtesy of Chrysler Corporation*

tinuous compressor operation in a case of a solenoid malfunction. Turning the ignition off and on resets the electronic timer circuit to renew the 3 1/2 minute maximum run time. The height sensor is mounted to the frame cross member in the rear. The sensor actuator arm is attached to the rear upper control arm by a link. The link should be attached to the metal arm when making any trim adjustment.

When the air line is attached to the shock absorber fittings or compressor dryer fitting, the retainer clip snaps into a groove in the fitting, locking the air line in position. To remove the air line, spread the retainer clip, release it from the groove, and pull on the air line.

SERVICING ELECTRONIC SUSPENSION COMPONENTS

Most electronic suspension servicing requires the removal of the component from the system, replacing or repairing it, and then reinstalling the component back into the system. Procedures for individual component replacement are covered in the vehicle's service manual. Serviceable components include the air compressor, charger, mounting brackets, height sensors, air springs, air lines and connections, gas struts, strut mounts, control arm components, shock absorbers, and stabilizer bars.

Failure to keep the following procedures in mind might result in a sudden failure of the air spring or suspension system. Suspension fasteners are impor-

tant attaching parts. They could affect performance of vital components and systems or could result in major service expenses. They must be replaced with fasteners of the same part number, or with an equivalent part, if replacement becomes necessary. Do not use a replacement part of lesser quality or substitute design. Torque values must be used, as specified, during assembly to ensure proper retention of parts. New fasteners must be used in the place of the old ones whenever they are loosened or removed and when new component parts are installed.

⚠ *WARNING!*

Do not remove an air spring under any circumstances when there is pressure in the air spring. Do not remove any components supporting an air spring without either exhausting the air or providing support for the air spring. Power to the air system must be shut off by turning the air suspension switch (in the luggage compartment) off or by disconnecting the battery when servicing any air suspension components. Most air suspension systems are equipped with a warning light. The light comes on if there is a problem, or when servicing the system. ◼

Do not attempt to install or inflate any air spring that has become unfolded. Any spring that has unfolded must be refolded as shown in Figure 36–55 prior to being installed in a vehicle. The air spring refolding

FIGURE 36–55 Air spring folding: (A) unroll spring membrane; (B) remove solenoid to expand membrane, then reinstall solenoid to trap air; (C) reroll spring membrane; and (D) release air to trap membrane position.

procedure should only be used to service an air spring that has never supported the vehicle's weight while in the improperly folded position. Improperly folded air springs found on vehicles during predelivery inspection or after customer mileage must be replaced. Do not attempt to inflate any air spring that has been collapsed while it is hanging from the rebound position to the jounce stop. When installing a new air spring, care must be taken not to apply a load to the suspension until springs have been inflated using air spring fill procedures. When front air springs are replaced, the height sensor must be checked and replaced if damaged.

CUSTOMER CARE

Because the technician is seldom present when a vehicle requires towing. It is important to advise the customer proper procedures so the tow operator does not damage the electronic suspension system. You must also know the proper hoist lifting and jacking restrictions. While it is necessary to check the service manual for specific instructions, the following are the basics for electronic suspension.

When towing, it must be remembered that when the ignition is off, the automatic leveling suspension is still on. Before lifting the vehicle, be sure the ignition switch is turned off and the trunk switch deactivated. When towed from the front, towing should not exceed a speed of 35 mph or a distance of 50 miles. When the car is towed from the rear, speeds should not exceed 50 mph (or 35 mph on bumpy pavement).

A body hoist is usually the only type of lift recommended. In most service manuals, manufacturers warn against using a suspension hoist. The proper sequence is to position the car over the lift, shut off the ignition, then deactivate the system.

If a body hoist is not available, a floor jack and jack stands will do. Lift the car by the front cross member and the rear jacking points that are just in front of the rear wheel wells. Jack stands should be used to support the car.

In all situations, the lifting theory is the same. The suspension should be free to hang down while the car is in the air. This allows the wheels to be supported by the struts in the front and the shocks at the rear, both in their full extension (rebound) positions. Thus, the membrane of each air spring retains its proper shape while the car is in the air. ∎

Vehicle Alignment

Aligning a vehicle with an electronic suspension system is essentially the same as the aligning procedure described in a later chapter—with one notable exception, and that is curb height.

Curb height is an important dimension because it affects the other alignment angles. Caster is the most obvious one that is affected, but front camber and toe can also be included. Curb height is especially critical when checking rear camber and toe on independent rear suspensions. With electronic suspension, the ride can vary depending on various circumstances. The only way to guarantee the suspension at curb height is to preset it.

ACTIVE SUSPENSIONS

Some of the advanced adaptive suspension systems may be called **active suspensions**. In this text, active suspensions refer to those controlled by double-acting hydraulic cylinders or solenoids (usually called actuators) that are mounted at each wheel. Each actuator maintains a sort of hydraulic equilibrium with the others to carry the vehicle's weight, while maintaining the desired body attitude. At the same time, each actuator serves as its own shock absorber, eliminating the need for yet another traditional suspension component.

In other words, each hydraulic actuator acts as both a spring (with variable-rate damping characteristics) and a variable-rate shock absorber. This is accomplished in an active suspension system by varying the hydraulic pressure within each cylinder and the rate at which it increases or decreases. By bleeding or adding hydraulic pressure from the individual actuators, each wheel can react independently to changing road conditions.

The components that make such a system possible are the actuator control valves, various sensors, and the chassis computer (Figure 36–56). Feeding information to a computer are a number of specialized sensors. Each actuator has a linear displacement sensor and an acceleration sensor to keep the computer informed about the actuator's relative position. This enables the computer to track the extension and compression of each actuator, and to know when each wheel is undergoing jounce or rebound. There are also load sensors and hub acceleration sensors in each wheel to measure how heavily each wheel is loaded.

A steering angle sensor is used to signal the computer when the vehicle is turning (Figure 36–57). To monitor body motions, a roll sensor and lateral acceleration and G-sensors are used. The computer also monitors hydraulic pressure within the system and the speed of the pump monitor.

FIGURE 36–57 Auto adjust suspension system.

FIGURE 36–56 Active suspension systems counteract body roll, tilting, and leaning. This diagram shows ACS system action during left turn. *Courtesy of Mitsubishi Motor Sales of America, Inc.*

Once it has all the necessary inputs, the computer can then regulate the flow of hydraulic pressure within each individual actuator according to any number of variables and its own built-in program. Another nice feature of a suspension such as this is that it can be programmed to behave in a variety of unique and currently impossible ways: leaning or rolling into turns, for example, or even raising a flat tire on command to change the tire without using a separate jack.

When the wheel of an active suspension hits a bump, the sensors detect the sudden upward deflection of the wheel. The computer recognizes the change as a bump, and instantly opens a control valve to bleed pressure from the hydraulic actuator. The rate at which pressure is bled from the actuator determines the cushioning of the bump and the relative harshness or softness of the ride. The rate can be varied at any point during jounce or rebound to produce a variable spring rate effect. In other words, the feel of the suspension can be programmed to respond in an almost indefinite variety of ways. Once the bump has been absorbed by the actuator, pressure is forced back into it to keep the wheel in contact with the road and to maintain the suspension's desired ride height.

During hard braking with a conventional suspension system, there is a tendency for a vehicle to make a dive. The weight of the vehicle seemingly pushes the front of the car downward and the back upwards. During hard braking, the active suspension increases air pressure in the front actuators and reduces air pressure in the rear actuators. These actions minimize dive to keep the vehicle level and make it easier for the driver to control. After braking, valves operate to equalize air pressures in front and rear air actuators and level the vehicle again.

Frequently, when a driver depresses the accelerator quickly during hard acceleration, the front end of the vehicle tends to lift up, while the rear end lowers. The action is known as **squat**. With an active suspension system, squat is controlled by the operating valve's solenoids, which increase the air pressure in rear wheel actuators and reduce air pressure in front wheel actuators. When the vehicle is no longer accelerating quickly, the control system operates valves to equalize air pressures and level the vehicle. Thus, an active suspension changes the height of the front, rear, or either side of the vehicle to counteract tilting, rolling, and leaning. These active attitude control functions improve vehicle stability and increase tire traction and driver control.

The power required for a totally active system is only 3 to 5 horsepower (about the same as a typical power steering pump). Power consumption is lowest when the system is least active, as when driving on a smooth road. Rough roads and hard maneuvers, on the other hand, put more of a demand on the system. The hydraulic pump works harder and thus requires more power.

Power consumption can be reduced by going with a semi-active suspension that uses small springs with the hydraulic actuators. The springs help to support the vehicle's weight, which reduces the load on the actuators. Smaller actuators that require less hydraulic power can then be used, which reduces the bulk and weight of the system. The addition of springs also adds a certain margin of safety to the system to keep it from going flat should the hydraulics spring a leak.

Although not as widely used as electronic leveling or adaptive suspension systems, hydraulic active suspensions are sure to become more common.

SONAR ROAD SURFACE SENSING

In the very near future, vehicles may be equipped with sonar-sensing devices that constantly monitor the surface of the road just ahead of the vehicle. The sensor would be similar to those used on automatic-focusing 35-millimeter cameras.

The sonar sensor would mount under the front of the vehicle. Its input would enable the system computer to anticipate bumps before they are struck, rather than react to bumps as they do in present systems.

The computer would then change the suspension settings before the bump or dip is encountered. A speed sensor would help the computer calculate the distance between the vehicle and the bump or dip. Other sensors would input steering and vehicle acceleration or braking data to help the computer make the finest adjustment possible to the suspension settings.

CASE STUDY

An eight-year-old vehicle is brought to the shop. The customer states the vehicle runs well, but the ride has become so bouncy he wants the shock absorbers replaced.

The work order is written and the technician replaces the shock absorbers that afternoon.

The following day, the customer returns, complaining of only a slight improvement in ride and handling. He states the shocks must be defective or mismatched to his vehicle. Faced with an angry customer, the technician now takes the time to do what he should have done the previous day. He takes the vehicle on a road test and performs a complete inspection. On checking the ride height of the vehicle, he finds the vehicle is riding extremely low. This is a sure sign the coil springs are severely weakened.

Showing the customer the ride height measurement and the factory specification for that measurement convinces the customer of the need for new coil springs.

With new coil springs and shock absorbers, ride and handling improve dramatically.

KEY TERMS

Active suspension
Adaptive suspension
A-frame
Antisway bar
Axle tramp
Ball joint
Chapman strut
Control arm
Dampers
Double wishbone
Fiber composite
IFS
Jounce
Linear rate
MacPherson strut
Main leaf
Monoleaf

Monoshock
Multiple-leaf
Rebound
Shock absorber
SLA
Spring rate
Sprung weight
Squat
Steering knuckle
Strut rod
Sway bar
Torsion bar
Trailing arm
Unsprung weight
Variable rate
Wheel spindle

SUMMARY

- Four types of springs are used in suspension systems: coil, leaf, torsion bar, and air.
- Springs take care of two fundamental wheel actions: jounce and rebound.
- Common coil spring materials include carbon steel, carbon boron, steel, and alloy steels. Alloy steels, such as those containing chromium and silicon, improve the coil's resistance to relaxation. Most coil springs are manufactured by either a cold coiling or a hot coiling process. Hot coiling usually requires hardening and tempering along with short peening to increase the fatigue strength of the base material.
- Two basic designs of coil springs are used in vehicles: linear rate and variable rate.
- Leaf springs are made of steel or a fiber composite.
- In torsion suspension, the bar may either run from front to rear or side to side across the chassis.
- Air springs are generally only used in microprocessor controlled suspension systems.
- Shock absorbers damp or control motion in a vehicle. Conventional shock absorbers are a velocity-sensitive hydraulic damping device. The faster it moves, the more resistance it has to the movement.
- Shock absorbers can be mounted either vertically or at an angle. Angle mounting of shock absorbers improves vehicle stability and dampens accelerating and braking torque.
- There are two basic adjustable air shock systems: the manual fill type and the automatic or electronic load-leveling type.
- MacPherson struts provide the damping function of a shock absorber. In addition, they serve to locate the spring and to fix the position of the suspension.
- Domestic struts have taken two forms: a concentric coil spring around the strut itself and a spring located between the lower control arm and the frame.
- MacPherson suspensions use sway or stabilizer bars. Coil springs are used on all strut suspensions.
- Independent front suspension (IFS) must keep the wheels rigidly positioned and at the same time allow them to steer right and left. In addition, because of weight transfer during braking, the front suspension system absorbs most of the braking torque. When accomplishing this, it must provide good ride and stability characteristics.
- The unequal length arm or short-long arm (SLA) suspension system is most commonly used on domestic vehicles.
- Live-axle is the traditional rear suspension system and consists of springs used in conjunction with a live-axle (one in which the differential axle, wheel bearings, and brakes act as a unit). The springs are either of leaf or coil type.
- Semi-independent suspension is used on many front-wheel-drive models.
- Three strut designs are frequently used in IFS systems. They are the conventional MacPherson strut, the modified MacPherson strut, and the Chapman strut.
- The two basic types of computer suspension systems are adaptive and active.
- Electronically controlled suspensions can be either simple load-leveling systems, adaptive systems, or fully active systems. Adaptive and active suspension systems are computer controlled. Most load-leveling systems do not use a computer.
- Adaptive suspensions can alter vehicle ride height and shock absorber damping while the vehicle is in motion. Such systems use air springs and electronic shock absorbers or struts.
- Active suspensions are hydraulically operated actuators to control up-and-down and side-to-side movement. They can be programmed to respond to certain road conditions and turning forces.

TECH MANUAL

The following procedures are included in Chapter 36 of the *Tech Manual* that accompanies this book:

1. *Inspect suspension components.*
2. *Replace a strut assembly.*
3. *Replace a cartridge in a strut.*
4. *Remove and install a control arm bushing.*

REVIEW QUESTIONS

1. How does a stabilizer bar work?
2. Explain the difference between sprung and unsprung weight.
3. What is the principle of the air spring?
4. Explain the action of the conventional shock absorber on both compression (jounce) and rebound strokes.
5. Describe the action of the independent front wheel suspension system.
6. The core of any suspension system is the ____.
   a. wheel spindle assembly
   b. spring
   c. ball joints
   d. control arm
7. What occurs when a wheel hits a dip or hole and moves downward?
   a. jounce   c. deflection
   b. free length   d. rebound
8. Which of the following is part of the sprung weight of a vehicle?
   a. steering linkage c. engine
   b. tires   d. all of the above
9. What occurs when a wheel hits a dip or hole and moves upward?
   a. jounce   c. deflection
   b. free length   d. rebound
10. When towing a vehicle with a computer-controlled suspension system, Technician A tows from the front at speeds of less than 35 mph. Technician B tows from the rear at speeds as high as 50 mph. Who is correct?
    a. Technician A   c. Both A and B
    b. Technician B   d. Neither A nor B
11. Suspension ball joints can be grouped into which classifications?
    a. load-carrying and nonload-carrying
    b. load-carrying, nonload-carrying, or stabilizing
    c. load-carrying or compression
    d. load-carrying or loaded
12. What controls the movement of a vehicle as it moves down a bumpy road?
    a. struts   c. both a and b
    b. shock absorbers   d. neither a nor b
13. The coil springs of the vehicle ____.
    a. support the weight of the vehicle
    b. provide axle location
    c. stabilize the up-and-down motion
    d. all of the above
14. Before replacing springs, vehicle height is checked on both sides of the front suspension, and tire pressure is checked. Should you check the amount of fuel in the vehicle?
    a. Yes, the fuel tank should be empty.
    b. Yes, the fuel tank should be full.
    c. No, it does not make any difference.
    d. None of the above.
15. When servicing an air suspension component, Technician A shuts off power to the system by disconnecting the battery. Technician B shuts off power to the system by turning the air suspension switch in the luggage compartment. Who is correct?
    a. Technician A   c. Both A and B
    b. Technician B   d. Neither A nor B
16. The two SLA systems in common use today are ____.
    a. coil spring and strut suspension
    b. coil spring and torsion bar suspension
    c. coil spring and single control arm suspension
    d. single and double control arm suspension
17. Coil springs are used ____.
    a. on all strut suspensions
    b. on selected strut suspensions
    c. not at all on strut suspensions
    d. only on modified MacPherson suspensions
18. When the wide bottom of a control arm is toward the front of the car and the point turns in to meet the upright, it is called a(n) ____.
    a. trailing arm   c. wishbone arm
    b. semitrailing arm d. A-shaped arm
19. The modified MacPherson strut rear suspension is very common in ____.
    a. front-wheel-drive vehicles
    b. rear-wheel-drive vehicles
    c. pick-up trucks
    d. station wagons
20. Technician A says the use of firmer, urethane bushings in the suspension system improves the vehicle's road holding ability and handling. Technician B says firmer bushings also help eliminate torque steer in FWD vehicles. Who is correct?
    a. Technician A   c. Both A and B
    b. Technician B   d. Neither A nor B

STEERING SYSTEMS AND WHEEL ALIGNMENT

37

OBJECTIVES

◆ *Describe the similarities and differences between parallelogram, worm and roller, and rack and pinion steering linkage systems.* ◆ *Identify the typical manual steering system components and their functions.* ◆ *Name the five basic types of steering linkage systems.* ◆ *Identify the components in a parallelogram steering linkage arrangement and describe the function of each.* ◆ *Identify the components in a manual rack and pinion steering arrangement, and describe the function of each.* ◆ *Describe the function and operation of the manual steering gearbox and the steering column.* ◆ *Explain the various manual steering service procedures.* ◆ *Describe the service conventional and nonconventional power-steering design arrangements.* ◆ *Perform general conventional power-steering system checks.* ◆ *Describe the common four-wheel steering systems.* ◆ *Explain the benefits of accurate wheel alignment.* ◆ *Explain the importance of correct wheel alignment angles.* ◆ *Describe the different functions of camber and caster with regard to the vehicle's suspension.* ◆ *Identify the purposes of steering axis inclination.* ◆ *Explain why toe is the most critical tire wear factor of all the alignment angles.* ◆ *Identify the purposes of turning radius or toe-out.* ◆ *Explain the condition known as tracking.* ◆ *Understand the importance of rear-wheel alignment.* ◆ *Know the difference between two-wheel and four-wheel alignment procedures.*

The purpose of the steering system is to turn the front wheels. In some cases, it also turns the rear wheels. The wheels constantly change direction, while switching lanes, rounding sharp turns, and avoiding roadway obstacles.

Swift and sure steering responses are needed at today's driving speeds. To accomplish this, the wheels must be in alignment. Wheel alignment allows the wheels to roll without scuffing, dragging, or slipping on different types of road conditions. This gives greater safety in driving, easier steering, longer tire life, reduction in fuel consumption, and less strain on the parts that make up the front end of the vehicle.

MANUAL STEERING SYSTEMS AND THEIR COMPONENTS

The steering system is composed of three major subsystems: the steering linkage, manual steering gear, and steering column and wheel. As the steering wheel is turned by the operator, the steering gear transfers this motion to the steering linkage. The steering linkage turns the wheels to control the vehicle's direction. Although there are many variations to this system,

these three major assemblies are in all steering systems.

Steering Linkage

The term **steering linkage** is applied to the system of pivots and connecting parts that is placed between the steering gear and the steering arms attached to the front or rear wheels, controlling the direction of vehicle travel. The steering linkage transfers the motion of the steering gear output shaft to the steering arms, turning the wheels to maneuver the vehicle.

The type of front-wheel suspension (independent wheel suspension as compared with a solid front axle) greatly influences steering geometry. Most passenger cars, and many light trucks and recreational vehicles, have independent front-wheel suspension systems. Therefore, a steering linkage arrangement that tolerates relatively large wheel movement must be used.

Parallelogram Steering Linkage A **parallelogram** type of steering linkage arrangement was at one time the most common type used on passenger cars. It is used with the recirculating ball steering gear and can be classified into two distinct configurations: parallelo-

FIGURE 37–1 Parallelogram steering system mounts (A) behind front suspension, and (B) ahead of front suspension.

gram steering linkage placed behind the front wheel suspension (Figure 37–1A) and parallelogram steering linkage placed ahead of the front-wheel suspension (Figure 37–1B). This type of steering linkage is most often used when motor and chassis components would interfere with normal operation of the steering linkage.

These designs are the basic steering systems used in conjunction with independent front-wheel suspensions. This type of linkage also provides good steering and suspension geometry. Road vibrations and impact forces are transmitted to the linkage from the tires, causing wear and looseness in the system (Figure 37–2A). The linkage wear concentration points are shown in Figure 37–2B. This looseness permits intermittent changes in the toe setting of the front wheels, allowing further tire wear.

In a parallelogram steering linkage, the **tie-rods** have ball socket assemblies at each end. One end is attached to the wheel's steering arm and the other end to the center link.

The components in a parallelogram steering linkage arrangement are the pitman arm, idler arm, links, and tie-rods.

PITMAN ARM The **pitman arm** connects the linkage to the steering column through a steering gear

located at the base of the column. It transmits the motion it receives from the gear to the linkage, causing the linkage to move left or right to turn the wheels in the appropriate direction. It also serves to maintain the height of the center link. This ensures that the tie-rods are able to be parallel to the control arm movement and avoid unsteady toe settings or **bump steer**.

FIGURE 37–2 (A) Linkage force diagram and (B) linkage wear concentration points.

FIGURE 37–3 Wear and nonwear pitman arms. *Courtesy of Dana Corporation*

Toe, a critical alignment factor, is a term that defines how well the tires point to the direction of the vehicle.

There are two basic types of pitman arms: **wear** and **nonwear** (Figure 37–3). Service needs differ, depending on which type of arm is used. Nonwear arms have tapered holes at their center link ends and normally need to be replaced only if they have been damaged in an accident or have been mounted with excessive tolerance. Wear arms have studs at the center link end and are subject to deterioration from normal operation. These arms must be inspected periodically to determine whether or not they are still serviceable.

IDLER ARM The **idler arm** or idler arm assembly is normally attached, on the opposite side of the center link, from the pitman arm and to the car frame, supporting the center link at the correct height. A pivot built into the arm or assembly permits sideway movement of the linkage. On some linkages, such as those on a few light-duty trucks, two idler arms are used.

Idler arms normally wear more than pitman arms because of this pivot function, with wear usually showing up at the swivel point of the arm or assembly (Figure 37–4). Worn bushings or stud assemblies on idler arms permit excessive vertical movement in the idler arms.

LINKS Links, depending on the design application, can be referred to as **center**, **drag**, or steering **links**. Their purpose is to control sideway linkage movement, which changes the wheel directions. Because they usually are also mounting locations for tie-rods, they are very important for maintaining correct toe settings. If they are not mounted at the correct height, toe is unstable and a condition known as the toe change or bump steer is produced. Center links and drag links can be used either alone or in conjunction with each other, depending on the particular steering design.

There are several common designs of center links (Figure 37–5). Like pitman arms, they can be broadly characterized as either wear or nonwear. Center links with stud or bushing ends are likely to become unserviceable from the effects of normal operation and should be inspected periodically. Links with open tapers are nonwear and usually need to be replaced only if they have been damaged in an accident or through excessive tolerance at the mounting position of the idler or pitman arms.

SHOP TALK

If a center link is nonwear, the pitman arm is normally a wear arm. If the link is wear, the arm is usually nonwear. Idler arms or assemblies are always subject to wear. ■

TIE-RODS Tie-rods are actually assemblies that make the final connections between the steering linkage and steering knuckles. They consist of inner tie-rod ends, which are connected to the opposite sides

FIGURE 37–4 Wear on idler arms occurs at the pivot. *Courtesy of Dana Corporation*

FIGURE 37–5 Center link designs. *Courtesy of Dana Corporation*

FIGURE 37–6 Tie-rods connect the steering linkage to the wheel assemblies and permit toe to be adjusted. *Courtesy of Dana Corporation*

of the center link; outer tie-rod ends, which connect to the steering knuckles; and adjusting sleeves or bolts, which join the inner and outer tie-rod ends, permitting the tie-rod length to be adjusted for correct toe settings (Figure 37–6).

Tie-rods are subject to wear and damage, particularly if the rubber or plastic dust boots covering the ball stud have been damaged or are missing. Contaminants such as dirt and moisture can enter and cause rapid part failure. A special bonded ball stud, in which no boot is used, is available for use on certain light-duty two-wheel-drive and four-wheel-drive trucks. An elastomer bushing bonded to the stud ball provides strong shock absorption and steering return in downsized vehicles.

> ⚠ **WARNING!**
> Never apply heat to any part of the steering linkage, while servicing it. If any parts must be heated to remove them, they must be replaced and not reinstalled. ∎

Rack and Pinion Steering Linkage **Rack and pinion** is lighter in weight and has fewer components than parallelogram steering. Tie-rods are used in the same fashion on both systems, but the resemblance stops here. Steering input is received from a pinion gear attached to the steering column. This gear moves a toothed rack that is attached to the tie-rods.

In the rack and pinion steering arrangement, there is no pitman arm, idler arm assembly, or center link. The **rack** performs the task of the center link. Its movement pushes and pulls the tie-rods to change the wheel's direction. The tie-rods are the only steering linkage parts used in a rack and pinion system.

Most rack and pinion constructions are composed of a tube in which the steering rack can slide (Figure 37–7A). The rack is a rod with gear teeth cut along one end—spur and helical. The other end is fitted with two balls to which the ends of the divided track rods are attached. The rack meshes with the teeth of a small pinion at the end of the steering column. The two inner tie-rod ends, which are attached to the rack, are covered by rubber bellows boots that protect the rack from contamination. The inner tie-rod connect to outer tie-rod ends, which connect to the steering arms. The rack and pinion housing is fastened to the vehicle at two or three points.

In some cases, the rack and pinion steering gear on unibody cars is bolted directly to a body panel, like a cowl (Figure 37–7B). When this is done, the body panel must hold the steering gear in its correct location. The unibody structure must maintain the proper relationship of the steering and suspension parts to each other. Along with other advantages, the rack and pinion steering system combined with the MacPherson strut suspension system is found in most front-wheel-drive unibody vehicles because of their weight- and space-saving feature.

The vehicle operator gets a greater feeling of the road with rack and pinion because there are less friction points. This means a higher probability of car owners with steering complaints. Fewer friction points can reduce the system's total ability to isolate and dampen vibrations.

FIGURE 37–7 Rack and pinion steering systems (A) on conventional frame and (B) bolted to body panel of a unibody.

RACK The rack is a toothed bar contained in a metal housing. The rack maintains the correct height of the steering components so the tie-rod movement is able to parallel control arm movement.

The rack is similar to the parallelogram center link in that its sideway movement in the housing is what pulls or pushes the tie-rods to change wheel directions.

PINION The pinion is a toothed or worm gear mounted at the base of the steering column assembly, where it is moved by the steering wheel. The pinion gear meshes with the teeth in the rack so the rack is propelled sideways in response to the turning of the pinion.

YOKE ADJUSTMENT The rack-to-pinion lash, or preload, affects steering harshness, feedback, and noise. It is set according to the manufacturer's specifications. An adjustment screw, plug, or shim pack is located on the outside of the housing at the junction of the pinion and rack to correct or set the **yoke lash** (Figure 37–8).

TIE-RODS Tie-rods are very similar to those used on parallelogram systems. They consist of inner and outer ends and adjusting sleeves or bolts. The inner tie-rod ends on rack and pinion units are usually spring-loaded ball sockets that screw onto the rack ends (Figure 37–9). They are preloaded and protected against contaminant entry by a rubber bellows or boot.

Manual Steering Gear

The purpose of the steering gear is to change the rotational motion of the steering wheel to a reciprocating motion to move the steering linkage. There are three styles currently in use. These are the recirculating ball, worm and roller, and the rack and pinion. The latter gear assembly incorporates the already

FIGURE 37–9 The inner tie-rod is a spring-loaded ball socket in a rack and pinion steering box.

described rack and pinion linkage system and steering gear as a single unit.

The **recirculating ball** is generally found in larger cars (Figure 37–10). A sector shaft is supported by needle bearings in the housing and a bushing in the sector cover. A ball nut is used that has threads that mate to the threads of the wormshaft via continuous rows or ball bearings between the two. Ball bearings recirculate through two outside loops, referred to as ball return guide tubes. The ball nut has gear teeth cut on one face that mesh with gear teeth on the sector shaft. As the steering wheel is rotated, the wormshaft rotates, causing the ball nut to move up or down the wormshaft. Since the gear teeth on the ball nut are meshed with the gear teeth on the sector

FIGURE 37–8 The rack preload (yoke lash) is adjusted by a screw, plug, or shim pack.

FIGURE 37–10 Side cutaway of a manual recirculating ball steering gear.

shaft, the movement of the nut causes the sector shaft to rotate and swing the pitman arm.

The design of two separate circuits of balls results in an almost friction-free operation of the ball nut and the wormshaft. When the steering wheel is turned, the ball bearings roll in the ball thread grooves of the wormshaft and ball nut. When the ball bearings reach the end of their respective circuit, they enter the guide tubes and are returned to the other end of the circuits.

The teeth on the sector shaft and the ball nut are designed so an interference fit exists between the two when the front wheels are straight ahead. This interference fit eliminates gear tooth lash for a positive feel when driving straight ahead. Proper mesh engagement between the sector and ball nut is obtained by an adjusting screw that moves the sector shaft axially.

WARNING!

Proper adjustment between the worm gear and the pitman gear is important for adequate steering response (Figure 37–11). Refer to the vehicle manual for specific adjustment procedures. ■

The worm thrust bearing adjuster can be turned to provide proper preloading of the worm thrust bearings. Worm bearing preload eliminates worm end play and is necessary to prevent steering free play and vehicle wander.

The sector can be either constant or variable ratio (Figure 37–12). The former's teeth are all identical, while the latter has one long tooth between two shorter teeth that changes the amount of mechanical advantage according to the position of the wheel. This serves to make the steering faster (maybe 13:1) in turns than

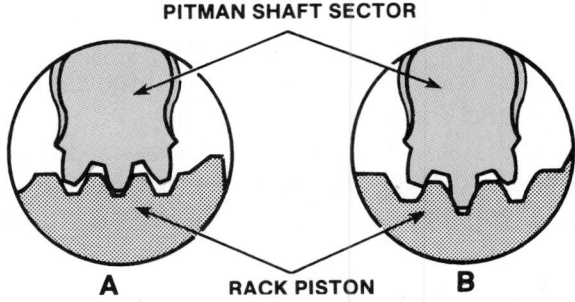

PITMAN SHAFT SECTOR

A   **RACK PISTON**   **B**

FIGURE 37–12   (A) Constant and (B) variable ratio.

in a straight direction (15 or 16:1). Variable ratio is ordinarily used only in power-steering units.

The **worm and roller** gearbox is similar to the recirculating ball except a single roller replaces the balls and ball nut (Figure 37–13). This reduces internal friction, making it ideal for smaller cars. The steering linkage used with a worm and roller gearbox typically includes a pitman arm, center link, idler

WORMSHAFT ADJUSTER PLUG (PRELOAD ADJUSTMENT)

WORMSHAFT   BALLS AND GUIDES   LOCKNUT

SEAL

WORM THRUST BEARING

BALL NUT

SECTOR SHAFT   WORM THRUST BEARING

FIGURE 37–11   Top cutaway of a manual recirculating ball steering gear.

1 STEERING SHAFT
2 STEERING BOX
3 WORM UPPER BEARING SHIMS
4 REAR BALL BEARING
5 WORM
6 FRONT BALL BEARING
7 WORM LOWER BEARING SHIMS
8 WORM THRUST COVER
9 ROLLER PIN
10 ROLLER
11 ROLLER SHAFT
12 SPRING WASHER UNDER PITMAN ARM NUT
13 ROLLER SHAFT OIL SEAL
14 ROLLER SHAFT BUSHING
15 ROLLER SHAFT ADJUSTING DISC
16 ROLLER SHAFT ADJUSTING SCREW
17 LOCKNUT
18 PLUG
19 STEERING BOX COVER
20 PITMAN ARM
21 PITMAN ARM NUT
22 STEERING SHAFT OIL SEAL

FIGURE 37–13   Worm and roller gearbox is similar to recirculating ball. *Courtesy of Fiat Corporation*

FIGURE 37–14 Rack slides sideways and pushes or pulls on tie-rods. This rotates the steering knuckles and front wheels. *Courtesy of Sealed Power Corporation*

FIGURE 37–15 Steering column components. Steering wheel is splined to shaft that extends through column and down to steering gearbox. *Courtesy of Toyota Motor Corporation*

arm, and two tie-rod assemblies. The function of these components is the same as the parallelogram steering linkage described earlier in this chapter.

In operation, the steering shaft rotates the worm gear. It, in turn, engages the roller, causing the roller shaft to turn. The shaft moves the pitman arm left or right to steer the vehicle.

Currently, the rack and pinion manual gear assembly is the most commonly used. When the steering shaft of the rack and pinion unit turns the pinion shaft, the pinion gear moves the rack gear. The rack then slides sideways inside the gear housing (Figure 37–14). The thrust spring preloads the rack and pinion gear teeth to prevent excessive gear backlash (play). Adjustment screws or shims may be used for setting thrust spring tension. Either bushings or roller bearings may be used on the pinion shaft and rack. Frequently, the pinion shaft uses roller bearings and the rack uses plain bushings.

It must be noted that the steering gear does not cause the vehicle to pull to one side nor does it cause road wheel shimmy.

Steering Wheel and Column

The purpose of the steering wheel and column is to produce the necessary force to turn the steering gear. The exact type of steering wheel and column depends on the year and the car manufacturer.

Major parts of the steering wheel and column are shown in Figure 37–15. The steering wheel is used to produce the turning effort. The lower and upper covers conceal parts. The universal joints rotate at angles. Support brackets are used to hold the steering column in place. Assorted screws, nuts, bolt pins, and seals are used to make the steering wheel and column perform correctly. Since 1968, all steering columns have a collapsible feature that allows the column to fold into itself on impact. This feature prevents injury to the driver.

In most vehicles equipped with a driver's side air bag, the air bag assembly is contained in the center

portion of the steering wheel. This assembly must be disarmed and removed before the steering wheel can be removed.

⚠ *WARNING!*

Always disconnect the negative battery cable and wait one full minute before beginning to remove an air bag assembly. Failure to do this may result in accidental air bag deployment (see Chapter 43). Air bag service precautions vary depending on the vehicle. Always follow the manufacturer's service precautions and recommendations when working with an air bag system. ∎

Differences in steering wheel and column designs include fixed column, telescoping column, tilt column, manual transmission, floor shift, and automatic transmission column shift. The tilt columns (Figure 37–16) feature at least five driving positions (two up, two down, and a center position). Both fixed and tilt columns may house an emergency warning flasher control, a turn signal switch, ignition key, lights (high/low beams), horn, windshield wipers and washers, and an antitheft device that locks the steering system. On automatic transmission-equipped vehicles, the transmission linkage locks also. Some vehicles have steering wheels that may be pushed to the side to permit easy entrance and exit from the vehicle. (It is not possible to start the car with this feature until the steering wheel has been returned to the driving position and locked in place.)

Most steering columns today are of the extruded absorber type. To reduce the chance of injury to the

FIGURE 37–16 Tilt steering column operation.

FIGURE 37–18 Collapsing mesh steering column. *Courtesy of Ford Motor Company*

driver, automotive engineers have designed steering columns that collapse in the event of a collision. Lower steering sections are linked by two or more universal joints. These joints allow the sections to fold (Figure 37–17). The upper column normally incorporates a solid shaft and a tube. The shaft is locked to the tube and is designed to give in the event of a collision.

Methods used to lock the shaft to the tube include a breakaway plastic capsule or a series of inserts or steel balls held in a plastic retainer that allows the shaft to roll forward inside the tube. There are also collapsible steel mesh (Figure 37–18) or accordion-pleated devices that give way under pressure. After the vehicle has been in an accident, the steering column should be checked for evidence of collapse. Although the car can be steered with a collapsed column that has been pulled back, the collapsed portion must be replaced. All service manuals provide explicit instructions for doing this.

The steering wheel is usually held in place on the steering column by either a bolt or nut. When the blocked tooth on the steering gear input shaft is in the 12 o'clock position, the front wheels should be in the straight-ahead position and the steering wheel spokes in their normal position (Figure 37–19). If the spokes

FIGURE 37–19 Typical acceptable steering wheel position—measured from normal spoke angle.

are not in their normal position, they can be adjusted by changing the toe adjustment (as described later in this chapter). This adjustment can be made only when the steering wheel indexing mark is aligned with the steering column indexing marks. As a rule, indexing teeth or mating flats on the wheel hub and steering shaft prevent misindexing of these components. The alignment of the notches on the steering wheel hub and steering shaft confirm correct orientation.

MANUAL STEERING SERVICE PROCEDURES

In this chapter only general manual steering service procedures are covered. For more details on how to diagnose specific problems and how to correct them,

FIGURE 37–17 Steering shaft universal joints. *Courtesy of Chrysler Corporation*

check the *Tech Manual* written for this book. Damaged or broken parts must be replaced as described in the appropriate service manual.

Parallelogram Steering Linkage

Carefully inspect the components of parallelogram steering linkage.

PITMAN ARM Because of its function, the pitman arm is the most heavily stressed point in the system. To inspect the pitman arm, grasp it and vigorously shake it to detect any looseness. Check the socket to reveal any damage or looseness. Either condition must be corrected by replacing the worn part.

IDLER ARM A worn or damaged idler arm can cause steering instability, uneven tire wear, front-end shimmy, hard steering, excessive play in steering, or poor returnability. Because an idler arm is the weakest link in a parallelogram steering system, it wears quicker than the rest of the system.

The procedure is simple for checking an idler arm for looseness or wear. The suspension should be normally loaded on the ground or on an alignment rack. When raised by a frame contact hoist, the vehicle's steering linkage is allowed to hang. Proper testing cannot be done. Check the idler arm ends for worn sockets or deteriorated bushings. Grasp the center link firmly with your hand at the idler arm end. Push up with approximately a 25-pound load. Pull down with the same load. The allowable movement of the idler arm and support assembly is ±1/8 inch for a total acceptable movement of 1/4 inch (Figure 37–20). The load can be accurately measured by using a dial indicator or pull spring scale located as near the center link end of the idler arm as possible. Keep in mind that the test forces should not exceed 25 pounds, as even a new idler arm might be forced to show movement due to steel flexing when excessive pressure is applied. It is also necessary that a scale or ruler be rested against the frame and used

to determine the amount of movement. Observers tend to overestimate the actual movement when a scale is not used. The idler arm should always be replaced if it fails this test. Jerking the right front wheel and tire assembly back and forth (causing an up and down movement in the idler arm) is not an acceptable method of checking, as there is no control on the amount of force being applied.

CENTER LINK Worn or bent center links can cause front-end shimmy, vehicle pull to one side, or change in the toe setting, causing excessive tire wear.

When inspecting the center link, look closely to ensure it has not been bent or damaged. Grasp the center link firmly and try moving it in all directions. Any movement, or sign of damage, is reason for replacement. Tapered openings seldom wear but should be checked for enlargement caused by a loose connection. If necessary, replace the center link.

TIE-ROD ASSEMBLY Worn tie-rod ends result in incorrect toe-in settings, scalloped and scuffed tires, wheel shimmy, understeering, or front-end noise and tire squeal on turns.

Tie-rod end and center link inspections are similar. Grasp the tie-rod end firmly. Push vertically with the stud, and inspect for movement at the joint with the steering knuckle. Any movement over 1/8 inch or observation of damaged or missing parts, such as seals, is sufficient evidence that replacement is necessary.

Adjusting sleeves resemble a piece of internally threaded pipe. They have a slot or separation that runs either their entire length or just partway. Adjusting sleeves also have two crimping or squeezing clamps located at each end to lock the toe adjustment. Badly rusted, worn, or damaged adjusting sleeves should be replaced.

An additional check of the tie-rods can be made by rotating each tie-rod end to feel for roughness or binding, which could indicate the socket has probably rusted internally.

STEERING DAMPER The steering dampers found in some steering linkage designs are generally nonadjustable and nonrefillable, and are not repairable. At each inspection interval, inspect the mountings and check the assembly for fluid leaks. A light film of fluid is evidence of fluid leakage. However, a light film of fluid is permissible on the body of the damper near the shaft seal. A dripping damper should be replaced.

DRY PARK CHECK An excellent overall check for worn or loose conventional steering components is the **dry park** check. With the full weight of the vehicle on the wheels, have an assistant rock the steering wheel back and forth. Start your inspection at one

FIGURE 37–20 Checking idler arm movement.

FIGURE 37–21 Circled areas indicate where a dry park check of steering linkage should be made.

side to the other side. Note any looseness in tie-rod, center link, idler arm, or pitman arm sockets (Figure 37–21). If a second person is not available, reach up under the vehicle and grasp the flexible coupling on the steering shaft. Rock the linkage.

Before assembling any steering linkage parts, thoroughly check all tapered holes for out-of-roundness and wear. Thoroughly clean all bores that the stud tapers mount in. On new and reused parts, firmly install the tapered stud into its tapered hole. The stud must seat firmly, without rocking. Only thread should protrude from the hole. If the parts do not meet these requirements, the mating part is worn and must be replaced, or the correct parts are not being used. Always follow the manufacturer's stud and mounting bolt torque specifications when installing chassis parts.

Worm and Roller Steering

Since the worm and roller steering linkage components are almost identical to those of a parallelogram linkage, the same methods of inspection are used.

CUSTOMER CARE

It is important for you to tell your customer that the steering linkage under normal conditions should be lubricated with any water-resistant EP chassis lubricant every 7,500 miles or 6 months, whichever occurs first. Lubricate every 3,000 miles or 2 months, whichever occurs first, when operating in dusty or muddy conditions or if the vehicle is used off-road. Lubrication points and additional information on the chassis lubricant recommended can be found in the vehicle's service manual. ∎

Rack and Pinion Steering

A rack and pinion system has no idler or pitman arms and no center link. Instead, they are replaced with a rack. Because the rack has no wear points, the number of wear points on rack and pinion systems is reduced to four—each of the tie-rod ends. Tie-rod ends are also wear points on the parallelogram steering system.

To solve customer complaints, a very thorough inspection of the entire system is needed. Everything, including ball joints, tires, outer tie-rods, bellows boots, inner tie-rods, rack mounting bushings, steering couplings, and gearbox adjustment must be checked. Rack and pinion steering inspection must be very thorough due to the system's sensitivity.

PROCEDURES
Rack and Pinion Steering Inspection

1. Check all working components (Figure 37–22) of the systems. Inspect the flexible steering coupling or the universal joints for wear or looseness. If any play is found, recommend replacement. Universal joints can also seize or bind. They should be checked closely.
2. Grasp the pinion gear shaft at the flexible steering coupling and try to move it in and out of the gear. If there is movement, the pinion bearing preload might need adjustment. If there is no adjustment, internal components have to be replaced.
3. Carefully inspect the rack housing. In most cases, the rack and pinion steering assemblies are mounted in rubber bushings. As the vehicle gets older, these mounting bushings deteriorate from heat, age, and oil leakage from the engine. When this happens, the housing moves within its mounting and causes loose and erratic steering. Also, be alert for excessive movement of the rack housing.
4. Stiffness in steering can be caused by a bent rack assembly, tight yoke bearing adjustment, loose power-steering belt, weak pump, internal leaks in power-steering system, and damaged CV joints in front-wheel-drive vehicles.
5. Check the inner tie-rod socket assemblies (Figure 37–23) located inside the bellows. The most foolproof way of checking these sockets is to loosen the inner bellows clamp and pull the bellows back, giving a clear view of the socket. During the dry park check, observe any looseness. The inner tie-rod socket can also be checked by squeezing the bellows boot until the inner socket can be felt. Push and pull on the tire. If loose-

ness is found in the tie-rod, it should be re-placed. On some vehicles the boot might be made of hard plastic. For this type of boot, lock the steering wheel and push and pull on the tire. Watch for in-and-out movement of the tie-rod. If movement is observed, replace the inner tie-rod.

6. One fact to keep in mind is that the condition of the bellows boot determines the life of the inner socket. The bellows boot protects the rack from contamination. It might also contain fluid that helps keep the rack lubricated. If any cracks, splits, or leaks exist, the boot should be replaced. Also, be sure clamps for the bellows are in their proper place and fastened tightly.

7. Inspect the outer tie-rod ends. In addition to the dry park check, grab each end and rotate to feel for any roughness that would indicate internal rusting. Be sure to check for bent or damaged forgings and studs; split or deteriorated seals; and, damaged, out-of-round, or loose tapers. If any of these conditions exist, the parts should be replaced.

FIGURE 37–23 Various inner tie-rod socket assemblies.

Manual Steering Gear

Before any adjustments are made or servicing procedures performed to the steering gear, a careful check should be made of front-end alignment, shock ab-sorbers, wheel balance, and tire pressure for possible steering system problems.

Before adjusting or servicing a manual steering gear, the technician must disconnect the battery

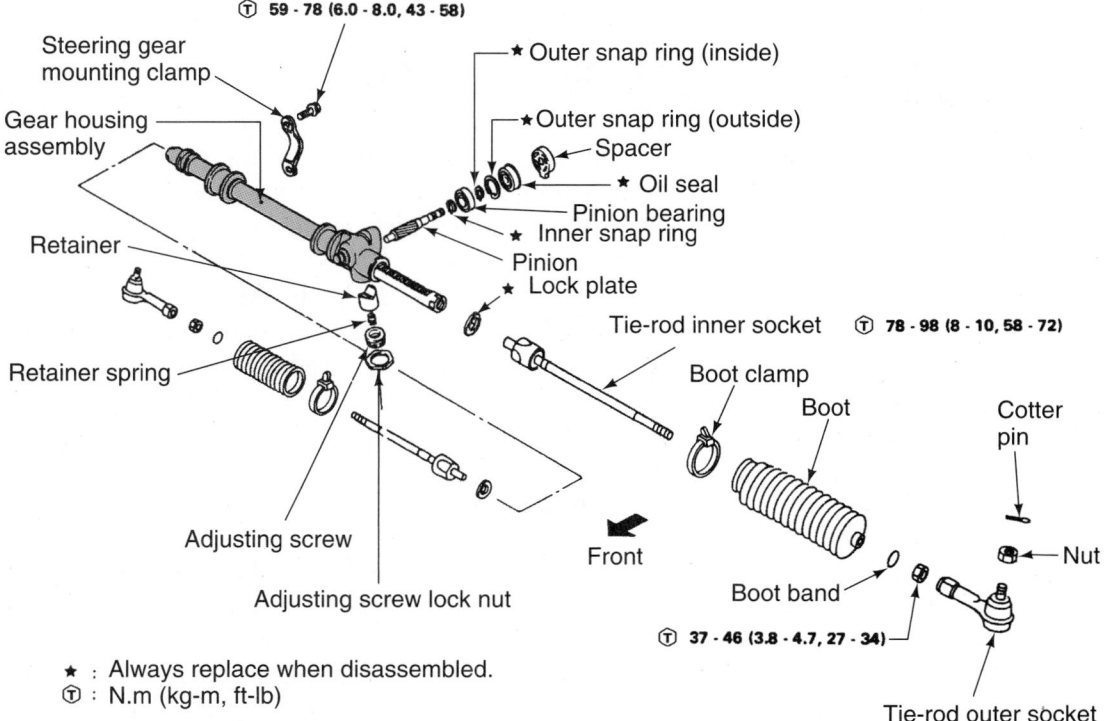

★ : Always replace when disassembled.
ⓣ : N.m (kg-m, ft-lb)

FIGURE 37–22 Rack and pinion steering components. *Courtesy of Nissan Motors*

FIGURE 37–24 Typical steering gear adjustment points.

ground cable. Raise the vehicle with the front wheels in the straight-ahead position. Remove the pitman arm nut. Mark the relationship of the pitman shaft. Remove the pitman arm with a pitman arm puller. Loosen the steering gear adjuster plug lock nut and back the adjuster plug off one-quarter turn (Figure 37–24). Remove the horn shroud or button cap. Turn the steering wheel gently in one direction until stopped by the gear; then, turn back one-half turn. Measure and record bearing drag by applying a torque wrench with a socket on the steering wheel nut and rotating through a 90-degree arc (Figure 37–25). Check the service manual for the correct amount of drag.

Once these steps are taken, the steering gear is ready for adjusting or servicing as per instructions in the vehicle's service manual.

Steering Columns

To perform service procedures on the steering column upper end components, it is not necessary to remove the column from the vehicle. The steering wheel, horn components, directional signal switch, ignition switch, and lock cylinder can be removed with the column remaining in the vehicle.

FIGURE 37–25 Measuring steering gear preload.

⚠ *WARNING!*

Set the parking brake before removing the steering column. Also, remove the battery cable from the negative terminal. Remember that special precautions must be observed before beginning disassembly and during assembly to ensure the correct fitting together of the steering column shaft and steering gear shaft connections. ■

To determine if the energy-absorbing steering column components are functioning as designed, or if repairs are required, a close inspection should be made. An inspection is called for in all cases in which damage is evident or whenever the vehicle is being repaired due to a front-end collision. If damage is evident, the affected parts must be replaced. Because of the differences in the steering column styles and various components, consult the service manual for more explicit inspection and servicing procedures.

⚠ *WARNING!*

When working on a collapsible steering column, do not hammer on or bump column components. With the column removed from the mounts, it is extremely susceptible to impact damage. A slight impact on the column end can collapse the steering shaft or loosen the plastic injections that maintain column rigidity. When removing the steering wheel, use a puller. Do not hammer or pound on any components to aid in removal. ■

POWER STEERING

The power-steering unit is designed to reduce the amount of effort required to turn the steering wheel. It also reduces driver fatigue on long drives and makes it easier to steer the vehicle at slow road speeds, particularly during parking.

Power steering can be broken down into two design arrangements: conventional and nonconventional or electronically controlled. In the conventional arrangement, hydraulic power is used to assist the driver. In the nonconventional arrangement, an electric motor and electronic controls provide power assistance in steering.

Conventional Power-Steering Systems

There are several power-steering systems in use on passenger cars and light-duty trucks. The most common ones are the external-piston linkage, integral-piston, and power-assisted rack and pinion system (Figure 37–26).

FIGURE 37–26 The three major power-steering systems. (A) Integral-piston linkage, (B) rack and pinion, (C) external-piston linkage. *Courtesy of Moog Automotive*

External-Piston Linkage System The **external-piston linkage** system, sometimes called nonintegral, is generally found on older cars. It consists of a power-steering pump and reservoir, control valve, power cylinder, and four hoses. The control valve and pressure cylinder are separate components that are not incorporated into the steering gear. The pressure hose connects the pump to the control valve and directs the pressurized fluid into the correct booster hoses to the power cylinder. The power cylinder piston provides the necessary power assistance.

Integral-Piston System The **integral-piston** system is one of the most common conventional power-steering systems in use today. It consists of a power-steering pump and reservoir, power-steering pressure and return hose, and steering gear. The power cylinder and the control valve are in the same housing as the steering gear.

On some recent-model cars and light trucks, instead of the conventional vacuum-assist brake booster, the hydraulic fluid from the power-steering pump is also used to actuate the brake booster. This brake system is called the hydro-boost system (Figure 37–27).

Power-Assisted Rack and Pinion System The power-assisted rack and pinion system is similar to

the integral system because the power cylinder and the control valve are in the same housing. The rack housing acts as the cylinder and the power piston is part of the rack. Control valve location is in the pinion housing. Turning the steering wheel moves the valve, directing pressure to either end of the back piston. The system utilizes a pressure hose from the pump to the control valve housing and a return line to the pump reservoir. This type of steering system is common in front-wheel-drive vehicles.

Components Several of the manual steering parts described earlier in this chapter, such as the steering linkage, are used in conventional power-steering systems. The components that have been added for power steering provide the hydraulic power that drives the system. They are the power-steering pump, flow control and pressure relief valves, reservoir, spool valves and power pistons, hydraulic hose lines, and gearbox or assist assembly on the linkage.

POWER-STEERING PUMP The steering pump is used to develop hydraulic flow, which provides the force needed to operate the steering gear. The pump is belt driven from the engine crankshaft, providing flow any time the engine is running. It is usually mounted near the front of the engine (Figure 37–28).

FIGURE 37-27 Typical hydro-boost system that uses the power-steering pump to power assist brake applications. *Courtesy of Ford Motor Company*

There are four general types of power-steering pumps: roller, vane, slipper, and gear (Figure 37–29). Functionally, all pumps operate in the same basic manner. Hydraulic fluid for the power-steering pump is stored in a reservoir. Fluid is routed to and from the pump by hoses and lines. Excessive pressure is controlled by a relief valve.

FLOW CONTROL AND PRESSURE RELIEF VALVES A pressure relief valve controls the pressure output from the pump. This valve is necessary because of the variations in engine rpm and the need for consistent steering ability in all ranges from idle to highway speeds. It is positioned in a chamber that is exposed to pump outlet pressure at one end and supply hose pressure at the other. A spring is used at

FIGURE 37-29 Four basic types of power-steering pumps.

FIGURE 37-28 Typical power-steering pump location.

DISCHARGE

INTAKE

STATIC

FLOW BYPASS

PRESSURE RELIEF   **FLOW CONTROLLING**   **IDLE FLOW**

FIGURE 37–30 Flow control valve operation.

the supply pressure end to help maintain a balance (Figure 37–30).

As the fluid leaves the pump rotor, it passes the end of the flow control valve and is forced through an orifice that causes a slight drop in pressure. This reduced pressure, aided by the springs, holds the flow control valve in the closed position. All pump flow is sent to the steering gear.

When engine speed increases, the pump can deliver more flow than is required to operate the system. Since the outlet orifice restricts the amount of fluid leaving the pump, the difference in pressure at the two ends of the valve becomes greater until pump outlet pressure overcomes the combined force of supply line pressure and spring force. The valve is pushed down against the spring, opening a passage that returns the excess flow back to the inlet side of the pump.

A spring and ball contained inside the flow control valve are used to relieve pump outlet pressure. This is done to protect the system from damage due to excessive pressure when the steering wheel is held against the stops. Since flow in the system is severely restricted, the pump would continue to build pressure until a hose ruptured or the pump destroyed itself.

When outlet pressure reaches a preset level, the pressure relief ball is forced off its seat, creating a greater pressure differential at the two ends of the flow control valve. This allows the flow control valve to open wider, permitting more pump pressure to flow back to the pump inlet and pressure is held at a safe level.

POWER-STEERING GEARBOX A power-steering gearbox is basically the same as a manual recirculating ball gearbox with the addition of a hydraulic assist. A power-steering gearbox is filled with hydraulic fluid and uses a control valve.

In a power rack and pinion gear, the movement of the rack is assisted by hydraulic pressure. When the wheel is turned, the rotary valve changes hydraulic flow to create a pressure differential on either side of the rack. The unequal pressure causes the rack to move toward the lower pressure, reducing the effort required to turn the wheels.

The integral power steering has the spool valve and a power piston integrated with the gearbox. The spool valve directs the oil pressure to the left or right power chamber to steer the vehicle. The spool valve is actuated by a lever (Figure 37–31) or a small torsion bar (Figure 37–32).

In linkage systems, the control valve is connected directly to the steering center link and the pitman arm on the steering gear. Any movement of the steering wheel and the pitman arm compresses the centering spring and moves the valve spool. This opens and closes a series of ports directing fluid under pressure from the pump to one side, or the other, of the power cylinder piston.

The power cylinder in the linkage system is attached to the steering center link and the piston shaft is attached to the frame. As fluid under pressure is directed to one side of the piston by the control valve, power assist is provided to aid the driver in moving the steering linkage and road wheels. Two lines connect the cylinder to the control valve. Each one functions as both return line or supply line, depending on the direction of the turn.

POWER-ASSISTED RACK AND PINION STEERING Power-assisted rack and pinion components are basically the same as for manual rack and pinion steering, except for the hydraulic control housing. As mentioned earlier, the power rack and pinion steering unit may be classified as integral. The rack functions

Pressure   Return

Return oil

Valve spool
Valve body

Pressure   Return

Return oil

Valve spool
Valve body

FIGURE 37–31 Constant control-type spool valves direct oil pressure to the left or right power chamber to steer the vehicle. *Courtesy of Buick Motor Division, General Motors Corporation*

as the power piston and the spool valve is connected to the pinion gear.

In a power rack and pinion gear the piston is mounted on the rack, inside the rack housing. The rack housing is sealed on either side of the rack piston to form two separate hydraulic chambers for the left and right turn circuits. When the wheel is turned to the right, the rotary valve creates a pressure differential on either side of the rack piston. This causes the rack to move toward the lower pressure and reduces the total effort required to turn the wheels. Movement of the rack during a left and right turn is shown in Figure 37–33.

FIGURE 37–32 Torsion bar moves the spool valve to direct the oil flow to the piston.

FIGURE 37–33 Left and right turn with power-assisted rack and pinion system. *Courtesy of Ford Motor Company*

POWER-STEERING HOSES The primary purpose of power-steering hoses is to transmit power (fluid under pressure) from the pump, to the steering gearbox, and to return the fluid ultimately to the pump reservoir. Hoses also, through material and construction, function as additional reservoirs and act as sound and vibration dampers.

Hoses are generally a reinforced synthetic rubber material coupled to metal tubing at the connecting points. The pressure side must be able to handle pressures up to 1,500 psi. For that reason, wherever there is a metal tubing to a rubber connection, the connection is crimped. Pressure hoses are also subject to surges in pressure and pulsations from the pump. The reinforced construction permits the hose to expand slightly and absorb changes in pressure.

Where two diameters of hose (Figure 37–34) are used on the pressure side, the larger diameter or pressure hose is at the pump end. It acts as a reservoir and as an accumulator absorbing pulsations. The smaller diameter or return hose reduces the effects of kickback from the gear itself. By restricting fluid flow, it also maintains constant back pressure on the pump, which reduces pump noise. If the hose is of one diameter, the gearbox is performing the damping functions internally.

Because of working fluid temperature and adjacent engine temperatures, these hoses must be able to withstand temperatures up to 300°F. Due to various weather conditions, they must also tolerate subzero temperatures as well. Hose material is specially formulated to resist breakdown or deterioration due to oil or temperature conditions.

CAUTION:

Hoses must be carefully routed away from engine manifolds. Power-steering fluid is very flammable. If it comes in contact with hot engine parts, it could start an underhood fire. ■

POWER-STEERING DIAGNOSIS

Because there are so many different factors that can affect a vehicle's steering, proper diagnostics are vital for locating the exact cause of a condition without performing unnecessary tests or repairs. By eliminating the simple or obvious items first, it is possible to pinpoint the condition quickly and accurately (Figure 37–35).

The first step in the diagnostic process is a thorough visual inspection. Make notes of anything that appears abnormal, such as tire inflation, size, match,

FIGURE 37–34 Power-steering hoses may have two internal diameters.

BELLOWS LEAK POINTS
OIL LEAK AT BELLOWS MAY ORIGINATE AT THE FOLLOWING POINTS:
1. INNER RACK SEAL (INNER DIAMETER LIP)
2. OUTER RACK SEAL (INNER DIAMETER LIP)
3. OUTER RACK SEAL (OUTSIDE DIAMETER)
4. PINION SEAL

IF THE PINION SEAL LEAKS, IT WILL SHOW UP AS A BELLOWS LEAK SINCE IT CANNOT BE DISTINGUISHED FROM AN INNER RACK SEAL LEAK. A COMPLETE SEAL KIT REPLACEMENT IS REQUIRED.

PINION SEAL

OUTER RACK SEAL

INNER RACK SEAL

RIGHT BELLOWS

OIL LEAK AT THE INSIDE DIAMETER OF THE INNER RACK SEAL WILL SHOW UP AS A BELLOWS LEAK.

NOTE: OIL CAN TRANSFER FROM ONE BELLOWS TO THE OTHER THROUGH THE BREATHER TUBE.

LEFT BELLOWS

HOSE FITTING LEAK POINTS

IF LEAK OCCURS HERE, REPLACE INPUT SHAFT SEAL KIT.

TORSION BAR O-RING

DUST SEAL

INPUT SHAFT SEAL

TUBE NUT

SEAL

HOUSING

SNAP RING

O-RING

HOSE OR TUBE ASSEMBLY

IF LEAK OCCURS HERE, REPLACE VALVE ASSEMBLY ALONG WITH INPUT SHAFT SEAL KIT.

LEAK HERE REQUIRES AN O-RING REPLACEMENT.

IF LEAK OCCURS HERE, TIGHTEN NUT TO SPECIFICATION. REPLACE PLASTIC SEAL IF NECESSARY. DO NOT OVERTIGHTEN.

NOTE: ALWAYS REPLACE THIS SEAL WHEN A LINE IS REMOVED.

FIGURE 37–35   Possible leakage points on power-steering systems.

and general condition. Inspect the power-steering belts and hoses. Give the steering linkage special attention. In most cases, an owner's concerns related to steering prove to be something relatively minor and rarely involve the steering gear or pump.

Check the fluid level in the reservoir after the engine has been run at idle for two or three minutes and the wheel has been cycled from lock to lock several times. This warms the fluid to its normal operating temperature and gives a more accurate reading.

Examine the condition of the fluid carefully. Check for evidence of contamination, such as solid particles or water. If either of these conditions is present or the fluid has a burnt odor, the system should be flushed before returning to service.

If in the course of the inspection a defect is found, do not correct it until after the road test. Doing so could change the condition and make final diagnosis more difficult. The obvious exception to this would be a condition such as broken linkage or other conditions that would make driving the vehicle hazardous.

After the visual inspection is completed, a road test is necessary to verify the owner's concern. It is very important that during the road test the vehicle is driven under conditions similar to the owner's normal driving. While it may be somewhat inconvenient to seek out a particular type of road surface, this may be the only way to verify the condition. Take plenty of time since it could save hours of service time in the final diagnosis.

Once the road test has been completed and it has been determined there is an abnormal condition, certain tests are necessary to pinpoint the exact cause. In some cases, partial disassembly of the system may be required to complete a test. Do not shortcut test steps to save time. Doing so can alter the results, leading to an inaccurate diagnosis and unnecessary replacement of parts. It is also vital that specifications be confirmed in the service manual. Guessing gives incorrect results.

GENERAL POWER-STEERING SYSTEM CHECKS

The steering linkage operates as a system. All components between the tires and the steering wheel can affect the way a vehicle steers. It may be the problem is not related to the power-steering system. Therefore, first make the following checks.

TIRES Check for correct pressure, construction, size, wear, and damage, and for defects including ply separations, sidewall knots, concentricity problems, and force problems.

TIRE AND WHEEL ASSEMBLY Check for radial and lateral runout, static, and dynamic imbalance.

WHEEL BEARINGS Check for correct adjustment.

STEERING AND SUSPENSION PIVOTS Check for wear, looseness or tightness, physical damage, and lubrication.

STEERING GEARBOX Check for loose mounting bolts and for internal maladjustment.

ALIGNMENT (FRONT AND REAR) Check for correct caster, camber, toe, toe-out on turns (turning radius), and chassis height.

When all other areas have been checked and the power-steering system is still suspect, the following checks should be made.

BELT CONDITION AND TENSION If the belt shows evidence of cracking or glazing, it should be replaced. Adjust belt tension according to service manual instructions and specifications.

FLUID LEVEL The fluid is checked at the pump reservoir with a dipstick attached to the reservoir cap. However, it is not simply a matter of pulling the cap and reading the dipstick, so follow the manufacturer's procedure.

FLUID LEAKS Clean the suspected area, then cycle the wheel from lock to lock several times. Fluid leakage will not only cause abnormal noises, but may result in unequal and abnormal steering efforts (Figure 37–36). If no signs of leakage are apparent, repeat the wheel cycling process and inspection several more times. Consult the appropriate section of the service manual for detailed information about the action necessary to correct any leaks.

TURNING EFFORT If an owner's concern indicates excessive turning effort, a pull scale should be used to read the actual force required to turn the wheel (Figure 37–37). Compare the test results to the specifications in the service manual. If the effort exceeds the maximum, carefully inspect the entire steering system before performing a pressure test.

TIE-ROD ARTICULATION EFFORT The effort required to move the tie-rod or its inner ball socket should be checked with a pull scale if excessive steering effort or looseness is noted during the road test. If the effort is not within the specified limits, the tie-rod must be replaced.

AIR IN THE SYSTEM Air in the system is usually determined during a fluid level check. If the fluid looks foamy, it is likely that air is in the system. The method of bleeding depends on the type of power-steering system. Follow the service manual procedure.

ADEQUATE PRESSURE If the preliminary tests indicate the possibility of an internal pump or gear malfunction, a steering system analyzer (Figure 37–38) provides an accurate method for evaluating the pump, rotary valve, and internal seals. The analyzer provides a direct readout of base pump pressure and flow, pump relief pressure, and steering gear seal integrity. Check the system's pressure following manufacturer's instructions.

POWER-STEERING SYSTEM SERVICING

Vehicles with power-steering systems have the same types of steering linkage as manual steering. The power-steering linkage is checked and serviced as previously described. Actually, the only difference is the servicing of the hydraulic components, such as the hoses, pump, and power-steering gear, that are fully covered in the vehicle's service manual.

FIGURE 37–36   Leaking seals can cause a steering imbalance. *Courtesy of Chrysler Corporation*

FIGURE 37–37   A pull scale is used to measure steering effort.

ELECTRONICALLY CONTROLLED POWER-STEERING SYSTEMS

The object of power steering is to make steering easier at low speeds, especially while parking. However, higher steering efforts are desirable at higher speeds to provide improved down-the-road feel. The electronically controlled power-steering (EPS) systems provide both of these benefits. The hydraulic boost of these systems is tapered off by electronic control as road speed increases. Thus, these systems require well under 1 pound of steering effort at low road speeds and 3 pounds plus of steering effort at higher road speeds to enable the driver to maintain control of the steering wheel for improved high-speed handling.

FIGURE 37–38   Typical power-steering analyzer hookup.

Presently, true electronically controlled power-steering systems appear primarily on imported cars. One of the more popular systems uses a by-pass flow control valve in the hydraulic line (Figure 37–39). Central to this system is the speed at which the steering wheel is being turned.

A rotary valve electronic power-steering system consists of the power-steering gearbox, power-steering oil pump, pressure hose, and the return hose.

FIGURE 37–39 By-pass flow control valve in hydraulic line. *Courtesy of Nissan Motors*

The amount of hydraulic fluid flow (pressure) used to boost steering is controlled by a solenoid valve that is identified as its PCV (pressure control valve).

SHOP TALK

The PCV (pressure control valve) is not to be confused with the PCV (positive crankcase ventilator) used with emission controls systems. ∎

The electronic power-steering (EPS) system's PCV (Figure 37–40) is exposed to spring tension on the top and plunger force on the bottom. The plunger slips inside an electromagnet. By varying the electrical current to the electromagnet, the upward force exerted by the plunger can be varied as it works against the opposing spring. Current flow to the electromagnet is variable with vehicle road speed and, therefore, provides steering to match the vehicle's road speed.

When servicing, as with any power-steering system, the first step is to look for fluid leaks, damaged components, a slipping drive belt, and so on. Only after these things have been checked and no problems have been found should the electronics be suspected as the problem. Check the appropriate service manual for the correct troubleshooting procedures of the electronics.

Electric/Electronic Rack and Pinion System

The electric/electronic rack and pinion unit replaces the hydraulic pump, hoses, and fluid associated with conventional power-steering systems with electronic controls and an electric motor located concentric to the rack itself (Figure 37–41). The design features a DC motor armature with a follow shaft to allow passage of the rack through it (Figure 37–42). The outboard housing and rack are designed so the rotary motion of the armature can be transferred to linear movement of the rack through a ball nut with thrust bearings. The armature is mechanically connected to

FIGURE 37–40 Outline of electronic power-steering components. EPS PCV is exposed to spring tension and plunger force. *Courtesy of Mitsubishi Motor Sales of America, Inc.*

ELECTRIC RACK AND PINION
STEERING SYSTEM

FIGURE 37-41   The vehicle's generator becomes the power source for electronically driven rack and pinion systems, replacing the hydraulic pump of conventional systems.

These units are readily retrofitted to conventionally equipped vehicles. As for servicing, there are currently no replacement parts available; therefore, if the rack should become faulty, the entire unit should be replaced. Rebuilt kits, with complete installation instructions, are planned for the near future.

Unlike conventional power steering, electric/electronic units provide power assistance even when the engine stalls, since the power source is the battery rather than the engine driven pump. The feel of the steering can also be adjusted to match the particular driving characteristics of cars and drivers, from high performance to luxury touring cars. It also eliminates hydraulic oil, which means no leaks.

the ball nut through an internal/external spline arrangement.

The basis of system operation is its ability to change the rotational direction of the electric motor, while being able to deliver the necessary amount of current to meet torque requirements at the same time. The system can deliver up to 75 amperes to the motor. The higher the current, the greater the force exerted on the rack. The direction of the turn is controlled by changing the polarity of the signal to the motor.

The field assembly houses permanent ceramic magnets while providing structural integrity for the gear system. In essence, the electronic/electric rack design allows for a direct power source to the rack and steering linkage. The system monitors steering wheel movement through a sensor mounted on the input shaft of the rack and pinion steering gear. After receiving directional and load information from the sensor, an electronic controller activates the motor to provide power assistance.

FOUR-WHEEL STEERING SYSTEM

Four-wheel independent suspensions have been around for years and continue to be an important part of the automotive industry. Now the industry is offering four-wheel independent steering systems, in which the rear wheels also help to turn the car by electrical, hydraulic, or mechanical means. Because these systems are going to be more common in the future, the automotive technician should be aware of them.

Production-built cars tend to understeer or, in a few instances, oversteer. If a car could automatically compensate for an understeer/oversteer problem, the driver would enjoy nearly neutral steering under varying operating conditions. Four-wheel steering (**4WS**) is a serious effort on the part of automotive design engineers to provide near-neutral steering with the following advantages.

CORNERING CAPABILITY The vehicle's cornering behavior becomes more stable and controllable at

FIGURE 37-42   Electric/electronic rack and pinion system. *Courtesy of Chrysler Corporation*

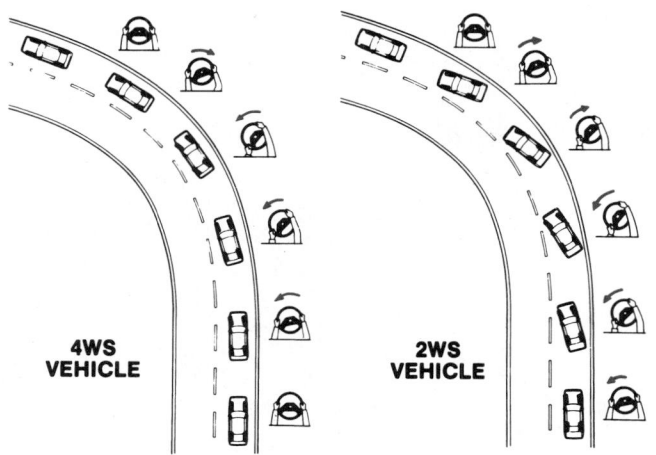

FIGURE 37–43 Comparison of 2WS and 4WS vehicle behavior during cornering.

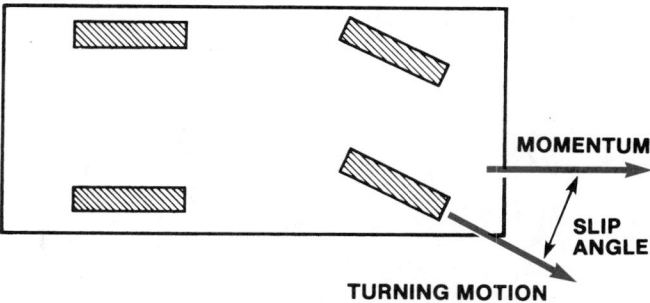

FIGURE 37–44 When a turn is initiated with front steering, the momentum wants to move the car forward while the steering input causes a directional change. This creates a tire slip angle as the vehicle momentarily resists turning.

high speeds as well as on wet or slippery road surfaces (Figure 37–43).

STEERING RESPONSE The vehicle's response to steering input becomes quicker and more precise throughout the vehicle's entire speed range.

STRAIGHT-LINE STABILITY The vehicle's straight-line stability at high speeds is improved. Negative effects of road irregularities and crosswinds on the vehicle's stability are minimized.

LANE CHANGING Stability in lane changing at high speeds is improved. High-speed slalom-type operations become easier. The vehicle becomes less likely to go into a spin even in situations when the driver must make a sudden and relatively large change of direction.

LOW-SPEED MANEUVERABILITY By steering the rear wheels in the direction opposite the front wheels at low speeds, the vehicle's turning circle is greatly reduced. Therefore, vehicle maneuvering on narrow roads and during parking becomes easier.

To understand the advantages of four-wheel steering, it is wise to review the dynamics of typical steering maneuvers with a conventional front-steered vehicle. The tires are subject to the forces of grip, momentum, and steering input when making a movement other than straight-ahead driving. These forces compete with each other during steering maneuvers. With a front-steered vehicle, the rear end is always trying to catch up to the directional changes of the front wheels. This causes the vehicle to sway. As a normal part of operating a vehicle, the driver learns to adjust to these forces without thinking about them.

When turning, the driver is putting into motion a complex series of forces. Each of these must be balanced against the others. The tires are subjected to

road grip and slip angle. Grip holds the car's wheels to the road, and momentum moves the car straight ahead. Steering input causes the front wheels to turn. The car momentarily resists the turning motion, causing a tire slip angle to form (Figure 37–44). Once the vehicle begins to respond to the steering input, cornering forces are generated. The vehicle sways as the rear wheels attempt to keep up with the cornering forces already generated by the front tires. This is referred to as rear-end lag, because there is a time delay between steering input and vehicle reaction. When the front wheels are turned back to a straight-ahead position, the vehicle must again try to adjust by reversing the same forces developed by the turn. As the steering is turned, the vehicle body sways as the rear wheels again try to keep up with the cornering forces generated by the front wheels.

The idea behind four-wheel steering is that a vehicle requires less driver input for any steering maneuver if all four wheels are steering the vehicle. As with two-wheel-steer vehicles, tire grip holds the four wheels on the road. However, when the driver turns the wheel slightly, all four wheels react to the steering input, causing slip angles to form at all four wheels. The entire vehicle moves in one direction rather than the rear half attempting to catch up to the front. There is also less sway when the wheels are turned back to a straight-ahead position. The vehicle responds more quickly to steering input because rear wheel lag is eliminated.

Currently, there are three types of production four-wheel-steering systems: mechanical, hydraulic, and electro/hydraulic designs. Since each system is unique in its construction and repair needs, the vehicle's service manual must be followed for proper diagnosis, repair, and alignment of a four-wheel system.

Mechanical 4WS

In a straight-mechanical type of 4WS, two steering gears are used—one for the front and other for the

FIGURE 37–45 Inside a rear-steering gearbox is a simple planetary gear setup. *Courtesy of American Honda Motor Company, Inc.*

rear wheels. A steel shaft connects the two steering gearboxes. Conventional steering linkage is used fore and aft. But, the heart of the system is the double crank. The shaft that runs from the forward-steering gearbox to the rear-steering gearbox terminates at an eccentric shaft. This shaft is fitted with an offset pin (Figure 37–45) that engages a second offset pin that fits into a planetary gear.

The planetary gear meshes with the matching teeth of an internal gear. The internal gear is secured in a fixed position to the gearbox housing. This means that the planetary gear can rotate but the internal gear cannot. The eccentric pin of the planetary gear fits into a hole in the slider that is part of the stroke end.

A 120-degree turn of the steering wheel rotates the planetary gear to move the slider and stroke rod in the same direction that the front wheels are headed. Proportionately, the rear wheels turn the steering wheel about 1.5 to 10 degrees (Figure 37–46). Further rotation of the steering wheel, past the 120-degree point, causes the rear wheels to start straightening out due to the double-crank action (two eccentric pins) and rotation of the planetary gear. Turning the steering wheel to a greater angle, about 230 degrees, finds the rear wheels in a neutral position regarding the front wheels. Further rotation of the steering wheel results in the rear wheels going counterphase with regard to the front wheels. About 5.3 degrees maximum counterphase rear steering is possible.

Because front and rear steering systems are linked together mechanically, it stands to reason that when the front wheels are turned to make a caster check, the rear wheels are going to move as well. The same is true for checking toe-out on turns.

This setup makes it mandatory for all four wheels to rest on turntables or full-floating slip plates to prevent the car from crabbing to one side or the other as the front wheels are turned during wheel alignment.

Mechanical 4WS is steering angle sensitive. It is not sensitive to vehicle road speed.

Hydraulic 4WS The hydraulically operated four-wheel-steering system shown in Figure 37–47 is a simple design, both in components and operation.

In this system, the rear wheels turn only in the same direction as the front wheel. They also turn no more than 1 1/2 degrees. The system does not use electronic sensors, a computer control module, or

FIGURE 37–46 The steer angle of the rear wheels compared to the angle of the front wheels. *Courtesy of American Honda Motor Company, Inc.*

FIGURE 37–47 Simple hydraulic 4WS system. *Courtesy of Mitsubishi Motor Sales of America, Inc.*

FIGURE 37–48 Control valve/rear steering power cylinder fluid flow for (A) left turn and (B) right turn.

advanced gearing mechanisms. This system only activates at speeds above 30 mph. It does not operate when the vehicle moves in reverse.

A two-way hydraulic cylinder mounted on the rear stub frame turns the wheels. Fluid for this cylinder is supplied by a rear steering pump that is driven by the differential. The pump only operates when the front wheels are turning. A tank in the engine compartment supplies the rear steering pump with fluid.

When the steering wheel is turned, the front steering pump sends fluid under pressure to the rotary valve in the front rack and pinion unit. This forces fluid into the front power cylinder, and the front wheels turn in the direction steered. The fluid pressure varies with the turning of the steering wheel. The faster and farther the steering wheel is turned, the greater the fluid pressure.

The fluid is also fed under the same pressure to the control valve where it opens a spool valve in the control valve housing (Figure 37–48). As the spool valve moves, it allows fluid from the rear steering pump to move through and operate the rear power cylinder. The higher the pressure on the spool, the farther it moves. The farther it moves, the more fluid it allows through to move the rear wheels. As mentioned earlier, this system limits rear wheel movement to 1 1/2 degrees in either the left or right direction.

Electro/Hydraulic 4WS Several 4WS systems combine computer electronic controls with hydraulics to make the system sensitive to both steering angle and road speeds. The system shown in Figure 37–49 consists of two hydraulic pumps, a reverse tank, solenoid valve, steering angle sensor, controller (ECU), cutoff valve, vehicle speed sensor, and the power cylinder.

In this design, the speed sensor and the steering wheel angle sensor feed information to the electronic control unit (ECU). By processing the information received, the ECU commands the hydraulic system to steer the rear wheels. At low road speed, the rear wheels of this system are not considered a dynamic factor in the steering process.

At moderate road speeds, the rear wheels are steered momentarily counterphase, through neutral, then in phase with the front wheels. At high road speeds, the rear wheels turn only in phase with the

FIGURE 37–49
Electro/hydraulic 4WS system using an electrically controlled power cylinder. *Courtesy of Nissan Motors*

front wheels. The ECU must know not only road speed, but also how much and how quickly the steering wheel is turned.

These three factors—road speed, amount of steering wheel turn, and the quickness of the steering wheel turn—are interpreted by the ECU to maintain continuous and desired steering angle of the rear wheels.

A second electro/hydraulic 4WS system is shown in Figure 37–50. The basic working elements of the design are the control unit, a stepper motor, a swing arm, a set of beveled gears, a control rod, and a control valve with an output rod. Two electronic sensors tell the ECU how fast the car is going.

The yoke is a major mechanical component of this electro/hydraulic design. The position of the control yoke varies with vehicle road speed. For example, at speeds below 33 mph, the yoke is in its downward position, which results in the rear wheels steering in the counterphase (opposite front wheels) direction. As road speeds approach and exceed 22 mph, the control yoke swings up through a neutral (horizontal) position to an up position. In the neutral position, the rear wheels steer in phase with the front wheels.

The stepper motor moves the control yoke. A swing arm is attached to the control yoke. The position of the yoke determines the arc of the swing rod. The arc of the swing arm is transmitted through a control arm that passes through a large bevel gear. Stepper motor action eventually causes a push-or-pull movement of its output shaft to steer the rear wheels up to a maximum of 5 degrees in either direction.

The electronically controlled, four-wheel steering system regulates the angle and direction of the rear wheels in response to speed and driver's steering. This speed-sensing system optimizes the vehicle's dynamic characteristics at any speed, thereby, producing enhanced stability and, within certain parameters, agility.

The actual 4WS system consists of a rack and pinion front steering that is hydraulically powered by a main twin-tandem pump. The system also has a rear-steering mechanism, hydraulically powered by the main pump. The rear-steering shaft extends from the rack bar of the front steering assembly to the rear steering-phase control unit (Figure 37–51).

The rear steering is comprised of the input end of the rear-steering shaft, vehicle speed sensors, and steering-phase control unit (deciding direction and degree), a power cylinder and an output rod. A centering lock spring is incorporated, which locks the rear system in a neutral (straight-ahead) position in the event of hydraulic failure. Additionally, a solenoid valve that disengages the hydraulic boost (thereby activating the centering lock spring in case of an electrical failure) is included.

All 4WS systems have fail-safe measures. For example, with the electro/hydraulic setup, the system automatically counteracts possible causes of failure, both electronic and hydraulic, and converts the entire steering system to a conventional two-wheel steering type. Specifically, if a hydraulic defect should reduce pressure level (by a movement malfunction or a broken driving belt), the rear-wheel-steering mechanism is automatically locked in a neutral position, activating a low-level warning light.

In the event of an electrical failure, it would be detected by a self-diagnostic circuit integrated in the four-wheel-steering control unit. The control unit stimulates a solenoid valve, which neutralizes hydraulic pressure, thereby alternating the system to two-wheel steering. The failure would be indicated by the system's warning light in the main instrument display.

On any 4WS system, there must be near-perfect compliance between the position of the steering wheel, the position of the front wheels, and the position of the rear wheels. it is usually recommended that the car

FIGURE 37–50 An electronically and hydraulically controlled 4WS system using a stepper motor and control yoke. *Courtesy of Mazda*

be driven about 20 feet in a dead-straight line. Then, the position of the front/rear wheels is checked with respect to steering wheel position. The base reference point is a strip of masking tape on the steering wheel hub and the steering column. When the wheel is positioned dead center, draw a line down the tape. Run the car a short distance straight ahead to see if the reference line holds. If not, corrections are needed, such as repositioning the steering wheel.

Even severe imbalance of a rear wheel on a speed-sensitive 4WS system can cause problems and make basic troubleshooting a bit frustrating.

PRINCIPLES OF WHEEL ALIGNMENT

Proper alignment of both the front and the rear wheels ensures easy steering, comfortable ride, long tire life, and reduced road vibrations.

Steering Geometry and Alignment Angles

There is a multitude of angles and specifications automotive manufacturers must consider when designing a car. The multiple functions of the suspension system complicate things a great deal for design engineers. They must take into account more than basic geometry. Durability, maintenance, tire wear, available space, and production cost are all critical elements. Most elements contain a degree of compromise to satisfy the minimum requirements of each.

Most technicians do not need to be concerned with all of this. All they need to do is restore the vehicle to the condition the design engineer specified. To do this, however, the technician must be totally familiar with the purpose of basic alignment angles.

The alignment angles are designed in the vehicle to properly locate the vehicle's weight on moving parts and to facilitate steering. If these angles are not correct, the vehicle is misaligned. The effects of mis-

FIGURE 37–51 Front- and rear-steering systems. *Courtesy of Mazda*

alignment are given in Table 37–1. It is important to remember that alignment angles, when specified in the text, are those specific angles that should exist when the system is being measured under a given set of conditions. During regular performance, these angles change as the traveling surface and vehicle driving forces change.

Basic Wheel Alignment

Before making adjustments, conduct the following prealignment checks.

ROAD TEST Begin the alignment with a road test. While driving the car, check to see that the steering wheel is straight. Feel for vibration in the steering wheel as well as in the floor or seats. Notice any pulling or abnormal handling problems, such as hard steering, tire squeal while cornering, or mechanical pops or clunks. This helps find problems that must be corrected before proceeding with the alignment.

VISUAL INSPECTION This includes tire wear and mismatched tire sizes or types. Look for the results of collision damage and towing damage.

RIDE HEIGHT MEASUREMENT The car is designed to ride at a specific curb height. Curb height specifications and the specific measuring points are given in service manuals.

UNDER VEHICLE CHECKS With the vehicle raised, inspect all steering components, such as control arm bushings, upper strut mounts, pitman arm, idler arm, center link, tie-rod ends, ball joints, and shock absorbers. Check the CV joints (if equipped) for looseness, popping sounds, binding, and broken boots. Damaged components must be repaired before adjusting alignment angles.

Angle Alignment

The proper alignment of a suspension/steering system centers around the accuracy of the following angles.

TABLE 37–1 EFFECTS OF INCORRECT ALIGNMENT	
Problem	**Effect**
Incorrect camber setting	Tire wear Ball joint/wheel bearing wear Pull to side of most positive/least negative camber
Too much positive caster	Hard steering Excessive road shock Wheel shimmy
Too much negative caster	Wander Weave Instability at high speeds

Unequal caster	Pull to side most
	  negative/least positive
	  caster

Incorrect SAI	Instability Poor return Pull to side of lesser inclination Hard steering
Incorrect toe setting	Tire wear
Incorrect turning radius	Tire wear Squeal in turns

CASTER Caster is the angle of the steering axis of a wheel from the vertical, as viewed from the side of the vehicle. The forward or rearward tilt from the vertical line (Figure 37–52) illustrates caster. Caster is the first angle adjusted during an alignment. Tilting the wheel forward is negative caster. Tilting backward is positive caster.

Caster is designed to provide steering stability. The caster angle for each wheel on an axle should be equal. Unequal caster angles cause the vehicle to steer toward the side with less caster. Too much negative caster can cause the vehicle to have sensitive steering at high speeds. The vehicle might wander as a result of negative caster.

Caster is affected by worn or loose strut rod and control arm bushings. Caster adjustments are not possible on some strut suspension systems. Where they are provided, they can be made at the top or bottom mount of the strut assembly.

CAMBER Camber is the angle represented by the tilt of either the front or rear wheels inward or outward from the vertical as viewed from the front of the car (Figure 37–53). Camber is designed into the vehicle to compensate for road crown, passenger weight, and vehicle weight. Camber is usually set equally for each wheel. Equal camber means each wheel is tilted outward or inward the same amount. Unequal camber causes tire wear and causes the vehicle to steer toward the side that is more positive.

Camber angle changes, through the travel of the suspension system are controlled by pivots. Camber is affected by worn or loose ball joints, control arm bushings, and wheel bearings. Anything that changes chassis height also affects camber. Camber is adjustable on most vehicles. Some manufacturers prefer to include a camber adjustment at the spindle assembly. Camber adjustments are also provided on some strut suspensions systems at the top mounting of the strut. Very little adjustment of camber (or caster) is required on strut suspensions if the tower and lower control arm positions are in their proper place. If serious camber error has occurred and the suspension mounting positions have not been damaged, it is an indication of bent suspension parts. In this case, diagnostic angle and dimensional checks should be made on the suspension parts. Damaged parts should be replaced.

TOE Toe is the distance comparison between the leading edge and trailing edge of the front tires. If the leading edge distance is less, then there is toe-in. If it is greater, there is toe-out (Figure 37–54). Actually, toe is critical as a tire-wearing angle. Wheels that do

FIGURE 37–52 Three types of caster: (A) zero, (B) positive, and (C) negative.

FIGURE 37–53 (A) Positive and (B) negative camber.

FIGURE 37–54 Typical rear toe condition.

not track straight ahead have to drag as they travel forward. Excessive toe measurements (in or out) cause a sawtooth edge on the tread surface from dragging the tire sideways.

Toe adjustments are made at the tie-rod. They must be made evenly on both sides of the car. If the toe settings are not equal, the car may tend to pull due to the steering wheel being off-center. This pull condition is especially common with power-assisted rack and pinion gears. It can be corrected by making the toe adjustments equal on both sides of the car. Toe is the last adjustment made in an alignment.

THRUST LINE ALIGNMENT A main consideration in any alignment is to make sure the vehicle runs straight down the road, with the rear tires tracking directly behind the front tires when the steering wheel is in the straight-ahead position. The geometric centerline of the vehicle should parallel the road direction. This is the case when rear toe is parallel to the vehicle's geometric centerline in the straight-ahead position. If rear toe does not parallel the vehicle centerline, a thrust direction to the left or right is created (Figure 37–55). This difference of rear toe from the geometric centerline is called the **thrust angle**. The vehicle tends to travel in the direction of the thrust line, rather than straight ahead.

To correct this problem, begin by setting individual rear wheel toe equally in reference to the geometric centerline. Four-wheel-alignment machines check individual toe on each wheel. Once the rear wheels

are in alignment with the geometric centerline, set the individual front toe in reference to the thrust angle. Following this procedure ensures that the steering wheel is straight ahead for straight-ahead travel. If you set the front toe to the vehicle geometric centerline, ignoring the rear toe angle, a cocked steering wheel results.

STEERING AXLE INCLINATION (SAI) This angle locates the vehicle weight to the inside or outside of the vertical centerline of the tire. The **SAI** is the angle between true vertical and a line drawn between the steering pivots as viewed from the front of the vehicle (Figure 37–56). It is an engineering angle designed to project the weight of the vehicle to the road surface for stability. The SAI helps the vehicle's steering system return to straight ahead after a turn.

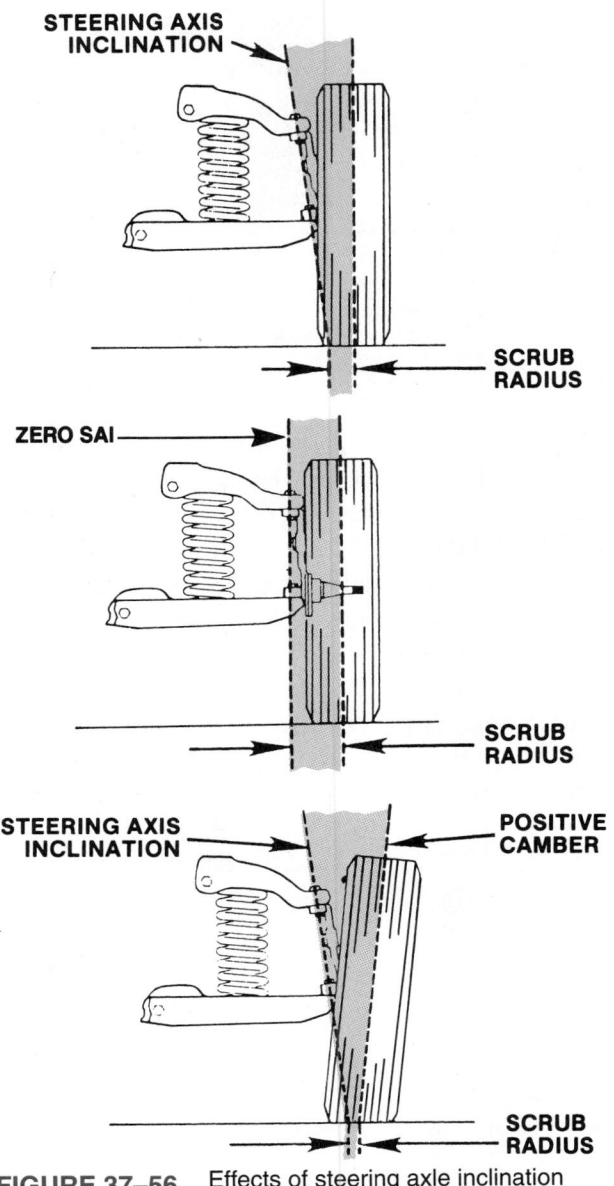

FIGURE 37–56 Effects of steering axle inclination changes.

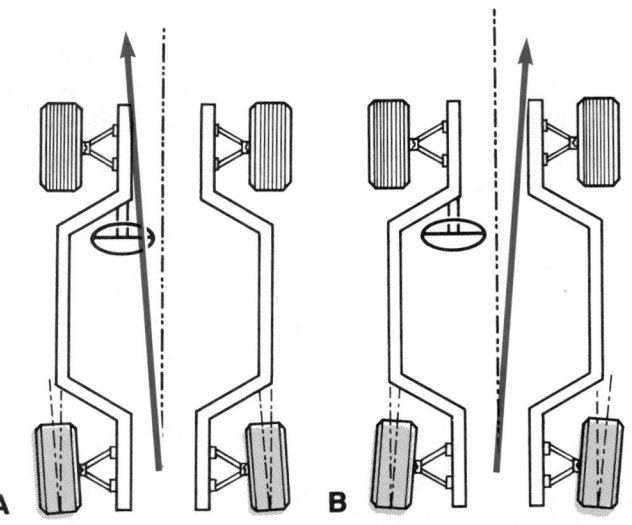

FIGURE 37–55 (A) Left and (B) right thrust direction.

If the vehicle has 0 (zero) SAI, the upper and lower ball joints (or strut pivot points) would be located directly over one another. Problems associated with this simple relationship include tire scrub in turns, lack of control, and increased effort during turn recovery. If the SAI is tilted, a triangle is formed between ball joints and spindle. An arc is then formed when turning. There is a high point at straight-ahead position and a drop downward turning to each side. This motion travels through the control arms to the springs and finally to the weight of the vehicle. The forces generated in a turn are actually trying to lift the vehicle. The tilting and loading effect of SAI offsets the lifting forces and helps to pull the tires back to straight ahead when the turn is finished.

Front-wheel drive vehicles with strut suspensions typically have a higher SAI angle (12 to 18 degrees) than a short-long arm rear-wheel-drive suspension (6 to 8 degrees). This is because the extra leverage provided by a larger angle helps directional stability.

If the SAI angles are unequal side-to-side, torque steer, brake pull, and pump steer (jerking from side to side) can occur even if static camber angles are within specifications.

Checking the SAI angle can help locate various problems that affect wheel alignment. For example, an SAI angle that varies from side to side may indicate an out-of-position upper strut tower, a bowed lower control arm, or a shifted center cross member.

On a short-long arm suspension, SAI is the angle between true vertical and a line drawn from the upper ball joint through the lower ball joint. In a strut equipped vehicle this line is drawn through the center of the strut's upper mount down through the center of the lower ball joint.

When the camber angle is added to the SAI angle, the sum of the two is called the included angle. Comparing SAI included, and camber angles can also help identify damaged or worn components. For example, if the SAI reading is correct, but the camber and included angles are less than specifications, the steering knuckle or strut tower may be bent. Table 37–2 summarizes the various angle combinations used to troubleshoot short-long arm, strut, and twin I-beam suspension system alignment problems.

TURNING RADIUS Turning radius or cornering angle is the amount of toe-out present in turns (Figure 37–57). As a car goes around a corner, the inside tire must travel in a smaller radius circle than the outside tire. This is accomplished by designing the steering geometry to turn the inside wheel sharper than the outside wheel. The result can be seen as toe-out in turns. This eliminates tire scrubbing on the road surface by keeping the tires pointed in the direction they have to move.

When a car has a steering problem, the first diagnostic check should be a visual inspection of the

TABLE 37–2 SAI DIAGNOSTIC REFERENCE CHART				
Suspension Systems	**SAI**	**Camber**	**Included Angle**	**Probable Cause**
Short Arm/	Correct	Less	Less	Bent knuckle
Long Arm	Less	Greater	Correct	Bent lower control arm
Suspension	Greater	Less	Correct	Bent upper control arm
System	Less	Greater	Greater	Bent knuckle
MacPherson	Correct	Less	Less	Bent knuckle and/or bent strut
Strut	Correct	Greater	Greater	Bent knuckle and/or bent strut
Suspension	Less	Greater	Correct	Bent control arm or strut tower (out at top)
	Greater	Less	Correct	Strut tower (in at top)
	Greater	Greater	Greater	Strut tower (in at top) and spindle and/or bent strut
	Less	Greater	Greater	Bent control arm or strut tower (out at top) plus bent knuckle and/or bent strut
	Less	Less	Less	Strut tower (out at top) and knuckle and/or strut bent or bent control arm
Twin I	Correct	Greater	Greater	Bent knuckle
Beam	Greater	Less	Correct	Bent I beam
Suspension	Less	Greater	Correct	Bent I beam
	Less	Greater	Greater	Bent knuckle

FIGURE 37–57 Turning radius is affected by toe-out in turns.

entire vehicle for anything obvious: bent wheels, misalignment of the cradle, and so on. If there is nothing obviously wrong with the car, make a series of diagnostic checks without disassembling the vehicle. One of the most useful checks that can be made with a minimum of equipment is a jounce-rebound check.

This jounce-rebound check determines if there is misalignment in the rack and pinion gear. For a quick check, unlock the steering wheel and see if it moves during the jounce or rebound. For a more careful check, use a pointer and a piece of chalk. Use the chalk to make a reference mark on the tire tread and place the pointer on the same line as the chalk mark. Jounce and rebound the suspension system a few times while someone watches the chalk mark and the pointer. If the mark on the wheel moves unequally in and out on both sides of the car, chances are there is a steering arm or gear out of alignment. If the mark does not move or moves equally in and out on both sides of the car, the steering arm and gear are probably all right. Each wheel or side should be checked.

TRACKING All vehicles are built around a geometric centerline that runs through the center of the chassis from the back to the front. The **thrust line** is the direction the rear axle would travel if unaffected by the front wheels. This condition is also called tracking. An ideal alignment has all four wheels parallel with the centerline, making the thrust line parallel with the centerline. However, the rear-wheel thrust line of a vehicle might not always be parallel to the actual centerline of the vehicle, so the angle of the thrust line must be checked first.

Rear-wheel-drive vehicles rarely need thrust line adjustment unless they have been in an accident or experienced severe usage. Independent rear suspension can have offset thrust angles from unequal rear toe adjustments. An offset thrust angle affects handling by pulling in the direction away from the thrust line and can cause tire wear similar in pattern to that of incorrect toe settings. As a general rule, minor variations between the thrust line and centerline are not noticeable and do not cause handling problems as long as the front wheels are aligned parallel with the thrust line.

Correct **tracking** refers to a situation with all suspension and wheels in their correct location and condition and aligned so that the rear wheels follow directly behind the front wheels while moving in a straight line (Figure 37–58). For this to occur, all wheels must be parallel with one another and axle and spindle lines must be at 90-degree angles to the vehicle centerline. Simply stated, all four wheels should form a perfect rectangle.

LOAD DISTRIBUTION Load distribution refers to the load placed on each wheel. Every vehicle is engineered to operate at a designed curb height (also called **trim height**). At this height, each wheel must carry the correct amount of weight. Excessive loading to either the front, gear, or one side of the vehicle changes the curb height, upsetting vehicle balance and steering geometry.

In correct alignment, sagging springs and bent suspension parts can also change this condition,

FIGURE 37–58 When a car is tracking correctly, its rear wheels are the same distance from the front wheels on both sides.

upsetting geometry and placing excessive load on only one or two wheels.

All of these elements—springs, shocks, suspension, and geometry—are engineered to work together as a balanced team to provide good riding and handling. Quite naturally, if one wheel is running under a different condition of weight load and steering geometry, the vehicle does not ride and handle as it is capable.

ALIGNMENT PROCEDURES

The equipment used to check wheel alignment can vary from a simple alignment gauge to computerized four-wheel alignment systems. A typical alignment device of computerized systems gives information on a CRT screen to guide the technician step-by-step through the alignment process.

The technician selects the make of the car that is to be worked on. Then the same procedure is performed to select the specific year and model. The electronic wheel runout compensation takes just a few seconds per wheel. When compensation is complete, alignment measurements are instantly displayed.

The CRT readings are often in color. Specification memory matches OE data including asymmetric tolerances, different left- and right-side specifications, and cross specifications (difference allowed between left and right side). Graphics and text on the screen show the technician where and how to make adjustments.

As the adjustments are made on the vehicle, the technician can observe the center block slide toward the target. When the block aligns with the target, the adjustment is within half the specified tolerance.

The computerized system for alignment, such as the one here, can perform other services. For example, it can provide an undercar checklist for the technician to use as prealignment inspection. The technician can check or bypass any item. In addition, a printout of the inspection data can be given to the car owner as proof of the status of the vehicle.

Another popular wheel alignment system uses a combination scale as a target for a laser beam. Errors in wheel angle are shown immediately on the scale and given measurements are easily read. Measurements can be made continually while errors are being corrected. This scale/laser system makes measuring of the rear-wheel camber and toe-in as simple and exact as for the front wheels.

The technician is cautioned to follow the instructions provided by the manufacturer of the particular brand of wheel alignment equipment that is to be used. Test readings obtained from the equipment are to be compared with the vehicle manufacturer's specifications. If adjustments are necessary and can be

made, proceed. Use only authorized replacement parts if a replacement should be necessary.

All wheel alignment angles are interrelated. Regardless of the make of a car or the type of suspension, the same adjustment order—caster, camber, toe—should be followed, as far as the car permits such adjustments to be made. Many MacPherson suspensions do not provide for caster or camber adjustments. Additionally, adjustment methods vary from model to model and, occasionally, even in different model years.

Caster/Camber Adjustment

Although caster and camber are vital alignment angles, only conventional suspensions generally allow for their adjustment. Caster, or both caster and camber, might be preset on many MacPherson suspensions by the manufacturer and can be adjusted only by replacing either the strut assembly or control arm.

Conventional Suspension Adjustments Several methods are used on conventional suspensions to adjust caster and camber (Figure 37–59).

SHIMS Many cars use shims for adjusting caster and camber. The shims can be located between the control arm pivot shaft and the inside of the frame. Both caster and camber can be adjusted in one operation requiring the loosening of the shim bolts just once. Caster is changed by adding or subtracting shims from one end of the pivot shaft only. Then, camber is adjusted by adding or subtracting an equal amount of shims from the front and rear bolts. This procedure allows camber to change without affecting the caster setting.

Some cars use shims located between the control arm pivot shaft and the outside of the frame. The adjustment procedure is the same as just described. Always look at the shim arrangements to determine the desired direction of change before loosening the bolts.

ECCENTRICS AND SHIMS Eccentrics and shims are used on some vehicles to adjust caster and camber. In some designs, an eccentric bolt and cam on the upper control arm adjust both caster and camber. To adjust, the nuts on the upper control arm are loosened first. Then, one eccentric bolt at a time is turned to set caster. Both bolts are turned equally to set camber.

The **eccentric bolt and cam** assembly (Figure 37–60) is located on the inner upper control arm. Unlike other designs, camber is adjusted first. The front lower arm pivot nut is loosened, and the cam is rotated to the proper camber setting. Caster is set by applying the same procedure to the rear cam.

CASTER AND CAMBER
(ECCENTRIC BUSHING)

CAMBER
(CAMS)

CASTER
STRUT

CASTER AND
CAMBER (SHIMS)

CASTER AND
CAMBER (SHIMS)

CAMBER (SHIMS)

CASTER STRUT

CASTER AND CAMBER
(ELONGATED HOLES)

CASTER AND
CAMBER (SHIMS)

CASTER AND CAMBER
(ECCENTRIC WASHER)

CAMBER (SHIMS)

CASTER STRUT

CAMBER (BALL JOINT ECCENTRIC)
(OR SLOTS FOR BALL JOINT)

CASTER
STRUT

CASTER
STRUT

CAMBER (ECCENTRIC
WASHER)

CASTER (ECCENTRIC WASHER)

CAMBER (ECCENTRIC WASHER)

FIGURE 37–59 Different suspension designs showing various locations for adjusting caster and camber. *Courtesy of Snap-on Tools Corporation*

Figure 37–61 shows another type of eccentric bolt and cam that is located on the lower control arm. With this type of suspension, camber is corrected before caster.

Some car models have a camber eccentric in the steering knuckle of the upper support arm. A locknut is loosened, and the camber eccentric is rotated to set camber. Caster is set with an adjustable strut rod.

SLOTTED FRAME The slotted frame adjustment has slotted holes under the control arm inner shaft that allow the shaft to be repositioned to the correct caster and camber settings. Caster and camber adjusting tools help in making adjustments. One end of the shaft is moved for caster adjustment. Both ends of the shaft are moved for camber adjustment. Turning a nut on one end of the rod changes its length and adjusts caster. Camber is set by an eccentric at the inner end of the lower control arm, or by a camber eccentric in the steering knuckle of the upper support arm, as described earlier.

FIGURE 37–60 Eccentric bolt and cam (upper control arm).

ECCENTRIC
CAM

FIGURE 37–61 Another type of eccentric bolt and cam on a lower control arm.

ROTATING BALL JOINT AND WASHERS In this design, camber is increased by disconnecting the upper ball joint, rotating it 180 degrees, and reconnecting. This positions the flat of the ball joint flange inboard and increases camber approximately 1 degree. Caster angle is changed with a kit containing two washers, one 0.12 inch thick and one 0.36 inch thick. The washers are placed at opposite ends of the locating tube between the legs of the upper control arm. Placement of the large washer at the rear leg of the control arm increases caster by 1 degree. Placement of the large washer at the front leg of the control arm decreases caster by 1 degree.

MacPherson Suspension Adjustments

Caster/camber adjustments are made only on certain models with MacPherson suspensions. There are two general OEM procedures for doing this, although aftermarket kit adapters are available for some models. Service information must be consulted for an accurate listing of models on which adjustments can be made.

In one version, a cam bolt at the base of the strut assembly is used to adjust camber (Figure 37–62). On different models, this bolt can be either the upper or the lower of the two bolts connecting the strut assembly to the steering knuckle. Both bolts must be loosened to make the adjustment, and the wheel assembly must be centered. Turn the cam bolt to reach the correct alignment, then retighten the bolts to the appropriate torque specifications. There is no caster adjustment on this version.

In the other form of kit adapter, both caster and camber are adjustable at the strut upper mount. Slots in the mounting plate permit the strut assembly to be shifted to reach the alignment specifications. To adjust caster, loosen the three locknuts on the mounting studs and relocate the plate. Do not remove the nuts (Figure 37–63). Loosen the center locknut and slide it toward or away from the engine as needed to adjust camber correctly.

While caster cannot be adjusted on many MacPherson strut front suspensions, camber can be adjusted. Although it is locked in place with a pop rivet, it can be adjusted by removing the rivet from the camber plate and loosening the three nuts that hold the plate to the body apron (Figure 37–64). Camber is changed by moving the top of the shock strut to the position where the desired camber setting is achieved. The nuts are then tightened to specifications. (It is not necessary to install a new pop rivet.)

SLIDE THE UPPER PLATE TOWARD THE FRONT OR REAR OF THE CAR UNTIL THE DESIRED CASTER READING IS OBTAINED.

SLIDE THE LARGE LOCKNUT TOWARD OR AWAY FROM THE ENGINE UNTIL THE DESIRED CAMBER READING IS OBTAINED.

FIGURE 37–62 Some MacPherson suspensions use cam bolts at the connection to the steering knuckle for camber adjustments.

FIGURE 37–63 Caster and camber adjustment of locknuts.

FENDER APRON

STRUT

SPINDLE

FIGURE 37–64 Camber adjustment—spring on single control arm with modified MacPherson strut.

FIGURE 37–65 Steering wheel holder is handy when making wheel adjustments. *Courtesy of Ammco Tools*

Most suspension inspection and adjustment work is best performed on a rack. Some camber checks, however, can be made to diagnose the condition of a strut and can be measured easily with a magnetic caster/camber gauge. Photo Sequence 25 shows a typical procedure for measuring front wheel camber and caster.

Toe Adjustment

Toe is the last alignment angle to be set. The same procedure is followed on all vehicles, except those with bonded ball stud sockets. Photo Sequence 26 shows the procedure for checking toe using optical toe gauges.

To adjust toe, start by being sure the steering wheel is centered when the front wheels point straight ahead (Figure 37–65). Then loosen the retaining bolts on the tie-rod adjusting sleeves. Turn the sleeves to move the tie-rod ends as shown in Figure 37–66.

An ideal toe condition is with both wheels exactly straight ahead, which would minimize tire wear. This, however, is not possible because of the many factors affecting alignment. As a result of these numerous conditions dealing with both tire wear and handling, all suspensions are designed with a slight toe-in or toe-out.

Any misalignment of the steering linkage pivot point or control arm pivot point (such as the center link or rack and pinion out of place) causes the condition known as **toe-change**. Toe-change involves turning the wheels from their straight-ahead position as the suspension moves up and down.

The change might be only one wheel, both wheels in the same direction, or both wheels in the opposite direction. Regardless of the condition, any change of one or more wheels is a toe-change condition. The results are tire wear and a hard-to-handle vehicle. The poor handling effects can be to the point that the vehicle is dangerous to drive.

Toe change is not a specification, it is a condition where the toe setting constantly varies. It must be determined by equipment or a method that measures

TURN DOWNWARD TO DECREASE ROD LENGTH. TURN UPWARD TO INCREASE ROD LENGTH.

TURN DOWNWARD TO INCREASE ROD LENGTH. TURN UPWARD TO DECREASE ROD LENGTH.

LEFTHAND SLEEVE

RIGHTHAND SLEEVE

FIGURE 37–66 Adjusting toe.

TYPICAL PROCEDURE FOR MEASURING FRONT WHEEL CAMBER AND CASTER

P25–1 Position the vehicle on the alignment rack with the front tires located properly on the turn tables, and remove the turn table locking pins.

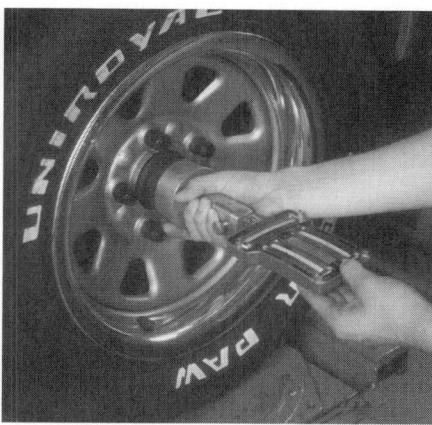

P25–2 Attach the magnetic gauges to the front wheel hubs.

P25–3 Jounce the front bumper several times to stabilize suspension.

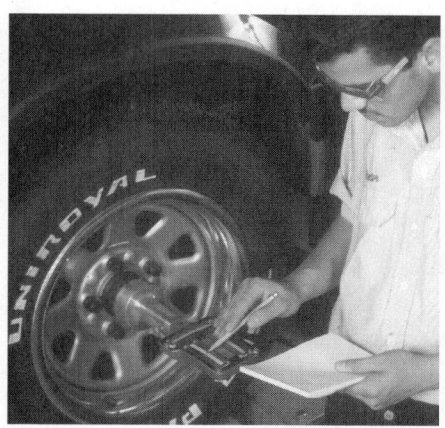

P25–4 Read the camber on each front wheel.

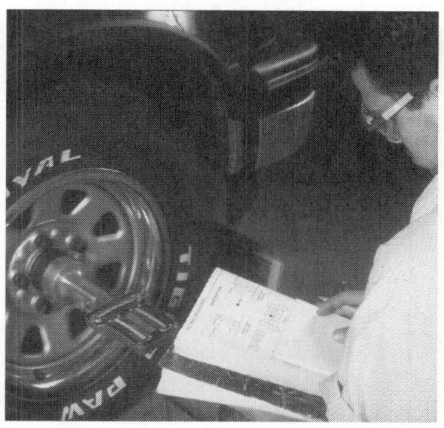

P25–5 Compare the camber reading to specifications.

P25–6 Install a brake pedal jack between the brake pedal and the front seat.

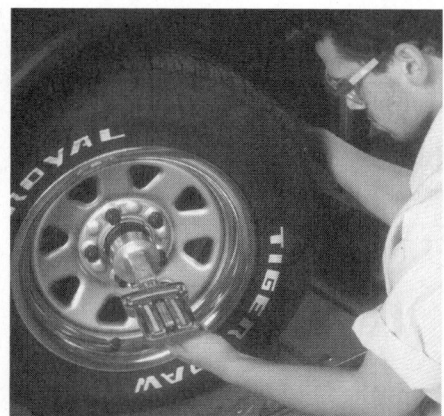

P25–7 Turn the wheel outwardly to 20 degrees on the turn table, then adjust the caster vial to zero.

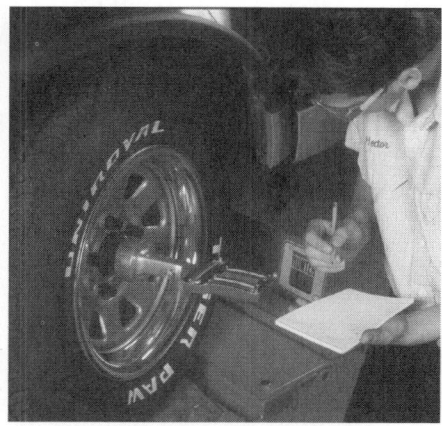

P25–8 Turn the wheel inward to 20 degrees on the turn table, then record the caster reading.

P25–9 Measure the caster on the opposite front wheel using the same procedure and compare the caster readings to specifications.

PHOTO SEQUENCE 26

TYPICAL PROCEDURE FOR MEASURING FRONT WHEEL TOE

P26–1 Position the vehicle on the alignment rack with the front tires located properly on the turn tables, and remove the turn table locking pins. Make sure the wheels are straight ahead and the turn tables are in the zero position.

P26–2 Install a steering wheel clamp. If the car has power steering, run the engine when the clamp is installed.

P26–3 Install a brake pedal jack between the brake pedal and the front seat. If the car has power brakes, run the engine while installing the jack.

P26–4 Remove the wheel covers and grease caps. Be sure the outer hub surfaces are free from grease, dirt, and metal burrs.

P26–5 Jounce the front suspension several times to allow it to stabilize.

P26–6 If the steering linkage is at the rear of the front wheels, push outward simultaneously on the rear of the front tires. When the steering linkage is at the front of the front wheels, perform this action at the front edge of the front tires.

P26–7 Mount the optical toe gauges on the front wheel hubs.

P26–8 Use the level indicators on the gauges to be sure the gauges are level.

P26–9 Read the front wheel toe on the toe gauges and compare the reading to specifications.

individual wheel toe at all suspension heights. There must be a change in suspension heights for any changes to occur.

Lightweight front-wheel-drive vehicles can be affected greatly by toe change. With these vehicles, the front wheels are no longer being pushed. They actually pull the vehicle forward and as a result, if the wheels are not maintaining a straight-ahead position, they affect directional control. Adverse road conditions, such as wet or icy conditions, can also increase the handling effects created by toe-change in the front-wheel-drive car.

REAR ALIGNMENT

A car with a perfect front alignment can still experience poor handling and premature tire wear—particularly on front-wheel-drive cars and cars with independent rear suspensions—if the rear suspension is misaligned. Approximately 80 percent of today's vehicles not only have front-end alignment specifications but also require rear-wheel alignment.

REAR CAMBER Like front camber, rear camber affects both tire wear and handling. The ideal situation is to have zero running camber on all four wheels to keep the tread in full contact with the road for optimum traction and handling.

Camber is not a static angle. It changes as the suspension moves up and down. Camber also changes as the vehicle is loaded and the suspension sags under the weight.

To compensate for loading, most vehicles with independent rear suspension often call for a slight amount of positive camber. A collapsed or mislocated strut tower, bent strut, collapsed upper control arm bushing, bent upper control arm, sagging spring, or an overloaded suspension can allow the rear wheels to assume a negative camber attitude. A bent spindle, strut or bowed lower control arm can cause too much positive camber. Even rigid rear-axle housings in rear-wheel-drive vehicles can become bowed by excessive torque, severe overloading, or road damage.

⚠ *WARNING!*

Never jack up or lift a FWD vehicle on its rear axle. The weight of the vehicle may cause the axle to bend and result in misalignment of the rear wheels. Always lift the vehicle at the recommended lifting points. ∎

Besides wearing the tires unevenly across the tread, uneven side-to-side camber (as when one

wheel leans in and the other does not) creates a steering pull just like it does when the camber readings on the front wheels do not match. It is like leaning on a bicycle. A vehicle always pulls toward a wheel with the most positive camber. If the mismatch is at the rear wheels, the rear axle pulls toward the side with the greatest amount of positive camber. If the rear axle pulls to the right, the front of the car drifts to the left. The result is a steering pull even though the front wheels may be perfectly aligned.

REAR TOE Rear toe, like front toe, is a critical tire rear angle. If toed-in or toed-out, the rear tires scuff just like the front ones. Either condition can also contribute to steering instability as well as reduced braking effectiveness. (Keep this in mind with antilock brake systems.)

Like camber, rear toe is not a static alignment angle. It changes as the suspension goes through jounce and rebound. It also changes in response to rolling resistance and the application of engine torque. With FWD vehicles, the front wheels tend to toe-in under power while the rear wheels toe-out in response to rolling resistance and suspension compliance. With RWD vehicles, the opposite happens: the front wheels toe-out while the rear wheels on an independent suspension try to toe-in as they push the vehicle ahead.

If rear toe is not within specifications, it affects tire wear and steering stability just as much as front toe. A total toe reading that is within specifications does not necessarily mean the wheels are properly aligned, especially when it comes to rear toe measurements. If one rear wheel is toed-in while the other is toed-out by an equal amount, total toe would be within specifications. However, the vehicle would have a steering pull because the rear wheels would not be parallel to center.

Remember, the ideal situation is to have all four wheels at zero running toe when the car is traveling down the road. This is especially true with antilock brakes where improper toe can affect brake balance when braking on slick or wet surfaces, causing the antilock brakes to cycle on and off to prevent a skid. Without antilock brakes, this condition may upset traction enough to cause an uncontrollable skid.

Thrust Line

If both rear wheels are square to one another and the rest of the vehicle, the thrust line is perpendicular to the rear axle and coincides with the vehicle's centerline. But if one or both rear wheels are toed in or out, or one is **setback** slightly with respect to the other, the thrust line is thrown off-center. This creates a thrust angle that causes a steering pull in the opposite direction. For example, a thrust line that is off-center to the right makes the car pull left.

The presence of a thrust angle can cause poor directional stability on ice, snow, or wet pavement. It can sometimes make a vehicle pull during braking or hard acceleration. It can also increase tire wear as the front wheels fight the rear ones for steering control.

The only way to eliminate the problem is to eliminate the thrust angle. The thrust line can be recentered by realigning rear toe. On most FWD applications, that can be easily done by using the factory-provided toe adjustments, by placing toe/camber shims between the rear spindles and axle (Figure 37–67), or by using eccentric bushing kits. With rear-wheel-drive vehicles that have a solid rear axle, changing rear toe is not as easy. Sometimes the floorpan or frame rails are misaligned from the factory or from collision damage. Short of pulling the chassis on a collision bench to restore the correct control arm or spring-mount geometry, the only other options are to try some type of offset trailing arm bushing with the coil springs, or to reposition the spring shackles or U-bolts with leaf springs.

If rear toe cannot be easily changed, the next best alternative is to align the front wheels to the rear axle thrust line rather than the vehicle centerline. Doing this puts the steering wheel back on center and eliminates the steering pull—but it does not eliminate dog tracking.

USING SERVICE MANUALS

Consult the appropriate service manual for details on these rear-end alignment procedures. Also, use good alignment procedures and a good alignment specifications book. Several aftermarket companies have complete and accurate specification books with front/rear-end specifications for domestic and imported cars, as well as light trucks. ■

FOUR-WHEEL-DRIVE VEHICLE ALIGNMENT

Most aftermarket parts manufacturers have camber adjustment shims available in various thicknesses and three diameters, 4 3/4 inches, 6 inches, and 6 5/8 inches (Figure 37–68). Never stack the shims. Only one shim per side should be used.

⚠ *WARNING!*

Do not use shims on vehicles on which brakes are mounted to the steering knuckle flange. The brakes can be misaligned and brake performance and wear can be seriously affected. ■

With front-wheel-drive and full-time 4WD vehicles, the front wheels are also driving wheels. As the front wheels pull the vehicle, the wheels tend to toe-in when torque is applied. To offset this tendency, the front wheels usually need less static toe-in to produce zero running toe. In fact, the preferred toe alignment specifications in this instance can be zero to slightly toed-out (1/16-inch toe-out).

It is important to note that when the front wheels of a part-time 4WD system are freewheeling, they behave the same as the front wheels in a rear-wheel-drive vehicle. That is, they roll rather than pull. The wheels tend to toe-out, so the static toe setting would have to toe-in to achieve zero running toe when dri-

FIGURE 37–67 Aligning rear wheels by installing shims to eliminate an off-unit thrust angle condition. *Courtesy of Chrysler Corporation*

FIGURE 37–68 Typical camber shim used on 4WD vehicles.

ving in the two-wheel mode. The kind of tires being used can also make a difference in suspension compliance. Bias-ply tires give more than radial tires.

The tires suffer in proportion to toe misalignment. For a tire that is only 1/8-inch off (1/4 degree), the tire is scrubbed sideways 12 feet for every mile traveled. That may not sound like much, but 12 feet of sideway scrub every mile can cut a tire's life in half.

If rapid tire wear seems to be the problem, look for the telltale feathered wear pattern. If the wheels are running toe-in, the feathered wear pattern leaves sharp edges on the inside edges of the tread. If the wheels are running toe-out, the sharp edges are toward the outside of the tread. It is usually easier to feel the feathered wear pattern than to see it. To tell which way the wear pattern runs, rub your fingers sideways across the tread.

Worn tie-rod ends or an idler arm are the most common causes of the tire wear. A bent steering arm, which is not uncommon with off-road vehicles, causes wear. One of the most common mistakes that is made when aligning 4WD vehicles is that of aligning every vehicle to the same set of specifications. If the factory specifications do not work, chances are something is bent.

Toe alignment can also be caused by misalignment in the steering linkage. To hold the tires in the same toe position as the suspension travels through jounce and rebound, the tie-rods must be parallel to the control arms.

If the rods are not parallel to the control arms, unequal toe changes result, causing bump steer. If severe enough, a bump steer can cause a noticeable jerk or pull to one side every time the vehicle hits a bump.

Bump steer can be caused by a steering rack (rack and pinion steering) or a center link (parallelogram steering) that is not level. When one side is high and the other side is low, both wheels change toe in the same direction as the suspension travels through jounce and rebound.

The parallelism of the steering linkage on an alignment rack cannot be checked unless toe measurements are compared with the suspension raised 4 inches, then lowered 4 inches.

If the amount of toe-change is not equal side-to-side, the steering linkage is misaligned. Measure the distance from each end of the steering rack or center link to the ground to see if one end is higher than the other. If it is, the chassis is probably bent and has to be tweaked to restore proper steering linkage alignment.

To align a modified 4WD vehicle that has been raised and fitted with oversized tires on off-set rims, keep in mind that off-set rims tend to increase compli-

ance and exaggerate camber. The technician should still aim for zero running toe and a static camber setting of zero to plus 1/4 degree.

Four-Wheel Alignment

The primary objective of **four-wheel** (or **total wheel alignment**, as it is frequently called), whether front or rear drive, solid axle, or independent rear suspension, is to align all four wheels so the vehicle drives and tracks straight with the steering wheel centered. To accomplish this, the wheels must be parallel to one another and perpendicular to a common centerline.

Total toe for all four wheels must be determined and rear toe adjusted where possible to bring the rear axle or wheels into square with the chassis. The front toe setting can then be adjusted to compensate for any rear alignment deviation that might persist.

Four-wheel alignment also includes checking and adjusting rear-wheel camber as well as toe, and doing all the traditional checks of front camber, toe, caster, toe-out on turns and steering axis inclination. The most important thing a four-wheel alignment job tells the technician is whether or not the rear axle or rear wheels are square with respect to the front wheels and chassis.

With two-wheel alignment equipment that aligns the front wheels to the geometric centerline, the assumption is made that the rear wheels are square with respect to the centerline. If that is true, the alignment job produces satisfactory results. If not, steering and tracking might be a problem.

Rear-wheel alignment can be checked on a two-wheel machine by simply backing the vehicle onto the rack. The rear wheels can also be checked for square by measuring the wheelbase on both sides with a track bar to make sure it is equal. The obvious drawback to this approach is that four-wheel alignment involves several extra steps. There is also the question of aligning the wheels to the centerline or thrust line.

The best approach in terms of both accuracy and completeness for wheel alignment is to reference the front wheels to the rear wheels. With this approach, individual rear toe is measured so the thrust line can be determined and the front wheels adjusted to the centerline. It also eliminates the need to back the vehicle onto the alignment machine because heads are provided for the rear wheels.

Total four-wheel alignment is measuring rear toe (and camber) and correcting any misalignment to bring the thrust line into the same plane as the centerline. This produces a vehicle that drives and tracks straight with a centered steering wheel. It minimizes rolling resistance, tire wear, and wind resistance. It improves fuel economy and tire life. In short, it does

TYPICAL PROCEDURE FOR PERFORMING FOUR-WHEEL ALIGNMENT WITH A COMPUTER WHEEL ALIGNER

P27–1 Position the vehicle on the alignment rack.

P27–2 Be sure the front tires are positioned properly on the turn tables.

P27–3 Position the rear wheels on the slip plates.

P27–4 Attach the wheel units.

P27–5 Select the vehicle make and model year.

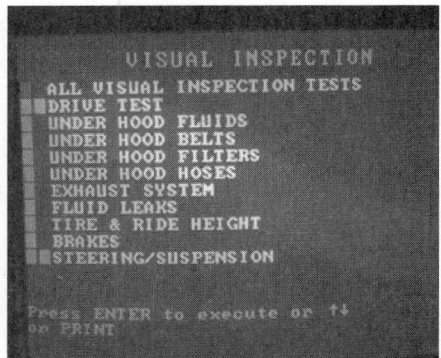

P27–6 Check the items on the screen during the preliminary inspection.

P27–7 Display the ride height screen.

P27–8 Check tire condition for each tire on the tire condition screen.

P27–9 Display wheel runout compensation screen.

P27–10 Display turning angle screen and perform turning angle check.

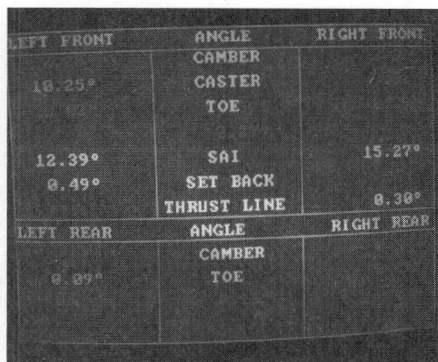

P27–11 Display front and rear wheel alignment angle screen.

P27–12 Display adjustment screen.

all the things a complete alignment job is supposed to do.

The actual procedure for total four-wheel alignment, as with two-wheel alignment, begins with a thorough inspection of the tires and suspension. Tires should be checked for unusual wear patterns that might indicate toe or camber misalignment, inflation pressure, or balance problems. Tires should be the same size and condition side to side, with matching tread patterns and should be inflated to the recommended specifications before any measurements are taken.

All steering and suspension components, front and rear, should be visually checked for wear or obvious damage. Check ball joints, tie-rods, idler arms, pitman arm, control arms and bushings, struts, shocks, springs, sway bars and brackets, rack and pinion steering bellows, and rack mountings. (Loose or deteriorated mountings can cause steering shimmy and wander.)

Check the steering gear for play. Do not forget to check the front and rear wheel bearings. Finally, check the ride height based on the normal vehicle load.

Once the alignment heads are installed and compensated for wheel runout, read front and rear camber, front and rear toe. The thrust angle created by the rear wheels can then be determined. A typical procedure for checking the alignment of all four wheels with a computerized alignment machine is shown in Photo Sequence 27.

Read caster by turning the front wheels side to side. Most alignment machines compensate for wheel setback. Some show how much setback is present and where.

Steering axis inclination, an angle frequently neglected on quick alignment jobs, is important to include because it can help pinpoint damaged parts.

If the SAI does not match specifications, compare both sides. Problems can be caused by bent struts, control arm spindles, or steering knuckles. A mislocated strut tower or control arm anchor can also throw off the reading.

Once the basic measurements have been taken, the suspension can be adjusted. Do so in this sequence: rear camber, rear toe, caster/camber one side front, caster/camber other side front, then front toe.

CASE STUDY

Two days after having a complete alignment performed on her late-model vehicle, a customer returns to the shop complaining of improper service. Since having the alignment work done, the vehicle now consistently pulls to the right.

The technician who performed the work road tests the vehicle and verifies that the car is drifting to the right. The technician rechecks the alignment against factory specifications. All settings appear to be within range. A check of the suspension system finds nothing wrong. Desperately trying to figure out why the vehicle is drifting, the technician reviews some notes she kept from an alignment class attended several months before. Here, she finds the answer. When setting the right wheel, she forgot to allow for road crown. The technician readjusts the right wheel to account for road crown angle and test drives the vehicle. The drifting has been eliminated.

KEY TERMS

4WS	Rack and pinion
Bump steer	Rack
Camber	SAI
Caster	Setback
Center link	Steering linkage
Drag link	Thrust angle
Dry park	Thrust line
Eccentric bolt and cam	Tie-rod
External-piston linkage	Toe
Four-wheel alignment	Toe-change
Idler arm	Total wheel alignment
Integral-piston	Tracking
Nonwear arm	Trim height
Parallelogram	Wear arm
Pitman arm	Worm and roller
Recirculating ball	Yoke lash

SUMMARY

- The components of a manual steering system include the steering linkage, steering gear, and the steering column and wheel.
- The term steering linkage is applied to the system of pivots and connecting parts that is placed between the steering gear and the steering arms attached to the front wheels, controlling the direction of vehicle travel. The steering linkage transfers the motion of the steering gear output shaft to the steering arms, turning the wheels to maneuver the vehicle.
- Basic components of a parallelogram steering linkage system include the pitman arm, idler arm, links, tie-rods, and in some designs, a steering damper.
- The worm and roller steering components are basically the same found in the parallelogram system.
- In rack and pinion steering linkage, steering input is received from a pinion gear attached to the steering column. This gear moves a toothed rack that is attached to the tie-rods that move the wheels.
- There are three types of manual steering gears in use today: recirculating ball, worm and roller, and rack and pinion.
- The steering wheel and column produce the necessary force to turn the steering gear.
- The power-steering unit is designed to reduce the amount of effort required to turn the steering wheel. It also reduces driver fatigue on long drives and makes it easier to steer the vehicle at slow road speeds, particularly during parking.
- There are several power-steering systems in use on passenger cars and light-duty trucks. The most

common ones are the integral, linkage, hydroboost, and power-assisted rack and pinion systems.
- The major components of a conventional power-steering system are the steering linkage, power-steering pump, flow control and pressure relief valves, reservoir, spool valves and power pistons, hydraulic hose lines, and gearbox or assist assembly on the linkage.
- Electronic rack and pinion systems replace the hydraulic pump, hoses, and fluid associated with conventional power-steering systems with electronic controls and an electric motor located concentric to the rack itself.
- Four-wheel steering (4WS) advantages include cornering capability, steering response, straight-line stability, lane changing, and low-speed maneuverability.
- Currently there are three types of production 4WS systems: mechanical, hydraulic, and electro/hydraulic.
- Caster is the angle of the steering axis of a wheel from the vertical, as viewed from the side of the vehicle. Tilting the wheel forward is negative caster. Tilting backward is positive.
- Camber is the angle represented by the tilt of either the front or rear wheels inward or outward from the vertical as viewed from the front of the car.
- Toe is the distance comparison between the leading edge and trailing edge of the front tires. If the edge distance is less, then there is toe-in. If it is greater, there is toe-out.
- The difference of rear toe from the geometric centerline of the vehicle is called the thrust angle. The vehicle tends to travel in the direction of the thrust line, rather than straight ahead.
- Steering axis inclination (SAI) angles locate the vehicle weight to the inside or outside of the vertical centerline of the tire. The SAI is the angle between the true vertical and a line drawn between the steering pivots as viewed from the front of the vehicle.
- Turning radius or cornering angle is the amount of toe-out present on turns.
- In correct tracking all suspension and wheels are in their correct locations and conditions and are aligned so the rear wheels follow directly behind the front wheels while moving in a straight line.
- Load distribution refers to the load placed on each wheel.
- It is important to remember that approximately 80 percent of today's vehicles not only have front-end alignment but require rear-wheel alignment as well.

◆ The primary objective of four-wheel or total-wheel alignment, whether front or rear drive, solid axle, or independent rear suspension, is to align all four wheels so the vehicle drives and tracks straight with the steering wheel centered. To accomplish this, the wheels must be parallel to one another and perpendicular to a common centerline.

TECH MANUAL

The following procedures are included in Chapter 37 of the *Tech Manual* that accompanies this book:

1. Inspect power steering fluid.

2. Inspect, adjust, and/or replace power-steering belt.

3. Inspect steering components.

4. Measure vehicle ride height.

5. Measure and adjust toe, camber, and caster.

6. Perform a four-wheel alignment.

REVIEW QUESTIONS

1. Describe how a rack and pinion steering, parallelogram steering, and worm and roller system operate.

2. What checks should be made before undertaking a wheel alignment?

3. What is an integral power-steering system?

4. Define the term *gearbox ratio*.

5. What are the basic features of all four-wheel steering systems?

6. What is the primary purpose of power-steering hoses?
   a. to lubricate the pump
   b. to relieve pressure
   c. to transmit power through fluid under pressure
   d. none of the above

7. Technician A says electronically controlled power steering systems allow for power assistance even when an engine stalls. Technician B says an electronic rack and pinion system provides power assistance even when the engine stalls. Who is correct?
   a. Technician A
   b. Technician B
   c. Both A and B
   d. Neither A nor B

8. Technician A says the manual steering gear is the probable cause of a shimmy. Technician B says it could be loose steering linkage. Who is correct?
   a. Technician A
   b. Technician B
   c. Both A and B
   d. Neither A nor B

9. Technician A says adjusting the steering gear too tightly can cause hard steering. Technician B says adjusting the steering gear too tightly can cause poor returnability. Who is correct?
   a. Technician A
   b. Technician B
   c. Both A and B
   d. Neither A nor B

10. Technician A says a worn or damaged idler arm can cause front-end shimmy. Technician B says a worn or damaged idler arm can cause hard steering. Who is correct?
    a. Technician A
    b. Technician B
    c. Both A and B
    d. Neither A nor B

11. Worn tie-rod ends can result in ____.
    a. scalloped and scuffed tires
    b. vehicle pull to one side
    c. poor returnability
    d. all of the above

12. In a rack and pinion steering system, what protects the rack from contamination?
    a. the inner tie-rod socket
    b. the outer tie-rod socket
    c. grommets
    d. the bellows boot

13. A variable ratio can be normally found in ____.
    a. manual-steering units
    b. power-steering units
    c. both a and b
    d. neither a nor b

14. Hydro-boost provides power to the steering system and to what other system?
    a. braking
    b. electrical
    c. both a and b
    d. neither a nor b

15. All of the following angles are adjustable during wheel alignment except ____.

   a. toe-in
   b. toe-out
   c. camber
   d. steering axis inclination

16. An owner's concern indicates excessive turning effort. Technician A road tests the car to determine the actual force required to turn the wheel. Technician B uses a pull scale. Who is correct?

   a. Technician A
   b. Technician B
   c. Both A and B
   d. Neither A nor B

17. Which of the following is true of the steering linkage system?

   a. The power cylinder is integrated with the steering gear.
   b. The power cylinder has four hydraulic lines connected to it.
   c. The power cylinder is attached to the steering center link.
   d. All of the above.

18. What is another name for the circle mode of 4WS?

   a. parallel
   b. same-phase
   c. contra phase
   d. none of the above

19. Rack and pinion steering ____.

   a. is lighter in weight and has fewer components than parallelogram steering
   b. does not provide as much feel for the road as parallelogram steering
   c. does not use tie-rods in the same fashion as parallelogram steering
   d. all of the above

20. What connects the steering column to the wheels

   a. steering shaft
   b. steering linkage
   c. gearbox
   d. pitman arm

SECTION 8

BRAKES

As with the steering and suspension systems, a properly operating brake system is vital to the safe operation and control of any vehicle. A full understanding of hydraulic principles, brake lines and hoses, and disc and drum brake components is needed to perform accurate brake service.

Antilock braking systems (ABS) and traction-assist systems are rapidly gaining popularity. They will soon be standard equipment on most vehicles. ABS and traction assist add yet another electronically controlled system to the increasingly complex modern vehicle.

The information found in Section 8 corresponds to materials covered on the ASE certification test on brakes.

WE ENCOURAGE
PROFESSIONALISM

THROUGH TECHNICIAN
CERTIFICATION

BRAKE SYSTEMS 38

OBJECTIVES

◆ *Explain the basic principles of braking, including kinetic and static friction, friction materials, application pressure, and heat dissipation.* ◆ *Describe the components of a hydraulic brake system and their operation, including brake lines and hoses, master cylinders, system control valves, and safety switches.* ◆ *Perform both manual and pressure bleeding of the hydraulic system.* ◆ *Briefly describe the operation of drum and disc brakes.* ◆ *Inspect and service hydraulic system components.* ◆ *Describe the operation and components of both vacuum-assist and hydraulic-assist braking units.*

The brake system is designed to slow and halt the motion of a vehicle. To do that, various components within a hydraulic brake system must convert the momentum of the vehicle into heat. They do so by using friction.

FRICTION

Friction is the resistance to movement exerted by two objects in contact with each other. Two forms of friction play a part in controlling a vehicle (Figure 38–1): **kinetic**, or moving; and static, or stationary. The amount of friction, or resistance to movement, depends on the type of materials in contact, the smoothness of their rubbing surfaces, and the pressure holding them together (often gravity or weight).

For example, slide your hand lightly across a polished table top. Very little effort is required because of the smooth texture of the rubbing surfaces and the small amount of pressure exerted. Now, rub your hand over a piece of sandpaper. Feel the difference in friction? The rough texture of the sandpaper resists the movement of your hand.

Rub any surface long enough or hard enough and you begin to feel heat (Figure 38–2). Friction always converts moving, or kinetic, energy into heat. The greater the friction between two moving surfaces, the greater the amount of heat produced.

As the brakes on a moving automobile are actuated, rough-textured pads or shoes are pressed against rotating parts of the vehicle, either rotors (discs) or drums (Figure 38–3). The kinetic energy, or momentum, of the vehicle is then converted into heat energy by the kinetic friction of rubbing surfaces and the car or truck slows down.

When the vehicle comes to a stop, it is held in place by static friction. The friction between the surfaces of the brakes, as well as the friction between the tires and the road, resist any movement. To over-

FIGURE 38–1 Braking action creates kinetic friction in the brakes and static friction between the tire and road to slow the vehicle. When brakes are applied, the vehicle's weight is transferred to the front wheels and is unloaded on the rear wheels.

FIGURE 38–2 Friction produces heat.

FIGURE 38–3 Basic disc brake operation.

come the static friction that holds the car motionless, the brakes are released. The heat energy of combustion in the engine crankcase is converted into kinetic energy by the transmission and drivetrain, and the vehicle moves.

Static friction also plays an important part in controlling a moving vehicle. The rotating tires grip the road, and the static friction between these two surfaces enables the driver to control the speed and direction of the car. When the brakes are applied, the kinetic friction of the rubbing brake components slows the rotation of the tires. This increases the static friction between the tires and the road, decreasing the motion of the car. If the kinetic or sliding friction of the brake components overcomes the static friction between the tires and road, the wheels lock up and the car begins to skid. Static friction then exists between the components in the brakes and kinetic friction between the skidding tires and the road. The car is out of control. Obviously, the most effective braking effort is achieved just below the brake component kinetic friction levels that result in wheel lockup. This is the role antilock braking systems play in modern vehicles. By electronically pumping the brakes on and off many times each second, antilock systems keep kinetic friction below the static friction between the tires and road.

Factors Governing Braking

There are four basic factors that determine the braking power of a system. The first three factors govern the generation of friction: pressure, coefficient of friction, and frictional contact surface. The fourth factor is a result of friction. It is heat, or more precisely heat dissipation.

PRESSURE The amount of friction generated between moving surfaces contacting one another depends in part on the pressure exerted on the surfaces. For example, if you slowly increase the downward pressure on the palm of your hand as you move it

across a tabletop, you feel a gradual increase in friction.

In automobiles, hydraulic systems provide application pressure. Hydraulic force is used to move brake pads or brake shoes against spinning rotors or drums mounted to the wheels.

COEFFICIENT OF FRICTION The amount of friction between two surfaces is expressed as a coefficient of friction (**COF**). The coefficient of friction is determined by dividing the force required to pull an object across a surface by the weight of the object (Figure 38–4). For example, if it requires 100 pounds of pull to slide a 100-pound metal part across a concrete floor, the coefficient of friction is 100 ÷ 100 or 1. To pull a 100-pound block of ice across the same floor might require only 2 pounds of pull. The coefficient of friction then would be only 0.02. As it applies to automotive brakes, the COF expresses the frictional relationship between pads and rotors or shoes and drums and is carefully engineered to ensure optimum performance. Therefore, when replacing pads or shoes, it is important to use replacement parts with similar COF. If, for example, the COF is too high, the brakes are too sticky to stop the car smoothly. Premature wheel lockup or grabbing would result. If the coefficient is too low, the friction material tends to slide over the machined surface of the drum or rotor rather than slowing it down. Most automotive friction materials are thus engineered with a COF of between 0.25 and 0.55, depending on their intended application.

FRICTIONAL CONTACT SURFACE The third factor is the amount of surface, or area, that is in

FIGURE 38–4 Coefficient of friction is equal to the pounds of pull divided by the weight of the object.

contact. Simply put, bigger brakes stop a car more quickly than smaller brakes used on the same car. Similarly, brakes on all four wheels slow or stop a moving vehicle faster than brakes on only two wheels, assuming the vehicles are equal in size.

HEAT DISSIPATION Any braking system must be able to effectively handle the heat created by friction within the system. The tremendous heat created by the rubbing brake surfaces must be conducted away from the pad and rotor (or shoe and drum) and be absorbed by the air. The greater the surface areas of the brake components, the faster the heat can be dissipated. Thus, the weight and potential speed of the vehicle determine the size of the braking mechanism and the friction surface area of the pad or shoe. Brakes that do not effectively dissipate heat experience brake fade during hard, continuous braking. The linings of the pad and shoe become glazed, and the rotor and drum become hardened. Therefore, the coefficient of friction is reduced and excessive foot pressure must be applied to the brake pedal to produce the desired braking effect.

Brake Lining Friction Materials

For many decades, asbestos was the standard brake lining material. It offers good friction qualities, long wear, and low noise. New materials are being used because of the health hazards of breathing asbestos dust. In fact, the federal government has banned the use of asbestos in new vehicles and in aftermarket replacement parts.

FULLY METALLIC Fully **metallic** linings of sintered iron have been used for years in heavy-duty and racing applications because they have great fade resistance. However, they require very high pedal pressure and tend to quickly wear out drums and rotors.

SEMIMETALLIC Semimetallic lining materials were developed to eliminate the disadvantages of fully metallic linings. Semimetallic linings are made of iron fibers molded with an adhesive matrix. Semimetallic material offers excellent fade resistance that meets the needs of today's vehicles. It has good frictional characteristics so only a moderate amount of application pressure is needed. Finally, semimetallic pads and shoes do not cause excessive wear on rotor or drum surfaces.

NONASBESTOS Other **nonasbestos** lining materials made of synthetic substances are now available. The major brake lining manufacturers are constantly experimenting with new materials that meet all established criteria for long life, friction characteristics, drum and rotor wear, and heat dissipation.

FIGURE 38–5 Schematic of a basic automotive hydraulic brake system.

PRINCIPLES OF HYDRAULIC BRAKE SYSTEMS

A hydraulic system (Figure 38–5) uses a brake fluid to transfer pressure from the brake pedal to the pads or shoes. This transfer of pressure is reliable and consistent because liquids are not compressible. That is, pressure applied to a liquid in a closed system is transmitted by that liquid equally to every other part of that system. Apply a force of 5 pounds per square inch (psi) through the master cylinder and you can measure 5 psi anywhere in the lines and at each wheel where the brakes operate.

For example, move piston 1 a distance of 1 inch and piston 2 also moves 1 inch (Figure 38–6). The force can be increased at output (that is, at the wheel) by increasing the size of the wheel's piston, though piston travel decreases. The force at output can be decreased by decreasing the size of the wheel piston, but the piston travel increases.

Thus, to double the output force of the 5 psi at the master cylinder to 10 psi at the wheels, simply use a wheel cylinder piston with a surface area of 2 square inches (Figure 38–7). To triple the force of 100 psi, use a piston with 3 square inches and 300 pounds of output result (Figure 38–8). No matter what the fluid pressure is, the output force can be

FIGURE 38–6 Force and movement are transmitted equally.

FIGURE 38-7 Force increases—movement decreases.

FIGURE 38-9 Typical hydraulic brake layout.

FIGURE 38-10 Multiplied force in a master cylinder.

increased with a larger piston, though piston travel decreases proportionately. In actual practice, however, fluid movement in an automotive hydraulic brake system is very slight. In an emergency, when the pedal goes all the way to the floor, the volume of fluid displaced amounts to only about 20 cubic centimeters. About 15 cubic centimeters goes to the front discs and 5 cubic centimeters goes to the rear drums. Even under these conditions, the wheel cylinder and caliper pistons move only slightly.

Of course, the hydraulic system does not stop the car all by itself. In fact, it really just transmits the action of the driver's foot on the brake pedal out to the wheels (Figure 38-9). In the wheels, sets of friction pads are forced against rotors or drums to slow their turning and bring the car to a stop. Mechanical force (the driver stepping on the brake pedal) is changed into hydraulic pressure, which is changed back into mechanical force (brake shoes and disc pads contacting the drums and rotors). The amount of force acting on the friction pads and shoes is equivalent to the psi applied to the pedal multiplied by the area of the piston affected. A force of 25 psi applied to the pedal times 4 square inches of piston area equals 100 pounds of pressure in the system (Figure 38-10).

Single Braking System

With very few exceptions, the single circuit hydraulic system (Figure 38-11) was used on cars made through 1966. This system used a master cylinder with one piston that operated the brakes on all four wheels. Later, its use was confined to trucks and industrial and construction equipment.

Dual Braking Systems

Since 1967, federal law has required that all cars be equipped with two separate brake systems. If one circuit fails, the other provides enough braking power to safely stop the car.

The dual system differs from the single system by employing a tandem master cylinder, which is essentially two master cylinders formed by installing two separate pistons and fluid reservoirs into one cylinder bore. Each piston applies hydraulic pressure to two wheels.

FIGURE 38-8 Output force increases with piston size.

FIGURE 38-11 Single system braking.

Front/Rear Split System In early dual systems, the hydraulic circuits were separated front and rear (Figure 38–12). Both front wheels were on one hydraulic circuit and both rear wheels on another. If a failure occurred in one system, the other system was still available to stop the vehicle. However, the front brakes do approximately 70 percent of the braking work. A failure in the front brake system would only leave 20 to 40 percent braking power. This problem was somewhat reduced, with the development of diagonally split systems.

Diagonally Split System The **diagonally split** system operates on the same principles as the front and rear split system. It uses primary and secondary master cylinders that move simultaneously to exert hydraulic pressure on their respective systems.

The hydraulic brake lines on this system, however, have been diagonally split front to rear (left front to right rear and right front to left rear) (Figure 38–13). The circuit split can occur within the master cylinder or externally at a proportioning valve or pressure differential switch.

In the event of a system failure, the remaining good system would do all the braking on one front wheel and the opposite rear wheel, thus maintaining 50 percent of the total braking force.

FIGURE 38–12   Front/rear split hydraulic system.

FIGURE 38–13   Dual diagonally split hydraulic system.

HYDRAULIC BRAKE SYSTEM COMPONENTS

The following sections describe the major components of a hydraulic brake system, including power-assisted systems and antilock braking systems.

Brake Fluid

Brake fluid is the lifeblood of any hydraulic brake system and is what makes the system operate properly.

Modern brake fluid is specially blended to enable it to perform a variety of functions. Brake fluid must be able to flow freely at extremely high temperatures (500°F) and at very low temperatures (–104°F). Brake fluid must also serve as a lubricant to the many parts with which it comes into contact to ensure smooth and even operation. In addition, brake fluid must fight corrosion and rust in the brake lines and various assemblies and components in services. Another important property of brake fluid is that it must resist evaporation. All brake fluids are hydroscopic; that is, they readily absorb water. This is why brake fluid should always be kept in a sealed container and should only be exposed to outside air for limited periods of time.

Some of the earliest brake fluids had chemicals in them that ate away at the rubber components in the brake system (i.e., cups and seals). Modern brake fluid must be compatible with rubber to avoid damage to the cups and seals in the system. Brake fluid must provide a controlled amount of swell to the brake system cups and seals. There must be just enough swell to form a good seal. However, the swell cannot be too great. If it is, drag and poor brake response occur. Every can of brake fluid carries the identification letters of SAE and **DOT**. These letters (and corresponding numbers) indicate the nature, blend, and performance characteristics of that particular brand of brake fluid.

There are three basic types or classifications of hydraulic brake fluids. DOT 3 is a conventional brake fluid with a minimum dry **ERBP** (equilibrium reflux boiling point) of 401°F and a minimum wet ERBP of 284°F. It is generally recommended for most ABS systems and some power brake setups. DOT 4 is a conventional brake fluid with a minimum dry ERBP of 446°F and a minimum wet ERBP of 356°F. It is the most commonly used brake fluid for conventional brake systems. DOT 5 is a unique silicone-based brake fluid with a minimum dry ERBP of 500°F and a minimum WET ERBP of 356°F. In the last few years, DOT 5 has lost its demand by brake servicing experts. However, remember that it is best to follow the vehicle manufacturer's recommendations.

WARNING!

Use only approved brake fluid in a brake system. Any other lubricant, such as power steering fluid, automatic transmission fluid, or engine oil, which has a petroleum base, must never be used in the brake system. Petroleum-based fluids attack the rubber components in the brake system, like the piston cups and seals, and cause them to swell and disintegrate. ∎

Some vehicles have brake fluid level sensors that provide the driver with an early warning message that the brake fluid in the master cylinder reservoir has dropped below the normal level.

As the brake fluid in the master cylinder reservoir drops below the designated level, the sensor closes the warning message circuit. About 15 seconds later, the message "brake fluid low" appears on the instrument panel. At this time, the master cylinder reservoir should be checked and filled to the correct level with the specified brake fluid.

Brake Pedal

The brake pedal is where the brake's hydraulic system gets its start. When the brake pedal is depressed, force is applied to the master cylinder. On a basic hydraulic brake system (where there is no power assist), the force applied is transmitted mechanically. As the pedal in Figure 38–14 pivots, the force applied to it is multiplied mechanically. The force that the pushrod applies to the master cylinder piston is, therefore, much greater than the force applied to the brake pedal.

Master Cylinders

The heart of the hydraulic brake system is the master cylinder. It converts the mechanical force of the driver's foot on the brake pedal to hydraulic pressure. The master cylinder has a bore that contains a piston assembly and return spring. Seals on the piston prevent fluid leakage. A cup seal on the forward end keeps the brake fluid ahead of the piston when it is

FIGURE 38–14 Brake pedal action.

FIGURE 38–15 (A) Typical cast-iron dual master cylinder and (B) typical aluminum/composite dual master cylinder.

put under pressure. Although master cylinders differ in number of pistons, reservoir design, and integrated hydraulic components, the operation of all master cylinders is basically the same.

Master cylinders are generally constructed of cast iron (Figure 38–15A) with an integral fluid reservoir or weight-saving aluminum with a separate molded nylon or fiberglass reinforced plastic reservoir. Aluminum body master cylinders feature an anodized body (Figure 38–15B) to protect against corrosion and to extend bore life.

WARNING!

It is recommended that aluminum master cylinders not be rebuilt if pitting or scoring of the cylinder bore is evident. A new unit should be installed. ∎

Single System Master Cylinders To understand how a master cylinder works, it is easier to examine a single piston master cylinder before studying dual master cylinders. A cross section of a typical single piston cylinder is shown in Figure 38–16. The cylinder and the fluid reservoir are an integral unit. A vent port and compensating or replenishing port pass from the reservoir into the piston chamber. The chamber contains a piston, a return spring, and a residual pressure check valve. On the brake pedal end of the cylinder, a pushrod connects the cylinder

FIGURE 38–16   Typical single master cylinder system.

to the power booster or brake pedal clevis. The opposite end of the cylinder contains the threaded fluid outlet to which the hydraulic line is connected.

When the brake pedal is depressed, the force from the brake pedal is transferred to the piston by a pushrod. The piston exerts pressure on the fluid, which flows out through the fluid outlet port into a single hydraulic system, serving both front and rear brakes. When the brake pedal is released, the return spring in the cylinder forces the piston back to its original position. If the piston returns too quickly, vacuum is generated in the cylinder. Fluid from the reservoir then enters the cylinder through a vent port to fill the void. As the brakes are fully released, excess fluid is returned to the reservoir through the replenishing or **compensating port** to relieve pressure in the system. Single piston master cylinders have not been used in passenger vehicles for many years. Safety considerations dictated the use of dual (one cylinder for two wheels) master cylinders.

SHOP TALK

Master cylinder terminology is often confusing. For example, replenishing and compensating ports are synonymous terms. That is, they serve the same function but are called different names by different manufacturers and in different parts of the country. The same is true of the master cylinder's vent port, by-pass port, or relief passage. All these things actually perform the same function and in basically the same manner, but are called by different names. ■

Dual Master Cylinders   The important parts of a typical dual master cylinder are shown in Figure

38–17. Their functions are described here. The cap is also known as the bail, cover, or gasket. This part keeps an airtight seal on the master cylinder while letting it breathe. It keeps moisture from entering the system. Moisture breaks down the ability of brake fluid to lubricate properly. It also causes corrosion. The cap, or **cover gasket**, acts like a diaphragm. It expands and contracts as the fluid pressure rises or falls. When the brakes are applied, the demand for brake fluid could create a vacuum below the diaphragm. This would keep fluid from flowing out of the reservoir. For the gasket to expand or contract, the space between the gasket and the cover must be vented. The venting is accomplished with small grooves or drilled holes in the cap or cover. (Most seals have a bellow design. As the fluid goes down, the space above the gasket fills with air. When the brakes are released, the fluid returns to the master cylinder reservoirs and the air is forced out the vent holes.) The wire bail retainer (Figure 38–18) or a bolt is typically used to hold on the cap or cover.

Extra brake fluid is stored in two separate reservoirs. Made of either cast iron or specially blended plastic, they are designed to function independently as a protection against lost brake fluid which can cause the brake system to fail. It is important to keep the reservoir filled to its proper level.

The dual master cylinder reservoir has a single piston bore that contains the two pistons (primary and secondary) lined up in tandem. Each piston has a return spring in front of it. This holds the piston cup slightly behind the replenishing port for each reservoir. In addition to keeping the replenishing ports uncovered, the return springs also return the brake pedal when the force has been removed from it. As the brakes are applied, the stiffer primary piston spring pushes the secondary piston and spring slight-

Reservoir cover

*Manual brake master cylinders only

*Push rod retainer
(variation)

*Boot

Diaphragm

*Push rod

Primary
piston

*Push rod
retainer

*Washer

Lock ring

Tube
seat
insert

Residual
pressure
check valve

Piston
stop bolt

Spring

Cup retainer

Primary cup

Cup protector

Check valve spring

Secondary
piston

Secondary cups

FIGURE 38–17   Typical dual master cylinder system, disassembled.

INSTALL

REMOVE

BAIL

FIGURE 38–18   Cover and retainer bail wire.

ly. The cup at the front end of the secondary piston passes and closes off the primary replenishing port on the secondary side of the master cylinder.

A retaining ring fits into a groove near the end of the bore and holds the piston.

The primary outlet (or port) is the one closer to the cowl panel. It is off the primary piston (the one which receives the initial, or primary movement).

The function of the **residual check valve**, found only on vehicles with rear drum brakes, is to keep light (or residual) pressure in the brake lines and also

at the wheel cylinders. Without residual pressure, air can be sucked past the wheel cylinder cups and into the wheel cylinders. This could occur when the brake pedal is released quickly. Residual check valves are designed to permit hydraulic fluid and pressure to flow from the master cylinder into the hydraulic lines when the pressure in the master cylinder becomes great enough to open the valve. After allowing the fluid to flow back into the master cylinder when the pedal is released, the outlet check valve spring (Figure 38–19) takes over and keeps the hydraulic lines and wheel cylinders full of fluid, ready for the next application of the brakes. On most of the newer car mod-

FIGURE 38–19   Outlet check valve springs.

FIGURE 38–20 (A) Reservoir replenishing pressure chamber; (B) fluid returns to the reservoir.

els, automobile manufacturers have eliminated residual pressure check valves from the brake system. Wheel cylinders are equipped with cup expanders. The cup expanders keep the cup seals tightly pressed against the cylinder walls to prevent air from entering the system.

Light residual pressure is needed for operating the drum brakes. However, when the brakes are used repeatedly, too much pressure can build up. The replenishing or compensating port (Figure 38–20) takes care of this problem. After many stops, like in city driving, the brake drums and wheel cylinders get very hot. This causes the brake fluid to heat up and expand. Such a pressure buildup can become so strong that it keeps the brake shoes from returning after releasing the brake pedal. If the brake shoes do not return properly, they might drag against the drums. This causes more heat to build up and pressure is further increased.

SHOP TALK

Extra brake fluid is forced into the hydraulic system by pumping the brakes. Pressure builds until the brake pedal is released and the piston moves back far enough to uncover the replenishing ports. This removes the excess pressure from the brake lines and wheel cylinders and allows the fluid to return to the brake master cylinder reservoir.   ■

Vent ports help to pump up a low brake pedal by allowing more fluid in the lines. There are several reasons for a brake pedal to be lower than normal. One is that the clearance between the brake lining and the drum is too large. This can happen when the automatic brake adjusters, if the vehicle is so equipped, are not working properly. Another reason could be the result of air leaking into the brake system. If a brake pedal is pumped too rapidly, the return springs in the master cylinder might move the pistons back very fast. At the other end of the system, the brake shoe return springs move the wheel cylinder pistons much more slowly. The flow of brake fluid from the wheel cylinders is then delayed. It cannot match the fast return of the master cylinder pistons. As a result, pressure drops in the master cylinder. The pressure in the master cylinder actually becomes lower than the pressure in the reservoir. Fluid then rushes through the vent ports, through holes in the piston, past the piston cup, and back into the area ahead of the piston cups. Vent ports are important because the replenishing ports are not large enough to handle the extra flow of fluid needed when the pedal is pumped.

The design of the master cylinder used on a particular model car depends on the capacity of the reservoir and the displacement of the pistons at the wheel. Disc brakes require larger reservoirs than drum brakes because the caliper cylinder is much larger than that of a wheel cylinder.

Some internal parts of the master cylinder may also change with application. For example, in the 1980s General Motors introduced caliper pistons that had a low-drag. These were designed to retract farther into the caliper's cylinder when the brake pedal was released. This reduction of drag increased fuel economy. However, since the piston had to move farther to push the pads against the rotor, more fluid had to be moved by the master cylinder. This caused a delay in pedal response and the feeling of a low pedal. To correct this problem, General Motors uses a **quick-take-up** master cylinder, with a larger rear piston to move more fluid. A quick-take-up valve in the master cylinder controls the flow of fluid from the reservoir to the master cylinder's rear piston.

OPERATION OF THE DUAL SYSTEM MASTER CYLINDER To understand the operation of a dual master cylinder, it is important to know how the various parts of the unit work together. Actually, the oper-

FIGURE 38-21 Master cylinder—brakes applied.

FIGURE 38-23 The reservoir returns fluid to the bore.

ation of the dual master cylinder is like that of two single piston types placed end to end in the same bore. The two pistons in the master cylinder are not rigidly connected. Each half really operates like a single system. As just mentioned, each piston has its own reservoir with vent and replenishing ports. Stepping on the brake pedal moves a pushrod forward, causing the first or primary piston to move forward. The fluid ahead of it cannot be compressed, so the secondary piston moves. As the pistons progress deeper into the cylinder bore, the brake fluid that is put under pressure transmits this force through both systems to friction pads in the wheels (Figure 38-21).

The pistons have seals at both ends: a cup seal with a one-way sealing property at the forward end and a secondary cup at the rear. Each piston has a return spring with the primary piston spring between the two pistons. On the forward stroke, the lip of each cup seal is forced against the bore wall. When the piston springs quickly back to place, the brake fluid cannot return through the lines fast enough to avoid creating a low-pressure condition ahead of it. Fluid must reach the low-pressure area in time for another stroke of the cylinder. On the return stroke, the edges of the cup pull away from the bore enough to allow fluid to pass around the piston assembly to the area of low pressure (Figure 38-22).

FIGURE 38-22 When the pedal is released, brake fluid flows around piston cup.

At the same time, the reservoir returns the small amount of fluid it had taken in during piston action (Figure 38-23). This way, the master cylinder returns to normal before all the fluid returns from the lines. Finally, the pads and shoes return to position. That is, once the brake pedal is released and the master cylinder piston has returned to the rest position, shoe return springs (in the drum brakes) and piston seals (in the disc brakes) cause these pistons to retract.

HYDRAULIC TUBES AND HOSES

Steel tubing and flexible synthetic rubber hosing serve as the arteries and veins of the hydraulic brake system. These brake lines transmit brake fluid pressure (the blood) from the master cylinder (the heart) to the wheel cylinders and calipers (the muscles and working parts) of the drum and disc brakes.

Fluid transfer from the driver-actuated master cylinder is usually routed through one or more valves and then into the steel tubing and hoses (Figure 38-24). The design of the brake lines offers quick fluid transfer response with very little friction loss. Engineering and installing the brake lines so they do not wrap around sharp curves is very important in maintaining this good fluid transfer.

BRAKE LINE TUBING Most brake line tubing consists of copper-fused double-wall steel tubing in diameters ranging from 1/8 to 3/8 inch. Some OEM brake tubing is manufactured with soft steel strips, sheathed with copper. The strips are rolled into a double-wall assembly and then bonded in a furnace at extremely high temperatures. Corrosion protection is often added by tin-plating the tubing.

FITTINGS Assorted fittings are used to connect steel tubing to junction blocks or other tubing sections. The most common fitting is the double or inverted flare style. Double flaring is important to maintain the strength and safety of the system. Single flare or sleeve compression fittings may not hold up

FIGURE 38–24 Typical hydraulic brake assembly.

in the rigorous operating environment of a standard vehicle brake system.

Fittings are constructed of steel or brass. The 37 degree inverted flare or standard flare fitting is the most commonly used coupling. Newer vehicles may use the **ISO** or metric bubble flare fitting.

Never change the style of fitting being used on the vehicle. Replace ISO fittings only with ISO fittings. Replace standard fittings with standard fittings.

The metal composition of the fittings must also match exactly. Using an aluminum-alloy fitting with steel tubing may provide a good initial seal, but the dissimilar metals create a corrosion cell that eats away the metal and reduces the connection's service life.

BRAKE LINE HOSES Brake line hoses offer flexible connections to wheel units so steering and suspension members can operate without damaging the brake system. Typical brake hoses range from 10 to 30 inches in length and are constructed of multiple layers of fabric impregnated with a synthetic rubber. Brake hose material must offer high heat resistance and withstand harsh operating conditions.

SHOP TALK

Many brake hose failures can be traced to errors made in the original installation or repair of the hose. Hoses twisted into place become stressed and are prime candidates for leaks and bursting. Most manufacturers now print a natural lay indicator or line on the hose. By making sure this line is not spiralled after fittings are tightened, you can ensure the hose is not overly stressed. Also, always use a hose of

the same length and diameter as the original during servicing to maintain brake balance at all wheels. ■

HYDRAULIC SYSTEM SAFETY SWITCHES AND VALVES

Switches and valves are installed in the brake system hydraulic lines to act as warning devices to pressure control devices.

Pressure Differential (Warning Light) Switches

A pressure differential valve is used in all dual brake systems to operate a warning light switch. Its main purpose is to tell the driver if pressure is lost in either of the two hydraulic systems. Since each brake hydraulic system functions independently, it is possible the driver might not notice immediately that pressure and braking are lost. When a pressure loss occurs, brake pedal travel increases and a more-than-usual effort is needed for braking. Should the driver not notice the extra effort needed, the warning light is actuated by the hydraulic system safety switch.

Under normal conditions, the hydraulic pressure on each side of the pressure differential valve piston is balanced. The piston is located at its center point, so the spring-loaded warning switch plunger fits into the tapered groove of the piston. This leaves the contacts of the warning switch open. The brake warning light stays off.

If there is a leak in the front or rear braking system, the hydraulic pressure in the two systems is unequal. For example, if there is a leak in the system supplying the front brakes, there is lower pressure in

FIGURE 38–25 Pressure differential valve under normal conditions.

the front system when the brake pedal is applied. The hydraulic pressure in the rear system then pushes the piston toward the front side, where the pressure is lower. As the piston moves, the plunger is pushed out (Figure 38–25). This closes the switch and illuminates the brake warning light.

While all brake warning light switches serve the same function, there are three common variations in the design of these switches. These variations include switches with centering springs, without centering springs, and with centering springs and two pistons.

Metering and Proportioning Valves

Metering and proportioning valves are used to balance the braking characteristics of disc and drum brakes.

The braking response of the disc brakes is immediate when the brake pedal is applied. It is directly proportionate to the effort applied at the pedal. Drum brake response is delayed while rear brake hydraulic pressure moves the wheel cylinder pistons to overcome the force of their return springs and force the brake shoes to contact the drum. Their actions are self-energizing and tend to multiply the pedal effort.

Metering Valve A **metering valve** in the front brake line holds off pressure going from the master cylinder

to the front disc calipers. This delay allows pressure to build up in the rear drums first. When the rear brakes begin to take hold, the hydraulic pressure builds to the level needed to open the metering valve (Figure 38–26). When the metering valve opens, line pressure is high enough to operate the front discs. This process provides for better balance of the front and rear brakes. It also prevents lockup of the front brakes by keeping pressure from them until the rear brakes have started to operate. The metering valve has the most effect at the start of each brake operation and all during light braking conditions.

FIGURE 38–26 Metering valve.

FIGURE 38–27 Typical proportioning valve cross section.

Proportioning Valve The self-energizing action of the delayed response rear drum brakes can cause them to lock the rear wheels at a lower hydraulic pressure than the front brakes. The **proportioning valve** is used to control rear brake pressures, particularly during hard stops. When the pressure to the rear brakes reaches a specified level, the proportioning valve overcomes the force of its spring-loaded piston, stopping the flow of fluid to the rear brakes (Figure 38–27). By doing so, it regulates rear brake system pressure and adjusts for the difference in pressure between front and rear brake systems. This keeps front and rear braking forces in balance.

SHOP TALK

Distribution and weight on some vehicles, such as station wagons, is such that a rear-to-front weight transfer does not present a similar problem. For this reason, standard proportioning valves are not required on all station wagon models. ■

Combination Valves Most newer cars have a **combination valve** in their hydraulic system. This valve is simply a single unit that combines the metering and proportioning valves with the pressure differential valve. Combination valves are described as three-function or two-function valves, depending on the number of functions they perform in the hydraulic system.

THREE-FUNCTION VALVE This type of valve (Figure 38–28) performs the functions of the metering valve, brake warning light switch, and proportioning valve.

TWO-FUNCTION VALVES There are two variations of the two-function combination valve. One variation does the proportioning valve and brake warning light switch functions. The other performs the metering valve and brake warning light switch functions.

If any one of its several operation fails, the entire combination valve must be replaced, because these units are not repairable.

FIGURE 38–28 Three-function combination valve.

FIGURE 38–29 Mechanically activated stop light switch.

Stop Light Switches

The stop light (stop light/speed control) switch and mounting bracket assembly (Figure 38–29) is attached to the brake pedal bracket and is activated by pressing the brake pedal.

The mechanical stop light switch is operated by contact with the brake pedal or with a bracket attached to the pedal. The hydraulic switch is operated by hydraulic pressure developed in the master cylinder. In both types, the circuit through the switch is open when the brake pedal is released. When the brakes are applied, the circuit through the switch closes and causes the stop lights to come on. Hydraulic brake light switches are not commonly used today because they provided one more area for possible fluid leaks.

DRUM AND DISC BRAKE ASSEMBLIES

Although drum and disc brakes are explained in great detail in later chapters, a brief explanation of their components and operating principles is essential at this point.

Drum Brakes

A drum brake assembly consists of a cast-iron drum, which is bolted to and rotates with the vehicle's wheel, and a fixed backing plate to which the shoes, wheel cylinders, automatic adjusters, and linkages are attached (Figure 38–30). Additionally, there might be some extra hardware for parking brakes. The shoes are surfaced with frictional linings, which contact the inside of the drum when the brakes are applied. The shoes are forced outward by pistons located inside the wheel cylinder. They are actuated by hydraulic pressure. As the drum rubs against the shoes, the energy of the moving drum is transformed into heat. This

FIGURE 38–30 Typical drum brake.

FIGURE 38–31 Typical disc brake.

heat energy is passed into the atmosphere. When the brake pedal is released, hydraulic pressure drops and the pistons are pulled back to their unapplied position by return springs.

Disc Brakes

Disc brakes resemble the brakes on a bicycle: the friction elements are in the form of pads, which are squeezed or clamped about the edge of a rotating wheel. With automotive disc brakes, this wheel is a separate unit, called a **rotor**, inboard of the vehicle wheel (Figure 38–31). The rotor is made of cast iron. Since the pads clamp against both sides of it, both sides are machined smooth. Usually the two surfaces are separated by a finned center section for better cooling (such rotors are called **ventilated rotors**). The pads are attached to metal shoes, which are actuated by pistons, the same as with drum brakes. The pistons are contained within a caliper assembly, a housing that wraps around the edge of the rotor. The caliper is kept from rotating by way of bolts holding it to the car's suspension framework.

The **caliper** is a housing containing the pistons and related seals, springs, and boots as well as the cylinders and fluid passages necessary to force the friction linings or pads against the rotor. The caliper resembles a hand in the way it wraps around the edge of the rotor. It is attached to the steering knuckle. Some models employ light spring pressure to keep the pads close against the rotor. In other caliper designs, this is achieved by a unique type of seal that allows the piston to be pushed out the necessary amount, then retracts it just enough to pull the pad off the rotor.

Unlike shoes in a drum brake, the pads act perpendicular to the rotation of the disc when the brakes are applied. This effect is different from that produced in a brake drum, where frictional drag actually pulls the shoe into the drum. Disc brakes are said to

be nonenergized and so require more force to achieve the same braking effort. For this reason, they are ordinarily used in conjunction with a power brake unit.

HYDRAULIC SYSTEM SERVICE

Hydraulic system service is relatively uncomplicated, but it is vital to the vehicle's safe operation.

Brake Fluid Inspection

The master cylinder is usually located under the hood and near the fire wall on the driver's side.

 WARNING!

Clean the cover before removal to avoid dropping dirt into the reservoir. ∎

Remove the cover and check the gasket, or diaphragm. Inspect the cover for damage or plugged vent holes. Clean the vent holes, if necessary.

Check the brake fluid level in the master cylinder. A cast-iron reservoir is usually filled to within 1/4 inch of the top. A plastic reservoir may have fluid level marks. Do not overfill a reservoir. If fluid must be added, a leak probably has developed or the shoes and/or pads are worn. Check the system carefully to locate the leak.

To check for contaminated fluid, place a small amount of brake fluid in a clear glass jar. If the fluid is dirty or separates into layers, it is contaminated. Contaminated fluid must be replaced.

Contaminated brake fluid can damage rubber parts and cause leaks. When replacing contaminated brake fluid, it is necessary to flush and refill the brake system with new fluid. Always use fluid with a DOT rating of 3 or higher. Follow manufacturer's recommendations.

Check the master cylinder for dampness and leaks around the body fittings, especially at the rear. A leak where it is mounted to the fire wall or power brake unit indicates a defective rear piston seal. The master cylinder must be rebuilt or replaced.

Brake Line Inspection Check all tubing, hoses, and connections from under the hood to the wheels for leaks and damage (Figure 38–32). Wheels and tires should also be inspected for signs of brake fluid leaks. Check all hoses for flexibility, bulges, and cracks. Check parking brake linkage, cable, and connections for damage and wear. Replace parts where necessary.

Brake Pedal Inspection Depress and release the brake pedal several times (engine running for power

A

B

FIGURE 38–32 (A) Check the rear brake backing plate on each rear wheel for signs of brake fluid leakage, or oil spray; (B) inspect all hoses and connections.

brakes). Check for friction and noise. Pedal movement should be smooth, with no squeaks from the pedal or brakes. The pedal should return quickly when it is released.

When operating the engine, be sure the transmission lever is in neutral or park. Be sure the area is properly ventilated for the exhaust to escape.

Apply heavy foot pressure to the brake pedal (engine running for power brakes). Check for a spongy pedal and pedal reserve. Spongy pedal action is springy. Pedal action should feel firm. **Pedal reserve** is the distance between the brake pedal and the floor after the pedal has been depressed fully. The pedal should not go lower than 1 or 2 inches above the floor.

With the engine off, hold light foot pressure on the pedal for about 15 seconds. There should be no pedal movement during this time. Pedal movement indicates a leak. Repeat the procedure using heavy pedal pressure (engine running for power brakes).

If there is pedal movement, but the fluid level is not low, the master cylinder has internal leakage. It must be rebuilt or replaced. If the fluid level is low, there is an external leak somewhere in the brake system. The leak must be repaired.

Depress the pedal and check for proper stop light operation.

To check power brake operation, depress and release the pedal several times while the engine is stopped. This eliminates vacuum from the system. Hold the brake down with moderate foot pressure and start the engine. If the power unit is operating properly, the brake pedal moves downward when the engine is started.

Master Cylinder Rebuilding A master cylinder is rebuilt to replace leaking seals or gaskets. If a more serious problem exists, the master cylinder should be replaced.

To remove a master cylinder, disconnect the brake lines at the master cylinder. Install plugs in the brake lines and master cylinder to prevent dirt from entering. Remove the nuts that attach the master cylinder to the fire wall power brake unit, and remove the cylinder.

Remove the cover and seal. Drain the master cylinder and carefully mount it in a vise. Remove the piston assembly and seals according to the manufacturer's instructions. New pistons, pushrods, and seals are usually included in rebuilding kits.

Clean master cylinder parts only with brake fluid, brake cleaning solvent, or alcohol. Do not use a solvent containing mineral oil, such as gasoline. Mineral oil is very harmful to rubber seals.

Inspect the master cylinder. Damage, cracks, porous leaks, and worn piston bores mean the master cylinder must be replaced. Check very carefully for pitting or roughness in the bore. If any are present, the cylinder must be replaced.

Reassemble, install, and bleed the master cylinder according to the manufacturer's directions.

Hydraulic System Bleeding

Fluids cannot be compressed, while gases are compressible. Any air in the brake hydraulic system is compressed as the pressure increases. This action reduces the amount of force that can be transmitted by the fluid. This is why it is very important to keep all air out of the hydraulic system. To do this, air must be bled from brakes. This procedure is called **bleeding** the brake system.

Bleeding is a process of forcing fluid through the brake lines and out through a bleeder valve or bleeder screw. The fluid eliminates any air that might be in the system. Bleeder screws and valves are fastened to the wheel cylinders or calipers. The bleeder must be cleaned. A drain hose then is connected from the bleeder to a glass jar (Figure 38–33).

FIGURE 38-33 While bleeding the brake system, releasing the fluid into a glass jar will help to determine when the system is free of air.

CUSTOMER CARE

Remind your customers to use only approved brake fluid in a brake system. Any other lubricant, such as power steering fluid, automatic transmission fluid, or engine oil, which has a petroleum base, must never be used in the brake system. Petroleum-based fluids attack the rubber components in the brake system, like the piston cups and seals, and cause them to swell and disintegrate. If you open a brake fluid reservoir and find the diaphragm is swelled out of shape and is larger than it should be, you can be sure someone has previously put some kind of petroleum-based fluid in it. Such a discovery is costly to the vehicle's owner as all rubber components in the entire brake system will need to be replaced. ∎

Two types of brake bleeding procedures are used: manual bleeding and pressure bleeding. Always follow the manufacturer's recommendations when bleeding brakes. The sequence in which bleeding is performed can be critical. When bleeding a power brake system, remove the vacuum line from the power unit and plug the unit. To remove vacuum, the engine must be off. Pump the brake pedal several times.

WARNING!

Always use fresh brake fluid when bleeding the system. Do not use fluid that has been drained. Drained fluid may be contaminated and can damage the system. ∎

Manual Bleeding A manual bleeding procedure requires two people. One person operates the bleeder; the other, the brake pedal. Bleed only one wheel at a time.

WARNING!

Be sure the bleeder hose is below the surface of the liquid in the jar at all times. Do not allow the master cylinder to run out of fluid at any time. If these precautions are not followed, air can enter the system, and it must be bled again. The master cylinder cover must be kept in place. ∎

Place the bleeder hose and jar in position. Have a helper pump the brake pedal several times and then hold it down with moderate pressure. Slowly open the bleeder valve. After fluid/air has stopped flowing, close the bleeder valve. Have the helper slowly release the pedal. Repeat this procedure until fluid that flows from the bleeder is clear and free of bubbles.

Discard all used brake fluid. Fill the master cylinder reservoir. Check the brakes for proper operation.

WARNING!

Clean the master cylinder and cover before adding fluid. This is important for preventing dirt from entering the reservoir. ∎

Pressure Bleeding A pressure bleeding procedure can be done by one person. Pressure bleeding equipment uses pressurized fluid that flows through a special adapter fitted into the master cylinder (Figure 38-34).

The use of pressure bleeding equipment varies with different automobiles and different equipment makers. Always follow the automobile manufacturer's recommendations when using pressure bleeding equipment.

On automobiles with metering valves, the valve must be held open during pressure bleeding. Figure 38-35 shows a special tool used to hold open the metering section of a combination valve.

USING SERVICE MANUALS

Consult the service manual to be sure the proper bleeding sequence is followed. If a vehicle requiring a special sequence is bled in the conventional manner, air might be chased throughout the system. ∎

Open the bleeder valves one at a time until clear, air-free fluid is flowing. Progress from the wheel

FIGURE 38-34 Pressure bleeding.

FIGURE 38-35 Special tool to hold the metering valve open while bleeding the system.

cylinder farthest from the master cylinder to the cylinder closest.

Do not exceed recommended pressure while bleeding the brakes. Always release air pressure after bleeding. Clean and fill the master cylinder after pressure bleeding. Check the brakes for proper operation. Be sure to remove the special tool used to hold the metering valve.

Power Brakes

Power brakes are nothing more than a standard hydraulic brake system with a booster unit located between the brake pedal and the master cylinder to help activate the brakes.

Two basic types of power-assist mechanisms are used. The first is **vacuum assist**. These systems use engine vacuum, or sometimes vacuum pressure developed by an external vacuum pump, to help apply the brakes. The second type of power assist is **hydraulic assist**. It is normally found on larger vehicles. This system uses hydraulic pressure developed by the power steering pump or other external pump to help apply the brakes.

Both vacuum and hydraulic assist act to multiply the force exerted on the master cylinder pistons by the driver. This increases the hydraulic pressure delivered to the wheel cylinders or calipers while decreasing driver foot pressure.

Vacuum-Assist Power Brakes

All vacuum-assisted units are similar in design. They generate application energy by opposing engine vacuum to atmospheric pressure. A piston and cylinder, flexible diaphragm or bellows use this energy to provide braking assistance.

All modern vacuum-assist units are vacuum-suspended systems. This means the diaphragm inside the unit is balanced using engine vacuum until the brake pedal is depressed. Applying the brake allows atmospheric pressure to unbalance the diaphragm and allows it to move generating application pressure.

Atmospheric pressure is normally 14 to 15 psi. So, if the diaphragm is 12 inches in diameter, it would have an area of about 113 square inches. With an atmospheric pressure of 14 psi, this results in an application force of 1,552 psi.

Vacuum boosters may be single diaphragm (Figure 38–36) or tandem diaphragm (Figure 38–37). The unit consists of three basic elements combined into a single power unit.

The three basic elements of the single diaphragm follow.

1. A vacuum power section that includes a front and rear shell, a power diaphragm, a return spring, and a pushrod.
2. A control valve built as an integral part of the power diaphragm and connected through a valve rod to the brake pedal. It controls the degree of brake application or release in accordance with the pressure applied to the brake pedal.

FIGURE 38–36 Cross section of tandem master cylinder and vacuum-operated power booster.

FIGURE 38–37 Cross section of a tandem master cylinder with a tandem diaphragm power booster.

3. A hydraulic master cylinder, attached to the vacuum power section that contains all the elements of the conventional brake master cylinder except for the pushrod. It supplies fluid under pressure to the pressure applied by the brake booster.

Operation When the brakes are applied, the valve rod and plunger move to the left in the power diaphragm. This action closes the control valve's vacuum port and opens the atmospheric port to admit air through the ralve at the rear diaphragm chamber. With vacuum in the rear chamber, a force develops that moves the power diaphragm, hydraulic

pushrod, and hydraulic piston or pistons to close the compensating port or ports and force fluid under pressure through the residual check valve or valves and lines into the front and rear brake assemblies.

As pressure develops in the master cylinder, a counterforce acts through the hydraulic pushrod and reaction disc against the vacuum power diaphragm and valve plunger. This force tends to close the atmospheric port and reopen the vacuum port. Since this force is in opposition to the force applied to the brake pedal by the operator, it gives the operator a feel for the amount of brake applied.

Servicing Vacuum-Assist Booster Units The fact that a vehicle's brakes still operate when the vacuum-assist unit fails indicates that the hydraulic brake system and the vacuum-assist system are two separate systems. This means you should always check for faults in the hydraulic system first. If it checks out satisfactorily, start inspecting the vacuum-assist circuit.

For a fast check of vacuum-assist operation, press the brake pedal firmly and then start the engine. The pedal should fall away slightly and less pressure should be needed to maintain the pedal in any position.

PRESSURE CHECK Another simple check can be made by installing a suitable pressure gauge in the brake hydraulic system. Take a reading with the engine off and the power unit not operating. Maintain the same pedal height, start the engine, and read the gauge. There should be a substantial pressure increase if the vacuum assist booster is operating correctly.

PEDAL TRAVEL Pedal travel and total travel are critical on vacuum-assisted vehicles. Pedal travel should be kept strictly to specifications listed in the vehicle's service manual.

VACUUM READING If the power unit is not giving sufficient assistance, take a manifold vacuum reading. If manifold vacuum level is below specifications, tune the engine and retest the unit. Loose or damaged vacuum lines and clogged air intake filters reduce braking assistance. Most units have a check valve that retains some vacuum in the system when the engine is off. A vacuum gauge check of this valve indicates if it is restricted or stays open.

RELEASE PROBLEMS Failure of the brakes to release is often caused by a tight or misaligned connection between the power unit and the brake linkage. Broken pistons, diaphragms, bellows, or return springs can also cause this problem.

To help pinpoint the problem, loosen the connection between the master cylinder and the brake booster. If the brakes release, the problem is caused by internal binding in the vacuum unit. If the brakes do not release, look for a crimped or restricted brake line or similar problem in the hydraulic system.

HARD PEDAL Power brakes that have a **hard pedal** may have collapsed or leaking vacuum lines of insufficient manifold vacuum. Punctured diaphragms or bellows and leaky piston seals all lead to weak power unit operation and hard pedal. A steady hiss when the brake is held down indicates a vacuum leak that causes poor operation.

GRABBING BRAKES First, look for all the usual causes of brake grab, such as greasy linings, or scored rotors or drums. If the trouble appears to be in the power unit, check for a damaged reaction control. The reaction control is made up of a diaphragm, spring, and valve that tend to resist pedal action. It is put into the system to give the driver more brake pedal feel.

CHECK OF INTERNAL BINDING Release problems, hard pedal, and dragging (slow releasing) brakes can all be caused by internal binding. To test a vacuum unit for internal binding, place the transmission/transaxle in neutral and start the engine. Increase engine speed to 1,500 rpm, close the throttle, and completely depress the brake pedal. Slowly release the brake pedal and stop the engine. Remove the vacuum check valve and hose from the vacuum assist unit. Observe for backward movement of the brake pedal. If the brake pedal moves backward, there is internal binding and the unit should be replaced.

PUSHROD ADJUSTMENT

Proper adjustment of the master cylinder pushrod is necessary to ensure proper operation of the power brake system. A pushrod that is too long causes the master cylinder piston to close off the replenishing port, preventing hydraulic pressure from being released and resulting in brake drag. A pushrod that is too short causes excessive brake pedal travel and causes groaning noises to come from the booster when the brakes are applied. A properly adjusted pushrod that remains assembled to the booster with which it was matched during production should not require service adjustment. However, if the booster, master cylinder, or pushrod are replaced, the pushrod might require adjustment.

There are two methods that can be used to check for proper pushrod length and installation: the gauge method and the air method.

Gauge Method In most vacuum power units, the master cylinder pushrod length is fixed, and length is usually checked only after the unit has been overhauled or replaced. A typical adjustment using the gauge method is shown in Figure 38–38.

Air Method The air testing method uses compressed air applied to the hydraulic outlet of the master cylinder. Air pressure is regulated to a value of approximately 5 psi to prevent brake fluid spraying from the master cylinder.

If air passes through the replenishing port, which is the smaller of the two holes in the bottom of the master cylinder reservoir, the adjustment is satisfac-

FIGURE 38–38 Delco-Moraine pushrod adjustment. *Courtesy of Robinair Division, SPX Corporation*

tory. If air does not flow through the replenishing port, adjust the pushrod as required, either by means of the adjustment screw (if provided) or by adding shims between the master cylinder and power unit shell until the air flows freely.

HYDRAULIC-ASSIST POWER BRAKES

Decreases in engine size, plus the continued use of engine vacuum to operate other engine systems, such as emission control devices, led to the development of hydraulic-assist power brakes. These systems use fluid pressure, not vacuum pressure, to help apply the brakes.

The hydraulic pressure in the hydraulic booster should not be confused with the hydraulic pressure in the brake lines. Remember, they are two separate systems.

Two of the more popular hydraulic systems in use today are the hydro-boost system produced by Bendix (Figure 38–39) and the Powermaster system produced by General Motors.

Hydro-Boost

The **hydro-boost** system uses pressurized fluid from the power-steering pump to obtain its power assist.

FIGURE 38–39 Hydro-boost power brake boosters.

FIGURE 38–40 Hydro-boost components.

The components of a hydro-boost system are shown in Figure 38–40.

The booster assembly itself consists of an open center spool valve and sleeve assembly, a lever assembly, an input rod assembly, a power piston, an output pushrod, and the accumulator. The booster assembly is mounted on the vehicle in much the same manner as a vacuum booster. The pedal rod is connected at the booster input rod end.

A dual master cylinder is bolted to the brake booster and is operated by a pushrod projecting from the booster cylinder bore.

The power-steering pump, which is unmodified, except for a larger reservoir and an additional return port for the hydro-boost return line, supplies hydraulic pressure to the hydro-boost unit through external lines. When the engine is running, the fluid enters the unit through the pump port from which most of the fluid is directed to the gear port and then to the steering gear by an external line.

The small quantity of power steering fluid that does not go to the power steering gear circulates inside the hydro-boost unit and then returns to the steering pump reservoir by an external line.

Power-steering fluid flow in the hydro-boost unit is controlled by a hollow center spool valve. The spool valve has lands, annular grooves, and drilled passages. These mate with grooves and lands in the valve bore. The flow pattern of the fluid depends upon the alignment of the valve in the bore.

TESTING THE HYDRO-BOOST

Any investigation of a hydro-boost complaint should begin with an inspection of the power-steering pump belt, fluid level, and hose condition and connections. Hydro-boost does not work properly if it is not supplied with a continuous supply of clean, bubble-free power-steering fluid at the proper pressure.

WARNING!

Always depressurize the accumulator of any hydraulic boost system before disconnecting any brake lines or hoses. This is usually done by turning the engine off and depressing and releasing the brake pedal up to ten times. ∎

Basic Operational Test

The basic operational test of hydro-boost is as follows. With the engine off, pump the brake pedal numerous times to bleed off the residual hydraulic pressure that is stored in the accumulator. Hold firm pressure on the brake pedal and start the engine. The brake pedal should move downward, then push up against the foot.

Accumulator Test

To be sure the **accumulator** is performing properly, rotate the steering wheel with the engine running until it stops and hold it in that position for no more than 5 seconds. Return the steering wheel to the center position and shut off the engine. Pump the brake pedal. You should feel two to three power-assisted strokes. Now repeat steps 1 and 2. That pressurizes the accumulator. Wait 1 hour, then pump the brake pedal. There should be two or three power-assisted strokes. If the system does not perform as just described, the accumulator is leaking and should be replaced.

Noise Troubleshooting

The hydro-boost unit is also part of another major subsystem of the vehicle, the power-steering system. Problems or malfunctions in the steering system may affect hydro-boost operation. The following are some common troubleshooting tips.

Moan or low-frequency hum usually accompanied by a vibration in the pedal or steering column might be encountered during parking or other very low-speed maneuvers. This can be caused by a low fluid level in the power-steering pump or by air in the power-steering fluid due to holding the pump at relief pressure (steering wheel held all the way in one direction) for an excessive amount of time (more than 5 seconds). Check the fluid level and add fluid if necessary. Allow the system to sit for 1 hour with the cap removed to eliminate the air. If the condition persists, it might be a sign of excessive pump wear. Check the pump according to the vehicle manufacturer's recommended procedure.

At or near power runout (brake pedal near fully depressed position), a high-speed fluid noise (like a faucet can make) might occur. This is a normal con-

dition and will not be heard, except in emergency braking conditions.

Whenever the accumulator pressure is used, a slight hiss is noticed. It is the sound of the hydraulic fluid escaping through the accumulator valve and is completely normal.

After the accumulator has been emptied and the engine is started again, another hissing sound might be heard during the first brake application or the first steering maneuver. This is caused by the fluid rushing through the accumulator charging orifice. It is normal and will only be heard once after the accumulator is emptied. However, if this sound continues even though no apparent accumulator pressure assist was made, it could indicate the accumulator is not holding pressure. Check for this using the accumulator test discussed previously.

After bleeding, a gulping sound might be present during brake applications, as noted in the bleeding instructions. This is normal and should disappear with normal driving and braking.

POWERMASTER HYDRAULIC BOOSTER

In 1985, General Motors introduced its **Powermaster** power brake system. Used primarily on full-sized passenger cars, the system incorporates a self-contained hydraulic booster that is built directly onto the master cylinder. Instead of relying on the power steering pump for hydraulic pressure as is done in the hydro-boost system, the Powermaster has its own vane pump and electric motor to provide the hydraulic pressure required for booster operation (Figure 38–41).

Pump

The vane pump is driven by an electric motor that is mounted below the master cylinder. Brake fluid is drawn through a low-pressure hose from the reservoir to the pump. There it is pressurized and exits through a high-pressure hose to the accumulator. Pump motor operation is controlled through a dual-pressure switch and relay.

Accumulator

The accumulator stores brake fluid under pressure at approximately 675 psi (maximum). It has a heavy, flexible diaphragm that separates brake fluid on one side from high-pressure nitrogen gas on the other.

Master Cylinder

In the Powermaster system, the master cylinder is similar to a conventional dual or tandem master cylinder in both design and operation.

FIGURE 38–41 Powermaster components. *Courtesy of Chrevrolet Motor Division, General Motors Corporation*

Dual-Pressure Switch

This switch controls the pump operation in conjunction with a relay attached to the pump motor. Three lead wires are attached to the switch. One leads to the pump motor relay, one leads to the brake warning light (dash mounted), and the third leads to ground. When accumulator pressure drops below 510 psi, one contact set in the switch closes, completing the ground for the relay. At this point, the relay is able to supply battery voltage to the pump motor. With the pump operating, accumulator pressure increases to approximately 675 psi. At that point, the contact set opens, breaking the ground to the relay and shutting off the pump. If accumulator pressure should drop below 400 psi, the second contact closes. This illuminates the dash-mounted brake warning light.

Reservoir

The reservoir is a removable, plastic container internally divided into three chambers. Two chambers (primary and secondary) supply the master cylinder with brake fluid as in a conventional master cylinder. Both chambers are sealed to the atmosphere. The third chamber supplies the booster pump with brake fluid and is vented to the atmosphere because of the large amount of fluid movement in this portion of the reservoir.

Booster

The booster assembly consists of a power piston, inner and outer control valves, and the reaction components. The power piston uses the high-pressure fluid from the accumulator against its large diameter to produce the force needed to apply (push) the master cylinder pistons. The reaction components fit between the power piston and master cylinder primary piston. These components consist of a reaction body group, reaction disc, and reaction piston. In operation, the reaction components provide pedal feel. The apply (outer control) valve and discharge (inner control) valve regulate fluid movement through the booster according to brake pedal movement and brake pedal pressure (force). Both valves are located in the power piston Figure 38–42.

Testing the Powermaster Unit

Diagnosis and testing of the Powermaster unit requires the use of a special adapter and test gauge or aftermarket equivalents. The Powermaster pressure switch is removed and the adapter and test gauge are installed in its port. The unit can then be energized, and the switch's high pressure cut-off and low pressure turn-on points observed and checked against specifications. Follow service manual instructions for the connection and operation of the test gauge and all system test procedures.

FIGURE 38–42 (A) Apply and (B) discharge valve in a power piston.

CASE STUDY

A customer brings her late-model vehicle to a brake specialty shop, complaining of occasional rear brake lockup when the brakes are lightly applied. She is nervous because she feels the vehicle is unsafe to drive. The vehicle is equipped with front disc and rear drum brakes.

A thorough road test by the technician does not verify the complaint. Talking to the customer, the technician learns the problem most often occurs in damp or cold weather, or when the vehicle has been sitting for a length of time.

The technician performs a complete visual and operational inspection. He checks the action of the brake pedal, the power brake booster, and the combination valve. All systems are working fine. He then removes the rear drums and inspects the shoes and drums. Nothing appears out of order or broken. The technician turns to his supervisor for a second opinion.

After listening to a summary of the inspection and checks made to date, the shop supervisor checks the file on factory service bulletins for that model vehicle. The answer is found in a bulletin issued about a year after the vehicle was introduced. The OEM brake shoes were found to have a tendency to swell when subjected to cold and wet. The factory recommended another type of shoe should be installed to correct the problem. Had the technician the experience to check the service bulletin file on the vehicle, valuable diagnostic time would have been saved.

The correct shoe is installed, and the vehicle is road tested. The rear brakes no longer lock up.

KEY TERMS

Accumulator	Hard pedal
Bleeding	Hydraulic assist
Caliper	Hydro-boost
COF	ISO
Combination valve	Kinetic
Compensating port	Metallic
Cover gasket	Metering valve
Diagonally split	Nonasbestos
DOT	Pedal reserve
ERBP	Pedal travel
Friction	Powermaster
Proportioning valve	Semimetallic
Quick-take-up	Static friction
Residual check valve	Vacuum assist
Rotor	Ventilated rotor

SUMMARY

◆ The four factors that determine a vehicle's braking power are pressure, which is provided by the hydraulic system; coefficient of friction, which represents the frictional relationship between pads and rotors or shoes and drums and is engineered to ensure optimum performance; frictional contact surface, meaning that bigger brakes stop a car more quickly than smaller brakes; and heat dissipation, which is necessary to prevent brake fade.

◆ With asbestos banned as a brake lining material, today full metallics and semimetallics are used, as well as other nonasbestos substances.

◆ Since 1967, all cars have been required to have two separate brake systems. The dual brake system uses a tandem master cylinder, which is two master cylinders formed by installing two separated pistons and fluid reservoirs in one cylinder bore.

◆ Brake fluid is the lifeblood of any hydraulic brake system. DOT 4 is the type most commonly used on conventional systems. DOT 3 is recommended for most ABS systems and some power brake systems.

◆ The brake lines transmit brake fluid pressure from the master cylinder to the wheel cylinders and calipers of drum and disc brakes. Brake hoses offer flexible connections to wheel units and must offer high heat resistance.

◆ A pressure differential valve is used in all dual brake systems to operate a warning light switch that alerts the driver if pressure is lost in either hydraulic system.

◆ The metering valve, located in the front brake line, provides for better balance of the front and rear brakes, while also preventing lockup of the front brakes. The proportioning valve controls rear brake pressure, particularly during hard stops.

◆ Hydraulic brake system service is vital to safe vehicle operation. It includes brake fluid, brake line, and brake pedal inspection.

◆ Bleeding removes air from the hydraulic system.

◆ Power brakes can be either vacuum assist or hydraulic assist. Vacuum-assisted units use engine vacuum or vacuum developed by an external pump to help apply the brakes. Hydraulic-assisted units use fluid pressure.

TECH MANUAL

The following procedures are included in Chapter 38 of the *Tech Manual* that accompanies this book:

1. Bench bleed a master cylinder.

2. Make double flare and ISO flares on the end of a brake line.

3. Pressure bleed a brake system.

4. Perform power vacuum brake test.

REVIEW QUESTIONS

1. Explain why bleeding air out of a hydraulic system is so important.

2. Explain why modern hydraulic braking systems are dual designs, and why this is important.

3. Define the different types of power brake designs and tell how they operate.

4. Describe the purpose of a pressure differential valve.

5. Describe the functions of the hydraulic system combination valve.

6. The friction that is generated between a vehicle's tires and the road when the vehicle is in a non-skidding state is called ____ friction.

   a. static   **c.** heat
   b. kinetic   **d.** coefficient

7. Bleeding a hydraulic system involves ____ from the system.

   a. removing water
   b. removing contaminated brake fluid
   c. removing air pockets
   d. filtering out dirt

8. The purpose of the master cylinder is to ____.

   a. generate the hydraulic pressure needed to apply the brake mechanisms
   b. automatically pump the brakes during panic stops
   c. apply braking power when wheel slippage occurs
   d. all of the above

9. After bleeding a hydraulic system, Technician A examines the brake fluid and returns it to the master cylinder if the fluid is clean. Technician B always refills the master cylinder with new brake fluid. Who is correct?

   a. Technician A   **c.** Both A and B
   b. Technician B   **d.** Neither A nor B

10. Which of the following can lead to brake hose failure?

    a. improperly matched fittings
    b. stressing the hose during installations
    c. deterioration from heat and contaminants
    d. all of the above

11. When the brakes are applied, which type of brake offers immediate response?

    a. drum   **c.** both a and b
    b. disc   **d.** neither a nor b

12. Which type of brake requires greater application force and is commonly used with power-boost units?

    a. drum   **c.** both a and b
    b. disc   **d.** neither a nor b

13. What type of power-assist unit uses pressure developed by an external pump, such as the power steering pump?

    a. hydraulic assist   **c.** ABS
    b. vacuum assist   **d.** ASC

14. The power brakes in a vehicle are grabbing. Technician A immediately investigates the power unit. Technician B first checks for other causes, such as greasy lining or scored drums. Who is correct?

    a. Technician A   **c.** Both A and B
    b. Technician B   **d.** Neither A nor B

15. While discussing what affects the amount of pressure exerted by the brakes, Technician A says the shorter the line, the more pressure there will be. Technician B says braking force will increase if the size of the pistons in a master cylinder are increased. Who is correct?

    a. Technician A   **c.** Both A and B
    b. Technician B   **d.** Neither A nor B

16. Which of the following is *not* a component of a typical dual master cylinder?

    a. primary piston   **c.** pressure relief valve
    b. piston stop bolt   **d.** secondary cup

17. The metering valve portion of a combination valve fails. Technician A says this means the entire combination valve must be replaced. Technician B says the metering part can be repaired. Who is correct?

    a. Technician A   **c.** Both A and B
    b. Technician B   **d.** Neither A nor B

18. While discussing quick-take-up master cylinders, Technician A says this design allows for increased braking power. Technician B says this design is only used on drum brake systems. Who is correct?

    a. Technician A   **c.** Both A and B
    b. Technician B   **d.** Neither A nor B

19. Technician A says metallic brake linings cause the rotors and drums to wear quickly. Technician B says semimetallic brake linings do not quickly wear out rotors and drums but have a tendency to easily fade after repeated applications. Who is correct?

    a. Technician A   **c.** Both A and B
    b. Technician B   **d.** Neither A nor B

20. Technician A says if the brake pedal pushrod is too long, brake drag will result. Technician B says if the brake pedal pushrod is too short, a groaning noise will be heard from the brake booster when the brakes are applied. Who is correct?

    a. Technician A   **c.** Both A and B
    b. Technician B   **d.** Neither A nor B

DRUM BRAKES 39

OBJECTIVES

◆ *Explain how drum brakes operate.* ◆ *Identify the major components of a typical drum brake and describe their functions.* ◆ *Explain the difference between duo-servo and nonservo drum brakes.* ◆ *Perform a cleaning and inspection of a drum brake assembly.* ◆ *Recognize conditions that adversely affect the performance of drums, shoes, linings, and related hardware.* ◆ *Reassemble a drum brake after servicing.* ◆ *Explain how typical drum parking brakes operate.* ◆ *Adjust a typical drum parking brake.*

For many years, drum brakes were used on all four wheels on virtually every vehicle on the road. Today, disc brakes have replaced drum brakes on the front wheels of most vehicles, and some models are equipped with both front and rear disc brakes. One reason for their continued use is that drum brakes can easily handle the 20 to 40 percent of total braking load placed on the rear wheels. Another is that drum brakes can also be built with a simple parking brake mechanism.

DRUM BRAKE OPERATION

Drum brake operation is fairly simple. The most important fact contributing to the effectiveness of the braking force supplied by the drum brake is the brake shoe pressure or force directed against the drum (Figure 39–1). With the vehicle moving in either the forward or reverse direction with the brakes on, the applied force of the brake shoe pressing against the brake drum increasingly multiplies itself. This is because the brake's anchor pin acts as a brake shoe stop and prohibits the brake shoe from its tendency to follow the movement of the rotating drum. The result is a wedging action between the brake shoe and brake drum. The wedging action combined with the applied brake force creates a self-multiplied brake force.

DRUM BRAKE COMPONENTS

The major components of a typical drum brake are shown in Figure 39–2. The **backing plate** provides a

THE RELATIVE SIZE OF THE ARROWS INDICATES THE INCREASE OF BRAKE FORCE OR PRESSURE.

FIGURE 39–1 The wheel cylinder pushes the primary and secondary shoes against the inside surface of the rotating brake drum.

foundation for the brake shoes and associated hardware. The plate is secured and bolted to the axle flange or spindle. The wheel cylinder, under hydraulic pressure, forces the brake's shoes against the drum. There are also two linked brake shoes attached to the backing plate. Brake shoes are the backbone of a drum brake. The shoes must support the lining and carry it into the drum so the pressure is distributed across the lining surface during brake application. Shoe return springs and shoe hold-down

FIGURE 39–2 Components of a typical rear-wheel drum brake.

parts maintain the correct shoe position and clearance. Some drum brakes are self-adjusting. Others require manual adjustment mechanisms. Brake drums provide the rubbing surface area for the linings. Drums must withstand high pressures without excessive flexing and must also dissipate large quantities of heat generated during brake application. Finally, the rear drum brakes on most vehicles include the parking brakes.

Wheel Cylinders

Wheel cylinders convert hydraulic pressure supplied by the master cylinder into a mechanical force at the wheel brakes. The space in the wheel cylinder bore between the cups is filled with fluid. When the brake pedal is depressed, additional brake fluid is forced into the cylinder bore. The additional fluid, which is under pressure, moves the cups and pistons outward in the bore. This piston movement forces the shoe links and brake shoes outward to contact the drum and thus apply the brakes.

Brake Shoes and Linings

The workhorse of the drum brake is the brake shoe. In the same brake sizes, there can be differences in

web thickness, shape of web cutouts, and positions of any reinforcements.

The shoe rim is welded to the web to provide a stable surface for the lining. The web thickness might differ to provide the stiffness or flexibility needed for a specific application. Many shoes have nibs or indented places along the edge of the rim. These nibs rest against shoe support ledges on the backing plate and keep the shoe from hanging up.

Each drum in the drum braking system contains a set of shoes. The **primary shoe** (or leading shoe) is the one that is toward the front of the vehicle. The friction between the primary shoe and the brake drum forces the primary shoe to shift slightly in the direction that the drum is turning (an **anchor pin** permits just limited movement). The shifting of the primary shoe forces it against the bottom of the secondary shoe, which causes the secondary shoe to contact the drum. The **secondary shoe** (or trailing shoe) is the one that is toward the rear of the vehicle. It comes into contact as a result of the movement and pressure from the primary shoe and wheel cylinder piston and increases the braking action.

The brake shoe lining provides friction against the drum to stop the car. It contains heat-resistant fibers. The lining is molded with a high-temperature synthetic bonding agent.

The two general methods of attaching the lining to the shoe are riveting and bonding. Regardless of the method of attachment, brake shoes are usually held in a position by spring tension. They are either held against the anchor by the shoe return springs or against the support plate pads by shoe **hold-down springs**. The shoe webs are linked together at the end opposite the anchor by an adjuster and a spring. The adjuster holds them apart. The spring holds them against the adjuster ends.

Mechanical Components

In the unapplied position, the shoes are held against the anchor pin by the return springs. The shoes are held to the backing plate by hold-down springs or spring clips. Opposite the anchor pin, a star wheel adjuster links the shoe webs and provides a threaded adjustment that permits the shoes to be expanded or contracted. The shoes are held against the star wheel by a spring.

Shoe Return Springs

Return springs can be separately hooked into a link or a guide (Figure 39–3) or strung between the shoes. Springs are normally installed on the anchor in the order shown under each category listed in Figure 39–4.

While shoe brake springs look the same, they are usually not interchangeable. Sometimes to help distinguish between them, they are color coded. Pay close attention to the colors and the way they are hooked up.

SEPARATE SPRING LINK

SEPARATE SPRING GUIDE

FIGURE 39–3   Typical brake shoe return spring alignments.

WITH MANUAL ADJUSTER

WITH GM LEVER AUTOMATIC ADJUSTER

WITH CABLE AUTOMATIC ADJUSTER; WITH AUXILIARY (THIRD) SPRING

WITH CRANK AUTOMATIC ADJUSTER

FIGURE 39–4   Typical brake shoe return spring anchoring points.

Shoe Hold-Downs

Various shoe hold-downs are illustrated in Figure 39–5. To unlock or lock the straight pin hold-downs, depress the locking cup and coil spring or the spring clip, and rotate the pin or lock 90 degrees. On General Motors' lever adjusters, the inner (bottom) cup has a sleeve that aligns the adjuster lever.

Shoe Anchors

As shown in Figure 39–6 there are various types of **shoe anchors** such as the fixed nonadjustable type; self-centering shoe sliding type; or, on some earlier models, adjustable fixed type providing either an eccentric or a slotted adjustment. On some front brakes, fixed anchors are threaded into or are bolted through the steering knuckle and also support the wheel cylinder.

On adjustable anchors, when it is necessary to recenter the shoes in the drum or drum gauge, loosen

ADJUSTABLE FIXED ANCHORS

ECCENTRIC

ECCENTRIC

FIGURE 39–7 Eccentric anchor adjustment.

FIGURE 39–5 Types of brake shoe hold-downs.

PRIMARY SHOE

SWAGED TO BACKING PLATE

SELF-CENTERING (SLIDING) ANCHOR

THREADED INTO STEERING ARM

BOLTED ON

BOLTED TO BACKING PLATE

FIXED ANCHOR PINS

FIGURE 39–6 Types of brake shoe anchors.

drum rotates freely. Repeat this sequence until drag cannot be relieved. Tighten the anchor nut. Back off the star wheel to a normal manual adjustment.

On the slotted type anchor, tighten the star wheel to heavy drag. Tap the support plate until the anchor moves and frees the brake. Repeat this sequence until drag cannot be relieved. Tighten the lock nut to 100 to 200 foot-pounds torque. Back off the star wheel to a normal manual adjustment.

Drums

Modern automotive brake drums are made of heavy cast iron (some are aluminum with an iron or steel sleeve or liner) with a machined surface inside against which the linings on the brake shoes generate friction when the brakes are applied. This results in the creation of a great deal of heat. The inability of drums to dissipate as much heat as disc brakes is one of the main reasons discs have replaced drums at the front of all late-model cars and light trucks, and at the rear of some sports and luxury cars.

Sometimes the rear drums of FWD cars are integral with the hub and cannot be removed without disassembling the wheel bearing. The rear drums of other FWD and most RWD cars are held in place by the wheel lugs, so they can be removed without tampering with the wheel bearings.

DRUM BRAKE DESIGNS

There are two brake designs in common use. They are **duo-servo** (or self-energizing) drum brakes and **nonservo** (or leading-trailing) drum brakes.

Most large American cars use the duo-servo design of brake. However, the nonservo type has become popular as the size of cars have become smaller. Because the smaller cars are lighter, this type of brake helps reduce rear brake lockup without reducing breaking ability.

the locknut enough to permit the anchor to slip but not so much that it can tilt.

On eccentric anchors, tighten the star wheel to heavy brake drag (Figure 39–7). Rotate the eccentric anchor in the direction that frees the brake until drag is again encountered. Return the eccentric to the position between the two points of drag where the

FIGURE 39–8   Typical duo-servo drum brake.

FIGURE 39–10   Duo-servo braking forces.

Duo-Servo Drum Brakes

The name duo-servo brake drum is derived from the fact that the **self-energizing** force is transferred from one shoe to the other with the wheel rotating in either direction. Both the primary (front) and secondary (rear) brake shoes are actuated by a double-piston wheel cylinder (Figure 39–8). The upper end of each shoe is held against a single anchor by a heavy coil return spring. An adjusting screw assembly and spring connect the lower ends of the shoes.

The wheel cylinder is mounted on the backing plate at the top of the brake. When the brakes are applied, hydraulic pressure behind the wheel cylinder cups forces both pistons outward causing the brakes to be applied. Some wheel cylinders have extensions on the pistons that contact the brake shoes, while others have separate links (Figure 39–9).

When the brake shoes contact the rotating drum in either direction of rotation, they tend to move with the drum until one shoe contacts the anchor and the other shoe is stopped by the star wheel adjuster link (Figure 39–10). With forward rotation, frictional forces

between the lining and the drum of the primary shoe result in a force acting on the adjuster link to apply the secondary shoe. This adjuster link force into the secondary shoe is many times greater than the wheel cylinder input force acting on the primary shoe. The force of the adjuster link into the secondary shoe is again multiplied by the frictional forces between the secondary lining and rotating drum, and all of the resultant force is taken on the anchor pin. In normal forward braking, the friction developed by the secondary lining is greater than the primary lining. Therefore, the secondary brake lining is usually thicker and has more surface area. The roles of the primary and secondary linings are reversed in braking the vehicle when backing up.

Automatically Adjusted Servo Brakes

Since the early 1960s, automatic drum brake adjusters have been used on all American and most import vehicles. There are several variations of automatic adjusters used with servo brakes. The more common types available follow.

BASIC CABLE Figure 39–11 shows a typical automatic adjusting system. Adjusters, whether cable,

FIGURE 39–9   Wheel cylinder designs.

FIGURE 39–11   Cable self-adjusters.

FIGURE 39–12 Cable automatic adjustment with overtravel springs.

crank, or lever, are installed on one shoe and operated whenever the shoe moves away from its anchor. The upper link, or cable eye, is attached to the anchor. As the shoe moves, the cable pulls over a guide mounted on the shoe web (the crank or lever pivots on the shoe web) and operates a lever (pawl), which is attached to the shoe so it engages a star wheel tooth. The pawl is located on the outer side of the star wheel and, on different styles, slightly above or below the wheel centerline so it serves as a ratchet lock, which prevents the adjustment from backing off. However, whenever lining wears enough to permit sufficient shoe movement, brake application pulls the pawl high enough to engage the next tooth. As the brake is released, the adjuster spring returns the pawl, thus advancing the star wheel one notch.

On most vehicles, the adjuster system is installed on the secondary shoe and operates when the brakes are applied as the vehicle is backing up. On a few models, it is located on the primary shoe and operates when the brakes are applied as the vehicle is moving forward. Left-hand and right-hand threaded star wheels are used on opposite sides of the car, so parts should be kept separated. If the wrong star wheel thread is installed, the system does not adjust at all.

Another system uses a cable and pawl, with the left brake having right-hand threads and the right brake left-hand threads. The first cable guide is usually retained on the shoe web by the secondary shoe return spring, and the lever-pawl engages a hole in the shoe web. The adjuster operates in either direction of vehicle movement.

CABLE WITH OVERTRAVEL SPRING Figure 39–12 shows a system with an upstroke pawl advance. The left brake has left-hand threads, and the right brake has right-hand threads. The lever (pawl) is installed on a web pin with an additional pawl return mousetrap spring. The cable is hooked to the lever (pawl) by means of an **overtravel spring** installed in the cable hook. The overtravel spring dampens movements and prevents unnecessary adjustment should sudden hard braking cause excessive drum deflection and shoe movement.

LEVER WITH OVERRIDE The system illustrated in Figure 39–13 uses a downstroke pawl advance. The left brake has right-hand threads, and the right brake has left-hand threads.

FIGURE 39–13 Adjusting lever with pivot and override spring.

The lever (pawl) is mounted on a shoe hold-down, pivoting on a cup sleeve. It has a separate lever-pawl return spring located between the lever and the shoe table. A pivot lever and an override spring assembled to the upper end of the main lever dampen movement, preventing unnecessary adjustment in the event of excessive drum deflection.

LEVER AND PAWL The system illustrated in Figure 39–14 uses a downstroke pawl advance. The left brake has right-hand threads, and the right break has left-hand threads. The lever is mounted on a shoe hold-down, pivoting on a cup sleeve, and engages the pawl. A separate pawl return spring is located between the pawl and the shoe.

Nonservo Drum Brakes

The nonservo (or as it is better known today as the leading-trailing shoe) drum brake is often used on small cars. The basic difference between this type and the duo-servo brake is that both brake shoes are held against a fixed anchor at the bottom by a retaining spring (Figure 39–15). Nonservo brakes have no servo action.

On a forward brake application, the forward (leading) shoe friction forces are developed by wheel cylinder fluid pressure forcing the lining into contact with the rotating brake drum. The shoe's friction forces work against the anchor pin at the bottom of the shoe. The trailing shoe is also actuated by wheel cylinder pressure but can only support a friction force equal to the wheel cylinder piston forces. The trailing shoe anchor pin supports no friction load. The leading shoe in this brake is energized and does most of the braking in comparison to the nonenergized trailing shoe. In reverse braking, the leading and trailing brake shoes switch functions.

FIGURE 39–15 Typical nonservo drum brake.

SHOP TALK

It is important for the technician to remember that on nonservo drum systems the forward shoe is called the leading shoe and the rear one is known as the trailing shoe (when the vehicle is moving in the forward direction). On duo-servo designs, the forward shoe is the primary, and the rear is the secondary. ■

Nonservo, or leading-trailing shoe, drum brakes can be either manually adjusted or can have an automatic adjustment feature.

Manually Adjusted Nonservo Drum Brakes

There are several types of manually adjusted nonservo drum brake designs available. The two most common are lockheed manual and adjustable strut adjusters.

LOCKHEED MANUAL ADJUSTER This is a very simple brake system. The shoes are located on the top and bottom rather than the sides. The shoes are held tightly against the wheel cylinder and the adjusters by two retracting springs. Each shoe has to be adjusted individually by tightening it against the drum and then backing it off until the drum turns freely.

Depending upon what car this type of brake is used on, there will be differences in the brake shoes, adjusters, anchors, wheel cylinders, or parking brake linkage. It is best to work on one wheel at a time and use the other for reference.

ADJUSTABLE STRUT ADJUSTER On this design (Figure 39–16) the bottoms of the leading and trailing shoes are held against the anchor plate by shoe-to-anchor retaining springs. The top webs engage the wheel cylinder pistons and are straddled by a specially designed adjuster screw assembly. Return springs

FIGURE 39–14 Lever and pawl automatic adjustment.

FIGURE 39–16 Nonservo manually adjusted brake.

attached to the adjuster hole in the backing plate hold the shoes in against the adjuster screw assembly. One end engages the trailing shoe web and parking brake lever and the other end engages the leading shoe web.

The upper end of the parking brake lever is pinned to the upper end of the trailing shoe and the lower end is attached to the parking brake cable. When the cable is pulled, force is transmitted through the special adjuster assembly to the leading shoe. Shoe adjustment is done manually by inserting a thin bladed screwdriver through the hole in the backing plate and rotating the adjuster screw to spread the shoes.

Automatically Adjusted Nonservo Brakes

While some standard automatic adjusters similar to the one already discussed are employed on small cars, some of the automatic adjuster mechanisms are unique and varied, using expanding struts between the shoes, or special ratchet adjusting mechanisms. Among the more common of these designs are automatic cam, ratchet automatic, and semiautomatic adjusters.

AUTOMATIC CAM ADJUSTERS This rear nonservo drum brake is for use with front disc brakes and has one forward acting (leading) and one reverse acting (trailing) shoe. Shoes rest against the wheel cylinder pistons at the top and are held against the anchor plate by a shoe-to-shoe pull-back spring. The anchor plate and retaining plate are riveted to the backing plate. Adjustment of the brake shoes takes place automatically as needed when the brakes are applied. The

automatic cam adjusters are attached to each shoe by a pin through a slot in the shoe webbing. As the shoes move outward during application, the pin in the slot moves the cam adjuster, rotating it outward. Shoes always return enough to provide proper clearance because the pin diameter is smaller than the width of the slot (Figure 39–17).

RATCHET AUTOMATIC ADJUSTER These popular brakes are a leading-trailing shoe design with a ratchet self-adjusting mechanism. The shoes are held to the backing plate by spring and pin hold-downs, and are held against the anchors at the top by a shoe-to-shoe spring. At the bottom, the shoe webs are held against the wheel cylinder piston ends by a return spring (Figure 39–18).

The self-adjusting mechanism consists of a spacer strut and a pair of toothed ratchets attached to the secondary brake shoe. The parking brake actuating lever is pivoted on the spacer strut.

The self-adjusting mechanism automatically senses the correct lining-to-drum clearance. As the linings wear, the clearance is adjusted by increasing the effective length of the spacer strut. This strut has projections to engage the inner edge of the secondary shoe via the hand brake lever and the inner edge of the large ratchet on the secondary shoe. As wear on the linings increases, the movement of the shoes to bring them in contact with the drums becomes greater than the gap. The spacer strut, bearing on the shoe web, is moved together with the primary shoe to

FIGURE 39-17   Nonservo drum brake with automatic cam adjusters.

close the gap. Further movement causes the large ratchet behind the secondary shoe to rotate inward against the spring-loaded small ratchet, and the serrations on the mating edges maintain this new setting until further wear on the shoe results in another adjustment. On releasing brake pedal pressure, the return springs cause the shoes to move into contact with the shoulders of the spacer strut/hand brake actuating lever. This restores the clearance between the linings and the drum proportionate to the gap.

SEMIAUTOMATIC ADJUSTER This brake was designed to be used only as a rear wheel drum for a small car with front disc brakes (Figure 39-19). It has one forward-acting and one reverse-acting shoe.

A hold-down clip has replaced the hold-down spring, cup, and pin. A specially designed parking brake strut and rod assembly straddles the shoe webs just below the wheel cylinder. A shoe-to-shoe spring at the top and another at the bottom under the anchor plate hold the shoes in place.

The strut and rod assembly for the parking brake has the strut part on the forward shoe and the rod part connected to a hole in the reverse shoe. When the parking brake is applied, rear brake shoe adjustment is made. The strut and rod spread the shoes enough to pass the spring locks mounted in the assembly. The shoes are prevented from returning to their original position. Pressure on the brake shoes is released when the rod is relaxed, providing enough clearance for the wheels to turn.

FIGURE 39-18   Typical nonservo self-adjusting mechanism.

FIGURE 39–19 Nonservo drum brake featuring semiautomatic adjustments.

Inspection and Service

The first rule of quality brake service is to perform a complete job. For example, if new linings are installed without regard to the condition of the hydraulic system, the presence of a leaking wheel cylinder quickly ruins the new linings. Braking power and safety are also compromised.

Problems such as spongy pedal, excessive pedal travel, pedal pulsation, poor braking ability, brake drag, lock, or pulling to one side, and braking noises can be caused by trouble in the hydraulic system or the mechanical components of the brake assembly. To aid in doing a complete inspection and diagnosis, a form like the one shown in Figure 39–20 is very helpful. Working with such a form helps the technician avoid missing any brake test and components that may cause problems.

Brake Noise

All customer complaints related to brake performance must be carefully considered. The number one customer complaint is brake noise. Noise is often the first indication of wear or problems within the braking system, particularly in the mechanical components. Rattles, clicking, grinding, and hammering from the wheels when the brake is in the unapplied position should be carefully investigated. Be sure the noise is not caused by the bearings or various suspension parts. If the noise is coming from the brake assembly, it is most likely caused by worn, damaged, or missing brake hardware, or the poor fastening or mounting of brake components. Grinding noises usually occur when a stone or other object becomes trapped between the lining material and the rotor or drum.

When the brakes are applied, a clicking noise usually indicates play or hardware failure in the attachment of the pad or shoe. On recent systems, the noise could be caused by the lining tracking cutting tool marks in the rotor or drum. A nondirectional finish on rotors eliminates this and so does a less pointed tip on the cutting tool used to refinish drums.

Grinding noises on application can mean metal-to-metal contact, either from badly worn pads or shoes, or from a serious misalignment of the caliper, rotor, wheel cylinder, or backing plate. Wheel cylinders and calipers that are frozen due to internal corrosion can also cause grinding or squealing noises.

Other noise problems and their solutions are covered later in this chapter.

ROAD TESTING BRAKES

Road testing allows the brake technician to evaluate brake performance under actual driving conditions. Whenever practical, perform the road test before beginning any work on the brake system. In every case, road test the vehicle after any brake work to make sure the brake system is working safely and properly.

⚠️ WARNING!

Before test driving any car, first check the fluid level in the master cylinder. Depress the brake pedal to be sure there is adequate pedal reserve. Make a series of low-speed stops to be sure the brakes are safe for road testing. Always make a preliminary inspection of the brake system in the shop before taking the vehicle on the road. ∎

PREBRAKE JOB INSPECTION CHECKLIST

Owner _____   Phone _____   Date ___|___|___
       LAST   FIRST

Address _____   License No. _____

Make _____   Model _____   Mileage _____   Serial No. _____   Year _____

Special Key for Hubcaps/Wheels   Location _____   Owner Use Parking Brake Yes ☐ No ☐

      4 Drum ☐ 4 Disc ☐ Disc/Drum ☐ P/B No ☐ Yes ☐ Vacuum ☐ Hydro ☐ ABS ☐

Owner Comments _____

1. CHECKS BEFORE ROAD TEST	Safe	Unsafe
Stoplight Operation		
Brake Warning Light Operation		
Master Cylinder Checks		
Fluid Level		
Fluid Contamination		
Under Hood Fluid Leaks		
Under Dash Fluid Leaks (No Power)		
Bypassing		

BRAKE PEDAL HEIGHT AND FEEL

Check One		Check One	
Low		Spongy	
Med		Firm	
High			

Power Brake Unit Checks

VACUUM	Safe	Unsafe	HYDRO	Safe	Unsafe
Vacuum Unit			Hydro Unit		
Engine Vacuum			P/S Fluid		
Vacuum Hose			P/S Belt Tension		
Unit Check Valve			P/S Belt Condition		
Reserve Braking			P/S Fluid Leaks		
			Reserve Braking		

3. In Shop Checks On Hoist	Yes	No	RF	LF	RR	LR
Brake Drag						
Intermittent Brake Drag						
Brake Pedal Linkage Binding						
Wheel Bearing Looseness						
Missing or Broken Wheel Fasteners						
Suspension Looseness						

Tire Pressure Specs	Front	Rear
Record Pressure Found		

RF _____ LF _____ RR _____ LR _____

Tire Condition

RF _____ LF _____ RR _____ LR _____

2. ROAD TEST	Yes	No	RF	LF	RR	LR
Brake Pull						
Brake Clunk						
Brake Scraping						
Brake Squeal						
Brake Grabby						
Brakes Lock Prematurely						
Wheel Bearing Noise						
Vehicle Vibrates						

STEERING WHEEL MOVEMENT WHEN STOPPING
FROM 2-3 MPH YES/NO/RGT/LFT

Does ABS Work	YES	NO
Pedal Pulsation when Braking	YES	NO
Steering Wheel Oscillation when Braking	YES	NO
No Stopping Power	YES	NO
Warning Light Comes on when Braking	YES	NO
Difference in Pedal Height after Cornering	YES	NO
Nose Dive	YES	NO

	Front					Rear				
	Right		Left			Right			Left	
	Spec	Safe	Unsafe	Safe	Unsafe	Spec	Safe	Unsafe	Safe	Unsafe
Mark Wheels and Remove										
Caliper/Piston Stuck RF LF RR LR										
Mark Drums and Remove										
Measure Rotor Thickness or Drum Diameter.										
Measure Rotor Thickness Variation.										
Measure Rotor Runout.										
Lining Thickness										
Tubes and Hoses										
Fluid Leaks										
Broken Bleeders										
Leaky Seals										
Self-Adjuster Operation									Safe	Unsafe
Parking Brake Cables and Linkage										

FIGURE 39-20 Sample of prebrake job inspection checklist. *Courtesy of Hennessy Industries, Inc.*

Brakes should be road tested on a dry, clean, reasonably smooth, and level roadway. A true test of brake performance cannot be made if the roadway is wet, greasy, or covered with loose dirt. All tires do not grip the road equally. Testing is also adversely affected if the roadway is crowned so as to throw the weight of the vehicle toward the wheels on one side, or if the roadway is so rough that wheels tend to bounce.

Test brakes at different speeds with both light and heavy pedal pressure. Avoid locking the wheels and sliding the tires on the roadway. There are external conditions that affect brake road-test performance. Tires having unequal contact and grip on the road cause unequal braking. Tires must be equally inflated, and the tread pattern of right and left tires must be approximately equal. When the vehicle has unequal loading, the most heavily loaded wheels require more braking power than others and a heavily loaded vehicle requires more braking effort. A loose front-wheel bearing permits the drum and wheel to tilt and have spotty contact with the brake linings, causing erratic brake action. Misalignment of the front end causes the brakes to pull to one side. Also, a loose front-wheel bearing could permit the disc to tilt and have spotty contact with brake shoe linings, causing pulsations when the brakes are applied. Faulty shock absorbers that do not prevent the car from bouncing on quick stops can give the erroneous impression that the brakes are too severe.

DRUM BRAKE INSPECTION

Before inspecting drum brakes, place the vehicle in neutral, release the parking brake, and raise the vehicle on the hoist. Once the vehicle is raised, mark the wheel-to-drum and drum-to-axle positions so the components can be accurately reassembled. Relieve all tension from the parking brake cable by loosening or removing the adjusting nut at the equalizer. To access the drum brake assembly, remove the lug nuts and pull the wheel off the hub.

● CAUTION:

When servicing wheel brake parts, do not create dust by cleaning with a dry brush or with compressed air. Asbestos fibers can become airborne if dust is created during servicing. Breathing dust containing asbestos fibers can cause serious bodily harm. To clean away asbestos from brake surfaces, use an OSHA-approved washer (Figure 39–21). Follow manufacturer's instructions when using the washer. ■

Shoe and Lining Removal

Several different methods are used to mount the drum to the wheel hub flange. It can be fastened with rivets or by swaging the piloting shoulders of the wheel studs, or with speed nut fasteners installed over the threads of the wheel studs.

The most common mounting method is to use the tire rim and lug nuts. The drum is a slip fit over the axle flange and studs. Speed nuts are installed at the vehicle manufacturing plant for temporary reten-

FIGURE 39–21 Washer used to safely remove asbestos fibers from brake surfaces.

tion of the drum on the assembly line until the wheel is installed.

A **floating drum** can be retained by a nut and cotter pin. The drum can also be secured to the axle flange by one or two bolts. Some import applications have two additional holes threaded into the drum face so bolts can be used to press the drum from the hub or flange.

After removing the retaining devices that hold the drum to the axle flange or hub, the drum can be removed for servicing. If the brake drum is rusted or corroded to the axle flange and cannot be removed, lightly tap the axle flange to the drum mounting surface with a plastic mallet. Remember that if the drum is worn, the brake shoe adjustment has to be backed off for the drums to clear the brake shoes. Do not force the drum or distort it. Do not allow the drum to drop.

If the brake shoes have expanded too tightly against the drum or have cut into the friction surface of the drum brake, the drums might be too tight for removal. In such a case, the shoes must be adjusted inward before the brake drum is removed. On most cars with self-adjusting mechanisms, reach through the adjusting slot with a thin screwdriver (or similar tool) and carefully push the self-adjusting lever away from the star wheel a maximum of 1/16 inch (Figure 39–22). While holding the lever back, insert a brake adjusting tool into the slot and turn the star wheel in the proper direction until the brake drum can be removed.

On cars that have the adjusting slot in the drum rather than in the backing plate, reach through the slot with a thin wire hook and pull the adjuster lever away from the star wheel slackening the adjustment. If the

ADJUSTER HOLE

ADJUSTER LEVER
PUSH BACK 1/16-IN.
MAX (1.5 mm)

MOVE HANDLE UPWARD
TO RETRACT BRAKE
SHOES AND DOWNWARD
TO EXPAND.

FIGURE 39–22 Removing brake drums equipped with self-adjusters.

slot in the drum is not open, knock out the center of the slot-shaped lanced area with a punch or chisel.

Be sure to inspect the rear wheel axle gaskets and wheel seals for leaks. Replace worn components as needed.

Drum Inspection

One of the most important safety inspections to be made is that of the brake drum (Figure 39–23). First, visually inspect the brake shoes, as installed on the car. Their condition can, many times, reveal defects in the drums. If the linings on one wheel are worn more than the others, it might indicate a rough drum. Uneven wear from side to side on any one set of shoes can be caused by a tapered drum. If some linings are worn badly at the toe or heel, it might indicate an out-of-round drum.

Thoroughly clean the drums with a water-dampened cloth or a water-based solution. Equipment for washing brake parts is commercially available. Wet cleaning methods must be used to prevent asbestos fibers from becoming airborne. If the drums have been exposed to leaking oil or grease, thoroughly clean them with a non-oil-based solvent after washing to remove dust and dirt. It is important to determine the source of the oil or grease leak and correct the problem before reinstalling the drums.

FIGURE 39–23 Checking the condition of the drum.

Brake drums act as a heat sink. They absorb heat and dissipate it into the air. As drums wear from normal use or are machined, their cooling surface area is reduced and their operating temperatures increase. Structural strength also reduces. This leads to over-distortion, which causes some of the drum conditions covered here.

SCORED DRUM SURFACE Figure 39–24A shows a scored drum surface. The most common cause of this condition is buildup of brake dust and dirt between the brake lining and drum. A glazed brake lining, hardened by high heat or in some cases by very hard inferior grade brake lining, can also groove the drum surface. Excessive lining wear that exposes the rivet head or shoe steel will score the drum surface. If the grooves are not too deep, the drum can be turned.

BELL-MOUTHED DRUM Figure 39–24B shows a distortion due to extreme heat and braking pressure. It occurs mostly on wide drums and is caused by poor support at the outside of the drum. Full drum-to-lining contact cannot be achieved and fading can be expected. Drums must be turned.

CONCAVE DRUM Figure 39–24C shows an excessive wear pattern in the center area of the drum brake surface. Extreme braking pressure can distort the shoe platform so braking pressure is concentrated at the center of the drum.

CONVEX DRUM This wear pattern is greater at the closed end of the drum (Figure 39–24D). It is the result of excessive heat or an oversized drum, which allows the open end of the drum to distort.

HARD SPOTS ON THE DRUM This condition in the cast-iron surface (Figure 39–24E), sometimes called chisel spots or islands of steel, results from a change in metallurgy caused by braking heat. Chatter, pulling, rapid wear, hard pedal, and noise occur. These spots can be removed by grinding. However, only the raised surfaces are removed, and they can reappear when heat is applied. The drum must be replaced.

THREADED DRUM SURFACE An extremely sharp or chipped tool bit or a lathe that turns too fast can result in a threaded drum surface (Figure 39–24F). This condition can cause a snapping sound during brake application as the shoes ride outward on the thread, then snap back. To avoid this, recondition drums using a rounded tool and proper lathe speed. Check the edge of the drum surface around the mounting flange side for tool marks indicating a previous rebore. If the drum has been rebored, it might have worn too thin for use. Check the diameter.

FIGURE 39–24 Drum conditions that require servicing or replacement of the drum.

HEAT CHECKS Heat checks are visible, unlike hard spots that do not appear until the machining of the drum (Figure 39–25A). Extreme operating temperatures are the major cause. The drum might also show a bluish/gold tint, which is a sign of high temperatures. Hardened carbide lathe bits or special grinding attachments are available through lathe manufacturers to service these conditions. Excessive damage by heat checks or hard spots requires drum replacement.

CRACKED DRUM Cracks in the cast-iron drum are caused by excessive stress (Figure 39–25B). They can be anywhere but usually are in the vicinity of the bolt circle or at the outside of the flange. Fine cracks in the drums are often hard to see and, unfortunately, often do not show up until after machining. Nevertheless, should any cracks appear, no matter how small, the drum must be replaced (Figure 39–25C).

OUT-OF-ROUND DRUMS Drums with eccentric distortion might appear good to the eye but cause pulling, grabbing, and pedal vibration or pulsation. An out-of-round or egg-shaped condition (Figure 39–26) is often caused by heating and cooling during normal brake operation. Out-of-round drums can be detected before the drum is removed by adjusting the brake to a light drag and feeling the rotation of the drum by hand. After removing the drum, gauge it to determine the amount of eccentric distortion. Drums with this defect should be machined or replaced.

Drum Measurements

Measure every drum with a drum micrometer (Figure 39–27) even if the drum passed a visual inspection to make sure that it is within the safe oversize limits. If the drum is within safe limits, even though the surface appears smooth, it should be turned to assure a true drum surface and to remove any possible contamination in the surface from previous brake linings, road dust, etc. Remember that if too much metal is removed from a drum, unsafe conditions can result.

FIGURE 39–25 (A) Heat checks, (B) cracks, and (C) broken areas. The latter two conditions require replacement.

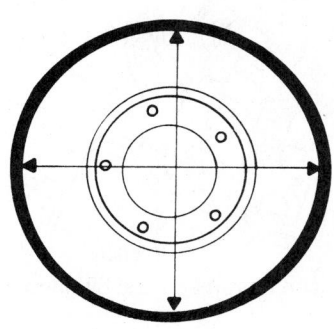

FIGURE 39–26 Measure the inside diameter of the drum in several spots to determine out-of-roundness.

FIGURE 39–27 Measuring the inside diameter with a drum micrometer.

Take measurements at the open and closed edges of the friction surface and at right angles to each other. Drums with taper or out-of-roundness exceeding 0.006 inch are unfit for service and should be turned or replaced. If the maximum diameter reading (measured from the bottom of any grooves that might be present) exceeds the new drum diameter by more than 0.060 inch, the drum cannot be reworked. If the drums are smooth and true but exceed the new diameter by 0.090 inch or more, they must be replaced.

If the drums are true, smooth up any slight scores by polishing with fine emery cloth. If deep scores or grooves are present that cannot be removed by this method, the drum must be turned or replaced.

Drum Refinishing

Brake drums can be refinished by either turning or grinding on a **brake lathe** (Figure 39–28).

Only enough metal should be removed to obtain a true, smooth friction surface. When one drum must be machined to remove defects, the other drum on the same axle set must also be machined in the same manner and to the same diameter so braking is equal.

FIGURE 39–28 Brake drums can be remachined by grinding or turning on a brake lathe.

FIGURE 39–29 The drum's discard diameter is stamped on the drum.

Brake drums are stamped with a discard dimension (Figure 39–29). This is the allowable wear dimension and not the allowable machining dimension. There must be 0.030 inch left for wear after turning the drums. Some states have laws about measuring the limits of a brake drum.

Machining or grinding brake drums increases the inside diameter of the drum and changes the lining-to-drum fit. When remachining a drum, follow the equipment instructions for the specific tool you are using.

Cleaning Newly Refaced Drums

The friction surface of a newly refaced drum contains millions of tiny metal particles. These particles not only remain free on the surface, they always lodge themselves in the open pores of the newly machined surface. If the metal particles are allowed to remain in the drum, they become imbedded in the brake lining. Once the brake lining gets contaminated in this manner, it acts as a fine grinding stone and scores the drum.

These metal particles must be removed by washing or cleaning the drum. Do not blow out the drum with air pressure. Either of the following methods is recommended to clean a newly refaced brake drum. The first method involves washing the brake drum thoroughly with hot water and wiping with a lint-free rag. Then, use the air pressure to thoroughly dry it. If the front hub and drums are being cleaned, be very careful to avoid contaminating the wheel bearing grease. Or, completely remove all the old grease, then regrease and repack the wheel bearing after the drum has been cleaned and dried. The wheel bearings and the grease seals must be removed from the drum before cleaning. The second method involves wiping the inside of the brake drum (especially the newly machined surface) with a lint-free white cloth dipped in one of the many available brake cleaning solvents that do not leave a residue. This operation should be repeated until dirt is no longer apparent on the wiping cloth. Allow the drum to dry before reinstalling it on the vehicle.

Both of these procedures are also good for cleaning disc brake rotors.

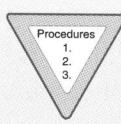

PROCEDURES

Mechanical Component Service of Duo-Servo Drum Brakes

1. Disconnect the cable from the parking brake lever.
2. If required, install wheel cylinder clamps on the wheel cylinders to prevent fluid leakage or air from getting into the system while the shoes are removed. Some brakes have wheel cylinder stops; therefore, wheel cylinder clamps are not required. Regardless of whether or not the clamps are needed, do not press down on the brake pedal after shoe return springs have been removed. To prevent this, block up the brake pedal so it cannot be depressed.

SHOP TALK

Keep the adjusting screws and automatic adjuster parts for left and right brakes separate. These parts usually are different. For example, on many automatic adjusters, the adjusting screws on the right brakes have left-hand threads and the adjusting screws on the left brakes have right-hand threads. ■

3. Remove the brake shoe return springs. Use a brake spring removal and installation tool to unhook the springs from the anchor pin or anchor plate (Figure 39–30). In some cases, the return springs might not be attached directly to the anchor pin. One spring might be hooked over the adjusting mechanism link, which is in turn installed over the anchor pin. Or, both springs can be hooked onto an anchor plate. Regardless of how springs are attached, carefully note the location, position, and color of all springs before removing any so they can be reinstalled properly.

WARNING!

Do not use the brake spring tool to remove the adjusting link from the anchor pin or anchor plate. ■

4. Remove the shoe retaining or hold-down cups and springs. Special tools are available, but the hold-down springs can be removed by using pliers to compress the spring and rotating the cup with relation to the pin.

5. Self-adjuster parts can now be removed. Lift off the actuating link, lever and pivot assembly, sleeve (through lever), and return spring. No advantage is gained by disassembling the lever and pivot assembly unless one of the parts is damaged.
6. Spread the shoes slightly to free the parking brake strut and remove the strut with its spring. Disconnect the parking brake lever from the secondary shoe. It can be attached with a retaining clip, bolt, or simply hooked into the shoe.
7. Slip the anchor plate off the pin. No advantage is gained by removing the plate if it is bolted on or riveted. Spread the anchor ends of the shoes and disengage from the wheel cylinder links, if used. Remove the shoes connected at the bottom by the adjusting screw and spring, as an assembly.
8. Overlap the anchor end of the shoes to relieve spring tension. Unhook the adjusting screw spring, and remove the adjusting screw assembly.

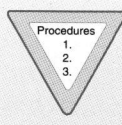

PROCEDURES

Disassembling Nonservo or Leading-Trailing Brakes

1. Install the wheel cylinder clamp. Then unhook the adjuster spring from the parking brake strut and reverse shoe.
2. Unhook the upper shoe-to-shoe spring from the shoes and unhook the antinoise spring from the spring bracket.
3. Remove the parking brake strut and disengage the shoe webs from the flat, clamp shoe hold-down clips.

(continued)

FIGURE 39–30 Using a spring removal tool to remove the return springs.

4. Unhook the lower shoe-to-shoe spring and remove the forward shoe. Disconnect the parking brake cable, then remove the reserve shoe.
5. Remove the shoe hold-down clips from the backing plate.
6. Press off the C-shaped retainers from the pins and remove the parking brake lever, automatic adjuster lever, and adjuster latch.

SHOP TALK

Mark the shoe positions if shoe and linings are to be reused. When disassembling an unfamiliar brake assembly, work on one wheel at a time and use the other wheel as a reference. ∎

7. Remove the parking brake lever.

Cleaning, Inspecting, and Lubricating Brake Parts

CAUTION:

When servicing wheel brake parts, do not create dust by cleaning with a dry brush or compressed air. ∎

PROCEDURES

Cleaning and Inspecting Brake Parts

1. Clean the backing plates, struts, levers, and other metal parts to be reused using a water-dampened cloth or a water-based solution. Equipment is commercially available to perform washing functions of brake parts. Wet cleaning methods must be used to prevent asbestos fibers from becoming airborne.
2. Carefully examine the raised shoe pads on the backing plate to make sure they are free from corrosion or other surface defects that might prevent the shoes from sliding freely. Use fine emery cloth to remove surface defects, if necessary. Clean them thoroughly.
3. At the rear wheels, look for evidence of oil or grease leakage past the wheel bearing seals. Such leakage could cause brake failure and indicates the need for additional service work.

4. Check that the backing plates are not cracked or bent. If so, they must be replaced. Make sure backing plate bolts and bolted-on anchor pins are torqued to specifications.
5. If replacement of the wheel cylinder is needed, it should be done at this time. To determine wheel cylinder condition, carefully inspect the boots. If they are cut, torn, heat-cracked, or show evidence of excessive leakage, the wheel cylinders should be replaced. On cylinders with external boots, carefully pull back the lower edge of the boot. If more than a drop of fluid spills out, leakage is excessive and indicates that replacement is necessary. If the wheel cylinders have internal boots, carefully remove one of the wheel cylinder connecting links to check for leakage.

SHOP TALK

A slight amount of fluid behind the boot is normal. This lubricates the piston. However, if enough fluid is present to run or spill out, this indicates excessive leakage. ∎

6. Disassemble the adjusting screw assembly (Figure 39–31) and clean the parts in a suitable solvent. Make sure the adjusting screw threads into the pivot nut over its complete length without sticking or binding. Check that none of the adjusting screw teeth are damaged, particularly on self-adjusting brakes. Lubricate the adjusting screw threads with brake lubricant, being careful not to get any on the adjusting teeth, and reassemble. Most adjusting screw assemblies use a thrust washer between the adjusting screw and socket. Some might also have the antinoise spring washer. Thread the adjusting screw in as far as it goes.

WARNING!

Do not use ordinary grease to lubricate drum brake parts. It does not hold up under high temperatures. ∎

7. Apply a thin film of a brake lubricant to the raised shoe pads on the backing plate lands. Check that there are no burrs on the edges of the replacement shoes where they contact the pads. On the rear brakes, lubricate the parking brake lever pivot point.

Antiseize lubrication works very well as brake lubricant. ∎

8. Examine the shoe anchor, support plate, and small parts for signs of looseness, wear, or damage that could cause faulty shoe alignment. Check springs for spread or collapsed coils, twisted or nicked shanks, and severe discoloration. Operate star wheel automatic adjusters by prying the shoe lightly away from its anchor or by pulling the cable to make sure the adjuster advances easily, one notch at a time. Adjuster cables tend to stretch, and star wheels and pawls become blunted after a long period of use. For rear-axle parking brakes, pull on the cable and shoe linkage to make sure no binding condition is present that could cause the shoes to drag when the parking brake is released.

Some brake technicians check brake spring tension by the drop method. This method is not overly scientific and the results are not always correct. Drop the brake spring on a clean concrete floor. If it bounces with a chunky sound, it is good. If the bounced spring gives off a tinny sound, it is tired and should be replaced. ∎

To complete the drum brake inspection, examine wheel bearings and hub grease seals for signs of damage. Service or replace, if necessary.

FIGURE 39–31 Exploded view of adjusting screw assembly.

BRAKE SHOES AND LININGS

Lining materials influence braking operation. The use of a lining with a friction value that is too high can result in a severe grabbing condition. A friction value that is too low can make stopping difficult because of a hard pedal.

Overheating a lining accelerates wear and can result in dangerous lining heat fade—a friction-reducing condition that hardens the pedal and lengthens the stopping distance. Continual overheating eventually pushes the lining beyond the point of recovery into a permanent fade condition. In addition to fade, overheating can cause squeal.

Overheating is indicated by a lining that is charred or has a glass-hard glazed surface, or if severe, random cracking of the surface is present.

CAUTION:

Automotive friction materials often contain substantial amounts of asbestos. Studies indicate that exposure to excessive amounts of asbestos dust can be a potential health hazard. It is important that anyone handling brake linings understands this and takes the necessary precautions to avoid injury. ∎

Inspect the linings for uneven wear, imbedded foreign material, loose rivets, and to see if they are oil soaked. If linings are oil soaked, replace them.

If linings are otherwise serviceable, tighten or replace loose rivets, remove imbedded foreign material, and clean the rivet counterbores.

If linings at any wheel show a spotty wear pattern or an uneven contact with the brake drum, it is an indication that the linings are not centered in the drums. Linings should be circle ground to provide better contact with the drum.

Brake Relining

Brake linings that are worn to within 1/32 inch of a rivet head or that have been contaminated with brake fluid, grease, or oil must be replaced (Figure 39–32). Failure to replace worn linings results in a scored drum. When it is necessary to replace brake shoes, they must also be replaced on the wheel on the opposite side of the vehicle. Inspect brake shoes for distortion, cracks, or looseness. If these conditions exist, the shoe must be discarded.

Do not let brake fluid, oil, or grease touch the brake lining. If a brake lining kit is used to replace the linings, follow the instructions in the kit and install all the parts provided.

FIGURE 39–32 Checking drum brake lining thickness using a depth gauge.

The two general methods of attaching the linings to the brake shoes are bonding and riveting (Figure 39–33). The **bonded linings** are fastened with a special adhesive to the shoe, clamped in place, then cured in an oven. Instead of using an adhesive, some linings are riveted to the shoe. Riveted linings allow for better heat transfer than bonded linings.

Sizing New Linings

Modern brake shoes are usually supplied with what is known as cam, offset, contour, or eccentric shape (Figure 39–34), which is ground in at the factory. That is, the full thickness of the lining is present at the middle of the shoe, but is ground down slightly at the heel and toe. The diameter of the circle the shoes make is slightly smaller than that of the drum. This compensates for the minor tolerance variations of drums and brake mountings and promotes proper wearing-in of the linings to match the drum.

FIGURE 39–33 Examples of riveted and bonded brake shoe linings.

CONCENTRIC GRIND

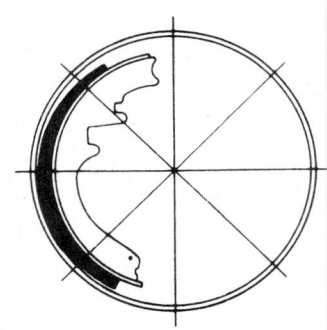

TYPICAL OEM OFFSET GRIND (FURNISHED ON NEW VEHICLES)

CONTOUR (ECCENTRIC) GRIND [SERVO, 0.050 IN. (1.3 mm) UNDERSIZE]

CONTOUR (ECCENTRIC) GRIND [NON-SERVO, 0.030 IN. (0.75 mm) UNDERSIZE]

FIGURE 39–34 Various types of brake shoe lining grinds.

On duo-servo shoe designs, the forward shoe is the primary and the rear, the secondary. The secondary shoe lining is longer.

Lining Adjustment

New **eccentric-ground** linings tolerate a closer new lining clearance adjustment than concentric ground linings. With manual adjusters, the shoes should be expanded into the drums until the linings are at the point of drag but not dragging heavily against the drum. With star wheel automatic adjusters, a drum/shoe gauge provides a convenient means of making the preliminary adjustment. This type of gauge, when set at actual drum diameter, automatically provides the working clearance of the shoes. If new linings have been concentrically ground, the initial clearance adjustment must be backed off an amount that provides sufficient working clearance.

Many technicians take pride in showing the customer a high pedal, but it should be remembered that with new linings an extremely high pedal indicates tight clearances and can cause seating problems.

Drum Shoe and Brake Installation

Before installing the shoes, be sure to sand or stone the inner edge of the shoe to dress down any slight lining or metal nicks and burrs that could interfere with the sliding upon the support pads.

A support (backing) plate must be tight on its mount and not bent. Stone the shoe support pads brightly and dress down any burrs or grooves that could cause the shoes to bind or hang up.

Using an approved lubricant, lightly coat the support pads and the threads of servo star wheel adjusters. On rear axle parking brakes, lubricate any point of potential binding in the linkage and the cable. Do not lubricate nonservo brake adjusters other than to free a frozen adjuster with penetrating oil.

Reassemble the brakes in the reverse order of disassembly. Make sure all parts are in their proper locations and that both brake shoes are properly positioned in either end of the adjuster. Also, both brake shoes should correctly engage the wheel cylinder pushrods and parking brake links. They should be centered on the backing plate. Parking brake links and levers should be in place on the rear brakes. With all of the parts in place, try the fit of the brake drum over the new shoes. If not slightly snug, pull it off and turn the star wheel until a slight drag is felt when sliding on the drum. A brake preset gauge makes this job easy and final brake adjustment simple. Then install the brake drum, wheel bearings, spindle nuts, cotter pins, dust caps, and wheel/tire assemblies, and make the final brake adjustments as specified in individual instructions in the vehicle's service manual. Torque the spindle and lug nuts to specifications.

WHEEL CYLINDER INSPECTION AND SERVICING

Wheel cylinders might need replacement when the brake shoes are replaced or when they begin to leak.

Inspecting and Cleaning Wheel Cylinders

Wheel cylinder leaks reveal themselves in several ways: (1) fluid can be found when the dust boot is peeled back; (2) the cylinder, linings, and backing plate, or the inside of a tire might be wet; or (3) there might be a drop in the level of fluid in the master cylinder reservoir.

Such leaks can cause the brakes to grab or fail and should be immediately corrected. Note the amount of fluid present when the dust boot is pulled back. A small amount of fluid seepage dampening the interior of the boot is normal. A dripping boot is not.

WARNING!

Hydraulic system parts should not be allowed to come in contact with oil or grease. They should not be handled with greasy hands. Even a trace of any petroleum-based product is sufficient to cause damage to the rubber parts.

Cylinder binding can be caused by rust deposits, swollen cups due to fluid contamination, or by a cup wedged into an excessive piston clearance. If the clearance between the pistons and the bore wall exceeds allowable values, a condition called heel drag might exist. It can result in rapid cup wear and can cause the piston to retract very slowly when the brakes are released.

Evidence of a scored, pitted, or corroded cylinder bore is a ring of hard, crystal-like substance. This substance is sometimes noticed in the cylinder bore where the piston rests after the brakes are released.

Light roughness or deposits can be removed with crocus cloth or an approved cylinder hone. While honing lightly, brake fluid can be used as a lubricant. If the bore cannot be cleaned up readily, the cylinder must be replaced.

PROCEDURES

Replacing a Wheel Cylinder

1. Since brake hoses are an important link in the hydraulic system, it is recommended they be replaced when a new cylinder is to be installed or when the old cylinder is to be reconditioned. Remove the brake shoe assemblies from the backing plate before proceeding. The smallest amount of brake fluid contaminates the friction surface of the brake lining.

2. Using two appropriate wrenches, disconnect the hydraulic hose from the steel line located on the chassis. On solid rear axles, use the appropriate tubing wrench and disconnect the hydraulic line where it enters the wheel cylinder. Care must be exercised in removing this steel line. It might be bent at this point and be difficult to install once new wheel cylinders are mounted to the backing plate.

3. Remove the plates, shims, and bolts that hold the wheel cylinder to the backing plate (Figure 39–35). Some later designed wheel cylinders are held to the backing plate with a retaining ring (Figure 39–36) that can be removed with two small picks.

4. Remove the wheel cylinder from the backing plate and clean the area with a proper cleaning solvent.

FIGURE 39–35   Lock plates and shims can be used to hold the wheel cylinder to the backing plate.

FIGURE 39–36   Example of a wheel cylinder retaining ring.

Care must be taken when installing new or reconditioned wheel cylinders on cars equipped with wheel cylinder piston stops. The rubber dust boots and the pistons must be squeezed into the cylinder before it is tightened to the backing plate. If this is not done, the pistons jam against the stops causing hydraulic fluid leaks and erratic brake performance.

DRUM PARKING BRAKES

The parking brake keeps a vehicle from rolling while it is parked. It is important to remember that the parking brake is not part of the vehicle's hydraulic braking system. It works mechanically, using a lever assembly connected through a cable system to the rear drum service brakes.

Types of Parking Brake Systems

Parking brakes can be either hand or foot operated. In general, downsized cars and light trucks use hand-operated self-adjusting lever systems (Figure 39–37). Full-size vehicles normally use a foot-operated park-

FIGURE 39–37   Typical center-mounted hand-operated parking brake.

FIGURE 39–38 Typical pedal-operated parking brakes: (A) mechanical release and (B) vacuum release.

ing brake pedal (Figure 39–38A). The pedal or lever assembly is designed to latch into an applied position and is released by pulling a brake release handle or pushing a release button.

On some vehicles, a vacuum power unit (Figure 39–38B) is connected by a rod to the upper end of the release lever. The vacuum motor is actuated to release the parking brake whenever the engine is running and the transmission is in forward driving gear. The lower end of the release lever extends down for alternate manual release in the event of vacuum power failure or for optional manual release at any time. Hoses connect the power unit and the engine manifold to a vacuum release valve on the steering column.

The starting point of a typical parking brake cable and lever system is the foot pedal (Figure 39–39) or hand lever. This assembly is a variable ratio lever mechanism that converts input effort of the operator

and pedal/lever travel into output force with less travel. In the system shown in Figure 39–39, as the pedal is being depressed, the attached front cable assembly tightens increasingly as it moves a short distance (by comparison to the pedal's travel distance). Tensile force from the front cable is transmitted through the car's brake cable system to the rear brakes. This tension pulls the flexible steel cables attached to each of the rear brakes. It serves to operate the internal lever and strut mechanism of each rear brake, expanding the brake shoes against the drum. Springs return the shoes to the unapplied position when the parking brake pedal is released and tensile forces in the cable system are relaxed.

CUSTOMER CARE

Drivers of vehicles equipped with an automatic transmission may sometimes develop the bad habit of resting their left foot on the brake pedal. The effect of this slight pressure is constant braking action that can quickly wear out components. Wear normally occurs in the brake assembly where the

FIGURE 39–39 Typical parking brake cable and lever system.

return springs, seals, and pistons have slightly less mechanical resistance than the other three wheels. In effect, this brake is constantly applied.

On vehicles driven in stop-and-go traffic only, the weak brake assembly may be affected. In vehicles driven at constant highway speeds, all four assemblies may quickly become worn and burnt. The true danger involved is that excessive heat may lead to hydraulic fluid evaporation and brake failure.

Suspect this problem when signs of accelerated wear are present. Ask the customer how often the braking system requires service. Inspect the brake pedal for signs of wear. If the left foot brake condition is apparent, let the customer know that the cause of the problem is not the quality of the replacement parts or service. ∎

An electronic switch, triggered when the brake pedal is applied, lights the brake indicator in the instrument panel when the ignition is turned on. The light goes out when either the pedal or control is released or the ignition is turned off.

The cable/lever routing system in a typical parking brake arrangement (Figure 39–40) employs a three lever setup to multiply the physical effort of the operator. First is the pedal assembly or hand grip. When moved, it multiplies the operator's effect and pulls the front cable. The front cable, in turn, pulls the equalizer lever.

The **equalizer lever** multiplies the effort of the pedal assembly, or hand grip, and pulls the rear cables. This pulling effort passes through an equalizer, which ensures equal pull on both rear cables. The equalizer functions by allowing the rear brake cables to slip slightly to balance out small differences in cable length or adjustment. Typical equalizer arrangements are shown in Figure 39–41.

USING SERVICE MANUALS

Service manuals list the standard brake drum inside diameter along with the discard dimension. They also state the standard and minimum lining thickness. Manual illustrations should be used to accurately identify all components plus the disassemble/reassembly procedure. Tightening torques for backing plate nuts and other components should always be followed. ∎

The rear cables pull the parking brake levers in the drum brake assembly (Figure 39–42). As for the parking brakes themselves, there are several types in use. The integral or conventional rear drum parking brake is part of the vehicle's ordinary rear drum system. It utilizes the same friction elements as the hydraulic brakes. The transmission or drive shaft parking brake system operates independently of the rear wheel brakes. These parking brakes are known in the trade as drive shaft brakes.

FIGURE 39–40   Typical parking brake routing to the rear drum brakes.

FIGURE 39–41 Types of equalizers used to apply even application force to each rear brake.

3. LEVER WORKS AGAINST LINK, AND PIVOT FORCES SECONDARY SHOE AGAINST THE DRUM.

2. LEVER MOVES LINK AGAINST PRIMARY SHOE AND SHOE AGAINST DRUM.

CONDUIT

1. CABLE PULLS LEVER.

FIGURE 39–42 Integral drum brake parking brake operation.

INTEGRAL PARKING BRAKES

Integral parking brakes are for vehicles with rear wheel drum brakes. Figure 39–43 shows a typical integral parking brake. When the parking brake pedal is applied, the cables and equalizer exert a balanced pull on the parking brake levers of both rear brakes. The levers and the parking brake struts move the shoes outward against the brake drums. The shoes are held in this position until the parking brake pedal is released. The portion of the parking brake from the equalizer on back to the rear wheel drum brake is shown in Figure 39–43. Also, the parking brake components are shown removed from the wheel brake for identification.

The rear cable enters each rear brake through a conduit (Figure 39–44). The cable end engages the lower end of the parking brake lever. This lever is hinged to the web of the secondary shoe and linked with the primary shoe by means of a strut. The lever and strut expand both shoes away from the anchor and wheel cylinder and into contact with the drum as the cable and lever are drawn forward. The shoe return springs reposition the shoes when the cable is slacked.

To remove and replace the rear brake shoes, it might be necessary to relieve the parking brake cable tension by backing off the adjusting check nuts at the equalizer. Count the turns backed off in order to restore the nuts to their original position.

Adjusting and Replacing Parking Brakes

Regular wheel brake service should be completed before adjusting the parking brake. Then, check the parking brake for free movement of the parking brake cables in the conduits. If necessary, apply a lubricant to free the cables. Check for worn equalizer and linkage parts. Replace any defective parts. Finally, check for broken strands in the cables. Replace any cable that has broken strands or shows signs of wear.

TESTING Test the parking brake by parking the vehicle facing up on an incline of 30 degrees or less. Set the parking brake fully and place the transmission in neutral. The vehicle should hold steady. Reverse the vehicle position so it is facing down the incline and repeat the test. If the vehicle creeps or rolls in either case, the parking brake requires adjustment. A typical adjustment procedure is shown in Photo Sequence 28.

ADJUSTING REAR DRUM PARKING BRAKE

P28–1 Proper adjustment of the parking brake begins with setting the parking brake to a near full on position.

P28–2 Raise the car. Make sure it is safe to work under and that you will be able to rotate the wheels. (If the parking brake is adjusted and working properly, you should be unable to rotate the wheels.)

P28–3 Carefully inspect the entire length of the parking brake cable. Look for signs of fraying, breakage, and deterioration.

P28–4 Spray all exposed metal areas of the cable assembly with a penetrating oil. This will ensure a free-moving system.

P28–5 Inspect the adjustment mechanism. Clean off the threaded areas and make sure the tightening nuts are not damaged.

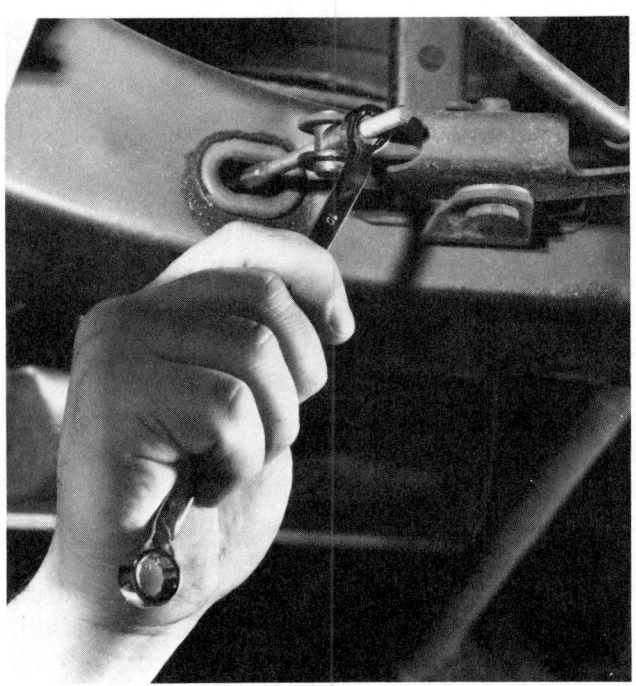

P28–6 Loosen the adjustment lock nut. Adjust the parking brake.

P28–7 When the wheels are unable to be turned, stop tightening the adjusting nut.

P28–9 Raise the vehicle and rotate the wheels. If the wheels turn with only a slight drag, the parking brake is properly adjusted.

P28–8 Lower the vehicle and release the parking brake lever.

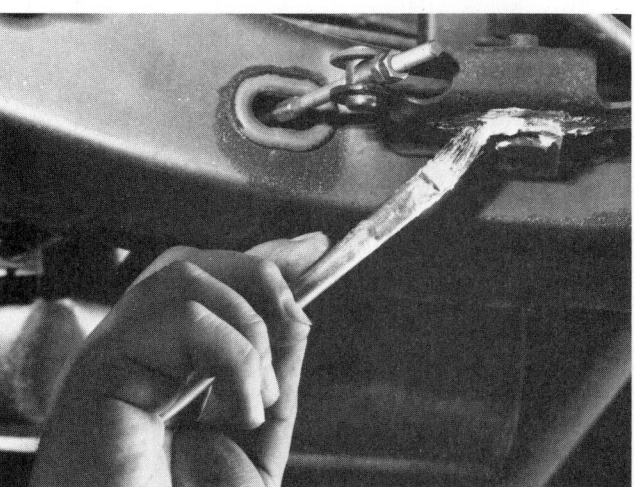

P28–10 After proper adjustment is made, tighten the adjustment lock nut. Apply a coat of white grease to all contacting surfaces of the adjustment assembly.

FIGURE 39–43 Integral parking brake components.

FIGURE 39–44   Rear cable and conduit details.

CASE STUDY

*S**hortly** after new brake shoes and hardware were installed on a vehicle, it is returned to the shop on the rear of a tow truck. An extremely irate and distressed customer is heard throughout the entire service bay area. It seems when the customer applied the brakes while traveling at a high speed, there was a sudden loss of braking power and fine metallic grinding noise was heard. Luckily, the customer was able to control the vehicle and avoid an accident, but the situation was potentially disastrous.*

The vehicle is immediately placed on a hoist and the drum brakes are disassembled. Although all the parts are new, they had failed. The shoes are pulled away from the backing plate and the hold-down pins and retainers are broken.

The technician replaces all broken components with new parts from the shop's parts department. Everything appears to be installed correctly and in good working order.

The technician is reluctant to release the vehicle to the owner without uncovering the cause of the first failure. Inspecting the assembly, the technician compares the new shoes with the failed shoes. He notices the hold-down pin bores on the defective shoes do not line up perfectly with the pins. More comparisons between the new and failed parts uncover slight differences. The shoes and hardware that had failed were the wrong parts for the vehicle. Although similar in many ways, these slight differences were enough to cause a major failure. The technician who had performed the original replacement should have visually compared the new parts with the old parts.

KEY TERMS

Anchor pin	Hold-down spring
Backing plate	Nonservo
Bonded linings	Overtravel spring
Brake lathe	Primary shoe
Duo-servo	Return spring
Eccentric-ground	Secondary shoe
Equalizer lever	Self-energizing
Floating drum	Shoe anchor
Heat checks	Web

SUMMARY

◆ Drum brakes are still used on the rear wheels of many cars and light trucks.

◆ The drum is mounted to the wheel hub. When the brakes are applied, a wheel cylinder uses hydraulic power to press two brake shoes against the inside surface of the drum. The resulting friction between the shoe's lining and drum slows the drum and wheel.

◆ The brake's anchor pin acts as a brake shoe stop, keeping the shoes from following the rotating drum. This creates a wedging action that multiplies braking force.

◆ The shoes and wheel cylinder are mounted on a backing plate. Hardware, such as shoe return springs, hold-down parts, and linkages are also mounted on the backing plate.

◆ The primary or leading shoe is toward the front of the vehicle while the secondary or trailing shoe is toward the rear of the vehicle.

◆ Brake lining can be attached to the shoes by riveting or a special adhesive bonding process.

◆ Brake drums act as a heat sink to dissipate the heat of braking friction. Drums can be refinished on a brake lathe provided the inside diameter is not increased above a safe limit (discard dimension).

- ◆ Servicing brakes requires performing a complete system inspection. Partial replacement of worn or damaged parts does not solve the braking problems and may ruin the new parts installed.
- ◆ When servicing brakes, extreme care must be taken to avoid generating asbestos dust.

- ◆ Wheel cylinders should be replaced if they show any signs of hydraulic fluid leakage or component wear.
- ◆ Drum brakes allow for the use of a simple parking brake mechanism that can be activated with a hand lever or foot pedal. This is a mechanical system, completely separate from the service brake hydraulic system.

TECH MANUAL

The following procedures are included in Chapter 39 of the *Tech Manual* that accompanies this book:

1. *Inspect and measure brake drums.*
2. *Inspect brake hardware and shoes.*
3. *Adjust parking brake linkage (cable).*

REVIEW QUESTIONS

1. Name the two methods of attaching brake lining materials to the brake shoes.
2. Explain how drum brakes create a self-multiplying brake force.
3. List at least five separate types of wear and distortion to look for when inspecting brake drums.
4. What is the job of wheel cylinder stops?
5. Explain the operation of an integral drum brake parking brake.
6. In a typical drum brake, which component provides a foundation for the brake shoes and associated hardware?
   - **a.** wheel cylinder
   - **b.** drum
   - **c.** backing plate
   - **d.** lining
7. The function of the wheel cylinder is to ____.
   - **a.** provide the rubbing surface area for the linings
   - **b.** convert hydraulic pressure into a mechanical force at the wheel brakes
   - **c.** maintain correct shoe position and clearance
   - **d.** prohibit the shoe from following the movement of the rotating drum
8. Which of the following statements concerning drum brake shoes is incorrect?
   - **a.** Web thickness never varies.
   - **b.** Many shoes have nibs along the edge of the rim.
   - **c.** The shoe rim is welded to the web.
   - **d.** The primary shoe is the one toward the front of the vehicle.
9. Brake linings should be replaced when ____.
   - **a.** linings are worn to within 1/32 inch of a rivet head
   - **b.** linings are contaminated with oil or grease
   - **c.** linings are contaminated with brake fluid
   - **d.** all of the above
10. In the unapplied position, drum brake shoes are held against the anchor pin by the ____.
    - **a.** hold-down springs
    - **b.** star wheel adjuster
    - **c.** shoe hold-down
    - **d.** return springs
11. Duo-servo drum brakes are also known as what type of brake assembly ____.
    - **a.** leading-trailing brakes
    - **b.** self-energizing brakes
    - **c.** nonservo brakes
    - **d.** none of the above
12. On most vehicles, the automatic adjuster system is ____.
    - **a.** installed on the secondary shoe
    - **b.** set up to operate when the brakes are applied as the vehicle moves forward
    - **c.** installed on the primary shoe
    - **d.** set up to operate when the brakes are not applied.
13. When the original drum is mounted against a wheel hub flange, it can be fastened by ____.
    - **a.** swaging the piloting shoulders of the wheel studs
    - **b.** riveting
    - **c.** using speed nut fasteners
    - **d.** all of the above

14. Backing plates, struts, levers, and other metal brake parts should be ____.
    a. wet-cleaned using water or a water-based solution
    b. wet-cleaned using an alcohol-based solvent
    c. wet-cleaned using gasoline
    d. dry-cleaned only

15. A buildup of brake dust and dirt between the lining and the drum is the most common cause of ____.
    a. concave/barrel-shaped drum
    b. convex/tapered drum
    c. threaded drum surface
    d. scored drum surface

16. A drum with a taper or out-of-roundness of 0.006 inch is ____.
    a. unacceptable and should be turned
    b. unacceptable and must be replaced
    c. borderline, and probably should be turned
    d. acceptable

17. The effort of the parking brake pedal assembly or hand grip is multiplied and passed on to the rear cables by the ____.
    a. equalizer lever   c. rear disc
    b. front cable   d. drive shaft

18. It has been determined that chatter and brake pull are being caused by hard spots on the brake drum. Technician A says the problem can be solved by grinding off the hard spots. Technician B says the drum must be replaced. Who is correct?
    a. Technician A   c. Both A and B
    b. Technician B   d. Neither A nor B

19. Technician A says the discard dimension of a brake drum is the drum's allowable machining dimension. Technician B says the discard dimension is the allowable wear dimension. There must be 0.030 inch left for wear after machining. Who is correct?
    a. Technician A   c. Both A and B
    b. Technician B   d. Neither A nor B

20. After resurfacing a brake drum, Technician A cleans it using hot water and a lint-free cloth. He then uses compressed air to thoroughly dry it. Technician B cleans the drum using a special brake cleaning solvent dipped in a lint-free cloth. She then allows the drum to dry before reinstallation. Who is correct?
    a. Technician A   c. Both A and B
    b. Technician B   d. Neither A nor B

DISC BRAKES

40

OBJECTIVES

◆ List the advantages of disc brakes. ◆ List disc brake components and describe their functions. ◆ Explain the difference between the three types of calipers commonly used on disc brakes. ◆ Describe the two types of parking brake systems used with disc brakes. ◆ Explain what precautions should be taken when servicing disc brake systems. ◆ Describe the general procedure involved in a complete caliper service or overhaul. ◆ List and describe five typical disc brake rotor problems.

Disc brakes resemble the brakes on a bicycle. The friction elements are in the form of pads, which are squeezed or clamped about the edge of a rotating wheel. With automotive disc brakes, this wheel is a separate unit, called a **rotor**, inboard of the wheel (Figure 40–1). The rotor is typically made of cast iron. However, there is much research being done with composite materials in the design of rotors. Since the pads clamp against both sides of a rotor, both sides are machined smooth. Usually the two surfaces are separated by a finned center section for better cooling. Such rotors are called ventilated rotors. The pads are attached to metal shoes, which are actuated by pistons, the same as with drum brakes. The pistons are contained within a **caliper** assembly, a housing that wraps around the edge of the rotor. The caliper is kept from rotating by way of bolts holding it to the steering knuckle.

The caliper is a housing containing the pistons and related seals, springs, and boots as well as the cylinder(s) and fluid passages necessary to force the friction linings or pads against the rotor. The caliper resembles a hand in the way it wraps around the edge of the rotor. It is attached to the steering knuckle. Some models employ light spring pressure to keep the pads close against the rotor. In other caliper designs, this is achieved by a unique seal that allows the piston to be pushed out the necessary amount, then retracts it just enough to pull the pad off the rotor.

Unlike shoes in a drum brake, the pads act perpendicular to the rotation of the disc when the brakes are applied. This effect is different from that produced in a brake drum, where frictional drag actually pulls the shoe into the drum. Disc brakes are said to be nonenergized. They require more force to achieve the same braking effort. For this reason, they are ordinarily used in conjunction with a power brake unit.

Disc brake calipers fall into two categories: fixed and moving designs. The latter includes both sliding and floating calipers.

Disc brakes offer four major advantages over conventional drum brakes. They are resistant to heat fade. Disc brakes are generally more resistant to heat fade during high-speed brake stops or repeated stops. The design of the disc brake rotor exposes more surface to the air and thus dissipates heat more efficiently. They are also resistant to water fade because the rotation of the rotor tends to throw off moisture. The squeeze of the sharp edges of the pads clears the surface of water. Disc brakes perform more straight-line

FIGURE 40–1   Typical disc brake assembly.

stops. Due to their clamping action, disc brakes are less apt to pull. Finally, disc brakes automatically adjust as pads wear.

DISC BRAKE COMPONENTS AND THEIR FUNCTIONS

The disc brakes used on American cars are typically of two basic designs: **fixed** or floating **caliper**. There is also a sliding caliper, but its design is very similar to the **floating caliper**. The only difference is that **sliding calipers** slide on surfaces that have been machined smooth for this purpose, and floating calipers slide on special pins or bolts. The disc brake, regardless of its design, consists of a hub and rotor assembly, a caliper assembly, and a brake pad assembly.

Hub and Rotor Assembly

Many of the advantages of disc brakes can be attributed to the disc, or rotor, as it is more commonly called. The typical rotor is made of cast iron. Iron has a high coefficient of friction and withstands wear exceptionally well. The rotor is attached to and rotates with the hub assembly (Figure 40–2). Solid rotors are used on lightweight vehicles, and trucks generally have ventilated rotors (Figure 40–3).

The ventilated rotor is cast with a weblike construction between two friction surfaces. The webs radiate out from the center of the rotor, much like vanes or fins in a fan. As the rotor turns, air is drawn into the rotor at its center, flows between the friction surfaces, and is discharged along the outer edge. This

A   **B**

FIGURE 40–3 (A) Downsized solid rotor; (B) full-size ventilated rotor.

cools the rotor vent effectively, drastically reducing the incidence of brake fade, even during multiple hard stops.

Rotors are cooled by splash shields or plates. The **splash shield** protects the rotor and pads from road splashes and dirt. It is also shaped to channel the flow of air over the exposed rotor surfaces. As long as the car is moving, this flow of air helps to cool the rotor. The splash shield cannot be removed unless the rotor and caliper are first removed. Replacement of the splash shield is necessary only when it has been damaged or when the spindle is replaced.

Caliper Assembly

Caliper action converts hydraulic pressure into mechanical force. The caliper assembly (Figure 40–4) is composed of the following components.

Caliper Housing

The caliper housing is usually a one-piece construction of cast iron or aluminum and has an inspection hole in the top to allow for lining wear inspection. A cylinder bore is located in that portion of the casting nearest the engine. In the cylinder bore is a groove that seats a square-cut seal. This groove is tapered toward the bottom of the bore to increase the compression on the edge of the seal that is nearest hydraulic pressure. The top of the cylinder bore is also grooved as a seat for the dust boot. A fluid inlet hole is machined into the bottom of the cylinder bore and a bleeder valve outlet hole is located near the top of the casting. The caliper has inner ears with holes for mounting on the anchor plate.

Caliper Pistons

A caliper can contain one, two, or four cylinder bores and pistons that provide uniform pressure distribu-

Caliper assy.

Combination spindle and anchor plate

Combination caliper locating and attaching pin

Inner bearing assy.

Grease retainer

Rotor assy.

Gasket

Screw

Splash shield

FIGURE 40–2 A wheel hub and disc brake assembly. *Courtesy of Ford Motor Company*

FIGURE 40–4 Parts of a typical sliding caliper. *Courtesy of Ford Motor Company*

tion against the brake's friction pads. Because there is no self-energizing action with disc brakes, the pistons are relatively large in diameter and short in stroke to provide high pressure on the friction pad assemblies with a minimum of fluid displacement.

Basically, the hydraulics of disc brakes are the same as for drum brakes, where the master cylinder piston forces the brake fluid into the wheel cylinders and against the wheel pistons.

The disc brake piston is made of either steel, aluminum, or fiberglass-reinforced **phenolic piston** resin. The steel pistons are usually nickel-chrome plated for improved durability and smoothness. The pistons usually have a larger diameter to provide the necessary braking force with little fluid movement. The top of the pistons is grooved to accept the **dust boot**.

Dust Boot

The dust boot seats in a groove at the top of the cylinder bore and also in a groove in the piston. The dust boot prevents moisture and road contamination from entering the bore.

Piston Hydraulic Seal

The piston hydraulic seal prevents fluid leakage between the cylinder bore wall and the piston. This rubber sealing ring also acts as a retracting mechanism for the piston when hydraulic pressure is released, causing the piston to return in its bore (Figure 40–5). When hydraulic pressure is diminished, the seal functions as a return spring to retract the piston.

In addition, as the disc brake pads wear, the seal allows the piston to move further out to adjust auto-

FIGURE 40–5 Function of a low-drag caliper seal.

matically for the wear and to maintain the lining in proper relationship with the rotor. Additional brake fluid in the caliper bore compensates for lining wear. In this manner, the caliper assembly maintains the inboard and outboard shoe and lining in the proper relationship with the rotor surface throughout the full life of the lining.

FIGURE 40–6   Typical pad linings.

FIGURE 40–8   Visual disc brake pad wear sensor.

Brake Pad Assembly

Brake shoe pads with disc brakes are metal plates with the linings either riveted or bonded to them. Pads are placed one in each side of the caliper and together straddle the rotor. The inner brake pad, which is positioned against the piston, is not interchangeable with the outer brake pad (Figure 40–6). The linings are made of semimetallic or other nonasbestos material.

Disc Pad Wear Sensors

Some brake shoe pads have wear-sensing indicators. The three most common design wear sensors are audible, visual, and tactile.

Audible sensors are thin, spring steel tabs that are riveted to the edge of the pad backing plate and are bent to contact the rotor when the lining wears down to a point that replacement is necessary. At that point, the sensor causes a high-pitched squeal at all times the wheel is turning, except when the brakes are applied; then the noise goes away. The noise gives a warning to the driver that brake service is needed and perhaps saves the rotor from destruction (Figure 40–7). The tab is generally installed toward the rear of the wheel.

Visual sensors inform the driver of the need for new linings. This method employs electrical contacts recessed in the pads that touch the rotor when the linings are worn out. This completes a circuit and turns on a dashboard warning light (Figure 40–8). This system is found mostly on imports.

Tactile sensors create pedal pulsation as the sensor on the rotor face contacts the sensor attached to the lower portion of the disc pad (Figure 40–9).

> ⚠️ **WARNING!**
> As disc brake pad linings wear thin, more brake fluid is needed in the system. ∎

> 🔒 **CUSTOMER CARE**
> Excessive heat liquefies the resin binder that holds the brake pad material together. Once liquefied, the binder rises to the surface of the pad to form a glaze. A glazed pad surface may cause squealing because more heat must be created to achieve an amount of friction equal to a pad in good condition. One common cause of pad glazing is the improper break-in of the pads. Remember to inform customers that unnecessary hard braking during the first 200 miles of a pad's life can generate enough heat to glaze the pads and ruin the quality of the work just performed. ∎

FIGURE 40–7   Audible disc brake pad wear indicator.

FIGURE 40–9   Location of the tactile sensor, which causes the brake pedal to pulsate when the brake pads are worn.

FIGURE 40–10 Cross section of a fixed caliper.

FIGURE 40–12 Cross section of a caliper in the applied position.

Fixed Caliper Disc Brakes

Fixed caliper disc brakes include a caliper assembly that is bolted in a fixed position and does not move when the brakes are applied. The pistons in both sides come inward to force the pads against the rotor (Figure 40–10). Import cars use the fixed caliper more widely than domestics.

Floating Caliper Disc Brakes

The Ford floating caliper disc brake shown in Figure 40–11 is a typical example of a floating caliper. The caliper on this brake is a one-piece casting that has one hydraulic cylinder and a single piston.

The caliper is attached to the **spindle anchor plate** with two threaded locating pins. A Teflon® sleeve separates the caliper housing from each pin. The caliper slides back and forth on the pins as the brakes are actuated. Upon brake application, hydraulic pressure builds in the caliper cavity behind the piston and seal. Because hydraulic pressure exerts equal force in all directions, pressure against the piston is equal to that exerted against the caliper housing. The piston seal offers the point of least resistance. Initial movement is of the piston outward in the bore.

The piston presses the inboard pad against the rotor. As the pad contacts the revolving rotor, greater resistance to outward movement is increased, forcing pressure to push the caliper away from the piston. This action forces the outboard pad against the rotor (Figure 40–12). However, both pads are applied with equal pressure.

Sliding Caliper Disc Brakes

Sliding caliper disc brakes get their name from the fact that the caliper slides or moves sideways when the brakes are applied. As mentioned previously, in operation these brakes are almost identical to the floating type.

But unlike the floating caliper, the sliding caliper does not float on pins or bolts attached to the anchor plate. The sliding caliper has angular machined surfaces at each end that slide in mating machined surfaces on the anchor plate.

Figure 40–13 is an example of a typical sliding caliper disc brake. The caliper on this brake is a one-piece casting that has one hydraulic cylinder and a single piston. Machined surfaces on the caliper are

FIGURE 40–11 Ford/Kelsey floating caliper disc brake.

FIGURE 40–13 Sliding caliper disc brake.

FIGURE 40–14　Typical parking brake that uses a drum built into the center of a rotor. *Courtesy of Chrysler Corporation*

FIGURE 40–15　Delco-Moraine disc parking brake.

positioned against mating machined surfaces on the anchor, which is where the caliper then slides back and forth.

REAR DISC/DRUM (AUXILIARY DRUM) PARKING BRAKE

The rear disc/drum or auxiliary drum parking brake arrangement is found on some General Motors' and Chrysler vehicles that use discs on the rear wheels. On these brakes, the inside of each rear wheel hub and rotor assembly is used as the parking brake drum. Figure 40–14 shows a typical rear disc/drum parking brake.

REAR DISC PARKING BRAKES

Instead of using an auxiliary drum and shoes to hold the vehicle when parked, these brakes have a mechanism that forces the pads against the rotor mechanically. One method for doing this is the ball-and-ramp arrangement. Another method used in the General Motors' rear calipers for E-body cars, uses a high lead thrust screw to hold the piston out and maintain contact with the pads and rotors (Figure 40–15). Other types of actuating systems for rear disc brakes include the use of a variety of cams.

SERVICE PRECAUTIONS

The following general service precautions apply to all disc brake systems and should be reviewed before studying the specific servicing techniques in this chapter.

1. Road test the vehicle to determine the condition of the brakes.
2. Be sure the vehicle is properly centered and secured on stands or a hoist.

3. Disconnect the battery ground cable.
4. Before any service is performed, inspect the wheel and brake assembly for obvious damage that could affect braking. Check the following.
    - Tires for excessive wear or improper inflation
    - Wheels for bent or warped rims
    - Wheel bearings for looseness or wear
    - Suspension components to see if they are worn or broken
    - Brake fluid level
    - Master cylinder, brake lines or hoses, and each wheel for leaks
5. During servicing, grease, oil, brake fluid, or any other foreign material must be kept off the brake linings, caliper, surfaces of the disc, and external surfaces of the hub. Handle the brake disc and caliper in such a way to avoid deformation of the disc and nicking or scratching brake linings.
6. Work on one wheel at a time to avoid popping pistons out of the other caliper and allow the other caliper assembly to be used as a guide.
7. When removing wheels, be sure to avoid damage to the rotor, external lines, bleeder screws, and splash shield.
8. When a hydraulic hose is disconnected, plug it to prevent any foreign material from entering.
9. Do not attempt to remove the hub with the wheel and tire still mounted. The wheel and tire must be dismounted and the caliper removed before the hub and rotor can be dismounted.
10. Never permit the caliper assembly to hang with the weight on the brake hose. Support it on the suspension or hang it by a piece of wire.
11. Inspect the caliper for leaks. If leakage is present, the caliper must be overhauled.
12. Use crocus cloth to remove rust, corrosion, pitting, and scratches from the piston bore. If the

bore cannot be cleaned with crocus cloth, light honing is permitted. Do not hone a plated bore.

13. When using compressed air to remove caliper pistons, avoid high pressures. A safe pressure to use is 30 psi.

14. Clean the brake components in either denatured alcohol or clean brake fluid. Do not use mineral-based cleaning solvent such as gasoline, kerosene, carbon tetrachloride, acetone, or paint thinner to clean the caliper. It causes rubber parts to become soft and swollen in an extremely short time.

15. Lubricate any moving member such as the caliper housing or mounting bracket to ensure a free-moving action. Use only recommended lubricant.

16. Before the brake pads are installed, apply a disc brake noise suppressor to the back of the pads to prevent brake squeal. For best results, follow the directions on the container.

17. The front-wheel bearing should be adjusted to the manufacturer's specifications.

18. Check the master cylinder fluid level and be sure the reservoirs are filled when the brake job is completed.

19. Obtain a firm brake pedal after servicing the brakes and before moving the vehicle. Be sure to road test the vehicle.

20. Always torque the lug nuts when installing a wheel on a vehicle with disc brakes. Never use an impact gun to tighten the lug nuts. Warpage of the rotor could result if an impact gun is used.

Before beginning brake work, remove about two-thirds of the brake fluid from the front or disc brake reservoir on a front/rear split system (Figure 40–16). On a diagonally split system, remove fluid from both reservoirs. If this is not done, the fluid could overflow and spill when the pistons are forced back into the caliper bore, possibly damaging the painted surfaces. Replace the cover. Discard old brake fluid.

Another common procedure (and perhaps a better way) is to open the caliper bleeder screw and run

FIGURE 40–16
Removing brake fluid from master cylinder reservoir.

a hose down to a container to catch the fluid that is expelled when the piston is forced back into its bore. This also makes it easier to move the piston.

If the bleeder screws are frozen tight with corrosion, it is sometimes possible to free them using a propane torch and penetrating oil. Of course, the caliper has to be removed from the car, taken to a bench, and worked on there. If the bleeder screws cannot be loosened, they can be drilled out and the caliper retapped for an insert, or the caliper can be replaced with a new or rebuilt unit. The bleeder screw should be removed when doing an overhaul.

⬤ CAUTION

When using the propane torch to loosen a bleeder screw, use it with extreme care. ■

GENERAL CALIPER INSPECTING AND SERVICING

The general procedures involved in a complete caliper service or overhaul include tasks such as:

◆ Caliper removal
◆ Brake pad removal
◆ Caliper disassembly
◆ Caliper assembly
◆ Brake pad installation
◆ Caliper installation

Not all caliper work includes every one of these tasks. Frequently, caliper service involves only the removal and installation of the brake pads. However, since the new pads are thicker than the worn-out set they replace, they locate the piston farther back in the bore where dirt and corrosion might cause the seals to leak. For this reason, it is often good practice to rebuild the calipers whenever installing new pads. Of course, it is also good practice to true up or replace the rotors when replacing brake pads.

When bench working a caliper assembly, use a vise that is equipped with protector jaws. Excessive vise pressure causes bore and piston distortion.

🔧 SHOP TALK

Some shops do not rebuild calipers. They contract them out to specialty shops. However, the brake technician must at least know how to rebuild calipers. ■

Caliper Removal

The first step in proper caliper service is to remove the caliper assembly from the vehicle. Depending on the caliper design, this operation is accomplished in various ways. Specific caliper removal procedures are given in service manuals. General details of the task follow.

FIGURE 40–17   Bottoming piston in the bore.

PROCEDURES

Removing Calipers

1. Remove the brake fluid from the master cylinder.
2. Raise the vehicle and remove the wheel and tire assembly. Use care to avoid damage to or interference with bleeder screw fitting during removal.
3. Mark the right-hand and left-hand caliper assemblies with chalk prior to removing from the vehicle, so they can be positioned correctly during installation.
4. On a sliding or floating caliper, install a C-clamp on the caliper with the solid end of the clamp on the caliper housing and the screw end on the metal portion of the outboard brake pad. Tighten the clamp until the piston bottoms in the caliper bore (Figure 40–17), then remove the clamp. Bottoming the piston allows room for the brake pad to slide over the ridge of rust that accumulates on the edge of the rotor.
5. Disconnect the brake hose from the caliper and remove the copper gasket or washer and the cap end of the brake end. If only the brake pads are to be replaced, do not disconnect the brake hose.
6. Remove the two mounting brackets to the steering knuckle bolts. Support the caliper when removing the second bolt to prevent the caliper from falling.
7. On a sliding caliper, remove the top bolts, retainer clip, and **antirattle springs** (Figure 40–18). On a floating caliper, remove the two special pins that hold the caliper to the anchor plate (Figure 40–19). On an older type fixed caliper, remove the bolts holding it to the steering knuckle. On all three types, get the caliper off by prying it straight up and lifting it clear of the rotor.

FIGURE 40–18   Sliding caliper removal.

FIGURE 40–19   Floating caliper removal.

Brake Pad Removal

Disc brake linings should be checked periodically or whenever the wheels are removed. Some calipers have inspection holes in the caliper body. If they do not, the brake pads can be visually inspected from the outer ends of the caliper.

If the friction pads appear worn and in need of replacement, measure them at the thinnest part of the pad. Compare this measurement to the minimum brake pad lining thickness listed in the vehicle's service manual, and replace the pads if needed.

FIGURE 40-20
Normal pad wear pattern.

FIGURE 40-22 Removing guide pins.

Uneven pad wear on a sliding caliper often means the caliper is sticking and not giving equal pressure to both pads. On a sliding caliper, the problem could be that the caliper ways are not allowing a smooth sliding movement. Check these machined ways for proper clearance. A slightly tapered wear pattern on the pads of certain models is caused by caliper twist during braking. It is normal if it does not exceed 1/8-inch taper from one end of the pad to the other (Figure 40-20).

Sliding or floating calipers must always be lifted off the rotor for pad replacement. Fixed calipers might have pads that can be replaced by removing the retaining pins or clips instead of having to lift off the entire caliper. They can be held in position by retaining pins (Figure 40-21), guide pins (Figure 27-22), or a support key (Figure 40-23). Note the position of the shims, antirattle clips, keys, bushings, or pins during disassembly. A typical procedure for replacing brake pads is outlined in Photo Sequence 29.

If only the pads have to be replaced, lift the caliper off the rotor and hang it up by a wire. Remove the outer pad and inner pad. Remove the old sleeves and bushings and install new ones. Replace rusty pins on a floating caliper to provide for free movement. Transfer shoe retainers, which can be clips or springs, onto the new pads.

FIGURE 40-23 Removing caliper support key.

SHOP TALK

If new pads and plates are not to be installed immediately, insert several thicknesses of clean cardboard or plastic in the caliper. This keeps the pistons from coming out of caliper cylinders. ∎

Caliper Disassembly

If the caliper must be rebuilt, it should be taken to the workbench for servicing. Drain any brake fluid from the caliper by way of bleeder screws. Remove the bleeder valve protector, if so equipped.

On a floating caliper, examine the mounting pins for rust that could limit travel. Most manufacturers recommend that these pins and their bushings be replaced each time the caliper is removed. This is a good idea because the pins are inexpensive and a good insurance against costly comebacks. On a fixed caliper, check the pistons for sticking and rebuild the caliper if this problem is found.

To disassemble the caliper, the piston and dust boot must first be removed. Use compressed air to pop the piston out of the bore.

FIGURE 40-21
Removing brake
pad retaining pins.

REMOVING AND REPLACING BRAKE PADS

P29–1 Front brake pad replacement begins with removing brake fluid from the master cylinder reservoir. Using a siphon, remove enough fluid to cause the reservoir to be half-full.

P29–2 Raise the car. Make sure it is safely positioned on the lift. Remove its wheel assemblies.

P29–3 Inspect the brake assembly. Look for signs of fluid leaks, broken or cracked lines, or a damaged brake rotor. If any problem is found, correct it when installing the new brake pads.

P29–4 Loosen the bolts and remove the pad locator pins.

P29–5 Lift and rotate the caliper assembly from the rotor.

P29–6 Remove the brake pads from the caliper assembly.

P29–7 Fasten a piece of wire to the car's frame and support the caliper with the wire.

P29–8 Check the condition of the locating pin insulators and sleeves.

P29–9 Place a piece of wood over the caliper's piston and install a C-clamp over the wood and caliper. Tighten the clamp to force the piston back into its bore.

P29–11 Install the new pads into the caliper.

P29–10 Remove the clamp and install new locating pin insulators and sleeves, if necessary.

P29–12 Set caliper with pads over the rotor and install the locating pins. After the assembly is in the proper position, torque the pins according to specifications

PROCEDURES

Disassembling a Caliper

1. Position the caliper face down on a bench.
2. Insert the used outer pad into the caliper. Place a folded shop towel on the face of the lining to cushion the piston.
3. Apply low air pressure (never more than 30 psi) to the fluid inlet port of the caliper to force the piston from the caliper housing (Figure 40–24).

CAUTION:

Be careful to apply air pressure very gradually. Be sure there are enough cloths to catch the piston when it comes out of the bore. Never place your fingers in front of the piston for any reason when applying compressed air. Personal injury could occur if the piston is popped out of the bore. ■

4. If a piston is frozen, release air pressure and tap the piston into its bore with a soft-headed hammer or mallet. Reapply air pressure.
5. Frozen phenolic (plastic) pistons can be broken into pieces with a chisel and hammer.

CAUTION:

Protect the eyes with safety glasses. Avoid damaging the caliper bore and seal groove with the chisel. ■

6. Internal expanding pliers are sometimes used to remove pistons from caliper bores.

FIGURE 40-24 Using air to remove a piston.

FIGURE 40-25 Inspect phenolic piston for surface irregularities.

FIGURE 40-26 Peeling off dust boot.

FIGURE 40-27 Prying out dust boot with a screwdriver.

groove. In some cases it might be necessary to pry the dust boot out with a screwdriver (Figure 40-27). The old boot can be discarded since it must be replaced along with the seal.

⚠️ *WARNING!*

Be careful not to scratch the cylinder bore while prying out the dust boot. ■

Remove a stroking seal by prying it out of the piston with a wooden or plastic tool. Pry a fixed seal out of the cylinder with the same type of tool (Figure 40-28). Do not use a screwdriver or other metal tool. Any of these could nick the metal in the caliper bore and cause a leak. Inspect the bore for pitting or scoring. A bore that shows light scratches or corrosion can usually be cleaned with crocus cloth. However, a

Inspect phenolic pistons for cracks, chips, or gouges (Figure 40-25). Replace the piston if any of these conditions are evident. If the plated surface of a steel piston is worn, pitted, scored, or corroded, it also should be replaced.

Dust boots vary in design depending on the type of piston and seal, but they all fit into one groove in the piston and another groove in the cylinder. One type comes out with the piston and peels off. Another type stays in place and the piston comes out through the boot, and is then removed from the cylinder (Figure 40-26). In either case, peel the boot from its

FIGURE 40-28 Removing piston seal with a wooden or plastic stick.

FIGURE 40–29 Honing caliper bore.

bore that has deep scratches or scoring must be honed, provided the diameter of the bore is not increased more than 0.002 inch. If the bore does not clean up within this specification, a new caliper housing should be installed. Black stains on the bore walls are caused by piston seals. They do no harm.

When using a hone (Figure 40–29), be sure to install the hone baffle before honing the bore. The baffle protects the hone stones from damage. Use extreme care in cleaning the caliper after honing. Remove all dust and grit by flushing the caliper with alcohol. Wipe it dry with a clean lint-free cloth and then clean the caliper a second time in the same manner.

Loaded Calipers

There is now a trend toward installing loaded calipers, rather than overhauling calipers in the shop. Loaded calipers are completely assembled with friction pads and mounting hardware included. Besides the convenience and the savings of installation time, preassembled calipers also reduce the odds of errors in installation.

Mistakes that are frequently made when replacing calipers include forgetting to bend pad locating tabs that prevent pad vibration and noise, leaving off anti-rattle clips and pad insulators, and reusing corroded caliper-mounting hardware that can cause a floating caliper to bind up and wear the pads unevenly.

One of the major causes of premature brake wear is rust. It causes improper slider and piston operation that leads to uneven pad wear. Tests have shown that when only the pads are replaced, the new pads can wear out in half the mileage as the originals when rust affects caliper operation. Installing a loaded caliper ensures that all parts requiring replacement are replaced.

SHOP TALK

Make sure the supplier tells you what type of friction material is used on their loaded caliper

assemblies. Some suppliers use lower grade friction material to keep cost down. Also, avoid mismatching friction materials from side to side. When one caliper is bad, both calipers should be replaced using the same friction material on both sides. ■

Caliper Assembly

Before assembling the caliper, clean all metal parts to be reused and the phenolic piston (if so equipped) in clean denatured alcohol or brake fluid. Then, clean out and dry the grooves and passageways with compressed air. Make sure that the caliper bore and component parts are thoroughly clean.

Some designs of disc brakes require that the piston-to-bore clearance be checked with a feeler gauge (Figure 40–30). If clearances exceed the limits listed in the service manual, the piston must be replaced.

To replace a typical piston seal, dust boot, and piston, first lubricate the new piston seal with clean brake fluid or assembly lubricant (usually supplied with the caliper rebuild kit). Make sure the seal is not distorted. Insert it into the groove in the cylinder bore so it does not become twisted or rolled. Install a new dust boot by setting the flange squarely in the outer groove of the caliper bore. Next, coat the piston with brake fluid or assembly lubricant and install it in the cylinder bore (Figure 40–31). Be sure to use a wood block or other flat stock when installing the piston back into the pis-

FIGURE 40–30 Checking piston clearance with feeler gauge.

FIGURE 40–31 When installing a piston in a caliper bore, make sure the piston is lubricated.

FIGURE 40–32 Some installation procedures require the dust boot to be pulled over the end of the piston.

FIGURE 40–33 Seating a dust boot with a boot installer.

FIGURE 40–34 Applying sealer to dust boot groove.

FIGURE 40–35 Applying sealer between dust boot ring and caliper housing.

ton bore. Never apply a C-clamp directly to a phenolic piston, and be sure the pistons are not cocked. Spread the dust boot over the piston as it is installed. Seat the dust boot in the piston groove.

With some types of boot/piston arrangements, the procedure of installation is slightly different from that already described. That is, the new dust boot is pulled over the end of the piston (Figure 40–32). Lubricate the piston with brake fluid before installing it in the caliper. Then, by hand, slip the piston carefully into the cylinder bore, pushing it straight, so the piston seal is not damaged during installation. Use an installation tool or wooden block to seat the new dust boot (Figure 40–33).

The installation of some dust boots requires that its groove be filled with a bead of silicone sealer (Figure 40–34). After lubricating the dust boot, insert the piston. Bottom the piston in the cylinder bore and seat the dust boot in the recess next to the bore. Seal the area between the dust boot ring and caliper housing with a bead of silicone sealer (Figure 40–35).

⚠️ *WARNING!*

Be sure no sealant gets between the piston and cylinder since it retards its action. ■

Another point to keep in mind is that some caliper designs have a slot cut in the face of the pistons that must align with an **antisqueal shim**. Make sure the piston and shim align. It might be necessary to turn the piston to achieve proper alignment.

To complete the caliper assembly job, install the bleeder screw.

⚠️ *WARNING!*

On fixed calipers, bridge bolts are used to hold the two caliper halves together. These are high-tensile bolts are ordered only by specific part number. They require accurate torque tightness to prevent leakage. Do not attempt to use standard bolts in place of bridge bolts. ■

Brake Pad Installation

It is a good practice to replace disc brake hardware when replacing disc brake pads. Hardware life is drastically affected by intense heat, weather conditions, abrasive particles, and normal wear. Replacement of the disc brake hardware ensures proper caliper movement and brake pad retention. Hardware replacement aids in preventing brake noise and uneven brake pad wear.

Fixed Caliper Brake Pads

The designs of fixed caliper disc brakes vary slightly. Generally, to replace the pads insert new pads and

FIGURE 40–36 Clinching down pad ears with channel lock pliers.

FIGURE 40–38 Bend the retaining flange if there is excessive free play.

plates in the caliper with the metal plates against the end of the pistons. Be sure the plates are properly seated in the caliper. Spread the pads apart and slide the caliper into position on the rotor. With some pads, mounting bolts are used to hold them in place. These bolts are usually tightened 80 to 90 foot-pounds. On some fixed disc brakes, the pads are held in place by retaining clips or, as with some Delco-Moraine designs, both retaining pins and clips are used. Figure 40–36 shows channel lock pliers being used to clinch down the ear clips of the outer pads. Reinstall the antirattle spring/clips and other hardware (if so equipped).

Sliding Caliper Brake Pads
Push the piston carefully back into the bore until it bottoms. Slide a new outer pad and lining assembly into the recess of the caliper (Figure 40–37). No free play between the brake pad flanges and caliper fingers should exist. If free play is found, remove the pad from the caliper and bend the flanges to eliminate all vertical free play (Figure 40–38). Install the pad.

FIGURE 40–37 Installing an outboard pad on the caliper.

Place the inner pad into position on the adapter with the pad flange in the adapter's machined ways. Slide the adapter assembly into position in the adapter and over the disc. Align the caliper on the adapter's ways. Do not pull the dust boot from its groove when the piston and boot slide over the inboard pad. Install the antirattle springs (if so equipped) on top of the retainer plate and tighten the retaining screws to specification.

Floating Caliper Brake Pads
For floating or pin caliper disc brakes, compress the flanges of the outer bushing in the caliper fingers and work them into position in the hole from the outer side of the caliper. Compress the flanges of the inner guide pin bushings and install them.

Slide the new pad and lining assemblies into position in the adapter and caliper. Be sure the metal portion of the pad is fully recessed in the caliper and adapter and the proper pad is on the outer side of the caliper.

Hold the outer pad and carefully slide the caliper into position in the adapter and over the disc. Align the guide pin holes of the adapter with those of the inner and outer pads. Install the guide pins through the bushings, caliper, adapter, and inner and outer pads into the outer bushings in the caliper and antirattle spring.

Caliper Installation
To reinstall the caliper on the vehicle, first install the caliper assembly over the rotor with the outer brake pad against the rotor's braking surface. This prevents pinching the piston boot between the inner brake pad and the piston. Make sure the correct caliper is installed on the correct anchor plate according to the way they were marked during disassembly. Next, lubricate the rubber insulators (if so equipped) with

silicone dielectric compound. Install the caliper assembly back on its mounting brackets. Connect the brake hose to the caliper. If copper washers or gaskets are used, be sure to use new ones. The old ones might have taken a set and might not form a tight seal if reused. Fill the master cylinder reservoirs and bleed the hydraulic system. Check for fluid leaks under maximum pedal pressure. Lower the vehicle and road test it.

ROTOR INSPECTING AND SERVICING

The cause for braking complaints on cars equipped with drum brakes can usually be found by visually examining the brake drum. In cases where the same complaints involve disc brakes, visual inspection of the rotor does not give the answer. Tolerances on rotor thickness, parallelism, runout, flatness, and depth of scoring are very critical and must be measured with exacting gauges and micrometers. To perform a proper servicing job on rotors, accurate measuring tools and up-to-date rotor resurfacing equipment are required.

⚠️ WARNING!

Never turn the rotor on one side of the vehicle and not the other. ∎

The rotors should be inspected whenever brake pads are required and when the wheels are removed for other types of service. The following are typical disc brake rotor conditions that need careful inspection.

Lateral Runout

Excessive **lateral runout** is a wobbling of the rotor from side to side when it rotates. The excessive wobble knocks the pads farther back than normal, causing the pedal to pulse and vibrate during braking. Chatter can also result. It also causes excessive pedal travel because the pistons have farther to travel to reach the rotor. If runout exceeds specifications, the rotor must be turned or replaced.

Lack of Parallelism

Parallelism refers to variations in thickness of the rotor. If the rotor is out of parallel, it can cause excessive pedal travel, front end vibration, pedal pulsation, chatter, and on occasion, grabbing of the brakes. It must be resurfaced or replaced.

Scoring

Rotor wear or scoring can be caused by linings that are worn through to the rivets or backing plate or by friction material that is harsh or unkind to the mating surface. Rust, road dirt, and other contamination could also cause rotor scoring.

Light scoring (less than a depth of 0.015 inch) of the disc braking surface can occur during normal brake use. This does not affect brake operation. However, this can result in a higher-than-average brake shoe lining wear rate. But, any rotor having score marks more than 0.15 inch should be refinished or replaced.

Bluing or Heat Checking

If the lining surface is charred, blued, or hard-ended with a heavy glaze, or if the rotor is severely heat checked, machine the rotor or replace it.

Hard or chill spots of steel in a rotor cast-iron surface usually result from a change in the metallurgy caused by braking heat. Pulling, rapid wear, hard pedal, and noise occur. These spots can be removed by grinding. However, only the raised surfaces are removed, and they could reappear when heat is again encountered. The rotor must be replaced.

Rusty Rotor

If the vehicle has not been driven for a period of time, the discs rust in the area not covered by the lining and cause noise and chatter. Excessive wear and scoring of the discs and lining result. Wear ridges on the discs can cause temporary improper pad lining contact if ridges are not removed before installation of new lining. Lining deposits on the disc can cause erratic friction characteristics if a new lining is installed without resurfacing or cleaning the disc.

🔧 SHOP TALK

Specific inspection and repair procedures can be found in the service manuals. Always refer to them when performing a brake job. ∎

CASE STUDY

An obviously embarrassed customer explains his problem to the brake shop technician. He just finished installing new disc pads on his light truck, but the disc brakes are dragging.

The young man insists he performed the work correctly and the rest of the braking system is in fine working order.

The technician inspects the front brakes and finds the owner cleaned all components well and installed the pads correctly. The technician checks the action of the caliper. Its piston shows no signs of sticking, but the caliper appears to be binding. Removal and inspection of the caliper locates the problem. Although the owner had carefully cleaned the slides of the caliper, he had failed to apply any lubricant to the surface. This was causing the calipers to bind and the brakes to drag.

Omitting the simplest of tasks when performing repairs can often lead to failure and wasted time.

KEY TERMS

Antirattle spring	Lateral runout
Antisqueal shim	Parallelism
Audible sensor	Phenolic piston
Caliper	Rotor
Dust boot	Sliding caliper
Fixed caliper	Spindle anchor plate
Floating caliper	Splash shield

SUMMARY

- Disc brakes offer four major advantages over drum brakes: resistance to heat fade, resistance to water fade, increased straight-line stopping ability, and automatic adjustment.
- The typical rotor is attached to and rotates with the wheel hub assembly. Heavier vehicles generally use ventilated rotors. Splash shields protect the rotors and pads from road moisture and dirt.
- The caliper assembly includes cylinder bores and pistons, dust boots, and piston hydraulic seals.

- Brake pads are placed in each side of the caliper and together straddle the rotor. Some brake pads have wear sensors.
- Fixed caliper disc brakes do not move when the brakes are applied. Floating caliper disc brakes slide back and forth on pins or bolts. Sliding calipers slide on surfaces that have been machined smooth for this purpose.
- The rear disc/drum parking brake in a rear disc brake in which the inside of each rear wheel hub and rotor assembly is used as the parking brake drum.
- Rear disc parking brakes have a mechanism that forces the pads against the rotor mechanically.
- The general procedures involved in a complete caliper overhaul include tasks such as caliper removal, brake pad removal, caliper disassembly, caliper assembly, brake pad installation, and caliper installation.
- The first step in proper caliper service is to remove the caliper assembly from the vehicle.
- Disc brake pads should be checked periodically or whenever the wheels are removed. They should be replaced if they fail to exceed minimum lining thickness as listed in the service manual.
- To disassemble the caliper, the piston and dust boot must first be removed. Compressed air is used to pop the piston out of the bore.
- Before assembling the caliper, all metal parts and the phenolic piston are cleaned in denatured alcohol or brake fluid. The grooves and passageways of the caliper are cleaned out and dried with compressed air.
- It is a good practice to replace disc brake hardware when replacing disc brake pads.
- The caliper assembly is installed over the rotor with the outer brake pad against the rotor's braking surface.
- Disc brake rotor conditions that must be corrected include lateral runout, lack of parallelism, scoring, blueing or heat checking, and rusty rotors.

TECH MANUAL

The following procedures are included in Chapter 40 of the *Tech Manual* that accompanies this book:

1. Inspect brake hardware and pads.

2. Remove and replace a front rotor from a FWD vehicle.

3. Inspect and measure brake rotors.

REVIEW QUESTIONS

1. Name four major advantages of disc brakes over drum brakes.

2. Name the three assemblies that make up a disc brake.

3. Name the three types of calipers used on disc brakes.

4. What type of brake uses the inside of each rear wheel hub and rotor assembly as a parking brake drum?

5. How many cylinder bores and pistons can a caliper assembly contain?

6. Which of the following statements concerning disc brakes is incorrect?
   a. Disc brakes can handle more heat than drum brakes.
   b. Disc brakes are not as likely to fade during heavy braking as are drum brakes.
   c. Disc brakes stay in adjustment automatically.
   d. Disc brakes do not tolerate water well.

7. Disc brakes are not ____.
   a. self-adjusting   c. easy to reline
   b. rapid acting   d. self-energizing

8. Solid rotors are used on ____.
   a. lightweight vehicles
   b. heavy vehicles
   c. high-performance vehicles
   d. none of the above

9. What channels the flow of air over the exposed rotor surfaces?
   a. webs   c. splash shield
   b. hub assembly   d. caliper assembly

10. Which of the following statements concerning the caliper assembly is incorrect?
   a. The caliper housing is usually a two-piece construction of aluminum and cast iron.
   b. Caliper action converts hydraulic pressure into mechanical force.
   c. A caliper assembly can contain as many as four cylinder bores and pistons.
   d. The caliper assembly provides a means of applying brake pads to the rotor.

11. What prevents moisture from entering the cylinder bore?
   a. phenolic piston   c. splash shield
   b. drag caliper   d. dust boot

12. When servicing disc brakes on a vehicle, Technician A works on one wheel before beginning work on another. Technician B uses a mini-

mum of 50 psi of air pressure to force the piston from the caliper housing. Who is correct?
   a. Technician A   c. Both A and B
   b. Technician B   d. Neither A nor B

13. When examining disc brakes, Technician A visually inspects the rotor for wear. Technician B uses a propane torch and penetrating oil to free a bleeder screw frozen tight with corrosion. Who is correct?
   a. Technician A   c. Both A and B
   b. Technician B   d. Neither A nor B

14. What should be used to remove rust, corrosion, pitting, and scratches from the piston bore?
   a. an oily rag   c. abrasive paper
   b. crocus cloth   d. all of the above

15. Which term refers to variations in thickness of the rotor?
   a. torque   c. parallelism
   b. lateral runout   d. pedal pulsation

16. Technician A cleans brake components in denatured alcohol. Technician B cleans brake components in clean brake fluid. Who is correct?
   a. Technician A   c. Both A and B
   b. Technician B   d. Neither A nor B

17. Technician A says rotor wear can be caused by worn pad linings. Technician B says hard spots on a rotor usually result from manufacturing defects. Who is correct?
   a. Technician A   c. Both A and B
   b. Technician B   d. Neither A nor B

18. When replacing the brake pads, Technician A disconnects the brake hose. When removing the caliper, Technician B supports the caliper before removing the second bolt. Who is correct?
   a. Technician A   c. Both A and B
   b. Technician B   d. Neither A nor B

19. Technician A replaces the pads if they are 1/32-inch thick or less. Technician B says the calipers must be replaced if the pads have a slightly tapered wear pattern. Who is correct?
   a. Technician A   c. Both A and B
   b. Technician B   d. Neither A nor B

20. While discussing how to remove the piston from a brake caliper, Technician A says the dust boot should be removed then a large dull screwdriver should be inserted into the piston groove to pry the piston out. Technician B says air pressure should be injected into the bleeder screw's bore to force the piston out of the caliper. Who is correct?
   a. Technician A   c. Both A and B
   b. Technician B   d. Neither A nor B

ANTILOCK BRAKE SYSTEMS

41

OBJECTIVES

◆ *Explain how antilock brake systems work to bring a vehicle to a controlled stop.* ◆ *Describe the differences between an integrated and a nonintegrated ABS.* ◆ *Briefly describe the major components of a two-wheel antilock brake system.* ◆ *Briefly describe the major components of a four-wheel antilock brake system.* ◆ *Describe the operation of the major components of an antilock brake system.* ◆ *Describe the operation of the major components of an automatic stability control system.*

Antilock brake systems (ABS) and traction control systems are rapidly gaining popularity. They will soon be standard equipment on most vehicles. ABS and traction control add yet another electronically controlled system to the increasingly complex modern vehicle.

Modern antilock (skid) brake systems can be thought of as electronic/hydraulic pumping of the brakes for straightline stopping under panic conditions (Figure 41–1). Good drivers have always pumped the brake pedal during panic stops to avoid wheel lockup and the loss of steering control. Antiskid brake systems simply get the pumping job done much faster and in a much more precise manner than the fastest human foot. Keep in mind that a tire on the verge of slipping produces more friction with respect to the road than one which is locked and skidding. Once a tire loses its grip, friction is reduced and the vehicle takes longer to stop.

PRESSURE MODULATION

When the driver quickly and firmly applies the brakes and holds the pedal down, the brakes of a vehicle not equipped with ABS will almost immediately lock the wheels. The vehicle slides rather than rolls to a stop. During this time, the driver also has a very difficult time keeping the vehicle straight and the vehicle will skid, out of control. The skidding and lack of control was caused by the locking of the wheels. If the driver was able to release the brake pedal just before the wheels locked up then reapply the brakes, the skidding could be avoided.

This release and apply of the brake pedal is exactly what an antilock system does. When the brake pedal is pumped or pulsed, pressure is quickly applied and released at the wheels. This is called **pressure modulation**. Pressure modulation works to prevent wheel locking. Antilock brake systems can modulate the pressure to the brakes as often as 15 times per second. By modulating the pressure to the brakes, friction between the tires and the road is maintained and the vehicle is able to come to a controllable stop.

The only time reduced friction aids in braking is when a tire is on loose snow. A locked tire allows a small wedge of snow to build up ahead of it, which allows it to stop in a shorter distance than a rolling tire.

Steering is another important consideration. As long as a tire does not slip, it goes only in the direction in which it is turned. But once it skids, it has lit-

FIGURE 41–1 The four-wheel antilock braking system has few parts and operates at very high pressures.

tle or no directional stability. One of the big advantages of ABS, therefore, is the ability to keep control of the vehicle under all conditions.

CUSTOMER CARE

Remind your customers that pumping the brake pedal while stopping will prevent the ABS from activating. They should always keep firm steady pressure on the brake pedal during braking. ■

PEDAL FEEL

The brake pedal on a vehicle equipped with ABS has a different feel than that of a conventional braking system. When the ABS is activated, a small bump followed by rapid pedal pulsations will continue until the vehicle comes to a stop or the ABS turns off. These pulsations are the result of the modulation of pressure to the brakes and are felt more on some systems than on others. This is due to the use of damping valves in some modulation units. If pedal feel is of concern during diagnosis of a brake problem, compare the brake pedal feel with that of a similar vehicle with a normal operating antilock brake system.

TYPES OF ANTILOCK BRAKE SYSTEMS

During normal operation, all antilock brake systems operate like conventional power-assisted braking systems. During heavy braking, however, the ABS modulates hydraulic pressure to each wheel according to the wheel's speed.

All antilock brake systems found on today's vehicles are manufactured by one of the following companies: Bendix, Bosch, Delco Moraine, ITT Teves, Kelsey-Hayes, or Lucas Girling. Each manufacturer has a unique way to accomplish the same thing—no skid during braking. When working with ABS, it is important that you identify the exact system you are working with and follow the specific service procedures for that system.

The exact manner in which hydraulic pressure is controlled depends on the exact ABS design. The great majority of antilock brake systems are integrated systems. They combine the master cylinder, hydraulic booster, and ABS hydraulic circuitry into a single hydraulic assembly.

Other antilock brake systems are nonintegrated. They use a conventional vacuum-assist booster and master cylinder. The system's hydraulic control unit is a separate mechanism.

FIGURE 41–2 Typical two-wheel antilock braking system.

In addition to being classified as integral and non-integral antilock brake systems, systems can be broken down into the level of control they provide. Antilock brake systems can be 1-, 2-, 3-, or 4-channel two- or four-wheel systems.

TWO-WHEEL SYSTEMS These basic systems offer antilock brake performance to the rear wheels only. They do not provide antilock performance to the steering wheels. Two-wheel systems are most often found on light trucks and some sport utility vehicles (Figure 41–2).

These systems can be either 1- or 2-channel systems. In **1-channel** systems, the rear brakes on both sides of the vehicle are modulated at the same time to control skidding. These systems rely on the input from a centrally located **speed sensor**. The speed sensor is normally positioned on the ring gear in the differential unit (Figure 41–3), transmission, or transfer case. Ford's single channel system for the rear wheels is called **RABS**, Rear ABS. Chrysler and General Motors call their 1-channel, two-wheel antilock brake systems, a rear wheel antilock (**RWAL**) system.

Two-channel, two-wheel systems modulate the pressure to each of the rear wheels independently of each other. Modulation is controlled by the speed variances recorded by speed sensors located at each wheel (Figure 41–4).

DIAGONALLY SPLIT SYSTEMS This type of system uses two speed sensors to provide wheel speed data for the regulation of all four wheels. One sensor has input that controls the right front wheel; the other sensor performs likewise for the left front wheel.

Brake hydraulic pressure to the opposite rear wheel is controlled simultaneously with its diagonally located front wheel. For example, the right rear wheel receives the same pumping instructions as the left front wheel.

This system is an upgrade from the two-wheel system since it does provide steering control. However, it

FIGURE 41-3 Speed sensor for both rear wheels located on the differential unit. *Courtesy of Chrysler Corporation*

FIGURE 41-4 Four-channel ABS. *Courtesy of Ford Motor Company*

FIGURE 41–5 General Motors' 4WAL ABS. *Courtesy of Chevrolet Division, General Motors Corporations*

can have shortcomings under certain operating conditions.

FRONT/REAR SPLIT SYSTEMS These systems have individual hydraulic circuits to each of the two front wheels, and a single circuit to the two rear wheels. This is a **3-channel** circuit. General Motors' **4WAL** (4-wheel antilock) system is an example of this type of system (Figure 41–5).

FULL (FOUR-WHEEL) SYSTEMS This system is the most effective ABS available. This is a **4-channel** system, in which sensors monitor each of the four wheels. With this continuous information, the ABS electronic control module ensures each wheel receives the exact braking force it needs to maintain both antilock and steering control.

INTEGRATED ANTILOCK BRAKE SYSTEM COMPONENTS

Delco ABS III, Teves Mark I/Mark II, Bendix ABS 10, and Bosch ABS-3 are commonly used integrated antilock brake systems.

The following sections describe the main components found in a typical four-wheel, 3-channel, **integrated** or **integral** ABS (Figure 41–6). Four-wheel, 4-

FIGURE 41–6 Master brake cylinder in the typical system uses an electric pump for power boost. *Courtesy of Ford Motor Company*

channel systems are similar and are used as the basis for automatic traction control systems, which will discussed later in this chapter.

HYDRAULIC UNIT This hydraulic unit (Figure 41–7) serves the purpose of the booster and master cylinder. It contains the electrical and mechanical components needed to modulate brake fluid pressure in each hydraulic circuit while in the antilock mode.

FIGURE 41–7 Typical ABS hydraulic control unit.

BOOSTER/MASTER CYLINDER ASSEMBLY

The booster/master cylinder assembly contains the valves and pistons needed to produce hydraulic pressure in the wheel circuits during brake application. Power brake assist is provided by pressurized brake fluid supplied by the hydraulic **accumulator**.

VALVE BLOCK ASSEMBLY The valve block assembly attaches to the side of the booster/master cylinder and contains the hydraulic wheel circuit solenoid valves (Figure 41–8). The electronic brake control module controls the position of these solenoid valves. The **valve block** is serviceable separate from the booster/master cylinder but should not be disassembled. An electrical connector links the valve block to the ABS control module.

WHEEL CIRCUIT VALVES The system has three separate wheel circuits: left front, right front, and rear. Two solenoid valves are used to control each circuit. One controls the inlet valve of the circuit, the other the outlet valve.

When inlet and outlet valves of a circuit are used in combination, pressure can be increased, decreased,

or held steady in the circuit. The position of each valve is determined by the control module. Outlet valves are normally closed, and inlet valves are normally open. Valves are activated when the ABS control module switches 12 volts to the circuit solenoids. During normal driving, the circuits are not activated.

MAIN VALVE This two-position valve is also controlled by the ABS control module and is open only in the ABS mode. When open, pressurized brake fluid from the booster circuit is directed into the master cylinder (front brake) circuits to prevent excessive pedal travel.

PRESSURE SWITCH This switch controls pump motor operation and the low pressure warning light circuit. The pressure switch grounds the pump motor relay coil circuit, activating the pump when accumulator pressure drops below 2,030 psi. The switch cuts off the motor when the pressure reaches 2,610 psi. The pressure switch also contains switches to activate the dash mounted warning light if accumulator pressure drops below 1,500 psi.

PUMP/MOTOR ASSEMBLY An integral pump/motor assembly is used to provide pressurized brake fluid to the hydraulic unit accumulator. The pump/motor is mounted on the hydraulic unit with pressure and return hoses running to the booster inlet and reservoir (Figure 41–9). The pump/motor assembly keeps the hydraulic accumulator pressure at required levels anytime the ignition switch is in the run position.

ACCUMULATOR The accumulator itself is a small, sealed chamber mounted to the pump/motor assembly (Figure 41–10). It holds the highly pressurized nitrogen gas that is used to generate this charging pressure.

RESERVOIR WITH FLUID LEVEL WARNING SWITCHES The reservoir assembly is a translucent plastic container with two main chambers. Integral

FIGURE 41–8 Solenoid valve body assembly from a Teves Mark II system. *Courtesy of Ford Motor Company*

FIGURE 41–9 Reservoir with fluid level warning switches.

FIGURE 41–10 An accumulator from a Teves Mark II system. *Courtesy of Ford Motor Company*

fluid level switches are part of the reservoir cap assembly with one electrical connector pointing forward for wire harness connections. Two low-pressure hoses lead from the reservoir. One hose attaches to the hydraulic pump assembly and the other to the master cylinder housing.

WHEEL-SPEED SENSORS The ABS control module continuously receives data from four wheel-speed sensors. One sensor is mounted at each wheel and generates a signal whenever the wheel turns.

The sensors use electromagnetic principles to generate a voltage pulse. Like the magnetic pulse generators discussed under ignition systems, the wheel sensor uses a toothed sensor ring that is moved past a stationary sensor (Figure 41–11). The stationary sen-

FIGURE 41–11 Typical ABS wheel sensors: (A) front and (B) rear wheel.

sor consists of a permanent magnet and pickup coil. As the teeth on the ring approach and move away from the stationary sensor, they expand and contract the magnetic lines of force around the permanent magnet. This movement of magnetic force induces a voltage in the pickup coil that can be read by the ABS control module.

ABS CONTROL MODULE This small control computer is normally mounted inside the trunk on the wheel housing. It monitors system operation and controls antilock function when needed. The module relies on inputs from the wheel speed sensors and feedback from the hydraulic unit to determine if the antilock brake system is operating correctly and to determine when the antilock mode is required. The module has a self-diagnostic function including numerous trouble codes.

INTEGRATED ANTILOCK BRAKE SYSTEM OPERATION

When a wheel speed sensor signals the ABS control module that a high rate of deceleration is taking place at its wheel (that is, that the wheel is likely to lock and skid), the controller initially signals the hydraulic unit to keep hydraulic pressure at the wheel constant. If the wheel continues to decelerate, the controller then signals the circuit valve solenoids to reduce hydraulic pressure to the affected wheel. This reduces braking at the wheel, reducing the risk of lockup (Figure 41–12).

The wheel accelerates again as a result of the reduced braking pressure. Once a specific limit has been reached, the controller registers the fact that the wheel is not being sufficiently braked. The wheel is decelerated again by increasing the pressure, which was initially reduced. The control cycles may be executed every second depending upon the road conditions.

In operation, when the brakes are released, the piston in the master cylinder is retracted. The booster chamber is vented to the reservoir, and the fluid in the chamber is at the same low pressure as the reservoir (Figure 41–13).

When the brakes are applied, under normal conditions, the brake pedal actuates a pushrod (Figure 41–14). This operates a scissors lever, which moves a spool valve. When the spool valve moves, it closes the port from the booster chamber to the reservoir and partially opens the port from the accumulator in proportion to the pressure on the brake pedal. This allows hydraulic fluid under pressure from the accumulator to enter the booster chamber. As hydraulic pressure enters, it pushes the booster piston forward,

2. SENSORS RELAY ANALOG SIGNAL INDICATING IMPENDING LOCKING CONDITION.

3. ANALOG SIGNAL CONVERTED TO DIGITAL SIGNAL.

4. MICROPROCESSOR COMPARES INPUT WITH INFORMATION IN RAM AND DETERMINES POTENTIAL BRAKE LOCKUP.

INPUT CONDITIONERS

REFERENCE VOLTAGE REGULATOR

MICROCOMPUTER

OUTPUT DRIVERS

ANALOG-TO-DIGITAL CONVERTER

MICRO-PROCESSOR

5. OUTPUT DRIVERS CLOSE.

6. ACTUATOR GROUND CIRCUITS CLOSE.

7. CURRENT FLOWS TO SOLENOIDS

RAM

ANTI-LOCK BRAKE PROCESSOR

AMP

FROM MASTER CYLINDER

TO RESERVOIR

FROM BOOSTER CHAMBER.

8. HYDRAULIC PRESSURE TO BRAKE IS REDUCED.

SOLENOID VALVE

CALIPER

ROTOR

1. SENSORS DETECT WHEEL ROTATION.

10. NORMALLY OPEN INLET VALVES CLOSED.

9. NORMALLY CLOSED OUTLET VALVES OPEN.

FIGURE 41–12   ABS operation—potential brake lock condition.

BRAKE PEDAL

MASTER CYLINDER PISTON

RETRACTION SLEEVE

KEY

ATMOSPHERIC PRESSURE
ACCUMULATOR PRESSURE
BOOSTER PRESSURE

FRONT LEFT   FRONT RIGHT   REAR AXLE

FIGURE 41–13   ABS operation—no braking.

FIGURE 41–14 Normal braking with ABS.

providing hydraulic assist to the mechanical thrust from the pushrod.

When the controller determines the wheels are locking up, it opens a valve that supplies one chamber between the two master cylinder pistons and another chamber between the retraction sleeve and the first master cylinder piston (Figure 41–15). The hydraulic pressure on the retraction sleeve retracts the pushrod, pushing back the brake pedal. In effect, the hydraulic pressure to the front wheels is now supplied by the accumulator, not by the brake pedal action. The controller also opens and closes the solenoid valves to cycle the brakes on the wheels that have been locking up.

When the solenoid valves are open, the master cylinder pistons supply hydraulic fluid to the front brakes and the boost pressure chamber provides hydraulic pressure to the rear. When the solenoid valves are closed, the hydraulic fluid from the master cylinder pistons and booster pressure chamber is cut off. The hydraulic fluid is returned from the brakes to the reservoir.

FIGURE 41–15 ABS in operation.

The electronic controller monitors the electro-mechanical components of the system. Malfunction of the ABS causes the electronic controller to shut off or inhibit the system. However, normal power-assisted braking remains. Malfunctions are indicated by one or two warning lights inside the vehicle. Loss of hydraulic fluid or power booster pressure disables the antilock brake system.

In most malfunctions in the anti-lock brake system, the check antilock brakes or brake light is illuminated. The sequence of illumination of these warning lights combined with the problem symptoms determine the appropriate diagnostic tests to perform. The diagnostic tests then pinpoint the exact component needing service.

NONINTEGRATED ANTILOCK BRAKE SYSTEMS

Typical **nonintegrated** or **independent systems** include the Bendix Antilock 6, Bosch ABS-2/2S/2U, Bosch ABS/ASR, Delco ABS VI, Kelsey-Hayes RWAL/4WAL/RABS, and Teves Mark IV.

Nonintegrated systems do not integrate the hydraulic boost, master cylinder, and ABS hydraulic valve unit into a single assembly. Instead the master cylinder and hydraulic valve unit are separate assemblies and a vacuum boost is used. In some nonintegrated systems, the master cylinder supplies brake fluid to the hydraulic unit. Although the hydraulic unit is a separate assembly, it still uses a high-pressure pump/motor, accumulator, and fast-acting solenoid valves to control hydraulic pressure to the wheels. Wheel speed sensor and control module operation are also similar to integrated systems described earlier.

General Motors' Electromagnetic Antilock Brake Systems

Beginning in 1991, General Motors began equipping certain small and mid-size vehicles with an antilock braking system called the Delco ABS-VI. This system is an add-on system that uses a conventional vacuum power booster and master brake cylinder. It does not use a high pressure pump/motor and accumulator and fast-acting solenoid valves to control hydraulic pressure. Instead, it uses a hydraulic modulator (Figure 41–16) that operates using a principle General Motors calls electromagnetic braking.

As in integrated systems, wheel speed is monitored using individual speed sensors. When one wheel begins to decelerate faster than the others while braking, the control module signals the hydraulic modulator assembly to reduce pressure to the affected brake.

MODULATOR OPERATION The ABS-VI modulator contains three small screw plungers—one for each front brake circuit and one for the rear brake circuit. These plungers are driven by electric motors. At the top of each plunger cavity is a check ball that controls hydraulic pressure within the brake circuit.

The hydraulic modulator and motor pack (Figure 41–17) is mounted to the master cylinder. The hydraulic brake circuit for each front wheel is con-

FIGURE 41–16 The hydraulic modulator is an add-on component to the conventional master cylinder. The electric motors can be replaced separately, as can the two solenoids. *Courtesy of Chevrolet Division, General Motors Corporation*

1 **ELECTROMAGNETIC BRAKE COIL**
2 **MOTOR PACK**

1 **MOTOR DRIVE DOG RELEASES SPRING BRAKE AND DRIVES PINION**
2 **CIRCLIP**
3 **MOTOR PINION**
4 **PINION DRIVE DOG**
5 **EXPANSION SPRING BRAKE (ESB)**
6 **MOTOR DRIVE DOG**
7 **MOTOR SHAFT**
8 **STEEL SLEEVE**
9 **MOTOR DRIVE DOG RELEASES SPRING BRAKE (SPRING LEG BENEATH PINION DOG) AND DRIVES PINION**
10 **PINION DOG EXPANDS SPRING AND LOCKS AGAINST SLEEVE**

FIGURE 41–17 A motor pack from an ABS VI. _Courtesy of Pontiac Division, General Motors Corporation_

trolled by a motor, gear-driven ball screw, solenoid, piston, and check valve. The rear wheel circuit is controlled by check balls and a single motor; therefore, both rear brakes are modulated together.

The motors are high-speed, bi-directional motors that quickly and precisely position the ball screws. Each motor has a brake which allows its ball screw to maintain its position against hydraulic pressures. The front motors have an electromagnetic brake (**EMB**) and the rear motor uses an expansion spring brake (**ESB**).

During normal braking conditions, each plunger is all the way up. The check ball at the top is unseated and the by-pass solenoid is normally open. This allows brake pressure from the master cylinder and vacuum power booster to apply the brakes during normal stopping.

During panic stops, the ABS mode operates. In this situation, brake pressure must be reduced to prevent wheel lockup. This is done by closing the normally open solenoid to isolate the circuit and then turning

the plunger down to reduce braking pressure. As the plunger turns down, it increases the volume within the brake circuit. This causes a drop in pressure that keeps the wheel from locking. The amount of pressure applied is controlled by running the plunger up and down as required. To decrease pressure further, the plunger is run down. To reapply pressure, the plunger moves back up.

The system can cycle the brakes seven times per second. Because the system does not have a high-pressure pump and accumulator, it cannot increase brake pressure above what can be provided by the master cylinder and vacuum-assist booster.

The ABS-VI control module has five separate diagnostic modes. Data available for troubleshooting includes wheel speed sensor readings, vehicle speed, battery voltage, individual motor and solenoid command status, warning light status, and brake switch status. Numerous trouble codes are programmed into the controller to help pinpoint problems. Other diagnostic modes store past trouble codes. This data can help technicians determine if an earlier fault code, such as an intermittent wheel speed sensor, is linked to the present problem such as a completely failed wheel sensor. Another mode enables testing of individual system components.

ANTILOCK BRAKE SYSTEM SERVICE

Most of the service done to the brakes of an antilock brake system is identical to those in a conventional brake system. There are, however, some important differences. One of these is the bleeding of the brake system. Always refer to the appropriate procedures in the service manual before attempting to service the brakes on an ABS-equipped vehicle.

CAUTION:

Always check the service manual for special precautions before checking brake fluid level, bleeding the system, loosening a hydraulic line or hose, or replacing a part. It may be necessary to de-pressurize the system to safely service it. ■

Brake System Bleeding

The front brakes of an antilock brake system can be bled in the conventional manner, with or without the accumulator being charged. However, bleeding the rear brakes requires a full-charged accumulator or a pressure bleeder attached to the reservoir cap opening, with a minimum of 35 psi.

System Bleeding with Accumulator Charged

Once accumulator pressure is available to the system, the rear brakes can be held by opening the rear brake caliper bleeder screws for 10 seconds at a time while holding the brake pedal in the applied position with the ignition switch in the run position. Repeat until an air-free flow of brake fluid has been observed at each caliper, then close the bleeder screws. Pump the brake pedal several times to complete the bleeding procedure. Adjust the brake fluid level in the reservoir to the maximum level with a fully charged accumulator.

CAUTION:

Care must be used when opening the rear caliper bleeder screws, due to the high pressure from a fully charged accumulator. ■

System Bleeding with Pressure Bleeder

When using a pressure bleeder, it must be attached to the reservoir cap opening, and a minimum of 35 psi must be maintained on the system. With the brake pedal at rest and the ignition switch off, open the rear caliper bleeder screws for 10 seconds at a time. Once an air-free flow of brake fluid has been observed at each caliper, close the bleeder screws and place the ignition switch in the run position. Pump the brake pedal several times to complete the bleeder procedure. Siphon off the excess fluid in the reservoir to adjust the level to the maximum level with a full-charged accumulator.

DIAGNOSIS AND TESTING

Always follow the vehicle manufacturer's specified diagnostic and replacement procedures when servicing ABS systems. In general, ABS diagnostics require three to five different types of testing that must be performed in the specified order listed in the service manual. Types of testing may include the following.

1. Pretest checks or inspections.
2. On-board ABS control module testing (trouble code reading).
3. Warning light symptom troubleshooting.
4. Individual trouble code or component troubleshooting.

WARNING!

Following the wrong sequence or bypassing steps may lead to unnecessary replacement of parts or incorrect resolution of the symptom. The information and procedures given in this chapter are typical of the various antilock systems on the market. For specific instructions, consult the vehicle's service manual. ■

The prediagnosis inspection consists of a quick visual check of specific system components that could create an apparent antilock system malfunction. Inspecting the system before diagnosing specific symptoms can result in the detection of a simple defect, which could be the cause of an inoperative system. This inspection should be the first step in diagnosing a complaint.

If a malfunction in the ABS occurs, be sure the control module connector is securely connected and that all ABS connectors are securely connected. Check for a blown fuse. If the malfunction is still present, refer to the procedure for reading trouble codes.

If pretest checks or inspections do not determine the problem, the ABS control module is then accessed

LOWER STEERING COLUMN COVER

FUSE PANEL ACCESS COVER

ABS DIAGNOSTIC CONNECTOR

FIGURE 41–18 Typical location of the ABS diagnostic connector on Chrysler passenger cars. *Courtesy of Chrysler Corporation*

for individual trouble codes. Some antilock brake systems have over fifty trouble codes, each corresponding to a different problem in the system. These codes are keyed to individual pinpoint tests and troubleshooting sequences listed in the service manual.

To retrieve trouble codes, a scan tool is used. Often the same scan tool recommended for diagnosing engine performance problems is used to retrieve ABS trouble codes. These scan tools are plugged into the vehicle's ABS diagnostic connector (Figure 41–18). The location of this connector can be found in the appropriate service manual.

The brake and anti-lock warning lights are also designed to signal potential problems in the system. On/off combinations of the two lights are keyed to specific troubleshooting sequences listed in the service manual.

Many antilock brake systems components are simply remove-and-replace items. On some systems, wheel speed sensors can be reused or adjusted.

Normal brake repairs, such as replacing brake pads, caliper replacement, rotor machining or replacement, brake hose replacement, master cylinder or power booster replacement, or parking brake repair, can all be performed as usual. In other words, brake service on an ABS-equipped vehicle is similar to service on a conventional system with a few exceptions.

First, before beginning service, depressurize the accumulator to prevent personal injury from high-pressure fluid. This is accomplished by pumping the brake pedal (ignition off) until the pedal becomes hard. Air gaps between the speed sensors and toothed ring do not have to be adjusted after machining rotors if wheel bearing adjustment is made to manufacturer's specifications. Disc or drum brake service is per-

formed as on a conventional vehicle. Always bleed the system after performing any service that allows air to enter the lines.

AUTOMATIC STABILITY (TRACTION) CONTROL

Auto makers are now applying the technology used in antilock braking systems to design automatic traction or stability control systems. As explained earlier, an ABS pumps the brakes when a braking wheel attempts to go into a locked condition. Automatic traction control systems (**ATC**) apply the brakes when a drive wheel attempts to spin and lose traction (Figure 41–19).

The system works best when one drive wheel is working on a good traction surface and the other is not. The system also works well when the vehicle is accelerating on slippery road surfaces, especially when climbing hills.

ATC is most helpful on four-wheel or all-wheel drive vehicles where loss of traction at one wheel could hamper driver control. It is also desirable on high-powered front-wheel-drive vehicles for the same reason.

During road operation, the ATC system uses an electronic control module to monitor the wheel-speed sensors. If a wheel enters a loss-of-traction situation, the module applies braking force to the wheel in trouble. Wheel spin is normally limited to a 10 percent slippage. Some traction control systems use separated hydraulic valve units and control modules for the ABS and ATC, while others integrate both systems into one hydraulic control unit and a single control module. The pulse rings and wheel-speed sensors remain unchanged from the ABS to the ATC.

Some ATC systems function only at low road speeds to 5 to 20 miles per hour. More advanced systems work at higher speeds and usually integrate some engine control functions into the control loop. For example, if the ATC system senses a loss of traction, it not only cycles the brakes but also signals the engine control module to retard ignition timing and partially close the throttle as well. Timing and throttle reduce engine output. If wheel slippage continues, the ATC controller may also cut fuel delivery to one or more engine cylinders. This action relieves engine stress and prevents the driver from overspeeding the engine in extremely slippery conditions.

Many systems are equipped with a dash mounted warning light to alert the driver that the system is operating. There may also be a manual cut-off switch so the driver can turn off ATC operation.

Front wheel
speed sensor

ABS
relays

Rear wheel speed sensor

TCC/antilock
brake switch

Pressure modulator
valve assembly (PMV)

Electronic brake (and
traction) control module
(EBCM/EBTCM)

FIGURE 41–19 A typical ATC system.
Courtesy of General Motors Corporation

CASE STUDY

A customer brings her 1992 Chevrolet Lumina into the service department because her brake warning light is on at all times. Her expressed concern is that she paid for an ABS and is sure the system doesn't work, which is why the light is lit. It seems she read in the owner's manual that when the ABS light remains on, there is a problem with the system and the ABS is inoperative.

The technician verifies the complaint and finds the red brake light to be lit at all times. He further verifies that the vehicle is equipped with an ABS VI. He then retrieves the ABS test procedures from the service manual. After the preliminary tests are completed, he uses a scan tool to retrieve any trouble codes from the system. No trouble codes were found and the brake light remained on.

Confused and frustrated, the technician seeks help from a fellow certified technician. He summarizes the problem and the tests he conducted. The other technician goes over to the car to see what could be the problem and immediately identifies the major cause of the problem. The red brake warning light was on, not the amber one. The amber light will light if a problem has affected the ABS. It will also light to indicate that the ABS is inoperative. The red light, however, will light when there is a problem of low brake fluid, a closed parking brake switch, or if there is a hydraulic problem in the base brake system.

Through a basic inspection, the technician found the brake fluid level to be low. Once the fluid level was corrected, the light went out. It seems that the technician was side tracked by the customer's concern over the light and her desire to have a working ABS. The moral of the story is simply make sure you understand the function of all warning and alert lights before jumping to conclusions.

KEY TERMS

1-channel	Independent system
2-channel	Integral ABS
3-channel	Integrated ABS
4-channel	Nonintegrated system
4WAL	Pressure modulation
Accumulator	RABS
ATC	RWAL
EMB	Speed sensor
ESB	Valve block

SUMMARY

◆ Brake fluid is the lifeblood of any hydraulic brake system. DOT 4 is the type most commonly used on conventional systems. DOT 3 is recommended for most antilock brake systems and some power brake systems.

◆ Modern antilock brake systems provide electronic/hydraulic pumping of the brakes for straight-line stopping under panic conditions.

◆ In addition to being classified as integral and non-integral, antilock brake systems can be broken down into the level of control they provide. They can be 1-, 2-, 3-, or 4-channel two- or four-wheel systems.

◆ Pressure modulation works to prevent wheel locking. Antilock brake systems can modulate the pressure to the brakes as often as 15 times per second.

◆ Integrated antilock brake systems combine the master cylinder, hydraulic booster, and hydraulic circuitry into a single assembly. The great majority of antilock brake systems systems are of this type.

◆ On a nonintegrated ABS, the master cylinder and hydraulic valve unit are separate assemblies and a vacuum boost is used. In some nonintegrated systems, the master cylinder supplies brake fluid to the hydraulic unit.

◆ Automatic traction control (ATC) is a system that applies the brakes when a drive wheel attempts to spin and lose traction.

◆ Malfunction of the ABS causes the electronic controller to shut off or inhibit the system. However, normal power-assisted braking remains. Malfunctions are indicated by one or two warning lights inside the vehicle. Loss of hydraulic fluid or power booster pressure disables the antilock brake system.

TECH MANUAL

The following procedures are included in Chapter 41 of the *Tech Manual* that accompanies this book:

1. Perform ABS electronic checks with warning lights.

2. Perform ABS tests with a scan tool.

3. Adjust wheel sensor gap.

REVIEW QUESTIONS

1. Describe the three ways antilock brake systems can be classified.

2. Explain the role of the wheel sensor(s) in the ABS.

3. Define the difference between an integrated and non-integrated antilock braking system.

4. Briefly describe the proper steps and testing needed to accurately diagnose antilock braking systems.

5. An ABS modulates brake pressure. What does this mean?

6. Describe the normal pedal feel when the ABS is activated during hard braking.

7. What is the purpose of the hydraulic unit in an integrated ABS?

8. What is the basic difference between a Delco ABS VI and other typical systems?

9. Technician A says in 1-channel systems, the rear brakes on both sides of the vehicle are modulated, at the same time, to control skidding. Technician B says most single channel systems are called either RABS or RWAL. Who is correct?

   a. Technician A   **c.** Both A and B
   b. Technician B   **d.** Neither A nor B

10. Technician A says a malfunction of the ABS causes the electronic controller to shut off or inhibit the system. Technician B says a loss of hydraulic fluid or power booster pressure disables the antilock brake system. Who is correct?

    a. Technician A   **c.** Both A and B
    b. Technician B   **d.** Neither A nor B

11. Which of the following is a true statement?
    a. In some antilock brake systems, the power brake assist is provided by pressurized brake fluid supplied by the hydraulic accumulator.
    b. The accumulator is a small, sealed chamber mounted to the pump/motor assembly.
    c. The accumulator holds a highly pressurized nitrogen gas that is used to generate a charging pressure.
    d. All of statements are true.

12. Technician A says some traction control systems have separate hydraulic valve units and control modules for an ABS and ATC. Technician B says some integrate both systems into one hydraulic control unit and a single control module. Who is correct?
    a. Technician A   c. Both A and B
    b. Technician B   d. Neither A nor B

13. Which of the following is *not* a true statement about servicing ABS components or the entire system?
    a. Before beginning service, depressurize the accumulator by pumping the brake pedal (ignition off) until the pedal becomes hard.
    b. All base brake parts can be serviced the same way they would be if they were part of a non-ABS.
    c. Air gaps between the speed sensors and toothed ring must be adjusted after machining the brake rotors.
    d. Wheel bearing adjustment must be made to exact manufacturer's specifications.

14. While road testing a car equipped with an ABS, Technician A says during heavy braking, several pulses should be felt through the brake pedal. Technician B says a spongy pedal during normal braking is normal. Who is correct?
    a. Technician A   c. Both A and B
    b. Technician B   d. Neither A nor B

15. What is the name for the gas-filled pressure chamber that is part of the antilock braking system's pump and motor assembly?
    a. controller   c. sensor
    b. accumulator   d. reservoir

16. Which of the following is *not* a component of an antilock brake system?
    a. power-steering pump
    b. master cylinder
    c. solenoid valve body assembly
    d. wheel sensors

17. Technician A says the accumulator in an ABS is used to store hydraulic fluid to provide residual pressure for power-assist braking. Technician B says the booster pump in an antilock system provides pressurized hydraulic fluid for the ABS. Who is correct?
    a. Technician A   c. Both A and B
    b. Technician B   d. Neither A nor B

18. Technician A says the front brakes of an ABS can be bled without the accumulator being charged. Technician B says bleeding the front brakes requires a fully-charged accumulator. Who is correct?
    a. Technician A   c. Both A and B
    b. Technician B   d. Neither A nor B

19. Technician A says it is normal for the amber brake lamp to light when the ABS is activated during braking. Technician B says it is normal for the red brake lamp to be on whenever the ignition is on and the engine is off. Who is correct?
    a. Technician A   c. Both A and B
    b. Technician B   d. Neither A nor B

20. Technician A uses a pressure tester to check the operation of the accumulator, hydraulic pump, and controls of an ABS during diagnosis. Technician B checks an ABS by checking the codes in the control computer's memory. Who is correct?
    a. Technician A   c. Both A and B
    b. Technician B   d. Neither A nor B

SECTION 9

PASSENGER COMFORT

Chapter 42 Heating and Air Conditioning

Chapter 43 Other Comfort, Safety, and Security Equipment

Modern vehicles are designed to provide passengers with comfort, convenience, and safety. Such accessory systems can be quite elaborate, adding electronic circuits and components to an already complex vehicle.

In addition, service to items such as air bags, passive restraint systems, and air-conditioning equipment must be performed both safely and accurately. Concerns over the proper handling of air-conditioning refrigerant are particularly important.

The information covered in Section 9 corresponds to materials found on the ASE certification tests on heating and air-conditioning systems and electrical systems.

HEATING AND AIR CONDITIONING

42

OBJECTIVES

◆ Identify the purpose of a ventilation system. ◆ Identify the common parts of a heating system. ◆ Compare the vacuum and mechanical controls of a heating system. ◆ Describe how an automotive air-conditioning system operates. ◆ Locate, identify, and describe the function of the various air-conditioning components. ◆ Understand the special handling procedures for automotive refrigerants. ◆ Describe methods used to check refrigerant leaks. ◆ Use approved methods and equipment to discharge, reclaim/recycle, evacuate, and recharge an automotive air-conditioning system. ◆ Describe the operation of the three types of air-conditioning control systems.

The discomforts of motoring's early days would daunt the toughest motorcross racer (Figure 42–1). Paper-thin tires blew out if the vehicle ran over a good-size pebble. Headlights were so dim they could barely illuminate a locomotive in their path. There was no climate control. In winter, heavy coats and blankets were all that allowed passengers to survive behind a woefully inadequate windscreen. In summer, the breeze generated by 15 mph travel was the only thing that retarded heat prostration.

Today, ventilation, heating, and air-conditioning systems are very important elements for providing passenger comfort. Ventilation and heating systems are standard equipment on all passenger vehicles and air conditioning is standard on some and available for nearly all.

The large number of vehicles with air conditioning plus recent changes in the methods used to cool a vehicle and to service the systems makes a basic knowledge of air conditioning systems a must for automotive technicians.

VENTILATION SYSTEM

The **ventilation** system on most vehicles is designed to supply outside air to the passenger compartment through upper or lower vents or both. There are several systems used to vent air into the passenger compartment. The most common is the flow-through system (Figure 42–2). In this arrangement, a supply of outside air, which is called **ram air**, flows into the car when it is moving. When the car is not moving, a steady flow of outside air can be produced by the heater fan. In operation, ram air is forced through an inlet grille. The pressurized air then circulates throughout the passenger and trunk compartment. From there the air is forced outside the vehicle through an exhaust area.

FIGURE 42–1 Early-model cars did not offer the conveniences of today's vehicles.

FIGURE 42–2 A flow-through ventilation system is used on some vehicles. Ram air is forced into the inlet grille and sent throughout the passenger and trunk compartment. The air then flows out of the vehicle through exhaust areas. *Courtesy of Chevrolet Division, General Motors Corporation*

On certain older vehicles, air is admitted by opening or closing two vent knobs under the dashboard. The left knob controls air through the left inlet. The right knob controls air through the right inlet. The air is still considered ram air and is circulated through the passenger compartment.

Rather than using ram air (especially if the vehicle is stopped), a ventilation fan can be used. It can be accessible from under the dashboard or from inside the engine compartment. A blower assembly is placed inside the blower housing. As the squirrel cage blower rotates, it produces a strong suction on the intake. A pressure is also created on the output. When the fan motor is energized by using the temperature controls on the dashboard, air is moved through the passenger compartment.

AUTOMOTIVE HEATING SYSTEMS

The automotive heating system has been designed to work hand in hand with the cooling system to maintain proper temperatures inside the car. The heating system's primary job is to provide a comfortable passenger compartment temperature and to keep car windows clear of fog or frost. The primary components of the automotive heating system are the heater core, the heater control valve, the blower motor and the fan, and the heater and defroster duct hoses (Figure 42–3).

In the liquid-cooling system, heat from the coolant circulating inside the engine is converted to hot air, which is blown into the passenger compartment. Hot coolant from the engine is transferred by a heater hose to the heater control valve and then to the **heater core** inlet. As the coolant circulates through the core, heat is transferred from the coolant to the tubes and fins of the core. Air blown through the core by the blower motor and fan then picks up the heat from the surfaces of the core and transfers it into the passenger compartment of the car. After giving up its heat, the coolant is then pumped out through the heater core outlet, where it is returned to the engine to be recirculated by the water pump.

The heater core is generally designed and constructed much like a miniature radiator. It features two tanks, each with an inlet or outlet tube and a tube and fin core to facilitate coolant flow between them.

Although all heater cores basically function in the same manner, several variations in design and materials are used by different auto makers to achieve the same results. Although the core construction varies, this type has an aluminum core with plastic tanks.

Like the radiator, heater core tanks, tubes and fins can become clogged over time by rust, scale, and mineral deposits circulated by the coolant. Heater core failures are generally caused by leakage or clogging. Feel the heater inlet and outlet hoses while the engine is idling and warm with the heater temperature control on hot. If the hose downstream of the heater valve does not feel hot, the valve is not opening.

With cable-operated control valves, check the cable for sticking, slipping (loose mounting bracket) or misadjustment. With valves that are vacuum operated, there should be no vacuum to the valve when the heater is on (except for those that are normally closed and need vacuum to open).

If the heater core appears to be plugged, the inlet hose may feel hot up to the core but the outlet hose remains cool. Reverse flushing the core with a power flusher may open up the blockage, but usually the core has to be removed for cleaning or replacement. Air pockets in the heater core can also interfere with proper coolant circulation. Air pockets form when the coolant level is low or when the cooling system is not properly filled after draining.

When the heater core leaks and must be repaired, or replaced, it is a very difficult, and time-consuming job, primarily because of the core's location deep within the fire wall of the car. For this reason always leak test a replacement heater core before installation. Also flush the cooling system and replace the coolant seasonally.

SHOP TALK

Engines with aluminum cylinder heads or blocks sometimes lose coolant through microscopic porosity leaks in the castings. Though the amount of coolant that is lost this way is not great, over time it can contaminate the oil enough to cause premature engine wear, especially in the cylinders and bearings. Pressure testing the cooling system usually does not reveal microscopic porosity leaks because the cracks are too small to allow a noticeable pressure drop. ∎

FIGURE 42–3 Components of a typical heating system.

Porosity leaks can be sealed by adding a hot melt sealer product to the cooling system. Some experts recommend adding stop-leak products as a preventive measure when changing the coolant in late-model engines with aluminum heads or blocks.

Heater Control Valve

The **heater control valve** (sometimes called the water flow valve) controls the flow of coolant into the heater core from the engine. In a closed position, the valve allows no flow of hot coolant to the heater core, keeping it cool. In an open position, the valve allows heated coolant to circulate through the heater core, maximizing heater efficiency. Heater control valves are operated in three basic ways: by cable, thermostat, or vacuum.

Cable-operated valves are controlled directly from the heater control lever on the dashboard (Figure 42–4). Thermostatically controlled valves (feature a liquid-filled capillary tube located in the discharge airstream off the heater core. This tube senses air temperature, and the valve modulates the flow of water to maintain a constant temperature, regardless of engine speed or temperature.

Most heater valves, utilized on today's car are vacuum operated. These valves are normally located in the heater hose line or mounted directly in the engine block. When a vacuum signal reaches the valve, a diaphragm inside the valve is raised, either opening or closing the valve against an opposing spring. When the temperature selection on the dashboard is changed, vacuum to the valve is vented and the valve returns to its original position. Vacuum-actuated heater control valves are either normally open or normally closed designs.

On late-model vehicles, heater control valves are typically made of plastic for corrosion resistance and light weight. These valves feature few internal working parts and no external working parts. With the reduced weight of these valves, external mounting brackets are not required.

The thermostat, which helps regulate the coolant temperature in the cooling system, plays a large part in the heating system. A malfunctioning thermostat can cause the engine to overheat or not reach normal operating temperature, or it can be the cause of poor heater performance.

Blower Motor

The blower motor is usually located in the heater housing assembly. It ensures that air is circulated through the system (Figure 42–5). Its speed is controlled by a multiposition switch in the control panel. The switch works in connection with a resistor block that is usually located on the heater housing.

On some vehicles, when the engine is running, the blower motor is in constant operation at low speed. On automatic temperature control systems, the blower motor is activated only when the engine reaches a predetermined temperature. The blower motor circuit is protected by a fuse located in the fuse panel. The fuse rating is usually 20 to 30 amperes.

The blower motor resistor block is used to control the blower motor speed. The typical resistor block is composed of three or four wire resistors in series with the blower motor, which control its volt-

FIGURE 42–5 Blower motor assembly.

FIGURE 42–6 Blower motor wiring diagram.

FIGURE 42–4
Cable-operated heater valve used to control the flow of water or coolant through the heater core.

age and current (Figure 42–6). The speed of the motor is determined by the control panel switch, which puts the resistors in series. Increasing the resistance in the system slows the blower speed.

If the blower does not operate, use a test light to make sure there is voltage on both sides of the fuse. Then, check to see if current is arriving at the motor. On cars where the blower motor is behind the inner fender shell, hunt out the wiring and check for current. If the blower motor is getting current, the problem is either a burned out blower motor or a bad ground on the motor. In situations where no current is available at the motor, backtrack to check for an open resistor. Check also for burned or corroded connections in the blower relays or bulkhead connectors. In-line fuses are another potential problem.

Sliding the heat selector control switch off on a vehicle without factory air conditioning closes a door that blocks the flow of air into the heater core. Even if the blower is turned on, no heat comes out because the air inlet is closed. On vehicles with factory air conditioning, a **blend door** usually routes some air through the heater core and some through the evaporator depending on the temperature range selected (Figure 42–7).

If the blower motor runs but no air comes out of the ducts, the problem is either a stuck on inoperative airflow control or blend door. This can also affect the operation of the defrosters. These doors may be cable or vacuum operated.

Change the position of the temperature selector knob, sliding it from hot to cold. If the sound of doors opening and closing is not heard, the control cables can sometimes slip loose from the dash switch or door arm rendering the door inoperative. If this is the case, little or no resistance is felt when sliding the temperature control knob. A kinked or rusted cable can also

prevent a door from working. If this is the case, resistance is felt trying to move the control knob. In either case, it is necessary to get under the dash, find the cable, and replace, reroute, or reconnect it. Doors can also be jammed by objects that have fallen down the defroster ducts. Remove the obstruction from the plenum by fishing through the heater outlet with a coat hanger or magnet, or remove the plenum. Be careful when fishing for the obstruction, some heater cores are easily pierced.

With vacuum-controlled doors, the most common reasons for failure are leaky or loose vacuum hoses, or defective diaphragms in the little vacuum motors that move the doors. Check the vacuum by starting the engine and disconnecting the small hose that goes to the vacuum motor that works one of the doors. If you feel a vacuum or hear a hissing sound when trying different temperature settings, the vacuum source is good. If by applying vacuum to it with a hand-held pump, it moves and holds vacuum for about one minute (Figure 42–8), the problem is a bad vacuum motor. If it does not, check for leaky vacuum hose connections, a defective temperature control switch, or a leaky vacuum reservoir or check valve under the dash or in the engine compartment.

A low coolant level can starve the heater resulting in little or no heat output. Check the coolant level in the radiator (not the overflow tank) to see if it is low. If low, adding coolant does not cure the problem until the problem of low coolant is found and fixed.

Air pockets can form in long heater hoses or where the heater is mounted higher than the radiator.

FIGURE 42–7 Typical blended air heater system. *Courtesy of General Motors Corporation*

FIGURE 42–8 The operation of vacuum-actuated valves can be checked using a hand-held vacuum pump. *Courtesy of Stant, Inc.*

To vent the trapped air, some vehicles have bleeder valves on the hoses. Opening the valves allows air to escape as the system is filled. The valves are then closed when coolant reaches their level. On vehicles that lack these special bleeder valves, it may be necessary to temporarily loosen the heater outlet hose so air can bleed out as the system is filled.

Heater and Defroster Duct Hoses

Transferring heated air from the heater core to passenger compartment heater and defroster outlets is the job of the heater and defroster duct hoses. These hoses vary in diameter from 1-1/2 inches to 6 inches. They are generally made by wrapping a continuous ply of **elastomer** (impregnated-and-coated fabric tape) and a plated reinforcing spring wire simultaneously so the wire is completely enclosed and bonded within the tape overlap. This construction improves rust protection since the wire is not exposed to condensation, and metal-to-metal contact is eliminated.

HEATING SYSTEM SERVICE

When performing any checks and service procedures, always follow the procedures recommended in the manufacturer's service manual. In some cases, it is possible to make repairs to vacuum hose and electrical connections without removing the heater assembly. If it is necessary to remove the heater assembly, the cooling system must be drained before removing the heater core.

THEORY OF AUTOMOTIVE AIR CONDITIONING

It is important for the technician to know the basic theory of automotive air-conditioning systems. Understanding how a system moves heat from the confined space of the passenger compartment and dissipates it into the atmosphere (Figure 42–9) will assist the technician in analyzing system failures and performing the required maintenance and service.

All air-conditioning systems are based on three fundamental laws of nature.

HEAT FLOW An air-conditioning system is designed to pump heat from one point to another. All materials or substances, as cold as –459 degrees Fahrenheit, have heat in them. Also, heat always flows from a warmer object to a colder one. For example, if one object is at 30°F and another object is 80°F, heat flows from the warmer object (80°F) to the colder one (30°F). The greater the temperature difference between the objects, the greater the amount of heat flow.

HEAT FROM SUN AND OUTSIDE AIR

FIGURE 42–9 Heat flow from inside the car to outside. *Courtesy of Everco Industries, Inc.*

HEAT ABSORPTION Objects can be in one of three forms: solid, liquid, or gas. When objects change from one state (form) to another, large amounts of heat can be transferred. For example, when water temperature goes below 32°F, water changes from a liquid to a solid (ice). If the temperature of water is raised to 212°F, the liquid turns into a gas (steam). But an interesting thing occurs when water, or any matter, changes from a solid to a liquid and then from a liquid to a gas. Additional heat is necessary to change the state of the substance, even though this heat does not register on a thermometer. For example, ice at 32°F requires heat to change into water, which will also be at 32°F. Additional heat raises the temperature of the water until it reaches the boiling point of 212°F. More heat is required to change water into steam. But if the temperature of the steam was measured, it would also be 212°F. The amount of heat necessary to change the state of a substance is called **latent heat**—or hidden heat—because it cannot be measured with a thermometer. This hidden heat is the basic principle behind all air-conditioning systems.

PRESSURE AND BOILING POINTS Pressure also plays an important part in air conditioning. Pressure on a substance, such as a liquid, changes its boiling point. The greater the pressure on a liquid, the higher the boiling point. If pressure is placed on a vapor, the vapor condenses at a higher than normal temperature. In addition, as the pressure on a substance is reduced, the boiling point can also be reduced. For example, the boiling point of water is 212°F. The boiling point can be increased by increasing the pressure on the fluid. It can also be decreased by reducing the pressure or placing the fluid in a vacuum.

REFRIGERANTS IN AIR-CONDITIONING SYSTEMS

The substance used to remove heat from the inside of an air conditioned vehicle is called the refrigerant. Up to recently, the refrigerant was Refrigerant-12 (commonly referred to as R-12 and Freon). **R-12** is dichlorodifluoromethane (CCl_2F_2). This chemical is used to carry heat from the inside of the vehicle to outside the vehicle.

R-12 has a low boiling point (the point at which **evaporation** occurs). At any temperature above $-21.6°F$, liquid R-12 can become a vapor. As it changes state, it absorbs a large amount of heat. Since the heat that it absorbs is from the inside of the vehicle, passengers are cooler.

R-12 is colorless, odorless, non-corrosive, non-toxic (although it can displace oxygen), oil soluble, and will not damage rubber seals, gaskets, or hoses.

To understand how R-12 is used to cool the interior of a vehicle, the effects of pressure and temperature on R-12 must be first understood. If the pressure of R-12 is high, so is its temperature. Likewise if the pressure is low, so is its temperature. When the pressure of R-12 is between 20 to 80 psi, any change in pressure results in a proportional change in temperature. An increase of one psi will cause an increase of $1°F$ (Figure 42–10). Therefore the temperature of R-12 can be changed by changing its pressure.

To absorb heat, the temperature and pressure of R-12 is kept low. To dissipate heat, the temperature and pressure is high. Remember that the heat from something hot always moves to something colder. The R-12 absorbs heat from the inside of the vehicle and dissipates it to the cooler outside air. As the R-12 absorbs heat it changes from a liquid to a vapor. As it dissipates heat, it changes from a vapor to a liquid. The change from a vapor to a liquid is called **condensation**. These two changes of state—evaporation and condensation—occur continuously as the R-12 circulates through the air conditioning system.

An amendment to the United States' Clean Air Act and international agreements have mandated that R-12 be phased out as the refrigerant of choice. This came as a result of research that found the earth's ozone layer was being deteriorated by the chemicals found in R-12. The ozone layer is the earth's outermost shield of protection. This delicate layer protects against harmful effects of the sun's ultraviolet rays. The thinning of the ozone layer has become a worldwide concern. The ozone depletion is caused in part by release of chlorofluorocarbons (**CFC**s) into the atmosphere. R-12 is in the chemical family of CFCs. Since air conditioning systems with R-12 are susceptible to leaks, further damage to the ozone layer could be avoided by not using R-12 in air conditioning units.

Of the many chemicals that could be used in place of R-12, the automobile manufacturers have decided to use **R-134a**. This refrigerant may also be referred to as SUVA. R-134a is a hydrofluorocarbon (**HFC**) that causes less damage to the ozone layer when released to the atmosphere.

Although R-134a air conditioners operate in the same way and with the same basic components as R-12 systems, the two refrigerants are not interchangeable. Because it is less efficient than R-12, R-134a operates at higher pressures to make up for the loss of performance and requires new service techniques and system component designs. Basically, the higher system pressures of R-134a mean the system must be designed for those higher pressures.

The production phaseout for all CFCs, including R-12, was scheduled for December 1, 1995. To keep systems operating that were originally equipped with R-12, there are retrofit kits available for a changeover to R-134a. Although R-134a is less likely to have an adverse effect on the ozone layer, it still has the capability of contributing to the "greenhouse effect" when released into the air. Therefore, the recovery and recycling of R-134a became mandatory on November 15, 1995.

THE AIR-CONDITIONING SYSTEM AND ITS COMPONENTS

An automotive air-conditioning system is a closed, pressurized system. It consists of a compressor, condenser, receiver/dryer or accumulator, expansion valve or orifice tube, and an evaporator (Figure 42–11).

FIGURE 42–10 The relationship between temperature and pressure for R-12.

FIGURE 42–11 Major and secondary components of a typical air-conditioning system.

In a basic air-conditioning system, the heat is absorbed and transferred in the following steps (Figure 42–12).

1. Refrigerant leaves the compressor as a high-pressure, high-temperature vapor.
2. By removing heat via the condenser, the vapor becomes a high-pressure, high-temperature liquid.
3. Moisture and contaminants are removed by the receiver/dryer, where the cleaned refrigerant is stored until it is needed.
4. The expansion valve controls the flow of refrigerant into the evaporator.
5. Heat is absorbed from the air inside the passenger compartment by the low-pressure, warm refrigerant, causing the liquid to vaporize and greatly decrease its temperature.
6. The refrigerant returns to the compressor as a low-pressure, low-temperature vapor.

To understand the operation of the five major components, remember that an air-conditioning system is divided into two sides: the high side and the low side. **High side** refers to the side of the system that is under high pressure and high temperature. **Low side** refers to the low-pressure, low-temperature side of the system.

The Compressor

The compressor is the heart of the automotive air-conditioning system. It separates the high-pressure and low-pressure sides of the system. The primary purpose of the unit is to draw the low-pressure and low-temperature vapor from the evaporator and compress this vapor into high-temperature, high-pressure vapor. This action results in the refrigerant having a higher temperature than surrounding air, and enables the condenser to condense the vapor back to a liquid. The secondary purpose of the compressor is to circulate or pump the refrigerant through the A/C system under the different pressures required for proper operation. The compressor is located on the engine and is driven by the engine's crankshaft via a drive belt.

Although there are numerous types of compressors in use today, they are usually one of three types.

PISTON COMPRESSOR This type of compressor (Figure 42–13) can have its pistons arranged in an in-line, axial, radial, or V design. It is designed to have an intake stroke and a compression stroke for each cylinder. On the intake stroke, the refrigerant from the low side of the system (evaporator) is drawn into the compressor. The intake of refrigerant occurs through intake reed valves. These one-way

FIGURE 42–12 Basic refrigerant flow cycle.

FIGURE 42–13 (A) Piston on the downstrike (intake) pulls low-pressure refrigerant into the cylinder cavity. The intake (suction) valve is open, and the discharge valve is closed. (B) Piston on the upstroke (discharge) compresses refrigerant vapor and forces it out through the discharge valve. The intake (suction) valve is closed, and the discharge valve is open.

valves control the flow of refrigerant vapors into the cylinder. During the compression stroke, the vaporous refrigerant is compressed. This increases both the pressure and the temperature of the heat-carrying refrigerant. The outlet or **discharge** side reed valves then open to allow the refrigerant to move to the condenser. The outlet reed valves are the beginning of the high side of the system. Reed valves are made of spring steel, which can be weakened or broken if improper charging procedures are used, such as liquid charging with the engine running.

ROTARY VANE COMPRESSOR The **rotary vane compressor** does not have pistons (Figure 42–14). It consists of a rotor with several vanes and a carefully shaped housing. As the compressor shaft rotates, the vanes and housing form chambers. The refrigerant is drawn through the suction port into these chambers, which become smaller as the rotor turns. The discharge port is located at the point where the gas is completely compressed. No sealing rings are used in a vane compressor. The vanes are sealed against the housing by centrifugal force and lubricating oil. The oil sump is located on the discharge side, so the high pressure tends to force it around the vanes into the low-pressure side. This action ensures continuous lubrication. Because this type of compressor depends on a good oil supply, it is subject to damage if the system charge is lost. A protection device is used to disengage the clutch if pressure drops too low.

SCROLL-TYPE COMPRESSOR The **scroll-type compressor** has a movable scroll and a fixed or nonmovable scroll that provide an eccentriclike motion. As the compressor's crankshaft rotates, the movable scroll forces the refrigerant against the fixed scroll and toward the center of the compressor. This motion pressurizes the refrigerant. The action of a scroll-type compressor can be compared to that of a tornado. The pressure of air moving in a circular pattern increases as it moves toward the center of the circle. A delivery port is positioned at the center of the compressor and allows the high-pressure refrigerant to flow into the air-conditioning system (Figure 42–15). This type of compressor operates more smoothly than other designs.

Every compressor is equipped with an electromagnetic clutch as part of the compressor pulley assembly (Figure 42–16). It is designed to engage the pulley to the compressor shaft when the clutch coil is energized. The purpose of the clutch is to transmit power from the engine to the compressor and to provide a means of engaging and disengaging the refrigeration system from engine operation.

THRUST AND BELLEVILLE WASHERS

COMPRESSOR SHELL

MAIN BEARING — FRONT

CLUTCH COIL TERMINALS

PULLEY RIM

PULLEY RIM MTG. SCREW

DISCHARGE PORT

PULLEY RIM MTG. SCREW LOCKWASHER

ROTOR BEARING

ROTOR BEARING RETAINER

SUCTION PORT

SEAL SEAT RETAINER

SHAFT KEY

SHAFT NUT

SHAFT SEAL

MAIN BEARING — REAR

SEAL SEAT

SEAL SEAT O-RING

PISTON ASSEMBLY

CLUTCH DRIVE ASSEMBLY

ROTOR AND HUB ASSEMBLY

FRONT HEAD

CLUTCH COIL AND HOUSING ASSEMBLY

SHELL RETAINER

VALVE PLATE RETAINER RING

VALVE PLATE ASSEMBLY

FIGURE 42–14 Cutaway view of a typical rotary vane compressor. *Courtesy of Oldsmobile Division, General Motors Corporation*

The clutch is driven by power from the engine's crankshaft, which is transmitted through one or more belts (a few use gears) to the pulley, which is in operation whenever the engine is running. When the clutch is engaged power is transmitted from the pulley to the compressor shaft by the clutch drive plate. When the clutch is not engaged, the compressor shaft does not rotate, and the pulley freewheels.

The clutch is engaged by a magnetic field and disengaged by springs when the magnetic field is broken. When the controls call for compressor operation, the electrical circuit to the clutch is completed, the magnetic clutch is energized, and the clutch engages the compressor. When the electrical circuit is opened, the clutch disengages the compressor.

Two types of electromagnetic clutches have been in use for many years. Early-model air-conditioning systems used a rotating coil clutch. The magnetic coil, which engages or disengages the compressor, is mounted within the pulley and rotates with it. Electrical connections for the clutch operation are made through a stationary brush assembly and rotating slip rings, which are part of the field coil assembly. This older rotating coil clutch, now in limited use, has been largely replaced by the stationary coil clutch.

With the stationary coil, wear has been measurably reduced, efficiency increased, and serviceability made much easier. The clutch coil does not rotate. When the driver first energizes the air-conditioning system from the passenger compartment dashboard, the pulley assembly is magnetized by the stationary coil on the compressor body, thus engaging the clutch to the clutch hub which is attached to the compressor shaft. This activates the air-conditioning system. Depending on the system, the magnetic clutch is usually pressure controlled to cycle the

FIGURE 42–15 Scroll-type compressor. From Green/Green/Dwiggins, Australian Automotive Air Conditioning 1E © 1993 by Thomas Nelson Holdings, Ltd.

FIGURE 42–16   Parts of a compressor clutch assembly.

operation of the compressor (depending on system temperature or pressure). In some system designs, the clutch might operate continually when the system is turned on. With stationary coil design, service is not usually necessary except for an occasional check on the electrical connections.

Condenser   The **condenser** (Figure 42–17) consists of coiled refrigerant tubing mounted in a series of thin cooling fins to provide maximum heat transfer in

a minimum amount of space. The condenser is normally mounted just in front of the vehicle's radiator. It receives the full flow of ram air from the movement of the vehicle or airflow from the radiator fan when the vehicle is standing still.

The purpose of the condenser is to condense or liquefy the high-pressure, high-temperature vapor coming from the compressor. To do so, it must give up its heat. The condenser receives very hot (normally 200 to 400°F), high-pressure refrigerant vapor from the compressor through its discharge hose. The refrigerant vapor enters the inlet at the top of the condenser and as the hot vapor passes down through the condenser coils, heat (following its natural tendencies) moves from the hot refrigerant into the cooler air as it flows across the condenser coils and fins. This process causes a large quantity of heat to be transferred to the outside air and the refrigerant to change from a high-pressure hot vapor to a high-pressure warm liquid. This high-pressure warm liquid flows from the outlet at the bottom of the condenser through a line to the receiver/dryer or to the refrigerant metering device if an accumulator instead of a dryer is used.

In an air-conditioning system which is operating under an average heat load, the condenser has a combination of hot refrigerant vapor in the upper two-thirds of its coils. The lower third of the coils contains the warm liquid refrigerant, which has condensed. This high-pressure, liquid refrigerant flows from the condenser and on toward the evaporator. In effect, the condenser is a true heat exchanger.

1. CONDENSER
2. INSULATOR
3. INSULATOR
4. BRACKET
5. 11.5 N·m (101 LBS. IN.)
6. BRACKET
7. INSULATOR

FIGURE 42–17   Typical condenser. *Courtesy of Buick Division, General Motors Corporation*

Receiver/Dryer

Used on many systems, the **receiver/dryer** (Figure 42–18) is a storage tank for the liquid refrigerant from

FIGURE 42–18 Typical receiver/dryer. *Courtesy of Nissan Motors*

1 High & Low pressure switch:
   Turns off when refrigerant
   pressure reaches at more than
   2,452 kPa (25 kg/cm², 356
   psi) and less than 216 kPa (2.2
   kg/cm², 31 psi), cutting compressor power supply.
2 High pressure valve:
   Opens at pressures above 3,727
   kPa (38 kg/cm², 540 psi),
   thereby discharging refrigerant
   to the atmosphere.
3 Sight glass
4 Strainer:
   Removes foreign material in
   refrigerant.
5 Desiccant:
   Removes water in refrigerant.

the condenser, which flows into the upper portion of the receiver tank containing a bag of **desiccant** (moisture-absorbing material such as silica alumina or silica gel). As the refrigerant flows through an opening in the lower portion of the receiver, it is filtered through a mesh screen attached to a baffle at the bottom of the receiver. The desiccant in this assembly is to absorb any moisture present that might enter the system during assembly. These features of the assembly prevent obstruction to the valves or damage to the compressor.

Depending on the manufacturer, the receiver/ dryer may be known by other names such as filter or dehydrator. Regardless of its name, the function is the same. Included in many receiver/dryers are additional features such as high-pressure fitting, a pressure relief valve, and a sight glass for determining the state and condition of the refrigerant in the system.

The receiver/dryer is often neglected when the air-conditioning system is serviced or repaired. Failure to replace it can lead to poor system performance or replacement part failure. It is recommended that the receiver/dryer and/or its desiccant be changed whenever a component is replaced, the system has lost the refrigerant charge, or the system has been open to the atmosphere for any length of time.

⚠️ WARNING!

The dessicant draws moisture like a magnet and it can become contaminated in less than 5 minutes if it is exposed to the atmosphere. Keep it sealed. Once opened, put it under a vacuum quickly. ∎

Accumulator Systems not equipped with a receiver/dryer use an **accumulator** to accomplish the same thing. The accumulator is connected into the low side, at the outlet of the evaporator. The accumulator also contains a desiccant and is designed to store excess refrigerant and to filter and dry the refrigerant. If liquid refrigerant flows out of the evaporator, it will be collected by and stored in the accumulator.

Thermostatic Expansion Valve/Orifice Tube

The refrigerant flow to the evaporator must be controlled to obtain maximum cooling, while ensuring complete evaporation of the liquid refrigerant within the evaporator. This is accomplished by a thermostatic expansion valve (**TEV** or **TXV**) or a fixed orifice tube.

The TEV is mounted at the inlet to the evaporator and separates the high-pressure side of the system from the low-pressure side. The TEV regulates refrigerant flow to the evaporator to prevent evaporator flooding or starving. In operation, the TEV regulates the R-12 flow to the evaporator by balancing the inlet flow to the outlet temperature.

Both externally and internally equalized TEVs are used in air-conditioning systems (Figure 42–19). The only difference between the two valves is that the external TEV uses an equalizer line connected to the evaporator outlet line as a means of sensing evaporator outlet pressure. The internal TEV senses evaporator inlet pressure through an internal equalizer passage. Both valves have a capillary tube to sense evaporator outlet temperature. The tube is filled with a

FIGURE 42–19 Typical thermostatic expansion valves: (A) internally equalized and (B) externally equalized. From Whitman/Johnson, Refrigeration and Air Conditioning Technology, 2E © 1991 by Delmar Publishers

gas, which, if allowed to escape due to careless handling, will ruin the TXV.

During stabilized conditions (vehicle shutdown), the pressure on the bottom of the expansion valve diaphragm becomes equal to the pressure on the top of the diaphragm. This allows the valve spring to close the valve. When the system is started, the pressure on the bottom of the diaphragm drops rapidly, allowing the valve to open and meter liquid refrigerant to the lower evaporator tubes where it begins to vaporize.

Compressor suction draws the vaporized refrigerant out of the top of the evaporator at the top tube where it passes the sealed sensing bulb. The bottom of the valve diaphragm internally senses the evaporator pressure through the internal equalization passage around the sealed sensing bulb. As evaporator pressure is increased, the diaphragm flexes upward pulling the sensing bulb and pushrod away from the ball seat of the expansion valve. The expansion valve spring forces the ball onto the tapered seat and the liquid refrigerant flow is reduced.

As the pressure is reduced due to restricted refrigerant flow, the diaphragm flexes downward again, opening the expansion valve to provide the required controlled pressure and refrigerant flow condition. The sensing bulb produces the required pressure on top of the diaphragm. As the cool refrigerant passes the body of the sensing bulb, the gas above the diaphragm contracts and allows the expansion valve spring to close the expansion valve. When heat from the passenger compartment is absorbed by the refrigerant, it causes the gas to expand. The pushrod again forces the expansion valve to open, allowing more refrigerant to flow so that more heat can be absorbed.

Like the thermostatic expansion valve, the **orifice tube** (Figure 42–20) is the dividing point between the high- and low-pressure parts of the system. However,

FIGURE 42–20 Typical orifice expansion tube.

its metering or flow rate control does not depend on comparing evaporator pressure and temperature. It is a fixed orifice. The flow rate is determined by pressure difference across the orifice and by subcooling. Subcooling is additional cooling of the refrigerant in the bottom of the condenser after it has changed from vapor to liquid. The flow rate through the orifice is more sensitive to subcooling than to pressure difference.

Evaporator

The **evaporator**, like the condenser, consists of a refrigerant coil mounted in a series of thin cooling fins (Figure 42–21). It provides a maximum amount of heat transfer in a minimum amount of space. The evaporator is usually located beneath the dashboard or instrument panel.

Upon receiving the low-pressure, low-temperature liquid refrigerant from the thermostatic expansion valve or orifice tube in the form of an atomized (or droplet) spray, the evaporator serves as a boiler or vaporizer. This regulated flow of refrigerant boils immediately. Heat from the core surface is lost to the boiling and vaporizing refrigerant, which is cooler than the core, thereby cooling the core. The air passing over the evaporator loses its heat to the cooler surface of the core, thereby cooling the air inside the car. As the process of heat loss from air to the evaporator core surface is taking place, any moisture (humidity) in the air condenses on the outside of the evaporator

FIGURE 42–21 Typical evaporator. *Courtesy of Ford Motor Company*

core and is drained off as water. A drain tube in the bottom of the evaporator housing leads the water outside the vehicle. This dehumidification of air is an added feature of the air-conditioning system that adds to passenger comfort. It can also be used as a means of controlling fogging of the vehicle windows. Under certain conditions, however, too much moisture can accumulate on the evaporator coils. An example would be when humidity is extremely high and the maximum cooling mode is selected. The evaporator temperature might become so low that moisture would freeze on the evaporator coils before it can drain off.

Through the metering, or controlling, action of the thermostatic expansion valve or orifice tube, greater or lesser amounts of refrigerant are provided in the evaporator to adequately cool the car under all heat load conditions. If too much refrigerant is allowed to enter, the evaporator floods. This results in poor cooling due to the higher pressure (and temperature) of the refrigerant. The refrigerant can neither boil away rapidly nor vaporize. On the other hand, if too little refrigerant is metered, the evaporator starves. Poor cooling again results because the refrigerant boils away or vaporizes too quickly before passing through the evaporator.

The temperature of the refrigerant vapor at the evaporator outlet will be approximately 4 to 16°F higher than the temperature of the liquid refrigerant at the evaporator inlet. This temperature differential is the superheat that ensures that the vapor will not contain any droplets of liquid refrigerant that would be harmful to the compressor.

Refrigerant Lines

All the major components of the system have inlet and outlet connections that accommodate either flare or O-ring fittings. The refrigerant lines that connect between these units are made up of an appropriate length of hose or tubing with flare or O-ring fittings at each end as required. In either case the hose or tube end of the fitting is constructed with sealing beads to accommodate a hose or tube clamp connection.

There are three major refrigerant lines. Suction lines are located between the outlet side of the evaporator and the inlet side or **suction side** of the compressor. They carry the low-pressure, low-temperature refrigerant vapor to the compressor where it again is recycled through the system. Suction lines are always distinguished from the discharge lines by touch and size. They are cold to the touch. The suction line is larger in diameter than the liquid line because refrigerant in a vapor state takes up more room than refrigerant in a liquid state.

The other types of refrigerant lines are the **discharge** and liquid lines. Beginning at the discharge outlet on the compressor, the discharge or high-pressure line connects the compressor to the condenser. The liquid lines connect the condenser to the receiver/dryer and the receiver/dryer to the inlet side of the expansion valve. Through these lines, the refrigerant travels in its path from a gas state (compressor outlet) to a liquid state (condenser outlet) and then to the inlet side of the expansion valve where it vaporizes on entry to the evaporator. Discharge and liquid lines are always very warm to the touch and easily distinguishable from the suction lines.

Sight Glass

The **sight glass** allows the technician to see the flow of refrigerant in the lines. It can be located on the receiver/dryer or in-line between the receiver/dryer and the expansion valve or tube (Figure 42–22).

To check the refrigerant, open the windows and doors, set the controls for maximum cooling, and set the blower on its highest speed. Let the system run for about five minutes. Be sure the vehicle is in a well-ventilated area, or connect an exhaust gas ventilation system.

Use care to check the sight glass while the engine is running. If oil-streaking is seen, this indicates the system is empty. Bubbles, or foam, indicate the refrigerant is low. A sufficient level of refrigerant is indicated by what looks like a flow of clear water, with no bubbles. A clouded sight glass is an indication of desiccant contamination with subsequent infiltration and circulation through the system.

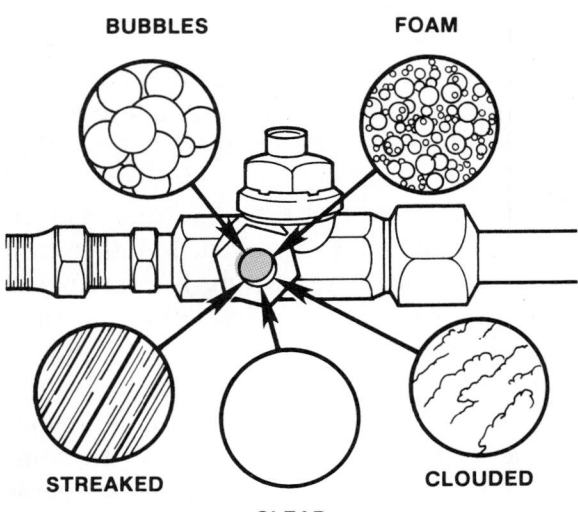

FIGURE 42–22 Typical sight glass location, and possible appearance of refrigerant.

Accumulator systems do not have a receiver-drier to separate the gas from the liquid as it flows from the condenser. The liquid line will always have a certain amount of bubbles in it. Therefore it would be useless to have a sight glass in these systems. Pressure and performance testing are the only ways to identify low refrigerant levels.

Blower Motor/Fan

The blower motor/fan assembly is located in the evaporator housing. Its purpose is to increase airflow in the passenger compartment (Figure 42–23). The blower, which is basically the same type as those used in heater systems, draws warm air from the passenger compartment, forces it over the coils and fins of the evaporator, and blows the cooled, cleaned, and dehumidified air into the passenger compartment. The blower motor is controlled by a fan switch.

During cold weather, the blower motor/fan provides the air flow, and the heater core provides the heat for the passenger compartment.

FIGURE 42–23 Blower fan increases airflow.

AIR-CONDITIONING SYSTEMS AND CONTROLS

There are two basic types of automotive air-conditioning systems. They are classified according to the method used in obtaining temperature control and are known as a cycling clutch system or an evaporator pressure or temperature control system.

Cycling Clutch System

In every **cycling clutch** system, the compressor is run intermittently through controlling the application and release of its clutch by a thermostatic or pressure switch. The thermostatic switch senses the evaporator's outlet air temperature, through a capillary tube that is part of the switch assembly. With a high sensing temperature, the thermostatic switch is closed and the compressor clutch is energized. As the evaporator outlet temperature drops to a preset level, the thermostatic switch opens the circuit to the compressor clutch. The compressor then ceases to operate until such time as the evaporator temperature rises above the switch setting. From this on and off operation is derived the term cycling clutch. In effect, the thermostatic switch is calibrated to allow the lowest possible evaporator outlet temperature that would prevent the freezing of condensation that might form on the evaporator.

Variations of the cycling clutch system include a system with a thermostatic expansion valve and a system with an orifice tube.

Cycling Clutch System with Thermostatic Expansion Valve
Some factory installations utilize a cycling clutch system that incorporates a TEV and receiver/dryer, as do some add-on units. The evaporator and control components are either in the engine compartment or an integral part of the cowl. In such cases there is a common blower and duct work for both heating and air-conditioning purposes. Also in these installations, the thermostatic switch has no temperature control knob and is usually mounted on the evaporator or its case. Temperature control is accomplished by using fresh or recirculating air and by reheating the cooled air in the heater core. The clutch cycles only to prevent evaporator icing.

A common form of the cycling clutch system is the field-installed (add-on) unit. With this installation, the evaporator, the thermostatic expansion valve, and thermostatic switch are self-contained in an underdash assembly. An installation of this type operates solely on passenger compartment recirculated air. Temperature control depends on intermittent operation of the compressor. The thermostatic switch has a control knob to cycle at higher temperatures when less cooling is desired.

●●● LOW PRESSURE LIQUID
■■■ LOW PRESSURE VAPOR

▬ HIGH PRESSURE LIQUID
▭ HIGH PRESSURE VAPOR

1 SWITCH, PRESSURE FAN	7 TUBE, EXPANSION (ORIFICE)	13 PORT, LOW-SIDE SERVICE
2 MUFFLER	8 EVAPORATOR	14 LINE, LOW-SIDE (SUCTION)
3 LINE, HIGH-SIDE (DISCHARGE)	9 SWITCH, PRESSURE CYCLING	15 SWITCH, HIGH PRESSURE CUT OUT
4 PORT, HIGH-SIDE SERVICE	10 ACCUMULATOR	16 VALVE, HIGH PRESSURE RELIEF
5 CONDENSER	11 DESICCANT	17 COMPRESSOR
6 LINE, LIQUID	12 HOLE, OIL BLEED	

FIGURE 42–24 Typical cycling clutch system with expansion (orifice) tube. *Courtesy of General Motors*

Cycling Clutch System with Orifice Tube (CCOT)

A typical **CCOT** system is illustrated in Figure 42–24. The system is factory installed and can use a thermostatic clutch cycling switch mounted on the evaporator case or a pressure cycling switch located on the accumulator. An expansion (orifice) tube is used in place of the TEV. Also, the system has an accumulator in the evaporator outlet. The accumulator is used primarily to separate vapor from liquid refrigerant before it enters the compressor. It also contains a drying agent or desiccant to remove moisture. The CCOT system has no receiver/dryer or sight glass. This system does have a special orifice, the oil bleed orifice, that allows refrigerant oil to return to the compressor rather than collect in the accumulator.

Evaporator Pressure Control System

In this type of system the compressor operates continually when dash controls are in the air-conditioning position. Evaporator outlet air temperature is automatically controlled by an evaporator pressure control valve such as the **STV** or **EPR** (POA). These types of valves throttle the flow of refrigerant out of the evaporator as required to establish a minimum evaporator pressure and thereby prevent freezing of condensation on the evaporator core. Maximum evaporator pressure is also established by this valve.

Valves-In-Receiver (VIR) System

This assembly incorporated the evaporator pressure control valves and receiver/dryer into one assembly. The **VIR** assembly is mounted close to the evaporator and is connected to both the evaporator inlet and outlet pipes. The basic refrigeration system components for a VIR system are shown in Figure 42–25.

To improve the efficiency of the compressor and evaporator, special supplemental controls are needed.

Compressor Controls

There are many controls used to monitor and trigger the compressor during its operational cycle. Each of

FIGURE 42–25 Typical evaporator pressure control system with VIR assembly.

these represents the most common protective control devices designed to ensure safe and reliable operation of the compressor.

Ambient Temperature Switch This switch senses outside air temperature and is designed to prevent compressor clutch engagement when air conditioning is not required or when compressor operation might cause internal damage to seals and other parts.

The switch is in series with the compressor clutch electrical circuit and closes at about 37°F. At all lower temperatures, the switch is open, preventing clutch engagement.

On some vehicles, the ambient switch is located in the air inlet duct of the air-conditioning systems that are regulated by evaporator pressure controls. Other makes have it installed near the radiator. It is not required on systems with a thermostatic or pressure switch.

Thermostatic Switch In cycling clutch systems, the thermostatic switch is placed in series with the compressor clutch circuit so it can turn the clutch on or off. It has two purposes. It de-energizes the clutch and stops the compressor if the evaporator is at the freezing point. On hang-on units or systems without reheat temperature control, it also controls the air temperature by turning the compressor on and off intermittently. For this purpose, it has a control knob to change the switch setting.

When the temperature of the evaporator approaches the freezing point (or the low setting of the switch), the thermostatic switch opens the circuit and disengages the compressor clutch. The compressor remains inoperative until the evaporator temperature rises to the preset temperature, at which time the switch closes and compressor operation resumes.

Pressure Cycling Switch This switch is electrically connected in series with the compressor electromagnetic clutch. Like the thermostatic switch, the turning on and off of the pressure cycling switch controls the operation of the compressor.

Low-Pressure Cutoff or Discharge Pressure Switch This switch is located on the high side of the system and senses any low-pressure conditions (Figure 42–26). It is tied into the compressor clutch circuit, allowing it to immediately disengage the clutch when the pressure falls too low.

High-Pressure Cutout Switch This switch, normally located in the vicinity of the compressor or discharge (high side) muffler, is wired with the compressor clutch (in series). Designed to open (cut out) and disengage the clutch at 350 to 375 psi, it again

FIGURE 42–26 Low-pressure cutoff switch.

closes and normally reengages the clutch when pressure returns to 250 psi.

Thermal Limiter and Superheat Switch A **thermal limiter** (fuse) and superheat switch, designed to protect the air-conditioning compressor against damage when the refrigerant charge is partially or totally lost, are incorporated in some vehicles. The thermal fuse can be found in various underhood locations. The **superheat switch** is located in the rear head of the compressor (Figure 42–27). The fuse and switch are connected in series by an electrical lead.

The thermal limiter on underhood applications should not be moved from its initial location because varying underhood ambient temperatures could result in improper operation of the switch.

During normal air-conditioning system operation, current flows through the control head switch, ambient switch, and thermal fuse to the clutch coil to actuate the compressor clutch. If a partial or total loss of refrigerant occurs in the system, the contacts in the superheat switch close as the switch senses low system pressure and high suction gas temperature. When the contacts close, current flows to energize a resistor heater in the thermal fuse.

The resultant heat melts the fuse link, and the circuit to the compressor clutch coil opens. Compressor

FIGURE 42–27 Superheat switch.

operation ceases and damage due to the loss of refrigerant charge is prevented. Before thermal fuse replacement, the cause of the refrigerant loss must be corrected and the system charged. It is serviceable only as a unit.

The superheat switch is sealed in the rear head by means of an O-ring between the switch housing and head. A specially formed retainer ring holds the switch in place and electrically grounds the switch housing to the compressor.

High-Pressure Relief Valve A high-pressure relief valve is incorporated into many air-conditioning systems. This valve may be installed on the receiver/dryer, compressor, or elsewhere in the high side of the system. It is a high-pressure protection device that opens (normally at 440 psi) to bleed off excessive pressure that might occur in the system.

Compressor Control Valve This valve regulates the crankcase pressure in some compressors (commonly General Motors' V5 compressor). It has a pressure-sensitive bellows exposed to the suction side. This bellows acts on a ball and pin valve, which is exposed to high side pressure. The bellows also controls a bleed port that is also exposed to the low side. The control valve is continuously modulating, changing the displacement of the compressor according to pressssure or temperature.

Evaporator Controls

Evaporator controls maintain a back pressure in the evaporator. Because of the refrigerant temperature/pressure relationship, the effect is to regulate evaporator temperature. The temperature is controlled to a point that provides effective air cooling but prevents the freezing of moisture that condenses on the evaporator.

Suction Throttling Valve (STV) The suction throttling valve determines the temperature of the evaporator core by limiting the minimum evaporator pressure. The valve in this manner also protects the core against freeze-up, which would result in a partial or complete loss of cooling capacity. While the system is in operation, the evaporator is held to a minimum pressure of 28 psi and provides maximum cooling at all times. The evaporator pressure holds at this level as long as maximum cooling is desired by the occupants of the car.

The STV valve (Figure 42–28) is located in the evaporator outlet line. It operates on a spring pressure versus evaporator pressure principle. In operation, the flow of low-pressure vapor from the evaporator to the compressor is determined and controlled by the position of the piston in the valve body, which is in turn

FIGURE 42–28 Action of a suction throttling valve (STV). Located in the evaporator outlet, it senses evaporator pressure to control R-12 flow and temperature. *Courtesy of General Motors Corporation*

determined by the balance of the forces applied to the diaphragm. Refrigerant vapor flows through the valve inlet, through three openings in the lower skirt of the piston, and from there through the valve outlet and the suction hose to the compressor. A very small portion of the vapor flow is diverted to the interior of the piston through drilled holes in the piston wall. This pressure, transmitted to the inner side of the diaphragm, permits it to sense the actual pressure in the evaporator. Evaporator vapor pressure applied on the inner side of the diaphragm and piston assembly is balanced and opposed by spring load plus atmospheric pressure applied to the outer surface of the diaphragm. An increase of temperature and pressure in the evaporator causes the piston to move against the opposing spring pressure, opening the valve and allowing an increasing amount of vapor to flow through the valve to the compressor. This in turn lowers the evaporator pressure and allows the piston to close as required. Evaporator pressure is controlled to a predetermined setting by the action of the valve in throttling or choking off the suction line when evaporator pressure drops below the established setting. With the line restricted, the evaporator pressure rises because the flow through the thermal expansion valve continues. As the pressure rises above the valve setting, the valve is forced open as required to bring the pressure down to the proper level.

Pilot-Operated Absolute Valve (POA) The function of the **POA** valve is to control evaporator pressure. This is accomplished in the same manner as with the previously described STV valve. That is, the evaporator outlet is throttled or restricted so the pressure within the evaporator is maintained at a predetermined point. Although the end result of using this valve in the system is the same as with the STV, there is no similarity in the operation of the two valves. As its name implies, the POA valve contains a pilot valve. This valve has a bronze evacuated bellows. The POA is referenced to the nearly perfect vacuum in this bellows rather than to atmospheric pressure as in the case of the STV. The POA, therefore, requires no external altitude compensating device.

Valves-In-Receiver (VIR) Assembly As stated earlier in this chapter, VIR is a combination of two different valves: the POA (or STV) valve and the thermostatic expansion valve, plus the receiver/dryer (Figure 42–29). Early series are called simply valves-in-receiver (VIR), and later series are called evaporator equalizer valves-in-receiver (EEVIR). Both are essentially the same device. They operate and are serviced in the same manner. Replacement parts or repair kits are available.

Evaporator Pressure Regulator (EPR) On Chrysler products, this valve is installed in the suction passage of the compressor. It is accessible after the suction line fitting is removed from the compressor. The EPR valve regulates evaporation outlet pressure to keep operation pressure between 22 to 31 psi. This valve func-

FIGURE 42–30 Electronic cycling clutch switch. *Courtesy of Chrysler Corporation*

tions the same as the STV described earlier. Its operation can be checked with a second low-side fitting on the right head of the compressor.

Electronic Cycling Clutch Switch (ECCS) The **ECCS** prevents evaporator freeze-up by sending a signal to the engine control computer (Figure 42–30). The computer, in turn, cycles the compressor on and off by monitoring suction line temperature. If the temperature gets too low, the ECCS will open the input circuit to the computer, which causes the A/C clutch relay to open, which disengages the compressor clutch.

MAINTENANCE PRECAUTIONS

Air-conditioning systems are extremely sensitive to moisture and dirt. Therefore, clean working conditions are extremely important. The smallest particle of foreign matter in an air-conditioning system contaminates the refrigerant, causing rust, ice, or damage to the compressor. For this reason, all replacement parts are sold in vacuum-sealed containers and should not be opened until they are to be installed in the system. If, for any reason, a part has been removed from its container for any length of time, the part must be completely flushed using only recommended flush solvent to remove any dust or moisture that might have accumulated during storage. When the system has been open for any length of time, the entire system must be purged completely and a new receiver/dryer must be installed because the element of the existing unit will have become saturated and unable to remove any moisture from the system once the system is recharged.

The following general practices should be observed to insure chemical stability in the system.

🔧 SHOP TALK

It is important to remember that just one drop of water added to the refrigerant will start chemical changes that can result in corrosion and

FIGURE 42–29 Cross section of VIR showing detail of components and direction of refrigerant flow.

eventual breakdown of the chemicals in the system. Hydrochloric acid is the result of an R-12 mixture with water. The smallest amount of moist air in the refrigerant system might start reactions that can cause malfunctions. ■

Whenever it becomes necessary to disconnect a refrigerant connection, wipe away any dirt or oil at and near the connection to eliminate the possibility of dirt entering the system. Both sides of the connection should be immediately capped or plugged to prevent the entrance of dirt, foreign material, and moisture. It must be remembered that all air contains moisture. Air that enters any part of the system carries moisture with it, and the exposed surface collects the moisture quickly.

Keep tools clean and dry. This includes the gauge set and replacement parts. Be careful not to overtighten any connection. Overtightening results in line and flare seat distortion and a system leak.

When adding oil, the container and the transfer tube through which the oil will flow should be exceptionally clean and dry. Refrigerant oil is as moisture-free as it is possible to make it. Therefore, it quickly absorbs any moisture it contacts. For this reason, the oil container should not be opened until ready for use and then it should be capped immediately after use.

When it is necessary to open a system, have everything needed ready and handy so as little time as possible is required to perform the operation. Do not leave the system open any longer than is necessary.

Cleanliness is especially important when servicing compressors because of the very close tolerances used in these units. Consequently, repairs to the compressor itself should not be attempted unless all proper tools are at hand and a spotless work area is provided.

Any time the system has been opened and sealed again, it must be properly evacuated. Keep in mind that the complete and positive sealing of the entire system is vitally important and that this sealed condition is absolutely necessary to retain the chemicals and keep them in a pure and proper condition.

REFRIGERANT SAFETY PRECAUTIONS

Always work in a well-ventilated and clean area. Refrigerant (R-12 and R-134a) is colorless and invisible as a gas. Refrigerant is heavier than oxygen and will displace oxygen in a confined area. Avoid breathing the refrigerant vapors. Exposure to refrigerant may irritate your eyes, nose, and throat.

Refrigerant evaporates quickly when it is exposed to the atmosphere. It will freeze anything it contacts.

If liquid refrigerant gets in your eyes or on your skin it can cause frostbite. Never rub your eyes or skin if refrigerant has contacted you. Immediately flush the exposed areas with cool water for 15 minutes and seek medical help.

An A/C system's high pressure can cause severe injury to your eyes and/or skin if a hose were to burst. Always wear eye protection when working around the A/C system and refrigerant. It is also advisable to wear protective gloves and clothing.

Never use R-134a in combination with compressed air for leak testing. Pressurized R-134a, in the presence of oxygen, may form a combustible mixture. Never introduce compressed air into R-134a containers (empty or full ones), A/C systems, or A/C service equipment.

Be careful when handling refrigerant containers. Never drop, strike, puncture, or burn the containers. Always use DOT-approved refrigerant containers.

Never expose A/C system components to high temperatures. Heat will cause the refrigerant's pressure to increase. Never expose refrigerant to an open flame. A poisonous gas, phosgene gas, will result. If breathed, this gas can cause severe respiratory irritation. This gas also occurs when an open flame leak detector is used. Phosgene fumes have an acrid (bitter) smell. If the refrigerant needs to be heated during service, the bottom of the refrigerant container should be placed in warm water (less than 125°F).

Never overfill refrigerant containers. The filling level of the container should never exceed 60 percent of the container's gross weight rating. Always store refrigerant containers in temperatures below 125°F and keep them out of direct sunlight.

Refrigerant comes in 30- and 50-pound cylinders. Remember that these drums are under considerable pressure and should be handled following precautions. Keep the drums in an upright position. Make sure that valves and safety plugs are protected by metal caps when the drums are not in use. Avoid dropping the drums. Handle them carefully. When transporting refrigerant, do not place containers in the vehicle's passenger compartment.

R-12 should be stored and sold in white containers, whereas R-134a should be stored in light blue containers. R-12 and R-134a should never be mixed. Their oils and desiccants are not compatible. If the two refrigerants are mixed, contamination will occur and may result in A/C system failure. Separate service equipment, including recovery/recycling machines and service gauges should be used for the different refrigerants. Always read and follow the instructions from the equipment manufacturer when servicing A/C systems.

To prevent cross-contamination, identify whether the A/C system being worked on uses R-12 or R-134a. Check the fittings in the system, all R-134a based systems use 1/2-inch-16 ACME threaded fittings and quick disconnect service couplings. Most R-134a systems can be identified by underhood labels that clearly state R-134a is used. Most manufacturers identify the type of refrigerant used by labelling the compressor. Also look for a label with the words, "CAUTION—SYSTEM TO BE SERVICED BY QUALIFIED PERSONNEL." This label or plate can be found under the hood, near a component of the system. This label will also tell you what kind refrigerant is used, as well as the type of refrigerant oil. When servicing an A/C system, determine the type of refrigerant used before beginning.

R-134a can also be identified by viewing the sight glass, if the system has one. The appearance of R-134a will be milky due to the mixture of refrigerant and the refrigerant oil.

AIR CONDITIONER TESTING AND SERVICING EQUIPMENT

There are several specially designed pieces of equipment that are required to perform test procedures. They include manifold gauge sets, thermometers, service valves, vacuum pumps, charging station, charging cylinders, recovery/recycling systems, and leak-detecting devices.

Manifold Gauge Set

The **manifold gauge set** shown in Figure 42–31 is one of the most valuable air-conditioning tools. It is used when discharging, charging, evacuating, and for diagnosing trouble in the system. With the new legislation on handling refrigerants, all gauge sets are required to have a valve device to close off the end of the hose so that the fitting not in use is automatically shut.

The gauge illustrated on the left in Figure 42–31 is known as the low-pressure gauge. This dial is graduated into pounds of pressure from 1 to 120 (with cushion to 250) in 1-pound graduations, and, in the opposite direction, in inches of vacuum from 0 to 30. This is the gauge that should always be used in checking pressure on the low-pressure side of the system. The gauge at the right is graduated from 0 to 500 pounds pressure in 10-pound graduations. This is the high-pressure gauge that is used for checking pressure on the high-pressure side of the system.

The center manifold fitting is common to both the low and the high side and is for evacuating or adding refrigerant to the system. When this fitting is not being used, it should be capped. A test hose con-

FIGURE 42–31   Manifold gauge set.

nected to the fitting directly under the low side gauge is used to connect the low side of the test manifold to the low side of the system. A similar connection is found on the high side.

The gauge manifold is designed to control refrigerant flow. When the manifold test set is connected into the system, pressure is registered on both gauges at all times. During all tests, both the low and high side hand valves are in the closed position (turned inward until the valve is seated).

Refrigerant flows around the valve stem to the respective gauges and registers the system's low-side pressure on the low-side gauge and the system's high-side pressure on the high-side gauge. The hand valves isolate the low and high side from the central portion of the manifold. When the gauges are first connected to the gauge fittings with the refrigeration system charged, the gauge lines should always be purged. Purging is done by cracking each valve on the gauge set to allow the pressure of the refrigerant in the refrigeration system to force the air to escape through the center gauge line. Failure to purge lines can result in air or other contaminants entering the refrigeration system.

⚠ *WARNING!*

Do not open the high-side hand valve with the system operating and a refrigerant can connected to the center hose. The refrigerant will flow out of the system under high pressure into the can. High-side pressure is between 150 and 300 psi and will cause the refrigerant tank to burst. The only occasion for opening both hand valves at the same time would be when evacuating the system or when reclaiming refrigerant with the system off. ∎

Because R-134a is not interchangeable with R-12, separate sets of hoses, gauges, and other equipment are required to service vehicles. All equipment used to service R-134a and R-12 systems must meet SAE standard J991. The service hoses on the manifold gauge set must have manual or automatic back-flow valves at the service port connector ends. This prevents the refrigerant from being released into the atmosphere during connection and disconnection. Manifold gauge sets for R-134a can be identified by one or all of the following: Labelled FOR USE WITH R-134a, Labelled HFC-134 or R-134a, and/or have a light blue color on the face of the gauges.

For identification purposes, R-134a service hoses must have a black stripe along their length and be clearly labelled SAE J2196/R-134a. The low pressure hose is blue with a black stripe. The high pressure hose is red with black stripe and the center service hose is yellow with a black stripe. Service hoses for one type of refrigerant will not easily connect into the wrong system, as the fittings for a R-134a system are different than those used in a R-12 system.

Service Valves

System service valves, which incorporate a service gauge port for manifold gauge set connections, are provided on the low and high sides of most air-conditioning systems. When making gauge connections, purge the gauge lines first by cracking the charging valve and allowing a small amount of refrigerant to flow through the lines; then connect the lines immediately.

Two basic types of service valves are used: stem and Schrader.

Stem Service Valve The **stem valve** is sometimes used on two-cylinder reciprocating-piston compressors. Access to the high-pressure and low-pressure sides of the system is provided through service valves mounted on the compressor head. The low pressure valve is mounted at the inlet to the compressor, while the high-pressure valve is mounted at the compressor outlet. Both these valves can be used to shut off the rest of the air-conditioning system from the compressor when the compressor is being serviced. These valves have a stem under a cap (Figure 42–32) with the hose connection directly opposite.

A special wrench is used to open the valve to one of three positions. The back seated position is the

BACK SEATED

MID POSITION

FRONT SEATED

FIGURE 42–32 Stem service valve positions.

normal operating position with the valve stem rotated counterclockwise to seat the rear valve face and seal off the service gauge port. The mid position is the test position with the valve stem turned clockwise (inward) 1 1/2 to 2 turns. This connects the service gauge port into the system so that gauge readings can be taken with the system operating. A service gauge hose must be connected with the valve completely back seated. In the front seated position, the valve stem has been rotated clockwise to seat the front valve face and to isolate the compressor from the system. This position allows the compressor to be serviced without discharging the entire system. The front seated position is for service only. It is never used while the air conditioner is operating.

Schrader Service Valve Systems that do not utilize stem service have **Schrader service valves** (Figure 42–33) in both the high and low portions of the system for test purposes. Closely resembling a tire valve, Schrader valves are usually located in the high-pressure line (from compressor to condenser) and in the low-pressure line (from evaporator to condenser) to permit checking of the high side and low side of the system. All test hoses have a Schrader core depresser in them. As the hose is threaded into the service port, the pin in the center of the valve is depressed, allowing refrigerant to flow to the manifold gauge set. When the hose is removed, the valve closes automatically.

FIGURE 42–33 Schrader service valve.

After disconnecting gauge lines, check the valve areas to be sure the service valves are correctly seated and the Schrader valves are not leaking.

Leak Testing a System

Testing the refrigerant system for leaks is one of the most important phases of troubleshooting. Over a period of time, all air conditioners lose or leak some refrigerant. In systems that are in good condition, R-12 losses up to 1/2 pound per year are considered normal. Higher loss rates signal a need to locate and repair the leaks.

Leaks are most often found at the compressor hose connections and at the various fittings and joints in the system. Refrigerant can be lost through hose permeation. Leaks can also be traced to pin-holes in the evaporator caused by acid, which forms when water and refrigerant mix. Since oil and refrigerant leak out together, oily spots on hoses, fittings, and components are a good indication that there is a refrigerant leak (Figure 42–34). Any suspected leak

FIGURE 42–34 Probable refrigerant leak locations.

FIGURE 42–35 Leak testing with a Halide torch.

should be confirmed by using any one of the four methods of detection. All leaks should be repaired before refrigerant is added to the system.

Flame (Halide) Leak Detector The Halide leak detector (Figure 42–35) is a propane torch designed to locate a leak in any part of the system. Refrigerant gas drawn into the sampling tube attached to the torch causes the torch flame to change color in proportion to the size of the leak.

⬤ CAUTION:

If a flame leak detector must be used, do the work outdoors where there is a constant supply of fresh air. When in contact with extreme heat, R-12 breaks down into poisonous phosgene gas, which, if breathed, causes severe respiratory irritation. Also, keep the flame away from all fire hazards, such as fuel lines and tanks and ether-injection starting systems. Do not use a flame leak detector inside the passenger compartment or when the engine is running. ■

The following is a guide for color changes.

◆ Pale blue flame: no refrigerant is escaping.
◆ Pale yellow flame: very small amount of refrigerant is escaping.

- Bright yellow flame: small amount of refrigerant is escaping.
- Purple-tinted blue flame: large amount of refrigerant is escaping.
- Violet flame: very large amount of refrigerant is escaping.

Electronic Leak Detector The hand-held battery-operated electronic leak detector contains a test probe that is moved about one inch per second in areas of suspected leaks. (Remember that refrigerant gas is heavier than air, thus the probe should be positioned below the test point.) An alarm or a buzzer on the detector indicates the presence of a leak. On some models, a light flashes to establish the leak. The electronic leak detector is the most sensitive of the two types.

Fluorescent Leak Tracer To find a refrigerant leak using the fluorescent tracer system, first introduce a fluorescent dye into the air-conditioning system by means of a special infuser. Run the air conditioner for a few minutes, giving the tracer dye fluid time to circulate and penetrate. Wear the tracer protective goggles and scan the system with a black-light glow gun. Leaks in the system will shine under the black light as a luminous yellow-green.

Fluid Leak Detector Leaks can also be located by applying leak detector fluid around areas to be tested. If a leak is present, it will form clusters of bubbles around the source. A very small leak will cause a white foam to form around the leak source within several seconds to a minute. Adequate lighting over the entire surface being tested is necessary for an accurate diagnosis.

Regardless of which type of leak detector is used, the system should have a minimum of 70 psi pressure to accurately detect a leak. Be sure to check the entire system. If a leak is found at a connection, tighten the connection carefully and recheck. If the leak is still apparent, discharge the system as described earlier. Replace the damaged components, evacuate, charge, and test the system for leaks.

Service Procedures

To put the air conditioning in the best condition, be sure to perform the following service procedures:

- System discharging
- System flushing
- Compressor oil level checks
- Evacuation
- System charging

System Discharging All refrigerant must be discharged from the system before repair or replacement of any component (except for compressors with stem service valves). This procedure is accomplished through the use of a manifold gauge set and a refrigerant reclaiming unit, which makes it possible to control the rate of refrigerant discharge, preventing any loss of oil from the system (Figure 42–36).

Until recently, each time an air-conditioning system was serviced, the old refrigerant was vented into the atmosphere. Today, the refrigerant must be reclaimed and recycled. This means the refrigerant cannot be released into the atmosphere. According to Section 609 of the Federal Clean Air Act, no one repairing or servicing a motor vehicle's air conditioning system can do so without the proper refrigerant recycling equipment. It further states that no one can do this service unless that person is properly trained and certified.

Certification To become certified, a technician must have and use approved refrigerant recycling equipment and must pass an exam on refrigerant recovery and recycling. (A common test for this certification is administered by ASE.)

Recycling collects old refrigerant from the system being serviced and cleans it up and prepares it to be used in the future.

The SAE has set standards for recycled R-12 and R-134a to make sure the refrigerants provide proper system performance and longevity. J1991 and J2099 are purity standards for recycled refrigerant and speci-

FIGURE 42–36 Typical discharging hookup.

fies a limit, in ppm (parts per million) by weight. These limits are placed on three potential contaminants. There can be no more than 15 ppm of moisture in recycled R-12 and R-134a. The limit for the amount of refrigerant oil in R-12 is 4,000 ppm and 500 ppm for R-134a. The additional contaminant looked at by the SAE was air or non-condensable gases. There should be no more than 330 ppm in R-12 and no more than 150 ppm in R-134a.

Refrigerant Recovery To minimize the amount of refrigerant released to the atmosphere when A/C systems are serviced, always follow these steps.

1. The recycling equipment must have shutoff valves within 12 inches of the hoses' service ends. With the valves closed, connect the hoses to the vehicle's air conditioning service fittings.
2. Always follow the equipment manufacturer's recommended procedures for use. Recover the refrigerant from the vehicle and continue the process until the vehicle's system shows vacuum instead of pressure. Turn off the recovery/recycling unit for at least five minutes. If the system still has pressure, repeat the recovery process to remove any remaining refrigerant. Continue until the A/C system holds a stable vacuum for two minutes.
3. Close the valves in the recovery/recycling unit's service lines and disconnect them from the system's service fittings. On recovery/recycling stations with automatic shutoff valves, make sure they work properly.
4. You may now make repairs and/or replace parts in the system.

All recycled refrigerant must be safely stored in DOT CFR Title 49 or UL-approved containers. Containers specifically made for R-134a should be so marked. Before any container of recycled refrigerant can be used, it must be checked for noncondensable gases.

There are currently two types of refrigerant recovery machines, the single-pass and the multi-pass. Both have the ability to draw the refrigerant from the vehicle, filter and separate the oil from it, remove moisture and air from it, and store the refrigerant until it's reused.

In a single-pass system, the refrigerant goes through each stage before being stored. In multi-pass systems, the refrigerant may go through all stages or some of the stages before being stored. Either system is acceptable if it has the UL approved label.

System Flushing Compressor failure causes foreign material to pass into the system. The condenser must be flushed and the receiver/dryer replaced. Filter screens are sometimes located in the suction side of the compressor and in the receiver/dryer. These screens confine foreign material to the compressor, condenser, receiver/dryer, and connecting hoses. Use only recommended flushing solvents. Never use CFCs or methylchloroform for flushing. Some recommend instead of flushing the system, replacing the clogged components and installing a liquid line (inline) filter just ahead of the expansion valve or orifice tube. If flushing is recommended by the manufacturer, use only the recommended flushing agent and follow the specified procedures. After the system has been flushed, be sure to oil all components that require it.

Compressor Oil Level Checks It is not recommended that the oil level of the compressor should be checked as a matter of course. Generally, compressor oil level is checked only where there is evidence of a major loss of system oil that could be caused by a broken refrigerant hose, severe hose fitting leak, badly leaking compressor seal, or collision damage to the system's components.

When replacing refrigerant oil, it is important to use the specific type and quantity of oil recommended by the compressor manufacturer. If there is a surplus of oil in the system, too much oil circulates with the refrigerant, causing the cooling capacity of the system to be reduced. Too little oil results in poor lubrication of the compressor. When there has been excessive leakage or it is necessary to replace a component of the refrigeration system, certain procedures must be followed to assure that the total oil charge in the system is correct after leak repair or the new part is on the car.

When the compressor is operated, oil gradually leaves the compressor and is circulated through the system with the refrigerant. Eventually a balanced condition is reached in which a certain amount of oil is retained in the compressor and a certain amount is continually circulated. If a component of the system is replaced after the system has been operated, some oil goes with it. To maintain the original total oil charge, it is necessary to compensate for this by adding oil to the new replacement part. Because of the differences in compressor designs, be sure to follow the manufacturer's instructions when adding refrigerant oil to their unit.

R-12 based systems use mineral oil, while R-134a systems use synthetic Polyalkylene Gycol (PAG) oils. Using a mineral oil with R-134a will result in A/C compressor failure because of poor lubrication. Use only the oil specified for the system.

Evacuating and Charging the System The system must be completely discharged before evacuation. Always wear safety goggles when working with refrigerant containers or servicing air-conditioning systems. After discharging the system, the low-pressure gauge hose remains connected to the low-pressure test fitting. Both the high- and low-pressure manifold gauge valves are closed. Proceed as in Photo Sequence 30.

SHOP TALK

The importance of the correct charge cannot be stressed enough. The efficient operation of the air-conditioning system greatly depends on the correct amount of refrigerant in the system. A low charge results in inadequate cooling under high heat loads, due to a lack of reserve refrigerant, and can cause the clutch cycling switch to cycle faster than normal. An overcharge can cause inadequate cooling because of a high liquid refrigerant level in the condenser. Refrigerant controls will not operate properly and compressor damage can result. In general, an overcharge of refrigerant will cause higher-than-normal gauge readings and noisy compressor operation. Controls and parts of a typical charging station are shown in Figure 42–37. ∎

Vacuum Pump

Any air or moisture that is left inside an air-conditioning system after the system has been evacuated reduces the system's efficiency and eventually leads to major problems, such as compressor failure.

Air causes excessive pressure within the system, restricting the refrigerant's ability to change its state from gas to liquid within the refrigeration cycle, which drastically reduces its heat absorbing and transferring ability. Moisture, on the other hand, can cause freeze-up at the cap tube or expansion valve, which restricts refrigerant flow or blocks it completely. Both of these problems result in intermittent cooling or no cooling at all. Moisture also forms hydrochloric acid when mixed with refrigerant, causing internal corrosion, which is especially dangerous to the compressor.

The main function, or responsibility, of the vacuum pump is to remove the contaminating air and moisture from the system (Figure 42–38). The vacuum pump reduces system pressure in order to vaporize the moisture and then exhausts the vapor along with all remaining air. The pump's ability to clean the system is directly related to its ability to reduce pressure—create a vacuum—low enough to boil off all the contaminating moisture.

Thermistor Vacuum Gauge The electronic thermistor vacuum gauge (Figure 42–39) is designed to work with the vacuum pump to measure the last,

FIGURE 42–37 Parts and controls of a typical charging station.

EVACUATING AND RECHARGING AN A/C SYSTEM WITH A RECYCLING AND CHARGING STATION

P30–1 Physically locate the pressure fittings of the system with which you will be working. Make sure you have the proper adapters for the fittings prior to starting any service work on air-conditioning systems.

P30–2 Connect a gauge set to the system.

P30–3 Typical refrigerant reclaiming machine.

P30–4 Connect the reclaiming unit to the gauge set.

P30–5 Activate the reclaimer and allow enough time for the machine to draw a vacuum in the system. Observe the gauge set to determine when a vacuum is created.

P30–6 A typical A/C charging station.

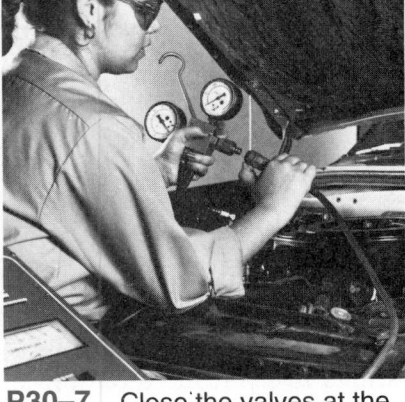

P30–7 Close the valves at the gauge set and disconnect the reclaiming machine. Connect the charging station and open the gauge set valves.

P30–8 Allow the charging station to pull a deep vacuum (at least 29 in. Hg). Set the unit to deliver the required amount of refrigerant for that system.

P30–9 After the system has been recharged, check the gauge readings while the system is in operation to make sure it is working properly.

FIGURE 42–38 Rotary vane vacuum pump. *Courtesy of Robinair Division, SPX Corporation*

most critical inch of mercury during evacuation. It constantly monitors and visually indicates the vacuum level so you know for sure when a system is free of air and moisture, eliminating guess-work and wasted time.

Charging Cylinder With an increase in temperature in any cylinder filled with refrigerant, there is a corresponding increase in pressure and a change in the volume of liquid refrigerant in the cylinder. To mea-

sure an accurate charge by weight from a cylinder using the liquid level in a sight glass as a point of measurement, it is absolutely necessary to compensate for liquid volume variations caused by temperature variations. These temperature variations are directly related to pressure variations and accurate measurements by weight can be calibrated in relation to pressure.

The charging cylinder is designed to meter out a desired amount of a specific refrigerant by weight. Compensation for temperature variations is accomplished by reading the pressure on the gauge of the cylinder and dialing the plastic shroud. The calibrated chart on the shroud contains corresponding pressure readings for the refrigerant being used.

When charging an air-conditioning system with refrigerant, the pressure in the system often reaches a point at which it is equal to the pressure in the cylinder from which the system is being charged. To get more refrigerant into the system to complete the charge, heat must be applied to the cylinder. The charging cylinder shown in Figure 42–40 eliminates the problem caused by equalization of pressure between the cylinder and the system being charged.

Performance Testing

Performance testing provides a measure of air-conditioning system operating efficiency. A manifold pressure gauge set is used to determine both high and low

FIGURE 42–39 Thermistor vacuum gauge. *Courtesy of Robinair Division, SPX Corporation*

FIGURE 42–40 Charging cylinder. *Courtesy of Robinair Division, SPX Corporation*

STANDARD TEMPERATURE/ PRESSURE CHART FOR R-134a

°F	PSI	°F	PSI	°F	PSI	°F	PSI	°F	PSI
65	69	77	86	89	107	101	131	113	158
66	70	78	88	90	109	102	133	114	160
67	71	79	90	91	111	103	135	115	163
68	73	80	91	92	113	104	137	116	165
69	74	81	93	93	115	105	139	117	168
70	76	82	95	94	117	106	142	118	171
71	77	83	96	95	118	107	144	119	173
72	79	84	98	96	120	108	146	120	176
73	80	85	100	97	122	109	149		
74	82	86	102	98	125	110	151		
75	83	87	103	99	127	111	153		
76	85	88	105	100	129	112	156		

METRIC TEMPERATURE/ PRESSURE CHART FOR R-134a

°C	kPa	°C	kPa	°C	kPa
18	476	29	676	40	945
19	483	30	703	41	979
20	503	31	724	42	1007
21	524	32	752	43	1027
22	545	33	765	44	1055
23	552	34	793	45	1089
24	572	35	814	46	1124
25	593	36	841	47	1158
26	621	37	876	48	1179
27	642	38	889	49	1214
28	655	39	917		

STANDARD TEMPERATURE/ PRESSURE CHART FOR R-12

°F	PSI	°F	PSI	°F	PSI	°F	PSI	°F	PSI
65	74	75	87	85	102	95	118	105	136
66	75	76	88	86	103	96	120	106	138
67	76	77	90	87	105	97	122	107	140
68	78	78	92	88	107	98	124	108	142
69	79	79	94	89	108	99	125	109	144
70	80	80	96	90	110	100	127	110	146
71	82	81	98	91	111	101	129	111	148
72	83	82	99	92	113	102	130	112	150
73	84	83	100	93	115	103	132	113	152
74	86	84	101	94	116	104	134	114	154

METRIC TEMPERATURE/ PRESSURE CHART FOR R-12

°C	kg/cm²	°C	kg/cm²	°C	kg/cm²
18	5.2	28	7.0	38	9.0
19	5.3	29	7.1	39	9.2
20	5.5	30	7.2	40	9.4
21	5.6	31	7.5	41	9.6
22	5.8	32	7.7	42	9.9
23	6.0	33	7.9	43	10.0
24	6.1	34	8.1	44	10.4
25	6.3	35	8.3	45	10.7
26	6.6	36	8.5	46	10.9
27	6.8	37	8.7	47	11.0

FIGURE 42–41 Refrigerant temperature and pressure charts. *Courtesy of ASE*

VENT NEAREST EVAPORATOR

DIAL THERMOMETER
FIGURE 42–42 Checking outlet air temperature.

pressures in the refrigeration system. The desired pressure readings will vary according to temperature. Use the charts in Figure 42–41 as a guide to determine the proper pressures. At the same time, a thermometer is used to determine air discharge temperature into the passenger compartment (Figure 42–42).

Before making this test, it should be established that the air distribution (air door) portion of a factory-installed system is functioning properly. This ensures that all air passing through the evaporator is being routed directly to the air outlet nozzles.

PROCEDURES
Performance Testing

1. Connect the manifold gauge set to the respective high- and low-pressure fittings as shown in Figure 42–43 with both valves closed. These fittings are found in various locations within the high- and low-pressure sides of the system.
2. Keep the hood open and close all the doors and windows of the car.
3. Adjust the air-conditioning controls to the maximum cooling and high blower position.
4. Idle the engine for 10 minutes in neutral or park with the brake on. For the best results, place a high volume fan in front of the radiator grille to insure an adequate supply of airflow across the condenser.
5. Increase engine speed to 1,500 to 2,000 rpm.
6. Measure the temperature at the evaporator air outlet grille or air duct nozzle (35 to 40°F).
7. Read high and low pressure, and compare to the normal range of the operating pressure given in the service manual.

Operating pressures vary with humidity as well as with outside air temperature. Accordingly, on more humid days, operating pressures will be on the high side of the range indicated in the service manual's performance chart. On less humid days, the operating pressures will read toward the lower side. If operating pressures are found to be within the normal range, the refrigeration portion of the air-conditioning system is functioning properly. This can be further confirmed with a check of evaporator outlet air temperatures.

Evaporator outlet air temperature also varies according to outside (ambient) air and humidity conditions. Further variations can be found, depending on whether the system is controlled by a cycling clutch compressor or an evaporator pressure control valve. Because of these variations, it is difficult to pinpoint what evaporator outlet air temperature should be on all applications. In general, with low side air temperatures (70 degrees) and humidity (20 percent), the evaporator outlet air temperature should be in the 35-to 40-degree range. On the other extreme of 80 degrees outside air temperatures and 90 percent humidity condition, the evaporator air outlet temperature might be in the 55- to 60-degree range.

1	SUCTION LINE	7	LOW PRESSURE GAUGE
2	SUCTION SERVICE PORT	8	CENTER MANIFOLD
3	LIQUID LINE	9	TO REFRIGERANT SUPPLY TANK VALVE
4	ACCUMULATOR/DRIER	10	HIGH PRESSURE GAUGE
5	HIGH PRESSURE GAUGE PORT VALVE	11	HIGH PRESSURE SERVICE HOSE
6	LOW PRESSURE SERVICE HOSE	12	TO VACUUM PUMP VALVE

FIGURE 42–43 Performance testing hookup. *Courtesy of Ford Motor Company*

Since it is impractical to provide a specific performance chart for all the different types of air-conditioning systems, it is desirable to develop an experience factor for determining the correlation that can be anticipated between operating pressures and outlet air temperatures on the various systems. For example, feel the discharge line from the compressor to the condenser. The discharge line should be the same temperature along its full length. Any temperature change is a sign of restriction, and the line should be flushed or replaced. Perform this test carefully because the discharge line will be hot.

There are other tests that can be performed with the engine running.

♦ Check the condenser by feeling up and down the face or along the return bends for a temperature change. There should be a gradual change from hot to warm as you go from the top to the bottom. Any abrupt change indicates a restriction, and the condenser has to be flushed or replaced.

♦ If the system has a receiver/dryer, check it. The inlet and outlet lines should be the same temperature. Any temperature difference or frost on the lines or receiver tank are signs of a restriction. The receiver/dryer must be replaced.

♦ If the system has a sight glass, check it as previously described.

♦ Feel the liquid line from the receiver/dryer to the expansion valve. The line should be warm for its entire length.

♦ The expansion valve should be free of frost, and there should be a sharp temperature difference between its inlet and outlet.

♦ The suction line to the compressor should be cool to the touch from the evaporator to the compressor. If it is covered with thick frost, this might indicate that the expansion valve is flooding the evaporator.

♦ On vehicles equipped with the orifice tube system, feel the liquid line from the condenser outlet to the evaporator inlet. A restriction is indicated by any temperature change in the liquid line before the crimp dimples the orifice tube in the evaporator inlet. Flush the liquid line or replace the orifice tube if restricted.

♦ The accumulator as well as the suction line must be cool to the touch from the evaporator outlet to the compressor.

By combining the results of both the hands-on checks and an interpretation of pressure gauge readings, the technician has a good indication that some unit in the system is malfunctioning and that further diagnosis is needed.

DIAGNOSTIC AND TROUBLESHOOTING PROCEDURES

The first step in air-conditioning diagnosis, as in all automotive diagnostic work, is to get the customer's story. Is the problem no cold air, the air from the ducts never gets cold enough, or the unit only cools at certain times of the day? The complaint could also be that the system does not work at all, or that the air blows out of the wrong ducts. An accurate description of the customer's problem helps pinpoint whether the problem is refrigerant, mechanical, or electrical related. It also reduces diagnosis time and, most important, satisfies the customer.

Because of the many construction and operational variations that exist, there is no uniform or standard diagnostic procedure applicable to all automotive air-conditioning systems. However, the information given in the *Tech Manual* can be used as a general guide to common air-conditioning problems and their possible remedies. For complete specific diagnostic information on a given air conditioner, check the manufacturer's service manual.

TEMPERATURE CONTROL SYSTEMS

Temperature control systems for air conditioners usually are connected with heater controls. Most heater and air-conditioning systems use the same plenum chamber for air distribution. Two types of air-conditioning controls are used: manual/semiautomatic and automatic (Figure 42–44).

Manual/Semiautomatic Temperature Controls

Air conditioner manual/semiautomatic temperature controls (MTC and SATC) operate in a manner similar to heater controls. Depending on the control setting, doors are opened and closed to direct airflow.

FIGURE 42–44 Typical air-conditioner control panels. (A) manual/semiautomatic and (B) automatic.

The amount of cooling is controlled manually through the use of control settings and blower speed.

Automatic Temperature Control

An automatic or electronic temperature control system maintains a specific temperature automatically inside the passenger compartment. To maintain a selected temperature, heat sensors send signals to a computer unit that controls compressor, heater valve, blower, and plenum door operation. A typical electronic control system might contain a coolant temperature sensor, in-car temperature sensor, outside temperature sensor, high-side temperature switch, low-side temperature switch, low-pressure switch, vehicle speed sensor throttle position sensor, sunload sensor, and power steering cutout switch.

The control panel is found in the instrument panel at a convenient location for both driver and front-seat passenger access. Three types of control panels may be found: manual, push-button (Figure 42–45A), or touch pad (Figure 42–45B). All serve the same purpose. They provide operator input control for the air-conditioning and heating system. Some control panels have features that other panels

do not have, such as provisions to display in-car and outside air temperature in degrees (Figure 42–46).

Provisions are made on the control panel for operator selection of an in-car temperature between 65 and 85°F in one-degree increments. Some have an override feature that provides for a setting of either 60 or 90°F. Either of these two settings overrides all in-car temperature control circuits to provide maximum cooling or heating conditions.

Usually, a microprocessor is located in the control head to input data to the programmer, based on operator-selected conditions. When the ignition switch is turned off, a memory circuit remembers the previous setting. These conditions are restored the next time the ignition switch is turned on. If the battery is disconnected, however, the memory circuit is cleared and must be reprogrammed.

Many automotive electronic temperature control systems have self-diagnostic test provisions in which an on-board microprocessor-controlled subsystem displays a code. This code (number, letter, or alphanumeric) is displayed to tell the technician the cause of the malfunction. Some systems also display a code to indicate which computer detected the malfunction.

A

HEATER AND A/C CONTROL

BUICK

PASSENGER
TEMPERATURE CONTROL

B

HEATER AND A/C CONTROL

OLDSMOBILE

PASSENGER
TEMPERATURE CONTROL

FIGURE 42–45 (A) Push-button control panel; (B) touch pad control panel. *Courtesy of General Motors Corporation*

FIGURE 42–46 ECC digital control panel.

Manufacturers' specifications must be followed to identify the malfunction display codes, since they differ from car to car. For example, in some General Motors car lines ".7,0" indicates no malfunction if "no trouble" codes are stored in the computer. in some Ford car lines the no trouble code is 888.

Case/Duct Systems

A typical automotive heater/air conditioner/case and duct system is shown in Figure 42–47. The purpose of the system is twofold. It is used to house the heater core and the air conditioner evaporator and to direct the selected supply air through these components into the passenger compartment of the vehicle. The supply air selected can be either fresh (outside) or recirculated air, depending on the system mode. After the air is heated or cooled, it is delivered to the floor outlet, dash panel outlets, or the defrost outlets.

In domestic vehicles, there are two basic duct systems employed. In the stacked core reheat system (Figure 42–48A) the basic control is in the water valve. For maximum air the water valve is completely closed. All air enters the vehicle compartment through the heater core.

The access door, which is activated by a cable, controls only fresh or recirculated air. Recirculated air is used during maximum cold operation, the air-conditioning unit is not operative and the evaporator will not be cold. The evaporator-only is used in the max air or maximum cold position. As the control level inside the car is moved, it controls the water valve by means of a vacuum or a cable to control the amount of hot water entering the heater core and the temperature of the air at the unit outlet.

The blend air reheat system (Figure 42–48B) is found on General Motors and Ford vehicles and some truck units with factory-controlled heater system units. During heater-only operation, the air-conditioning unit is shut off, and the evaporator performs no function in air distribution or temperature control. During maximum air or extreme cold air, the air-conditioning system operates, the evaporator is cold, and the blend air door damper is completely closed. Only conditioned air enters the car.

As the control lever is moved in the vehicle from max air towards heat with the air conditioner on, the blend air door is moving. In maximum cold, it is completely shut. On maximum hot, it is completely open. The water valve on this unit is a vacuum on/off unit to regulate water flow. Normal position would be open. This type of blend air system is extremely popular and can be used with or without a water valve.

FIGURE 42–47 Heater/air-conditioner ducts.

FIGURE 42–48 Two types of duct systems used in domestic cars: (A) stacked core reheat and (B) blend air reheat.

To check the proper functioning of the duct work, move the temperature control lever to see if any change occurs. If it does not, shut off the air conditioner and turn on the heater. Move the temperature control arm again to see if any change occurs. If not, check the cable and the flap door connected to the temperature control lever. You might be able to reach under the dash to reconnect the cable or free a stuck flap.

If no substantial airflow is coming out of the registers, check the fuses in the blower circuit. Remove the fan switch and test it. Check the blower motor by hot-wiring it directly to the battery with jumper cables.

USING SERVICE MANUALS

Many service manuals use block diagrams to show the component relationships and functions. Figure 42–49 illustrates such a diagram as it would pertain to typical automotive temperature control systems. ∎

ELECTRICAL SYSTEM INSPECTION

The electrical system must be checked periodically to prevent the vehicle's air-conditioning system from failing unexpectedly. Start by checking the battery because most electrical trouble begins there (Figure 42–50). Leaky battery acid and corrosion builds up on the terminals, which can disrupt contact or eat away the terminal connections. A regular scrubbing with baking soda and water keeps the corrosion at a minimum. Check the terminal leads to be sure they are free of corrosion and make good contact with the battery terminals.

Because vehicle air-conditioning systems contain various switches, there will be times when one of them malfunctions. Sometimes this is not due to the switch itself but instead is caused by a bad connection or corrosion that has built up on the switch leads, leading to a broken contact. The switch can sometimes function intermittently because of this. It is important to check the switches from time to time and clean off the leads. Check that each switch is making good contact and is free of dirt and corrosion.

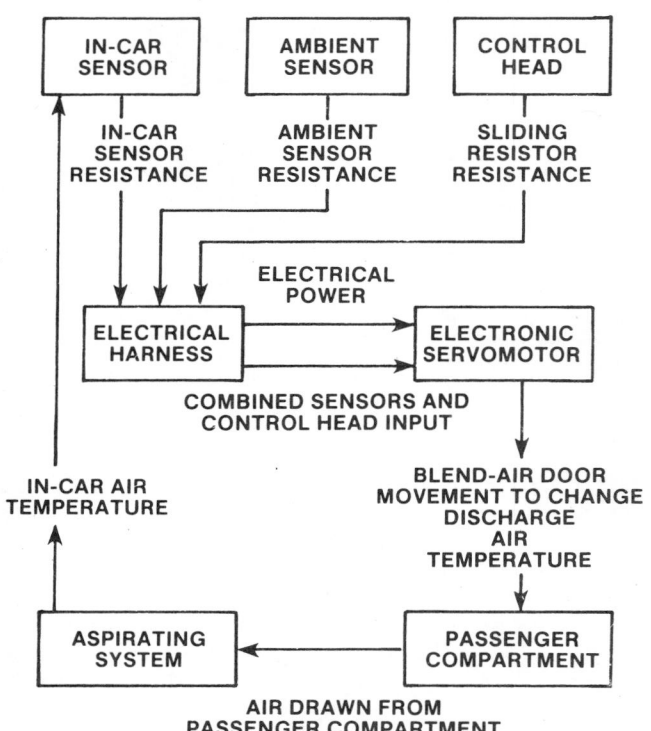

• LOW AIR TEMPERATURE AT SENSORS INCREASES RESISTANCE.
• HIGH TEMPERATURE LEVER SETTING INCREASES RESISTANCE.
• HIGH RESISTANCE CAUSES SERVOMOTOR TO MOVE BLEND-AIR DOOR TO HIGHER REHEAT POSITION.

FIGURE 42–49 Air-conditioning system component relationships are often found in service manuals.

CASE STUDY

*T*he first cold snap of winter brings a customer to the shop with the following complaint. When set on maximum, the heater does not produce sufficient heat to warm the vehicle.

First, the technician checks the coolant level. The radiator is full. She also checks the engine's operating temperature. It is normal, or more than enough to supply adequate heat.

The technician now knows the problem must be in the heating system itself. She measures the output temperature at the heater duct with the fan operating on high and the heater control positioned at its hottest setting. A lower-than-normal heat level is recorded. The technician checks the movement of the duct door and finds it to be open. She carefully checks the heater inlet and outlet hoses and finds them to be hot.

From these findings, the technician concludes the problem must be a plugged heater core. The core is removed and flushed, and the problem is solved.

FIGURE 42–50 Electrical circuit inspection and checkout.

KEY TERMS

Accumulator	Condensation	Discharge	Evaporator
Blend door	Condenser	Discharge side	Heater control valve
CCOT	Cycling clutch	ECCS	Heater core
CFC	Desiccant	Elastomer	HFC
		EPR	High side
		Evaporation	Latent heat

Low side
Manifold gauge set
Orifice tube
Phosgene gas
POA
R-12
R-134a
Ram air
Receiver/dryer
Rotary vane compressor
Schrader service valves

Scroll-type compressor
Sight glass
Stem valve
STV
Suction side
Superheat switch
TEV
Thermal limiter
Ventilation
VIR

SUMMARY

◆ Ventilation, heating, and air conditioning provide the vehicle's passengers with comfort.

◆ The ventilation system on most vehicles is designed to supply outside air to the passenger compartment through upper or lower vents or both. There are several systems used to vent air into the passenger compartment. The most common is the flow-through system. In this arrangement, a supply of outside air, which is called ram air, flows into the car when it is moving.

◆ Automotive heating systems have been designed to work with the cooling system to maintain proper temperature inside the car. The heating system's primary job is to provide a comfortable passenger compartment temperature and to keep car windows clear of fog or frost.

◆ The main components of an automotive heating system are the heater control valve, the heater core, the blower motor and fan, and heater and defroster duct hoses.

◆ All air-conditioning systems are based on three fundamental laws of nature: heat flow, heat absorption, and pressure and boiling points.

◆ The major components of an air-conditioning system are: compressor, condenser, receiver/dryer or accumulator, expansion valve or orifice tube, and evaporator.

◆ The compressor is the heart of an automotive air-conditioning system. It separates the high-pressure and low-pressure sides of the system. The primary purpose of the unit is to draw the low-pressure vapor from the evaporator and compress this vapor into high-temperature, high-pressure vapor. This action results in the refrigerant having a higher temperature than surrounding air, enabling the condenser to condense the vapor back to liquid.

◆ The secondary purpose of the compressor is to circulate or pump the refrigerant through the condenser under the different pressures required for proper operation. The compressor is located in the engine compartment.

◆ There are two basic types of compressors: piston and rotary vane.

◆ The condenser consists of a refrigerant coil tube mounted in a series of thin cooling fins to provide maximum heat transfer in a minimum amount of space. The condenser is normally mounted just in front of the vehicle's radiator.

◆ The receiver/dryer is a storage tank for the liquid refrigerant.

◆ The refrigerant flow to the evaporator must be controlled to obtain maximum cooling, while ensuring complete evaporation of the liquid refrigerant within the evaporator. This is accomplished by a thermostatic expansion valve or a fixed orifice tube.

◆ The evaporator, like the condenser, consists of a refrigerant coil mounted in a series of thin cooling fins. It provides a maximum amount of heat transfer in a minimum amount of space. The evaporator is usually located beneath the dashboard or instrument panel.

◆ The refrigerant currently in use in most air-conditioning systems is R-12. It is nontoxic, nonflammable, and nonexplosive. However, breathing large quantities of R-12 should be avoided, because doing so displaces oxygen in the lungs. Always wear safety glasses and nonleather gloves when handling R-12.

◆ An amendment to the United States' Clean Air Act and international agreements have mandated that R-12 be phased out as the refrigerant of choice. This came as a result of research that found the earth's ozone layer was being deteriorated by the chemicals found in R-12.

◆ The ozone depletion is caused in part by release of chlorofluorocarbons (CFCs) into the atmosphere. R-12 is in the chemical family of CFCs. Since air conditioning systems with R-12 are susceptible to leaks, further damage to the ozone layer could be avoided by not using R-12 in air-conditioning units.

◆ Of the many chemicals that could have been used in place of R-12, the automobile manufacturers have decided to use R-134a. R-134a is a hydrofluorocarbon (HFC) which causes less damage to the ozone layer when released to the atmosphere.

◆ Although R-134a air conditioners operate in the same way and with the same basic components as R-12 systems, the two refrigerants are not interchangeable. Because it is less efficient than R-12, R-134a operates at higher pressures to make up for the loss of performance and requires new service techniques and system component designs. Basically, the higher system pressures of R-134a mean the system must be designed for those higher pressures.

◆ The production phaseout for all CFCs, including R-12, was scheduled for December 1, 1995. To keep systems operating that were originally equipped with R-12, there are retrofit kits available for a changeover to R-134a. Although R-134a is less likely to have an adverse effect on the ozone layer, it still has the capability of contributing to the "greenhouse effect" when released to the air. Therefore, the recovery and recycling of R-134a became mandatory on November 15, 1995.

◆ There are two basic types of automotive air-conditioning systems. They are classified according to the method used in obtaining temperature control and are known as a cycling clutch system or an evaporator pressure control system.

◆ Evaporator controls maintain a back pressure in the evaporator. Because of the refrigerant temperature/pressure relationship, the effect is to regulate evaporator temperature. The temperature is controlled to a point that provides effective air cooling but prevents the freezing of moisture that condenses on the evaporator.

◆ Among the many controls used to monitor and maintain the compressor during its operational cycle within various systems are the pressure relief valve, the low- and the high-pressure cutout switches, the ambient temperature switch, and the thermostatic switch. Each of these represents the most common protective control devices designed to ensure safe and reliable operation of the compressor.

◆ Evaporator controls maintain a back pressure in the evaporator. Because of the refrigerant temperature/pressure relationship, the effect is to regulate evaporator temperature.

◆ Air-conditioning systems are extremely sensitive to moisture and dirt. Therefore, clean working conditions are extremely important. The smallest particle of foreign matter in an air-conditioning system contaminates the refrigerant, causing rust, ice, or damage to the compressor.

◆ Air conditioner testing and servicing equipment includes a manifold gauge set, service valves, vacuum pumps, charging station, charging cylinder, recovery/recycling systems, and leak-detecting devices.

◆ To put air-conditioning systems in their best condition, the following service procedures should be performed: system discharging, system flushing, compressor oil level checks, evacuation, and system charging.

◆ Temperature control systems for air conditioners are usually connected with heater controls. Most heater and air-conditioner systems use the same plenum chamber for air distribution. Two types of air-conditioner controls are used: manual/semiautomatic and automatic.

TECH MANUAL

The following procedures are included in Chapter 42 of the *Tech Manual* that accompanies this book:

1. Conduct system performance tests.
2. Inspect, adjust, and/or replace compressor drive belt.
3. Inspect, test, and service compressor clutch.
4. Identify and recover refrigerant.
5. Recycle refrigerant.
6. Label and store refrigerant.
7. Test recycled refrigerant for noncondensable gases.

REVIEW QUESTIONS

1. What is the amount of heat necessary to change the state of a substance called?

2. What type of electromagnetic clutch is used in late-model vehicles?

3. What type of valves do systems that do not utilize stem service valves use?

4. What causes condensed water to leak from the air-conditioning system?

5. On which of the following laws of nature is the air-conditioning system based?
   a. heat flow
   b. heat absorption
   c. pressure and boiling points
   d. all of the above

6. Technician A says a great amount of heat is transferred when a liquid boils or a vapor condenses. Technician B says a change in pressure does not change the boiling point of a substance. Who is correct?

   a. Technician A   c. Both A and B
   b. Technician B   d. Neither A nor B

7. Which of the following statements is true?

   a. Refrigerant leaves the compressor as a high-pressure, high-temperature liquid.
   b. Refrigerant leaves the condenser as a low-pressure, low-temperature liquid.
   c. Refrigerant returns to the compressor as a low-pressure, high-temperature vapor.
   d. None of the above.

8. Which of the following statements is false?

   a. The condenser is normally mounted just in front of the radiator.
   b. The receiver/dryer is a storage tank for the liquid refrigerant from the condenser.
   c. An accumulator is not used in any system with a receiver/dryer.
   d. All of the above.

9. Which of the following is true of R-12?

   a. It is toxic.
   b. It is flammable.
   c. It is destructive to the earth's ozone layer.
   d. All of the above.

10. Technician A says the thermostatic expansion valve and the fixed orifice tube perform the same function. Technician B says heat from the evaporator core surface is lost to the boiling and vaporizing refrigerant. Who is correct?

    a. Technician A   c. Both A and B
    b. Technician B   d. Neither A nor B

11. Technician A says suction lines are very warm to touch. Technician B says discharge lines connect the compressor to the condenser. Who is correct?

    a. Technician A   c. Both A and B
    b. Technician B   d. Neither A nor B

12. Technician A says the oil level of the compressor should be checked every year. Technician B says the system should be charged only after it has been completely evacuated. Who is correct?

    a. Technician A   c. Both A and B
    b. Technician B   d. Neither A nor B

13. Which of the following is electrically connected in series with the compressor electromagnetic clutch?

    a. ambient temperature switch
    b. thermostatic switch
    c. pressure cycling switch
    d. none of the above

14. When is the manifold gauge set used?

    a. discharging   c. evacuating
    b. charging   d. all of the above

15. Which of the following does *not* cause excessive heat?

    a. loose or damaged control cable
    b. water flow control valve stuck open
    c. flow control valve not opening fully
    d. faulty thermostatic fan

16. A heating system includes all of the following parts except a ____.

    a. heater core
    b. ventilation system
    c. receiver/dryer
    d. distribution plenum

17. All of the following statements are true except ____.

    a. the evaporator changes heated refrigerant to a liquid
    b. automatic temperature control operates to maintain a set temperature
    c. air conditioner/heater systems can be computer controlled
    d. heaters and air conditioners use the same plenum chambers

18. A heater does not supply enough heat. The coolant level and flow are correct. Technician A says a misadjusted heater control could be the cause. Technician B says a bad thermostat could be the cause. Who is correct?

    a. Technician A   c. Both A and B
    b. Technician B   d. Neither A nor B

19. Technician A says evacuating (pumping down) an air-conditioning system removes air and moisture from the system. Technician B says evacuating (pumping down) an air-conditioning system removes dirt particles from the system. Who is correct?

    a. Technician A   c. Both A and B
    b. Technician B   d. Neither A nor B

20. To charge an air-conditioning system while it is running, the refrigerant should be added to ____.

    a. the high side
    b. the low side
    c. both the high and low sides
    d. either the high or the low side

OTHER COMFORT, SAFETY, AND SECURITY EQUIPMENT

43

OBJECTIVES

◆ *Identify and describe devices that contribute to automotive safety.* ◆ *Detail the types of safety glass.* ◆ *Explain the difference between active and passive restraint systems.* ◆ *Identify the major parts of passive belt systems.* ◆ *Know how to service and repair passive belt systems.* ◆ *Describe the function and operation of air bags.* ◆ *Safely disarm and inspect an air bag assembly.* ◆ *Describe the operation of keyless entry systems.* ◆ *Identify the various security disabling devices.* ◆ *Understand the operation of the various security alarms.* ◆ *Identify the components of typical radio and audio systems.*

Safety is foremost in the minds of automobile manufacturers. According to a survey by the Insurance Institute for Highway Safety, occupant protection has emerged as a leading factor in determining which car Americans will buy. According to the institute, 68 percent of the households surveyed ranked the "degree to which the car protects people" as a very important purchase-decision factor. While only 2 percent of those surveyed were driving a car with an air bag, 48 percent said they want one on their next car.

There are some technological safety advancements that will be available in the very near future. Traction control is already available on quite a few models. But, one manufacturer presently has taken traction control a step further by reducing the engine's power if the computer senses a certain G-force level indicating the car is going into a corner too fast. No matter how far the accelerator is depressed, the engine will not generate more than nominal power.

Radar braking is still a way off, but it is definitely in development. Radar tracking, brakes, and the engine's throttle will be linked to determine when the brakes should be applied and then will apply them automatically. The system will take speed, weather conditions, and other factors into consideration. (The driver will still be able to apply the brakes, of course.) Manufacturers are also working with sonar near-obstacle detection systems for parking and backing up.

Sleepy-driver alerts, already being used in trucks, will very likely begin showing up in automobiles.

Communication systems will increase. Car telephones will be standard. Navigation systems using satellites will pinpoint the location of a vehicle. Signals will be transmitted from road signs to automatically display information to the driver or directly to the vehicle control system to increase driver safety.

It is important for auto technicians to keep up with all the safety developments of industry by reading trade publications and manufacturer's literature.

SAFETY GLASS

Safety glass is used in all auto windows and doors. The safety glass employed in today's vehicles is of two types: laminated or tempered. These types are considered to be safety glass because of their construction. They also have government approval.

Laminated plate glass is used to make all windshields. This type of glass consists of two thin sheets of glass with a thin layer of clear plastic between them. Some glass manufacturers have increased the thickness of the plastic material for greater strength. When this type of glass is broken, the plastic material tends to hold the shattered glass in place and prevent it from causing injury (Figure 43–1). The plastic or vinyl material is usually clear to provide an unimpeded view through the windshield from all angles.

Tempered glass is used for side and rear window glass but rarely for windshields. This type of glass is a single piece of heat-treated glass and has more resistance to impact than regular glass of the same thick-

FIGURE 43–1 Lamination kept windshield glass intact upon impact.

ness. The strength of tempered glass results from the high compression of its surfaces. This high compression is induced by rapidly heating the glass to approximately 1100 degrees Fahrenheit. The high temperature softens the glass. The glass is then cooled rapidly by blowing air on both flat surfaces. The resulting rapid contraction adds compressive stress to the surface of the glass, which strengthens the glass. Because of this compression, tempered glass cannot be cut, drilled, or ground after the tempering process.

When tempered glass is broken, the pieces of glass are small and have a granular texture. The shattered glass has an interlocked structure to it that obstructs visibility. This is one reason tempered glass is not used in windshields. Another reason is that this type of glass does not readily give and would, therefore, cause more severe head injuries in a collision. Tempered glass will also shatter if previously damaged or stressed. For example, a chipped edge or a stone striking it can weaken the glass so that it suddenly shatters some time after the initial defect is incurred.

Zone-tempered glass is sometimes used for windshields. Zone-tempered glass, which has a lesser degree of tempering in the area directly in front of the driver, prevents these small cracks from developing in the prescribed area in the event of glass breakage.

Antilacerative glass is similar to conventional multilayered glass, but it has one or more additional layers of plastic affixed to the passenger compartment side of the glass. This glass is used in the front windshield only and is added protection against shattering and cuts during impact.

Tinted glass can be laminated or tempered glass. Tinted laminated glass contains a light green shade of vinyl material to filter out most of the sun's glare. This type of windshield glass is helpful in reducing eye strain, driver tension and fatigue, and prevents fading

of the interior furnishings. Some windshields are shaded to reduce the sun's glare. This type uses only a dark band or section across the top part of the windshield. Tinted or shaded glass is usually recommended if the vehicle is equipped with air conditioning.

Glass can also be tinted by adding minute quantities of metal powder to the other normal ingredients of glass to give it a particular color. The addition of cobalt gives the glass a blue tint. Iron gives the glass a reddish tint. Another solar-control windshield glass has a virtually invisible layer of metal to reflect long-wavelength heat energy, reducing the solar load by 60 percent. Short-wavelength visible light is transmitted normally. The net result of solar safety glass is a reduced load for the air conditioner and longer life for interior trim components.

An antenna wire for radio reception can be placed either between the layers of laminated glass (windshield) or printed on the surface of the glass (rear window). Some rear windows have both antenna wires and heating wires side by side. That is, before heat treatment, metal powder, which conducts electricity, is printed on the glass surface in the form of heating wires. The metal powder is baked on the surface during the tempering process. In some rear window glass, a wire grid is unobtrusively embedded in it to provide the antenna function.

There are two types of glass found in heated windshield systems. One system uses glass that contains three layers of material. That is, a plastic laminate is sandwiched between two layers of glass. A silver and zinc oxide coating is fused onto the back of the outer glass layer to carry the electrical current. This coating gives the windshield a slight gold tint. Silver busbars fused into the coating at the top and bottom of the windshield connect the coating to power and ground circuits (Figure 43–2). A sensor watches for windshield damage. The control module checks to see if there is a voltage drop across the sensor before starting the system. A voltage drop means

FIGURE 43–2 Silver busbars connect the silver and zinc oxide coating to the power and ground circuits. *Courtesy of Ford Motor Company*

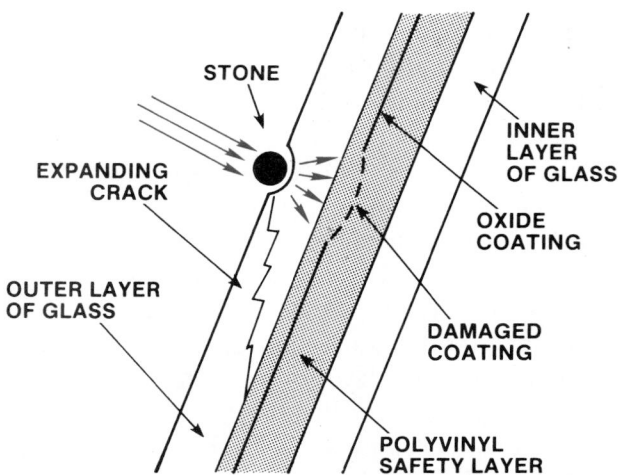

FIGURE 43–3 A stone hitting a heated windshield system could damage the inner silver and zinc oxide coating. This could cause an open in the circuit. *Courtesy of Ford Motor Company*

there is an open in the windshield circuit, which may be the result of a crack in the windshield (Figure 43–3). The manufacturer recommends replacing the windshield if there is any damage at all.

The other type of glass used in heated windshields also has three layers. The inner layer is not a plastic laminate, but a thin film of resistive coating sprayed between the inner and outer windshield. The coating is transparent, so there is no tint. While there is a sensing resistor in the circuit, the windshield glass does not require replacement when cracks or chips are not deep enough to break the inner coating. The standard methods of chip and "bull's eye" repair systems are given in the manufacturer's service manual.

Instructions for the replacement of cracked or broken glass can be found in the vehicle's service manual.

RESTRAINT SYSTEMS

All vehicles built or sold in the United States must now have one or both of these passive restraints: automatic seat belts or air bags. Both have made a tremendous impact on driver and passenger safety over the last few years. It is very important that technicians are able to service these systems.

Seat Belts

Prior to 1990, there were two types of seat belts in common use. The **active restraint system** is one that a vehicle's occupant must make a manual effort to use (Figure 43–4). For example, in most vehicles the passenger must fasten the seat belts for crash protection. The **passive restraint system** operates automatically (Figure 43–5). No action is required of the occupant to make it functional. Federal law requires that all cars sold in the United States after 1990 be equipped with a passive restraint. In some vehicles, this means that air bags are standard equipment. In others, passive seat belts are employed.

The passive seat belt system automatically puts shoulder belts on the driver and front seat passenger (Figure 43–6). It operates by means of electric motors. The movement is accomplished with carriers and track assemblies at the top of the door frames. One end of each belt attaches to the carriers. The other ends are secured to **inertia lock retractors**. The retractors are

FIGURE 43–4 Active seat belt restraint system. *Courtesy of Ford Motor Company*

FIGURE 43–5 Passive seat belt restraint system. *Courtesy of Ford Motor Company*

mounted in the center console. When the doors are closed and the ignition turned on, the belts move rearward and secure the occupants.

The shoulder harness webbing is attached to a retractor. The retractor for the front seat is located in the B-pillar. The rear seat belt retractor is located in the C-pillar. The webbing then passes through a guide above and behind the occupant's shoulder that directs the webbing at the proper downward angle over the occupant's shoulder and chest and attaches to the lap safety belt buckle. Manually operated (active) lap belts must always be used with the passive shoulder belts.

Servicing Seat Belts

When servicing or replacing lap and shoulder belts, refer to the following precautionary items.

1. Lap and shoulder belts should be serviced as follows:
   ◆ Retractor portions of front seat lap and shoulder belt for passenger and driver.
   ◆ Buckle portion of front seat lap belt for passenger and driver.
   ◆ All belts other than those mentioned will be serviced in complete sets.
   ◆ Do not intermix standard and deluxe belts on front or rear seats.
2. Keep sharp edges from damaging any portion of the belt buckle or latch plate.
3. Avoid bending or damaging any portion of the belt buckle or latch plate.
4. Do not attempt repairs on lap or shoulder belt

FIGURE 43–6 Motorized seat belt in operation. *Courtesy of Ford Motor Company*

FIGURE 43–7 Examples of webbing defects.

retractor mechanisms or lap belt retractor covers. Replace them with new replacement parts.

5. Tighten all seat and shoulder belt anchor bolts as specified in the service manual.

A visual and functional inspection of the belts themselves is very important to assure maximum safety. The following inspections provide typical, detailed procedures for seat belt inspection.

Webbing Inspection Pay special attention to where the webbing contacts maximum stress points, such as the buckle, D-ring, and retractor. Collision forces center on these locations and can weaken the belt. Signs of damage at these points require belt replacement. Check for twisted webbing due to improper alignment when connecting the buckle. Fully extend the webbing from the retractor. Inspect the webbing and replace with a new assembly if the following conditions are noted (Figure 43–7): cut or damaged webbing, broken or pulled threads, cut loops at belt edge, color fading as a result of exposure to sun or chemical agents, or bowed webbing.

If the webbing cannot be pulled out of the retractor or will not retract to the stowed position, check for the following conditions and clean or correct as necessary: dirty webbing coated with gum, syrup, grease, or other foreign material, twisted webbing, or retractor or loop on B-pillar out of position.

SHOP TALK

Do not bleach or dye the belt webbing. Clean with a mild soap solution and water. ∎

Buckle Inspection The technician must find out whether or not the buckle works and if the buckle housing cover has been damaged. Insert the tongue of the seat belt into the buckle until a click is heard. Pull back on the webbing quickly to ensure that the buckle is latched properly. Replace the seat belt assembly if the buckle does not latch. Depress the button on the buckle to release the belt. The belt should release with a pressure of approximately 2 pounds. Replace the seat belt assembly if the buckle cover is cracked, the push button is loose, or the pressure required to release the button is too high.

Retractor Inspection Retractors for lap belts should lock automatically once the belt is out fully. The two types of seat belt retractors used with passive seat belt systems are either webbing sensitive or vehicle sensitive. Webbing sensitive seat belt retractors can be tested by grasping the seat belt and jerking it. The retractor should lock up. If it does not, replace the seat belt retractor.

Vehicle seat belt retractors will not lock up using the same procedure as the webbing sensitive retractors. To test these belts, a braking test is required. Perform this test in a safe place. A helper is required to check the retractors on the passenger side and in the back if the vehicle is equipped with rear lap/shoulder belts.

Do the brake test for each belt by driving the car at 5 to 8 mph and quickly applying the brakes. If a belt does not lock up, replace the seat belt assembly. During this test, it is important for the driver and helper to brace themselves in the event the retractor does not lock up. Replace any belt assembly that does not lock up. If the car is not driveable when it first comes into the shop, check the retractors after the vehicle has been repaired. Make note of their conditions on the damage report.

Most retractors are not interchangeable. That is, an *R* marked on the retractor tab indicates that it is for the right side only, and an *L* should be used on the left side only.

On some vehicles both retractor tests are required. Check the service manual.

SHOP TALK

The passive seat belt system is a part of the inertia switch circuit. During an impact, the inertia switch cuts off the power to the restraint system and the fuel pump. Reset the switch to restore operation. It is also important that both shoulder belts are replaced whenever either belt is stressed in a collision. The reason is that the dual retractor assembly might be distorted when either belt absorbs the energy of a collision.

Drive Track Assembly and Anchorage Inspection
The seat belt anchors are found where the retractors attach to the car body. High impact forces occur here during a collision; therefore, be sure to carefully inspect the anchor areas. Look for cracks and distortion in the metal where the retractors and D-rings anchor. The use of shims on the track drive assembly is not recommended. Upper body damage must be properly repaired, returning the vehicle to exact dimensional specifications, before any repairs are performed on the seat belt system. Check for cracks, distortion, and looseness in the bolts that attach the retractors to the body. These bolts are usually large, prevailing torque fasteners. Finally, look for dirt and corrosion in the anchor area.

Loose bolts should be replaced. If there is damage to the metal in the mounting area, proper repairs must be completed before reattaching the anchor. Clean the area prior to welding. Be sure to apply correct MIG welding procedures and restore corrosion protection to the area. When spraying anticorrosion materials, make sure they do not enter the retractor. This can keep it from operating properly.

The drive motor is usually located at the base of the track assembly behind the rear seat side trim panel. Its purpose is to pull the tape that positions the belt. If a check of the drive motor reveals that it is faulty, replace it. Like any motorized system, the seat belt parts need periodic lubrication.

To service the motorized seat belt system, follow the instruction given in the service manual (Figure 43–8).

Seat Belt Tensioners
Some vehicles are equipped with seat belt tensioners. These contain a small explosive charge that is detonated during a collision. This causes the seat belts to tighten during several frontal impacts. The tensioners, located in the B-pillar, can be used on vehicles with or without air bags. Tensioners will not be deployed if the seat belt is not buckled.

To determine if the tensioner has been deployed or to replace a deployed tensioner, follow the procedures given in the service manual.

Rear Seat Restraint System
Removal and installation of a rear seat restraint system is obvious upon inspection. Check the position of the factory-installed lap belt and single loop belt anchors and reinstall and tighten the anchor plates in the same position and torque as specified in the vehicle's service manual.

FIGURE 43–8 Typical motorized seat belt system. The service manual is required to dismantle the system. *Courtesy of Chrysler Corporation*

Some models have a rear center seat belt and a few have them in the front as well. These belts do not have a retractor. In addition to checking the webbing and anchorages, the adjustable slide locking of the belt must be checked.

Fasten the tongue to the buckle and adjust by pulling the webbing end at a right angle to the connector and buckle. Release the webbing and pull upward on the connector and buckle. If the slide lock does not hold, remove and replace that seat belt assembly.

Child Seat
There are three types of child car seats: rear facing, forward facing, or a combination. The car seat is secured with a lap and shoulder seat belt (using a locking clip provided by the car seat manufacturer) or just a lap belt (Figure 43–9). Some child safety sets provide a tether strap that goes over the back of

FIGURE 43–9 Typical integrated child seat arrangement. *Courtesy of Chrysler Corporation*

the vehicle seat and attaches to an anchorage in the floor or panel behind the rear seat. If a tethered safety seat is installed in the front seat, the tether strap should be hooked to the rear seat lap belt tongue or the webbing of the buckled rear seat lap belt behind the child safety seat. Attachment holes (at each rear seating position) have been provided to attach the tether anchor hardware kit. Some manufacturers have included integral child seats. These seats are built into a normal passenger seat. They are exposed by moving the back cushion of the seat.

SHOP TALK

All vehicles built for sale in Canada include a tether anchor hardware kit for use with Canadian child safety seats. ■

When using any infant or child restraint system, follow the instructions provided by the manufacturer concerning its installation and use. Failure to follow each of the restraint manufacturer's instructions can result in a child striking the vehicle's interior during a sudden stop or collision.

Warning Light and Sound Systems

When the ignition is turned to the on or run position, the fasten seat belt light should come on. There should also be a buzzer or chime. In some cars, there is a computerized voice that directs the occupants to fasten their seat belts. If these warning lights and sound systems do not come on, check for a blown fuse or circuit breaker. If those check out fine, and there is sound but no light, check for a damaged or burned out bulb. If the bulb lights but there is no sound, check for damaged or loose wiring, switches, or buzzer (voice module).

Running some basic electrical checks should locate the problem. Having the proper wiring diagram or service manual on hand can help (Figure 43–10).

Inspecting seat belt systems takes a systematic approach and a focus on detail. Their important function is passenger protection and as such, calls for careful attention.

Air Bags

A typical supplemental inflatable restraint (**SIR**) or air bag system (Figure 43–11) includes three important elements. The electrical system includes the impact sensors and the electronic control module. Its main functions are to conduct a system self-check to let the driver know that it is functioning properly, to

FIGURE 43–10 Typical seat belt alert system circuit schematic.

detect an impact, and to send a signal that inflates the air bag. The air bag module is located in the steering wheel for the driver and in the dash panel for passengers. It contains the air bag and the parts that cause it to inflate. The knee diverter cushions the driver's knee from impact and helps prevent the driver from sliding under the air bag during a collision. It is located underneath the steering column and behind the steering column trim.

Electrical System Components The electrical system generally has the following parts.

DIAGNOSTIC MONITOR ASSEMBLY The diagnostic monitor (Figure 43–12) contains a microcomputer that monitors the electrical system components and connections. The monitor performs a self-check of the microcomputer internal circuits and energizes the system readiness indicator during prove out and whenever a fault occurs. System electrical faults can be detected and translated into coded indicator displays. If a certain fault occurs, the microcomputer disables the system by opening a thermal fuse built into the monitor. If a system fault exists and the indicator is malfunctioning, an audible tone signals the need for service. If certain faults occur, the system is disarmed by a firing circuit disarm device incorporated within the monitor or diagnostic module.

An air bag system backup power supply is included in the diagnostic monitor to provide air bag deploy-

FIGURE 43–11 Crash sequence of a typical air bag system. *Courtesy of Chrysler Corporation*

ment power if the battery or battery cables are damaged in an accident before the crash sensors close. The power supply depletes its stored energy approximately one minute after the positive cable of the battery is disconnected.

⬤ CAUTION:

The backup power supply energy must be depleted before any air bag component service is performed. To deplete the backup power supply energy, disconnect the positive battery cable and wait one minute. ■

FIGURE 43–12 Electronic monitor assembly contains a microcomputer that monitors the electrical system components and connections. *Courtesy of Chrysler Corporation*

SENSORS The sensors detect impact and signal the air bag to inflate (Figure 43–13). At least two sensors must be activated for the air bag to inflate. There are usually five sensors: two at the radiator support, one at the right-hand fender apron, one at the left-hand fender apron, and one at the cowl in the passenger compartment. (A few systems use only two sensors—one in front of the radiator and another in the passenger compartment.) There is an interlock between

FIGURE 43–13 Air bag crash sensors consist of a sensing mass (either a ball or a roller) that rolls forward on impact and closes the contacts to activate the deployment circuit. *Courtesy of Chrysler Corporation*

the sensors, so two or more must work together to trigger the system. Keep in mind that air bag systems are designed to deploy in case of frontal collisions only. While the design of individual systems varies, deployment generally occurs anywhere between 12 to 28 mph.

All the sensors use some type of inertia switching mechanism, which provides for the breakaway of a metal ball from its captive magnet. This function causes a signal to activate a portion of the deployment program set up in the control processor. The system is still capable of directly applying battery power to the squib or detonator. At least two sensors, one safing and one front crash sensor, must be activated to inflate the air bag (Figure 43–14).

An integrated version within this network includes a safing sensor, sometimes attached to the original crash sensor. This device confirms the attitude and magnitude of the frontal deceleration forces and will offer the microprocessor a second opinion before actual deployment. This is all it takes to complete the firing sequence, and the bag will deploy.

WIRING HARNESS The harness connects all system components into a complete unit. The wires carry the electricity, which signals the air bag to inflate. The harness also passes the signals during the self-diagnosis sequence.

SIR OR AIR BAG READINESS LIGHT This light lets the driver know the air bag system is working and ready to do its job. The readiness lamp lights briefly when the driver turns the key from off to run. A malfunction in the air bag system causes the light to stay on continuously or to flash, or the light might not come on at all. Some systems have a tone generator that sounds if there is a problem in the system or if the readiness light is not functioning.

Air Bag Module The bag itself is composed of nylon and is sometimes coated internally with neoprene. All the air bag module components are packaged in a single container, which is mounted in the center of the steering wheel. This entire assembly must be serviced as one unit when repair of the air bag system is required. The air bag module is made up of the following components (Figure 43–15).

FIGURE 43–14 Typical air bag firing circuit diagram.

FIGURE 43–15 Components of a typical air bag module. The individual parts are not serviceable in the field. *Courtesy of Chrysler Corporation*

IGNITER ASSEMBLY Inflation of the air bag is caused by an explosive release of gas. For the explosion to occur, a chemical reaction must be started. The igniter (Figure 43–16) does this when it receives a signal from the air bag monitor. Actually, the igniter is a two-pin bridge device. When the electrical current is applied, it arcs across the two pins creating a spark that ignites a squib or canister of gas generating zerconic potassium perchlorate (**ZPP**). This material ignites the propellant. Some newer-model seat bags now use solid propellent and argon. This gas has a stable structure, cools more quickly, and is inert as well as nontoxic.

INFLATER MODULE This module contains the ZPP. Once it triggers the igniter, the propellent charge is progressive burning sodium azide, which converts to nitrogen gas as it burns. It is the nitrogen gas that fills the air bag.

Almost as soon as the bag is filled, the gas is cooled and vented, deflating the assembly as the collision energy is absorbed. The driver is cradled in the

FIGURE 43–16 Igniter assembly holds the chemical that generates the gas as well as the mechanism that provides the electrical impulse to start the chemical reaction.

envelope of the supplemental restraint bag instead of being propelled forward to strike the steering wheel or be otherwise injured by follow-up inertia energy from seat belt restraint systems. In addition, a certain degree of facial protection against flying objects is obtained just when it is needed.

It is important to remember that the tandem action of at least one main sensor and a safing sensor will initiate safety restraint system activation. The micro-controller also provides failure data and trouble codes for use in servicing various aspects of most systems.

MOUNTING PLATE AND RETAINER RING

These attach the air bag assembly to the inflator. They also keep the entire air bag module connected to the steering wheel.

LINER AND STEERING WHEEL TRIM COVER

The liner houses the air bag. The trim cover goes over the exterior of the steering wheel hub.

Passenger-side air bags are very similar in design to the driver's unit. The actual capacity of gas required to inflate the bag is much greater because the bag must span the extra distance between the occupant and the dashboard at the passenger seating location. The steering wheel and column make up this difference on the driver's side.

⚠️ *WARNING!*

When the air bag is deployed, a great deal of heat is generated. While the heat is not harmful to passengers, it may damage or melt the clock spring electrical connector (Figure 43–17). When replacing a deployed air bag module, examine all of the electrical connections for signs of scorching or damage. If damage exists, it must be repaired. ■

FIGURE 43–17 Removing the clock spring requires dismantling part of the steering column. The service manual details this procedure. *Courtesy of Chrysler Corporation*

STEERING WHEEL

CLOCK SPRING ELECTRICAL CONNECTOR

STEERING COLUMN

AIR BAG MODULE

VIBRATION DAMPER FWD AUTOMATIC TRANSMISSION ONLY

SERVICING THE AIR BAG SYSTEM

A structural service routine, beginning with a thorough visual inspection of sensor integrity, is the best place to start when diagnosing a system with a glowing light. Damage from a collision, or mishandling during a non-related repair, can set up a fault area, which will disarm the air bag system. If the vehicle is accessible with a service code procedure or display parameter, troubleshooting can be very straightforward.

Keep in mind that wiring difficulties of any kind call for careful removal of the air bag module and substitution of a jumper wire or special load simulator in its place. This step allows for a safe test sequence with an activated control circuit and should identify any continuity problems or short circuits.

Back-probing a live, powered-up supplemental restraint system with a self-powered multimeter or test light is a sure way to obtain a first-hand demonstration of a bag deployment. The cost involved in revitalizing this system is very expensive, so it would be prudent not to indiscriminately deploy a system.

Sodium hydroxide, a chemical used with the system, can cause severe skin reactions or other more serious side effects.

The removal of the ground battery cable should precede any component service operation. On vehicles with a backup power source, the backup power pack should likewise be disconnected according to the service manual.

Even though the control processor for the air bags keeps tabs on malfunction data and possible related sensor and inertia reel data, the bag itself can be deployed at any time. This holds true because the air bag is electrically coupled directly into the battery through the detonator and the various sensors or crash detectors.

An air bag unitized module is serviced as a complete assembly in all of the available systems to date. Technicians repairing this supplemental system are also advised to service crash sensors, mercury switches, and any other related components in assembly groupings. A crash sensor that has been damaged should be replaced. It would be a good idea to replace the entire set if a failure or degradation of any single sensor is found.

Extreme care must be taken when reinstalling an air bag module. The bag modules should be stored with the horn pad facing up and the aluminum or metallic housing facing down.

The steering column clock spring or spiral wrap, used to electrically link the controller to the bag as well as the crash sensors, should be maintained in its correct index position at all times. Failure to keep the centering spring straight ahead or in the neutral position, relative to the steering wheel, can cause damage to the enclosure, wiring, or module. Any of these situations can cause the air bag system to default into a nonoperative mode.

Removing and reinstalling the steering wheel can cause many installation errors, the first being damaging the spiral coupler or clock spring device. Another important consideration might include altering the deflection attitude of the bag for deployment. Even though the removal of the steering wheel itself is essentially similar to non-air bag vehicles, additional caution should be used when servicing these systems.

Safety precautions must be taken when working on or around air bag systems. Before beginning any kind of diagnostic procedures, repair, removal, or installation of any components of an air bag system, disconnect the battery to prevent accidental inflation of the bag. On some vehicles, wait 10 minutes for the auxiliary power supply to discharge. Check the service manual.

If you lay a module down on a surface, make sure the bag and trim cover face up to minimize a launch effect of the module if the bag suddenly inflates.

Defective or used air bag modules must be replaced as a whole unit. Do not attempt to service individual parts of these modules.

Wear safety glasses and protective gloves when handling inflated air bags, and wash your hands with soap and water when finished. Inflators in most cases contain irritating and toxic chemicals.

Never probe electrical connectors on an air bag module. This could set off the air bag. Never just toss out a faulty air bag module or uninflated air bag. Some manufacturers stipulate that a deployed air bag must be returned to the manufacturer. Follow specific U.S. Department of Transportation regulations when returning it.

A final inspection of the job should include checking to make sure the sensors are firmly fastened to their mounting fixtures, with the arrows on them facing forward. Be certain all the fuses are correctly rated and replaced. Make sure a final check is made for codes (Figure 43–18) using the approved scan tool. Carefully recheck the wire and harness routing before releasing the car.

USING SERVICE MANUALS

Many service manuals contain air bag testing system function diagrams similar to the two shown in Figures 43–19A and B. With the service manual in hand, connect the scan tool to the diagnos-

NUMBER OF FLASHES	PROBABLE CAUSE
NO LIGHT	INOPERATIVE AIR BAG LAMP CIRCUIT
CONTINUOUS FLASHING	DISCONNECTED OR LOOSE MONITOR ASSEMBLY CONNECTOR
LIGHT STAYS ON/NO FLASH	DIAGNOSTIC MODULE FAULT
3	LOSS OF AIR BAG DEPLOYMENT CIRCUIT POWER
5	SHORTED FORWARD CRASH SENSOR DEPLOYMENT CIRCUIT
10	DEFECTIVE FIRING CIRCUIT DISARM DEVICE
4	POTENTIAL SHORT IN AIR BAG DEPLOYMENT CIRCUIT OR IMPROPERLY GROUNDED DASH PANEL SENSOR (MUST USE DIAGNOSTIC FLOW CHART TO TROUBLESHOOT)
6	DRIVER AIR BAG CIRCUIT INOPERATIVE
7	OPEN CIRCUIT IN MONITOR CONNECTOR
8	FORWARD CRASH SENSOR IMPROPERLY ATTACHED OR GROUNDED
9	OPEN FORWARD CRASH SENSOR DEPLOYMENT CIRCUIT
11	OPEN EXTERNAL FLASHER CIRCUIT
2	ALL FORWARD CRASH SENSORS DISCONNECTED

FIGURE 43–18 Typical trouble code index. For specific index, check service manual. Each number repeats itself, and then, if there is another code, it will be displayed next.

tic connector jumper harness, and turn the ignition to the run position. Exit the vehicle and reconnect the battery cable disconnected earlier. The scan tool reads two types of fault codes—earlier and stored. Stored codes can only be erased with a scan tool and only after the problem has been corrected.

With the scan tool attached to the diagnostic connector, begin with test 1 (Figure 43–19A). By following the chart through the steps listed, we first get a blank screen (step 8) and then a no response message (step 9). This leads to the flow chart step that tells us to perform test 2.

For test 2 (Figure 43–19B), first check the cable between scan tool and the diagnostic circuit for damaged or open circuits. If none are found, go on. Following the chart, we find that the DRB II cable is good. Disconnect the DRB II and the diagnostic jumper harness. Check connectors for spread or damaged terminals. There are none. Connect an ohmmeter to both ends of DO4LG wire in the jumper harness. No open circuits are found.

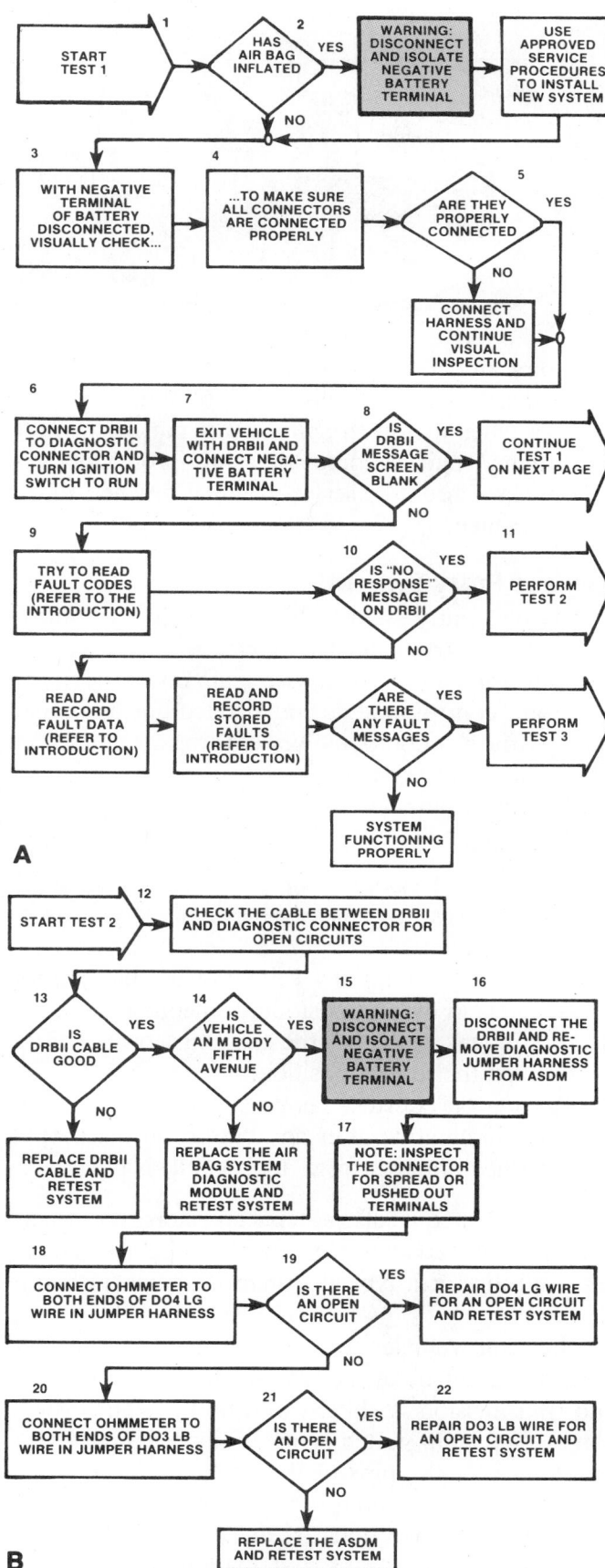

A

B

FIGURE 43–19 (A) Testing system function; (B) test for no response message on DRB. Test 1 is performed before proceeding. *Courtesy of Chrysler Corporation*

Connect an ohmmeter to both ends of DO3LB wire in the jumper harness. There is an open circuit. This is the problem. The damaged harness is repaired or replaced, and the system is retested. This time there is no trouble code. The vehicle is ready to go. ∎

⚠ *WARNING!*

The example illustrates that you are more likely to find loose connectors or damaged wiring or sensors than a faulty diagnostic module. So, do not be hasty to replace expensive parts before checking for simpler solutions. That is why following the directions in the manual is so important. ∎

SECURITY AND ANTITHEFT DEVICES

Every 26 seconds a car is stolen somewhere in the United States. Although more than half of the million plus cars stolen every year are luxury or sports cars, any vehicle can become a part of these statistics. However, there are some steps that can be taken to slow down thieves or even scare them off.

There are three basic types of antitheft devices available: locking devices, disabling devices, and alarm systems. Many of the devices are available as OE from the manufacturers; others are aftermarket installed. Like other electrical systems, computers control antitheft devices. The sensors and relays can be checked with a digital multimeter and a jumper wire. Read the service manual for their operation details.

Locks

A variety of locks are available that are designed to deny entry to the engine, passenger, and trunk compartments of the car as well as to prevent a thief from driving the car away. These locking systems include door and trunk locks, keyless entry systems, fuel tanks, light delay systems, and locking steering wheels. With locking steering wheels, when the ignition key is off, the steering wheel cannot be turned (Figure 43–20). A rack and sector are usually used to slide a steel pin into mesh with a slotted disc. Since the disc is splined to the steering shaft, the steering wheel does not turn.

There are both internal and external hood locks available to prevent theft of anything under the hood. These locks are especially useful on a vehicle with a battery-powered alarm system because they prevent a thief from disconnecting the power source or disabling the siren.

FIGURE 43–20 Steering wheel locking mechanism. When the ignition key is removed, the steering wheel is locked, which helps prevent theft of vehicle. *Courtesy of Cadillac Motor Car Division, General Motors Corporation*

Many cars are equipped with special fuel filler doors that help to prevent the theft of gas from the fuel tank. Voltage is present at the fuel filler door release switch at all times. When the switch is closed, the door release solenoid is energized and the fuel door opens.

Antitheft devices are very effective in preventing tires and wheels from being stolen. A special key wrench is required to remove antitheft wheel lug nuts, and it is available only from the manufacturer (Figure 43–21). Hubcap locks (Figure 43–22) are wheelcovers equipped with an antitheft locking system. A special key wrench is required to pry off the center hub ornament and remove the lock bolt.

CUSTOMER CARE

When doing any wheel or tire servicing, show the customer how to change a tire if the wheel is equipped with locking hubcaps. ◼

FIGURE 43–21 Antitheft lug nut and key.

FIGURE 43–22 Antitheft wire hubcaps.

Some door lock systems automatically engage when vehicle speed exceeds 8 mph (manual transmission) or when the driver shifts out of park or neutral. Also, many vehicles come with child-protection rear door locks. Check the service manual for their repair or replacement.

Keyless Entry System

The keyless entry system allows the driver to unlock the doors or trunk lid from outside of the vehicle without using a key. It has two main components: an electronic control module and a coded-button keypad on the driver's door. Some keyless systems employ an illuminated entry system.

The electronic control module typically performs the following functions.

◆ Unlocking all doors
◆ Unlocking the luggage compartment
◆ Locking all doors
◆ Automatic locking of all doors when the ignition switch is in the run position, someone is seated in the driver's seat, and the transmission is shifted through the reverse position.
◆ Turning on courtesy lamps and keypad and key-hole illumination after any button on the keypad is pushed or either front door handle is pulled

The control module also accepts and stores an owner's alternate entry code. Either code then operates the system. Wiring for a typical system is shown in Figure 43–23.

In some vehicles, the backup lamp switch contacts are also part of the keyless entry system. When the transmission is shifted into or through reverse, the backup lamp switch contacts close, applying voltage to one of the pins of the keyless entry module. This prompts the module to automatically lock all doors (if other conditions are met).

Remote keyless entry systems are now available. They use a hand-held transmitter, frequently attached as part of the key fob (Figure 43–24). With a press of the unlock button on the transmitter, the interior lights turn on, the driver's door unlocks, and the theft

FIGURE 43–23 Typical keyless door entry wiring. *Courtesy of Ford Motor Company*

security system is disarmed from any direction range from 25 to 50 feet, depending on the type of transmitter. The trunk can also be unlocked. When exiting the car, pressing the lock button locks all doors and arms the security system.

Disabling Devices

Disabling devices can be either actively or passively armed. Actively armed units are controlled with either a key, a coded sequence or a digital touch-pad, or a hidden button mounted under the dash. Passive devices are part of a combination antitheft system. The more expensive models have a by-pass provision that allows the owner to leave the car at a service station or valet parking lot without telling anyone about the alarm system.

Ignition-Kill System

An ignition-kill system interferes with the ignition to such an extent that the car cannot be hot-wired. In fact, when the ignition kill is activated, not even the ignition key starts the car.

FIGURE 43–24 Typical remote keyless system transmitter. *Courtesy of General Motors Corporation*

An ignition-kill system has definite advantages. There is nothing to transport, no codes to remember, and nothing visible to mar the exterior of the car or to alert a thief.

One of the latest ignition-kill systems is the passkey arrangement (Figure 43–25). This unique system features an electronic pellet in the vehicle's ignition key. The ignition lock reads the electronic coding. Without the proper key coding, the engine does not start.

Hydraulic Lock

Hydraulic locks are permanently installed in the brake lines. They block the flow of fluid and lock up all four brakes so the car cannot move. A key lock is used to release the pressure on the brakes.

Alarm Systems

The two methods for activating alarm systems are passive and active. Passive systems switch on automatically when the ignition key is removed or the doors are locked. They are often more effective than active systems.

Active systems are activated manually with a key, keypad, or toggle switch. They allow the driver to leave the car at a service station or parking garage without disclosing the secrets of the system to the attendant. The disadvantage is that you must remember to turn the alarm on and off.

Among the number of devices used to trigger an alarm system, mechanical switches are similar to those used to turn on the courtesy lights as the doors are opened. When a door, hood, or trunk is opened, the switch closes and the alarm sounds. It turns itself off automatically (provided the intruder has stopped

FIGURE 43–25   The passkey security system. *Courtesy of General Motors Corporation*

FIGURE 43–26
Ultrasonic sensor triggers the alarm when someone enters the car.

trying to enter the car) to prevent the battery from being drained. It then rearms itself automatically.

Ultrasonic sensors are like the ones used at the supermarket to open doors automatically. They sound the alarm if someone tries to enter the car, either through a door or window (Figure 43–26).

Current-sensitive sensors activate the alarm if a change in current occurs within a car's electrical system. When a courtesy light goes on or the ignition starts, the alarm is activated. However, it might not be practical to use this type of sensor in a car in which the light does not turn on when the back doors are opened.

The majority of law enforcement officials recommend siren alarms over silent page alarms. A siren alarm calls attention to the car and startles the intruder. With a silent page alarm, the owner carries a pager that beeps when someone tampers with the car. However, this can be dangerous because many people recklessly confront the thief alone rather than call the police.

While increased numbers of vehicles are being equipped with security and antitheft devices, the majority of installation and repair work is done by a general auto technician. It is important for you to keep abreast of both OE and aftermarket systems for the latest information on security and antitheft equipment.

OTHER ELECTRONIC EQUIPMENT

As was stated in the beginning of this chapter, there is a great deal of automobile electronic equipment at the drawing board stage. Of the important comfort and safety electronic and electrical, the most popular is the radio.

Radio and Audio Systems

Entertainment radios are available in a wide variety of models. The complexity of the system varies significantly from the basic AM radio to the compact disc (CD) player with high-power amplifiers and multiple speakers. However, the overall operation of the radio itself is electrically basically the same.

The major components in a basic AM system are a radio receiver and speaker (Figure 43–27A). In the

FIGURE 43–27   Typical radio systems: (A) AM radio and (B) AM/FM stereo electronic radio. *Courtesy of Ford Motor Company*

more complex stereo systems, the major components are an AM/FM radio receiver, a stereo amplifier, sound amplifier switch, several speakers, and a power antenna system (Figure 43–27B).

Internal diagnostic examination of the radio should be left to the authorized radio service center. However, the automotive technician should be able to analyze and isolate radio reception conditions to the area of component causing the condition. All radio conditions can be isolated to one of five general areas. The trouble will be found in the antenna system, radio chassis (receiver), speaker system, radio noise suppression equipment, or sound system.

Operation of the AM radio requires only the power from the fuse panel to be available at the radio. The radio intercepts broadcast signals with its antenna and produces a corresponding input to the system speaker. In addition, some radios have built-in memory circuits to ensure that the radio returns to the previously selected station when the radio or ignition switch is turned off and back on again. Some of these memory circuits require an additional power input from the fuse panel that remains hot at all times. The current draw is very small and requires no more power than a clock. However, if battery power is removed, the memory circuit has to be reset.

The service manual and owner's guide for the vehicle contain detailed information concerning radio operation. If the radio system is not working, check the fuse. If the fuses are okay, refer to the service manual. Remember, the radio chassis (receiver) itself should only be serviced by a qualified radio technician or specialty radio service shop. If a technician determines that the radio itself is the problem, remove the radio, and send it to a qualified radio person.

Power Antenna

Over the years, various methods have been made to hide the conventional mast radio antenna. The functional advantages of doing this are improved exterior appearance, elimination of one source of wind noise, and heightened resistance to antenna-snapping vandalism. As already mentioned, some radio antennas are embedded into the front windshield and rear window.

In spite of many efforts to hide the antenna, the most popular method is still the power antenna. In addition, an auto technician can service the power antenna switch and motor. The power antenna switch is a spring-loaded switch with up, down, and center positions. In either the up or down position, power from the fuse panel is applied to the power antenna motor to move the antenna up or down as desired (Figure 43–28). The power antenna motor is a two-directional motor. It is part of the antenna assembly (Figure 43–29) and is controlled by the power antenna switch. The antenna should be in its fully extended position for the radio to work properly.

If AM reception is extremely poor and FM reception appears to have trouble holding stations, make sure the antenna and antenna connectors are properly mated. If the antenna connectors are properly mated but the reception is still poor, replace the

FIGURE 43–28 Power antenna switch. *Courtesy of Ford Motor Company*

FIGURE 43–29 Typical power antenna motor. *Courtesy of Ford Motor Company*

antenna cable. If only FM reception is poor, it is unlikely that the antenna is at fault. Remove the radio chassis for service.

CUSTOMER CARE

Many customers do not understand the limitations of FM reception. Refer your customer to the owner's guide for information about the limitations of FM radio performance. ■

Noise Suppression

The vehicle's ignition system is a source of radio interference. This high-voltage switching system produces a radio frequency electromagnetic field that radiates at AM, FM, and CB frequencies. Although components have been designed into the vehicle to minimize this concern, the noise is more noticeable if the radio is tuned slightly off channel when listening to FM programs. Vehicle electrical accessories and owner add-on accessories may also contribute to radio interference. Furthermore, there are many noise sources that are external to the vehicle. These include power lines, communication systems, ignition systems of other vehicles, and neon signs.

The most effective method of evaluating ignition noise is to compare the radio performance with the engine on, versus engine off. To identify the source of ignition noise, check to see if the spark plug wires are suppressors and the spark plugs are the correct resistors.

Noise suppression components may be malfunctioning or missing. Check the band ground strap effectiveness. Wedge a large file between the metal parts, such as between the tailpipe and body, or between the fender and frame. This ensures a proper ground while the radio is playing and engine is run-

ning. Listen for a decrease in the objectionable radio noise. If a reduction in radio noise is noted, first try tightening body and exhaust system clamps and brackets. Then, if necessary, install a new band strap between the two metal parts to ensure proper ground.

CUSTOMER CARE

Be sure to alert your customer that before turning off the radio or the ignition of the vehicle, always eject any cassette being played. Leaving the tape mechanism stopped while a tape is engaged can result in damage to the tape, pinch roller, or capstan. Also, tell the customer not to leave a tape cassette engaged in the tape player slot when not in use. Remove it completely to permit the slot door to close and keep out airborne dirt. ■

Speaker and Sound Quality Poor speaker or sound quality is usually caused by one of the following.

Experience has shown that rattles and buzzes are caused more often by loose speakers, speaker mountings, speaker grilles, or trim panels than by inoperative speakers. Check the tightness of mountings and trim pieces.

Distortion can be caused by the speaker, radio chassis, or wiring. If the concern is in the radio chassis, both speakers on the same side of the vehicle exhibit poor quality. Distortion caused by damaged wiring is most often accompanied by lower than normal sound output.

Buzzes, rattles, or distorted or weak sound from package tray speakers are often caused by bent package tray sheet metal around the speaker opening, lack of mounting brackets, or by missing or loose attaching hardware or speaker covers. Bent sheet metal should be straightened and the speaker reinstalled. Loose hardware should be finger-tightened plus approximately one full turn. Be careful not to overtighten hardware as this may bend or deform the speaker baskets causing buzzes or distorted sound.

SHOP TALK

Antitheft audio systems (Figure 43–30) have built-in devices that make the audio system soundless if stolen. If the power source for the audio system is cut, the antitheft system operates so that even if the power source is reconnected, the audio system will not produce any sound unless the ID number selected by the customer is put in. When performing repairs on vehicles equipped with this

FIGURE 43–30 The radio antitheft display. *Courtesy of Toyota Motor Corporation*

system, before disconnecting the battery terminals or removing the audio system, the customer should be asked for the ID number so the technician can input the ID number afterwards, or request that the customer input the ID number after the repairs are completed. With antitheft radio installation, there is a procedure in the service manual to obtain the factory back-up code using a touch tone phone if the owner's code is not available. In still other models, if the ignition key is removed and the negative battery cable is disconnected, the antitheft device is deactivated. A back-up battery in the radio keeps the code in memory allowing the radio to be removed and reinstalled. The radio becomes inoperable if the power is cut off during a collision or theft. Refer to the vehicle service manual before removing a stereo to determine if it is equipped with any antitheft devices and the procedures for removal. ∎

Cellular Phones

More and more auto manufacturers are installing cellular or mobile telephones as optional equipment (Figure 43–31). These cellular phones offer call-from-anywhere security. The service manual of such equipped vehicles contains all the necessary servicing information.

FIGURE 43–31 Typical of the factory-installed cellular phone. The unit shown is mounted in the back of the driver's sun visor for hands-free operation. Conventional models are floor-mounted units with hand sets. *Courtesy of Chrysler Corporation*

CASE STUDY

A customer complains that the radio and stereo cassette player are not operating properly. The customer states it sometimes drops in volume, so low it cannot be heard. In fact, it almost seems the unit is turning itself on and off.

The technician test drives the vehicle. At first, the system operates normally, but when crossing railroad tracks, the system cuts out momentarily. The technician deliberately drives over a rough road on the way back to the shop. The intermittent volume problem repeats itself.

Back at the shop, the technician now knows the type of problem to look for. The radio unit is carefully removed from the dash. The technician inspects the wiring harness, but no loose wires are found. By checking the mounting brackets, the problem is discovered. The grounding strap for the unit is not securely fastened to the metal frame. This intermittent ground was the cause of the volume cutting in and out. The unit was indeed turning itself on and off on rough roads. Securing a good ground connection solves the problem.

KEY TERMS

Active restraint system	Safety glass
Antilacerative glass	SIR
Inertia lock retractors	Tempered glass
Laminated plate glass	Zone-tempered glass
Passive restraint system	ZPP

SUMMARY

◆ Safety glass is used in all auto windows. It is of two types: laminated and tempered. Both types are available in a variety of tints.

◆ Laminated glass is used for windshields. The thin layer of plastic manufactured within the laminated glass keeps it from shattering when broken.

◆ Tempered glass is used in side and rear windows. It is harder than laminated glass, and when broken has a granular texture.

◆ Antenna wire for radio reception can be embedded in laminated glass or printed on the surface of tempered glass.

◆ A silver and zinc oxide coating fused to the glass to carry electrical current is used for some heated windshields. Others may use a laminate material capable of carrying electrical current.

- All new vehicles built or sold in the United States must have one or both types of passive restraints: seat belts or air bags.
- Seat belts are of two types: active restraint and passive restraint.
- When servicing seat belts, inspect the webbing, buckles, retractors, and anchorage.
- Child seat installation procedures vary depending on where the seat is installed.
- The main components of a typical air bag system include an electrical control system, air bag module, and knee diverter.
- An air bag electrical system consists of the monitor assembly, wire harness, and air bag readiness light.
- An air bag module consists of an igniter assembly, inflater module, mounting plate and retainer ring, and linear and steering wheel trim cover.
- Before doing any work on an air bag system, disconnect the battery.
- Care must be taken when removing a live (not deployed) air bag. Be sure the bag and trim cover are pointed away from you.
- There are three basic types of antitheft devices available: locking devices, disabling devices, and alarm systems.
- A variety of locks are available that are designed to deny entry to the engine, passenger, and trunk compartments of the car as well as to prevent a thief from driving the car away.
- Keyless entry systems allow drivers to unlock the vehicle's door or trunk lid without using a key. There are two types: the coded-button keypad and remote keyless entry system.
- Ignition kill systems that prevent engine startup and hydraulic lock systems that lock up all four brakes are two popular disabling devices for vehicle security.
- The basic components of AM radio and audio systems are a radio receiver and speaker. In the more complex stereo systems, the major components are an AM/FM receiver, a stereo amplifier, several speakers, and a power antenna.
- Radio interference may be caused by electromagnetic fields generated by power lines, communications equipment, and some simple electrical devices.
- Radio or stereo equipment sound distortion may be caused by poor wiring, particularly if sound output is diminished.
- Cellular phones are now available as a factory-installed option.

TECH MANUAL

The following procedures are included in Chapter 43 of the *Tech Manual* that accompanies this book:

1. Test a bumper's energy absorbing shock.

2. Inspect seat belts.

REVIEW QUESTIONS

1. What type of glass breaks into small pieces with a granular texture?

2. What type of glass is similar to conventional multilayered glass but has one or more additional layers of plastic affixed to the passenger compartment side of the glass?

3. What air bag system device contains the ZPP?

4. What type of seat belt operates automatically, with no action required by the vehicle's occupant?
   - **a.** passive restraint
   - **b.** retractor
   - **c.** active restraint
   - **d.** anchorage

5. Technician A says air bags are inflated by high-pressure gas stored in large steel cylinders behind the steering wheel or dash. Technician B says air bags are inflated with chemicals combined to produce gas rapidly. Who is correct?
   - **a.** Technician A
   - **b.** Technician B
   - **c.** Both A and B
   - **d.** Neither A nor B

6. Technician A says laminated glass is used to make windshields. Technician B says laminated glass is a single piece of heat-treated glass and has more resistance to impact than regular glass of the same thickness. Who is correct?
   - **a.** Technician A
   - **b.** Technician B
   - **c.** Both A and B
   - **d.** Neither A nor B

7. Technician A says tempered glass cannot be cut, drilled, or ground. Technician B says only laminated glass can be tinted. Who is correct?

a. Technician A   **c.** Both A and B
b. Technician B   **d.** Neither A nor B

8. Technician A says seat belt webbing should be replaced if it is bowed. Technician B says it does not need to be replaced if the color has merely faded due to exposure to the sun. Who is correct?

   a. Technician A   **c.** Both A and B
   b. Technician B   **d.** Neither A nor B

9. Which of the following is *not* an important element of a typical air bag system?

   a. electrical system   **c.** knee diverter
   b. air bag module   **d.** none of the above

10. Technician A says the monitor assembly will disarm the air bag system if certain faults occur. Technician B says at least two sensors must signal the air bag in order to trigger it. Who is correct?

    a. Technician A   **c.** Both A and B
    b. Technician B   **d.** Neither A nor B

11. Which of the following is false?

    a. The air bag ignitor assembly is a two-pin bridge device.
    b. The air bag ignitor assembly creates a spark that ignites a canister of gas generating zerconic potassium perchlorate.
    c. The air bag ignitor assembly is housed in the monitor assembly.
    d. None of the above.

12. Technician A checks the clock spring electrical connections for signs of damage when replacing a deployed air bag module. Technician B back probes an air bag system with a self-powered multimeter to determine if the system is in good working order. Who is correct?

    a. Technician A   **c.** Both A and B
    b. Technician B   **d.** Neither A nor B

13. Technician A removes the ground battery cable before servicing any component in the air bag system. Technician B wears safety glasses and protective gloves when handling inflated air bags. Who is correct?

    a. Technician A   **c.** Both A and B
    b. Technician B   **d.** Neither A nor B

14. Which of the following is a type of antitheft device?

    a. locking devices   **c.** alarm systems
    b. disabling devices   **d.** all of the above

15. Technician A says disabling devices can be either actively or passively armed. Technician B says only the ignition key will start the car when the ignition-kill system is activated. Who is correct?

    a. Technician A   **c.** Both A and B
    b. Technician B   **d.** Neither A nor B

16. Technician A says the majority of law enforcement officials recommend silent page alarms over siren alarms. Technician B says devices used to trigger an alarm system include mechanical switches, ultrasonic sensors, and current-sensitive sensors. Who is correct?

    a. Technician A   **c.** Both A and B
    b. Technician B   **d.** Neither A nor B

17. Technician A says air bag systems are designed to deploy in case of frontal collisions only. Technician B says some air bag systems only have two sensors. Who is correct?

    a. Technician A   **c.** Both A and B
    b. Technician B   **d.** Neither A nor B

18. Technician A says some heated windshields use a silver and zinc oxide coating fused to the outer glass layer to carry the electric current needed for heating. Technician B says other heated windshields use a special laminate material in the glass that is capable of carrying the electrical current. Who is correct?

    a. Technician A   **c.** Both A and B
    b. Technician B   **d.** Neither A nor B

19. Technician A says in a passive restraint system, a webbing-sensitive belt retractor can be tested by grasping it and pulling on it. It should lock up. Technician B says vehicle-sensitive retractors in passive systems can be tested by carefully performing a braking test on the road. Who is correct?

    a. Technician A   **c.** Both A and B
    b. Technician B   **d.** Neither A nor B

20. Which of the following can be sources of radio interference?

    a. ignition system wiring
    b. electrical power lines
    c. neon signs
    d. all of the above

DECIMAL AND METRIC EQUIVALENTS

Decimal and Metric Equivalents

Fractions	Decimal (in.)	Metric (mm)	Fractions	Decimal (in.)	Metric (mm)
1/64	0.015625	0.397	33/64	0.515625	13.097
1/32	0.03125	0.794	17/32	0.53125	13.494
3/64	0.046875	1.191	35/64	0.546875	13.891
1/16	0.0625	1.588	9/16	0.5625	14.288
5/64	0.078125	1.984	37/64	0.578125	14.684
3/32	0.09375	2.381	19/32	0.59375	15.081
7/64	0.109375	2.778	39/64	0.609375	15.478
1/8	0.125	3.175	5/8	0.625	15.875
9/64	0.140625	3.572	41/64	0.640625	16.272
5/32	0.15625	3.969	21/32	0.65625	16.669
11/64	0.171875	4.366	43/64	0.671875	17.066
3/16	0.1875	4.763	11/16	0.6875	17.463
13/64	0.203125	5.159	45/64	0.703125	17.859
7/32	0.21875	5.556	23/32	0.71875	18.256
15/64	0.234275	5.953	47/64	0.734375	18.653
1/4	0.250	6.35	3/4	0.750	19.05
17/64	0.265625	6.747	49/64	0.765625	19.447
9/32	0.28125	7.144	25/32	0.78125	19.844
19/64	0.296875	7.54	51/64	0.796875	20.241
5/16	0.3125	7.938	13/16	0.8125	20.638
21/64	0.328125	8.334	53/64	0.828125	21.034
11/32	0.34375	8.731	27/32	0.84375	21.431
23/64	0.359375	9.128	55/64	0.859375	21.828
3/8	0.375	9.525	7/8	0.875	22.225
25/64	0.390625	9.922	57/64	0.890625	22.622
13/32	0.40625	10.319	29/32	0.90625	23.019
27/64	0.421875	10.716	59/64	0.921875	23.416
7/16	0.4375	11.113	15/16	0.9375	23.813
29/64	0.453125	11.509	61/64	0.953125	24.209
15/32	0.46875	11.906	31/32	0.96875	24.606
31/64	0.484375	12.303	63/64	0.984375	25.003
1/2	0.500	12.7	1	1.00	25.4

ABBREVIATIONS

The following abbreviations are some of the more common ones used today in the automotive industry.

SAE J1930 Revised JUN93

Existing Usage	Acceptable Usage	Acceptable Acronized Usage
3GR (Third Gear)	Third Gear	3GR
4GR (Fourth Gear)	Fourth Gear	4GR
A/C (Air Conditioning)	Air Conditioning	A/C
A/C Cycling Switch	Air Conditioning Cycling Switch	A/C Cycling Switch
A/T (Automatic Transaxle)	Automatic Transaxle	A/T
A/T (Automatic Transmission)	Automatic Transmission	A/T
AC (Air Conditioning)	Air Conditioning	A/C
ACC (Air Conditioning Clutch)	Air Conditioning Clutch	A/C Clutch
Accelerator	Accelerator Pedal	AP
ACCS Air Conditioning Cyclic Switch)	Air Conditioning Cycling Switch	A/C Cycling Switch
ACH (Air Cleaner Housing)	Air Cleaner Housing1	ACL Housing[1]
ACL (Air Cleaner)	Air Cleaner[1]	ACL[1]
ACL (Air Cleaner) Element	Air Cleaner Element[1]	ACL Element[1]
ACL (Air Cleaner) Housing	Air Cleaner Housing[1]	ACL Housing[1]
ACL (Air Cleaner) Housing Cover	Air Cleaner Housing Cover[1]	ACL Housing Cover[1]
ACS (Air Conditioning System)	Air Conditioning System	A/C System
ACT (Air Charge Temperature)	Intake Air Temperature[1]	IAT[1]
Adaptive Fuel Strategy	Fuel Trim[1]	FT[1]
AFC (Air low Control)	Mass Air Flow[1]	MAF[1]
AFC (Air Flow Control)	Volume Air Flow[1]	VAF[1]
AFC (Air Flow Sensor)	Mass Air Flow Sensor[1]	MAF Sensor[1]
AFS (Air Flow Sensor)	Volume Air Flow Sensor[1]	VAF Sensor[1]
After Cooler	Charge Air Cooler[1]	CAC[1]
AI (Air Injection)	Secondary Air Injection[1]	AIR[1]
AIP (Air Injection Pump)	Secondary Air Injection Pump[1]	AIR Pump[1]
AIR (Air Injection Reactor)	Pulsed Secondary Air Injection[1]	PAIR[1]
AIR (Air Injection Reactor)	Secondary Air Injection[1]	AIR[1]
AIRB (Secondary Air Injection Bypass)	Secondary Air Injection Bypass[1]	AIR Bypass[1]
AIRD (Secondary Air Injection Diverter)	Secondary Air Injection Diverter[1]	AIR Diverter[1]
Air Cleaner	Air Cleaner[1]	ACL[1]
Air Cleaner Element	Air Cleaner Element[1]	ACL Element[1]
Air Cleaner Housing	Air Cleaner Housing[1]	ACL Housing[1]
Air Cleaner Housing Cover	Air Cleaner Housing Cover[1]	ACL Housing Cover[1]
Air Conditioning	Air Conditioning	A/C
Air Conditioning Sensor	Air Conditioning Sensor	A/C Sensor
Air Control Valve	Secondary Air Injection Control Valve[1]	AIR Control Valve[1]
Air Flow Meter	Mass Air Flow Sensor[1]	MAF Sensor[1]
Air Flow Meter	Volume Air Flow Sensor[1]	VAF Sensor[1]
Air Intake System	Intake Air System[1]	IA System[1]
Air Flow Sensor	Mass Air Flow Sensor[1]	MAF Sensor[1]
Air Management 1	Secondary Air Injection Bypass[1]	AIR Bypass[1]
Air Management 2	Secondary Air Injection Diverter[1]	AIR Diverter[1]
Air Temperature Sensor	Intake Air Temperature Sensor[1]	IAT Sensor[1]
Air Valve	Idle Air Control Valve[1]	IAC Valve[1]
AIV (Air Injection Valve)	Pulsed Secondary Air Injection[1]	PAIR[1]
ALCL (Assembly Line Communication Link)	Data Link Connector[1]	DLC[1]
Alcohol Concentration Sensor	Flexible Fuel Sensor[1]	FF Sensor[1]
ALDL (Assembly Line Diagnostic Link)	Data Link Connector[1]	DLC[1]
ALT (Alternator)	Generator	GEN
Alternator	Generator	GEN
AM1 (Air Management 1)	Secondary Air Injection Bypass[1]	AIR Bypass[1]

---

[1] Emission-Related Term

FIGURE 1—CROSS REFERENCE AND LOOK UP

SAE J1930 Revised JUN93

Existing Usage	Acceptable Usage	Acceptable Acronized Usage
AM2 (Air Management 2)	Secondary Air Injection Diverter[1]	AIR Diverter[1]
APS (Absolute Pressure Sensor)	Barometric Pressure Sensor[1]	BARO Sensor[1]
ATS (Air Temperature Sensor)	Intake Air Temperature Sensor[1]	IAT Sensor[1]
Automatic Transaxle	Automatic Transaxle[1]	A/T[1]
Automatic Transmission	Automatic Transmission[1]	A/T[1]
B+ (Battery Positive Voltage)	Battery Positive Voltage	B+
Backpressure Transducer	Exhaust Gas Recirculation Backpressure Transducer[1]	EGR Backpressure Transducer[1]
BARO (Barometric Pressure)	Barometric Pressure[1]	BARO[1]
Barometric Pressure Sensor	Barometric Pressure Sensor[1]	BARO Sensor[1]
Battery Positive Voltage	Battery Positive Voltage	B+
Block Learn Matrix	Long Term Fuel Trim[1]	Long Term FT[1]
BLM (Block Learn Memory)	Long Term Fuel Trim[1]	Long Term FT[1]
BLM (Block Learn Multiplier)	Long Term Fuel Trim[1]	Long Term FT[1]
BLM (Block Learn Matrix)	Long Term Fuel Trim[1]	Long Term FT[1]
Block Learn Memory	Long Term Fuel Trim[1]	Long Term FT[1]
Block Learn Multiplier	Long Term Fuel Trim[1]	Long Term FT[1]
BP (Barometric Pressure) Sensor	Barometric Pressure Sensor[1]	BARO Sensor[1]
C3I (Computer Controlled Coil Ignition)	Electronic Ignition[1]	EI[1]
CAC (Charge Air Cooler)	Charge Air Cooler[1]	CAC[1]
Camshaft Position	Camshaft Position[1]	CMP[1]
Camshaft Position Sensor	Camshaft Position Sensor[1]	CMP Sensor[1]
Camshaft Sensor	Camshaft Position Sensor[1]	CMP Sensor[1]
Canister	Canister[1]	Canister[1]
Canister	Evaporative Emission Canister[1]	EVAP Canister[1]
Canister Purge Valve	Evaporative Emission Canister Purge Valve[1]	EVAP Canister Purge Valve[1]
Canister Purge Vacuum Switching Valve	Evaporative Emission Canister Purge Valve[1]	EVAP Canister Purge Valve[1]
Canister Purge VSV (Vacuum Switching Valve)	Evaporative Emission Canister Purge Valve[1]	EVAP Canister Purge Valve[1]
CANP (Canister Purge)[1]	Evaporative Emission Canister Purge[1]	EVAP Canister Purge[1]
CARB (Carburetor)	Carburetor[1]	CARB[1]
Carburetor	Carburetor[1]	CARB[1]
CCC (Converter Clutch Control)	Torque Converter Clutch[1]	TCC[1]
CCO (Converter Clutch Override)	Torque Converter Clutch[1]	TCC[1]
CDI (Capacitive Discharge Ignition)	Distributor Ignition[1]	DI[1]
CDROM (Compact Disc Read Only Memory)	Compact Disc Read Only Memory[1]	CDROM[1]
CES (Clutch Engage Switch)	Clutch Pedal Position Switch	CPP Switch
Central Multiport Fuel Injection	Central Multiport Fuel Injection[1]	Central MFI[1]
CFI (Continuous Fuel Injection)	Continuous Fuel Injection[1]	CFI[1]
CFI (Central Fuel Injection)	Throttle Body Fuel Injection[1]	TBI[1]
Charcoal Canister	Evaporative Emission Canister	EVAP Canister[1]
Charge Air Cooler	Charge Air Cooler[1]	CAC[1]
Check Engine	Service Reminder Indicator[1]	SRI[1]
Check Engine	Malfunction Indicator Lamp[1]	MIL[1]
CID (Cylinder Identification) Sensor	Camshaft Position Sensor	CMP Sensor[1]
CIS (Continuous Injection System)	Continuous Fuel Injection[1]	CFI[1]
CIS-E (Continuous Injection System-Electronic)	Continuous Fuel Injection[1]	CFI[1]
CKP (Crankshaft Position)	Crankshaft Position[1]	CKP[1]
CKP (Crankshaft Position) Sensor	Crankshaft Position Sensor[1]	CKP Sensor[1]
CL (Closed Loop)	Closed Loop[1]	CL[1]
Closed Bowl Distributor	Distributor Ignition[1]	DI[1]
Closed Throttle Position	Closed Throttle Position[1]	CTP[1]

[1] Emission-Related Term

FIGURE 1—CROSS REFERENCE AND LOOK UP (CONTINUED)

SAE J1930 Revised JUN93

Existing Usage	Acceptable Usage	Acceptable Acronized Usage
Closed Throttle Switch	Closed Throttle Position Switch[1]	CTP Switch[1]
CLS (Closed Loop System)	Closed Loop[1]	CL[1]
Clutch Engage Switch	Clutch Pedal Position Switch[1]	CPP Switch[1]
Clutch Pedal Position Switch	Clutch Pedal Position Switch[1]	CPP Switch[1]
Clutch Start Switch	Clutch Pedal Position Switch[1]	CPP Switch[1]
Clutch Switch	Clutch Pedal Position Switch[1]	CPP Switch[1]
CMFI (Central Multiport Fuel Injection)	Central Multiport Fuel Injection[1]	Central MFI[1]
CMP (Camshaft Position)	Camshaft Position[1]	CMP[1]
CMP (Camshaft Position) Sensor	Camshaft Position Sensor[1]	CMP Sensor[1]
COC (Continuous Oxidation Catalyst)	Oxidation Catalytic Converter[1]	OC[1]
Condenser	Distributor Ignition Capacitor[1]	DI Capacitor[1]
Continuous Fuel Injection	Continuous Fuel Injection[1]	CFI[1]
Continuous Injection System	Continuous Fuel Injection System[1]	CFI System[1]
Continuous Injection System-E	Electronic Continuous Fuel Injection System[1]	Electronic CFI System[1]
Continuous Trap Oxidizer	Continuous Trap Oxidizer[1]	CTOX[1]
Coolant Temperature Sensor	Engine Coolant Temperature Sensor[1]	ECT Sensor[1]
CP (Crankshaft Position)	Crankshaft Position[1]	CKP[1]
CPP (Clutch Pedal Position)	Clutch Pedal Position[1]	CPP[1]
CPP (Clutch Pedal Position) Switch	Clutch Pedal Position Switch	CPP Switch[1]
CPS (Camshaft Position Sensor)	Camshaft Position Sensor[1]	CMP Sensor[1]
CPS (Crankshaft Position Sensor)	Crankshaft Position Sensor[1]	CKP Sensor[1]
Crank Angle Sensor	Crankshaft Position Sensor[1]	CKP Sensor[1]
Crankshaft Position	Crankshaft Position[1]	CKP[1]
Crankshaft Position Sensor	Crankshaft Position Sensor[1]	CKP Sensor[1]
Crankshaft Speed	Engine Speed[1]	RPM[1]
Crankshaft Speed Sensor	Engine Speed Sensor[1]	RPM Sensor[1]
CTO (Continuous Trap Oxidizer)	Continuous Trap Oxidizer[1]	CTOX[1]
CTOX (Continuous Trap Oxidizer)	Continuous Trap Oxidizer[1]	CTOX[1]
CTP (Closed Throttle Position)	Closed Throttle Position[1]	CTP[1]
CTS (Coolant Temperature Sensor)	Engine Coolant Temperature Sensor[1]	ECT Sensor[1]
CTS (Coolant Temperature Switch)	Engine Coolant Temperature Switch[1]	ECT Switch[1]
Cylinder ID (Identification) Sensor	Camshaft Position Sensor[1]	CMP Sensor[1]
D-Jetronic	Multiport Fuel Injection[1]	MFI[1]
Data Link Connector	Data Link Connector[1]	DLC[1]
Detonation Sensor	Knock Sensor[1]	KS[1]
DFI (Direct Fuel Injection)	Direct Fuel Injection[1]	DFI[1]
DFI (Digital Fuel Injection)	Multiport Fuel Injection[1]	MFI[1]
DI (Direct Injection)	Direct Fuel Injection[1]	DFI[1]
DI (Distributor Ignition)	Distributor Ignition[1]	DI[1]
DI (Distributor Ignition) Capacitor	Distributor Ignition Capacitor[1]	DI Capacitor[1]
Diagnostic Test Mode	Diagnostic Test Mode[1]	DTM[1]
Diagnostic Trouble Code	Diagnostic Trouble Code[1]	DTC[1]
DID (Direct Injection - Diesel)	Direct Fuel Injection[1]	DFI[1]
Differential Pressure Feedback EGR (Exhaust Gas Recirculation) System	Differential Pressure Feedback Exhaust Gas Recirculation System[1]	Differential Pressure Feedback EGR System[1]
Digital EGR (Exhaust Gas Recirculation)	Exhaust Gas Recirculation[1]	EGR[1]
Direct Fuel Injection	Direct Fuel Injection[1]	DFI[1]
Direct Ignition System	Electronic Ignition System[1]	EI System[1]
DIS (Distributorless Ignition System)	Electronic Ignition System[1]	EI System[1]
DIS (Distributorless Ignition System) Module	Ignition Control Module[1]	ICM[1]

[1] Emission-Related Term

FIGURE 1—CROSS REFERENCE AND LOOK UP (CONTINUED)

SAE J1930 Revised JUN93

Existing Usage	Acceptable Usage	Acceptable Acronized Usage
Distance Sensor	Vehicle Speed Sensor[1]	VSS[1]
Distributor Ignition	Distributor Ignition[1]	DI[1]
Distributorless Ignition	Electronic Ignition[1]	EI[1]
DLC (Data Link Connector)	Data Link Connector[1]	DLC[1]
DLI (Distributorless Ignition)	Electronic Ignition[1]	EI[1]
DS (Detonation Sensor)	Knock Sensor[1]	KS[1]
DTC (Diagnostic Trouble Code)	Diagnostic Trouble Code[1]	DTC[1]
DTM (Diagnostic Test Mode)	Diagnostic Test Mode[1]	DTM[1]
Dual Bed	Three Way + Oxidation Catalytic Converter[1]	TWC+OC[1]
Duty Solenoid for Purge Valve	Evaporative Emission Canister Purge Valve[1]	EVAP Canister Purge Valve[1]
E2PROM (Electrically Erasable Programmable Read Only Memory)	Electrically Erasable Programmable Read Only Memory[1]	EEPROM[1]
Early Fuel Evaporation	Early Fuel Evaporation[1]	EFE[1]
EATX (Electronic Automatic Transmission/ Transaxle)	Automatic Transmission	A/T
	Automatic Transaxle	A/T
EC (Engine Control)	Engine Control[1]	EC[1]
ECA (Electronic Control Assembly)	Powertrain Control Module[1]	PCM[1]
ECL (Engine Coolant Level)	Engine Coolant Level	ECL
ECM (Engine Control Module)	Engine Control Module[1]	ECM[1]
ECT (Engine Coolant Temperature)	Engine Coolant Temperature[1]	ECT[1]
ECT (Engine Coolant Temperature) Sender	Engine Coolant Temperature Sensor[1]	ECT Sensor[1]
ECT (Engine Coolant Temperature) Sensor	Engine Coolant Temperature Sensor[1]	ECT Sensor[1]
ECT (Engine Coolant Temperature) Switch	Engine Coolant Temperature Switch[1]	ECT Switch[1]
ECU4 (Electronic Control Unit 4)	Powertrain Control Module[1]	PCM
EDF (Electro-Drive Fan) Control	Fan Control	FC
EDIS (Electronic Distributor Ignition System)	Distributor Ignition System[1]	DI System[1]
EDIS (Electronic Distributorless Ignition System)	Electronic Ignition System[1]	EI System[1]
EDIS (Electronic Distributor Ignition System) Module	Distributor Ignition Control Module[1]	Distributor ICM
EEC (Electronic Engine Control)	Engine Control[1]	EC[1]
EEC (Electronic Engine Control) Processor	Powertrain Control Module[1]	PCM[1]
EECS (Evaporative Emission Control System)	Evaporative Emission System[1]	EVAP System[1]
EEPROM (Electrically Erasable Programmable Read Only Memory)	Electrically Erasable Programmable Read Only Memory[1]	EEPROM[1]
EFE (Early Fuel Evaporation)	Early Fuel Evaporation[1]	EFE[1]
EFI (Electronic Fuel Injection)	Multiport Fuel Injection[1]	MFI[1]
EFI (Electronic Fuel Injection)	Throttle Body Fuel Injection[1]	TBI[1]
EGO (Exhaust Gas Oxygen) Sensor	Oxygen Sensor[1]	O2S[1]
EGOS (Exhaust Gas Oxygen Sensor)	Oxygen Sensor[1]	O2S[1]
EGR (Exhaust Gas Recirculation)	Exhaust Gas Recirculation[1]	EGR[1]
EGR (Exhaust Gas Recirculation) Diagnostic Valve	Exhaust Gas Recirculation Diagnostic Valve[1]	EGR Diagnostic Valve[1]
EGR (Exhaust Gas Recirculation) System	Exhaust Gas Recirculation System[1]	EGR System[1]
EGR (Exhaust Gas Recirculation) Thermal Vacuum Valve	Exhaust Gas Recirculation Thermal Vacuum Valve[1]	EGR TVV[1]
EGR (Exhaust Gas Recirculation) Valve	Exhaust Gas Recirculation Valve[1]	EGR Valve[1]
EGR TVV (Exhaust Gas Recirculation Thermal Vacuum Valve)	Exhaust Gas Recirculation Thermal Vacuum Valve[1]	EGR TVV[1]
EGRT (Exhaust Gas Recirculation Temperature)	Exhaust Gas Recirculation Temperature[1]	EGRT

[1] Emission-Related Term

FIGURE 1—CROSS REFERENCE AND LOOK UP (CONTINUED)

SAE J1930 Revised JUN93

Existing Usage	Acceptable Usage	Acceptable Acronized Usage
EGRT (Exhaust Gas Recirculation Temperature) Sensor	Exhaust Gas Recirculation Temperature Sensor[1]	EGRT Sensor[1]
EGRV (Exhaust Gas Recirculation Valve)	Exhaust Gas Recirculation Valve[1]	EGR Valve[1]
EGRVC (Exhaust Gas Recirculation Valve Control)	Exhaust Gas Recirculation Valve Control[1]	EGR Valve Control[1]
EGS (Exhaust Gas Sensor)	Oxygen Sensor[1]	O2S[1]
EI (Electronic Ignition) (With Distributor)	Distributor Ignition[1]	DI[1]
EI (Electronic Ignition) (Without Distributor)	Electronic Ignition[1]	EI[1]
Electrically Erasable Programmable Read Only Memory	Electrically Erasable Programmable Read Only Memory[1]	EEPROM[1]
Electronic Engine Control	Electronic Engine Control[1]	Electronic EC[1]
Electronic Ignition	Electronic Ignition[1]	EI[1]
Electronic Spark Advance	Ignition Control[1]	IC[1]
Electronic Spark Timing	Ignition Control[1]	IC[1]
EM (Engine Modification)	Engine Modification[1]	EM[1]
EMR (Engine Maintenance Reminder)	Service Reminder Indicator[1]	SRI[1]
Engine Control	Engine Control[1]	EC[1]
Engine Coolant Fan Control	Fan Control	FC
Engine Coolant Level	Engine Coolant Level	ECL
Engine Coolant Level Indicator	Engine Coolant Level Indicator	ECL Indicator
Engine Coolant Temperature	Engine Coolant Temperature[1]	ECT[1]
Engine Coolant Temperature Sender	Engine Coolant Temperature Sensor[1]	ECT Sensor[1]
Engine Coolant Temperature Sensor	Engine Coolant Temperature Sensor[1]	ECT Sensor[1]
Engine Coolant Temperature Switch	Engine Coolant Temperature Switch[1]	ECT Switch[1]
Engine Modification	Engine Modification[1]	EM[1]
Engine Speed	Engine Speed[1]	RPM[1]
EOS (Exhaust Oxygen Sensor)	Oxygen Sensor[1]	O2S[1]
EPROM (Erasable Programmable Read Only Memory)	Erasable Programmable Read Only Memory[1]	EPROM[1]
Erasable Programmable Read Only Memory	Erasable Programmable Read Only Memory[1]	EPROM[1]
ESA (Electronic Spark Advance)	Ignition Control[1]	IC[1]
ESAC (Electronic Spark Advance Control)	Distributor Ignition[1]	DI[1]
EST (Electronic Spark Timing)	Ignition Control[1]	IC[1]
EVAP CANP	Evaporative Emission Canister Purge[1]	EVAP Canister Purge[1]
EVAP (Evaporative Emission)	Evaporative Emission[1]	EVAP[1]
EVAP (Evaporative Emission) Canister	Evaporative Emission Canister[1]	EVAP Canister[1]
EVAP (Evaporative Emission) Purge Valve	Evaporative Emission Canister Purge Valve[1]	EVAP Canister Purge Valve[1]
Evaporative Emission	Evaporative Emission[1]	EVAP[1]
Evaporative Emission Canister	Evaporative Emission Canister[1]	EVAP Canister[1]
EVP (Exhaust Gas Recirculation Valve Position) Sensor	Exhaust Gas Recirculation Valve Position Sensor[1]	EGR Valve Position Sensor[1]
EVR (Exhaust Gas Recirculation Vacuum Regulator) Solenoid	Exhaust Gas Recirculation Vacuum Regulator Solenoid[1]	EGR Vacuum Regulator Solenoid[1]
EVRV (Exhaust Gas Recirculation Vacuum Regulator Valve)	Exhaust Gas Recirculation Vacuum Regulator Valve[1]	EGR Vacuum Regulator Valve[1]
Exhaust Gas Recirculation	Exhaust Gas Recirculation[1]	EGR[1]
Exhaust Gas Recirculation Temperature	Exhaust Gas Recirculation Temperature[1]	EGRT[1]
Exhaust Gas Recirculation Temperature Sensor	Exhaust Gas Recirculation Temperature Sensor[1]	EGRT Sensor[1]
Exhaust Gas Recirculation Valve	Exhaust Gas Recirculation Valve[1]	EGR Valve[1]

[1] Emission-Related Term

FIGURE 1—CROSS REFERENCE AND LOOK UP (CONTINUED)

SAE J1930 Revised JUN93

Existing Usage	Acceptable Usage	Acceptable Acronized Usage
Fan Control	Fan Control	FC
Fan Control Module	Fan Control Module	FC Module
Fan Control Relay	Fan Control Relay	FC Relay
Fan Motor Control Relay	Fan Control Relay	FC Relay
Fast Idle Thermo Valve	Idle Air Control Thermal Valve[1]	IAC Thermal Valve[1]
FBC (Feed Back Carburetor)	Carburetor[1]	CARB[1]
FBC (Feed Back Control)	Mixture Control[1]	MC[1]
FC (Fan Control)	Fan Control	FC
FC (Fan Control) Relay	Fan Control Relay	FC Relay
FEEPROM (Flash Electrically Erasable Programmable Read Only Memory)	Flash Electrically Erasable Programmable Read Only Memory[1]	FEEPROM[1]
FEPROM (Flash Erasable Programmable Read Only Memory)	Flash Erasable Programmable Read Only Memory[1]	FEPROM[1]
FF (Flexible Fuel)	Flexible Fuel[1]	FF[1]
FI (Fuel Injection)	Central Multiport Fuel Injection[1]	Central MFI[1]
FI (Fuel Injection)	Continuous Fuel Injection[1]	CFI[1]
FI (Fuel Injection)	Direct Fuel Injection[1]	DFI[1]
FI (Fuel Injection)	Indirect Fuel Injection[1]	IFI[1]
FI (Fuel Injection)	Multiport Fuel Injection[1]	MFI[1]
FI (Fuel Injection)	Sequential Multiport Fuel Injection[1]	SFI[1]
FI (Fuel Injection)	Throttle Body Fuel Injection[1]	TBI[1]
Flash EEPROM (Electrically Erasable Programmable Read Only Memory)	Flash Electrically Erasable Programmable Read Only Memory[1]	FEEPROM[1]
Flash EPROM (Erasable Programmable Read Only Memory)	Flash Erasable Programmable Read Only Memory[1]	FEPROM[1]
Flexible Fuel	Flexible Fuel[1]	FF[1]
Flexible Fuel Sensor	Flexible Fuel Sensor[1]	FF Sensor[1]
Fourth Gear	Fourth Gear	4GR
FP (Fuel Pump)	Fuel Pump	FP
FP (Fuel Pump) Module	Fuel Pump Module	FP Module
FT (Fuel Trim)	Fuel Trim[1]	FT[1]
Fuel Charging Station	Throttle Body[1]	TB[1]
Fuel Concentration Sensor	Flexible Fuel Sensor[1]	FF Sensor[1]
Fuel Injection	Central Multiport Fuel Injection[1]	Central MFI[1]
Fuel Injection	Continuous Fuel Injection[1]	CFI[1]
Fuel Injection	Direct Fuel Injection[1]	DFI[1]
Fuel Injection	Indirect Fuel Injection[1]	IFI[1]
Fuel Injection	Multiport Fuel Injection[1]	MFI[1]
Fuel Injection	Sequential Multiport Fuel Injection[1]	SFI[1]
Fuel Injection	Throttle Body Fuel Injection[1]	TBI[1]
Fuel Level Sensor	Fuel Level Sensor	Fuel Level Sensor
Fuel Module	Fuel Pump Module	FP Module
Fuel Pressure	Fuel Pressure[1]	Fuel Pressure[1]
Fuel Pressure Regulator	Fuel Pressure Regulator[1]	Fuel Pressure Regulator[1]
Fuel Pump	Fuel Pump	FP
Fuel Pump Relay	Fuel Pump Relay	FP Relay
Fuel Quality Sensor	Flexible Fuel Sensor[1]	FF Sensor[1]
Fuel Regulator	Fuel Pressure Regulator[1]	Fuel Pressure Regulator[1]
Fuel Sender	Fuel Pump Module	FP Module
Fuel Sensor	Fuel Level Sensor	Fuel Level Sensor
Fuel Tank Unit	Fuel Pump Module	FP Module

[1] Emission-Related Term

FIGURE 1—CROSS REFERENCE AND LOOK UP (CONTINUED)

SAE J1930 Revised JUN93

Existing Usage	Acceptable Usage	Acceptable Acronized Usage
Fuel Trim	Fuel Trim[1]	FT[1]
Full Throttle	Wide Open Throttle[1]	WOT[1]
GCM (Governor Control Module)	Governor Control Module	GCM
GEM (Governor Electronic Module)	Governor Control Module	GCM
GEN (Generator)	Generator	GEN
Generator	Generator	GEN
Governor	Governor	Governor
Governor Control Module	Governor Control Module	GCM
Governor Electronic Module	Governor Control Module	GCM
GND (Ground)	Ground	GND
GRD (Ground)	Ground	GND
Ground	Ground	GND
Heated Oxygen Sensor	Heated Oxygen Sensor[1]	HO2S[1]
HEDF (High Electro-Drive Fan) Control	Fan Control	FC
HEGO (Heated Exhaust Gas Oxygen) Sensor	Heated Oxygen Sensor[1]	HO2S[1]
HEI (High Energy Ignition)	Distributor Ignition[1]	DI[1]
High Speed FC (Fan Control) Switch	High Speed Fan Control Switch	High Speed FC Switch
HO2S (Heated Oxygen Sensor)	Heated Oxygen Sensor[1]	HO2S[1]
HOS (Heated Oxygen Sensor)	Heated Oxygen Sensor[1]	HO2S[1]
Hot Wire Anemometer	Mass Air Flow Sensor[1]	MAF Sensor[1]
IA (Intake Air)	Intake Air	IA
IA (Intake Air) Duct	Intake Air Duct	IA Duct
IAC (Idle Air Control)	Idle Air Control[1]	IAC[1]
IAC (Idle Air Control) Thermal Valve	Idle Air Control Thermal Valve[1]	IAC Thermal Valve[1]
IAC (Idle Air Control) Valve	Idle Air Control Valve[1]	IAC Valve[1]
IACV (Idle Air Control Valve)	Idle Air Control Valve[1]	IAC Valve[1]
IAT (Intake Air Temperature)	Intake Air Temperature[1]	IAT[1]
IAT (Intake Air Temperature) Sensor	Intake Air Temperature Sensor[1]	IAT Sensor[1]
IATS (Intake Air Temperature Sensor)	Intake Air Temperature Sensor[1]	IAT Sensor[1]
IC (Ignition Control)	Ignition Control[1]	IC[1]
ICM (Ignition Control Module)	Ignition Control Module[1]	ICM[1]
IDFI (Indirect Fuel Injection)	Indirect Fuel Injection[1]	IFI[1]
IDI (Integrated Direct Ignition)	Electronic Ignition[1]	EI[1]
IDI (Indirect Diesel Injection)	Indirect Fuel Injection[1]	IFI[1]
Idle Air Bypass Control	Idle Air Control[1]	IAC[1]
Idle Air Control	Idle Air Control[1]	IAC[1]
Idle Air Control Valve	Idle Air Control Valve[1]	IAC Valve[1]
Idle Speed Control	Idle Air Control[1]	IAC[1]
Idle Speed Control	Idle Speed Control[1]	ISC[1]
Idle Speed Control Actuator	Idle Speed Control Actuator[1]	ISC Actuator[1]
IFI (Indirect Fuel Injection)	Indirect Fuel Injection[1]	IFI[1]
IFS (Inertia Fuel Shutoff)	Inertia Fuel Shutoff	IFS
Ignition Control	Ignition Control[1]	IC[1]
Ignition Control Module	Ignition Control Module[1]	ICM[1]
In Tank Module	Fuel Pump Module	FP Module
Indirect Fuel Injection	Indirect Fuel Injection[1]	IFI[1]
Inertia Fuel Shutoff	Inertia Fuel Shutoff	IFS
Inertia Fuel - Shutoff Switch	Inertia Fuel Shutoff Switch	IFS Switch
Inertia Switch	Inertia Fuel Shutoff Switch	IFS Switch
INT (Integrator)	Short Term Fuel Trim[1]	Short Term FT[1]
Intake Air	Intake Air	IA

[1] Emission-Related Term

FIGURE 1—CROSS REFERENCE AND LOOK UP (CONTINUED)

SAE J1930 Revised JUN93

Existing Usage	Acceptable Usage	Acceptable Acronized Usage
Intake Air Duct	Intake Air Duct	IA Duct
Intake Air Temperature	Intake Air Temperature [1]	IAT [1]
Intake Air Temperature Sensor	Intake Air Temperature Sensor [1]	IAT Sensor [1]
Intake Manifold Absolute Pressure Sensor	Manifold Absolute Pressure Sensor [1]	MAP Sensor [1]
Integrated Relay Module	Relay Module	RM
Integrator	Short Term Fuel Trim [1]	Short Term FT [1]
Inter Cooler	Charge Air Cooler [1]	CAC [1]
ISC (Idle Speed Control)	Idle Air Control [1]	IAC [1]
ISC (Idle Speed Control)	Idle Speed Control [1]	ISC [1]
ISC (Idle Speed Control) Actuator	Idle Speed Control Actuator [1]	ISC Actuator [1]
ISC BPA (Idle Speed Control By Pass Air)	Idle Air Control [1]	IAC [1]
ISC (Idle Speed Control) Solenoid Vacuum Valve	Idle Speed Control Solenoid Vacuum Valve [1]	ISC Solenoid Vacuum Valve [1]
K-Jetronic	Continuous Fuel Injection [1]	CFI [1]
KAM (Keep Alive Memory)	NonVolatile Random Access Memory [1]	NVRAM [1]
KAM (Keep Alive Memory)	Keep Alive Random Access Memory [1]	Keep Alive RAM [1]
KE-Jetronic	Continuous Fuel Injection [1]	CFI [1]
KE-Motronic	Continuous Fuel Injection [1]	CFI [1]
Knock Sensor	Knock Sensor [1]	KS [1]
KS (Knock Sensor)	Knock Sensor [1]	KS [1]
L-Jetronic	Multiport Fuel Injection [1]	MFI [1]
Lambda	Oxygen Sensor [1]	O2S [1]
LH-Jetronic	Multiport Fuel Injection [1]	MFI [1]
Light Off Catalyst	Warm Up Three Way Catalytic Converter [1]	WU-TWC [1]
Light Off Catalyst	Warm Up Oxidation Catalytic Converter [1]	WU-OC [1]
Lock Up Relay	Torque Converter Clutch Relay [1]	TCC Relay [1]
Long Term FT (Fuel Trim)	Long Term Fuel Trim [1]	Long Term FT [1]
Low Speed FC (Fan Control) Switch	Low Speed Fan Control Switch	Low Speed FC Switch
LUS (Lock Up Solenoid) Valve	Torque Converter Clutch Solenoid Valve [1]	TCC Solenoid Valve [1]
M/C (Mixture Control)	Mixture Control [1]	MC [1]
MAF (Mass Air Flow)	Mass Air Flow [1]	MAF [1]
MAF (Mass Air Flow) Sensor	Mass Air Flow Sensor [1]	MAF Sensor [1]
Malfunction Indicator Lamp	Malfunction Indicator Lamp [1]	MIL [1]
Manifold Absolute Pressure	Manifold Absolute Pressure [1]	MAP [1]
Manifold Absolute Pressure Sensor	Manifold Absolute Pressure Sensor	MAP Sensor [1]
Manifold Differential Pressure	Manifold Differential Pressure [1]	MDP [1]
Manifold Surface Temperature	Manifold Surface Temperature [1]	MST [1]
Manifold Vacuum Zone	Manifold Vacuum Zone [1]	MVZ [1]
Manual Lever Position Sensor	Transmission Range Sensor [1]	TR Sensor [1]
MAP (Manifold Absolute Pressure)	Manifold Absolute Pressure [1]	MAP [1]
MAP (Manifold Absolute Pressure) Sensor	Manifold Absolute Pressure Sensor [1]	MAP Sensor [1]
MAPS (Manifold Absolute Pressure Sensor)	Manifold Absolute Pressure Sensor [1]	MAP Sensor [1]
Mass Air Flow	Mass Air Flow [1]	MAF [1]
Mass Air Flow Sensor	Mass Air Flow Sensor [1]	MAF Sensor [1]
MAT (Manifold Air Temperature)	Intake Air Temperature [1]	IAT [1]
MATS (Manifold Air Temperature Sensor)	Intake Air Temperature Sensor [1]	IAT Sensor [1]
MC (Mixture Control)	Mixture Control [1]	MC [1]
MCS (Mixture Control Solenoid)	Mixture Control Solenoid [1]	MC Solenoid [1]
MCU (Microprocessor Control Unit)	Powertrain Control Module [1]	PCM [1]
MDP (Manifold Differential Pressure)	Manifold Differential Pressure [1]	MDP [1]
MFI (Multiport Fuel Injection)	Multiport Fuel Injection [1]	MFI [1]

Recommended Terms and Recommended Acronyms See Figure 2
[1] Emission-Related Term

FIGURE 1—CROSS REFERENCE AND LOOK UP (CONTINUED)

SAE J1930 Revised JUN93

Existing Usage	Acceptable Usage	Acceptable Acronized Usage
MIL (Malfunction Indicator Lamp)	Malfunction Indicator Lamp[1]	MIL[1]
Mixture Control	Mixture Control[1]	MC[1]
Modes	Diagnostic Test Mode[1]	DTM[1]
Monotronic	Throttle Body Fuel Injection[1]	TBI[1]
Motronic	Multiport Fuel Injection[1]	MFI[1]
MPI (Multipoint Injection)	Multiport Fuel Injection[1]	MFI[1]
MPI (Multiport Injection)	Multiport Fuel Injection[1]	MFI[1]
MRPS (Manual Range Position Switch)	Transmission Range Switch	TR Switch
MST (Manifold Surface Temperature)	Manifold Surface Temperature[1]	MST[1]
Multiport Fuel Injection	Multiport Fuel Injection[1]	MFI[1]
MVZ (Manifold Vacuum Zone)	Manifold Vacuum Zone[1]	MVZ[1]
NDS (Neutral Drive Switch)	Park/Neutral Position Switch[1]	PNP Switch[1]
Neutral Safety Switch	Park/Neutral Position Switch[1]	PNP Switch[1]
NGS (Neutral Gear Switch)	Park/Neutral Position Switch[1]	PNP Switch[1]
Nonvolatile Random Access Memory	Nonvolatile Random Access Memory[1]	NVRAM[1]
NPS (Neutral Position Switch)	Park/Neutral Position Switch[1]	PNP Switch[1]
NVM (Nonvolatile Memory)	Nonvolatile Random Access Memory[1]	NVRAM[1]
NVRAM (Nonvolatile Random Access Memory)	Nonvolatile Random Access Memory[1]	NVRAM[1]
O2 (Oxygen) Sensor	Oxygen Sensor[1]	O2S[1]
O2S (Oxygen Sensor)	Oxygen Sensor[1]	O2S[1]
OBD (On Board Diagnostic)	On Board Diagnostic[1]	OBD[1]
OC (Oxidation Catalyst)	Oxidation Catalytic Converter[1]	OC[1]
Oil Pressure Sender	Oil Pressure Sensor	Oil Pressure Sensor
Oil Pressure Sensor	Oil Pressure Sensor	Oil Pressure Sensor
Oil Pressure Switch	Oil Pressure Switch	Oil Pressure Switch
OL (Open Loop)	Open Loop[1]	OL[1]
On Board Diagnostic	On Board Diagnostic[1]	OBD[1]
Open Loop	Open Loop[1]	OL[1]
OS (Oxygen Sensor)	Oxygen Sensor[1]	O2S[1]
Oxidation Catalytic Converter	Oxidation Catalytic Converter[1]	OC[1]
OXS (Oxygen Sensor) Indicator	Service Reminder Indicator[1]	SRI[1]
Oxygen Sensor	Oxygen Sensor[1]	O2S[1]
P/N (Park/Neutral)	Park/Neutral Position[1]	PNP[1]
P/S (Power Steering) Pressure Switch	Power Steering Pressure Switch	PSP Switch
P- (Pressure) Sensor	Manifold Absolute Pressure Sensor[1]	MAP Sensor[1]
PAIR (Pulsed Secondary Air Injection)	Pulsed Secondary Air Injection[1]	PAIR[1]
Park/Neutral Position	Park/Neutral Position[1]	PNP[1]
PCM (Powertrain Control Module)	Powertrain Control Module[1]	PCM[1]
PCV (Positive Crankcase Ventilation)	Positive Crankcase Ventilation[1]	PCV[1]
PCV (Positive Crankcase Ventilation) Valve	Positive Crankcase Ventilation Valve[1]	PCV Valve[1]
Percent Alcohol Sensor	Flexible Fuel Sensor[1]	FF Sensor[1]
Periodic Trap Oxidizer	Periodic Trap Oxidizer[1]	PTOX[1]
PFE (Pressure Feedback Exhaust Gas Recirculation) Sensor	Feedback Pressure Exhaust Gas Recirculation Sensor[1]	Feedback Pressure EGR Sensor[1]
PFI (Port Fuel Injection)	Multiport Fuel Injection[1]	MFI[1]
PG (Pulse Generator)	Vehicle Speed Sensor[1]	VSS[1]
PGM-FI (Programmed Fuel Injection)	Multiport Fuel Injection[1]	MFI[1]
PIP (Position Indicator Pulse)	Crankshaft Position[1]	CKP[1]
PNP (Park/Neutral Position)	Park/Neutral Position[1]	PNP[1]
Positive Crankcase Ventilation	Positive Crankcase Ventilation[1]	PCV[1]
Positive Crankcase Ventilation Valve	Positive Crankcase Ventilation Valve[1]	PCV Valve[1]

[1] Emission-Related Term

FIGURE 1—CROSS REFERENCE AND LOOK UP (CONTINUED)

SAE J1930 Revised JUN93

Existing Usage	Acceptable Usage	Acceptable Acronized Usage
Power Steering Pressure	Power Steering Pressure	PSP
Power Steering Pressure Switch	Power Steering Pressure Switch	PSP Switch
Powertrain Control Module	Powertrain Control Module[1]	PCM[1]
Pressure Feedback EGR (Exhaust Gas Recirculation)	Feedback Pressure Exhaust Gas Recirculation[1]	Feedback Pressure EGR[1]
Pressure Sensor	Manifold Absolute Pressure Sensor[1]	MAP Sensor[1]
Pressure Transducer EGR (Exhaust Gas Recirculation) System	Pressure Transducer Exhaust Gas Recirculation System[1]	Pressure Transducer EGR System[1]
PRNDL (Park, Reverse, Neutral, Drive, Low)	Transmission Range	TR
Programmable Read Only Memory	Programmable Read Only Memory[1]	PROM[1]
PROM (Programmable Read Only Memory)	Programmable Read Only Memory[1]	PROM[1]
PSP (Power Steering Pressure)	Power Steering Pressure	PSP
PSP (Power Steering Pressure) Switch	Power Steering Pressure Switch	PSP Switch
PSPS (Power Steering Pressure Switch)	Power Steering Pressure Switch	PSP Switch
PTOX (Periodic Trap Oxidizer)	Periodic Trap Oxidizer[1]	PTOX[1]
Pulsair	Pulsed Secondary Air Injection[1]	PAIR[1]
Pulsed Secondary Air Injection	Pulsed Secondary Air Injection[1]	PAIR[1]
Radiator Fan Control	Fan Control	FC
Radiator Fan Relay	Fan Control Relay	FC Relay
RAM (Random Access Memory)	Random Access Memory[1]	RAM[1]
Random Access Memory	Random Access Memory[1]	RAM[1]
Read Only Memory	Read Only Memory[1]	ROM[1]
Recirculated Exhaust Gas Temperature Sensor	Exhaust Gas Recirculation Temperature Sensor[1]	EGRT Sensor[1]
Reed Valve	Pulsed Secondary Air Injection Valve[1]	PAIR Valve[1]
REGTS (Recirculated Exhaust Gas Temperature Sensor)	Exhaust Gas Recirculation Temperature Sensor[1]	EGRT Sensor[1]
Relay Module	Relay Module	RM
Remote Mount TFI (Thick Film Ignition)	Distributor Ignition[1]	DI[1]
Revolutions per Minute	Engine Speed[1]	RPM[1]
RM (Relay Module)	Relay Module	RM
ROM (Read Only Memory)	Read Only Memory[1]	ROM[1]
RPM (Revolutions per Minute)	Engine Speed[1]	RPM[1]
SABV (Secondary Air Bypass Valve)	Secondary Air Injection Bypass Valve[1]	AIR Bypass Valve[1]
SACV (Secondary Air Check Valve)	Secondary Air Injection Control Valve[1]	AIR Control Valve[1]
SASV (Secondary Air Switching Valve)	Secondary Air Injection Switching Valve[1]	AIR Switching Valve[1]
SBEC (Single Board Engine Control)	Powertrain Control Module[1]	PCM[1]
SBS (Supercharger Bypass Solenoid)	Supercharger Bypass Solenoid[1]	SCB Solenoid[1]
SC (Supercharger)	Supercharger[1]	SC[1]
Scan Tool	Scan Tool[1]	ST[1]
SCB (Supercharger Bypass)	Supercharger Bypass[1]	SCB[1]
Secondary Air Bypass Valve	Secondary Air Injection Bypass Valve[1]	AIR Bypass Valve[1]
Secondary Air Check Valve	Secondary Air Injection Check Valve[1]	AIR Check Valve[1]
Secondary Air Injection	Secondary Air Injection[1]	AIR[1]
Secondary Air Injection Bypass	Secondary Air Injection Bypass[1]	AIR Bypass[1]
Secondary Air Injection Diverter	Secondary Air Injection Diverter[1]	AIR Diverter[1]
Secondary Air Switching Valve	Secondary Air Injection Switching Valve[1]	AIR Switching Valve[1]
SEFI (Sequential Electronic Fuel Injection)	Sequential Multiport Fuel Injection[1]	SFI[1]
Self Test	On Board Diagnostic[1]	OBD[1]
Self Test Codes	Diagnostic Trouble Code[1]	DTC[1]
Self Test Connector	Data Link Connector[1]	DLC[1]

[1] Emission-Related Term

FIGURE 1—CROSS REFERENCE AND LOOK UP (CONTINUED)

SAE J1930 Revised JUN93

Existing Usage	Acceptable Usage	Acceptable Acronized Usage
Sequential Multiport Fuel Injection	Sequential Multiport Fuel Injection[1]	SFI[1]
Service Engine Soon	Service Reminder Indicator[1]	SRI[1]
Service Engine Soon	Malfunction Indicator Lamp[1]	MIL[1]
Service Reminder Indicator	Service Reminder Indicator[1]	SRI[1]
SFI (Sequential Fuel Injection)	Sequential Multiport Fuel Injection[1]	SFI[1]
Short Term FT (Fuel Trim)	Short Term Fuel Trim[1]	Short Term FT[1]
SLP (Selection Lever Position)	Transmission Range	TR
SMEC (Single Module Engine Control)	Powertrain Control Module[1]	PCM[1]
Smoke Puff Limiter	Smoke Puff Limiter[1]	SPL[1]
SPI (Single Point Injection)	Throttle Body Fuel Injection[1]	TBI[1]
SPL (Smoke Puff Limiter)	Smoke Puff Limiter[1]	SPL[1]
SRI (Service Reminder Indicator)	Service Reminder Indicator[1]	SRI[1]
SRT (System Readiness Test)	System Readiness Test[1]	SRT[1]
ST (Scan Tool)	Scan Tool[1]	ST[1]
Supercharger	Supercharger[1]	SC[1]
Supercharger Bypass	Supercharger Bypass[1]	SCB[1]
Sync Pickup	Camshaft Position[1]	CMP[1]
System Readiness Test	System Readiness Test[1]	SRT[1]
TAB (Thermactor Air Bypass)	Secondary Air Injection Bypass[1]	AIR Bypass[1]
TAD (Thermactor Air Diverter)	Secondary Air Injection Diverter[1]	AIR Diverter[1]
TB (Throttle Body)	Throttle Body[1]	TB[1]
TBI (Throttle Body Fuel Injection)	Throttle Body Fuel Injection[1]	TBI[1]
TBT (Throttle Body Temperature)	Intake Air Temperature[1]	IAT[1]
TC (Turbocharger)	Turbocharger[1]	TC[1]
TCC (Torque Converter Clutch)	Torque Converter Clutch[1]	TCC[1]
TCC (Torque Converter Clutch) Relay	Torque Converter Clutch Relay[1]	TCC Relay[1]
TCM (Transmission Control Module)	Transmission Control Module	TCM
TFI (Thick Film Ignition)	Distributor Ignition[1]	DI[1]
TFI (Thick Film Ignition) Module	Ignition Control Module[1]	ICM[1]
Thermac	Secondary Air Injection[1]	AIR[1]
Thermac Air Cleaner	Air Cleaner[1]	ACL[1]
Thermactor	Secondary Air Injection[1]	AIR[1]
Thermactor Air Bypass	Secondary Air Injection Bypass[1]	AIR Bypass[1]
Thermactor Air Diverter	Secondary Air Injection Diverter[1]	AIR Diverter[1]
Thermactor II	Pulsed Secondary Air Injection[1]	PAIR[1]
Thermal Vacuum Switch	Thermal Vacuum Valve[1]	TVV[1]
Thermal Vacuum Valve	Thermal Vacuum Valve[1]	TVV[1]
Third Gear	Third Gear	3GR
Three Way + Oxidation Catalytic Converter	Three Way + Oxidation Catalytic Converter[1]	TWC+OC[1]
Three Way Catalytic Converter	Three Way Catalytic Converter[1]	TWC[1]
Throttle Body	Throttle Body[1]	TB[1]
Throttle Body Fuel Injection	Throttle Body Fuel Injection[1]	TBI[1]
Throttle Opener	Idle Speed Control[1]	ISC[1]
Throttle Opener Vacuum Switching Valve	Idle Speed Control Solenoid Vacuum Valve[1]	ISC Solenoid Vacuum Valve[1]
Throttle Opener VSV (Vacuum Switching Valve)	Idle Speed Control Solenoid Vacuum Valve[1]	ISC Solenoid Vacuum Valve[1]
Throttle Position	Throttle Position[1]	TP
Throttle Position Sensor	Throttle Position Sensor[1]	TP Sensor[1]
Throttle Position Switch	Throttle Position Switch[1]	TP Switch[1]
Throttle Potentiometer	Throttle Position Sensor[1]	TP Sensor[1]
TOC (Trap Oxidizer - Continuous)	Continuous Trap Oxidizer[1]	CTOX[1]
TOP (Trap Oxidizer - Periodic)	Periodic Trap Oxidizer[1]	PTOX[1]

[1] Emission-Related Term

FIGURE 1—CROSS REFERENCE AND LOOK UP (CONTINUED)

SAE J1930 Revised JUN93

Existing Usage	Acceptable Usage	Acceptable Acronized Usage
Torque Converter Clutch	Torque Converter Clutch[1]	TCC[1]
Torque Converter Clutch Relay	Torque Converter Clutch Relay[1]	TCC Relay[1]
TP (Throttle Position)	Throttle Position[1]	TP[1]
TP (Throttle Position) Sensor	Throttle Position Sensor[1]	TP Sensor[1]
TP (Throttle Position) Switch	Throttle Position Switch[1]	TP Switch[1]
TPI (Tuned Port Injection)	Multiport Fuel Injection[1]	MFI[1]
TPS (Throttle Position Sensor)	Throttle Position Sensor[1]	TP Sensor[1]
TPS (Throttle Position Switch)	Throttle Position Switch[1]	TP Switch[1]
TR (Transmission Range)	Transmission Range	TR
Transmission Control Module	Transmission Control Module	TCM
Transmission Position Switch	Transmission Range Switch	TR Switch
Transmission Range Selection	Transmission Range	TR
TRS (Transmission Range Selection)	Transmission Range	TR
TRSS (Transmission Range Selection Switch)	Transmission Range Switch	TR Switch
Tuned Port Injection	Multiport Fuel Injection[1]	MFI[1]
Turbo (Turbocharger)	Turbocharger[1]	TC[1]
Turbocharger	Turbocharger[1]	TC[1]
TVS (Thermal Vacuum Switch)	Thermal Vacuum Valve[1]	TVV[1]
TVV (Thermal Vacuum Valve)	Thermal Vacuum Valve[1]	TVV[1]
TWC (Three Way Catalytic Converter)	Three Way Catalytic Converter[1]	TWC[1]
TWC + OC (Three Way + Oxidation Catalytic Converter)	Three Way + Oxidation Catalytic Converter[1]	TWC+OC[1]
VAC (Vacuum) Sensor	Manifold Differential Pressure Sensor[1]	MDP Sensor
Vacuum Switches	Manifold Vacuum Zone Switch	MVZ Switch[1]
VAF (Volume Air Flow)	Volume Air Flow[1]	VAF[1]
Vane Air Flow	Volume Air Flow[1]	VAF[1]
Variable Fuel Sensor	Flexible Fuel Sensor	FF Sensor[1]
VAT (Vane Air Temperature)	Intake Air Temperature[1]	IAT[1]
VCC (Viscous Converter Clutch)	Torque Converter Clutch[1]	TCC[1]
Vehicle Speed Sensor	Vehicle Speed Sensor[1]	VSS[1]
VIP (Vehicle In Process) Connector	Data Link Connector[1]	DLC[1]
Viscous Converter Clutch	Torque Converter Clutch[1]	TCC[1]
Voltage Regulator	Voltage Regulator	VR
Volume Air Flow	Volume Air Flow[1]	VAF[1]
VR (Voltage Regulator)	Voltage Regulator	VR
VSS (Vehicle Speed Sensor)	Vehicle Speed Sensor[1]	VSS[1]
VSV (Vacuum Solenoid Valve) (Canister)	Evaporative Emission Canister Purge Valve[1]	EVAP Canister Purge Valve[1]
VSV (Vacuum Solenoid Valve) (EVAP)	Evaporative Emission Canister Purge Valve[1]	EVAP Canister Purge Valve[1]
VSV (Vacuum Solenoid Valve) (Throttle)	Idle Speed Control Solenoid Vacuum Valve[1]	ISC Solenoid Vacuum Valve[1]
Warm Up Oxidation Catalytic Converter	Warm Up Oxidation Catalytic Converter[1]	WU-OC[1]
Warm Up Three Way Catalytic Converter	Warm Up Three Way Catalytic Converter[1]	WU-OC[1]
Wide Open Throttle	Wide Open Throttle[1]	WOT[1]
WOT (Wide Open Throttle)	Wide Open Throttle[1]	WOT[1]
WOTS (Wide Open Throttle Switch)	Wide Open Throttle Switch[1]	WOT Switch[1]
WU-OC (Warm Up Oxidation Catalytic Converter)	Warm Up Oxidation Catalytic Converter[1]	WU-OC[1]
WU-TWC (Warm Up Three Way Catalytic Converter)	Warm Up Three Way Catalytic Converter[1]	WU-TWC[1]

[1] Emission-Related Term

FIGURE 1—CROSS REFERENCE AND LOOK UP (CONTINUED)

GLOSSARY

Note: Terms are highlighted in color, followed by Spanish translation in bold.

Abrasion Wearing or rubbing away of a part.

Abrasión El desgaste o consumo por rozamiento de una parte.

Abrasive cleaning Cleaning that relies on physical abrasion, such as wire brushing and glass bead blasting.

Limpieza abrasiva La limpieza que cuenta con un abrasión físico, tal como el limpiar con cepillo de alambre o con un chorro de perlitas de vidrio.

Accumulator A device that cushions the motion of a clutch and servo action in an automatic transmission; a component used to store or hold liquid refrigerant in an air-conditioning system.

Acumulador Un dispositivo que suaviza los movimientos de un embrague y la acción del servo de una transmisión automática; un componente que se usa para guardar o reservar el refrigerante líquido de un sistema de un acondicionador del aire.

Acidity In lubrication, acidity denotes the presence of acid-type chemicals, which are identified by the acid number. Acidity within oil causes corrosion, sludges, and varnish to increase.

Acidez En la lubricación, la acidez se refiere a la presencia de los químicos de tipo ácido, que se identifican por un número de ácido. La acidez en los aceites causa aumentos en la corrosión, la grasa y el barnís.

Ackerman principle The geometric principle used to provide toe-out on turns. The ends of the steering arms are angled so the inside wheel turns more than the outside wheel when a car is making a turn.

El principio Ackerman El principio geométrico que provee la divergencia en las vueltas. Las extremidades de los brazos de dirección estan en un ángulo para que el interior de la rueda gira más que el exterior de la rueda cuando un coche da la vuelta.

Active restraint A manual seat and shoulder belt assembly that must be activated by an occupant.

Sujeción activo Una asamblea manual de cinturón de seguridad que debe ser implementado por el ocupante.

Actuator A control device that delivers mechanical action in response to an electrical signal.

Solenoide Un dispositivo de control que entrega una acción mecánica como respuesta a un señal eléctrico.

A/D converter An electronic device that changes analog signals to digital signals.

Convertidor de A/D Un dispositivo electrónico que cambia los señales análogos a los señales digitales.

Adaptive learning An operational mode of a control computer that adjusts operation parameters according to various conditions.

Operación de adaptación Un modo de operación de una computadora de control que ajusta los parámetros de operación según varias condiciones.

Additive In automotive oils, a material added to the oil to give it certain properties; for example, a material added to engine oil to lessen its tendency to congeal or thicken at low temperatures.

Aditamento En los aceites automotrices, una materia añadida al aceite para que ésta tenga ciertas propiedades; por ejemplo, una materia agregada al aceite de motor para disminuir su tendencia a solidificarse o ponerse espeso en las temperaturas bajas.

Adhesion The property of lubricating oil that causes it to stick or cling to a bearing surface.

Adhesión La propriedad del aceite de lubricación que causa que se pega o se adhiera a una superficie portante.

Adhesive Substance that causes adjoining bodies to stick together.

Adhesivo Una substancia que causa que dos cuerpos contiguos se pegan.

Aeration The process of mixing air with a liquid. Aeration occurs in a shock absorber from rapid fluctuation in movement.

Aeración El proceso de mezclar el aire con un líquido. La aeración ocurre en un amortiguador de barquinazos por causa de una variación rápida en el movimiento.

Aerobic Typically refers to a sealant or adhesive that dries in the presence of oxygen.

Aeróbico Típicamente se refiere a un sellante o un adhesivo que se seca cuando esta presente el oxígeno.

Air ducts Tubes, channels, or other tubular structures used to carry air to a specific location.

Conductos de aire Los tubos, las canalizaciones, u otras estructuras tubulares que sirven para traer el aire a una posición específica.

Air gap The space between spark plug electrodes, motor and generator armatures, and field shoes.

Entrehierro El espacio entre los electrodos de las bujías, el enducido del motor y del generador, y las piezas inductoras.

Air injection The introduction of fresh air into an exhaust manifold for additional burning and to provide oxygen to a catalytic converter.

Inyección por aire La introducción del aire fresco al múltiple de escape para mejor combustión y para proveer el oxígeno al convertidor catalítico.

Air lock   A bubble of air trapped in a fluid circuit that interferes with normal circulation of the fluid.

Bolsa de vapor   Una burbúja del aire atrapado en un circuito líquido que es un obstáculo en la circulación normal del líquido.

Air pump   A device to produce a flow of air at higher-than atmospheric pressure. Normally referred to as a thermactor air supply pump.

Bomba del aire   Un dispositivo que produce un corriente de aire con una presión más alta que la del atmósfera. Por lo común se refiere como bomba de aire termactor.

Align boring   A series of holes bored in a straight line.

Taladrado alineado   Una seria de perforaciones que se han taladrado en una linea recta.

Alignment   An adjustment to a line or to bring into a line.

Alineación   Un ajuste que se efectúa en una linea o alinear.

Alloy   A mixture of different metals such as solder, which is an alloy consisting of lead and tin.

Aleación   Una mezcla de metales distinctos como la soldadura, que es una aleación que consiste del plomo y el estaño.

All-wheel drive   System of driving all four wheels only when traction conditions dictate.

Tracción total (todoterreno)   Un sistema de tracción que maneja las cuatro ruedas sólo cuando indican las condiciones de la tracción.

Ambient temperature   Temperature of air surrounding an object.

Temperatura del ambiente   La temperatura en la atmósfera alrededor de un objeto.

Ammeter   The instrument used to measure electrical current flow in a circuit.

Amperímetro   El instrumento que

se usa para medir los corrientes eléctricos de un circuito.

Ampere   The unit for measuring electrical current; usually called an amp.

Amperio   La unidad para medir el corriente eléctrico; por lo común se refiere como amp en inglés.

Amplifier   A circuit or device used to increase the voltage or current of a signal.

Amplificador   Un circuito o un dispositivo que se usa para aumentar el voltage o el corriente de un señal.

Amplify   To enlarge or strengthen original characteristics; a term associated with electronics.

Amplificar   Aumentar o fortalecer las características originales; un término que se asocia con lo electrónico.

Anaerobic   Typically refers to a sealant or adhesive that dries without being exposed to oxygen.

Anaerobio   Típicamente se refiere a un sellante o un adhesivo que se seca sin ser expuesto al oxígeno.

Anaerobic sealer   Liquid or gel that operates to bond two parts together in the absence of air.

Sellante anaerobio   Un líquido o un gel cuyo propósito es adherir dos partes en la ausencia del aire.

Analog   A nondigital measuring method that uses a needle to indicate readings. A typical dashboard gauge with a moving needle is an analog instrument.

Análogo   Un método no numérico de medir que usa una aguja para indicar las lecturas. Un indicador típico de un tablero de intrumentos con una aguja que se mueve es un instrumento análogo.

Analog display signal   An instrument panel display in which an indicator moves in front of a fixed scale to give variable readout.

Señal del indicador análogo   Una presentación en el tablero de instrumento en la cual un indi-

cador se mueve ante una escala fija para indicar una lectura variada.

AND gate   A logic gate with at least two inputs and one output.

Puerta Y   Una puerta lógica que tiene al menos dos entradas y una salida.

Aneroid bellows   A device that responds to atmospheric pressure and can be used to move a metering needle within a jet to automatically compensate for altitude changes.

Fuelle aneroide   Un dispositivo que se ajusta a la presión atmosférica y mueve una aguja de medición dentro de un chorro para compensar automáticamente por los cambios en el altitud.

Anodize   An electrochemical process that coats and hardens the surface of aluminum.

Anodizar   Un proceso electroquímico que cubre y endurece la superficie del aluminio.

Antifreeze   A material, such as alcohol or glycerin, added to water to lower its freezing point.

Anticongelante   Una materia, tal como el alcohol o la glicerina, que se agrega al agua para disminuir su punto de congelación.

Antilock braking system   A series of sensing devices at each wheel that control braking action to prevent wheel lockup.

Sistema de frenos antideslizante   Una seria de dispositivos sensibles en cada rueda que controla la acción del enfrenamiento y previene que las ruedas se bloquean.

Antiseize compounds   A type of lubrication that prevents dissimilar metals from reacting with one another and seizing.

Compuestas antiagarrotamiento   Un tipo de lubricación que previene que los metales desemejantes se reaccionan y se agarran.

Apply side   The side of a piston on which force or pressure is exerted to move the piston to do work.

Superficie de empuje El lado del pistón en el cual la fuerza o la presión se aplica para mover el pistón y hacerlo trabajar.

Arbor A shaft to which other parts may be attached.

'Arbol Una flecha a la cual otras partes se pueden conectar.

Arcing Electrical energy jumping across a gap. Arcing across ignition points causes pitting and erosion.

Arco La energía eléctrica que salta por una holgura. Un arco entre los platinos del encendido causa las picaduras y la erosión.

Aspect ratio The height of a tire, from bead to tread, expressed as a percentage of the tire's section width.

Relación de aspecto La altura de un neumático, de la ceja a la banda, que se expresa como un porcentaje de lo ancho de una sección del neumático.

Asymmetric Unequal surfaces or sizes.

Asimétrico Desigual en las superficies o en los tamaños.

Atmospheric pressure The weight of the air at sea level (about 14.7 pounds per square inch or less at higher altitudes).

Presión atmosférica El peso del aire a nivel del mar (aproximadamente unas 14.7 libras por pulgada cuadrada o menos en las altitudes más altas).

Atomization The stage in which the metered air/fuel emulsion is drawn into the airstream in the form of tiny droplets.

Atomización La etapa en la cual la emulsión calibrada del aire/combustible se introduce al chorro del aire en la forma de pequeñas gotas.

Automotive aftermarket The network of businesses that supplies replacement parts and services to independent service shops, specialty repair shops, car and truck dealerships, fleet and industrial operations, and the general buying public.

Mercado de repuestas no originales La cadena de negocios que proveen las repuestas y los servicios a los talleres de servicio independientes, los talleres de refacción especializadas, los comerciantes de coches y camiones, las operaciones de flete e industrias, y las compras del público común.

Axial Having the same direction or being parallel to the axis or rotation.

Axial Teniendo el mismo dirección o siendo paralelo al eje o la rotación.

Axial load A type of load placed on a bearing that is parallel to the axis of the rotating shaft.

Carga axial Un tipo de carga puesto en un cojinete paralelo al eje de una flecha que gira.

Axial play Movement that is parallel to the axis or rotation.

Holgura axial El movimiento que es paralelo al eje o a la rotación.

Back pressure Pressure created by restriction in an exhaust system.

Contrapresión La presión creada por una restricción en un sistema de escape.

Backlash The clearance or play between two parts, such as meshed gears.

Juego La cantidad de holgura o juego entre dos partes, tal como los engranajes endentados.

Balancer shaft A weighted shaft used on some engines to reduce vibration.

Eje equilibrador Una flecha con un peso usado en algunos motores para disminuir la vibración.

Balancing coil gauge A type of gauge that utilizes coils to create magnetic fields instead of a permanent magnet.

Bobina equilibrada Un tipo de manómetro que utiliza las bobinas para crear un campo magnético en vez de un imán permanente.

Ball bearing An antifriction bearing that uses a series of steel balls

held between inner and outer bearing races.

Cojinete de bolas Un cojinete de antifricción que usa una serie de bolas del acero sujetados entre pistas interiores e exteriores.

Ball joint A pivot point for turning a front wheel to the right or left. Ball joints can be considered either nonloaded or loaded when carrying the car's weight.

Unión esférica Un punto de pivote en el cual gira una rueda delantera hacia la derecha o a la izquierda. Las uniones esféricas se pueden considerar como sin carga o con carga al sostener el peso del coche.

Ballast resistor A resistor in the primary side of the ignition system used to reduce the voltage approximately 4 to 5 volts.

Resistor autocompensador Un resistor en el circuito primario del sistema de encendido que disminuye el voltaje por aproximadamente 4 o 5 voltios.

Barometric pressure A sensor or its signal circuit that sends a varying frequency signal to the processor relating actual barometric pressure.

Presión barométrico Un sensor o su circuito de señal que manda un señal de frecuencia variada al procesor refiriendo la presión barométrico actual.

Barrel An opening in a carburetor that directs the air flow through it. This is sometimes referred to as the venturi although the venturi is part of the barrel.

Garganta Una apertura en un carburador que dirije el corriente del aire. Algunas veces se refiere como el venturi aunque el venturi forma parte de la garganta.

Base The center layer of a bipolar transistor.

Base La capa central de un transistor bipolar.

Battery cell That part of a storage battery made from two dissimilar metals and an acid solution. A cell stores chemical energy for use later as electrical energy.

Célula de batería   Aquella parte de una batería acumuladora hecha de dos metales desemejantes y una solución de ácido. Una célula almacena la energía química para usarse después como energía eléctrica.

Bead   The edge of a tire's sidewall, usually made of steel wires wrapped in rubber, used to hold the tire to the wheel.

Ceja   La extremidad del refuerzo lateral de un neumático, suele ser hecho de alambres de acero cubiertos en caucho, que sujeta el neumático a la rueda.

Bearing clearance   The amount of space left between a shaft and the bearing surface for lubricating oil to enter.

Holgura del cojinete   La cantidad del espacio que se deja entre la flecha y la superficie portante por la cual entra el lubricante.

Bearing crush   The process of compressing a bearing into place as the bearing cap is tightened.

Aplastamiento del cojinete   El proceso de colocar un cojinete comprimiéndolo cuando se aprieta la tapa del cojinete.

Bearing race   The machined circular surface of a bearing against which the roller or ball bearings ride.

Pista del cojinete   La superficie circular maquinada del cojinete en la cual ruedan los rodillos o bolas.

Bearing spread   The condition in which the distance across the outside parting edges of the bearing insert is slightly greater than the diameter of the housing bore.

Aplastamiento del cojinete   La condición en la cual la distancia de las extremidades exteriores de la pieza inserta del cojinete es un poco más grande que el diámetro de la caja.

Bellows   A movable cover or seal, usually of rubberlike material,

that is pleated or folded like an accordion to allow for expansion and contraction.

Fuelle   Una cubierta o un sello removible, normalmente de una materia parecida al caucho, que es plegado o doblado como un acordión para permitir la expansión y contracción.

Bias   A diagonal line of direction. In relationship to tires, bias means that belts and plies are laid diagonally or crisscrossing each other.

Bies   Una linea de dirección diagonal. Perteneciente a los neumáticos, bies quiere decir que las bandas y los pliegues se colocan diagonalmente y se cruzán entre sí.

Bimetal   Two dissimilar metals with different expansion rates used to switch a circuit on and off.

Aleación bimetálica   Dos metales desemejantes que se expanden en una tasa diferente que sirven para prender y apagar un circuito.

Binary code   A series of numbers represented by 1's and 0's or offs and ons.

Código binario   Una serie de números representados por los 1s y los 0s o por apagado y prendido.

Blowby   The unburned fuel and products of combustion that leak past the piston rings and into the crankcase during the last part of the combustion stroke.

Fuga   El combustible no consumido y los productos de la combustión que se escapan alrededor de los anillos de los pistones y entran al cárter en las últimas etapas de la carrera de combustión.

Blower   A fan that pushes, or blows, air through a ventilation, heater, or air-conditioning system.

Ventilador   Un ventilador que empuja, o sopla, el aire por un ventilador, un calentador o un sistema de aire acondicionado.

Body-over-frame   Type of vehicle construction in which the frame is the foundation, with the body

and all major parts of the vehicle attached to it.

Carrocería sobre armazón   Un tipo de construcción de vehículos en el cual el armazón es la fundación, al cual se conectan la carrocería y los componentes principales del vehículo.

Bolt diameter   The measurement across the major diameter of a bolt's threaded area, or across the bolt shank.

Diámetro del perno   La medida del diámetro mayor de la parte fileteada de un perno, o atravéz del asta del perno.

Bolt head   The part of a bolt that the socket or wrench fits over in order to torque or tighten the bolt.

Cabeza del perno   La parte del perno sobre la cual se pone el dado o la llave para apretar o torcer al perno.

Boot   Rubber protective cover with accordion pleats used to contain lubricants and exclude contaminating dirt, water, and grime. Located at each end of rack and pinion assembly and front-wheel-drive CV joints.

Protectores de caucho   Una cubierta protectora hecho de caucho que tiene pliegues estilo acordión que sirve para contener las lubricantes y prevenir la entrada de los contaminantes como el lodo, el agua y el mugre. Se ubican en cada extremidad de la asamblea de piñon y cremallera.

Bore   A dimension of cylinder size representing the diameter of the cylinder.

Diámetro del orificio   Una dimensión de tamaño del cilindro que representa el diámetro del cilindro.

Bourdon tube   A flexible hollow tube that uncoils and straightens as the pressure inside it is increased. A needle attached to the Bourdon tube moves over a scale to indicate the oil pressure.

Tubo bourdon   Un tubo hueco y flexible que se desenreda y se endereza al aumentar el presión en su interior. Una aguja conectada al tubo bourdon mueve por encima de una escala para indicar la presión del aceite.

Bracket An attachment used to secure parts to the body or frame.

Soporte Una fijación que se usa para enganchar las parte a la carrocería o al armazón.

Brake band A circle-shaped part lined with friction material that acts as a brake or holding device to stop and hold a rotating drum that has a gear train member connected to it.

Banda de freno Una parte circular recubierta con materia fricativa que sirve para frenar o como un dispositivo de asir para detener y sostener un tambor giratorio al cual esta conectado un miembro del tren de engrenaje.

Brake fade Occurs when friction surfaces become hot enough to cause the coefficient of friction to drop to a point where the application of severe pedal pressure results in little actual braking.

Amortiguamiento de frenar Ocurre cuando la superficie de fricción se sobrecalienta al punto de causar que caiga el coeficiente de fricción a tal punto que la aplicación de presión riguroso en el pedal de frenos resulta en muy poco enfrenamiento.

British thermal unit (Btu) A measurement of the amount of heat required to raise the temperature of 1 pound of water 1 degree Fahrenheit.

Unidad térmica Británica Una medida de la cantidad del calor que se requiere para aumentar la temperatura de 1 libra de agua por 1 grado fahrenheit.

Buffer Any device used to reduce the shock or motion of opposing forces.

Parachoques Qualquier dispositivo que sirve para disminuir los choques o el movimiento de las fuerzas opuestas.

Bump steer Erratic steering that is caused from rolling over bumps, cornering, or heavy braking; same as orbital steer and roll steer.

Dirección de choques La dirección errática que se causa al pasar por encima de los topes, a dar la vuelta, o en el enfrenamiento violento; quiere decir lo mismo que la dirección orbital y la dirección de inclinación.

Burnish To smooth or polish with a sliding tool under pressure.

Bruñir Pulir o suavizar por medio de una herramienta deslizandola bajo presión.

CAFE standards Law requiring auto makers to not only manufacture clean-burning engines but also to equip vehicles with engines that burn gasoline efficiently.

Normas CAFE El ley requeriendo que los fabricantes de automóviles no sólo fabrican los motores de combustión limpia sino que tambien equipan los vehículos con los motores que consumen la gasolina en una manera eficiente.

Camber The attitude of a wheel and tire assembly when viewed from the front of a car. If it leans outward, away from the car at the top, the wheel is said to have positive camber. If it leans inward, it is said to have negative camber.

Camber (comba) La actitud de una asamblea de la rueda y el neumático al verse desde la frente del coche. Si se inclina hacia afuera, se dice que la rueda tiene una comba positiva. Si se inclina hacia el interior, se dice que tiene una comba negativa.

Candlepower A measurement of the brightness of light.

Unidad de intensidad luminosa Una medida del brillantez de la luz.

Capacitor A device for holding and storing a surge of current.

Capacitor Un dispositivo que sostiene y almacena una sobretensión de corriente.

Carbon dioxide Compressed into solid form, this material is known as dry ice and remains at a temperature of -109 degrees. It goes directly from a solid to a vapor state.

Anhídrido carbónico Comprimido para formar un sólido, esta materia se conoce como hielo seco y sostiene una temperatura de -109 grados F. Va directamente del estado sólido a un vapor.

Carbon monoxide Poisonous gas formed in engine exhaust.

'Oxido de carbono Un gas venenoso producido en el escape de un motor.

Carbonize The process of carbon formation within an engine, such as on the spark plugs and within the combustion chamber.

Carbonizar El proceso de la formación del carbono en un motor, tal como en las bujías y en el interior de la cámara de combustión.

Case harden To harden the surface of steel.

Cementar Endurecer la superficie del acero.

Castellated nut A nut with slots through which a cotter pin can be passed to secure the nut to its bolt or stud.

Tuerca con entallas Una tuerca que tiene muescas por las cuales se puede insertar un pasador de chaveta para retener la tuerca al perno o a la espiga.

Caster Angle formed between the kingpin axis and a vertical axis as viewed from the side of the vehicle. Caster is considered positive when the top of the kingpin axis is behind the vertical axis.

Angulo de caster El ángulo formado entre la linea de pivote y un eje vertical al verse del lado del vehículo. El caster se considera positivo cuando la extremidad superior de la linea de pivote es atrás del eje vertical.

Catalyst A compound or substance that can speed up or slow down the reaction of other substances without being consumed itself. In an automatic catalytic converter, special metals (for example, platinum or palladium) are used to promote more complete combustion of unburned hydrocarbons and a reduction of carbon monoxide.

Agente catalítico Una compuesta o una substancia que puede acelerar o retardar la reacción de otras substancias sin ser consumida. En un convertidor catalítico automático, se usan metales especiales (por ejemplo, el platino y el paladio) para promover la combustión completa del hidrocarburo sobrante y para reducir el óxido de carbono.

Caustic Something that causes corrosion.

Cáustico Algo que causa la corrosión.

CC-ing The process of measuring a volume in cubic centimeters, commonly used to measure combustion chamber size.

Medida en CC El proceso de medir un volumen en centímetros cúbicos, suelen usarse al medir el tamaño de la cámara de combustión.

C-class oil Commercial engine oil designed for use in heavy-duty commercial applications.

Aceite tipo C El aceite del motor comercial que se diseñó para usarse en las aplicaciones comerciales de trabajo pesado.

Center link A steering linkage component connected between the pitman and idler arm.

Varilla central Un componente de enlace de dirección que conecta entre el brazo Pitman y el brazo loco.

Center of gravity The point about which the weight of a car is evenly distributed; the point of balance.

Centro de gravedad El punto en el cual el peso del coche es distribuido en una manera uniforme; el punto del equilibrio.

Centrifugal force A force tending to pull an object outward when it is rotating rapidly around a center.

Fuerza centrífuga Una fuerza que tiene la tendencia de jalar un objeto hacia afuera cuando éste gira rápidamente alrededor de un punto central.

Chaffing Damage caused by friction and rubbing.

Rozamiento Los daños incurridos por la fricción y el frotamiento.

Chamfer A bevel or taper at the edge of a hole.

Chaflán Un bisel o ahusamiento en la orilla de un hoyo.

Chamfering The process of removing the sharp edges around a bore or hole.

Achaflanar El proceso de quitar las orillas afiladas alrededor de un orificio o un hoyo.

Chase To straighten or repair damaged threads.

Embutir Enderezar o reparar los filetes dañados.

Check valve A gate or valve that allows passage of gas or fluid in one direction only.

Valvula de seguridad Una válvula que permite fluir la presión en un sólo sentido.

Chemical cleaning Cleaning that relies primarily on some type of chemical action to remove dirt, grease, scale, paint, or rust.

Limpieza química La limpieza que cuenta primariamente con la acción química para remover el lodo, la grasa, las incrustaciones, la pintura, o los óxidos.

Cherry picker A mobile crane that uses hydraulic power.

Burro Una grúa rodante que usa la energía hidráulica.

Chip A term commonly used for an integrated circuit that is small in size.

Pastilla Un término común que se refiere a circuito integrado que es de un tamaño pequeño.

Closed loop An electronic feedback system in which the sensors

provide constant information on what is taking place in the engine.

Bucle cerrado Un sistema de reacción electrónico en el cual los detectores proveen información constante de lo que esta pasando en el interior del motor.

Closed-cooling systems Cooling systems with expansion tanks designed to hold any coolant that passes through the pressure cap when the engine is hot.

Sistema de enfriamiento cerrado Los sistemas de enfriamiento que tienen tanques de expansión diseñados para contener a cualquier flúido refrigerante que pasa por la tapa de presión al calentarse el motor.

Clutch disc The part of a clutch that receives the driving motion from the flywheel and pressure plate assembly and transmits that motion to the transmission input shaft.

Disco del embrague La parte de un embrague que recibe el movimiento propulsor del volante y la asamblea del plato opresor y transmite esa acción a la flecha de entrada de la transmisión.

Clutch fork A forked lever that moves the clutch release bearing and hub back and forth.

Horquilla del embrague Una palanca bifurcada que mueve al balero collarín del embrague hacia afrente y hacia atrás.

Clutch release bearing A sealed, prelubricated ball bearing that moves the pressure plate release levers or diaphragm spring through the engagement and disengagement process.

Collarín del embrague Un cojinete esférico, prelubricado y sellado, que mueve las palancas de liberación del plato opresor o el resorte diafragma por medio del proceso del enganche y el desenganche.

Coefficient of friction A relative measurement of the friction developed between two objects in contact with each other.

Coeficiente de la fricción La medida relativa de la fricción que ocurre entre dos superficies que estan en contacto la una con la otra.

Coil spring pressure plate assembly An assembly that uses weighted levers to increase or decrease the force holding the clutch disc against the flywheel according to engine speed.

Asamblea de muelle y plato opresor Una asamblea que usa las palancas con pesos para incrementar o disminuir a la fuerza que aprieta el disco del embrague contra el volante según la velocidad del motor.

Collector The portion of a bipolar transistor that receives the majority of electrical current.

Colector La porción de un transistor bipolar que recibe la mayoría del corriente eléctrico.

Combustion chamber The space between the top of a piston and the cylinder head where the engine's combustion takes place.

Cámara de combustión El espacio entre la parte superior del pistón y la cabeza del cilindro en donde se lleva acabo la combustión.

Compound A mixture of two or more ingredients.

Compuesta Una mezcla de dos o más ingredientes .

Compression ratio The ratio of the volume in the cylinder above the piston when the piston is at bottom dead center to the volume in the cylinder above the piston when the piston is at top dead center.

Relación índice de compresión La relación del volumen en el cilindro arriba del piston cuando el piston esta en el punto muerto inferior al volumen en el cilindro arriba del pistón cuando el piston esta en el punto muerto superior.

Compression stroke The second stroke of the four-stroke engine cycle, in which the piston moves from bottom dead center and the intake valve closes. This traps and compresses the air/fuel mixture in the cylinder.

Carrera de compresión La segunda carrera de un ciclo de un motor de cuatro tiempos, en la cual el pistón mueve del punto muerto inferior y se cierre la válvula de admisión. Esto encierre y comprime la mezcla de aire/combustible en el cilindro.

Concentric Two or more circles having a common center.

Concéntrico Dos círculos o más que comparten un centro común.

Condensation The process of a vapor becoming a liquid; the reverse of evaporation.

Condensación El proceso por el cual un vapor se convierte en un líquido; lo opuesto de la evaporación.

Condense The process of cooling a vapor to below its boiling point. The vapor condenses into a liquid.

Condensar El proceso de enfriar un vapor a una temperatura más baja de su punto de ebullición. El vapor condensa, formando un líquido.

Conductor A device that readily allows for current flow.

Conductor Un dispositivo que permite fácilmente el flujo del corriente.

Continuous injection system A system that uses fuel under pressure to modulate or change the fuel injection area.

Sistema de inyección continua Un sistema que usa al combustible bajo presión para moderar o cambiar el area del inyección de combustible.

Contraction A reduction in mass or dimension; the opposite of expansion.

Contracción Una reducción en la masa o en la dimensión; lo opuesto de la expansión.

Control arms Suspension parts that control coil spring action as a wheel is affected by road conditions.

Palanca de comando Las partes de suspención que controlan la acción del muelle de control al afectarse una rueda por las condiciones de la carretera.

Controller A term commonly used for an electronic control unit or module.

Controlador Un término que se usa comúnmente para indicar una unidad de control electrónica o un módulo.

Convection oven Thermal cleaning oven that uses indirect heat to brake parts.

Horno de convección Un horno termal de limpieza que aplica el calor indirecto a las partes de los frenos.

Coolant A mixture of water and ethylene glycol-based antifreeze that circulates through the engine to help maintain proper temperatures.

Fluido refrigerante Una mezcla del agua con el anticongelante a base de glicol etileno que circula por el motor y ayuda en mantener las temperaturas indicadas.

Cords The inner materials running through the plies that produce strength in the tire. Common cord materials are fiberglass and steel.

Cuerdas Las materiales interiores recorriendo por los pliegues que producen la solidez del neumático. Las materiales más comunes para las cuerdas son la fibra de vidrio y el acero.

Core The center of the radiator, made of tubes and fins, used to transfer heat from the coolant to the air.

Núcleo El centro de un radiador, hecho de tubos y aletas, que sirve para transferir el calor del líquido refrigerante a la atmósfera.

Core plug A plug used to seal openings where necessary for casting the object in a cast structure.

Tapón del núcleo Un tapón diseñado para sellar las aperturas necesarias para fundar el objeto en un molde.

Corrosivity The characteristic of a material that enables it to dissolve metals and other materials or burn the skin.

Corrosidad La característica de una materia que permite que disuelva a los metales u otras materias o quema al piel.

Counterbore To enlarge a hole to a given depth.

Ensanchar con taladro Aumentar el tamaño de un hoyo a la profundidad indicada.

Countersink To cut or form a depression to allow the head of a screw to go below the surface.

Avellenar Cortar o formar una depresión bastante grande para permitir que la cabeza de un tornillo queda abajo de la superficie.

Counterweight Weight forged or cast into the crankshaft to reduce vibration.

Contrapeso Un peso que se ha forjado o colado al cigueñal para reducir la vibración.

Crank pin The machined, offset area of a crankshaft where the connecting rod journals are machined.

Espiga de manívela La superficie maquinada, descentrada de un cigueñal en donde los muñones de la biela se maquinan.

Crank throw The distance from the crankshaft main bearing centerline to the connecting rod journal centerline. The stroke of any engine is the crank throw.

Carrera La distancia del eje de quilla del cojinete principal del cigueñal al eje de quilla del muñon de la biela. Una carrera del pistón de cualquier motor es una carrera.

Crank web The unmachined portion of a crankshaft that lies between two crank pins or between a crank pin and main bearing journal.

Alma de cigueñal La porción no maquinada de un cigueñal que queda entre dos espigas de manívela o entre una espiga de manívela y el muñon del cojinete principal.

Crimp The use of pressure to force a thin holding part to clamp to, or conform to the shape of, a part so it can't move.

Engarzar El uso de la presión en forzar una parte delgada de sujeción para agarrar, o conformar a la forma de, una parte sujetada.

Crossflow radiator A radiator in which coolant enters on one side, travels through tubes, and collects on the opposite side.

Radiador de flujo horizontal Un radiador en el cual el líquido refrigerante entra de un lado, viaja por los tubos, y se colecta en el lado opuesto.

Crude oil The natural state of oil as it is pulled from the earth and before it is refined.

Aceite crudo El estado natural del aceite cuando sale de la tierra y antes de que sea refinado.

Current The number of electrons flowing past a given point in a given amount of time.

Corriente El número de los electronos que fluyen al través de un punto específico en un dado período del tiempo.

CV joint Constant velocity joint.

Junta CV Junta de velocidad continua.

Cylinder bore dial gauge Tool used to determine cylinder bore size, out-of-round, and taper.

Calibrador del orificio del cilindro Una herramienta que se usa para determinar el tamaño, lo ovalado y lo cónico de un cilindro.

Dampen To slow or reduce oscillations or movement.

Amortiguar Retardar o reducir las vibraciones o el movimiento.

Dead axle An axle that does not rotate but merely forms a base on which to attach the wheels.

Eje muerto Un eje que no gira sino solamente forma una plataforma en la cual se puede conectar las ruedas.

Dead center The extreme upper or lower position of the crankshaft throw at which the piston is not moving in either direction.

Punto muerto La posición extrema superior o inferior de una carrera de cigueñal en la cual el pistón no mueve en ningúna dirección.

Deck The top of the engine block where the cylinder head mounts.

Cubierta del monoblock La parte superior de un bloque del motor en donde se conecta la culata.

Deflection Bending or movement away from normal due to loading.

Desviación Curvación o moviniento fuera de lo normal debido a la carga.

Deflection angle The angle at which the oil is deflected inside the torque converter during operation. The greater the angle of deflection, the greater the amount of torque applied to the output shaft.

'Angulo de desviación El ángulo en el que se desvia el aceite en el convertidor de par durante su operación. Cuanto más el ángulo de desviación, más torsión se aplica en la flecha de potencia.

Density Compactness; relative mass of matter in a given volume.

Densidad La firmeza; la masa relativa de la materia en un volumen indicado.

Desiccant A special substance that absorbs moisture.

Desicante Una substancia especial que absorbe la humedad.

Detergent A compound of soap-like nature used in engine oil to remove engine deposits and hold them in suspension in the oil.

Detergente Una compuesta parecida al jabón que se usa en el aceite de motor para quitar los depósitos del motor y mantenerlos suspendidos en el aceite.

Detonation As used in an automobile, indicates a hasty burning or explosion of the mixture in the engine cylinders. It becomes audible through a vibration of the combustion chamber walls and is sometimes confused with a ping or spark knock.

Detonación Aplicado al automóvil, indica una combustión apresurada o una explosión de la mezcla en los cilindros del motor. Se oye por medio de las vibraciones de los paredes de la cámara de combustión y a veces se confunde con un golpeteo o una detonación de las bujías.

Dial caliper Versatile measuring instrument capable of taking inside, outside, depth, and step measurements.

Calibre de carátula (pie de rey) Un instrumento de medir versátil que es capaz de tomar las medidas interiores, exteriores, de profundidad, y de paso a paso.

Dial indicator A measuring tool used to adjust small clearances up to 0.001 inch. The clearance is read on a dial.

Calibrador de carátula Una herramienta de medida que sirve para ajustar las pequeñas holguras hasta el 0.001 de una pulgada. La holgura se lee en un cuadrante.

Diaphragm A flexible, impermeable membrane on which pressure acts to produce mechanical movement.

Diafragma Una membrana flexible e impermeable sobre la cual tiene un efecto la presión para producir un movimiento mecánico.

Diaphragm spring pressure plate assembly An assembly that uses weighted levers to increase or decrease the force holding the clutch disc against the flywheel according to engine speed.

Asamblea del resorte diafragma del plato opresor Una asamblea que usa las palancas con pesos para incrementar o reducir la fuerza que aprieta el disco de embrague contra el volante según la velocidad del motor.

Dielectric An insulator material.

Dieléctrico Una material de aislador.

Differential A gear assembly that transmits power from the drive shaft to the wheels and allows two opposite wheels to turn at different speeds for cornering and traction.

Diferencial Una asamblea de engrenajes que transmite la potencia del árbol de mando a las ruedas y permite que dos ruedas opuestas giran a velocidades distinctos para ejecutar las vueltas y la tracción.

Digital A voltage signal that is pulsed on or off.

Digital Un señal del voltaje que pulsa prendida o apagada.

Dilution To make thinner or weaker. Oil is diluted by the addition of fuel and water droplets.

Dilución Desleir o debilitar. El aceite se diluye por la agregación de las gotas del combustible o del agua.

Diode A simple semiconductor device that permits flow of electricity in one direction but not in the opposite direction.

Diodo Un dispositivo sencillo de semiconductor que permite el flujo de la electricidad en una dirección pero no en la dirección opuesta.

Direct drive The downward gear engagement in which the input shaft and output shaft are locked together.

Transmisión directa El enganchamiento en descenso del engrenaje en el cual la flecha de entrada y la flecha de producción se enclavan.

Direct ignition A distributorless ignition system in which spark distribution is controlled by the vehicle's computer.

Encendido directo Un sistema del encendido sin distribuidor en el cual la distribución de la chispa se controla por medio de la computador del vehículo.

Direct injection A diesel fuel injection system in which fuel is injected directly onto the top of the piston.

Inyección directa Un sistema de inyección de diesel en el cual el combustible se inyecta directamente arriba del pistón.

Directional stability The ability of a car to travel in a straight line with a minimum of driver control.

Estabilidad direccional La abilidad de un coche de viajar en una linea recta con control mínimo del conductor.

Disable A type of microcomputer decision that results in an automotive system being deactivated and not permitted to operate.

Incapacitar Un tipo de decisión de la microcomputadora que resulta en que un sistema automotríz se deactiva y no permite que se opera.

Displacement The volume the cylinder holds between the top dead center and bottom dead center positions of the piston.

Desplazamiento (cilindrada) El volumen que contiene el cilindro entre las posiciones del punto muerto superior y el punto muerto inferior del pistón.

Dome Typically refers to the shape of the top of a piston.

Fondo hemisférico Típicamente se refiere al contorno de la parte superior de un pistón.

Dowel A pin extending from one part to fit into a hole in an attached part; used for both location and retention.

Espiga Una clavija que extiende de una parte para quedarse en el hoyo de otra parte conjunta; se usa para la localización y la retención.

Downflow radiator A radiator in which coolant enters the top of the radiator and is drawn downward by gravity.

Radiador de flujo vertical Un radiador en el cual el líquido refrigerante entra en la parte superior del radiador y fluye hacia abajo atraído por la gravedad.

Drive member A gear that drives, or provides power for, other gears in a planetary gearset.

Miembro de ataque Un engrenaje que impulsa, o provee la potencia para los otros engrenajes en un conjunto planetario.

Driveability The degree to which a vehicle operates properly. Includes starting, running smoothly, accelerating, and delivering reasonable fuel mileage.

Manejo El punto en el cual un vehículo opera correctamente. Incluye el encendido, marchar sin averías, la acceleración y la entregada de un kilometraje económico.

Dropping resistor A device that reduces the battery voltage.

Resistencia para bajar la tensión Un dispositivo que disminuye el voltaje de la bateria.

Duo-servo A drum brake design with increased stopping power due to the servo or self-energizing effect of the brake.

Frenos tipo servo Un diseño de freno de tambor que tiene más potencia de enfrenar debido al servo o al efecto autoenergético del freno.

Duty cycle The percentage of on-time to total cycle time of fuel injectors.

Ciclo del trabajo El porcentaje del tiempo de trabajar al tiempo del ciclo total de los inyectores del combustible.

Dwell time The degree of crankshaft rotation during which the primary circuit is on.

'Angulo de cierre El grado de rotación del cigueñal en el cual esta encendido el circuito primario.

Dynamic Refers to balance when the object is in motion.

Dinámico Refiere al balance mientras que un objeto esté en movimiento.

Eccentric The part of a camshaft that operates the fuel pump.

Eccéntrico La parte de un árbol de levas que opera la bomba del combustible.

Efficiency A ratio of the amount of energy put into an engine as compared to the amount of energy coming out of the engine; a measure of the quality of how well a particular machine works.

Eficiencia Un relación de la cantidad de energía que consume un motor comparado con la cantidad de energía que produce el motor; una medida de la calidad de la máquina y su marcha.

Elasticity The principle by which a bolt can be stretched a certain amount. Each time the stretching load is reduced, the bolt returns exactly back to its original, normal size.

Elasticidad El principio por el cual un perno puede extenderse por un cierta cantidad. Cada vez que la carga tensor se reduce, el perno regresa exactamente a su tamaño normal y original.

Electrode The firing terminals that are found in a spark plug.

Electrodo Los terminales de chispeo que se encuentran en una bujía.

Electrochemical The chemical action of two dissimilar materials in a chemical solution.

Electroquímico El acción químico de dos materiales desemejantes en una solución química.

Electrolysis A chemical and electrical decomposition process that can damage metals, such as brass, copper, and aluminum, in the cooling system.

Electrólisis (deposición) Un proceso de decomposición químico y eléctrico que puede dañar a los metales, tales como el latón, el cobre y el aluminio, en el sistema de enfriamiento.

Electrolyte A material that has atoms that become ionized, or electrically charged, in solution. Automobile battery electrolyte is a mixture of sulfuric acid and water.

Electrólito Una materia que tiene átomos que se han ionizado, o que tienen una carga eléctrica, en una solución. El electrólito para las baterías automotrices es una mezcla del ácido sulfúrico y el agua.

Electromagnet A magnet formed by electrical flow through a conductor.

Electroimán Un imán que se produce por un corriente eléctrico fluyendo por un conductor.

Electromagnetic induction Moving a wire through a magnetic field to create current flow in the wire.

Inducción electromagnético Crear un corriente eléctrico en un alambre al moverlo por un campo magnético.

Electromagnetism A form of magnetism that occurs when current flows through a conductor.

Electromagnetismo Una forma del magnetismo que ocurre al fluir un corriente por un conductor.

Electromechanical Refers to a device that incorporates both electronic and mechanical principles together in its operation.

Electromecánico Refiere a un dispositivo que incorpora ambos principios del electrónico y mecánico en su operación.

Electronic Pertaining to the control of systems or devices by the use of small electrical signals and various semiconductor devices and circuits.

Electrónico Perteneciente al control de los sistemas o de los dispositivos por medio de los pequeños señales eléctricos y por varios de los dispositivos semiconductores y los circuitos.

Embedability The ability of the bearing lining material to absorb dirt.

Incrustabilidad La abilidad que tiene una material de forro de un cojinete en absorber la suciedad.

Emitter A portion of a transistor from which electrons are emitted, or forced out.

Emisor Una porción de un transistor de la cual se emite o se expulsan los electrones.

Emulsion The mixture of air and fuel in the carburetor.

Mezcla vaporizada La mezcla del aire y el combustible en el carburador.

End clearance play The extent of the possible forward and backward movement of the crankshaft, rod bearing on the crank pin, or the camshaft.

Holgura de las extremidades La cantidad del movimiento recíprocal del cigüeñal, el cojinete del muñon o el árbol de levas.

End play The amount of axial or end-to-end movement in a shaft due to clearance in the bearings.

Juego axial La cantidad del movimiento axial o de una extremidad a otra de una flecha debido a la holgura de los cojinetes.

Energy The ability to do work.

Energía La abilidad de trabajar.

EP toxicity The characteristic of a material that enables it to leach one or more of eight heavy metals in concentrations greater than 100 times standard drinking water concentrations.

Toxicidad EP La característica de una materia que permite que disuelva uno o más de los ocho metales pesados en concentraciones mayores de 100 veces la concentración del agua potable.

Ethanol A widely used gasoline additive known for its abilities as an octane enhancer.

Etanol Un aditivo muy común que se reconoce por su capacidad de elevar los niveles del octano.

Evacuate The process of applying vacuum to a closed refrigeration system to remove air and moisture.

Vaciar El proceso de aplicar un vacío a un sistema cerrado de refrigeración para quitarle el aire y la humedad.

Evaporation A natural process in which the moisture contained by an object leaves and enters the atmosphere.

Evaporación Un proceso natural en el cual la humedad deja un objeto y entra la atmósfera.

Excessive wear Wear caused by overloading an out-of-balance condition of a factor affecting wear, resulting in lower-than-normal life expectancy of the part or parts being subjected to the adverse operating condition.

Gasto excesivo El gasto causado por la condición de sobrecarga o de desequilibración de un factor que afecta al gasto, resultando en una durabilidad disminuida y menos de lo deseado de una parte o las partes que se exponen a las condiciones adversas.

Exhaust stroke The final stroke of the four-stroke engine cycle, in which the compressed fuel mixture is ignited in the combustion chamber.

Carrera de escape La última carrera de un ciclo de un motor de cuatro tiempos, en la cual se enciende la mezcla de aire/combustible en la cámara del cilindro.

Expansion An increase in size. For example, when a metal rod is heated, it increases in length and perhaps also in diameter; expansion is the opposite of contraction.

Expansión Un aumento en el tamaño. Por ejemplo, al calentarse una varilla de metal, aumenta en longitud y quizá en su diámetro tambien; la expansión es lo contrario de la contracción.

Fatigue Deterioration of a bearing metal under excessive intermittent loads or prolonged operation.

Fatiga La deterioración de un metal de apoyo bajo las cargas intermitentes o durante la operación prolongada.

Feedback Normally refers to the process in which computer commands and the results of such are monitored by the computer.

Retroalimentación Normalmente se refiere al proceso en el cual la computadora manda y los resultados se regulan por la computadora.

Ferrous metal Metal that contains iron or steel and is, therefore, subject to rust.

Metal férreo Un metal que contiene el hierro o el acero y que, por lo tanto, puede oxidarse.

Field coil A coil of wire on an alternator rotor or starter motor frame that produces a magnetic field when energized.

Bobina inductora Una bobina de alambre en un rotor de un alternador o un armazón de un motor de arranque que produce un campo magnético al establecer el corriente.

Fillets The smooth curve where the shank flows into the bolt head.

Filetes La curva lisa en donde el asta se convierte a la cabeza del tornillo.

Firing order The order in which the cylinders of an engine move through the power stroke.

Orden de encendido El orden en el cual mueven los pistones de un motor en la carrera encendido-expansión.

Flange A projecting rim or collar on an object for keeping it in place.

Collarín Una orilla sobresaliente o un collar en un objeto que lo sujeta en su lugar.

Flare An expanded, shaped end on a metal tube or pipe.

Abocinado (abocardado) Una extremidad extendida o formada en un tubo de metal.

Flat-rate manuals Literature containing figures dealing with the length of time specific repairs are supposed to require. Flat-rate manuals often contain a parts list with prices as well.

Manuales de valuación   La literatura que se trata de los detalles del tiempo de obra requirido por varias reparaciones específicas. Los manuales de valuación suelen incluir tambien una lista de repuestas con sus precios.

Flex plate   A round, flywheel-like disc mounted to an engine's crankshaft when the vehicle is equipped with an automatic transmission.

Placa de flexión   Una placa redonda parecida al volante montada al cigueñal de un motor de un vehículo que ha sido equipado con una transmisión automática.

Flooding   A condition in which excess, unvaporized fuel in the intake manifold prevents the engine from starting.

Ahogo   Una condición en la cual un exceso de combustible no vaporizado se queda en el múltiple de admisión y previene que arranque el motor.

Flutter (bounce)   As applied to engine valves, refers to a condition wherein the valve is not held tightly on its seat during the time the cam is not lifting it.

Titilación (rebote)   Aplicado a las válvulas de los motores, se refiere a una condición en la cual la válvula no se asienta bien en cuando la leva no la tiene levantada.

Flux density   The number of flux lines per square centimeter.

Densidad de flujo   El número de lineas de flujo por centímetro cuadrado.

Flux field   The magnetic field formed by magnetic lines of force.

Campo de flujo   El campo magnético formado por lineas de fuerza magnética.

Foot-pound   A unit of measurement for torque. One foot-pound is the torque obtained by a force of 1 pound applied to a wrench handle 12 inches long.

Pies-libra   Una unidad de medida de torsión. Un pie-libra es la torsión que se obtiene por la fuerza de una libra que se aplica a una llave de tuercas cuyo mango mide 12 pulgadas en longitud.

Force   A push or pushing effort measured in pounds.

Fuerza   Un esfuerzo de jalar o empujar que se mide en libras.

Forge   The process of shaping metal by stamping it into a desired shape.

Forgar   El proceso de formar el metal al imprimirlo en una forma requerida.

Forward bias   A positive voltage that is applied to the P-material and a negative voltage that is applied to the N-material in a semiconductor.

Polarización directa   Un voltaje positivo que se aplica al cristal P y un voltaje negativo que se aplica al cristal N de un semiconductor.

Free play   Looseness in a linkage between the start of application and the actual movement of the device, such as the movement in the steering wheel before the wheels start to turn.

Juego libre   Flojedad en una biela que aparece entre el tiempo en que se comienza usar a una aplicación y el movimiento actual del dispositivo, tal como el movimiento en un volante de dirección antes de que comienzan a girar las ruedas.

Free travel   The distance a clutch pedal moves before it begins to take up slack in the clutch linkage.

Juego libre   La distancia que mueve el pedal de embrague antes de que comienza accionar la biela del embrague.

Freewheeling   A mechanical device that engages the driving member to impart motion to a driven member in one direction but not the other. Also known as an overrunning clutch.

Embrague de volante libre   Un dispositivo mecánico que engrana el miembro de impulso con el miembro de tracción y confiere el movimiente en una dirección, pero no en la otra. Tambien se conoce como un embrague de sobremarcha.

Frequency   The rate at which something occurs.

Frecuencia   La velocidad en la cual algo ocurre.

Friction   Resistance to motion that occurs when two objects rub against each other.

Fricción   La resistencia al movimiento que ocurre al frotarse dos objetos.

Fulcrum   The support or point of rest a lever rests on; also called the pivot point.

Punto de apoyo   El soporte o punto de descanso en el cual descansa una palanca; tambien se llama el punto de pivote.

Full-floating   A type of live axle arrangement in which the weight of the vehicle is not supported by the axle.

Flotante   Un tipo de dispositivo de eje motor en el cual el peso del vehículo no se soporta por el eje.

Galling wear   Uniting two solid surfaces that are in rubbing contact; used to describe the normal wear of valve lifters.

Desgaste por rozamiento   Uniendo a dos superficies sólidos que estan en contacto frotativo; se usa para describir el gasto normal de las levantaválvulas.

Ganged   A type of switch in which several circuits are controlled by moving one control or lever.

Acoplados   Un tipo de interruptor en el cual varios circuitos se controlan al mover un control o una palanca.

Gear pitch   The number of teeth per given unit of pitch diameter. Gear pitch is determined by dividing the number of teeth by the pitch diameter of the gear.

Paso del engranaje   El número de los dientes por una unidad dada de un diámetro de paso. El paso del engranaje se determine al dividir el número de los dientes por el diámetro del paso del engrenaje.

Gear pumps Positive displacement pumps that use two meshing external gears, one drive and one driven.

Bombas de engrenajes Las bombas de desplazamiento positivo que usan dos engrenajes externos engranados, uno propulsor y uno loco.

Gear ratio An expression of gear size and tooth count of gears that are meshed together. The ratio reflects torque multiplication.

Relación de engranes Una expresión del tamaño del engrenaje y el número de los dientes que se engranan. La relación refleja la multiplicación de par.

Glaze A thin residue on the cylinder walls formed by a combination heat, engine oil, and piston movement.

Porcelana (barniz) Un residuo en los paredes de los cilindros que se forma por una combinación del calor, el aceite del motor y el movimiento de los pistones.

Glow plug An electrical device used on diesel engines to warm the combustion chamber and/or fuel when outside temperatures are low. These allow for quicker cold starts.

Bujía incandescente Un dispositivo eléctrico en los motores de diesel que sirve para calentar la cámara de combustión y/o al combustible en bajas temperaturas ambientes. Permiten los arranques fríos más rápidos.

Governor A device that limits the speed of a device.

Regulador Un dispositivo que limite la velocidad de un dispositivo.

Grade markings Marks on fasteners that indicate strength.

Marcos de grado Las marcas en las fijaciones que indican su fuerza.

Ground The negatively-charged side of a circuit. A ground can be a wire, the negative side of the battery, or even the vehicle chassis.

Tierra El lado de un circuito que tiene una carga negativa. Una tierra puede ser un alambre, el lado negativo de una batería, u hasta el chasis del vehículo.

Gum In automotive fuels, gum refers to oxidized petroleum products that accumulate in the fuel system, carburetor, or engine parts.

Sarro (goma) En los combustibles automotrices, el sarro se refiere a los productos petróleos oxidados que acumulan en el sistema de combustible, el carburador, o en las partes del motor.

Hairspring A fine wire spring.

Muelle resorte espiral Un resorte de alambre fino.

Hall-effect The consequence of moving current through a thin conductor that is exposed to a magnetic field; as a result of this, voltage is produced.

Efecto Hall La consecuencia de pasar un corriente por un conductor delgado que se expone a un campo magnético; por consecuencia, se produce el voltaje.

Halogen The term used to define a group of chemically related nonmetallic elements.

Halógeno El termino para describir un grupo de elementos no metálicos del mismo género químico.

Hand tap Tool used for hand cutting internal threads.

Macho de roscar de mano Una herramiento que sirve para cortar a mano las roscas interiores.

Hand-threading dies Tools used to cut external threads on bolts, rods, and pipes.

Terraja Las herramientas que sirven para cortar las roscas exteriores en los pernos, las varillas, y los tubos.

Hard spots Areas in the friction surface of a brake drum or rotor that have become harder than the surrounding metal; sometimes called islands of steel.

Regiones endurecidos Las averías en la superficie de fricción del tambor o el rotor de un freno que se han endurecido más que el metal que los rodea; a veces se llaman islas de acero.

Harmonics Periods of vibration that occur when valve springs are opened and closed rapidly.

Armónico Los períodos de la vibración que ocurren cuando los resortes de las válvulas abren y cierran rapidamente.

Hazardous waste Any material found on the Environmental Protection Agency list of known harmful materials. Waste is also considered hazardous if it has one or more of the following characteristics: ignitability, corrosivity, reactivity, and EP toxicity.

Desechos tóxicos Cualquier material que se nombra en la lista de materiales dañosos de la agencia de protección del medio ambiente (EPA). Los desechos también se consideran tóxicos si tiene uno o más de las características siguientes: la inflamabilidad, la calidad corrosiva, la reactividad y la toxicidad EP.

Heat dam The narrow groove cut into the top of the piston. It restricts the flow of heat into the piston.

Borde hendido Una muesca estrecha cortada en la cabeza del pistón. Limita el flujo del calor al pistón.

Heat range A rating used to express how well a spark dissipates heat.

Rango de calor Una medida que expresa la abilidad de una chispa de dispersar el calor.

Heat sink A device used to dissipate heat and protect parts.

Fuente fría Un dispositivo que sirve para dispersar el calor y protejer las partes.

Helical gear A gear with teeth

that are cut at an angle or are spiral to the gear's axis of rotation.

Engranaje helicoidal Un engranaje cuyos dientes han sido cortados en un ángulo o que son un espiral al eje de rotación del engrenaje.

Heptane A standard reference fuel with an octane number of zero, meaning that it knocks severely in an engine.

Eptano Un combustible de norma cuyo índice de octano es el cero, lo que significa que causa que el motor golpetea severamente.

High tension High voltage. In automotive ignition systems, voltages (up to 40 kilovolts) in the secondary circuit of the system as contrasted with the low, primary circuit voltage (nominally 6 or 12 volts).

Alta tensión El voltaje alto. En los sistemas del encendido, los voltajes (hasta los 40 kilovoltios) en el circuito secundario del sistema en contraste del voltaje bajo del circuito principal (de 6 o 12 voltios nominalmente).

Hone An abrasive for correcting small irregularities of differences in diameter in a cylinder, such as an engine cylinder or brake cylinder.

Piedra de rectificar Un abrasivo que sirve para corregir las pequeñas irregularidades en los diámetros de un cilindro, tal como un cilindro de un motor o un cilindro de freno.

Hot spot Refers to a comparatively thin section of area of the wall between the inlet and exhaust manifold of an engine, the purpose being to allow the hot exhaust gases to heat the comparatively cool incoming mixture. Also, used to designate local areas of the cooling system, which have attained above average temperatures.

Región de calor Refiere a una sección delgada en el muro entre

la admisión y el escape del múltiple de un motor, su propósito es permitir que los gases calientes del escape calientan a la mezcla entrando que es comparativamente fría. Este término tambien sirve para designar las areas locales del sistema del enfriamento, que han alcanzado las temperaturas más altas que las normales.

Hotchkiss drive A suspension design that uses leaf springs and the frame to control rear-end torque.

Propulsión del tipo Hotchkiss Un diseño de suspensión que usa los meulles de hojas y el armazón para controlar una torsión de la parte trasera del vehículo.

Hunting gearset A differential gearset in which one drive pinion gear tooth contacts every ring gear tooth after several rotations.

Conjunto de engranaje con diente suplementario Un conjunto de engranajes del diferencial en el cual cada diente del piñon de mando se engrena con cada diente del engranaje de corona después de varias rotaciones.

Hydraulic valve lifter A lifter that provides a rigid connection between the camshaft and the valves. The hydraulic valve lifter differs from the solid type in that it uses oil to absorb the shock that results from movement of the valve train.

Levantaválvulas hidráulica Una levantaválvulas que provee una conexión rígida entre el árbol de levas y las válvulas. La levantaválvulas hidráulica es distincta del tipo sólido en que usa el aceite para amortiguar los choques que resulten del movimiento del tren de válvulas.

Hydrocarbons Particles of gasoline, present in the exhaust and in crankcase vapors, that have not been fully burned.

Hidrocarburos Las partículas de

la gasolina, presentes en los gases de escape y en los vapores de la caja de cigueñal, que no se han quemado completamente.

Hylomar A sealing supplement that never hardens, but remains soft and pliable.

Hylomar Un suplemento de sellante que nunca endurece, sino permanece blanda y flexible.

Hypoid gears A type of spiral, beveled ring and pinion gearset in a differential. Hypoid gears mesh below the ring gear centerline.

Engrenajes hipoíde Un conjunto de engranajes de un diferencial de anillo y piñon de forma espiral y biselado. Los engranajes hipoídes se engrenan abajo de la linea central de la corona.

Ignitability The characteristic of a solid that enables it to spontaneously ignite. Any liquid with a flash point below 140°F is also said to possess ignitability.

Inflamabilidad La característica de un sólido que lo permite encenderse espontáneamente. Cualquier líquido con una temperatura de inflamabilidad menos del 140°F posea la caracteristica de la inflamabilidad.

Impact sockets Heavier walled sockets made of hardened steel and designed for use with an impact wrench.

Dados de impacto Los dados cuyos muros gruesos son hechos de acero endurecido y se han diseñado para usarse con una llave neumática.

Impact wrench A portable handheld reversible power wrench.

Llave neumático Una llave de potencia de mano portátil con acción invertible.

Impeller The part of a torque converter that is driven by the engine's crankshaft.

Impulsor Una parte de un convertidor del par que es accionada por el cigueñal del motor.

Included angle The sum of the

angle of camber and steering axis inclination.

'Angulo comprendido La suma del ángulo del camber y la inclinación del eje de la dirección.

Indirect injection A diesel fuel injection system in which fuel is injected into a precombustion chamber for ignition.

Inyección indirecta Un sistema de inyección de diesel en el cual el combustible se inyecta en una cámara de precombustión para encenderse.

Induction The process of producing electricity through magnetism rather than direct flow through a conductor.

Inducción El proceso de producción de la electricidad por el magnetismo en vez de un corriente directo por un conductor.

Inertia The constant moving force applied to carry the crankshaft from one firing stroke to the next.

Inercia La fuerza del movimiento constante aplicada a un cigüeñal para progresar de una carrera a la próxima.

Inertia switch A switch that automatically shuts off the fuel pump if the vehicle is involved in a collision or rolls over.

Conmutador inercia Un interruptor que automáticamente apaga a la bomba de combustible si el vehículo se involucra en un choque o si se voltea.

Insert bearing A bearing made as a self-contained part and then inserted into the bearing housing.

Cojinete inserta Un cojinete fabricado como una parte autónoma y que se inserta en la caja del cojinete.

Installed spring height The distance from the valve spring seat to the underside of the retainer when it is assembled with keepers and held in place.

Altura del resorte instalado La distancia del asiento del resorte de la válvula a la parte inferior

del retén cuando ha sido instalado con las cuñas y se fija en su lugar.

Installed stem height The distance from the valve spring seat and to the stem tip.

Altura del vástago instalado La distancia del asiento del muelle de la válvula al punto extremo del vástago.

Insulated circuit A circuit that includes all of the high current cables and connections from the battery to the starter motor.

Circuito aislado Un circuito que incluye a todos los cables de alta tensión y las conexiones de la batería al motor de arranque.

Insulator A material that does not allow for good current flow.

Aislador Una materia que no permite un flujo del corriente.

Intake stroke The first stroke of the four-stroke engine cycle, in which the piston moves away from top dead center and the intake valve opens.

Carrera de admisión La primera carrera de un ciclo de un motor de cuatro tiempos, en la cual el pistón se aleja del punto muerto superior y se abre la válvula de admisión.

Integral Make in one piece.

Integral Hecho en una sóla pieza.

Integrated circuit A large number of diodes, transistors, and other electronic components, all mounted on a single piece of semiconductor material and able to perform numerous functions.

Circuito integrado La cantidad de diodos, transistores u otros componentes electronicos, todos montados en una sola pieza de material semiconductor y capable de ejecutar varias funciones.

Intercooler A device used on some turbocharged engines to cool the compressed air.

Refrigerante intermedio Un dispositivo que se usa en algunos motores turbocargados para enfriar al aire comprimido.

Isooctane A standard reference

fuel with an octane number of 100, meaning that it does not knock in an engine.

Iso-octano Un combustible de norma con un índice de octano de cien, lo que significa que resulta en que el motor no golpetea.

Jack stands Safety stands. Used to hold a vehicle up while using a floor jack.

Torres Los soportes de seguridad. Sirven para sostener un vehículo en alto mientras que se usa un gato de piso.

Jam nut A locknut; one nut is tightened against another nut.

Contra tuerca Una tuerca perturbador; una tuerca que se aprieta contra otra tuerca.

Jet A precisely sized, calibrated hole in a hollow passage through which fuel or air can pass.

Surtidor Un hoyo calibrado de medida precisa en un pasillo hueco por el cual puede pasar el combustible o el aire.

Jig Device that holds the work and guides the operation.

Plantilla Un dispositivo que sostiene al trabajo y guía a la operación.

Jounce Upward suspension movement.

Sacudo Un movimiento hacia arriba de la suspención.

Keep alive memory A series of vehicle battery-powered memory locations in the microcomputer that allows the microcomputer to store information on input failure, identified in normal operations for use in diagnostic routines. Keep alive memory adopts some calibration parameters to compensate for changes in the vehicle system.

Memoria de retención Una seria de localizaciones de memoria mantenidas por la batería del vehículo que permiten que la microcomputador registra la información de fallos de entrada, que se identifican en las operaciones normales para usarse en las pruebas diagnósticos. La memoria de retención utiliza algunos de los parámetros calibrados para compensar por los cambios en el sistema del vehículo.

Key A small block inserted between the shaft and hub to prevent circumferential movement.

Chaveta Un tope pequeño que se meta entre la flecha y el cubo para prevenir un movimiento circunferencial.

Kickdown Normally refers to an automatic transmission shifting into a lower gear to meet the demands of the driver or a heavier load.

Disparo descendente Normalmente se refiere a una transmisión automática que efectúa un cambio descendente para acomodar al chofer o para acomodar a una carga más pesada.

Kinetic balance Balance of the radial forces on a spinning tire. Determined by an electronic wheel balancer.

Balanceo cinético El balanceo dinámico de las fuerzas radiales en una llanta que gira. Se determine por un balanceador de ruedas electrónico.

Kinetic energy Energy in motion.

Energía cinético La energía en movimiento.

Knurling A technique used for restoring the inside diameter dimensions of a worn valve guide by plowing tiny furrows through the surface of the metal.

Moletear Un método para restorar las dimensiones del diámetro interior de una guía de la válvula gastada partiendo al metal de la superficie en pequeños surcos.

Lambda sensor A form of an oxygen sensor used on some European cars.

Sensor lambda Un tipo de detector del oxígeno que se usa en algunos coches europeos.

Lamination Thin layers of soft metal used as the core for a magnetic circuit.

Laminas Las hojas delgadas del metal blando que sirven de alma de un circuito magnético.

Land The areas on a piston between the grooves.

Meseta del pared Las areas de un pistón entre las muescas.

Lapping The process of fitting one surface to another by rubbing them together with an abrasive material between the two surfaces.

Pulido El proceso de ajustar a una superficie con otra por frotarlas juntas con una materia abrasiva entre las dos superficies.

Lash The operational gap between two objects.

Juego La holgura que permite operar dos objetos.

Leakdown The relative movement of the plunger with respect to the hydraulic valve lifter body after the check valve is seated by pressurized oil. A small amount of oil leakdown is necessary for proper hydraulic valve lifter operation.

Fuga por abajo El movimiento relativo del émbolo con respeto al cuerpo de la levantaválvula hidráulica después de que la válvula de un sólo paso se asienta por el aceite a presión. Una pequeña cantidad de fuga es necesario para asegurar una operación correcta de la levantaválvula hidráulica.

Lean An air/fuel mixture that has more air than is required for a stoichiometric mixture.

Mezcla pobre Una mezcla de combustible y aire que tiene más aire de lo que requiere una mezcla estoquiométrica.

Light-emitting diode (LED) A type of digital electronic display used as either single indicator lights or grouped to show a set of letters or numbers.

Diodo emisor de luz (LED) Un tipo de indicador electrónico digital que tiene luces indicadores individuales o en grupos para formar un conjunto de letras o números.

Limited-slip A type of differential that allows more torque to be sent to the wheel with the most traction.

Deslizamiento limitado Un tipo de diferencial que permite que más energía del par se envía a la rueda con más tracción.

Line boring An engine block machining operation in which the main bearing housing bores are rebored to standard size and in perfect alignment.

Rectificación en linea Una operación maquinaria del bloque del motor en la cual los taladros principales de la caja se taladran de nuevo para asegurar un tamaño uniforme y una alineación perfecta.

Line contact The contact made between the cylinder and the torsional rings, usually on one side of the ring. The contact made between the valve and the valve seat. When an interference angle is used, only a small line of contact is produced.

Contacto en linea El contacto entre el cilindro y los anillos de torsíon, normalmente en un sólo lado del anillo. El contacto entre la válvula y el asiento de la válvula. Al usarse un ángulo de interferencia, sólo se produce una pequeña linea del contacto.

Liner Usually a thin section placed between two parts, such as a replaceable cylinder liner in an engine.

Forro Típicamente una sección delgada que se coloca entre dos partes, tal como un forro reemplazable del cilindro de un motor.

Lip-type seal An assembly consisting of a metal or plastic casing, a sealing element made of rubber, and a garter spring to help hold the seal against a turning shaft.

Sellos con borde Una asamblea que consiste de un cárter de metal o de plástico, un elemento sellante hecho de caucho, y un resorte de liga que sirve para apretar al sello contra una flecha que gira.

Liquid crystal diode (LCD) A type of digital electronic display made of special glass and liquid and requiring a separate light source.

Diodo de cristal líquido Un tipo de presentación electrónico hecho de un tipo especial de vidrio y líquido que requiere un suministro de luz independiente.

Live axle An axle on which the wheels are firmly affixed. The axle drives the wheels.

Eje motor Un eje en el cual las ruedas se montan rígidamente. El eje acciona las ruedas.

Load The work an engine must do, under which it operates more slowly and less efficiently. The load could be that of driving up a hill or pulling extra weight.

Carga El trabajo que debe ejecutar el motor, bajo el cual opera más lentamente y con menos eficiencia. La carga puede ser el de viajar cuesta arriba o de arrastrar el peso extra.

Lockup The point at which braking power overcomes the traction of the vehicle's tires and skidding occurs. The most efficient stopping occurs just before lockup is reached. Locked wheels cause loss of control, long stopping distances, and flat-spotting of the tires.

Enclavamiento El punto en el cual el enfrenamiento supera la tracción de los neumáticos del vehículo y ocurre el patinaje. El enfrenamiento más eficiente se efectúa justo antes de que ocurre el enclavamiento. Las ruedas enclavadas causan una pérdida del control, el enfrenamiento dilatorio y el gasto irregular de los neumáticos.

Logic gate Electronic circuit that acts as gates to output voltage signals depending on different combinations of input signals.

Compuerta lógico El circuito electrónico que sirve como una puerta a las señales del voltaje de salida según las combinaciones distinctas de señales de entrada.

Look-up tables The part of a microcomputer's memory that indicates, in the form of calibrations and specifications, how an engine should perform.

Obtención de datos de una tabla La parte de una memoria del microcomputador que indica, en la forma de las calibraciones y las especificaciones, como debe funcionar el motor.

Low and reverse band Transmission brake engaged in manual low and reverse gear ranges.

Banda de baja-reversa El freno de transmisión engranado en una posición de la banda baja-reversa.

Low and reverse clutch Transmission brake device engaged in manual low and reverse ranges.

Embrague baja-reversa Un dispositivo del frenado de transmisión engranado en la banda manual baja-reversa.

LP gas Liquified petroleum gas, often referred to as propane, which burns clean in the engine and can be precisely controlled.

Licuados del petróleo El gas de petroleo en forma líquido, típicamente llamado el propano, que se quema completamente en el motor y que puede ser controlado precisamente.

Lubrication The process of reducing friction between the moving parts of an engine.

Lubricación El proceso de reducir la fricción entre dos partes que mueven en un motor.

Magnet Any body with the property of attracting iron or steel.

Imán Cualquier cuerpo que tiene la propiedad de atraer al hierro o al acero.

Magnetic field The area surrounding the poles of a magnet that is affected by its attraction or repulsion forces.

Campo magnético El area alrededor de los polos de un imán que se afectan por las fuerzas de atracción o repulsión.

Magnetic gauges Electrical analog gauges that use magnetic forces to move the needle left or right.

Indicador magnético Las galgas análogas eléctricas que usan a las fuerzas magnéticas para mover la aguja indicadora a la izquierda o a la derecha.

Magnetic pulse generator An engine position sensor used to monitor the position of the crankshaft and control the flow of current to the center base terminal of the switching transistor.

Generador de pulsos magnéticos Un detector del posición de motor que sirve para regular la posición de la cigueñal y controlar al flujo del corriente al terminal del base central del transistor interruptor.

Magnitude Normally refers to the height of an electrical signal.

Magnitúd Normalmente se refiere a la intensidad de un señal eléctrico.

Main journal The central area of a crankshaft, where the main bearings support the shaft in the block.

Muñon central El area central de un cigueñal, en donde los cojinetes principales soportan al eje en el bloque.

Mainline pressure Pressure that is regulated in an automatic transmission hydraulic system.

Presión de la linea procedente de la bomba La presión que se regula en un sistema de transmisión hidráulica automática.

Major thrust face The side of the piston to which most force is applied by side thrust.

Cara de empuje principal El lado del pistón al cual la mayoría de la fuerza se aplica en un empuje lateral.

Malleable Able to be shaped.

Maleable Capable de ser formado.

Manifold absolute pressure A measure of the degree of vacuum or pressure within an intake manifold; used to measure air volume flow.

Presión absoluta en el múltiple Una medida del grado del vacío o de la presión dentro de un múltiple de admisión; sirve para medir el volumen del flujo del aire.

MAP sensor The sensor that measures changes in the intake manifold pressure that result from changes in engine load and speed.

Sensor MAP El detector que mide los cambios de presión en el múltiple de admisión que resultan según los cambios de la carga y la velocidad del motor.

Margin The area between the valve face and the head of the valve.

Margen El area entre la cara de la válvula y la cabeza de la válvula.

Mass airflow sensor An EFI air intake sensor that measures the mass, not the volume, of the air flowing into the intake manifold.

Sensor de la masa del aire Un detector del admisión del aire de inyección de combustible electrónico que mide la masa, en vez del volumen, del aire que fluye al múltiple de admisión.

Material safety data sheets Information sheets containing chemical composition and precautionary information for all products that can present a health or safety hazard.

Folletos de información de materiales y precauciones El folleto que contiene la información pertinente a la composición química y la indicaciones precavidos para todos los productos que pueden presentar peligros a la salud o la seguridad.

Mechanical efficiency (engine) The ratio between the indicated horsepower and the brake horsepower of an engine.

Eficiencia mecánica (motor) La relación entre la potencia indicada en caballos y el caballo indicado al freno de un motor.

Memory The part of a computer that stores, or holds, the programs and other data.

Memoria La parte de una computador que archiva, o guarda, a las aplicaciones u otros datos.

Mercury switch A type of switch that uses the flow of liquid metal mercury to complete the electrical circuit. Mercury switches are frequently used to control trunk and underhood lights.

Interruptor de mercurio Un tipo de interruptor que usa el flujo del metal mercurio líquido para completar un circuito eléctrico. Los interruptores de mercurio se suelen usar en aplicaciones de los luces de la cajuela y bajo del cofre.

Mesh To fit together, as gear teeth.

Engrenar Ajustarse bien, tal como los dientes de un engranaje.

Metered To control the amount of fuel passing into an injector. Fuel is metered to obtain the correct measured quantity.

Medir Controlar la cantidad del combustible que pasa al inyector. El combustible se mide para asegurar una cantidad medida correcta.

Metering The process of controlling something in response to quantities of something else.

Medida El proceso de controlar algo según las cantidades de otra cosa.

Methanol The lightest and simplest of the alcohols; also known as wood alcohol.

Metano El más ligero y más sencillo del grupo de alcohol; tambien llamado el alcohol piroleñoso.

Microcomputer A smaller version of a computer that makes decisions based on information it receives from sensors.

Microcomputadora Una versión más pequeña de una computadora que forma las decisiones basado en la información que recibe de los detectores.

Microprocessor The portion of a microcomputer that receives sensor input and handles all calculations.

Microprocesor La parte de un microcomputador que recibe la información de los detectores y se encarga de todas las calculaciones.

Milling The process of using blades to remove metal from an object.

Fresado El proceso de usar las cuchillas para quitar el metal de un objeto.

Miscibility The ability of one chemical to mix well with another chemical.

Miscible La característica de una química a mezclarse bien con otra química.

Misfiring Failure of an explosion to occur in one or more cylinders while the engine is running; can be continuous or intermittent failure.

Fallo de encendido El fallo en que una detonación ocurre en uno o más cilindros mientras que este en marcha el motor; puede ser un fallo continuo o intermitente.

Missing A lack of power in one or more cylinders.

March irregular Una falta de potencia en uno o más cilindros.

Modulation Pulsing.

Modulación Pulsante.

Monolith A single body shaped like a pillar or long tubular structure used as a catalyst in a catalytic converter.

Monolito Un cuerpo sólo en forma de columna o una estructura larga y tubular que sirve de catalizador en un convertidor catalítico.

Multimeter A tool that combines

the voltmeter, ohmmeter, and ammeter together in one diagnostic instrument.

Multímetro Una herramienta que combina las funciones del voltiometro, del ohmímetro, y del amperímetro en un instrumento diagnóstico.

Multiplexing A means of transmitting information between computers. It is a system in which electrical signals are transmitted by a peripheral serial bus instead of common wires, allowing several devices to share signals on a common conductor.

Multiplexar Una manera de transferir la información entre las computadoras. Es un sistema en el cual los señales eléctricos se transmiten por medio de un bus serial periférico en vez de por los alambres comunes, así permitiendo que varios dispositivos comparten los señales en un conductor común.

Multiviscosity oil A chemically modified oil that has been tested for viscosity at cold and hot temperatures.

Aceite de viscosidad de grado múltiple Un aceite modificado químicamente cuyo viscosidad se ha probado en temperaturas bajas y altas.

Nodular iron A metal, used in pressure plates, that contains graphite, which acts as a lubricating agent.

Hierro nodular Un metal, usado en los platos opresores, que contiene el grafito, que funciona como un agente de lubricación.

Nonhunting gearset A differential gearset in which one drive pinion gear tooth contacts only three ring gear teeth after several rotations.

Conjunto de engranaje sin diente suplementario Un conjunto de engranaje en el cual un diente del engranaje de piñon engrane solamente con tres dientes

del engranaje del anillo después de varias rotaciones.

Normal wear The average expected wear when operating under normal conditions.

Desgaste normal El desgaste que se espera de una parte al operar bajo condiciones normales.

Normally aspirated The method by which an internal combustion engine draws air into the combustion chamber. As the piston moves downward in the cylinder, it creates a vacuum that draws air into the combustion chamber through the intake manifold.

Aspirado normalmente El método por el cual un motor de combustión interno hace entrar al aire en la cámara de combustión. Al moverse hacia abajo el pistón en el cilindro, crea un vacío que hace entrar el aire a la cámara de combustión al travéz del múltiple de admisión.

Octane number A unit of measurement on a scale intended to indicate the tendency of a fuel to detonate or knock.

'Indice de octano Una unidad de medida en una gama cuyo intención es de indicar la tendencia de un combustible de causar una detonación o los golpeteos.

OEM parts Parts made by the original vehicle manufacturer.

Partes EOF Las partes hechas por el fabricante original del vehículo.

Offset Placed off center. Also, the measurement between the center of the rim and the point where a wheel's center is mounted.

Descentrado Ubicado fuera del centro. Tambien, la medida entre el centro del ancho del rim y el punto en que se monta la rueda.

Ohm A unit of measured electrical resistance.

Ohmio Una unidad de medida de la resistencia eléctrica.

Ohm's law A basic law of electricity expressing the relationship between current, resistance, and voltage in any electrical circuit. It

states that the voltage in circuit is equal to the current (in amperes) multiplied by the resistance (in ohms).

Ley de los ohmios Una ley básica de la electricidad que describe la relación entre el corriente, la resistencia, y el voltaje en cualquier circuito eléctrico. Declare que el voltaje en un circuito egala al corriente (en amperios) multiplicado por la resistencia (en ohmios).

Open circuit An electrical circuit that has a break in the wire.

Circuito abierto Un circuito eléctrico que tiene una quebradura en el alambre.

Open loop An electronic control system in which sensors provide information, the microcomputer gives orders, and the output actuators obey the orders without feedback to the microcomputer.

Bucle abierto Un sistema de control electrónico en el cual los detectores proveen la información, el microcomputador da los ordenes, y los actuadores de salida obedecen a éstas ordenes sin realimentación a la microcomputadora.

Orifice A precisely sized hole that controls fluid flow. Also, an opening.

Orificio Un hoyo de tamaño preciso que controla el flujo de los líquidos. Tambien, una apertura.

Out-of-round An inside or outside diameter, designed to be perfectly round, having varying diameters when measured at different points across its diameter.

Ovulado Un diámetro interior o exterior, por diseño perfectamente redondo, que tiene varios diámetros cuando se mide en puntos distinctos al través de su diámetro.

Overbore The dimension by which a machined hole is larger than the standard size.

Rectificación sobremedida La dimensión por la cual un orificio maquinado es más grande del tamaño normal.

Overdrive Normally used to express a gear ratio that allows the driven gear to rotate faster than the drive gear.

Sobremarcha Normalemente se usa para describir una relación de engranaje que permite que el engrenaje arrastrado gira más rapidamente que el engranaje propulsor.

Overlap The period of time that the intake and exhaust valves are open at the same time.

Temporización El periódo del tiempo en el cual las válvulas de admisión y de escape estan abiertas a la misma vez.

Override clutch The mechanism that disengages the starter from the engine as soon as the engine turns more rapidly than the starter has cranked it.

Embrague de invalidación El mecanismo que desembraga el motor de arranque en el momento que el motor gira más rapidamente que el motor de arranque.

Oxidation The combination of a substance with oxygen to produce an oxygen-containing compound. Also, the chemical breakdown of a substance or compound caused by its combination with oxygen.

Oxidación La combinación de una sustancia con el oxígeno para producir una compuesta que tenga oxígeno. Tambien, una descomposición química de una sustancia o una compuesta causada por su combinación con el oxígeno.

Oxidation inhibitor Gasoline additives used to promote gasoline stability by controlling gum and deposit formation and staleness.

Inhibitor del oxígeno Los aditivos de la gasolina que promueban la estabilidad de la gasolina por medio de controlar la formación del sarro y los depósitos y el rancidez.

Oxidation rate Speed that oxygen is taken into a substance.

Tasa de oxidación . La velocidad en que el oxígeno se absorbe por una sustancia.

Oxides of nitrogen Various compounds of oxygen and nitrogen that are formed in the cylinders during combustion and are part of the exhaust gas.

'Oxido de nitrógeno Varias compuesta del oxígeno y el nitrógeno que se forman en los cilindros durante la combustión y son parte del vapor del escape.

Parallel circuit In this type of circuit, there is more than one path for the current to follow.

Circuito paralelo En este tipo de circuito, hay más que una senda en que puede viajar el corriente.

Parallelogram A four-sided figure in which opposite sides are parallel.

Paralelogramo Una figura de cuatro lados en la que los lados opuestos son paralelos.

Parasitic load An electrical load that is still present when the ignition switch is off.

Carga parásita Una carga eléctrica que siga presente cuando el interruptor de encendido esta apagado.

Peen To stretch or clinch over by pounding with the rounded end of a hammer.

Martillazo Estirar o remachar con la extremidad redondeado de un martillo de bola.

Periphery The external boundary of the torque converter.

Periferia El límite externo del convertidor de par.

Phase Refers to the rotational positions of the various elements of a driveline.

Fase Se refiere a las posiciones giratorias de los varios elementos de una flecha motríz.

Phosgene gas A poisonous gas formed when R-12 is heated.

Gas fosgeno Un gas venenoso que forma al calentarse el R-12.

Pick-up coil A weak permanent magnet and wire assembly that, in combination with a reluctor, forms a position sensor.

. **Bobina de captación** Una asamblea de alambre y un imán débil permanente que, en combinación con un reluctor, forma un detector de posición.

Piezoresistive A characteristic of something that changes resistances in relationship to changes in pressure.

Piezoresistivo Una característica de algo que cambia la resistencia relativamente con los cambios de la presión.

Pilot journal A mechanical journal that slides inside the pilot bearing and guides its movement.

Muñon piloto Un muñon mecánico que desliza dentro del cojinete piloto y guía su movimiento.

Pinning Cold crack repair process involving the installation of tapered plugs in the crack or on either side of the crack.

Chavetear Un proceso de reparar las grietas sin calor que involucra la instalación de los espárragos cónicos en las grietas o a un lado de la grieta.

Pintle The center pin used to control a fluid passing through a hole; a small pin or pointed shaft used to open or close a passageway.

Clavija La aguja central que controla al flúido que pasa por un hoyo; una pequeña clavija o flecha puntiaguda que sirve para abrir o tapar un pasillo.

Pitch The angle of the valve spring twist. A variable pitch valve spring has unevenly spaced coils.

Paso El ángulo de las espiras de un resorte de válvula. Un resorte de válvula con paso variable tiene separaciones inegales entre las espiras.

Pitch gauge A tool used to measure the thread pitch of a bolt.

Comprobador de paso de rosca Una herramienta que sirve para medir el paso de las roscas de un perno.

Pitting Surface irregularities resulting from corrosion.

Picadura Las irregularidades de la superficie causadas por la corrosión.

Plastigage A special wax used to measure bearing clearances.

Plastigage (calibrador de plástico) Una cera especial que sirve para medir las holguras.

Play Movement between two parts.

Juego El movimiento entre dos partes.

Pneumatic Operated by compressed air.

Neumático Operado por el aire comprimido.

Polarity The particular state, either positive or negative, with reference to the two poles or to electrification.

Polaridad Un estado particular, sea positivo o negativo, en referencia a los dos polos o a la electrificación.

Poppet valve A valve consisting of a round head with a tapered face, an elongated stem that guides the valve, and a machined slot at the top of the stem for the valve spring retainer.

Válvula champiñón Una válvula que consiste de una cabeza redonda de cara cónica, un vástago alargado que guía a la válvula, y una muesca maquinada en la parte superior del vástago para el retenedor del resorte de la válvula.

Porosity Tiny holes in a casting caused by air bubbles.

Porosidad Los pequeños agujeros en una pieza moldeada causados por las burbujas del aire.

Port fuel injection A fuel injection system that uses one injector at each cylinder, thus making fuel distribution exactly equal among all of the cylinders.

Inyección de combustible por aperturas Un sistema de inyección de combustible que usa un inyector en cada cilindro, así proporcionando una distribución del combustible exactamente igual en todos los cilindros.

Positive displacement pumps Oil pump through which a fixed volume of oil passes with each revolution of its drive shaft.

Bombas de desplazamiento positivo Una bomba de aceite por el cual pasa un volumen fijo de aceite con cada revolución del eje propulsor.

Post-combustion control systems Emission control systems that clean up the exhaust gases after the fuel has been burned.

Controles de escape poscombustión Los sistemas de control de emisiones que purifican los vapores de gas después de que se haya quemado el combustible.

Potentiometer A variable resistor that acts as a circuit divider to provide accurate voltage drop reading in response to the movement of an object.

Potenciómetro Un resistor variable que sirve de divisor de tensión para proveer una lectura precisa de una caída del voltaje según el movimiento de un objeto.

Power A measure of work being done.

Potencia Una medida del trabajo que se efectúa.

Power stroke The third stroke of the four-stroke engine cycle, in which the compressed fuel mixture is ignited in the combustion chamber.

Carrera encendido-expansión La tercera carrera de un ciclo de un motor de cuatro tiempos, en la cual se enciende la mezcla de aire/combustible en la cámara de combustión.

Precombustion control system Emission control systems that prevent emissions from being created in the engine, either during or before the combustion cycle.

Control de escape precombustión Los sistemas de control de emisión que previenen que se crean las emisiones en el motor, sea durante o antes del ciclo de combustión.

Preheating The application of heat as a preliminary step to some further thermal or mechanical treatment.

Precalentamiento La aplicación del calor como un paso preliminario de un tratamiento termal o mecánico.

Preignition The process of a glowing spark or deposit igniting the air/fuel mixture before the spark plug.

Detonación El proceso en que una chispa o un depósito caliente enciende la mezcla de aire/combustible antes de que lo haga la bujía.

Preload A thrust load applied to bearings that support a rotating part to eliminate axial play or movement.

Carga previa Una carga de empuje aplicada a los cojinetes que soportan una parte giratoria con el fin de eliminar el juego o movimiento axial.

Pressure The exertion of force upon a body in contact with it. Pressure is developed within the cooling system and is measured in pounds per square inch on a gauge.

Presión El esfuerzo de una fuerza sobre un cuerpo con el que esta en contacto. La presión se desarrolla dentro del sistema de enfriamiento y se mide en libras por pie cuadrado con un calibre.

Preventative maintenance Normally scheduled maintenance designed to prevent vehicle failures.

Mantenimiento preventativo El mantenimiento periódico con el fin de prevenir los fallos del vehículo.

Primary circuit The low-voltage circuit of an ignition system.

Circuito primario El circuito de bajo voltaje de un sistema de encendido.

Program A set of instructions or procedures that a computer must follow when controlling a system.

Programa Un conjunto de instrucciones o procedimientos que debe cumplir una computadora en el control de un sistema.

Proportioning valve A pressure reduction valve used in the rear brake circuit.

Válvula dosificadora Una válvula de reducción de presión que se usa en un circuito trasero de los frenos.

Pulse width The length of time in milliseconds that an injector is energized.

Anchura de impulso La cantidad del tiempo en milisegundos en la cual se acciona un inyector.

Purge To separate or clean by carrying off gasoline fumes. The carbon canister has a purge line to remove impurities.

Purgar Separar o limpiar al vaciar los vapores de la gasolina. El recipiente lleno de carbón tiene una linea de purgar para quitarle las impurezas.

Pushrod guide plates The devices used in some engines to limit side movement of the pushrods.

Placas de guía de varilla empujadora Los dispositivos que se usan en algunos motores para limitar el movimiento lateral de las varillas empujadoras.

Quenching The cooling of gases by pressing them into a thin area.

Templar El enfriamiento de los gases al oprimirlos en una area pequeña.

Race A channel in the inner or outer ring of an antifriction bearing in which the balls or roller operate.

Pista Un canal en el anillo interior o exterior de un cojinete an-

tifricción en el cual operan las bolas o los rodillos.

Radial Perpendicular to the shaft or bearing bore.

Radial Perpendicular a la flecha o al taladro del cojinete.

Radial load A load that is applied at 90 degrees to an axis of rotation.

Carga Radial Una carga aplicada a 90 grados del eje de la rotación.

Radiation The transfer of heat by rays, such as heat from the sun.

Radiación La transferencia del calor por medio de los rayos, tal como el calor del sol.

Random access memory A type of memory used to store information temporarily.

Memoria de acceso aleatorio Un tipo de memoria que sirve para archivar la información temporalmente.

Ratio The relation of proportion that one number bears to another.

Relación La relación entre la proporción de un número a otro.

Reach A design feature of a spark plug. It is the length of the threaded portion of a spark plug.

Alcance Un rasgo del diseño de una bujía. Se trata de la longitud de la porción fileteada de una bujía.

Reactivity The characteristic of a material that enables it to react violently with water or other materials. Materials that release cyanide gas, hydrogen sulfide gas, or similar gases when exposed to low pH acid solutions are also said to possess reactivity, as are materials that generate toxic mists, fumes, vapors, and flammable gases.

Reactividad La característica de una materia que facilita que reacciona violentamente con el agua o con otras materias. Las materias que descargan el gas cianuro, el gas sulfhídrico, o los gases semejantes al exponerse a las soluciones de bajo pH se consideran tener la propriedad de reactivi-

dad, así como son las materiales que crean la toxicidad en forma de la llovizna, el humo y el vapor y los gases inflamables.

Read only memory A type of memory in an automotive microcomputer used to store information permanently.

Memoria de sólo lectura Un tipo de la memoria en una computador automotríz que sirve para archivar la información permanentemente.

Reaming A technique used to repair worn valve guides either by increasing the guide hole size to take an oversize valve stem or by restoring the guide to its original diameter.

Escariado Un método para reparar las guías de las válvulas gastadas sea por aumentar el tamaño del hoyo de la guía para que acepta un vástago más grande o por restaurar el diámetro original de la guía.

Rebound An expansion of a suspension spring after it has been compressed as the result of jounce.

Repercusión Una expansión de un muelle de suspensión después de que se haya comprimido por razón de un sacudo.

Recess A shaped hollow space on a part.

Muesca Un espacio hueco formado en una parte.

Reciprocating An up-and-down or back-and-forth motion.

Reciprocante Un movimiento de arriba y abajo o de un lado a otro.

Rectify To change one type of voltage to another.

Rectificar Cambiar un tipo del voltaje por otro.

Reduction The removal of oxygen from exhaust gases.

Reducción Remover el oxígeno de los gases de escape.

Reference voltage A voltage provided by a voltage regulator to operate potentiometers and other sensors at a constant level.

Voltaje de referencia Un voltaje proporcionado por un regulador de voltaje para operar a los potenciómetros u otros detectores en un nivel constante.

Relay An electrical switching device that uses a low current circuit to control a high current circuit.

Relé Un dispositivo interruptor eléctrico que usa un circuito de bajo corriente para controlar un circuito de alta corriente.

Relief The amount one surface is set below or above another surface.

Relieve La cantidad por el cual una superficie queda arriba o abajo de otra superficie.

Reluctance A term used to indicate a material's resistance to the passage of magnetic lines of flux.

Reluctancia Un término que indica la resistencia de una materia al pasaje de las lineas de flujo magnético.

Residual Remaining or leftover pressure.

Residual La presión que queda o sobra.

Residue Surplus or what remains after a separation takes place.

Residuo Lo que sobra o se queda después de que se efectúa una separación.

Resilience Elastic or rebound action.

Resiliencia La acción elástica o de repercusión.

Resistance The opposition offered by a substance or body to the passage of electric current through it.

Resistencia La oposición que ofrece una sustancia o un cuerpo al pasaje de la corriente eléctrica que lo atraviesa.

Reverse bias A positive voltage applied to N-material and a negative voltage applied to the P-material in a semiconductor.

Polarización inversa Un voltaje positivo aplicado a un cristal N y un voltaje negativo aplicado al cristal P en un semiconductor.

Rheostat A two terminal variable resistor used to regulate electrical current.

Reóstato Un resistor variable con dos terminales que sirve para regular al corriente eléctrico.

Rich An air/fuel mixture that has more fuel than is required for a stoichiometric mixture.

Rica Una mezcla de aire/combustible que contiene más combustible de lo que requiere una mezcla estoquiométrica.

Right-to-know laws Laws requiring employers to provide employees with a safe work place as it relates to hazardous materials.

Leyes de derechos de los empleados Las leyes que requieren que los patrones proveen sus empleados con un ambiente del trabajo libre de los peligros asociados con las materiales tóxicas.

Ring lands The high parts of a piston between the grooves.

Tierras de las coronas Las partes altas de un pistón entre las ranuras.

Rolling resistance A term used to describe the amount of resistance a tire has to rolling on the road. Tires that have a lower rolling resistance usually get better gas mileage. Typically, radial tires have lower rolling resistance.

Resistencia a la rotación Un término que describe la cantidad de resistencia que tiene un neumático a rodar en el camino. Los neumáticos que tienen una resistencia a rodar más baja suelen proporcionar un kilometraje más económico.

Rotary A circular motion.

Rotativo Un movimiento circular.

Rotary flow Torque converter oil flow associated with the coupling stage of operation.

Flujo rotativo El flujo del aceite del convertidor de par que se asocia con la etapa de acoplamiento de su operación.

Rotor pump A type of oil pump that utilizes two rotors, a four-lobe inner, and a five-lobe outer; output per revolution depends on rotor diameter and thickness.

Bomba de tipo rotor Un tipo de bomba de aceite que utiliza dos rotores, uno interior con cuatro resaltes, y uno exterior con cinco rebajes; la producción por revolución depende del diámetro y espesor del rotor.

RTV A formed-in-place gasket product used in place of conventional paper, cork, and cork/rubber gaskets.

Sellador RTV Un empaque que se forma en sitio que se usa en vez de los sellos más convencionales del papel, del caucho o de caucho con corcho.

Runner A case tube on an intake or exhaust manifold used to carry air in or out of the engine.

Tubería Un cárter tubular en un múltiple de admisión o escape que sirve para hacer entrar o sacar el aire del motor.

Runout Out-of-round or wobble.

Corrimiento Ovulado o con una oscilación irregular.

Sampling The act of periodically collecting information, as from a sensor. A microcomputer samples input from various sensors in the process of controlling a system.

Muestreo Coleccionar la información periódicamente, tal como de un detector. Una microcomputadora toma las muestras de varios detectores en el proceso de controlar a un sistema.

Saturation The point reached when current flowing through a coil or wire has built up the maximum magnetic field.

Saturación El punto en que el corriente que fluye por una bobina o un alambre llega a lo máximo de un campo magnético.

Scale A flaky deposit occurring on steel or iron. Ordinarily used to describe the accumulation of minerals and metals in an automobile cooling system.

Incrustación Un depósito que ocurre en el acero o el hierro. Típicamente se usa para describir la acumulación de los minerales y los metales en un sistema de enfriamiento automotríz.

Scan tool A microprocessor designed to communicate with a vehicle's on-board computer to perform diagnosis and troubleshooting.

Herramienta de exploración Un microprocesador diseñado para comunicar con una computadora a bordo de un vehículo para efectuar los prognósticos y localización de fallas.

Schematics Wiring diagrams used to show how circuits are constructed.

Esquemáticos Los dibujos de los conexiones que sirven para enseñar cómo se han construídos los circuitos.

S-class oil Standard engine oil designed for use in passenger cars and light trucks.

Aceite de aplicaciones S El aceite de motor común que se ha diseñado para usarse en los coches de pasajeros y en los camiones ligeros.

Score A scratch, ridge, or groove marring a finished surface.

Rayo Un rasguño, una arruga, o una muesca que echa a perder una superficie acabada.

Screw pitch gauge A tool used to check the threads per inch (pitch) of a fastener.

Calibrador de pasos de rosca Una herramienta que sirve para examinar las cuerdas por pulgada (el paso) de un elemento de fijación.

Scuffing Scraping and heavy wear from the piston on the cylinder walls.

Rozamiento La raspadura y el gasto extremo de un pistón en los paredes del cilíndro.

Sealant Material used as a seal between two mating objects.

Sellante Una material que sirve de empaque entre dos objetos de contacto.

Seat A surface, usually machined, upon which another part rests or seats; for example, the surface upon which a valve face rests.

Asiento Una superficie, típicamente maquinada, sobre la cual otra parte descansa o se asienta; por ejemplo, una superficie en la que descansa la cara de la válvula.

Seize When one surface moving on another scratches. An example is a piston score or abrasion in a cylinder due to a lack of lubrication or overexpansion.

Agarrotar Cuando una superficie moviendo en otra la raya. Otro ejemplo sería un rayo o abrasión en un cilindro debido a la falta de lubricación o la sobreexpansión.

Semifloating A design of live axle in which only part of the vehicle's weight is supported by the axles.

Semiflotante Un diseño de un eje motor en el que sólo un porción del peso del vehículo se soporta por los ejes.

Sensor Any device that provides an input to the computer.

Detector Cualquier dispositivo que provee una entrada para la computadora.

Serpentine belts Multiple-ribbed belts used to drive water pumps, power steering pumps, air-conditioning compressors, alternators, and emission control pumps.

Correa serpentín Las bandas dentadas que sirven para propulsar las bombas de agua, las bombas de dirección hidráulica, los compresores acondicionadores, las alternadores y las bombas de control de emisiones.

Servo The part of a cruise control system that maintains the desired car speed by receiving a controlled amount of vacuum from the transducer.

Servo La parte de un sistema de control crucero que mantiene la velocidad deseada por medio de una cantidad de vacío que recibe y se controla por el transconductor.

Shift forks Semicircular castings connected to the shift rails that help control the movement of the synchronizer.

Horquillas de cambio de velocidades Partes moldeadas de forma semicircular conectadas a las palancas de cambio para ayudar en el control del movimiento del sincronizador.

Shift rails The parts of a transmission shift linkage that transfer motion from the driver-controlled gear shift lever to the shift forks.

Palancas de cambio Las partes de una biela de desembrague de una transmisión que transfieren el movimiento de la palanca del desembrague manual a las horquillas de desembrague.

Shim Thin sheets, usually metal, which are used as spacers between two parts, such as the two halves of a journal bearing.

Chapa Las hojas delgadas, por lo regular del metal, que sirven de arandelas entre dos partes, tal como las dos mitades de un cojinete de contacto plano.

Short and long arm suspension (SLA) A suspension system using an upper and lower control arm. The upper arm is shorter than the lower arm. This is done to allow the wheel to deflect in a vertical direction with a minimum change in camber.

Suspención de brazo corto y largo Un sistema de suspencíon que usa un brazo de control superior e inferior. El brazo superior es más corto que el brazo inferior. Este arreglo permite que la rueda se desvía en una dirección vertical con un cambio mínimo del camber.

Shrink fit The shaft or part is slightly larger than the hole in which it is to be inserted. The outer part is heated above its normal operating temperature or the inner part chilled below its normal operating temperature and assembled in this condition. Upon cooling, an exceptionally tight fit is obtained.

Calado por contracción La flecha o la parte que se debe insertar es un poquito más grande que el orificio. La parte exterior se calienta a una temperatura más alta de lo normal al funcionar, o la parte interior se enfría a una temperatura más baja de lo normal al funcionar y se asamblea en estas condiciones. Al regresar a la temperatura normal, se obtiene un ajuste extremadamente apretado.

Shudder Momentary shake or quiver; can sometimes be severe.

Estremecimiento Un sacudo o temblor momentáneo; a veces puede ser severo.

Shunt More than one path for current to flow, such as a parallel part of a circuit.

Shunt (en derivación) Cuando hay más que una senda en que puede fluir un corriente, tal como una parte paralela de un circuito

Sine wave Basically, this wave is a circle drawn over time. It appears as a wave with equal positive and negative magnitudes and amplitudes.

Onda senoidal Basicamente, esta onda es un círculo que se dibuja al través del tiempo. Aparece como una onda con magnitudes y amplitudes positivos y negativos egales.

Sleeving A means of reconditioning an engine by boring the cylinder oversize and installing a thin metal liner called a sleeve. The inside diameter of the sleeve is then bored, usually to the original or standard piston size.

Restaurar con manguito Un metodo de recondicionar a un motor por medio de taladrar más grande al cilindro e instalar un forro de metal delgado llamado un manguito. Luego se taladra al diámetro interior del manguito al tamaño normal o indicado según el pistón.

Sliding fit Where sufficient clearance has been allowed between the shaft and journal to permit free running without overheating.

Ajuste deslizante Cuando una holgura suficiente grande se ha dejado entro la flecha y el muñon para permitir la operación sín que se sobrecalienta.

Slip A condition caused when a driving part rotates faster than a driven part.

Deslizamiento Una condición causada cuando una parte propulsor gira más rapidamente que la parte arrastrada.

Sludge As used in connection with automobile engines, it indicates a composition of oxidized petroleum products along with an emulsion formed by the mixture of oil and water. This forms a pasty substance and clogs oil lines and passages and interferes with engine lubrication.

Sebo (grasa) En referencia con los motores automotrices, indica una composición de productos petroléos oxidados junta con una emulsión formada de una mezcla del aceite y el agua. Esto forma una sustancia pastosa y causa las obstrucciones en las lineas y pasajes del aceite previniendo la lubricación.

Smog Air pollution created by the reaction of nitrogen oxides to sunlight.

Smog La contaminación del aire producido por la reacción de los óxidos de nitrógeno a la luz del sol.

Solenoid An electromagnetic switch with a movable core.

Solenoide Un interruptor electromagnético con un núcleo portátil.

Spark plug A device that is used to plug a hole in the combustion chamber while allowing a spark to enter the chamber.

Bujía Un dispositivo que sirve para tapar un hoyo en la cámara de combustión mientras que permite pasar una chispa a la cámara.

Spark plug reach The length of the spark plug shell from the contact surface at the seat to the bottom of the shell, including both threaded and nonthreaded sections.

Alcance de la bujía La longitud del casco de la bujía desde la superficie de contacto del asiento a la parte inferior del casco, incluyendo a las partes fileteadas y no fileteadas.

Specific gravity The weight of a given volume of a liquid divided by the weight of the same volume of water.

Gravedad específica El peso de un volumen dado de un líquido dividido por el peso del mismo volumen del agua.

Speed ratio Comparison of the difference in speed between two moving parts, such as impeller speed and turbine speed.

Relación de la velocidad La comparación de la diferencia en velocidad entre dos partes en movimiento, tal como la velocidad del impulsor y la velocidad de la turbina.

Splay To spread or move outward from a central point.

Achaflanar Desplegar o moverse hacia afuera de un punto central.

Splice To join. Electrical wires can be joined by soldering or by using crimped connectors.

Empalmar Juntar. Los alambres eléctricos se pueden unir por soldado o por medio de los conectores de presión.

Splines External or internal teeth cut into a shaft that is used to keep a pulley or hub secured on a rotating shaft.

Espárragos Los dientes exteriores o interiores cortados en una flecha que sirven para fijar a una polea o un cubo en una flecha rotativa.

Sponginess A feel of a soft brake pedal.

Esponjoso Una sensación blanda en un pedal de freno.

Spontaneous combustion Process by which a combustible material ignites by itself and starts a fire.

Combustión espontánea Un proceso por el cual una material combustible se encienda sí mismo y causa un fuego.

Spur gear A gear with teeth that are cut straight across the gear.

Engrenaje recto Un engrenaje cuyos dientes atraviesan el engranaje en una linea recta.

Square wave Typically a digital waveform that shows the cycling of a circuit or device.

Onda cuadrada Típicamente una forma de onda digital que indica el ciclado de un circuito o un dispositivo.

Squirm To wiggle or twist about a body. When applied to tires, squirm is the wiggle or movement of the tread against the road surface. Squirm increases tire wear.

Encorvadura Torcerse o doblar alrededor de un cuerpo. Al aplicarse a los neumáticos, la encorvadura se refiere a la torción o el movimiento de la banda contra la superficie del camino. La encorvadura aumenta el desgaste de los neumáticos.

Stall speed With the engine operating at full throttle, the gear selection in D range, and the vehicle stationary, this speed can be read on a tachometer.

Velocidad de calar Al estar el motor en marcha a todo gas, el engrenaje selecionado en el rango D, el vehículo estacionario, este velocidad se lee en el taquímetro.

Stalling A condition in which the engine dies after starting.

Paro Una condición en la cual el motor para después de ser encendido.

Stamping A piece of sheet metal cut and formed into the desired shape with the use of dies.

Estampar Una pieza de metal de hoja que se corta y se forma a lo deseado con los matrices.

Static balance Balance at rest; still balance. It is the equal distribution of weight of the wheel and tire around the axis of rotation such that the wheel assembly has no tendency to rotate by itself regardless of its position.

Balanceo estático El equilibreo en descanso; el balanceo inmóvil. Es la distribución equilibrada del peso de la rueda y el neumático alrededor del eje de rotación para que la asamblea de la rueda no tenga tendencia a girar por sí mismo, sin que importa su posición.

Stator The name used to describe a part in a torque converter or the stationary windings of an alternator.

Estátor El nombre que describe una parte en un convertidor de par o el devanado estático de un alternador.

Step ratio Transmission with steps or gear ratios. A four-speed transmission has four steps.

Relación de paso La transmisión que tiene pasos o relaciones de engranajes. Una transmisión de cuatro velocidades tiene cuatro pasos.

Step-up transformer A transformer in which the voltage created in a secondary coil is greater than the voltage in the primary, or first, coil.

Transformador elevador Una transformador en la cual el voltaje creado en la bobina secundaria es más alta que el voltaje en la bobina primaria.

Stoichiometric Chemically correct. An air/fuel mixture is considered stoichiometric when it is neither too rich nor too lean; stoichiometric ratio is 14.7 parts of air for every part of fuel.

Estequiométrica Lo que es correcto químicamente. Una mezlca de aire/combustible se considera estequiométrica cuando no es demasiada rica o pobre; la relación estequiométrica es 14.7 partes del aire por cada parte del combustible.

Streamlining The practice of reducing the coefficient of drag of a vehicle's body.

Diseño aerodinámico La practica de reducir la coeficiente de resistencia aerodinámcia de la carrocería de un vehículo.

Stress The force of strain to which a material is subjected.

Esfuerzo La fuerza de la tensión a la cual se somete una materia.

Stroke A term used to describe cylinder size, it represents the amount of movement the piston has inside the bore.

Carrera Un término que describe el tamaño de un cilindro, representa la cantidad del movimiento que tiene el piston dentro del orificio.

Substrate A ceramic honeycomb grid structure coated with catalyst materials.

Sustrato Una estructura cerámica de rejilla agrietada cubierta con materiales de catalizador.

Suction Suction exists in a vessel when the pressure is lower than the atmospheric pressure.

Succión La succión existe en una vasija cuando la presión es más baja que la presión atmosférica.

Surging A condition in which the engine speeds up and slows down with the throttle held steady.

Operación pulsatorio Una condición en la cual el motor acelera y desacelera mientras que la presión de admisión se mantiene fijo.

Swirl combustion A swirling of the air/fuel mixture in a corkscrew pattern. The swirling effect improves combustion.

Combustión remolino Un movimiento circular de la mezcla aire/combustible en el patrón de un remolino. El efecto de este movimiento es de amejorar la combustión.

Tang A projecting piece of metal placed on the end of the torque converter on automatic transmissions. The tangs are used to rotate the oil pump.

Lengueta Una pieza sobresaliente de metal ubicado en la extremidad del convertidor del par de una transmisión automática. Las lenguetas sirven para girar a la bomba de aceite.

Tap To cut threads in a hole with a tapered, fluted, threaded tool.

Roscar con macho Cortar las roscas en un agujero con una herramienta cónica, acanalada y fileteada.

Taper The difference in diameter between the cylinder bore at the bottom of the hole and the bore at the top of the hole, just below the ridge.

Ahuso La diferencia en el diámetro del orificio del cilindro en la parte inferior y del orificio en la parte superior de la apertura, justo abajo del reborde.

Telescoping gauges Tools used for measuring bore diameters and other clearances; also known as snap gauges.

Calibradores telescópicos Las herramientas que sirven para medir los diámetros de los orificios y otras holguras; tambien se conocen como calibres de ensarte.

Tensile strength The amount of pressure per square inch the bolt can withstand just before breaking when being pulled apart.

Resistencia a la tracción La cantidad de presión por pulgada cuadrada que puede resistir un perno al estirarse justo antes de que se quiebra.

Tension Effort that elongates or stretches a material.

Tracción Un esfuerzo que alarga o estira a una materia.

Thermal cleaning Cleaning that relies exclusively on heat to bake off or oxidize surface contaminants.

Limpieza termal La limpieza que cuenta exclusivamente con el calor para quemar u oxidar los contaminantes de una superficie.

Thermistor A solid-state variable resistor made from semiconductor material that changes resistance in response to changes in temperature.

Termistor Un resistor variable de estado sólido hecho de material semiconductor que cambia su resistencia según los cambios de la temperatura.

Thermo efficiency A gallon of fuel contains a certain amount of potential energy in the form of heat when burned in the combustion chamber. Some of this heat is lost and some is converted into power. The thermal efficiency is the ratio of work accomplished compared to the total quantity of heat contained in the fuel.

Rendimiento térmico Un galón del combustible contiene una cierta cantidad de energía potencial en la forma de calor cuando se quema en la cámara de combustión. Algo de éste calor se pierde y algo se convierte a la fuerza. El rendimiento térmico es la relación del trabajo que se efectúa comparado con la cantidad total del calor que contiene el combustible.

Thread pitch The number of threads in one inch of threaded bolt length. In the metric system, thread pitch is the distance in millimeters between two adjacent threads.

Paso de rosca El número de las cuerdas por pulgada de un perno con rosca. En el sistema métrico, el paso de las roscas es la medida de la distancia entre dos pasos contiguos en milímetros.

Throw With reference to an automobile engine, usually the distance from the center of the crankshaft main bearing to the center of the connecting rod journal.

Recorrido Al referirse a un motor de automóvil, típicamente es la distancia del cojinete principal del cigueñal al centro de los muñones de la biela.

Thrust line A line that divides the total toe angle of the rear wheels.

Linea de empuje Una linea que divide el ángulo total de la convergencia de las ruedas traseras.

Thrust load Load placed on a part that is parallel to the center of the axis.

Carga de empuje Una carga en una parte que queda paralela al centro del eje.

Tolerance A permissible variation between the two extremes of a specification or dimension.

Tolerancia Una variación permitible entre dos extremos de una especificación o una dimensión.

Torque A twisting force applied to a shaft or bolt.

Par de ajuste Una fuerza torcedura que se aplica a una flecha o un perno.

Torque steer A twisting axle movement in front-wheel drive automobiles that causes a pulling action under acceleration toward the side with the longer driving axle.

Dirección de torsión Un movimiento de torsión del eje en un automóvil de tracción delantera que causa que jale mientras que accelera hacia el lado con un eje motor más largo.

Tracking The travel of the rear wheels in a parallel path with the front wheels.

Seguimiento El progreso de las ruedas traseras en una senda paralela con las ruedas delanteras.

Traction A tire's ability to hold or grip the road surface.

Tracción La abilidad de un neumático para agarrar o mantenerse en la superficie del camino.

Tractive effort Pushing force exerted by the vehicle's driving wheels against the road's surface.

Esfuerzo de tracción   Una fuerza de empujo que resulta de tracción de las ruedas contra la superficie del camino.

Tramp   Wheel hop caused by static balance.

Pisoteo   Un brinquito de la rueda causado por el balanceo estático.

Transistor   An electronic device produced by joining three sections of semiconductor materials. A transistor is very useful as a switching device, functioning as either a conductor or an insulator.

Transistor   Un dispositivo electrónico producido al unir tres secciones de materiales de semiconductor. Un transistor es muy útil como dispositivo interruptor, funciona como un conductor o como aislador.

Transverse   Perpendicular, or at right angles, to a front-to-back centerline.

Transverso   Perpendicular, o en ángulo recto, a una linea central de delantero a trasero.

Trimmer   A resistor or capacitor that is adjusted to meet the needs of a circuit.

Trimer   Un resistor o un condensador que se ajusta según los requerimientos de un circuito.

Turbo boost   The positive pressure increase created by a turbocharger.

Reforzar de turbo   Un aumento del presión positivo creado por un turbocargador.

Turning torque   Amount of torque required to keep a shaft or gear rotating; measured with a torque wrench.

Torsión giratorio   La cantidad de torsión requerida para mantener girando a una flecha o un engrenaje; se mide con una llave de torsión.

Type A fire   A fire resulting from the burning of wood, paper, textiles, and clothing.

Fuego tipo A   Un fuego que resulta de la combustión de la leña, el papel, los textiles, y la ropa.

Type B fire   A fire resulting from the burning of gasoline, grease, oils, and other flammable liquids.

Fuego tipo B   Un fuego que resulta de la combustión de la gasolina, la grasa, los aceites, y otros líquidos inflamables.

Type C fire   A fire resulting from the burning of electrical equipment, motors, and switches.

Fuego tipo C   Un fuego que resulta de la combustión del equipo eléctrico, los motores y los interruptores.

Ultrasonic cleaning   Method of cleaning that utilizes high-frequency sound waves to create microscopic bubbles that work to loosen soil from parts.

Limpieza ultrasónica   Un metodo de limpieza que usa las ondas de sonido de alta frecuencia para crear las burbújas microscópicas que hacen el trabajo de aflojar la suciedad de las partes.

Unibody   A stressed hull body structure that eliminates the need for a separate frame.

Monocasco   Una estructura de casco arriostrada que elimina la necesidad de un chassis aparte.

Union   A hydraulic coupling used to connect two brake lines.

Unión   Un acoplador hidráulico que sirve para conectar dos lineas de freno.

Universal joint   A joint that allows the driveshaft to transmit torque at different angles as the suspension moves up and down.

Junta universal   Una junta que permite que la flecha motríz transmite el par en los ángulos diferentes mientras que la suspensión mueve hacia arriba y hacia abajo.

Vacuum fluorescent   A type of digital electronic display utilizing glass tubes filled with argon or neon gas; when current is passed through the tubes, they glow brightly.

Flourescente en vacío   Un tipo de muestra digital que utiliza los tubos de vidrio llenos del vapor de argo o neo; al pasar el corriente por estos tubos, brillan mucho.

Valve float   A condition in which the valves fail to follow the actions of the valve train and remain open.

Acción flotante de la válvula   Una condición en la cual las válvulas no siguen los movimientos del tren de válvulas y quedan abiertas.

Valve margin   On a poppet valve, the space or rim between the surface of the head and the surface of the valve face.

Márgen de la válvula   En una válvula de champiñones, el espacio o el borde entre la superficie de la cabeza y la superficie de la cara de la válvula.

Vapor   A substance in a gaseous state. Liquid becomes a vapor when brought above the boiling point.

Vapor   Una substancia en un estado gaseoso. El líquido se convierte en un vapor al superar el punto de ebullición.

Vapor lock   A condition wherein the fuel boils in the fuel system forming bubbles that retard or stop the flow of fuel to the carburetor.

Tapón de vapor   Una condicion en la cual el combustible hierve en el sistema de combustible formando unas burbújas que retrasan o detienen al flujo del combustible al carburador.

Vaporization   The last stage of carburetion, in which a fine mist of fuel is created below the venturi in the bore.

Vaporización   La última etapa del carburacíon, en la cual una llovizna muy fina del combustible se crea en el orificio abajo del venturi.

Varnish   A deposit in an engine lubrication system resulting from oxidation of the motor oil. Varnish is similar to, but softer than, lacquer.

Barníz Un depósito en el sistema de lubricación de un motor que resulta de una oxidación del aceite del motor. El barníz parece a la laca, pero es más blando.

Venturi An hour-glass shaped restriction placed in the barrel of a carburetor to speed up the flow of incoming air.

Venturi Una restricción en forma de ampolleta ubicado en la garganta de un carburador para acelerar al chorro de aire de admisión.

Viscosimeter An instrument for determining the viscosity of an oil by passing a certain quantity at a definite temperature through a standard-size orifice or port. The time required for the oil to pass through, which is expressed in seconds, gives the viscosity.

Viscosímetro Un instrumento que determina la viscosidad de un aceite al hacer que pasa una cierta cantidad en una temperatura definida por un orificio o una puerta de un tamaño normal. El tiempo requerido para que el aceite atraviesa, expresado en segundos, define la viscosidad.

VNT The variable nozzle turbine unit designed to allow a turbocharger to accelerate quickly, thus reducing lag time.

VNT La unidad de turbina con boquilla variante diseñada para permitir que un turbocargador se acelerara rápidamente, así disminuyendo el tiempo del retraso.

Volatile liquid A liquid that vaporizes very quickly.

Líquido volátil Un líquido que se vaporiza muy rápidamente.

Volatility The tendency for a fluid to evaporate rapidly or pass off in the form of vapor. For example, gasoline is more volatile than kerosene because it evaporates at a lower temperature.

Volatilidad La tendencia de un flúido a evaporarse rápidamente o escaparse en la forma de un vapor. Por ejemplo, la gasolina es más volátil que el kerosén porque se evapora en las temperatura más bajas.

Volt A unit of measurement of electromotive force. One volt of electromotive force applied steadily to a conductor of one-ohm resistance produces a current of one ampere.

Voltio Una unidad de medida de la fuerza electromotor. Un voltio de la fuerza electromotor aplicado constantemente a un conductor que tiene una resistancia de un ohmio produce una corriente de un amperio.

Voltage drop Voltage lost by the passage of electrical current through resistance.

Caída de voltaje El voltaje que se pierde al pasarse un corriente eléctrico por la resistencia.

Voltmeter A tool used to measure the voltage available at any point in an electrical system.

Voltímetro Una herramienta que sirve para medir el voltaje disponible en cualquier punto del sistema eléctrico.

Volume The measure of space expressed as cubic inches, cubic feet, etc.

Volumen La medida del espacio expresado como pulgadas cúbicas, pies cúbicos, etc.

Volumetric efficiency A measure of how well air flows in and out of an engine.

Rendimiento volumétrico Una medida de lo fácil que circula el aire en un motor.

Vortex flow A swirling, twisting motion of fluid.

Flujo vórtice Un movimiento como remolino, o giratorio de un flúido.

Vulcanized A process of heating rubber under pressure to mold it into a special shape.

Vulcanizado Un proceso de calentar al caucho bajo presión para moldearlo en una forma especial.

Warpage Bending.

Alabeo Doblando.

Watt's law A basic law of electricity used to find the power of an electrical circuit expressed in watts. It states the power equals the voltage multiplied by the current (in amperes).

Ley de Watt Un ley básico de la electricidad que sirve para expresar la potencia de un circuito eléctrico en vatios. Declara que la potencia egala al voltaje multiplicado por el corriente (en ampérios).

Wheatstone bridge A series-parallel arrangement of resistors between an input terminal and ground.

Puente Wheatstone Un arreglo en series-paralelo de los resistores entre un terminal de entrada y la tierra.

Wheel base The distance between the center of a front wheel and the center of a rear wheel.

Batalla (empate) La distancia entre el centro de una rueda delantera y el centro de una rueda trasera.

Whip Flexing of a shaft that occurs during rotation.

Desviación (latigo) El doblar de una flecha que ocurre al girar.

Zener diode A diode that allows reverse current to flow above a set voltage limit.

Diodo zener Un diodo que permite que el corriente en reverso fluye en cantidades más altas del limite de voltaje predeterminado.

INDEX